Bird Families of the World

Ducks, Geese and Swans

Edited by
Janet Kear

Illustrated by
Mark Hulme

Volume 2
Species accounts (*Cairina* to *Mergus*)

OXFORD
UNIVERSITY PRESS
2005

OXFORD
UNIVERSITY PRESS

Great Clarendon Street, Oxford OX2 6DP

Oxford University Press is a department of the University of Oxford.
It furthers the University's objective of excellence in research, scholarship,
and education by publishing worldwide in

Oxford   New York

Auckland   Cape Town   Dar es Salaam   Hong Kong   Karachi
Kuala Lumpur   Madrid   Melbourne   Mexico City   Nairobi
New Delhi   Taipei   Toronto   Shanghai

With offices in

Argentina   Austria   Brazil   Chile   Czech Republic   France   Greece
Guatemala   Hungary   Italy   Japan   South Korea   Poland   Portugal
Singapore   Switzerland   Thailand   Turkey   Ukraine   Vietnam

Oxford is a registered trade mark of Oxford University Press
in the UK and in certain other countries

Published in the United States
by Oxford University Press Inc., New York

A catalogue record for this book is available from the British Library

Library of Congress Cataloging in Publication Data

Data available

ISBN 0 19 861009 2 (Volume 2)
ISBN 0 19 854645 9 (Set)

10 9 8 7 6 5 4 3 2 1

Typeset by Macmillan India Ltd

Printed on acid-free paper by Thomson Press, India

Contents

Summary of Volume 1 contents

Acknowledgements

Dedication

List of colour plates

List of abbreviations

Plan of the book

PART I *General chapters*

1 Introduction
2 Taxonomy and systematics
3 Feeding ecology
4 Ecology of social behaviour
5 Breeding strategies and biology
6 Movements and migrations
7 Population dynamics
8 Conservation and management

PART II *Species accounts (Anhima to Salvadorina)*

List of abbreviations

>	greater than
<	less than
†	extinct lineage and deceased authors
AEWA	African-Eurasian Migratory Waterbird Agreement
AOU	American Ornithologists' Union
Apr	April
asl	above sea level
Aug	August
BMR	basic metabolic rate
BOU	British Ornithologists' Union
bp	before present
BSC	Biological Species Concept
BTO	British Trust for Ornithology
c	about
CITES	Convention on Trade in Endangered Species
cm	centimetre
CWS	Canadian Wildlife Service
Dec	December
DEE	daily energy expenditure
DNA	deoxyribonucleic acid
EMR	existence metabolic rate
ENSO	El Ninõ Southern Oscillation
Feb	February
♀	female
FEPC	forced extra-pair copulation
Gr	Greek
ha	hectare(s)
h	hour
IUCN	The World Conservation Union
IWC	International Wildfowl Count
IWRB	International Waterfowl Research Bureau (now Wetlands International)
Jan	January
juv	juvenile (usually a first-winter bird)
km	kilometre
km^2	square kilometre
kHz	kilohertz
L	Latin
LRS	lifetime reproductive success
♂	male
m	metre(s)
Mar	March

min	minute(s)
mtDNA	mitochondrial DNA
mybp	million years before present
ND2	dehydrogenase subunit 2
N,S,E,W	north, south, east, west
n	number in sample
Nov	November
NZ	New Zealand
Oct	October
ppt	parts per thousand
PSC	Philogenetic Species Concept
RSPB	Royal Society for the Protection of Birds
SAFRING	South African Bird Ringing Unit
s.d.	standard deviation
s.e.	standard error
sec	second(s)
Sept	September
SGPP	Shortgrass Prairie Population
SONON	Samenwerkende Organisaties Vogelanderzock Nederland
srRNA	subunit ribosomal nucleic acid
TERA	Troy Ecological Research Associates
UK	United Kingdom of Great Britain and Northern Ireland
US	United States of America
USFWS	US Fish & Wildlife Service
ybp	years before present
WSGCOA	Waterbird Specialist Group of Chinese Ornithological Association
WWF	World Wide Fund For Nature
WWT	The Wildfowl & Wetlands Trust
ZICOMA	Zones d'Importance pour la Conservation des Oiseaux à Madagascar (Madagascar Important Bird Areas Project)

The dabbling or surface-feeding ducks

Dabbling ducks are considered to be the most successful of wildfowl since there are more species and a greater number of individuals than in any other tribe. Particularly widespread are the *Anas* ducks of the Arctic and temperate regions that breed at high latitudes and migrate to lower ones to spend the winter. Typically, the male is brightly coloured during the period of courtship and dull brown during the summer and early autumn when wing feathers are shed and the birds are flightless for a month or so. Usually, when the male has this dull eclipse plumage, he takes no part in family life, and pairbonds tend to be temporary, so that females are able to select several mates in the course of a lifetime. This inhibits inbreeding, but it also places a premium on male appearance and display. The conspicuously patterned males have elaborate courtship rituals that are seen every autumn as pairbonds are established for the next breeding season. The male Northern Mallard, for example, is devoted to the same female from October to April, but leaves her as soon as her clutch is laid, and may woo another mate for the following year. In most winter populations of migratory ducks there are more males than females, a situation arising partly because females suffer greater annual mortality. This means that not every male will get a mate. Those that are chosen usually follow their female back to the place where she was hatched. All these features are significant in speciation, as we saw in Chapter 4, and in the evolution of complex male displays and plumages (females and juveniles tend to resemble one another and are brown). A bright shiny patch, or speculum, is present on the trailing edge of the upperwing of both males and females.

Most dabbling ducks are able to breed at one year, and females lay large clutches so that there can be fairly rapid change to gene frequencies within the population. Nests are made usually on the ground where they are screened by waterside vegetation. The female alone builds, lining the nest with special dark down that grows in not long before laying; it differs from the white down of shelducks and other cavity-nesting ducks. The female alone warms the eggs against patches of bare skin that develop as a result of her plucking feathers from her breast. Dabbling ducks walk well on land and feed on seeds and invertebrates, mainly at the surface and by up-ending. They dive only rarely and, when they do, they must open their wings in order to submerge since they lack the short bodies, broad feet, and short tails that are characteristic of the true diving ducks.

Members of the tribe are closely related, a fact that is suggested by their ability to produce fertile hybrids, but can be grouped into the wigeon, green-winged teal, grey teal, mallards, pintails and blue-winged teal.

Adult wigeon obtain most of their food by grazing short pasture so that they have small bills and somewhat rounded, muscular heads.

The green-winged teal are small and have iridescent green patches on the wings of both male and female; included are the Eurasian and American Green-winged Teal, both of which are dimorphic and migratory, and the South American Teal, in which the sexes are similar; there is a long breeding season, no eclipse, and dual parental care.

The grey teal and New Zealand teal all have long breeding seasons, long pairbonds and shared parental care. While two grey teal species are isolated in islands, the Grey Teal is a nomadic bird of the arid, unpredictable interior of Australia that is self-introduced to New Zealand, where it has spread recently because of the provision of elevated nestboxes and protection from hunting.

The mallards make up a closely linked family with worldwide distribution, and are among the best known of wildfowl. They tend to replace one another geographically (they are not sympatric) and although, apart from the Northern Mallard, male and female look alike, the male takes no part in family life.

Pintails are found in every part of the world except Australasia. They have long necks and thus longer 'reaches' than other dabbling ducks, allowing them to gain food from greater depths. The single dimorphic species, the Northern Pintail, comes from the highest latitudes, and has the shortest laying season; it can occur in very large winter aggregations and is one of the world's most numerous ducks.

The blue-winged teal group includes seven dabbling ducks that feed in rather different ways; three of the smaller ones eat seeds, while the others, the shovelers, are small-headed, large-billed birds that filter the water surface for minute floating organisms, mostly of animal origin. This strategy means that they must feed for much of the day, with little time for loafing, and their foraging method has a significant influence on the timing of courtship, pairing, and of the male's moult out of eclipse into breeding plumage. The blue wing of the title refers not to the speculum (which is usually green) but to powder blue feathers on the shoulders of the upperwing. The Garganey and Blue-winged Teal are the long-distance travellers of the duck world, the first of the Old World and the second of the New. If a small brown duck turns up on a freshwater wetland on some remote oceanic island, then it is normally one of these, and usually a Garganey.

Common names can be a bit confusing. For instance, the names 'Black' and 'Grey' given to a number of mallards can mislead as the birds are mostly brown; and the designation 'teal' is used for any small duck species that may not be related. The first record of the word (spelt 'tele') dates from 1274 when carcases of Eurasian Teal sold in London markets were listed at a price of one and a half pennies for two—half the cost of a Northern Mallard. The word is said to derive from the attractive 'tutting' sound made by the males in winter gatherings. The Maori name of *tete* (pronounced *te-te*) for their Grey Teal likewise imitates the 'laughing' calls of the flock. The earliest English spelling (1513) of wigeon was 'wegyons'; it and the alternative 'whewer' again refer to the far-reaching whistling voice of the male, although the males were usually called wigeons and the females—which actually quack—known as whewers. Wigeon were recognized as different, and priced separately, from wild Mallard by London poulterers as recently as the 1540s.

Janet Kear

Taxonomy

Livezey (1991, 1997b) considered that the tribe Anatini consisted of all typical surface-feeding or dabbling ducks, together with the 'perching ducks' that were formerly grouped under the tribal name of Cairinini (Delacour and Mayr 1945). Although Livezey (1991) found only a single, partially ambiguous, character supportive of the tribe (a post-orbital stripe in duckling plumage), and although molecular data strongly support removal of several genera from a close relationship with *Anas* (Bottjer 1983, Madsen *et al.* 1988, Harshman 1996, Staml *et al.* 1996, Johnson and Sorenson 1998, Sorenson *et al.* 1999), his classification is retained here pending further evidence. Livezey's (1991) classification of *Anas* is largely in agreement with molecular data (Omland 1994, Johnson and Sorenson 1998).

Within the tribe, monogamy is typical, except perhaps for the Muscovy Duck (Johnsgard 1961a, McKinney 1985, Livezey 1991). In a minority of species, male and female attend the brood, and this is commoner among the tropical ones (Kear 1970). Most species are characterized by monosyllabic distress calls of the downy young (Lorenz 1951–53), and preflight 'intention' movements (McKinney 1965). They also share a number of display characteristics, including pre-copulatory Head-pumping (both sexes), marked Inciting (by females), variably long Decrescendo calls (females), post-copulatory bathing (females), ritualized Head-turning (by males) and Wing-preening (males) (Lorenz 1951–53, Johnsgard 1961a, 1965a, Livezey 1991). Interspecific hybridization is common, and intertribal hybrids with the pochards or diving ducks Aythyini have been recorded fairly frequently (Johnsgard 1960b).

The Anatini is the largest wildfowl tribe, and includes one of the largest bird genera (*Anas*) (Bock and Farrand 1980, Livezey 1991). Surface-feeding ducks occur throughout the world, but species diversity is highest in south and east Asia, North America, southern South America and east Africa (Figure 9.25). The group's origins may lie in the southern hemisphere (Livezey 1991). Four species are known to have become extinct during the Holocene, including *Anas marecula* of Amsterdam and St Paul Islands (Olson and Jouventin 1996), *Anas theoderi* of Mauritius and possibly Réunion Island (Cheke 1987, Cowles 1987) and Oustalet's or Marianas Mallard *Anas oustaleti* of the Mariana Islands (Reichel and Glass 1991, Reichel and Lemke 1994) which was

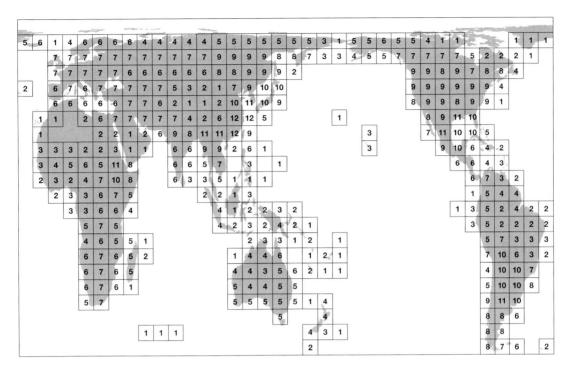

9.25 Species diversity of surface-feeding ducks (Anatini) that survived into the Holocene. The number of species that occur (or occurred) within each grid-cell is indicated.

probably a hybrid between Northern Mallard and Pacific Black Duck. In addition, a recently extinct, and as yet undescribed, duck of Rota Island (Steadman 1992), may be a dabbling duck.

The earliest known fossil belonging to the tribe is hard to determine, since many early fossils placed within *Anas* are of uncertain affinities (the early Miocene *Anas basaltica, A. luederitzensis, A. skalicensis* and *A.* cf. *velox*) (Brodkorb 1964, Howard 1964a, Cheneval 1987). However, following detailed analysis of many fossils, Cheneval (1987) listed *Anas risgoviensis, A. sansaniensis, A. velox, A. risgoviensis* and *Sinanas diatomas* from the mid-Miocene, while Bickart (1990) has described three as yet unnamed *Anas* species from the late Miocene of Arizona, US. The earliest fossil Wood Duck *Aix* was found in Pleistocene deposits in Kansas, Florida and New Mexico, US (Hepp and Bellrose 1995).

Members of the tribe have been subject to many taxonomic treatments. Several genera (*Cairina, Pteronetta, Aix, Chenonetta, Nettapus* and *Amazonetta*) were included in the perching ducks by Delacour and Mayr (1945), along with others of unclear affinity, the Spur-winged Goose and comb ducks. This grouping was followed by Johnsgard (1965a, 1978) who added the Ringed Teal (Johnsgard 1960c). Wolfenden (1961), however, suggested that the perching ducks should be merged with the dabbling ducks, except for the Spur-winged Goose. Subsequently, Livezey (1991) combined the two groups, exclusive of both the Spurwing and the comb ducks. His analysis suggested three subtribes, Cairinina (Muscovy and White-winged Ducks, Hartlaub's Duck, the American Wood Duck and Mandarin), Nettapodina (Australian Wood Duck and the pygmy-geese) and Anatina (Brazilian Teal, Ringed Teal and all other dabbling ducks). Donne-Gousé *et al.* (2002) found the Ringed Teal to be related, not to the dabblers, but to the seaduck (Mergini). DNA analysis supports a relationship between the Muscovy Duck and some other 'perching ducks' such as the American Wood Duck, but not with the White-winged Duck (Harshman 1996, Sorenson *et al.* 1999). Structurally, the White-winged Duck may look like the Muscovy (Sibley and Monroe 1990, Livezey 1991), but MacKenzie and Kear (1976) thought that they could not be closely related because of different breeding patterns in captivity in England. The White-winged Duck has egg-laying cycles that are typical of temperate wildfowl, in which a short laying season is stimulated by spring daylengths and ended by the long days of midsummer when birds enter a photorefractory phase. Other large perching ducks, such as Hartlaub's Duck and the Muscovy, have typically tropical egg-laying patterns that extend equally around the longest day. Johnson *et al.* (1999) later pointed out that it may be relatively difficult in evolutionary terms for ducks to make the transition from a short breeding season to a long one. Recently, linkage of the White-winged Duck to the pochards has been suggested from molecular data (Harshman 1996, Sorenson *et al.* 1999), and it has been returned to its own genus *Asarcornis*. Molecular data (Sorenson *et al.* 1999, Johnson and Sorenson 2000) also suggest that Hartlaub's Duck is linked to pochards rather than dabblers.

The closest relative of the American Wood Duck is the Mandarin with which, however, it rarely hybridizes. Hybrids between male Wood Duck and female dabbling ducks and shelducks are quite common in captivity (Johnsgard 1978), although infertile, and the failure of the Mandarin to hybridize at all frequently with the Wood Duck, or with any other duck, may relate to chromosomal differences (Yamashina 1952). Madsen *et al.* (1988) placed the Wood Duck and Mandarin outside a grouping of dabblers and pochards. Sraml *et al.* (1996) and Harshman (1996) found that pygmy-geese represent an early lineage that was well outside the Anatinae. Thus, the relationships of these basal anatines (*sensu* Livezey 1991) remain controversial. The classification of the Crested Duck, here placed within the monotypic genus *Lophonetta*, has also been subject to debate. It has been called a shelduck (Tadorninae) (Delacour and Mayr 1945, Delacour 1954, Boetticher 1958, Woolfenden 1961) because of shelduck-like aggressiveness, other reproductive behaviour and duckling coloration.

Johnsgard (1965a, 1978) felt that its aggressiveness was due to feeding ecology, and that similarities in courtship displays to the Bronze-winged Duck should place it within *Anas* (see Kaltenhäuser 1971 for a discussion on the use of *Lophonetta's* behaviour in determining taxonomy). Tuohy *et al.* (1992) thought it an aberrant species of unclear affinity, while Livezey (1991) wrote that the Crested and Bronze-winged Ducks are sister species, and form a sister group to the true dabblers. Data from DNA sequencing of mitochondrial genes (Johnson and Sorenson 1998) closely linked both species in a distinct, Neotropical group within the dabbling ducks, together with the steamer-ducks and the Brazilian Teal.

Livezey (1997b) split the remaining surface-feeding ducks to form two main groups, the wigeon and their allies (six species), and the typical dabbling ducks (40 species). He characterized the wigeon, for which he reinstated the generic name of *Mareca*, by 'primitive' syringeal bullae in the males and unique natal and definitive plumages (Livezey 1991), and assigned to the group three typical species (Eurasian Wigeon, American Wigeon and Chiloe Wigeon), the Cape Teal, plus two transitional forms, the Gadwall and Falcated Duck. Evidence from DNA sequencing of mitochondrial genes (Johnson and Sorenson 1998) suggested that the Chiloe Wigeon and American Wigeon are more closely related than they are to the Eurasian species. Additional phylogenetic studies may clarify whether the Chiloe Wigeon's behavioural specializations, such as a long pairbond and paternal care of the brood, are recently derived or an ancestral condition within the wigeon group (Brewer 1996). The Cape Teal has been the most difficult to classify. Although Livezey (1991) showed that it shared with the wigeon a number of duckling and adult plumage patterns, it had been placed earlier with the tropical pintails by Delacour and Mayr (1945), with the spotted Versicolor Teal by Delacour (1954–64), and with the Green-winged Teal by Johnsgard (1961a, 1965a). More recent DNA analysis (Johnson and Sorenson 1999) again linked Cape Teal to the pintails rather than the wigeon.

Within the typical surface-feeding ducks, Livezey (1991) recognized six subgenera: (a) *Anas* the mallards; (b) *Spatula* the blue-winged ducks; (c) *Nesonetta* the Australasian teal; (d) *Dafila* the pintails; (e) *Querquedula* the Holarctic teal; and (f) *Punanetta* the spotted teal. Within the mallards, the African Black Duck exhibits a number of peculiar behavioural characteristics that may be related to specialization for a riverine life. Some authors have considered this duck to be among the most ancient of the Anatini (Delacour 1956, Johnsgard 1961a, 1965a, 1978), and Johnson and Sorenson (1999) suggested that the mallard clade appeared first in Africa. Livezey (1991) recognized two groups within the remaining mallards, a northern-hemisphere group consisting of *Anas platyrhynchos*, *A. wyvilliana*, *A. laysanensis*, *A. oustaleti*, *A. fulvigula* and *A. diazi* (*A. oustaleti* is not treated in this book as a true species—see Pacific Black Duck account) and a southern-hemisphere group of *A.undulata*, *A. melleri*, *A. luzonica*, *A. superciliosa*, *A. poecilorhyncha* and *A. zonorhyncha* (the last two are considered here to be subspecies of the Spot-billed Duck).

A close relationship between the northern forms is recognized commonly; indeed many of the northern, and some of the southern species, have in the past been thought conspecific with the Northern Mallard (Delacour and Mayr 1945, Boetticher 1952, Johnsgard 1961a, 1961d, 1965a, 1978), but some species limits remain unresolved (Delacour and Mayr 1945, Johnsgard 1961a,b, Kessler and Avise 1984, Patton and Avise 1985, Livezey 1991). Palmer (1976) considered that the Mexican Duck was present, with the American Black Duck and the Mottled Duck, in North America before an invasion by the dimorphic Northern Mallard. Introgression, with more recent invasions, especially following extensive 'game' releases, has reduced the purity of the Mexican Duck, particularly in the US. DNA studies by Johnson and Sorenson (1999) found two major haplotypes in North American mallard, one linking the Northern Mallard to the Asian-Pacific *poecilorhyncha*, *zonorhyncha* and *luzonica*, and the other to the monomorphic North American *rubripes*, *diazi* and *fulvigula*. This suggests a high level of introgression with other North American species, and may support Palmer's (1976) view of Mallard invasions. McCracken *et al.* (2001) confirmed the distinct status of the Mexican Duck. DNA studies further

indicated that the Hawaiian Duck or Koloa is a full species, closely related to the North American mallard complex (Browne *et al.* 1993, Cooper *et al.* 1996, Rhymer 2001); however, it appears to be closer to the Mottled and American Black Ducks than to the Northern Mallard, and is believed to be a recent colonist of Hawaii. The Laysan Duck is sometimes supposed to have been derived independently from mallard-like isolates, or to have evolved secondarily from the Hawaiian Duck (Warner 1963, Lack 1970, Weller 1980). It is now shown by DNA analysis to be distinct, with its divergence from a mallard-type lineage occurring some 0.8 million years ago; it possibly evolved from an ancestor with similar sexes, such as Mottled or American Black Duck, rather than from the dimorphic Northern Mallard (Rhymer 2001).

Among the southern forms, Livezey (1991) thought that the Yellow-billed Duck and Meller's Duck of Africa were sister species and formed a sister group to the South Pacific mallards (Philippine, Pacific Black and Spot-billed Ducks). Johnsgard (1961a, 1965a) concluded that Meller's Duck was nearest to the Northern Mallard but later listed it following the Yellow-billed Duck (Johnsgard 1978, 1979), while some authors have put it next to the African Black Duck (Phillips 1923, Peters 1931, Johnsgard 1979). Studies in captivity (Young 1994) showed that the reproductive behaviour of Meller's Duck differs from both the Yellowbill's and the Northern Mallard's. The lack of a Down-up display, and its aggressiveness and territoriality when nesting, are similar to the African Black Duck, perhaps because of convergence; however, a relationship with the Yellow-billed Duck is confirmed by DNA analysis (Young and Rhymer 1998, Johnson and Sorenson 1999). A close kinship within the Pacific mallards is well established, although again species limits are debated; for example, Livezey (1991) splits the Indian and Chinese Spotbills into separate species, whereas the Pacific Black Duck is merged with the Spotbills into a single species by Delacour (1956) and Johnsgard (1961a, 1965a, 1978). The Philippine Duck is considered a close relative of the Pacific Black Duck, which Delacour and Mayr (1945) and Johnsgard (1978) thought doubtfully distinct from the Spot-billed Duck. The Spotbill is morphologically different, although resembling the Northern Mallard in behaviour, and replaces the Mallard in the Philippines and Australasian region. No wild hybrids are known between the Northern Mallard and Spotbills in India and Myanmar (Burma), and are evidently rare in China, although various hybrids are reported in captivity (Johnsgard 1965a).

After the mallards, the next group of dabbling ducks recognized by Livezey (1991) is the blue-winged ducks (subgenus *Spatula*), which includes the Blue-winged and Cinnamon Teals plus the shovelers. Johnson and Sorenson (1999) suggested that this group evolved relatively recently, and within the last 1.3 million years. A very close relationship between the Blue-winged and Cinnamon Teal is clear from morphological, behavioural and molecular studies, although their breeding ranges overlap somewhat, as is their affinity with the shovelers (Delacour and Mayr 1945, Johnsgard 1965a, 1978, Kessler and Avise 1984, Patton and Avise 1986, Tuohy et al. 1992). The Cape Shoveler is thought by Livezey (1991) to be the 'most primitive' shoveler, although the Red Shoveler is commonly described as such (Delacour and Mayr 1945, Delacour 1956, Johnsgard 1961a, 1965a, 1978, 1979).

Livezey's (1991, 1997b) third cohort of dabbling ducks is the Australasian teals (subgenus *Nesonetta*) which he splits into the grey teals (infragenus *Virago*), consisting of *Anas bernieri*, *A. gibberifrons*, *A. gracilis* and *A. albogularis*, and the reddish teals (infragenus *Nesonetta*) made up of *A. castanea*, *A. chlorotis*, *A. aucklandica* and *A. nesiotis*. A close relationship within the former group is recognized commonly; indeed, the Andaman and Grey Teals are often considered to be subspecies of the Indonesian Teal (Delacour and Mayr 1945, Delacour 1956, Johnsgard 1965a, 1978, 1979). Here they are treated as separate species. DNA studies of the Madagascar Teal confirmed its relationship with the Grey Teal (Young et al. 1997) and suggested that its nearest living relative is the Andaman Teal, although the extinct Sauzier's Teal *A. theodori* of Mauritius and Réunion (Mascarenes) may have been a sister species (Cheke 1987, Mourer-Chauviré 2000). A close affinity between three of the reddish teal is also recognized, and the Brown Teal and Campbell

Island Teal have been treated as subspecies of the Auckland Island Teal in the past (Delacour and Mayr 1945, Delacour 1956, Johnsgard 1965a, 1978, 1979). Accorded specific status in Marchant and Higgins (1990), they are considered separate species here. Molecular work suggested that all three may have arisen from independent radiations of the Chestnut Teal of Australia (Williams et al. 1991); however, Johnson and Sorensen (1999), Daugherty et al. (1999) and Kennedy and Spencer (2000) separated them from the Chestnut and Grey Teal while confirming their specific status through allozyme and mtDNA analysis.

The pintail group of dabbling ducks was split by Livezey (1991, 1997b) into three infragenera, *Paecilonitta* (the White-cheeked and Red-billed Pintails), *Dafilonettion* (the South American Teals), and *Dafila* (Brown, Northern and Eaton's Pintails). Eaton's Pintail appears genetically distinct from the Northern Pintail (Stahl et al. 1984) and perhaps results from the isolation of a small number of vagrant pintails settling many generations ago. The distinctive South Georgia Pintail was treated as a full species by Weller (1980); however, DNA studies have suggested that it and the Brown Pintail are closely related, with only 0.13% sequence divergence (Johnson and Sorenson 1999). Morphological studies (Livezey 1991) supported a link between all the pintails, and Johnson and Sorenson (1999) added the Cape Teal to the group. The South American Teal (including the Speckled Teal and the Andean Teal as subspecies) is more often allied with the green-winged teal (Delacour and Mayr 1945, Lorenz 1951–53, Boetticher 1952, Delacour 1956, Johnsgard 1965a, 1978, 1979), a relationship that is supported by recent studies of their DNA (Johnson and Sorenson 1999). The American Green-winged Teal seems to be a sister taxon to the South American Teal, not the Eurasian Teal as might be expected (Johnson and Sorenson 1999, Sangster et al. 2001).

In the Holarctic teal (subgenus *Querquedula*), Livezey (1991, 1997b) placed the Garganey, plus the Baikal, Eurasian and American Green-winged Teal (the last two here treated as separate species). The sister group relationship of the Garganey and the green-winged teal is controversial, since the former is invariably associated with the blue-winged ducks (subgenus *Spatula*, see above) (Salvadori 1895, Phillips 1923, Peters 1931, Delacour and Mayr 1945, Boetticher 1952, Verheyen 1955, Delacour 1956, Johnsgard 1961a, 1965a, 1978, 1979). However, Livezey (1991) argued that the pale grey forewing of the Garganey is derived from the light grey wing coverts of the green-winged and spotted teals and, thus, is only superficially similar to the powder blue forewings of the blue-winged ducks. The position of the Baikal Teal is also unsettled; it has been long considered an aberrant species of unclear affinities (Delacour and Mayr 1945, Boetticher 1952, Delacour 1956, Tuohy *et al.* 1992) and its molecular phylogeny suggests that it has no close relative within the dabbling ducks (Johnson and Sorenson 1999).

Livezey (1997b) considered the southern hemisphere group of spotted teal (subgenus *Punanetta*) to be composed of the Hottentot and Versicolor Teal (including the closely related Silver Teal and Puna Teal here treated as subspecies). This close relationship was not recognized by early taxonomists (Salvadori 1895, Phillips 1923, Peters 1931) but was by Delacour and Mayr (1945) and subsequently by Livezey (1991). DNA analysis (Johnson and Sorenson 1999) confirmed the link, while showing an affinity between these species and the blue-winged ducks, including the Garganey.

Des Callaghan

Muscovy Duck *Cairina moschata*
PLATE 12

Anas moschata Linnaeus, 1758, Syst. Nat., ed 10, p. 124
India; Brazil (any birds in India were introduced and domestic)
Cairina Fleming, 1822

Etymology: *Cairina* means native of Cairo in belief that bird came from Egypt; L *moschatus* means musky, as ♂ said to smell musky. Domesticated in tropical America centuries before arrival of Europeans, English name may refer to Russia, since ships of Muscovy Company, incorporated in London in 1555, could have brought Muscovies to England from France (Belon 1555, Donkin 1989).

Other names: French: Canard-musque d'Amerique; Mexican: Pato real; Portuguese: Pato or Pato silvestre; Spanish: Pato combined with several descriptive words, e.g. corillo, caseros.

Variation: no subspecies and no geographical variation in the wild; some variation in duckling pattern and in juvenile plumage.

Description

ADULT: somewhat dimorphic, particularly in size. Plumage of both sexes black with iridescent green and purplish sheen on back and wings. Mane-like crest of erectile head feathers. Badge of white feathers, variable in size, adorns each wing. Face of ♀ black, ♂ has black bare skin but, with age, small red caruncles appear especially over eye. Bill black except for bluish white band mid-length, tip hooked; short legs and large feet black; eye yellowish brown.

MOULT: no ♂ eclipse; however, black pigment fades in sunshine, so may look brown before body moult.

IMMATURE: like adult but less glossy, browner and with no or little white on forewing coverts until end of 1st year; lores feathered. Brown plumage of some juveniles mottled, or 'frosted', white. ♂ early becomes much larger than ♀ (Delacour 1954–64, Madge and Burn 1988).

DUCKLING: variable in pattern, most are similar to Northern Mallard and comb ducks. Yellow and dark brown, dark stripe from eye to dark cap and nape, short mane of longer down plumes at back of head, long fan-like tail. Prominent pale dorsal spots and wing patches. Large lustrous eyes, nail of grey bill hooked, legs and toes dark brown and yellow (Nelson 1993). Some ducklings almost entirely dark brown with yellow spot on chin, probably due to gene for melanism, particularly common in domestication (Coimbra-Filho 1965, Nelson 1993).

MEASUREMENTS AND WEIGHT: ♂ (*n* = 9) wing, 345–408 (385); tail, 164–184 (176); bill, 60.9–76.2 (67.9); tarsus, 62.1–69.1 (64.7). ♀ (*n* = 4) wing, 294–318 (307); tail 139–156 (148); bill, 47.2–54.3 (51.4); tarsus, 48.3–54.2 (51.9) (Palmer 1976). Smaller in size than usually described but ♂ almost twice as large as ♀, 1990–4000 and 1100–1470 respectively (Leopold 1959).

Field characters

Large (660–840 mm long), sedentary, tree-perching denizen of rainforests, where well camouflaged. Hybrids of domestic Mallard and Muscovies common in captivity but no evidence of hybridization in wild; hybrids sterile, thus 'differences in appearance (of wild birds) can sometimes be traced to hybridization with ducks of Mallard origin' (Donkin 1989) unlikely. Wild birds differentiated from feral or domestic Muscovies by more slender, fusiform shape and absence of, or reduced, red caruncles on face. Specimens of questionable appearance probably carry domestic genes.

Voice

Almost mute. ♂ has asthmatic wheeze, ♀ emits single *quack* when frightened, but communicates with ducklings by soft trilling. Ducklings twitter with 3 or 4-syllabled call when foraging and peep loudly when separated from brood.

Range and status

Inhabits rainforests near swamps, slow-moving tropical streams and coastal mangrove thickets. Ranges from Mexico through Central America to northern Argentina, east of high Andes, and including northern tropical and temperate areas of Andes in Columbia, Ecuador and eastern and Pacific Peru, Venezuela and Guianas. Groups of 2–20 seen on Upper Rupununi River, Guyana near Brazilian border, but becoming uncommon in Surinam. Rare visitor to Trinidad; recorded Chile. In Mexico

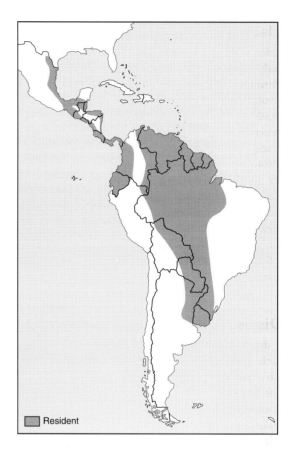

Resident

from Chaco, mid latitude at 7°S, has expanded northward with provision of nestboxes and now extends into Texas (Cruz 1991), although expanded population may contain domestic genes (Eitinear 1988). Several reports along Rio Grande between Texas and Mexico in vicinity of Santa Anna National Wildlife Refuge in southern Texas. Wetlands International (2002) suggested declining wild population of 100 000–1 000 000.

Domesticated in South America, though exact date and location unknown. Recorded in Columbia in 1514 and apparently seen by Columbus in Caribbean (Phillips 1922–26). Reached Europe *c* 1550 and, strangely, became widely 'known' to have originated in Turkey. Domesticated birds often become feral and may be found in many parts of world; deliberately introduced into Texas, Florida and Adams Island (Auckland Islands, New Zealand); probable that only Texas population survives (see Long 1981).

Habitat and general habits

Adept flyer through trees as travels to feeding grounds early in morning and evening (Leopold 1959), using stream as flyway. Rest of day spent perched in favourite tree. Prefers quiet oxbow ponds and forest creeks to main rivers. Non-migratory. Versatile and generalist feeder, straining organic matter from mud, grazing and gleaning grain (Woodyard and Bolen 1984). In Veracruz, took seeds (66%) and animal matter (34%), especially soldier flies Strationidae; in Tamaulipas, however, crop contents 100% maize. Adults also eat insect larvae, worms and flying insects, their usefulness as insectivores being major incentive for native peoples to domesticate them (Whitely 1973). Ducklings swim adroitly, snapping at tiny insects.

Displays and breeding behaviour

♂ display rhythmic Bobbing of head forward and back, crest spread, neck extended, wings slightly lifted and tail vibrated horizontally while uttering soft hisses. ♀ answers in similar, but less marked, manner (Delacour 1954–64). Before taking flight, make repeated Neck-craning movements diagonally upward with bill (Johnsgard 1965a). Polygyny often suggested. Despite claims that no pairbond occurs (Johnsgard 1978), Sibley (1967) in captivity in Massachusetts, and Rojas (1954) in Mexico found wild Muscovies usually in pairs. Rapacious copulation probably exaggerated (Raud and Faure 1988); ♂ induces cooperation of ♀ by treading her back. After coitus, ♀ performs ritual Bathing, swimming away splashing water over back. Notorious promiscuity of ♂♂ may be artifact of domestication, and studies of wild, marked individuals required. Non-territorial in breeding season, but ♂♂ aggressive to one another, and contest status in apparent social hierarchy using claws and wings (Fischer *et al.* 1982).

Breeding and life cycle

Few wild studies. Breeds in any month but rainy season may trigger egg production. ♂ deserts ♀ at egg-laying. Availability of nest sites limited by ♀ preference for laying clutch of 8–10 eggs in tree hollows; ground nests occur but more vulnerable to predation. Eggs white; 64.0×46.0 (56.5–67.5×42.7–48.0) ($n = 20$); weight 74 (calculated by Schönwetter 1960–66), or in captivity 71.1 (56.5–82.0) ($n = 100$); incubation, by ♀ alone, *c* 35 days, after which she calls young from nest. Ducklings, aided by sharp claws and hooked bill, climb to nest opening and jump; 46 hatched in captivity weighed 41.6. Nelson (1993) and Sibley (1967) reported captive ducklings wary and shy. Wing feathers grow slowly and fledging occurs in 3.5 months, putting young at risk of predation, and duck down found in 3 of 16 caimans shot on pond in Trinidad. No information on breeding success in wild. Strong bonds between brood members persist after fledging, and after parent has departed. Brood walks in single file, which may account for reported 'parades'. Hatching success in nestboxes high in Mexico (Woodyard and Bolen 1984). Captive ♀♀ can breed at one year old. No data on adult survival nor longevity.

Conservation and threats

Although greatly reduced in numbers by intensive hunting and destruction of habitat, small populations survive, Columbia being perhaps exception. Sanctuaries, and nestbox schemes to supplement holes in mature riparian trees, effective conservation measures. Crosses with domestic strains obviously detrimental to wild stock.

†Edmund Hoffmann

White-winged Duck *Asarcornis scutulata*
PLATE 12

Anas scutulata, S. Müller, 1842, Verh. Nat. Ges. Ned. Over. Bez., Land-Volkenk., p. 159
Java

Asarcornis Salvadori, 1895.

Etymology: *scutulata* from L. for diamond or checker-shaped, in reference to plumage marks.

Other names: White-winged Wood Duck; Forest Duck in Indonesia and Spirit Duck in Assam because of eerie, mournful honking call heard at dusk.

Variation: 2 subspecies described, *A. s. leucoptera* Blyth, 1849 and *A. s. scutulata*, but not recognized in recent literature due to quirk of ornithological history (see Green 1992a, 1993b). Indonesian *scutulata* reported different to continental ones when first compared (Blyth 1870), but extensive albinism in Indonesian birds attributed to hybridization or inbreeding, rather than racial differences, because of variety of plumage types observed (Blyth 1875, Hume and Marshall 1879–81, Salvadori 1895, Holmes 1977, MacKenzie 1990). Domestication excluded as explanation by both Phillips (1922–26) and Hoogerwerf (1950), as few Indonesian birds kept and none, apparently, bred in captivity; however, picture of captive pair in Sumatra appears in *Wildfowl* (8: 136). Structural and postural differences between Indonesian and continental birds suggest racial differentiation; further morphological and molecular studies needed.

Description

ADULT: slightly dimorphic. Continental *leucoptera* ♂ head and neck white, spotted black to varying degrees (often thickly spotted on crown, nape and hind neck). Back, mantle, rump and uppertail coverts black with metallic green iridescence. Upperwing coverts white and median coverts grey tipped greenish black, forming band. Secondaries bluish grey and primaries and primary coverts black. Outer tertiaries white with black margin. Tail dark brown. Lower neck glossy greenish black, merging into chestnut brown lower parts. Bill orange mottled black; legs orange-yellow; iris orange-yellow. In breeding season, base of bill swollen. ♀ similar but smaller and iris brown, usually with heavier speckling on head and neck. No swelling at base of bill during breeding season.

leucoptera adult ♂ and ♀ head and neck generally heavily speckled black, although some individuals speckled sparsely on head and upper neck. Adult ♂ Indonesian *scutulata* generally reported smaller with more extensive white plumage (Hoogerwerf 1950, Chambers 1990, Mackenzie 1990). Birds similar to continentals, with white speckling only on head and neck, present in Sumatra, but represent <20% of individuals (Chambers 1990, Mackenzie 1990, Burn

and Brickle 1992, Green 1992a); e.g. from minimum of 19 birds observed in Riau and Jambi provinces of southeast Sumatra, only one did not have completely white head and neck (Burn and Brickle 1992). Extent of white on body of Sumatran birds varies greatly (Chambers 1990, Mackenzie 1990, Burn and Brickle 1992). Museum specimens examined from Java and Sumatra showed more extensive white plumage than typical continental birds while birds in southeast Sumatra can be almost completely white except for black primaries, secondaries, scapulars and tail feathers (Burn and Brickle 1992). Most birds, especially ♂♂, exhibit white head, neck and breast, while underparts varied from almost wholly black to white down to undertail coverts. Mantle and uppertail coverts usually black, but some had white speckling or even fully white mantle and rump. All birds had black scapulars, remiges and rectrices, but secondary upperwing lesser and median coverts always white, with some birds also showing completely white primary coverts. All had white inner tertial stripe also present in continental birds. Structurally, Sumatran birds appear smaller than continental ones, with smaller, more rounded head, longer neck, smaller body and shorter, more curved bill. This results in more upright posture while sitting or standing, somewhat reminiscent of shelduck. Eye, leg and bill colour of Sumatran birds, especially of larger individuals presumed to be adult ♂♂, may be redder than continentals. Quantitative morphological data on Sumatran birds required to investigate suggested differences. Adult ♀ generally similar to ♂, but noticeably smaller with less extensive white plumage.

MOULT: no ♂ eclipse. Little known of moult cycle but, in Sumatra, wing moult complete by Sept.

IMMATURE: *leucoptera* similar to adult, but duller and browner with less extensive white on head and neck. Indonesian immature *scutulata* have more black spots on head than adult, and breast and back (often white in adult) always brown. Unlike Muscovy, has white wing patches in immature plumage.

DUCKLING: crown, nape, hind neck, upperparts and posterior underparts brown, with 2 buff yellow spots either side of rump. Wings brown with posterior buff yellow edge. Face, foreneck, chest and anterior underparts buff yellow. Highly distinctive orbital brown stripe divides anteriorly, with upper line running to nape and lower forming crescent on cheek. Bare parts grey (see Mackenzie and Kear 1976 for illustration).

MEASUREMENTS AND WEIGHT: from Baker (1908) of wild continental birds, sample size unknown: ♂ wing, 363–401; tail; 127–178; bill, 58–66; tarsus, 54–61; weight, 3800–4300. ♀ wing, 305–355; tail,127–178; bill, 56–61; tarsus, 53–61; weight, 2100–3600. Captive birds of Assam origin, WWT, Slimbridge, 1990–92, ♂ (n = 20) wing, 351–380 (367.2); bill, 57.3–67.2 (60.7); tarsus, 54.4–65.8 (60.3); weight, 2200–3225 (2666). ♀ (n = 7) wing, 327–358 (340.7); bill, 54.0–61.2 (57.4); tarsus, 55.0–57.6 (56.6); weight, 1700–2250 (1914). Vorderman (1892) gave dimensions of one, unsexed wild Indonesian bird: wing, 338; tail, 172; bill, 56; tarsus, 47. Hoogerwerf (1950) had weights of 'large number of males' collected in southern Sumatra ranging 2500–2800.

Field characters

Large size (660–810 mm long), white wing patches, habitat preferences and solitary nature distinctive. In northern part of range, may overlap with Comb Duck which uses more open wetlands, has no white on wings and whose ♂♂ have knobbed bills. Otherwise confusion likely only with domestic Muscovies seen near villages and identifiable by naked, warty faces.

Voice

Variety of sexually dimorphic honking and whistling calls made on water and in flight (Green 1993b). While flying in Sumatra, calls uttered at *c* one per sec (Burn and Brickle 1992), often by ♂ only, and more frequent just after taking flight. Five different calls recognized in Sumatra: *hong* (most common); *hongong*, second note lower and quieter than first; *hongongong*; *ink*, higher pitched version of *hong*, probably uttered by ♀; and *arnk* more rasping version of *hong*, probably as alarm. Calls given mainly when flying between feeding and roosting sites at dawn and dusk. Responds to playback in captivity (Green *et al.* 1992) and in field (Yahya 1994). Sonograms recorded at WWT, Slimbridge include 3, 2 and single-note calls.

Range and status

leucoptera found in India, Bangladesh and Thailand and rediscovered in Vietnam, Laos, Cambodia and Myanmar (Burma) (Green 1993c, Evans *et al.* 1996, Saw Han 1996). Nominate race extinct on Java but still quite widespread in Sumatra, where habitat being destroyed (Green 1993c). Highly fragmented and declining population mainly due to deforestation but also hunting (Green 1992a, 1993c).

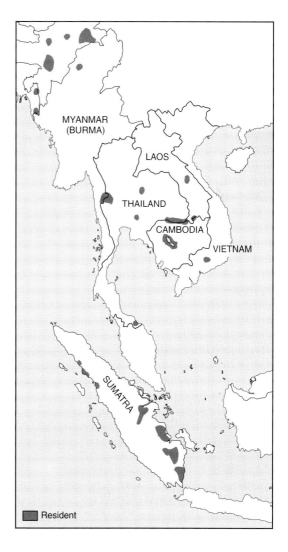

Resident

Wetlands International (2002) estimated 450 individuals in India, Bangladesh and Myanmar, 200 in southeastern Asia and 150 in Indonesia.

Habitat and general habits

Found on small wetlands among variety of moist forest types in lowland plains or upland plateaux (Green 1993c). Usually seen in groups of 1–3, with occasional family parties. Active around dawn and dusk, when seen in flight between feeding and roost sites. Often roosts high in forest trees during middle of day, and apparently active on moonlit nights. Little data on foraging behaviour. Omnivorous diet found mainly in shallow water by bill-dipping; aquatic snails, insects and small fish taken regularly, sometimes dives for fish (Green 1993b). No information on duckling diet. Many Sumatran birds feed in rice paddies in populated areas (Burn and Brickle 1992), roosting by day in nearby peat swamp forest.

Displays and breeding behaviour

Little information (Green 1993b). Inciting behaviour of ♀ common. Mutual Head-bobbing accompanied by honking apparently territorial display often seen in captive pairs and elicited by playback (Green *et al.* 1992). Zig-zag swimming display, with arching head movements, observed in possible courting groups in Sumatra (Chambers 1990). In Sumatra in 1992, display behaviour observed twice, between pair perched in tree and in pair feeding in rice paddy (Burn and Brickle 1992). On both occasions, display initiated by ♂ who performed elliptical Head-nodding reminiscent of those of ♂ shelduck. ♀♀ then began Head-nodding in response, but ♂ always performed more Head-nods than ♀. Intense periods of mutual Head-nodding lasted 1–2 minutes, but one ♂ Head-nodded for 10 mins. Johnsgard (1965a) described pre-copulatory display as silent vertical Head-pumping by both sexes, more obvious in ♂. After copulation, ♂ gives loud *kick* and may swim quickly in random directions while ♀ bathes. Monogamous, possibly with long-term pairbond.

Breeding and life cycle

Little known (Green 1993b). Nests at low density in pre-existing tree hollows up to 23 m above ground alongside forest wetlands. In Bangladesh, nests lined with leaves, grasses and roots of Water Hyacinth. Breeding season varies across range but generally timed so that hatching begins in early wet season when food supply probably increases. Egg-laying possibly Apr–July (Bangladesh, India, and Thailand), and Dec–June (southern Sumatra). Breeding seasons in captivity similar in Assam (26°N) and UK (52°N), laying lasting 18 Mar–4 June in Assam, and 30 Mar–5 June at WWT, Slimbridge (MacKenzie and Kear 1976).

Eggs white with faint green tinge; at WWT 67 × 49.5 (62.7–71.6 × 46.6–52.6) ($n = 40$) (Mackenzie and Kear 1976); in Sumatra 66–69 × 48–50 ($n = 8$) (Holmes 1977); in Indonesia (no sample size) 61.8–66 × 44.2–48.0 (Hoogerwerf 1950); weight at WWT 89 (66–107) ($n = 73$) (Mackenzie and Kear 1976), in Sumatra 80–87 ($n = 8$) (Holmes 1977). In captivity, incubation lasts *c* 33 days, and only ♀ incubates although ♂ remains close and accompanies ♀ on feeding trips. In captivity, clutch size mode 10 (6–13) ($n = 19$, Mackenzie and Kear 1976) while brood size in wild 4.4 (2–12) (mixed ages, $n = 19$). Broods recorded Jan (Sumatra), Mar (Sumatra), June (Myanmar, Thailand), July (Bangladesh, Thailand, Sumatra) and Aug (Myanmar). Duckling weights at WWT at 24 h, 48.7 (36–56) for ♀♀ ($n = 15$) and 48.4 (38–61) for ♂♂ ($n = 21$) (Mackenzie and Kear 1976). Brood often seen with 2 adults, suggesting that ♂ may help guard ducklings. Juveniles take *c* 14 weeks to fledge and may remain with parents afterwards; in Sumatra, families break up 3–5 weeks after fledging. Python shown to be predator in Sumatra.

Captive ♀♀ usually breed at 3 years of age, sometimes 2, while year-old ♀♀ known to lay fertile eggs (Mackenzie 1986). Captive ♂♂ can breed at 2 years old. No data on survival of wild birds. Maximum age of captive birds at WWT, 10 for ♂♂ and 7, possibly 12, for ♀♀ (Mackenzie 1986).

Conservation and threats

Globally Endangered (BirdLife International 2000, 2001). Rapid and accelerating destruction of lowland forest habitat (including massive forest fires in Sumatra) undoubtedly cause of decline; now mainly survives in small, fragmented populations in small patches of forest. Isolated populations unlikely to be viable long term (Ounsted *et al.* 1994). Hunting and egg collection secondary threats in many areas (Green 1992a, 1993c). Less significant or more localized threats include use of pesticides in paddy fields where birds feed, and contamination of some areas by oil, tea waste, etc. In recent years, various conservation projects carried out in India, Thailand, Indonesia, Laos and other countries, including site protection, surveys, education programmes and captive breeding; however, these insufficient to halt declines that are ongoing. Most populations remain outside protected areas (Green 1992a), and of 9 sites outside protection in Sumatra in 1988, 5 destroyed by 1994 (Ounsted *et al.* 1994).

Andy J. Green, Baz Hughes and Des Callaghan

Hartlaub's Duck *Pteronetta hartlaubii*
PLATE 12

Querquedula Hartlaubii Cassin, 1859, Proc. Acad. Nat. Sci. Philadelphia, p. 175
Camma River, Gabon
Pteronetta Salvadori, 1895.

Etymology: Gr. *pteron* is wing, *netta* duck, referring to distinctive wing patch; specific name after Karl Hartlaub (1814–1900), German ornithologist.

Other names: Hartlaub's Goose or Teal. French: Ptéronette de Hartlaub.

Variation: no subspecies. Birds from northeast Congo (now Zaire) formerly considered race *P. h. albifrons* Neumann, 1908 with larger white patches on forehead (Chapin 1932); however, this characteristic shown to be inconsistent (Bannerman 1921, Madge and Burn 1988).

Description

ADULT: sexes similar. ♂ head and neck black, with white patch on forehead that can occasionally extend to top of head. Rest of body rich chestnut, grading to dark olive-brown on longer scapulars, rump and tail. China blue upperwing coverts contrast sharply with olive-brown of rest of upperwing. Underwing dark brown. Wings have bony knobs at metacarpal joint. Bill black, with pinkish grey sub-terminal patch (on both maxilla and mandible), and base becomes swollen during breeding season; legs and feet dark brown, with yellowish or greenish tinge, and webs blackish; iris reddish brown, shading to dark greenish brown on inner edge. ♀ smaller and duller with little or no white patch on forehead; iris dark red (Chapin 1932, Delacour 1954–64, Brown *et al.* 1982).

MOULT: no ♂ eclipse plumage. Timing of wing and body moults unknown in wild.

IMMATURE: similar to ♀, but feathers on breast and lower parts pale edged (Chapin 1932, Brown *et al.* 1982). In captivity attains adult plumage at 6 months.

DUCKLING: blackish above and yellow below. Chin, neck and face with orange tinge, and yellow patches on wings, sides of back and rump. Strong black streak through eye and black spots on ear coverts (Delacour 1954–64, Brown *et al.* 1982).

MEASUREMENTS AND WEIGHT: ♂ (captive $n = 4$) wing, 270–287; tail, 100–115; culmen, 46–49; tarsus, 41.5–46; weight, 925–1140 (976). ♀ (captive $n = 2$) wing, 248–269; tail, 94–108; culmen, 44–47; tarsus, 40–45; weight, 770–805 (788) (Chapin 1932, Brown *et al.* 1982).

Field characters

Distinctive within range and unlikely to be confused with other wildfowl. Blue wing patch diagnostic in flight (Brown *et al.* 1982). Length 560–580 mm.

Voice

Includes quacking *ko-ko-ko-ko*, conversational *whit-whit-whit* and grating *ka-ka-kerr* or *karr-karr* (Mackworth-Praed and Grant 1970). ♂ in captivity has wheezy whistle and ♀ quacks (Lernould 1983). In distress, duckling utters series of evenly spaced, descending calls (10 in 2 sec); contact call faster than distress call (9 in 1 sec) and uttered in groups of 3 notes (Brown *et al.* 1982).

Range and status

Confined to equatorial rainforests of west and central Africa, from Sierra Leone east to southwest Sudan and south to southern Zaire (Brown *et al.* 1982, del Hoyo *et al.* 1992). At least 2 populations occur, although deforestation has undoubtedly formed other isolates; however, lack of data on distribution and abundance precludes accurate identification of boundaries.

Difficult to census due to forest perching habits. Western population probably numbers < 1000 individuals, and seems in sharp decline (Wetlands International 2002). Decline particularly acute in Ghana where described as not uncommon in 1970s (Grimes 1987) but now rare and confined to southern part of country east of Lake Volta. Uncommon in Ivory Coast, Sierra Leone and Liberia, and one published record for Guinea (del Hoyo *et al.* 1992). Not recorded in Benin or Togo (*contra* map in Brown

et al. 1982). Eastern population more numerous, perhaps 10 000–50 000 (Rose and Scott 1997). Appears most abundant in well-forested areas of Cameroon, Gabon, Congo and Zaire (Serle and Morel 1977, Brown *et al.* 1982, Madge and Burn 1988); at Lake Ossa, near Eden, Cameroon, Feb 2001, several pairs in every creek with population > 1000 (Demey 2001). However, numbers overall probably declining (Callaghan and Green 1993) and in Nigeria, where duck formerly not uncommon (Elgood 1994), now scarce. Also scarce in Sudan (del Hoyo *et al.* 1992).

Habitat and general habits

Sedentary, frequenting streams, small rivers and pools in rain and gallery forests and well-wooded savannas of coastal and inland regions (Johnsgard 1978, Brown *et al.* 1982, Grimes 1987, Elgood 1994). Readily perches in trees, and usually encountered

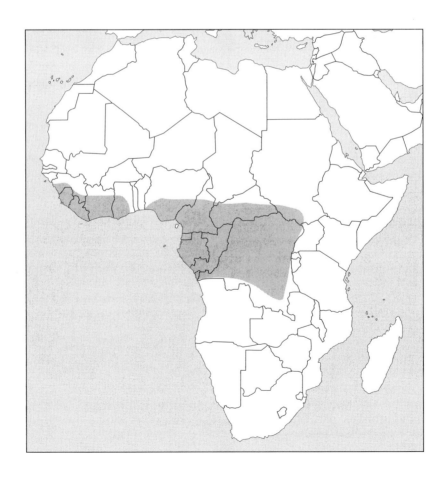

singly, in pairs or in small groups (Chapin 1932); however, larger numbers regularly observed (>30) which may be moulting parties (Johnsgard 1978).

Said to be nocturnal feeder (Brickell 1988). Eleven stomachs contained mostly aquatic invertebrates and some plant material (e.g. seeds) (Chapin 1932).

Displays and breeding behaviour

Pre-flight movements apparently consist of vertical Neck-jerking and Chin-lifting (Johnsgard 1965a). While perched on bough of tree, pairs seen to face one another, bow, rub bills and heads and make raucous noises (Delacour 1954–64). Similar behaviour described for captive birds, including circular movements of head while calling, but calls said to be quiet, high-pitched wheezing rather than raucous (Yealland 1951). Inciting by ♀ includes rotary Head-pumping accompanied by loud *quack* (Johnsgard 1965a). In threat, shows blue wing patches in sideways position to opponent (Lernould 1983).

Breeding and life cycle

Limited information. Nest not recorded from wild; however, thought to breed mainly during rainy season (Chapin 1932), although nesting probably protracted over many months and pairs likely to remain on territory year-round (Johnsgard 1978). Probably monogamous with firm pairbond, and captive individuals strongly territorial. Nests presumably located in hollow of tree although, in captivity, also made on ground amongst dense cover. In captivity, nest lined with pale grey down and clutch 8 (7–10) eggs ($n = 18$). Eggs cream coloured; 57.9×44.4 ($n = 20$); weight 68 (62–75) ($n = 56$); laid at daily intervals. Incubation by ♀ in captivity 32 days, and hatchlings weigh 41.5 (35–46) ($n = 19$). ♂ takes active parental role, and birds fledge in 56–60 days, after which ♂ becomes hostile to juveniles. Has bred at one year in captivity (Johnstone 1960, 1970, T. Jones 1972, Lernould 1983, Brickell 1988). No data on breeding success nor adult survival.

Conservation and threats

Given Near-threatened status by BirdLife International (2000). Rainforest clearance significant factor responsible for declining numbers, and no direct conservation action taken (Callaghan and Green 1993). Studies in wild required urgently.

Des Callaghan

American Wood Duck *Aix sponsa*
PLATE 13

Anas Sponsa Linnaeus, 1758, Syst. Nat., ed. 10, p. 128
North America = Carolina
Aix Boie, 1828

Etymology: *sponsa* refers to 'bridal dress' of ♂ in breeding plumage. *Aix* Gr. for diving bird, perhaps a duck mentioned by Aristotle.

Other names: Carolina, Acorn Duck, Squealer, Summer Duck, Woodie. French: Canard branchu; Spanish: Pato de charreteras, Pato Arcoiris.

Variation: no subspecies.

Description

ADULT: dimorphic. ♂ in breeding, or alternate, plumage has head, including long occipital crest, metallic green and purple with white lines and patches, chin and throat white; mantle dark greenish brown; wings metallic blue, green and black, primaries bordered outwards, secondaries and tertiaries tipped white; tail dark glossy green, coverts above long and curved, black and dark brown, some of upper ones with golden buff streaks; upperbreast vinous with white triangular spots, passing to white on lower breast and abdomen; broad black and white bars on sides, followed by buff feathers streaked with black, those in front of maroon flanks being buff yellow vermiculated black. Bill yellow, red, white and black; legs dull yellow and blackish brown; iris orange-red. ♀ olive-brown above and white below, with white chin and throat and white line around eyes and around culmen; breast and sides mottled; crest and mantle glossed purple and green; wings much as in ♂, but less bright and lacking enlarged tertiaries; tail bronzy brown. Bill black; legs as in ♂, but darker; iris dark brown (Delacour 1954–64).

MOULT: 2 body moults and one wing moult annually. Bright plumage of ♂ acquired late summer, retained through winter and into early summer. Eclipse, or basic, plumage, worn briefly by ♂ in summer while flight feathers replaced, resembles ♀ except for white throat and white cheek lines, red eye and colourful bill. Breeding ♀ flightless while young still unfledged. If single ovary of ♀ damaged or ceases to function, assumes dull ♂-like plumage at next body moult. For details of plumages and sequence of moults, see Palmer (1976) and Hepp and Bellrose (1995).

IMMATURE: ♂ much like ♀ but shows white on throat and face from *c* 3 months of age; juvenile ♀ starts to show white around eyes at same age.

DUCKLING: has dark, well-marked stripe from eye to occiput, short mane, dark almost glossy markings on pale yellowish base, slim boldly patterned tarsi and toes, and long fan-like blackish tail. Dark forehead, widening gradually and evenly from horns of dark bill past pale pre-ocular area, especially prominent in front view; golden or silvery aspect produced by many dull greenish yellow down tips (Nelson 1993). Large lustrous dark eyes particularly obvious. Long tail and sharp decurved claws enable ducklings to climb inner side of nest cavity (Siegfried 1974b).

MEASUREMENTS AND WEIGHT: ♂ (*n* = 12) wing, 218–240 (228); tail, 100–118 (115); bill, 32–36 (35); tarsus, 34–39 (36) (Palmer 1976); weight (*n* = 84), 544–862 (680); weight before mate lays (*n* = 5), 750; late in her incubation (*n* = 7), 584 (Hepp and Bellrose 1995). ♀ (*n* = 12) wing, 211–231 (221); tail, 91–106 (98); bill, 31–35 (34); tarsus, 33–36 (35) (Palmer 1995); weight (*n* = 60), 499–862 (671); weight at egg-laying, 706; during incubation, 542 (Hepp and Bellrose 1995).

Field characters

Fairly small perching duck, 470–540 mm long, that cannot easily be confused with any other, except in flight, since ♂ in breeding plumage distinctive and colourful. Except for short period of summer, when ♀ engages in parental duties, tends to fly in pairs when ♀'s call makes identification easy. Able to fly through woodland adroitly. Eclipsed ♂, ♀ and juvenile resemble those of Mandarin, and may be confused at sites where released birds occur. Mandarin has lighter grey head and eye encircled by narrow white line that continues towards nape.

Voice

Fairly silent. Calls described and sonograms given in Bellrose and Holm (1994) and Hepp and Bellrose (1995). ♂ has soft, high, rising whistle used in contact and Burp note *pfits* used in courtship. ♀ has various call notes including loud squealing *we-eek, we-eek* as pair flies off, and in warning or danger signal. Coquette call of ♀ given in courtship (Johnsgard 1965a) and at roost; probably functions to attract mate and reinforce bond. ♀'s maternal call coaxes young to leave hole nest at appropriate moment; ducklings presumably learn this call during hatching process, and in 1st hours of life spent in darkness of nest cavity. Young ducklings keep up constant conversation of high-pitched polysyllabic calls, especially when feeding, and have rapid, high-pitched distress call *ti-ti-ti-ti* (Nelson 1993); utter some adult vocalizations at 3 months.

Whistling sounds made by wings in flight.

Range and status

Widespread in North America. Small Pacific coast population, and larger one that reaches as far north as eastern Great Lakes, Québec and New Brunswick in summer. Partially migratory, northern populations move to southern parts of breeding range in autumn, mainly south of 35°N, some reaching Mexico, southern birds and most of those in California resident (Bellrose and Holm 1994). Breeding range overlaps that of Pileated Woodpecker *Dryocopus pileatus* whose holes often selected as nest site.

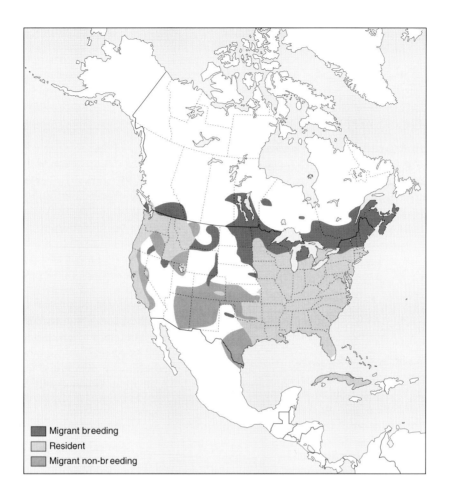

Migrant breeding
Resident
Migrant non-breeding

Rare at start of last century, has increased markedly due mainly to protection (Migratory Birds Treaty Act 1918), also possibly expanding Beaver populations and nestbox schemes (Bellrose 1990). Now commonest hole-nesting duck in North America. Wetlands International (2002) reported populations of 2 800 000 for eastern, 665 100 for interior and 66 000 for western North America, with eastern element increasing.

Habitat and general habits

Summers on lakes, marshes and slow water systems, often created by Beaver activity, with dense deciduous or mixed woodland cover. Typically spends part of day perched. In winter, found in more open waters, occasionally on brackish water near coast. Generally does not flock except at roosts in autumn and winter, when groups of 200–1000 possible, but less gregarious in breeding season.

Feeds more on acorns than other North American ducks, and eats mainly by dabbling and occasionally up-ending. Other foods include seeds of bald cypress, hickories, button bush, arrow arum and bur reed. Mulberries and wild grapes also taken in season, as is harvested corn and wheat. Feeds mainly on shoreline, using large eyes to select items, and only dives as duckling or to escape. Ducklings insectivorous until *c* 6 weeks of age, feeding on nymphs of mayfly and dragonfly, and newly emerged adult chironomids, taken from water surface. Breeding ♀ consumes more invertebrate food than ♂ or nonbreeding ♀♀ (Hepp and Bellrose 1995). In Missouri, breeding ♀♀ spent more time feeding (73%) than ♂♂ (34%) but *c* same amount of time (22–27%) in maintenance activities; ♂♂ spent remainder of time alert (Hepp and Bellrose 1995).

Displays and breeding behaviour

Well studied (Johnsgard 1965a, Hepp and Bellrose 1995). Pre-flight indicated by Neck-craning movement and lateral Head-shaking. In courtship, ♀ and ♂ often nibble head region of mate. Inciting by ♀ quite common, and performed also by paired ♂. Courtship seen more in autumn than spring. Turn-back-of-head, Chin-lift, Preen-behind-wing, Wing-and-tail-flash, Burp, Bill-jerk and Bill-jab all performed by ♂, and typically directed at single ♀. Preen-behind-wing frequent and striking, although not performed repeatedly, as in Mandarin. Burp display is whistle accompanied by vertical stretching of neck and raising of crest. Chin-lifting towards ♀ occurs independently or in sequence with Turn-back-of-head; in Turn-back-of-head, ♂ swims ahead and slightly to one side, with tail tilted to side away from ♀. Combination of Inciting by ♀ and Turn-back-of-head by ♂ has particular importance in pair formation. ♂♂ also perform elaborate Display Shake combined with whistling note, and sudden upward jerk of wing and tail called Wing-and-tail-flash. Pairs formed autumn and winter, and copulation occurs from autumn, probably reinforcing bond. At copulation, ♀ adopts prone position without prior mutual display; ♂ swims around her, usually Bill-dipping or Drinking, and pecks at her body. He mounts and, after treading, swims rapidly away Turning-back-of-head; she bathes. Forced extra-pair copulation rare. Monogamous, or serially monogamous at southern latitudes.

Not territorial; spacing of nests depends on location of suitable tree holes or nestboxes, and site not defended. ♂ will defend mate if approached closely.

Breeding and life cycle

Timing of nesting varies within breeding range; in south may start as early as Feb, in north peak nesting occurs mid Mar–mid Apr; in all cases, nesting ceases soon after longest day in late June (Murton and Kear 1978, Hepp and Bellrose 1995). Obligate hole-nesters, like Mandarin. Bellrose and Holm (1994) suggested that particular form and body size developed in evolution in order that ♀♀ might take advantage of holes created by Pileated Woodpeckers. Although woodpecker holes apparently preferred, other natural cavities selected, as well as man-made boxes.

In nest site selection, ♂ follows ♀. Pair may spend some part of every morning looking for and inspecting holes. Breeding pair maintain bond later into incubation than most North American ducks, which may benefit both sexes when breeding seasons long and 2nd broods more likely to occur (Manlove and Hepp 1998).

Dump nesting common in places, perhaps related to competition among ♀♀ for suitable holes. Also lays in nests of other cavity nesters, especially Hooded Merganser (Mallory 2003), but also Black-bellied Whistling-duck. Nest competitors include, importantly, introduced Common Starling *S. vulgaris*, Hooded Merganser, various other native birds, flying squirrels, mice and honey bees. Eggs laid every 24 h; elliptical ovate and dull white; in South Carolina 51.3 × 39.4 (46.5–61.2 × 36.8– 42.2) ($n = 105$), in Tennessee 49.9 × 38.5 (40.1–55.5 × 34.7–41.5) ($n = 203$); mass in South Carolina 44.2 (35.2– 57.6) ($n = 105$), in New York 42.9 (33.8–55.0) ($n = 174$) (Hepp and Bellrose 1995), in captivity at WWT, Slimbridge smaller at 38.6 (31.0–47.0) ($n = 100$). Clutch 12.2 (10.4–14.7) eggs ($n = 820$), declining as season progresses (Hepp and Bellrose 1995). ♀ covers first eggs with litter found in cavity, and starts to add down as 6th or 7th egg laid. Incubation, by ♀ alone, 30.9 days ($n = 44$); she leaves twice daily for average 98.6 min and covers eggs with down; meanwhile, her weight declines by 0.68 g per day (Manlove and Hepp 2000).

Up to 48 h before hatching, star-like cracks appear near blunt end of egg. Weight of day-old averages 23.7 (19–28) ($n = 43$) (Hepp and Bellrose 1995). Ducklings called from nest by ♀ standing on ground; have lively nervous disposition and, in captivity, make frequent attempts to jump towards light; in climbing vertical surfaces, proceed by series of leaps and use tail as brace (Siegfried 1974b); have no fear or avoidance of heights (Kear 1967). Hatching success of all nests in Illinois 62.6%, in New

York 51.6% (Hepp and Bellrose 1995). Nesting ♀ predated by foxes and Grey Squirrel *Sciurus carolinensis*, Raccoons, which are increasing, and Bull Snakes *Pituophis melanoleucus*. Predators of eggs include rat snakes, American Mink and various woodpeckers. Re-nesting common if eggs lost (birds move to new cavity), and a few ♀♀ in southern part of range renest after successfully hatching 1st clutch.

Parental care by ♀ alone who uses Distraction display feigning broken wings. As well as mammalian predators, ducklings taken by Snapping Turtles *Chelydra serpentina*, Bullfrogs *Rana catesbeiana*, Largemouth Bass *Micropterus salmoides* and Alligators *Alligator mississippiensis*. Fledge in 8–9 weeks. Proportion of young surviving from hatching to fledging 0.41–0.65, most mortality occurring in 1st 2 weeks. Annual survival of adult ♂♂ greater than ♀♀: 0.556 *v* 0.506 (Hepp and Bellrose 1995). Like Mandarin, particularly prone to avian TB in captivity. Both sexes can breed in year following hatching, but yearling ♀♀ usually lay later than older birds. ♀ probably tends to return to lay in site that resembles one in which hatched.

Conservation and threats

At start of 20th century, thought to be in danger of extinction; however, numbers never so low as supposed, and Migratory Bird Treaty Act of 1918, which protected birds in US and Canada, resulted in steady population growth until 1985. Since then, increases have slowed although harvest by hunters has declined (Bellrose 1990, Hepp and Bellrose 1995). After Northern Mallard, most commonly shot duck in Mississippi and Atlantic flyways, comprizing *c* 10% of annual wildfowl harvest. Major threats are drainage of swamps and, in particular, destruction of woodland with dead stumps and associated woodpeckers. Considerable proportion of population nests in boxes. Most successful boxes, that is, best accepted and which produce most young, resemble torpedoes and imitate cavity excavated in side branches by woodpeckers. An elliptical entrance hole may prevent access by Raccoons. A sharply pointed smooth top deters most mammalian predators; guards may be needed to prevent snakes from entering

Janet Kear

Mandarin Duck *Aix galericulata*
PLATE 13

Anas galericulata Linnaeus, 1758, Syst. Nat., ed. 10, p. 128
China

Etymology: *galericulata* refers to 'helmet' of bright feathers on head of ♂ in breeding plumage. English name dates from 1700s and derives from Sanskrit *mantrin* meaning counselor (Shurtleff and Savage 1996).

Other names: Mandarin. Chinese: Yuen Yang; Japanese: Oshidori; Russian: Mandarinka.

Variation: no subspecies.

Description

ADULT: dimorphic. ♂ in breeding, or alternate, plumage has forehead and crown glossy green to purplish, coppery red and green on long nuchal crest; sides of head, above eyes, and crest white; cheeks buff; ruff of pointed feathers on sides of neck and foreneck, chestnut with whitish shafts; mantle and back olive-brown; scapulars glossy blue with white and black; wings mostly olive-brown, ornamental tertiaries blue outside, 'sails' steel blue on inner web, orange-buff on large outer one, with black border in middle; upperbreast maroon; lowerbreast and abdomen white; sides of breast with alternate black and white bands; sides pale orange-brown vermiculated black, larger feathers tipped with black and white crescentic bands; tail brown glossed green, long upper coverts dark blue-green, lower white. Bill red, nail fleshy pink; legs orange-buff; iris dark brown with yellowish outer ring (Delacour 1954–64). ♀ head, neck and crest soft lilac-grey, with small greyish ruff; chin and throat white, and white spectacle stripe runs from around eye into crest at nape of neck; upperparts olive-brown with greenish sheen, and breast and sides browny grey with rows of whitish oval spots; wings and tail vary from pale brown to dark sepia with no colourful speculum as in Wood Duck; bill greyish brown with pale orange tip; legs brownish yellow; eyes brown (Lever 1989).

MOULT: both sexes moult body feathers twice annually, and undergo single wing moult after breeding. ♂ in eclipse closely resembles ♀ and, during this time, June–Sept, will lose all flight feathers and be temporarily flightless. Eclipsed ♂ can be distinguished from ♀ by red bill, yellower legs, less white marking around eyes and at base of bill, heavier crest, and glossier plumage with brown mottling on underparts (Lever 1989). ♀ flightless while still with brood.

IMMATURE: resembles adult ♀, but more uniformly grey-brown with less distinct face markings and less clearly dappled upper breast and flanks (Cramp and Simmons 1977).

DUCKLING: similar to Wood Duckling but slightly larger with yellow base colour instead of white. Crown, upperparts and sides dark olive-brown, longer filaments tipped olive-yellow. Spots on wing and on sides of back and rump yellow. One dark stripe from eye to nape, another less distinct below on cheek; sides of head, throat and chest yellow-buff, underparts pale yellow (Cramp and Simmons 1977). Bill grey-purple with pink nail.

MEASUREMENTS AND WEIGHT: ♂ wing (*n* = 11), 226–242 (235); tail (*n* = 13), 94–111 (101); bill (*n* = 15), 27–31 (28.6); tarsus (*n* = 14), 36–40 (38.1). ♀ (*n* = 8) wing, 215–234 (226); tail, 94–104 (99.3); bill 27–30 (28.2); tarsus, 35–38 (36.7). Weight in Russia (no sample size) ♂ 571–693 (628); ♀ 428–608 (512) (Cramp and Simmons 1977).

Field characters

Fairly small perching duck, 410–490 mm long, with short bill, large head, thick neck and relatively long tail that can be used as prop against substrate when moving along branch of tree. ♂ in breeding plumage exotic-looking and unmistakable, with great orange

wing sails and side whiskers. ♀ paler and greyer overall than ♀ Wood Duck, with smaller eye-patch (Madge and Burn 1988).

Voice

Not very vocal except during courtship and, rarely, in flight. ♂ has sharp staccato *hwick* or *uib uib*. ♀ has coquette call like that of Wood Duck, and Inciting call. Sonogram of ♂ and ♀ call in Cramp and Simmons (1977).

Range and status

Breeds in Russian Ussuriland in Amur, Khabarovsk and Primorye regions as far west as Zeya Estuary, northern China, Sakhalin Island, Kunashir in Kuril Islands and in Hokkaido, most northerly of Japan's main islands. Winters in eastern, central and southern China, Taiwan, Korea and Honshu; small numbers reach Myanmar (Burma) and northeast India (Brazil 1991, Green 1992b, Shurtleff and Savage 1996). Had wider breeding distribution in Palearctic before destruction of dominant broadleaf woodland; now has fragmented habitat *c* fifth of that available to North American Wood Duck on other side of Pacific Ocean. Introduced population breeding in Britain since 1930s. Uncertain what proportion of native population migrates—perhaps most; certainly those breeding in Ussuriland move south. Migrates mainly at night.

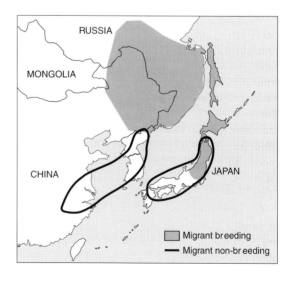

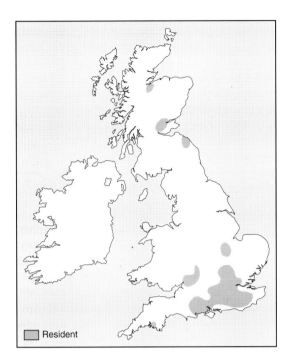

Resident

(1965a) noted, display especially on dark days. Diet mainly seeds and small nuts such as acorns, sweet chestnut and beechmast, but invertebrates, tadpoles and small fish and frogs taken, and invertebrates essential food for ducklings. Feeds by picking items from water surface and from shoreline; dabbles and up-ends but rarely dives. In winter, feeds in flooded rice fields after harvest in Oct.

Displays and breeding behaviour

♀♀ nibble facial plumes of mate, as Wood Ducks do, and ♀ Inciting displays and Coquette calls almost identical. However, ♂♂ tend to be more promiscuous in courtship. ♂ has Display Shake, similar to corresponding display of Wood Duck, plus Double Display Shake in which bill dipped and sneeze-like call uttered as head shaken, followed by another dipping movement and wheezy call as head withdrawn and tail shaken vigorously. Remarkable orange wing sails (enlarged inner secondaries) employed in ♂ Drinking and Preen-behind-wing display sequence (Johnsgard 1965a), ♂ does not spread whole wing but lifts sail on side towards ♀, quickly exposing metallic blue outer vane. ♂ also performs Wing-and-tail-flash, as does Wood Duck.

Pre-copulatory display consists of mutual Head-pumping; ♀ gradually flattens herself, ♂ may Bill-dip before mounting. After treading, ♂ swims rapidly away while Turning-back-of-head toward ♀ with tail slightly raised; she bathes.

Pairbond lasts until late in incubation or, more rarely, into early brood rearing, later than Wood Duck. Not territorial; nest spacing depends on distribution of tree holes. Obligate cavity nester; ♀, accompanied by ♂, selects tree holes as much as 15 m above ground.

Breeding and life cycle

Limited information from wild. Arrives in Ussuriland and Sakhalin already paired in Mar–early Apr. In Britain nests mid Apr–midsummer (Shurtleff and Savage 1996); in northern Honshu, breeds early June (Brazil 1991). Like Wood Duck, probably adopts woodpecker hole if available, but also nests in natural holes and nestboxes. Perhaps competes for these sites with other hole-nesters, such as Goosanders (Common Merganers) and Scaly-sided Mergansers.

Notoriously difficult to find and census (Davies 1988); Wetlands International (2002) suggested declining populations of 20 000 in China, 5000 in Korea and 350–500 resident in Taiwan; 40 000 estimated wintering in Japan (Miyabayashi and Mundkur 1999) where population appears stable. Introduced birds in Britain may exceed 7000 (Davies 1988).

Habitat and general habits

Asia's ecological equivalent of American Wood Duck, occupying similar mid-latitude broadleaf forest, with standing or slow moving freshwater, fringed by overhanging dense tree growth. Flies as easily through trees. Seems to have similar relationship to Black Woodpecker *Dryocopus martius* for providing nesting sites as Wood Duck has to Pileated Woodpecker. Introduced population in Britain, where Black Woodpecker absent, depends on natural holes, particularly in Beech *Fagus silvatica* that decays readily, and on nestboxes.

Gregarious and most active early morning and in evenings. Large eyes may be important in foraging under darkness of tree cover and, indeed, in observing conspicuous ♂♂ which, as Johnsgard

Will return to same hole year after year if successful. Nest building by ♀ only, using material already in hole, plus down from her breast. Eggs oval, white or buff, 51 × 37 (46–55 × 43–41) (*n* = 30) (Schönwetter 1960–66); weight in captivity 43.5 (35.5–51.5) (*n* = 100); clutch size *c* 10 (7–14), apparently smaller in Russia than in England where dump nesting common (Shurtleff and Savage 1996). Incubation, by ♀, 28–33 days, during which she leaves to feed once or twice daily. Hatching synchronous, weight of captive day-olds 26.9 (18.0–33.5) (*n* = 100). Ducklings have large eyes, and sharp claws with which to climb inside wall of dark nest cavity. ♀ calls them from hole with soft, melodious Exodus call, and has deep rolling Distraction call to warn brood and to divert predators (Cramp and Simmons 1977). Parental care entirely by ♀ up to fledging at 40–45 days. Both sexes can breed in year after hatching.

No data on breeding success in wild; egg predators include American Mink, Raccoon Dogs *Nyctereutes procyonoides* and martens *Martes*, but no information on numbers or proportion taken. Adult survival also unknown, but probably rather short-lived. In captivity especially prone, like Wood Ducks, to die of avian tuberculosis, although relatively immune to aspergillosis and candidiasis. Susceptibility to TB may be related to perching habit—if seldom on ground, may need no immunity to bacilli present in droppings, since does not normally contact them. And as hole-nesters in rotting tree stumps, may have developed some natural protection from pathogenic moulds and yeasts, such as *Aspergillus* and *Candida*. Oldest captive lived to 15 years (Hillgarth and Kear 1981), free-flying bird in England lived > 11 years, while oldest BTO ringed bird was > 8 years (Clark *et al.* 2002).

Conservation and threats

Wholesale cutting of Chinese Imperial Hunting Forests after 1911, when Manchu emperors deposed, and spread of agriculture, mining and other industry in Manchuria reduced drastically native woodland habitat, and caused great decline in numbers. Continuing deforestation, especially along river valleys, and consequent loss of nest holes, possibly greatest threat within natural range; food supply from mature oaks *Quercus* and other nut-bearing trees also crucial to survival before and during migration and in winter. Trapping of wintering flocks in China, and huge numbers exported West for aviculture, may have been one cause of decline; export ban imposed in 1975. Protected in Japan since 1947, and probably increasing there. Proposed logging of pristine coniferous forest of Sakhalin may affect Mandarins (and Black Woodpeckers) that breed in southern and central parts of that island; local Environment Watch called for creation of 700 km² refuge to protect this rich and wild corner of Sakhalin. Features in traditional Chinese and Japanese art and culture, often as symbol of marital fidelity and devotion (Shurtleff and Savage 1996); thus surprizing that so little known of its biology.

Janet Kear

Australian Wood Duck *Chenonetta jubata*
PLATE 13

Anas jubata Latham, 1801, Index Ornith., Suppl., p. 69 New South Wales
Chenonetta Brandt, 1836

Etymology: *Chen* Gr. means goose, plus *netta* meaning duck; *jubata* L. is crested or maned.

Other names: Maned Goose or Duck, Wood Duck, Blue Duck. Australian Aboriginal: Barndo, Eruwilla, Gnaroo, Goornabrinna, Gunali, Gunma, Irieerta, Kiri-kiri, Kooar, Loodnapina, Mar-ang-an-ner, Moodon-gnarie, Naneg, Neirey, Ngalawal, Ngowera, Purner, Tykewa, Walan, Woodla-arrie, Yarkalto; Dutch: Manengans; French: Canard à crinière; German: Mähnenente; Spanish: Pato de Crin.

Variation: no subspecies.

Description

ADULT: sexes differ in plumage but not in size. ♂ warm brown head and neck with black, mane-like crest down nape and hind neck that can expand in display. Body generally grey finely vermiculated on flanks, with dark line in scapulars extending through tertials. Back, rump, tail, vent and belly charcoal black. Bill dark grey; legs and feet grey-brown; eye dark brown. ♀ lacks intensity of ♂ pattern with lighter tone on head with distinctive pattern formed by white supercilium and white stripe below eye. Spotted breast similar to ♂ but underparts barred brown. Longitudinal stripe of scapulars and tertials similar to ♂ but belly, vent and undertail coverts white. Wings similar in ♂ and ♀ with upper forewing grey with broad white area on rear inner-wing crossed by narrow dark green iridescent speculum towards forward limit of white. Under-wings white.

MOULT: 2 plumages annually with simultaneous loss of flight feathers during major post-breeding moult. Moult, including wing replacement, sometimes skipped under drought conditions. ♂ often acquires eclipse plumage in summer that closely resembles ♀ but most often retains some dark belly and undertail characteristics. Eclipse in ♂ probably associated with successful brood rearing. Pre-breeding moult of most body feathers produces definitive alternate plumage in ♂ and fresh plumage in ♀.

IMMATURE: like ♀ but paler with breast distinctly streaked not spotted.

DUCKLING: dark brown upperparts with dark crown and two dark stripes on white face, one through eye, other across cheek. Rest of underparts white. Trailing edges of wing pads whiter, and white spot each side of rump.

MEASUREMENTS AND WEIGHT: ♂ (*n* = 16) wing, 265–293 (277); tail, 87–105 (96); bill, 25–31 (28); tarsus, 47–54 (51); weight (*n* = 45), 700–955 (815). ♀ (*n* = 8) wing, 270–286 (277); tail, 94–106 (98); bill, 26–30 (28); tarsus, 48–54 (50); weight (*n* = 26), 662–984 (800) (Frith 1982, Marchant and Higgins 1990).

Field characters

Medium-sized duck, 440–510 mm long, resembling small goose in shape and grazing behaviour. Plump body, relatively long legs, stubby bill, 'waisted' neck, large head and conspicuous black and white spotted breast all distinctive features (Madge and Burn 1988). In Australia unmistakable. Commonly seen in flocks when noisy mewing call of ♀ often draws attention. Usually found grazing in daytime and roosting on or near water at night. White upper-wing patches conspicuous in flight. Dark undertail and belly of ♂ good field marks.

Voice

Loud Identity call of ♀ long, drawn-out and mournful but distinctive mewing sound. ♀ uses similar call when Inciting and conversational cluck to maintain contact, e.g. when feeding, nest searching and as pre-flight signal. ♂ has large tracheal bulla but makes only weak sounds, soft wheezy and rather nasal call uttered during Burp display and more softly as parental contact call with brood. Deep rumbling sound produced during Display-shake. Further details, including sonograms, in Marchant and Higgins (1990).

Range and status

Endemic to Australia, vagrant in New Zealand. Generally widespread, except in far north, and mostly

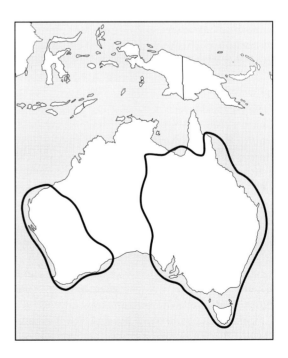

absent within arid zone running from northwest of continent to Australian Bight (Blakers *et al.* 1984, Marchant and Higgins 1990). Concentrations occur mostly in far southwest and throughout wetter regions of east. No comprehensive measures of abundance. Breeding population increasing in Tasmania. Recent counts on selected wetlands in southwest and in Victoria gave peak figures in both areas of *c* 10 000. Aerial surveys, used to provide indices of abundance of waterbirds, found numbers well in excess of 100 000 in some recent years (Marchant and Higgins 1990). Estimates, based on aerial surveys in eastern Australia, gave average figure of > 200 000 (Kingsford *et al.* 1999); however, doubtful that these surveys provide true picture because farmlands not sampled adequately. Likely, therefore, that numbers at times > 500 000, even 1 000 000.

Habitat and general habits

Particularly common in croplands and stock-grazed areas where benefiting from availability of short pastures used for feeding areas, and from presence of numerous farm dams for loafing and care of broods. Also found on most other wetlands, often associated with small bodies of water and commonly near ponds in urban areas. Mature trees with hollows of sufficient size required for nests, and this limits breeding at wetlands in many arid areas and where clearing has been severe; however, increased markedly in range and abundance as consequence of land clearing and development following European settlement (Marchant and Higgins 1990). Generally avoids only denser forested areas. Specialist grazer with almost all food obtained on land, usually by day, but also at night. Takes insects, etc, from water surface by picking but rarely up-ends, and dabbling may be to obtain grit rather than food (Kingsford 1989). Details of diet in Marchant and Higgins (1990). Ducklings start to graze when 2–3 days old (Kingsford 1989).

Displays and breeding behaviour

Gregarious at all times but breeding pairs solitary. Family groups form flocks after breeding, but mobile and composition seldom constant.

Chin-flick used to signal pre-flight with ♀ often calling. Threat indicated by thrusting head forward low on surface with open bill. Will rush at intruder in this posture moving quickly either on land or water. Pair formation involves Display-shake and Double-display-shake by ♂. From position with head buried in scapulars, body expanded to create impressive size, bill brought slowly to level of breast or, when on water, dipped to surface then returned abruptly back to resting position in shaking movement accompanied by rumbling sound. Sometimes 2nd shake immediately follows. Jump-flights frequent during communal display activities, when ♂ rises steeply from water in awkward flight with head thrust forward before pitching heavily and swimming back towards group. ♂ advertises with Burp display in which head held high, feathers expanded to create large disk shape, mane erect and wheezy call given. ♂ also Turns-back-of-head to lead away ♀. Inciting by ♀ involves Chin-lifting towards partner, then aggressive pointing with head lowered in direction of intruder while giving sharp repeated nasal call. Pre-copulatory Head-pumping with Bill-dipping and Head-dipping mainly by ♂ followed by ♀ stretching head forwards above water before ♂ mounts. After copulation, ♀ calls and ♂ Turns-back-of-head with elevated rear to reveal black undertail; both often then bathe. See Johnsgard (1965a) and Marchant and Higgins (1990) for more detail.

Breeding and life cycle

Sustained pairbond between breeding birds. Nests in tree hollow or suitable substitute (e.g. box). Pair search for nest hole together, usually in morning, both inspecting possible sites with constant calling by ♀, especially as move to another tree. Behaviour conspicuous and good indication that breeding will occur. Season usually starts July in regular rainfall areas, but erratic inland and can occur all year.

Eggs laid daily but sometimes interval 2 days, and sitting may not begin immediately on completion of clutch. Eggs oval or elliptical, close-grained, smooth, glossy, cream to creamy white (Marchant and Higgins 1990); 57 × 42 (53–62 × 40–45) (*n* = 88) (Frith 1982); in captivity 100 weighed on average 55.6 (45.0–62.0); clutch 10 ± 1. Plucked light grey down forms bulk of nest. Incubation by ♀, with long daily recesses, during which she feeds, becoming shorter nearer hatching; incubation 32–34 days, relatively long for size of duck. Dump laying often occurs, and pre-breeding condition of ♀ important in determining ability to carry through breeding routine (Briggs 1989). ♂ stationed nearby through incubation accompanying ♀ during recess and returning in flight to nest hole when he continues past as ♀ dives into hole. Ducklings, in captivity weighing 37.8 (*n* = 32), jump from nest to ground or water with vocal encouragement from ♀. Led by parents to water or brood rearing territory. Both parents closely tend young, injury feigning if threatened, often well after fledging. Ducklings fully feathered by 57 days and able to fly. Family party may remain together for longer, but usually gather in flocks. Most breed in 1st year when conditions allow. For more detail see Marchant and Higgins (1990).

Conservation and threats

In no immediate threat as widespread and abundant over large part of Australia. Ability to exploit modified rural lands, in particular development of improved pastures, means has been very successful, even moderately so within some urban environments (Kingsford 1992). Hunted widely in southeast Australia, sometimes forming high proportion of annual harvest (Marchant and Higgins 1990). World population at least 200 000 but probably considerably more as available counts may underestimate; however, steady decline detected in eastern Australia mid 1980s–1999 and this decline shown to be significant long-term trend (Kingsford *et al.* 1999, Kingsford *et al.* 2000).

Peter Fullagar

African Pygmy-goose *Nettapus auritus*
PLATE 13

Anas aurita Boddaert, 1783, Table Planches Enlum., p. 48
Madagascar
Nettapus Brandt, 1836

Etymology: *Nettapus* Gr. *Netta*, duck, *opos*, voice, meaning duck with squeaky voice; *aurita* L. means having ears, presumably referring to green 'ear' patches of ♂.

Other names: Dwarf Goose. Afrikaans: Zwerggans; French: Sarcelle pygmée d'Afrique, Sarcelle à oreillons, Anserelle naine; Malagasy: Vorontsara.

Variation: no subspecies; despite large range and relatively sedentary life-style, no distinguishable geographic variation.

Description

ADULT: dimorphic. ♂ face white with large distinctive black eye, short bill extends up forehead so, in profile, resembles goose rather than long flat face of most ducks. Crown black with some iridescence extending down back of neck and fringing powder-green oval patch on side of head and neck. Foreneck white merging into pale chestnut lower neck and breast and around sides of neck to form incomplete white collar at base. Flanks rich bright chestnut showing some lacing at junction with breast. Scapulars black with green iridescence, back black with rump feathers iridescent green almost covering 16 black tail feathers. Primaries and secondaries black with distinctive white diagonal bar across secondaries from alula joint to outer edge. All coverts and tertiaries black with considerable green iridescence; no speculum. Belly white. Bill yellow with black nail; feet and legs dark grey and black; iris brown-reddish. ♀ forehead, crown and hind neck dark brown with some black and minimal iridescence and dark brown to black eye. Lower mandible yellow and upper mottled brown with dark brown nail. Intensity of colour varies seasonally and possibly indicates breeding condition. Ground colour of face and upper neck pale grey brown with brown eyestripe, and individually variable smudged brown patches on cheek and nape. Breast and flanks chestnut; scapulars dark brown with iridescence. Back dark brown with extended rump feathers that also virtually cover dark brown tail. Primaries dark brown-black with white diagonal wing stripe as in ♂. Belly and feet as in ♂.

MOULT: no obvious eclipse plumage; however, outside breeding season, white face of ♂ has some dark grey tinges, and flank feathers appear less intensely chestnut. Further study of body moult required. In captivity, wing moult synchronized in ♂ and ♀ and occurs prior to brood dispersal.

IMMATURE: chestnut flank feathers appear at 15 days of age and, by Day 24, flank, scapular and tail feathers grown. By Day 45 feathering complete with exception of head, and first signs of flight seen. By Day 51 feathering complete and competent flight possible. At this stage young resemble adult ♀; however, signs of sexual dimorphism apparent with young ♂ developing pale grey to pink bill and less intense cheek patches. At 5 months young ♀ resembles adult, and ♂ has developed pale yellow bill, flank feathers have become quite intense chestnut and green oval 'ear' patch obvious. Immature, however, paler than adult ♂, with remainder of plumage still resembling young adult ♀. Adult plumage, with exception of green patch, which still lacks intensity, achieved at 10 months.

DUCKLING: bill grey with pink lower mandible and light brown nail and egg-tooth. Eyes dark grey with facial pattern as adult ♀ but markings black on white. Crown, extending in V from base of bill, and back of neck, black. Back, wings and tail black with distinctive white rump and flank patches. Neck, breast and belly pale grey to white; legs and feet dark grey-black.

MEASUREMENTS AND WEIGHT: ♂ wing, 150–165; tail, 62–70; culmen, 25–27; tarsus, 25–28; weight, 285. ♀ wing, 142–158; culmen, 23–25; weight, 260 (Delacour 1954–64, Madge and Burn 1988). Unsexed ($n = 18$) wing, 152–165 (157.4); culmen, 23–26 (24.9); tail, 52–73 (64.9) (Maclean 1993). Weight, ♂, 280, 290, ♀ 260 (Brown *et al.* 1982).

Field characters

Diminutive size (270–320 mm long) ensures unlikely to be confused with other wildfowl within range with possible exception of Hottentot Teal in south and in Madagascar. Found almost exclusively on still or slow moving lily-covered waters, not habitat that Hottentot Teal generally occupy.

Voice

Contrary to many reports, both sexes vocal from young age, at least in captivity, uttering repeated high-pitched twittering whistles. During displays, ♂ calls described as *chip, chip, chirrup, chiroo*, and when excited, as an explosive *chip, chip, chip* (Alder 1963). Sonogram in Maclean (1993). Observations in Zimbabwe and Botswana confirm that pairs, and particularly ♂, call repeatedly when approached by humans or other pairs. Reference made to ♀ quacking in Delacour (1954–64) and Johnsgard (1978), but quacks not heard from captive birds, nor in wild (see also Alder 1963). Most ♀ ducks that quack do so when handled, but this has not happened when ♀♀ picked up. In captivity, groups of ducklings utter frequent high-pitched twittering whistles, in particular when members of brood return after separation. If duckling catches insect and moves away to eat, other youngsters swim in pursuit calling almost constantly.

Range and status

Inhabits sub-Saharan Africa and Madagascar, from Senegal and Ethiopia to eastern subtropical regions of South Africa. Resident on Pemba, and, formerly, Zanzibar (Pakenham 1979); however, not recorded in Gulf of Guinea islands. Absent from arid areas and rare at elevation; range generally dependent on rainfall, possibly extending further south in exceptionally wet seasons. Relatively sedentary, limited migrations occur during drought, e.g. to coastal zone during dry season, or after exceptional rainfall. Stragglers reported in central South Africa, but pronounced seasonal changes in productivity of water-lilies may limit colonization. Only seasonally present in Chad and Sudan. In Madagascar, widespread but rare on Central Plateau, most common in west and north. Generally rare over much of range but locally common in East Africa, and abundant at Lake Tana, Ethiopia and Okavango Delta, Botswana. Population estimated at 20 000–30 000 in West Africa and 100 000–250 000 in eastern and southern Africa with possibly 15 000 in Okavanga

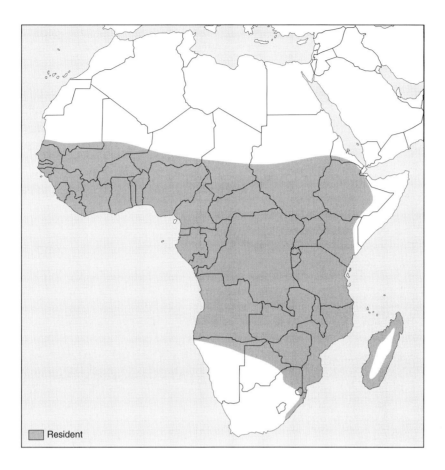

Resident

Delta; in Madagascar, estimated at 5000–10 000 and decreasing (Scott and Rose 1997).

Habitat and general habits

Found on open, slow-moving or still freshwater, frequently in proximity to White-backed Duck, with quantities of floating vegetation; water-lilies seem essential. Short legs means ungainly on land, and unusual in such situations. Mostly in pairs or family parties, rarely in large groups.

Diet poorly documented but probably consists of various parts of lily with ripe seed pods being particularly selected. Douthwaite (1980) analysed stomach contents taken on Thamalakane River, Botswana, and found 99% *Nymphaea* seeds. Bill short and robust, and nail well suited for tearing vegetation. Good diver and generally assumed to dive for food; Bell (1996a), however, did not observe birds diving or up-ending. Individuals seen

to swim away from group in attempt to conserve lily seed pods for themselves. Numerous other small seeds of grasses, etc, taken from surface. Bell (1998) observed two ♀♀ bending heads of grass *Papsalum urvillei*, their mates rushing to join as suitable seed found, ♂♂ not seen to bend over seed heads themselves; however, in captivity, ♂♂ pull down heads of sedge to water surface and call ♀♀ to feed. Fish fry, small insects and other invertebrates also consumed from above, below and on surface. Little seasonal variation in diet, and young eat similar food to adults. Feeds exclusively on water, and periods of greatest activity at dawn and dusk. Frequently loafs on or among lily pads, where surprizingly well camouflaged, or perches on dead branches hanging near surface during hottest times of day. Adept at swimming backwards, possibly as adaptation to life amongst water-lilies (Bell 1996a).

Displays and breeding behaviour

When many pairs present, ♀ may incite and ♂ makes mock attacks on neighbouring pairs, either rushing across surface with outstretched neck and wings, or flying low. Pairbond strong and may remain intact over successive seasons. Displays not elaborate and appear to consist of ♂ circling front of ♀ and Turning-side-of-head (Delacour 1954–64); while doing this, he calls and raises feathers on back of neck while green ear oval becomes more rectangular in appearance. ♀ actively Incites ♂ to drive intruders from territory, at same time giving considerable vocal support. In captivity, ♂ will chase White-backed Duck by flying above surface as victim dives to escape. Paired ♂ continues to defend territory while ♀ incubates, and takes active part in brood rearing and defence.

Breeding and life cycle

Long laying period variable through range and probably triggered by rain. Breeding in Nigeria July–Aug, Uganda June–Oct, Kenya and Tanzania June–July (Brown *et al.* 1982), Dec–Apr in Madagascar (Langrand 1990), July–Oct in The Gambia (Gore 1990), Sept–Mar in Botswana, mainly Jan in Zimbabwe, with peak in Mar–Apr in much of Southern Africa (Maclean 1997g). ♂ active in site selection and flies to trees with suitable hollows, or disused holes of barbets *Megalaima* and woodpeckers, and calls loudly from above entrance; ♂ not observed to enter nest cavity. Trees standing in water preferred, but other sites used; some nesting occurs in dense vegetation, such as papyrus, and disused nests of Hammerkop (Pitman 1965), but primary requirement is cavities in emergent trees or ones close to water edge. Where nests found on or close to ground, considered that snakes, notably Black Mamba *Dendroaspis polylepis*, may prevent use of tree holes (Pitman 1965); nests distant from water probably unsuccessful as family parties at great risk of predation.

Nest consists of small scrape with no material added but any debris in cavity pulled together; small quantities of pale grey or white down produced as clutch laid, and used to cover eggs thinly as ♀ leaves. Eggs creamy white; 1st ones slightly darker, and waxy covering thicker and more apparent; discoloration occurs in damp conditions; 43.3×32.9 ($41.6–44.8 \times 31.7–35.2$) ($n = 14$) (Brown *et al.* 1982) or, in captivity 38.5×26.0 ($n = 9$); weight in captivity 27 ($n = 2$) (Brown *et al.* 1982); clutch 9 (6–12). Incubation, by ♀ alone, 21–23 days. Hatching synchronous, and ducklings encouraged to leave, usually early in morning, by ♀ calling from below; have sharp toenails and climb from nest chamber. Hatch weight in captivity 14.2 (13.2– 15.0) ($n = 10$), or 15.3 and 17.5 (Brown *et al.* 1982). Fledge in captivity in 38–42 days (Bell 1997b).

Parental care primarily undertaken by ♀, with ♂ in attendance, and family remains together for period after fledging. No parental feeding seen, adults merely guiding young to suitable areas. No data from wild on breeding success, adult survival, nor on longevity.

Conservation and threats

Has declined in many parts of range and rare or threatened in Senegal, Kenya and Zimbabwe (Scott and Rose 1996). Large-scale habitat modification, particularly destruction of aquatic plant communities through introduction of exotic fish (notably cichlids such as *Tilapia*, e.g. in Madagascar), siltation and pollution have reduced numbers. Still hunted in places. With extensive range and low concentrations, establishment and management of key sites as refuges unlikely. Control of introduction of herbivorous fish, drainage schemes, herbicides and tourism, particularly water sports that destroy lily beds, needed to ensure long-term survival. Continued establishment of National Parks and Reserves, primarily for mammals of Africa, will help. Many farm dams and reservoirs in Zimbabwe and South Africa provide habitat for small populations of White-backed Ducks; such sites might be suitable for pygmy-geese except for shortage of nesting sites. Nestboxes might allow spread into otherwise apparently ideal locations.

Roger Cattermole and Glyn Young

Cotton Teal (Cotton Pygmy-goose) *Nettapus coromandelianus*

PLATE 13

Anas coromandeliana Gmelin, 1789, Syst. Nat., **1**, p. 522

Coromandel, India

Etymology: *coromandelianus* after type locality. Common name apparently from white plumage.

Other names: Cotton Pygmy-goose, Rice Teal, Goose Teal, Indian Pygmy-goose, White-quilled Dwarf Goose, White Pygmy-goose, White-bodied Goose Teal, Green-backed Goose Teal, Quacky-duck. French: Anserelle de Coromandel; German: Koromandelzwergente; Indian sub-continent: Girri, Girria, Girja or Gur-gurra (Hindustani); Ghangariel, Ghangani (Bengali); Bullia-hans (Dacca Faridpur, Sylhet); Lerreget-perriget, Merom-derebet (Kole); Ade, Adla (Ratnagiri) and Karagat (Burmese); Javanese: Meliwies-batoe; Malay: Itik-laut; Manila: Pa-ti-ki; Singhalese: Mal-saaru; Spanish: Gansito Asiático.

Variation: 2 subspecies recognized, nominate Indian Cotton Teal *N. c. coromandelianus* of tropical southeast Asia from Pakistan, India and China (north to Yangsi River), Malaysia, most of Indonesia to north Philippines and northern New Guinea, and Australian Pygmy-goose *N. c. albipennis* Gould, 1842 restricted to east coast of Queensland.

Description

ADULT: dimorphic. ♂ has green back with narrow dark breast band, head with dark crown and white face. Bill dark grey; legs and feet grey-olive; eye red. ♀ has distinct eyestripe, more extensive crown patch and duller eye, also has brown back and more dusky underparts. Wing pattern of ♂ differs from ♀ in being mostly green above and showing broad white line, visible from above and below, along trailing edge and expanding to clear sub-terminal mirror at wing tip. Wing in ♀ plain brown with white margin only on trailing edges of secondaries. Nominate subspecies smaller than Australian *albipennis* and often regarded as smallest extant duck.

MOULT: little information on moults but eclipse plumage occurs in ♂ following breeding, when resembles ♀ except for wing pattern and retention of whiter head.

IMMATURE: like ♀.

DUCKLING: similar to Green Pygmy-goose but separable (see that account).

MEASUREMENTS AND WEIGHT: nominate subspecies ♂ wing, 152–167; tail, 72–75; bill, 22–24; tarsus, 23–25 (Delacour 1954–64); weight ♂ *c* 255–312; ♀ *c* 185–255 (Madge and Burn 1988). *albipennis* ♂ wing (*n* = 18), 172–188 (177); tail (*n* = 5), 62–72 (67); bill (*n* = 18), 24–26 (25); tarsus (*n* = 5), 26–31 (28); weight (*n* = 52), 311–495 (403). ♀ wing (*n* = 15), 161–186 (174); tail (*n* = 3), 65, 69, 71; bill (*n* = 15), 23–26 (24); tarsus (*n* = 3), 27, 27, 28; weight (*n* = 37), 255–439 (380) (Frith 1982, Marchant and Higgins 1990).

Field characters

Diminutive pale duck, 300–370 mm long, with stubby bill. Different wing patterns and whiter appearance useful distinctions from similar Green Pygmy-goose. Small size makes confusion with other ducks unlikely.

Voice

Noisy at times. ♂ has loud distinctive rattling call given in flight. No ♂ tracheal bulla but calls of sexes seem to differ, with those of ♀ softer. Alder (1963) gave only useful descriptions; ♂ has nasal *grrr* used aggressively, nasal rattle *rick rick reoo* (presumed to be call given in flight), nasal *quack* when anxious and metallic *chak chak chak* also given in anxiety. ♀ has *tuck-it, tuck-it* call in aggression or excitement when disturbed, and conversational, musical *tick-a-tick-a-tick* or *wick, wick, wick*, like rusty hinge, probably when anxious.

Range and status

Indian sub-continent, including Sri Lanka, to south China and southeast Asia to isolated population in northeast Australia. Mostly resident, but in some areas concentrates at residual wetlands during dry season. Some populations locally migratory (Blakers *et al.* 1984, Madge and Burn 1988), including those from northern regions of lowland south China in winter. Vagrants reported from some distance, e.g. to Afghanistan, Iran, Iraq and often to Bahrain and Oman (Madge and Burn 1988). At Andaman islands and in northern Philippines, Borneo (Kalimantan), Sumatra, Java, Sulawesi and northern New Guinea, mostly locally sparse and occurrence in this region may be due to southward dispersals from main concentrations in Malay Peninsula, Asia and deltaic regions of Bengal (Phillips 1922–26, Madge and Burn 1988). Little information on present status except estimate in early 1960s of 1500 for Australian subspecies (Lavery 1966). Wetlands International (2002) suggested population of 7500 for *albipennis*, and < 1000 for nominate race in New Guinea, 25 000–100 000 in southern Asia, and up to 1 000 000 in eastern and southeastern Asia.

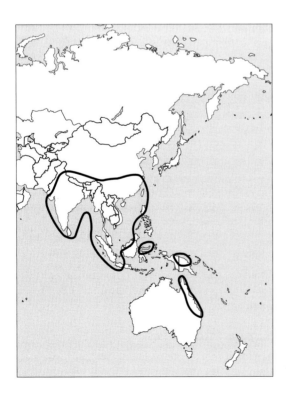

Habitat and general habits

Widespread throughout tropical southeast Asia on freshwater wetlands with floating and submerged vegetation. Feeds almost entirely on aquatic vegetation, taken by dabbling at surface and stripping seeds and flower heads. Feeding limited to water surface or just below, rarely diving (Lavery 1971b). Flattens head along water with rapid filtering while swimming, swallowing food with upward jerk of head (Marchant and Higgins 1990). Diet examined by Lavery (1970c, 1971a). Often found in pairs or small parties but gathers in larger flocks outside breeding season.

Displays and breeding behaviour

Social behaviour little studied or poorly described. Vertical Neck-jerking as pre-flight signal (Johnsgard 1965a). ♂ arches neck and jerks open wings to display white patches. Pre-copulatory mutual Bill-dipping occurs while ♂ circles ♀ before mounting and post-copulatory bathing by ♀ with ♂ arching wings and Bill-dipping (Johnsgard 1965a).

Breeding and life cycle

Little information. Hole nester usually using hollows in trees standing in water, but occasionally substitute sites in buildings. Breeds during wet season, at least Nov–Feb in northeastern Australia. Nest site chosen by pair during distinctive searching behaviour. Pair-bond almost certainly indefinite, involving close biparental care of ducklings, with ♀ only incubation. Clutch size, incubation period, length of brood rearing period and growth and development of young poorly documented. Broods of up to 10 ducklings noted in Australia (Marchant and Higgins 1990) possibly indicative of normal upper clutch limit; 6–9 eggs may be more usual (Beruldsen 1977). Single clutch likely in season. Behaviour of family parties not studied and details of life cycle, including age at 1st breeding and adult survival, not known. Eggs oval, smooth, finely grained surface; glossy and lustrous; creamy, ivory or pearly white (Marchant and Higgins 1990); measurements of nominate 46 × 39 (Delacour 1954–64) or 43.3 × 32.9 (38.0–47.0 × 29.7–35.6) (*n* = 110) (Schönwetter 1960–66), and for Australian subspecies 4 6.8 × 36.0

(n = 4) (Schönwetter 1960–66), see also Marchant and Higgins (1990). No egg weights recorded, but calculation suggested 27 for *coromandelianus* and 33 for *albipennis* (Schönwetter 1960–66).

Conservation and threats

Little information on which to base conservation action. Thought to be reasonably secure and, in past, not especially threatened by hunting. Destruction of natural wetlands, introduction of invasive water weeds and increased hunting might be serious future threat. Restricted range and small population size (possibly < 2000) of Australian subspecies means listed as Vulnerable by Threatened Waterfowl Specialist Group (2001).

Peter Fullagar

Green Pygmy-goose *Nettapus pulchellus*
PLATE 13

Nettapus pulchellus Gould, 1842, Birds Australia, pt. 6, pl. 4 and text
Port Essington, Northern Territory, Australia
Etymology: *pulchellus* from L. for pretty.

Other names: Australian Pygmy-goose, Little Goose, Green Dwarf Goose, Goose Teal, Teal. Australian Aboriginal: Loon-byte, Diwidj; Dutch: Australische Dwergeend; French: Anserelle élégante; German: Australische Zwergente; Spanish: Gansito Australiano.

Variation: no subspecies.

Description

ADULT: dimorphic. ♂ bottle-green neck and conspicuous white cheeks with distinctive pattern on bill. Wing green with dark primaries and white secondaries. Belly white with dusky vent. Bill greyish black with pink tip and patch either side; legs and feet dark greyish olive; eye dark brown. ♀ as ♂, lacks green neck and bill pattern but retains dark top to head and has pale stripe above eye.

MOULT: ♂ in eclipse resembles ♀. Annual postbreeding moult complete early in dry season, including simultaneous wing moult. Following this moult, ♂ most commonly has clear cheek patch; head pattern in ♂ sharpest in wet season.

IMMATURE: like ♀ but duller. Body moult at 2–3 months to adult plumage.

DUCKLING: very small, brownish above with dark cap to head; white underparts and broad white area across base of hindneck. Also small white patches either side of rump and along trailing edges of wing-rudiments. Tail relatively long. Differs from Cotton Teal in more prominent dark eyestripe and narrower supercilium (Marchant and Higgins 1990).

MEASUREMENTS AND WEIGHT: ♂ wing (n = 19), 167–181 (174); tail (n = 20), 63–71 (67); bill (n = 20), 23–27 (25); tarsus (n = 20), 25–29 (27); weight (n = 47), 300–430 (310). ♀ wing (n = 15), 163–182 (172); tail (n = 20), 58–78 (68); bill (n = 20), 23–27 (25); tarsus (n = 20), 25–30 (27); weight (n = 26), 245–340 (304) (Frith 1982, Marchant and Higgins 1990).

Field characters

Tiny compact duck with glossy, bottle-green back and scalloped flanks, 320–360 mm long. Diminutive size and squat appearance characteristic. Differs from Cotton Teal in darker appearance, different wing pattern with large white patch on secondaries. Both sexes of Cotton Teal have whiter appearance with dark narrow chest band in ♂.

Voice

Detailed information lacking but musical trills and whistles often given in flight and on landing. No ♂ tracheal bulla. Alarm call high-pitched *whit*; that of ♂ said to be more shrill than ♀. On landing, call sounds like 'don't-dig-it-up' or *cut-ka-ka-du*; further details, including sonogram, in Marchant and Higgins (1990).

Range and status

Largely restricted to northern Australia; also occurs in lowlands of southern New Guinea and on several islands of eastern Indonesia but status in these areas uncertain, with breeding not proven in most cases. Despite being common in parts of northern Australia, no measures of abundance (Blakers *et al.* 1984, Wetlands International 2002). Possible decline in range and numbers last century in Kimberley region of northwest Australia, with suggestion that decline linked to destruction of aquatic vegetation by cattle (Storr 1980b).

Habitat and general habits

Restricted to coastal and sub-coastal areas of tropical freshwater wetlands, occasionally found on brackish and saline waters and lower reaches of rivers. Wholly aquatic on range of water bodies. In dry season restricted to permanent freshwater with abundant floating or submerged vegetation, dispersing during wet season to other wetlands on floodplains. Avoids shallow or fast-flowing water and dense emergent vegetation. Usually found on swamps, pools, billabongs, channels, deep stable water storages, large lakes and still wide parts of rivers (Marchant and Higgins 1990). Feeds exclusively on aquatic vegetation, particularly water-lily seeds and flowers taken by dabbling and stripping; will occasionally up-end and dive to bring material to surface. Details of diet in Lavery (1966, 1970c, 1971a), Frith (1982) and further references in Marchant and Higgins (1990).

Displays and breeding behaviour

Social behaviour poorly known. Aggressive encounters between ♂♂ seen in wet season. Chin-lifts lead to short rushes by ♂ at other pairs with frequent open-bill attacks and vigorous fighting between ♂♂. ♀ incites by Chin-lifting while following ♂ (Scott 1958b, Johnsgard 1965a), and ♂ may perform simple Jump-flights (Scott 1958b). Preening wings and sideways presentation of head also noted as display. Copulation illustrated in Pringle (1985). Pairbond probably indefinite involving close biparental care of ducklings.

Breeding and life cycle

Little information on breeding, with few nests found during wet season (Jan–May). Assumed to be obligate hole-nester in hollow trees standing in water, with site chosen by pair during distinctive nest-searching behaviour. Eggs oval, textured glossy and white or creamy-white (Marchant and Higgins 1990); 44 × 32 (35–49 × 29–36) (*n* = 106) (Frith 1982); no weights recorded, but calculated at 30 by Schönwetter (1960–66); clutch (likely *c* 10 eggs), incubation period, length of brood rearing period and growth and development of young unrecorded. Only ♀ incubates. Behaviour of family parties not studied and details of life cycle, including age at 1st breeding and adult survival, unknown.

Conservation and threats

No immediate threat to survival perceived; still regarded as common in northern Australian tropical wetlands, especially in Northern Territories. However, restricted world range, habitat requirements and possibility that numbers may be < 10 000 suggest vulnerability. Introduced Water Buffalo and cattle accused of destroying water-lilies (Goodfellow 2001). Lack of information about many aspects of biology regrettable. More information on distribu-tion and abundance should be obtained in interests of conservation.

Peter Fullagar

Brazilian Teal *Amazonetta brasiliensis*
PLATE 13

Anas brasiliensis Gmelin, 1789, Syst. Nat., **1**, p. 517 northeastern Brazil
Amazonetta Boetticher, 1929

Etymology: *Amazonetta* means duck of the Amazon, and *brasiliensis* means of Brazil.

Other names: Brazilian Duck, Schuyl's Teal. Portuguese: Marreca-ananai; Spanish: Pato português, Pato brasileño.

Variation: in plumage and size, with 2 races recognized and 2 colour phases found within races. Delacour (1954–64) described 2 subspecies; however, mixing of migratory and sedentary populations may complicate ranges of subspecies and they may not warrant recognition (Coimbra-Filho 1964). Nominate *A. b. brasiliensis* occurs in central and eastern South America from Orinoco, western Brazil, eastern Bolivia, Paraguay, Uruguay, and possibly northern Argentina. Two colour phases (light and dark) noted within this population with slight geographical trend from smaller, darker individuals in northern parts of range and larger, paler ones in southern portions. *A. b. ipecutiri* Vieillot, 1816 found in southernmost regions of Brazil, Uruguay and central Argentina (Entre Rios and Buenos Aires provinces), is similar in plumage to nominate race but larger and typically dark phase. Population appears migratory, breeding over southern portions of range but mixing with nominate race in many areas.

Description

ADULT: dimorphic. ♂ has forehead and anterior part of cheeks pale chestnut brown with posterior parts pale yellowish grey; some individuals with dark crown running to nape of neck. Upper breast pale chestnut-brown with blackish brown rounded spots. Lower breast greyish buff blending into abdomen. Wings black with greenish purple sheen and large white band across posterior secondaries easily visible in flight. Flanks pale brown with rump patch velvety black. Tail black. Bill and foot colour ranges from coral-red to orange-red; light-coloured eyelids form ring surrounding brown iris. ♀ forehead and anterior part of cheeks pale chestnut colour marked by large white eye-spot and second white spot at base of bill below eye. Posterior cheeks and anterior portions of neck whitish blending down to pale chestnut breast. Upperbreast with small dark spots. Flanks pale brown similar to ♂. Wings and tail as ♂. Bill olive-grey; feet orange-red but generally duller than ♂; iris brown with eye distinguished by large white eye-spot.

MOULT: no ♂ eclipse plumage. Wing moult occurs following reproduction in conjunction with reduction in gonad size—peak mean length 19.08 mm in June decreasing to minimum mean 5.35 by Jan (Madriz 1979). Timing of moult varies across range, occurring Oct in Venezuela (Madriz 1979), Jan–Mar in Brazil (Nascimento and Antas 1990) and Feb in northern Argentina (Weller 1968b). No data on timing of body moults.

IMMATURE: in both sexes plumage similar to adult ♀, but somewhat duller and darker overall.

DUCKLING: dark brown above, yellow below, with light dorsal and wing spots as in Northern Mallard; large yellow eyebrow; yellow patch at base of bill and dark streak through eye to nape; bill dusky yellow (Delacour 1954–64).

MEASUREMENTS AND WEIGHT: *brasiliensis*: ♂ (*n* = 33) wing,174–204 (185.9); culmen, 35.9–43.2 (38); tarsus, 29.4–37.1 (33.5); weight (*n* = 50), 421–556 (411.5). ♀ (*n* = 20) wing,169.5–193 (182.7); culmen, 29.9–36.1 (33.5); tarsus, 34.2–40.4 (37.5); weight (*n* = 35), 434–542 (403.5) (Madriz 1979). *ipecutiri* ♂ (*n* = 60) wing, 191–229 (199.7); tarsus, 32.9–51.9 (36.7). ♀ (*n* = 41) wing, 180–206 (190.3); tarsus, 31.9–38 (35.4).

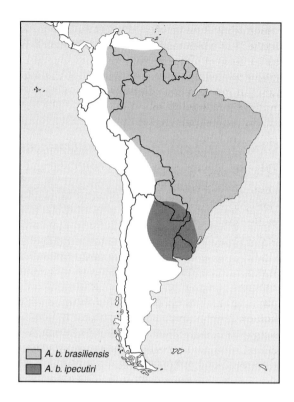

A. b. brasiliensis
A. b. ipecutiri

Field characters

Length 350–400 mm. Distinguished from Ringed Teal by larger size and bright red bill of ♂. Striking white triangular patch on posterior portion of secondaries of both sexes readily seen in flight. ♀ lacks white markings behind eye of Ringed Teal. Iridescent upperwing, long blunt-ended black tail, and brightly coloured bill and feet unmistakable.

Voice

♂ has strong piercing whistle *whee-whee-whee* as well as 2-note whistle *whe-wheeew* uttered both in flight and while stationary. ♀ has call similar to typical duck *quack*, loud, deep and repeated several times in rapid succession, often in response to disturbance or during flight. Sonogram of adult ♂ calls in Brewer (2001).

Range and status

Occurs in much of South America from southern Colombia and Venezuela, eastern Bolivia, throughout Paraguay, Uruguay and Brazil to northern half of Argentina. Found in tropical lowland forested regions east of Andes from Orinoco River valley in Venezuela, south through Brazil to eastern Bolivia and northeastern Argentina. *brasiliensis* race thought to be sedentary, although some dispersion occurs (Nascimento and Antas 1990) with *ipecutiri* partially or wholly migratory, perhaps moving as far north as Venezuela during austral autumn. Wetlands International (2002) suggested population of nominate race of 100 000–1 000 000, and guess at 10 000–100 000 for *ipecutiri*.

Habitat and general habits

Primarily inhabits tropical forested regions, wood-enclosed waters and flooded scrubland. Occurs mainly in smaller, shallow bodies of freshwater found in lowlands, up to 500 m elevation. Will also use flooded fields, marshes, and larger lagoons outside breeding season. Only rarely seen in coastal regions or mangrove swamps. Found singly, in pairs, or in groups of 15–20 outside breeding season. Pairs commonly observed together year-round. Pairs with older broods may join other families to form groups of up to 20 individuals. Flies with wings depressed exposing iridescence of wing and triangular patch on secondaries. Flight low and swift with ♀ often leading pair. Described as free percher throughout year (Phillips 1922–26), although observations on captives failed to indicate any preference for elevated perches.

Madriz (1983) examined diet in Venezuela and found higher percentage of vegetable material than other waterfowl of similar size and weight. Diet consists almost entirely of aquatic plant material both during rainy (98.0%) and dry (83.2%) seasons. Seeds decreased in diet from beginning of rainy season to dry season, with proportionately greater intake of animal material occurring as aquatic habitat became less available. Seed consumption during rains takes advantage of rapid growth and fruiting of plants including *Sagittaria*, *Brachiaria*, *Luziola*, and *Panicum*. Animal material consumed included primarily planarians, Coleoptera, Hemiptera and Homoptera.

Displays and breeding behaviour

Display repertoire simple, lacking elaborate courtship displays by ♂. ♂ displays consist primarily of Burping with simultaneous Chin-lifting. Whistled *whee-whee-whee* often given by displaying ♂. In courtship, ♂ swims in front of ♀ while displaying. Ritualized Wing-flapping appears important, although role undetermined. Post-copulatory display restricted to Wings-up-bill-down display homologous to that of blue-winged ducks and Versicolor Teal (Johnson *et al.* 2000). Pair formation occurs Mar in Venezuela, coinciding with enlargement of gonads (Madriz 1979), and May–June in south central Brazil (Coimbra-Filho 1964). Paired ♀♀ give vigorous Inciting display directed at courting ♂♂ consisting of rapidly alternating head movements towards mate and threatening bill-pointing movements towards opponent, together with repeated hoarse *week* calls (Johnsgard 1965a).

Breeding pairs highly aggressive toward conspecific and often interspecific intruders. Not known whether pairs defend territories during breeding season in wild, although evidence from captive pairs suggests they may. Pairs probably stay together throughout year but aggressiveness greatly reduced outside breeding season. Role of ♂ in rearing brood unknown but at least some ♂♂ present with brood and participating in care (Coimbra-Filho 1964). Both ♂ and ♀ give Distraction display, wing-flapping across water surface and calling loudly when brood threatened.

Breeding and life cycle

Little known. Laying dates vary widely with latitude. In Venezuela, gonad enlargement occurs in Mar, nest building in July, young seen Aug–Sept (Madriz 1979); in south central Brazil, captive-raised young hatched 13 Dec and 18 Mar (Coimbra-Filho 1964); Sao Paulo, year-round breeder but likely adaptation to man-made environmental conditions (Nascimento and Antas 1990); and northern Argentina, breeding Aug–Nov. Few wild nests described; generally located on ground, well hidden in vegetation near water. Nest in Venezuela consisted of cavity hollowed out in dense 1 m high vegetation entered through short tunnel (Madriz 1979). Nest in Argentina reported in top of Tala tree *Celtis tala* (Phillips 1922–26). Tree nesting common in central Paraguay. Wild nest also reported in grasslands 200 m from water (de la Peña 1987). Birds in captivity preferentially nested in dense grass when provided with ground cover and elevated cavities. Eggs creamy white with smooth texture, glossy, somewhat spherical; in Venezuela 45.9–47.2 × 34.3–35.1 ($n = 5$) (Madriz 1979), in central Brazil, 52 × 37 ($n = 18$) (Coimbra-Filho 1964); in Venezuela weight 29.5–30.7 ($n = 5$) (Madriz 1979); in captivity, eggs of *brasiliensis* weighed 29.8 ($n = 28$) and those of *ipecutiri* 34.2 ($n = 11$). Clutch commonly 6–8 although up to 11 not unusual (Madriz 1979) and 14 reported (Couto de Magalhaes 1939). Incubation 26–29 days, by ♀, with synchronous hatch. Captive ducklings of *brasiliensis* weighed 19.8 ($n = 16$) on hatching, and of *ipecutiri* 23.0 ($n = 17$). Pairs may raise 2 broods a year (Phillips 1922–26, Coimbra-Filho 1964). No data on age at 1st breeding, breeding success, survival nor on longevity.

Conservation and threats

Historically widespread and abundant (de Azara 1805, Goeldi 1894). Wide-ranging distribution and reports of being commonly observed in various parts of range indicate continued healthy status (Madriz 1983, Nascimento and Antas 1990). No known threats, although reliable information lacking over much of range. Occasionally occurs in agricultural areas but not considered pest. Not particularly wary; may be hunted in places, but not major quarry species and hunting unlikely to have major impact.

Jeff Port

Ringed Teal *Callonetta leucophrys*
PLATE 13

Anas leucophrys Vieillot, 1816, Nouv. Dict. Hist. Nat., nouv. éd., **5**, p. 156
Paraguay
Callonetta Delacour, 1936

Etymology: Gr. *kallos* for beauty, *netta* means duck; *leukos* means white, plus *phrus* browed, in reference to white stripe above eye of ♀. 'Ring' apparently refers to oval white patch on wings of both sexes, although possibly to collar.

Other names: Ring-necked Teal. French: Sarcelle or Callonette collier noir; German: Rotschulterente; Portuguese: Marreca-de-coleira; Spanish: Pato de collar.

Variation: no subspecies.

Description

ADULT: sexually dimorphic. ♂ top of head and back of neck black, terminating in half collar; sides of head, throat, and neck light grey to pale buff, finely streaked with darker reddish brown to black, back olive to grey-brown, scapulars orange chestnut, black wing coverts, brown primaries, oval white patch on secondary coverts above green metallic speculum, lower back, rump black; tail mostly black, with white patch on side outlined by anterior black bar, wing lining and axillaries black, buff pink breast with small black spots, belly whitish to light grey, white sides and flanks finely vermiculated black. Bill slaty blue-grey with black tip; legs and feet pink; iris brown. ♀ mainly brown, darkest on crown and hindneck and lightest on sides of head, lower back to tail black, white supra-orbital stripe and white lines behind eyes and cheeks, wings like ♂ but scapulars brown, throat and sides of neck white, darker on underside with mottled to banded brown, bill dull grey with dark saddle.

MOULT: no ♂ eclipse plumage. Presumably 2 body moults annually in both sexes but timing uncertain. Birds recently completed wing moult seen in May in northern Argentina (Weller 1968b).

IMMATURE: like ♀, but young ♂ does not have barred flanks or facial pattern of ♀, breast and upper abdomen spotted.

DUCKLING: grey-brown above and white below. Face white with dark line extending from bill through eye. White patches in scapular region and on either side of rump.

MEASUREMENTS AND WEIGHT: ♂ (*n* = 8) wing, 175–186 (182.2); tail, 59–65 (62.6); bill, 36–41 (37.9); tarsus (*n* = 1) 33. ♀ (*n* = 8) wing, 165–178 (172.6); tail, 56–62 (59.4); bill, 33–37 (35) (Blake 1977). Weight in early winter ♂ (*n* = 2) 350; ♀ (*n* = 1) 310 (Weller 1968b).

Field characters

Small, length 350–370 mm. Frequently perches in trees. Oval white patch on wings, and green metallic speculum, distinctive in both sexes. For ♂, black line along top of head, bright chestnut back, pink breast with black spots, and white spot on side of tail notable. Shy, springing rapidly into air when approached. Wings whistle in flight.

Voice

Limited information available for wild birds, but sonograms for most calls available from captives (Brewer 1988, 2001). In pair flights, ♂ gives Short Whistle and ♀ drawn-out *honk* (Gee Call) before landing. ♂ gives Long Whistle (*wheee-ooo* of Johnsgard 1965a) and ♀ loud *houii* (*hou-eee* of Johnsgard 1965a) when separated from mate, after disturbance, or in response to duckling distress. ♂ also utters *meow* call and Short Whistle when separated from mate. ♀ gives soft *peep* during Inciting and ♂ Long Whistles after some copulations. Both sexes use short *honks* when alarmed, and ♀ gives *honks* and soft *peeps* when accompanying brood. Both parents use hoarse, repeated hisses when brood approached closely. Ducklings have typical distress and contentment calls (Kear 1968).

Range and status

Found from southeastern Bolivia to northern Argentina, Paraguay, Uruguay, and southern Brazil. South to Argentine provinces of Santiago del Estero, Santa Fe, and northern Buenos Aires as winter visitor. Common in small numbers in much of range, with 800–1000 noted at Bañados de Figueroa in northern Argentina. Population estimated at 10 000–100 000 (Wetlands International 2002); not well studied but considered stable.

Habitat and general habits

Inhabits flooded forests and marshy clearings in wooded lowlands, including secluded pools and small streams. Most active during crepuscular period (Navas 1977). Arboreal, frequently found perching in trees. Generally seen in pairs or family groups, but

some larger concentrations noted during winter (Nores and Yzurieta 1980). Picks insects and seeds from surface and also head-dips in shallow water. Diet presumed to be mainly small seeds, other vegetable material, and invertebrates (del Hoyo *et al.* 1992).

Displays and breeding behaviour

Most information from captive birds (Brewer 1988, 2001). Strong pair and family bonds characteristic, as is vocal nature. Pairbonds long-term in captivity. Nestboxes not consistently defended by either sex, although intruding occupants driven out of occupied boxes. Extended nest-prospecting flights made by pairs early in breeding season. Pre-flight Neck-craning accompanied by soft calls synchronizes departure of paired birds, and both sexes call before landing after extended flights. When mates become separated, ♂ and ♀ call alternately until re-united when they may greet with Rotary head movements and soft calls. ♂♂ infrequently perform Preen-behind-wing broadside to mate. Pair copulations preceded by ♂ Head-bobs or Head-jerking, and ♀ assuming prone posture. ♂ faces ♀, remains alert broadside to her, or gives Long Whistle after copulation. Nine forced

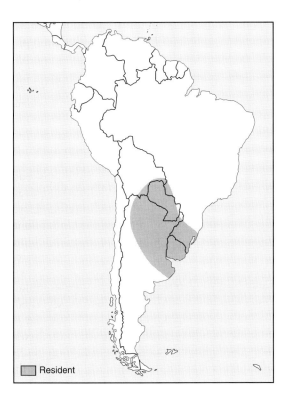

9.26 A pair of Ringed Teal with their brood.

extra-pair and two forced pair-copulation attempts observed in captivity, with mate defence strong and effective in all cases. ♀ Inciting consists of rotary movements of head accompanied by *peeps*. Both sexes and ducklings direct open-bill threats and pecks towards other birds. In captivity, both parents active in care of ducklings (Figure 9.26), with ♂ perching on high vantage point while ♀ and ducklings feed (Brewer 1989). Ducklings sometimes greet parents with rapid head movements, and families occasionally come together in Triumph Ceremony after other birds chased away by parents. Ducklings up to 4 weeks of age feign death when handled and both parents perform Distraction display.

Breeding and life cycle

Little information from wild. Some breeding noted in late summer and early fall, with ducklings seen early Feb and flying juveniles mid Jan in northern Argentina (Weller 1968b). Timing of breeding perhaps influenced by water availability. Nests in tree hollows or old stick nests of other birds. Eggs white; 46.5 × 35.2 ($n = 77$); weight 30.7 (23.5– 38.0) ($n = 100$); captives lay 5–8 eggs, although some clutches larger due to ♀♀ laying in same site; incubation, by ♀, 25–27 days ($n = 4$) (Brewer 1988); newly hatched ducklings weigh 19.4 ($n = 60$). Captive ♀ has laid again when ducklings *c* 3 weeks old ($n = 2$), with ♂ assuming care of young while ♀ incubated 2nd clutch (Brewer 1989). Breeds at one year in captivity. No data on breeding success in wild, adult survival nor longevity.

Conservation and threats

Status not well known, but not classified as globally threatened. Flooded forests with tree holes needed for successful nesting; forest destruction, hunting pressure and contamination of wetlands likely to be main threats.

Gwenda L. Brewer

Crested Duck *Lophonetta specularioides*
PLATE 18

Anas cristata Gmelin, 1789, Syst. Nat., **13** (2), p. 540
Anas specularioides King, 1828, Zool. Journ., **4**, p. 98
Strait of Magellan
Lophonetta Riley, 1914

Etymology: Gr. *lophos* for crest, and *netta* duck. *Specularioides* from L. *specularis*, which refers to metallic speculum; specific name based on Crested Duck's resemblance to Bronze-winged Duck.

Other names: Antarctic Duck, Grey Duck. Spanish: Pato crestón, Pato juarjual del sur (Chile: *specularioides*); Pato juarjual cordillerano (Chile: *alticola*).

Variation: 2 subspecies recognized: Patagonian Crested Duck *L. s. specularioides* of southern Chile, Argentina and Falkland Islands; and Andean Crested Duck *L. s. alticola* Ménégaux, 1909 of mountainous areas of Peru, Bolivia, northern Chile and Argentina.

Description

ADULT: sexes alike. Neck, chin and face pale grey, feathers of mantle, back and scapulars dark brown with pale centres, giving mottled appearance. Crown dark with blackish area around eye. Long tail feathers dark and wings may be black; speculum metallic purple or copper with broad white trailing edge. Axillaries white. *alticola* race larger, with less mottled underside, purplish speculum (without green-bronze reflections of *specularioides*) and yellow iris (red in *specularioides*) (Blake 1977). Bill, legs and feet of both races dark grey.

MOULT: no eclipse plumage, but assumed 2 body moults and one wing moult annually.

IMMATURE: resembles adult, lacks crest and has less black around eye.

DUCKLING: brown to dark grey with white markings, and long stiff tail. Young of *alticola* more vividly marked, with broad white eyebrows (Delacour 1954–64) and longer 'silkier' down than *specularioides* (Kear 1991).

MEASUREMENTS AND WEIGHT: *specularioides* ♂ (*n* = 10) wing, 260–273 (265.6); tail, 123–144 (131.1); bill, 43–48 (45.3). ♀ (*n* = 10) wing, 215–270 (244.7); tail, 132–145 (135); bill, 37–45 (41.1) (Blake 1977); tarsus, ♂ (no details) 46–50; ♀ (no details) 43–45 (Delacour 1954). *alticola* ♂ (*n* = 9) wing, 287–305 (294.8); tail, 145–170 (154.6); bill, 48–53 (49.9). ♀ (*n* = 9) wing, 270–302 (287.7); tail, 135–155 (141.4); bill, 43–48 (45.1) (Blake 1977); tarsus, ♂ (no details) 49–52, ♀ (no details) 44–46 (Delacour 1954–64). Weight *specularioides* (converted from imperial measure) ♂ (*n* = 1), 1077; ♀ (*n* = 1), 952 (Humphrey *et al.* 1970) or in captivity ♂ (*n* = 5) 785–940 (860); ♀ (*n* = 4) 705–776 (746).

Field characters

Medium-sized mottled grey-brown duck that appears long-bodied on water (500–600 mm). Dark, pointed tail may be prominent, and often raised. Both sexes have hanging occipital crest, longer in ♂, and dark smudging around eyes. Little likelihood of confusion with other South American ducks; Brown Pintail smaller, uniformly brown with slender neck and large head. Steamer-ducks bluish grey and massive; Bronze-winged Duck has prominent white facial markings.

Voice

Very vocal, as befits strong territorial behaviour, especially during courtship and aggressive interactions; ♀ may even call at nest. ♂ gives short, croaking *whorr* and buzzy *wheeeoo* (Fjeldså and Krabbe 1990). ♀ has low, barking, *grruf* and low nasal *quek-quek-quek*, while much harsher quacking calls given during displays, often with head thrown up (Woods 1988). Ducklings have multi-syllabic greeting trill (Kaltenhäuser 1971). No sonograms published.

Range and status

specularioides resident and partial migrant throughout southern South America from Talca in Chile and Mendoza in Argentina to Tierra del Fuego. Resident in Falkland Islands. Birds living at higher altitudes may migrate to coast in winter. *alticola* resident in high Andean lakes of southern Peru, north to Lake Junin, and Bolivia south to northern Chile and Argentina. May breed well above 4000 m, some birds moving to 2000 m in winter. Races meet and

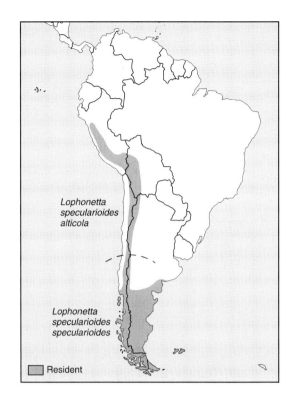

Lophonetta specularioides alticola

Lophonetta specularioides specularioides

☐ Resident

intergrade in northern Chile, in Talca area (Fjeldså and Krabbe 1990).

Both races still common; possibly 100 000 *alticola* occurring mostly in pairs and small parties on mountain lakes. More widespread *specularioides* less numerous, but may unite in large flocks outside breeding season. Rose and Scott (1997) suggested population of 10 000–25 000; 7–12 000 pairs estimated on Falklands where one of more numerous ducks (Woods and Woods 1997).

Habitat and general habits

Inhabits lakes, marshes and grassy areas; from coastal areas to high-altitude pools and bogs. Prefers shallow wetlands, often with exposed shorelines and rarely found in emergent aquatic vegetation. Will flock, and feeds readily in sheltered coastal bays and on sea beaches.

Feeds by sieving through mud, silt or gravel, often up-ending, but may come ashore to forage or feed offshore in kelp beds. Young dive with ease. Diet mostly animal material, e.g. molluscs and crustacea, particularly *specularioides*, but also feeds on aquatic plants such as water milfoil *Myriophyllum*. Two *alticola* collected at Lake Junin, Peru, had been feeding mostly on vegetable matter, *Noias* and *Potamogeton* (Phillips 1922–26). In Falklands, adults and young *specularioides* fed on marine isopods, amphipods, invertebrate larvae and minute clams (Weller 1972). Flocks may feed together, e.g. 45 birds feeding on fly (Helcomyzidae) larvae and pupae in rotting kelp (Weller 1972).

Displays and breeding behaviour

Noisy during courtship; calls used during several complex displays and formalized movements of Bill-shaking before every Grunt-whistle and Head-up-tail-up (Kaltenhäuser 1971). Pairs recorded giving Prolonged-lateral-dabble; members putting bills into water before swimming parallel, broadside to one another, dabbling, stiffly holding position and often finishing display with mutual Preen-behind-wing. Further ♂ displays include Head-shake, Head-flick and Body-shake, possibly independent, and not merely introductions to more complex movements. Display on land, where ♂ stretches, as on water, lowering head with bill downwards, before raising head rapidly, swinging face at right angles away from ♀ calling *wheeeoo* (Jones 1948) is probably a Head-flick. In specialized Head-up-tail-up (Head-back), head thrown rapidly down to back and then immediately brought forward as neck stretched vertically, ♂ calls and points bill towards courted ♀. Equally distinctive Double Grunt-whistle (or Pseudo-grunt-whistle); after Bill-dipping, ♂ lifts head before rising up with bill pointing downwards again, front of body raised high in water as head brought back and tail shaken (Von de Wall 1963, Johnsgard 1965a).

Both sexes Nod-swim; that of ♀ includes occasional Inciting movements with quick upward flick of bill, accompanied by *urr-uk* call. ♀ may have Head-shake and Body-shake, both sexes using Preen-behind-wing. Threat movements by ♀ may be followed by Quacking-towards-partner (Kaltenhäuser 1971). ♂ regularly swims backwards alongside ♀. Precopulatory pumping like that of dabbling ducks; postcopulatory Bridle not recorded, ♂ swims away from ♀ in manner resembling Steam of mallards.

Markedly aggressive towards own species and many other birds when breeding. In intraspecific disputes, ♂ and ♀ may chase whichever member of another family closest. Pairs nesting on plateau lakes in Argentina observed chasing large wildfowl such as Magellan Goose and Flying Steamerduck brood (Buitron and Nuechterlein 1989). Pairbond apparently long-term.

Breeding and life cycle

Limited information from wild. Season varies through range, Oct–Apr in Andes (*alticola*), Sept–Jan in south (*specularioides*) and Sept–Nov in Falklands; however, nesting birds found in most months. Pairs may be double, even treble, brooded. Nests on ground, usually close to water but may be well inland, built amongst grass, ferns or tussocks and down-lined. Eggs of both races ovate and cream coloured; *specularioides* 64.6 × 44.0 (59–71 × 39–48) ($n = 40$) (Schönwetter 1960–66) or (no sample size) 58.9 × 40.4 (Johnson 1965); *alticola* (no sample size) 61.3 × 42.2 (Johnson 1965); weight in captivity *specularioides* 57.3 (49.5–91.0) ($n = 100$), or 55.0 (Johnstone 1965), and *alticola* 62.8 ($n = 84$). Clutch of both races 5–8 (Johnson 1965). Incubation, by ♀, 30 days (Delacour 1954–64); *specularioides* ducklings hatched in captivity weighed 35.8 ($n = 57$) and *alticola* 39.7 ($n = 23$). ♂ accompanies brood, apparently to protect ducklings, and plays important role in their care from hatching to independence (Buitron and Nuechterlein 1989). In encounter with Magellan Goose, ♂ and ♀ cooperated by alternately luring goose away from young with repeated Distraction displays. High levels of vigilance, cooperation by both adults and aggressiveness undoubtedly allow species to nest in close proximity to gulls, e.g. Kelp or Southern Black-backed Gull, and skuas. Fledge in 10–11 weeks (Weller 1972). No data on breeding success, adult survival or longevity.

Conservation and threats

Sensible hunting practices and protection of wetlands throughout range of both subspecies should ensure that this remarkable duck remains common.

Glyn Young

Bronze-winged Duck *Speculanas specularis*
PLATE 18

Anas specularis King, 1828, Zool. Journ., **4**, p. 98
Strait of Magellan
Speculanas Boetticher, 1929

Etymology: *specularis* is L. for mirror, in reference to shining bronze speculum on wing.

Other names: Black Duck, Dog Duck, Spectacled Duck, Wood Duck. Spanish: Pato ante-ofillo.

Variation: no subspecies.

Description

ADULT: sexes alike. ♂ dark brown head and neck contrast with white oval patch in front of eye and white patch on throat that extends to sides of neck forming semi-collar. Mantle and scapulars dark brown to blackish with lighter edging. Breast and underparts barred or mottled with tan and dark brown, becoming large dark brown or blackish crescents on tan background on flanks. Tail dark brown and wing dark brown to purplish black. Speculum brilliant bronze bordered posteriorly with narrow black and narrow white line. Bill bluish grey; legs and feet orange-yellowish with darker markings; iris brown. ♀ closely resembles ♂, but slightly duller and smaller (Delacour 1954–64, Johnsgard 1978).

MOULT: no ♂ eclipse, but no data on wing and body moults.

IMMATURE: similar to adult but little or no white on face and heavy streaking on breast (Delacour 1954–64, Johnsgard 1978).

DUCKLING: brown above with whitish yellow face and underparts. Four spots on lateral and posterior part of back and narrow, posterior line on wings are also whitish yellow. Dark eyestripe and dark cheek stripe. Legs, feet and bill black (Delacour 1954–64). Johnson (1965) noted somewhat wigeon-like, with distinctive white areas on cheeks and throat.

MEASUREMENTS AND WEIGHT: ♂ wing, 260–280; tail, 105–116; culmen, 45–46; tarsus, 44–45; weight (*n* = 2), 1130 and 1460. ♀ wing, 252–277; culmen, 45–49; weight (*n* = 2), 900 and 1070 (Delacour 1954–64, Lack 1968a).

Field characters

Unmistakable. White facial patch conspicuous and dog-like 'bark' of ♀ distinctive. In flight, white axilliaries noticeable against dark underwing (Scott 1954, Johnsgard 1978, Fjeldså and Krabbe 1990).

Voice

Typical call of ♀ repeated, descending, raucous quacking of 5–6 syllables, while Inciting behaviour accompanied by loud, guttural note. ♂ emits trilled whistle during Inciting by ♀ (Phillips 1922–26, Scott 1954, Johnsgard 1978). No sonograms of adult calls published; sonogram of duckling's contact call in Kear (1968).

Range and status

Little known. Partial migrant; boundaries of breeding and wintering ranges unresolved. Breeds from about 37°S in western Argentina and Chile, south to Tierra del Fuego. In winter, some birds move to

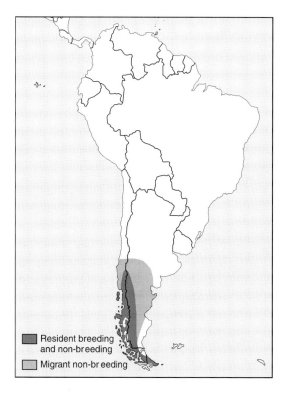

Resident breeding and non-breeding

Migrant non-breeding

lower altitudes and there may be significant movement north (to *c* 35°S) and east (to *c* 63°W). Vagrants recorded as far north as 33°S and east to 59°W (Humphrey *et al.* 1970, de Schauensee 1971, Narosky and Yzurieta 1987, Fjeldså and Krabbe 1990, Canevari *et al.* 1991, Araya and Chester 1993). Sparsely distributed, and surveys suggested 3000–3500 in Argentina; presumably, comparable numbers exist in Chile, indicating total population of 6000–7000; Rose and Scott (1997) estimated declining population of < 10 000.

Habitat and general habits

Generally encountered in pairs or family groups, but flocks of up to 18 individuals recorded. Mostly frequents lakes and fast-flowing streams and rivers in forested areas, but also seen on slower flowing rivers, lagoons and in more open habitats. Said to be commonest in valleys of Andean zone up to 1500 m (Phillips 1922–26, Scott 1954, de Schauensee 1971, Johnsgard 1978, Narosky and Yzurieta 1989, Fjeldså and Krabbe 1990, Canevari *et al.* 1991). Feeds by dabbling or probing on foot at water edge, up-ending in shallows and grazing on land. Four stomachs contained mostly roots, seeds, stems and leaves of aquatic plants and, in 2, smaller amounts of aquatic invertebrates (Phillips 1922–26, Humphrey *et al.* 1970, del Hoyo *et al.* 1992).

Displays and breeding behaviour

Inciting by ♀ involves strong chin-lifting movements, exposing white throat marks, and calling. ♂ responds with vigorous diagonal neck stretching and chin lifting (sometimes causing nape to touch back), accompanied by calling. ♂ also sometimes gapes with outstretched neck towards ♀. Copulatory behaviour not documented (Johnsgard 1978). Pairs establish fairly large foraging and breeding territories, some defended year-round (del Hoyo *et al.* 1992). Pairbond probably long-term.

Breeding and life cycle

Few studies in wild. Breeding starts Sept–Oct, with 1st eggs laid Oct–Nov and young hatching late Dec–early Jan (Johnson 1965). Nests on ground, often on river islets and in low vegetation; abundantly lined with down. Eggs deep cream, 63.6 × 44.2 (Johnson 1965) or, in captivity, somewhat larger at 70 × 51 (*n* = 5) (Johnstone 1965) and 71.5 (*n* = 55) in weight; clutch 4–6 (Johnson 1965), sometimes 7 (Humphrey *et al.* 1970). Incubation, by ♀, in captivity 30 days (Johnstone 1970). Newly hatched captives weigh 43.6 (*n* = 15). ♂ almost certainly participates in brood care. No information on growth, breeding success, age at first breeding, survival or longevity.

Conservation and threats

Despite relatively small population and occasional hunting, no obvious threats. Well represented in protected areas throughout breeding range, where many birds also winter (Scott and Carbonell 1986, del Hoyo *et al.* 1992, Callaghan and Green 1993). Considered Near-threatened by BirdLife International (2000), and studies required of bird in wild.

Des Callaghan

Cape Teal *Anas capensis*
PLATE 16

Anas capensis Gmelin, 1789, Syst. Nat., **1**, p. 527
Cape of Good Hope
Anas Linnaeus, 1758
   Etymology: *capensis* from Cape (of Good Hope, South Africa) where type specimen taken.
   Other names: Cape Wigeon. Afrikaans: Teeleend.
   Variation: no subspecies.

Description

ADULT: sexes alike, ♂ little larger than ♀. Grey uniform plumage, although back darker and browner than breast, with spotted flanks. Speculum, obvious in flight, emerald green with broad white borders. Bright pink bill, black at base of upper mandible, almost upturned; legs and feet dull yelowish; iris variably pale brown to orange-red.

MOULT: no ♂ eclipse. No information on timing of wing or body moults.

IMMATURE: similar to adult, duller with greyer bill.

DUCKLING: greyish brown upperparts with whitish underparts and white patches on wings, back. White line around pink-edged bill and broad white supercilium.

MEASUREMENTS AND WEIGHT: data from Cape Province (unsexed $n = 52$) wing, 168–206 (193.8); tail, 53–74 (64.3); bill, 36–44 (39.6), tarsus, 32–40 (37) (Winterbottom 1974); weight ♂ ($n = 31$), 352–502 (419); ♀ ($n = 25$), 316–451 (380) (Brown *et al.* 1982).

Field characters

Length 460 mm. Small to medium-sized, stocky, whitish grey duck; rounded, almost 'toy' shape and pink bill, unmistakable amongst African wildfowl. Sits high in water and regularly comes ashore, where can be fast runner. In flight, white and green speculum easily seen. Ranges of Cape Teal and Marbled Teal occasionally overlap in parts of Africa; Marbled Teal slightly larger, has dark face patch, grey bill and no speculum.

Voice

Generally quiet. ♂ has soft nasal squeak, ♀ low *quack*. During courtship, both sexes may be more vocal and ♀ has five-syllabled Decrescendo call (Brown *et al.* 1982). Sonogram of adult call in Maclean (1993).

Range and status

Widespread, but patchy distribution throughout eastern and southern Africa from Ethiopia to Cape, with three populations. Very small group in Chad valley centred on Lake Chad, principally in Sudan and Nigeria; this population may be nomadic and dispersive, i.e. has occurred Ghana, Niger, southern Libya and Sudan where may have bred, and vagrants recorded Israel. Further populations in east African Rift Valley (Ethiopia, Kenya, Tanzania, with

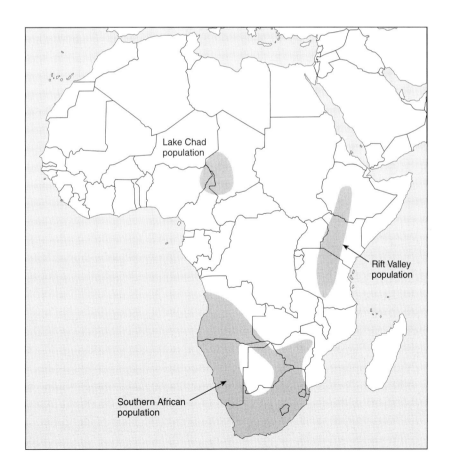

records from adjacent countries) and in southern Africa (South Africa, Namibia, Angola, Botswana and Zimbabwe). Can be common in parts of range, particularly in southern and eastern Africa, and especially in arid regions and Rift Valley soda lakes. Rose and Scott (1997) suggested 100 000–250 000 individuals in both of 2 populations, one in eastern Africa (but including Chad), and other in southern Africa. AEWA (2000) felt estimate much too high; > 33 500 recorded in southern Africa in Jan 1997, and perhaps < 25 000 appropriate for northern groups. Wetlands International (2002) estimate < 500 in Chad.

Habitat and general habits

Mostly found in shallow, saline and brackish waters, as well as saltpans, lagoons, estuaries and tidal mud-flats. Lives in pairs and small groups, with large flocks recorded rarely. Nomadic in parts of range, and may undertake long dry-season movements. Birds ringed in Cape recovered in Namibia (1850 km away) and Mozambique (2720 km) (Winterbottom 1974, Harrison *et al.* 1997). Usually crepuscular, feeding by dabbling, swimming in shallow water, or by up-ending; will also dive for food (Winterbottom 1974). Diet includes animal and vegetable material and, depending on availability, may feed almost exclusively on aquatic invertebrates and tadpoles.

Displays and behaviour

♂ uses Nod-swim, Preen-behind-wing, Burp, Head-up-tail-up and Preliminary-shake displays. Burp may be most commonly used display, and neck and head are extended forward rather than upward as in most *Anas*. Small crest, normally hidden, raised as ♂ gives clear whistle, of 3 syllables, *oo-whee-oo*. During Head-up-tail-up, tail spread rather than lifted and folded wings raised, flashing speculum, and then lowered as ♂ points bill towards ♀. ♂ Turns-back-of-head to Inciting ♀ (Johnsgard

1965a). Post-copulatory display consists of Bridle with call, and Erect Broadside. During Bridle, ♂ wings fanned partly open, exposing conspicuous white markings on secondaries (Johnson *et al.* 2000). May Burp.

Arrives at breeding area paired and may remain together for several seasons. Bigamy recorded (Stolen and McKinney 1983, Bannor 1997). ♂ does not defend territory but regularly accompanies and defends mate during brood rearing (Brand 1964, Siegfried 1974a).

Breeding and life cycle

Nesting recorded in all months, reproduction being dependent on high rainfall and associated increases in food supplies. Nests on ground or in aquatic vegetation, frequently on islands (Winterbottom 1974). Eggs ovate, smooth, pale to deep cream (Brown *et al.* 1982); in southwestern Cape 49.7×36.1 (46.2–54.8×33.0–39.4) ($n = 351$) (Winterbottom 1974), in southern Africa, 49.6×36.1 (43.0–56.8×31.0–45.5) ($n = 798$) (Maclean 1993); weight in captivity 30.5 (25.5–39.0) ($n = 46$) (Brown *et al.* 1982). Clutch in southern Africa 8.2 (5–11) ($n = 356$) (Maclean 1993); incubation, by ♀ alone, 26–30 days; hatch weight in captivity 18.9 ($n = 39$). Fledges in 42–56 days (Maclean 1993). Probably breeds at one year. No data on growth, breeding success, survival nor longevity.

Conservation and threats

No known threats to population but census coverage relatively poor. Conservation of nomadic species more difficult than of sedentary ones, since many ephemeral wetlands must receive protection. Hunting must be regulated, and restrictions should include provision for wide dispersal during dry conditions.

Glyn Young

Gadwall *Anas strepera*
PLATE 15

Anas strepera Linnaeus, 1758, Syst. Nat., ed. 10, p. 125
Europe

Etymology: *strepera* from L. *streperus* meaning noisy. Common name similar onomatopoeic origins, deriving from ♂'s chattering voice.

Other names: Grey Duck. Danish: Knarand; French: Canard chipeau; German: Schnatterente; Icelandic: Gargönd; Japanese: Okayoshi-gamo; Spanish: Pato Friso.

Variation: 2 subspecies. Common nominate race, plus sedentary race *A. s. couesi* Streets, 1876 now extinct. *A. s. couesi* formerly bred on Teraina (Washington and New York Islands) in Republic of Kirbati (Fanning Group) in Central Pacific, 1000 miles south of Hawaiian Islands; discovered in 1874 on lake and bogs of Washington Island, but never seen alive after discovery; probably descended from small group stranded birds of nominate race.

Description

ADULT: dimorphic. ♂ in breeding, or alternate, plumage has head greyish brown, forehead and chin that may be suffused cinnamon. Mantle, back and flanks delicately black-and-white vermiculated, appearing uniform grey at distance. Upper breast black, feathers edged white, lower breast and belly white with much reduced dark freckling. Tail grey-brown, strongly contrasting upper and undertail coverts black. White speculum often visible at rest. In flight, bold white inner speculum patch contrasts broad black forward band and warm chestnut wing coverts; white lower breast and belly also distinctive. Bill grey, but may have orangish patches along edges; legs yellowish orange usually with blackish webs, becoming dull olive-yellow during moult; iris brown. ♀ neck and head buffish brown, flecked with dark streaks, less warm brown than Northern Mallard. Chin and upper breast paler, but forehead, crown, nape and diffuse eyestripe darker than general head colour. Breast and much of body warm brown, but feathers all marked with dark sub-terminal markings, producing heavy scalloping on most body feathers, especially along flanks. Below

waterline, underparts whitish, highly conspicuous in flight. White speculum more restricted than ♂ (some ♀♀ have only one white secondary), bordered black in front, with variable chestnut marking (always less than ♂). Tail darker, also with dark sub-terminal markings. Bill greyish or greyish black, with dull orange patches along edges, becoming spotted with age; legs yellowish with grey to black webs; iris brown. ♂ of *couesi* resembled eclipsed ♂ of nominate race, but body size overall smaller.

MOULT: eclipsed ♂ in basic plumage resembles ♀, but retains chestnut patch and other patterning on wing, overall greyer than ♀. Bill of ♂ always less orange than ♀ during eclipse. Captive birds completely renewed wing feathers within 35–40 days, but regained powers of flight after only 25 (Oring 1968). ♂ in almost complete breeding plumage mid Aug.

IMMATURE: ♂ resembles adult ♀, but with greater contrast on body feathers, which show more spotting and streaking than scalloped effect of adult. Head and neck greyer than adult ♀, showing more contrast at range. Upperwing as adult ♀, but less chestnut and white than adult ♂. Bare parts as adult, but duller. ♀ body plumage also like adult ♀, but less scalloped. Upperwing dull, with restricted white patch (sometimes absent), no black or chestnut. Bare parts as adult, but duller.

DUCKLING: like Northern Mallard, but upperparts warm brown-sepia, lacking olive tinge. Pale patches of wing and flanks creamy rather than yellow, and more extensive. Bill grey with flesh-coloured edging; feet dark grey to olive-black (Nelson 1993).

MEASUREMENTS AND WEIGHT: nominate ♂ adult wing ($n = 148$), 269.5, juv (1st winter) ($n = 309$), 265.8; adult skull ($n = 115$), 98.9, juv ($n = 241$), 98.5; adult tarsus ($n = 115$), 40.4, juv ($n = 241$), 40.4; adult winter weight ($n = 150$), 782.5, juv ($n = 317$), 765.9. ♀ adult wing ($n = 102$), 251.1, juv ($n = 281$), 252.1; adult skull ($n = 96$), 93.3, juv ($n = 206$), 92.9; adult tarsus ($n = 97$), 38.8, juv ($n = 206$), 38.7; adult winter weight ($n = 127$), 706.3, juv ($n = 290$), 678.2; data from WWT, Abberton Reservoir, southeast England. ♂ adult wing ($n = 22$), 271.8, juv ($n = 58$), 266.7; weight ($n = 37$), 971.9, juv ($n = 204$), 862.4. ♀ adult wing ($n = 6$), 256.6, juv ($n = 56$) 248.9; weight ($n = 45$), 839.6, juv ($n = 200$), 780.3 (Bellrose 1980).

couesi (unsexed, no sample size) wing, 199; culmen, 37; tarsus, 36 (Delacour 1954–64).

Field characters

Medium-sized rather nondescript dabbling duck, 460–550 mm long, best identified by medium-sized slender bill and steep forehead. Adult ♂ black patch above and below tail surprizingly conspicuous, even at distance. In flight, pale belly and white speculum distinctive in most plumages. Juvenile and ♀ distinguished from Eurasian and American Wigeon by dull secondaries (contrast whitish wing bars framing glossed black panel), more uniformly dull upperwing, and pale uniform underwing.

Voice

Deep, croaking and fairly constant calls from ♂, ♀ makes quacking sound. Sonogram of adult calls in Cramp and Simmons (1977). For calls of ducklings, see Nelson (1993).

Range and status

Breeds between 40° and 60°N in lowland continental habitats and winters between 20° and 60°N throughout New and Old Worlds. Strongly migratory in north of range, may be sedentary further south.

Nests in greatest abundance across prairies of North America (densities varying 10.6–16.3 pairs per km², Bellrose 1980) but also occurs in parklands (4.9–15.8 pairs per km², Bellrose 1980) and great plains region (1.0–7.8 pairs per km², Bellrose 1980). Numbers decrease into boreal forest areas, but mild influence of Japanese Currents enables breeding in British Columbia and along Alaskan coast. Large numbers also breed in western US down into Central Valley of California. Numbers increased dramatically in eastern states since late 1950s (Henny and Holgerson 1974), mainly as result of colonization of freshwater impoundments in brackish areas. Appears to endure periods of drought better than many other prairie pothole species (Smith 1971, Stoudt 1971).

In America, winters over much of southern US, with up to 28 000 in California and up to 1.5 million (three-quarters of estimated North American population in early 1970s) recorded in Louisiana wetlands in autumn (Bellrose 1980). Others continue into

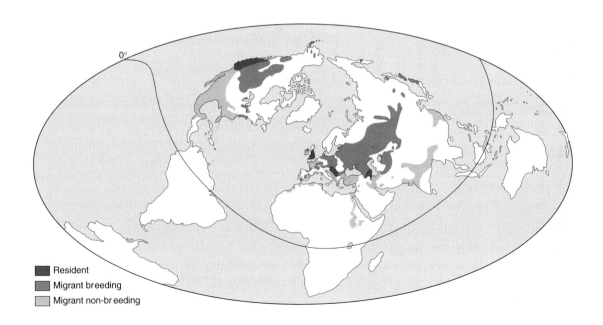

- Resident
- Migrant breeding
- Migrant non-breeding

Mexico, Cuba and other parts of West Indies. Declined 1.5% per annum in wintering numbers in North America 1967–86 (Boyd 1990). Continental numbers estimated at around 2.39 million (Rose and Scott 1997).

In Old World, breeds in Japan (rather uncommonly), China and Russian eastern Asia right across to lowlands of Caspian and Black Seas, through Mediterranean and eastern Europe across to Britain, Ireland and Iceland. Breeding distribution relatively discontinuous, western European populations augmented to variable extent by past introductions (as in UK, Fox 1988). Birds from eastern part winter in Japan (Brazil 1991), eastern China, Indian sub-continent, Caspian and Black Seas, with lesser numbers moving into Africa as far south as Kenya in east. Northern European flyway birds winter along milder coasts of North Sea, Britain and Ireland, France and Iberia, moving into west Africa as far south as Senegal. Vagrant to Hawaii, Mariana and Marshall Islands, Faeroes, Azores and Madeira.

Winter estimates suggest 30 000 in western Europe, 75 000–150 000 in Black Sea/eastern Mediterranean, 130 000 in former Soviet Union in mild winters (Rose and Scott 1994). There are estimates of 150 000 in southern Asia (Rose and Scott 1997) so, with 500 000–1 000 000 (Miyabayashi and Mundkur 1999) in eastern Asia, Old World population probably stands at >735 000. Dramatic increases in small western European wintering population, sustained at 8–10% per annum in recent years (Rose 1995), but signs that Russia breeding population declined at same time, reflected in decrease in Black Sea/eastern Mediterranean wintering population (Fox and Vinogradov 1994, Rose 1995).

Habitat and general habits

Found in freshwater marsh and lake habitats with high productivity, preferring shallow eutrophic sheltered waters with abundant vegetation. Large gatherings unusual away from coastal marshes of Louisiana where common in large groups. After breeding, may aggregate into modest moulting concentrations.

Consumes almost entirely green-vegetable diet throughout year, preferring green leaves and shoots to seeds. Unlike wigeon, rarely grazes terrestrial grassland, but prefers submerged or emergent vegetation, such as *Potamogeton*, *Ruppia*, *Zannichellia*, *Carex*, *Juncus* and *Scirpus*, as well as grasses and stoneworts *Chara* (Cramp and Simmons 1977, Bellrose 1980). Frequently obtains food by stealing from other species, such as Red-crested Pochard, Common Goldeneye and coots (Amat and Soriguer 1984, Knights 1984); character has enabled feeding in deeper water habitats than would be possible without parasitized partner, and implicated in recent spread in Britain (Fox and Salmon 1989). Also virtually vegetarian while moulting (Hohman *et al.* 1992).

Displays and breeding behaviour

Pair-formation conspicuous in late summer, and communal courtship often intense by mid Aug. Early pairing confers social advantage and hence access to limited poor-quality (usually green vegetation) food (Paulus 1983). Early courtship often involves pre-copulatory display even early in pair-formation. Pairbond lasts until soon after clutch initiation (Oring 1964), although re-pairing of free-flying birds at WWT, Slimbridge, known in subsequent seasons and recent studies show that pairs locate one another and re-establish bond after moult and brood raising (Köhler *et al.* 1995).

Pairs may arrive at breeding area up to month before laying, and ♂ shows increasing intolerance of others (Dwyer 1974). ♂ strongly defends territory before nest site selection often until some way into incubation (Dwyer 1974, Titman and Seymour 1981). Pairs may make low flights over suitable nesting areas to select site.

Breeding and life cycle

Because feeds mainly on protein-poor green plant material, almost certain that ♀ must store protein reserves in readiness for reproduction. Despite predominantly feeding on green vegetation through most of year, up to 72% of ♀ diet during laying may comprise macro-invertebrates, mainly cladocerans (Serie and Swanson 1976). Although much geographical variation in breeding season, nests generally late for temperate duck (May–July), becoming later in north of range. Often delays clutch initiation after arrival (e.g. 23–28 days in Utah, Gates 1962).

Will breed in 2nd summer, but late hatching individuals may not breed until 2 years old (Bellrose 1980). Young and inexperienced ♀♀ nest later than older ones (Johnson *et al.* 1992), are less likely to re-nest, with competition for nest sites perhaps involved in density regulation in some areas (Lokemoen *et al.* 1990). Homing rates for adult, 2-year-olds and year-lings were 63%, 47% and 22% respectively (allowing for mortality) and studies show young ♀♀ more likely to disperse short distances than older ones (Johnson *et al.* 1992). Successful ♀♀ more likely to show breeding philopatry than unsuccessful ones (61% *v* 38%, Lokemoen *et al.* 1990), but ♂ natal (2%) and breeding (10%) less than ♀ (6% and 41%), ensuring outbreeding (Lokemoen *et al.* 1990, Johnson *et al.* 1992). Such site fidelity makes habitat loss more serious than for some other ducks.

Nests on ground, usually amongst dense vegetation, often far from water, rarely over water. Nest baskets may be used (Kaminski and Weller 1992). Nest sites may be on islands (Kaminski and Weller 1992), sometimes in dense concentrations, where ♂ will defend stretches of mainland shoreline away from nest (Lokemoen *et al.* 1984). Nest parasitism recorded at 2–13% of studied nests (Sayler 1992). Eggs bluntly ovate, creamy white sometimes with pinkish tinge; 55×39 (51–59×35–44) ($n = 200$, Schönwetter 1960–66) in Europe, 55.7×39.7 (Bellrose 1980) in North America. Egg weight 44 (35–55, $n = 100$, Cramp and Simmons 1977). Clutch 8–11 (6–15) in Europe (Cramp and Simmons 1977), 10.04 (5–13) ($n = 2545$) in North America (Bellrose 1980); incubation 25.7 (24–27) days (Oring 1969). Single brood (but will replace lost clutch).

♀♀ lose up to 16% of body mass during incubation (Afton and Paulus 1992). Up to quarter of nests lost (Hines and Mitchell 1983), but this low among most dabbling ducks. Hatchability of eggs also high, losses varying 0.65–1.6 eggs (mean 0.98) per clutch (Miller and Collins 1954, Duebbert 1966). Late nesting (when cover thick and predators have switched to other prey) may be partly responsible for nesting success. Genetic analysis showed 75% of ducklings (14 of 261 ducklings) in 31% of broods (9 of 29 broods) in North Dakota were extrapair young, almost certainly due to extrapair paternity (Peters *et al.* 2003). Captive day-olds weigh 27.8 ($n = 63$). Losses of young in 1st 2 weeks recorded at 53% and pre-fledging at 73% (Duncan 1986b). ♀ leads brood to nursery area where young initially feed on invertebrates, but swiftly switch to vegetable food. Overall, less than 10% of studied pre-fledging diet animal material (Sugden 1973). Bellrose (1980) cited mean brood size at hatching (6.87, $n = 3891$) reduced to 6.10 for Class II age group ($n = 5035$), but increased to 6.28 for Class III age group ($n = 2545$) suggesting brood amalgamation (see Gollop and Marshall 1954 for definitions). Fledging takes minimum of 48 days, most fledge by 52 days and all by 63 (Oring 1968).

Adult survival higher for ♂ (75%) than ♀ (69%) (Szymczak and Rexstad 1991). Longevity record of BTO-ringed bird *c* 23 years (Toms and Clark 1998).

Conservation and threats

Presently increasing throughout much of range, there appear to be few threats, although declines in Russia give cause for concern. Has almost certainly benefited from effects of human eutrophication processes that have increased amount of aquatic plant biomass exploited through most of life cycle. Has also benefited from creation of artificial habitats, such as reservoirs and gravel pits, especially in semi-arid areas. Appears most susceptible to disturbance, e.g. from increasing pressures on freshwater for year-round recreational use, and pollution. Is quarry species throughout most of world range but, except where really abundant (as in Louisiana in US), rarely taken in large numbers. Adequate safeguard of all known internationally important sites remains a priority.

Tony Fox

Falcated Duck *Anas falcata*

PLATE 15

Anas falcata Georgi, 1775, Bemerkungen Reise Russischen Reich, p. 167

Lake Baykal, Asiatic Russia

Etymology: *falcatus* L. for sickle-shaped, from shape of ♂ scapulars.

Other names: Falcated Teal, Bronze-capped Duck. French: Canard à faucilles; German: Sichelente; Japanese: Yoshi-gamo; Russian: Kasatka; Spanish: Cerceta de alfanjes.

Variation: no subspecies.

Description

ADULT: dimorphic. ♂ in breeding, or alternate, plumage has head with bushy crest of dark metallic purple-chestnut on crown, green on sides, with crest falling onto back. White spot above base of upper bill. Neck white with narrow dark green half collar on lower part. Body silver-grey outlined with black crescents on breast and belly and fine vermiculation on flanks. Tail dark grey to black with black-bordered buff patches at sides and strip of white in front. Long black and white sickle-shaped inner secondaries extend over tail. Wing light grey to grey-brown above, white under wing. Speculum black and glossy green with whitish band at tip of secondaries. Bill black; legs yellowish to bluish grey with darker webs; eyes brown. ♀ head and neck dark brown with pale streaking. Short mane at back of head. Body and tail dark brown with reddish edging on back and dark crescent bands on breast. Belly yellow-brown with darker spots. Wings grey-black with black and green speculum (duller than ♂). Inner secondaries slightly elongated. Bill black or dark brown with black freckles; legs, feet and eyes as ♂.

MOULT: eclipse or basic plumage of ♂ like adult ♀ but head with some green gloss and darker cheeks. Inner secondaries not elongated and forewing clearer grey. ♂ starts head and body moult mid June, followed by moult of wing early July–late Aug. Moults comparable to Gadwall (Cramp and Simmons 1977).

IMMATURE: like adult ♀ but crown dark with greenish cast. ♀ has more brown inner secondaries, duller speculum, and lacks ochre bands on shoulder and hind neck feathers.

DUCKLING: back dark brown. Buff belly and markings near rump and scapular region. Sides of head reddish with indistinct line through eye.

MEASUREMENTS AND WEIGHT: ♂ (*n* = 12) wing, 244–268 (253); tail, 70–80 (73.5); bill, 39–48 (42.8); tarsus, 37–44 (39.8); weight (*n* = 4), 590–770 (713). ♀ (*n* = 9) wing, 226–236 (231); tail, 68–76 (71.3); bill, 36–40 (38.8); tarsus, 36–40 (37.7); weight (*n* = 5), 422–700 (585) (Shaw 1936, Palmer 1976). Dementiev and Gladkov (1952) gave heavier weights at ♂ *c* 750 and ♀ 640–660.

Field characters

Length 460–540 mm. Long bright green crest, white patches on chin and neck and near tail, and long inner secondaries distinguish ♂. Both ♂ and ♀ appear to have large head and squat posture on water. ♀ dark brown with rusty underparts and grey forewing. In flight, green and black speculum distinctive for both sexes. Flight fast and light.

Voice

Generally quiet except on breeding grounds. ♂ has shrill whistle *tyu-tyu-vit . . . tyu-vit . . . tyu-tyu-vit* (Dementiev and Gladkov 1952) and quiet whistle ending with wavering *uit-trr* (Flint *et al.* 1984). During sexual displays, ♂ gives vibrating *rruh-urr* (Burp), and *lili-fru-u-u* and soft whirring sound during Head-up-tail-up; ♀ has hoarse *quack*, short two-syllable Inciting call, and high-pitched, 2–4 syllable Decrescendo call (Lorenz and Von de Wall 1960). Both sexes give repeated short calls as greeting and during aggressive encounters. No published sonograms.

Range and status

Breeds south of Arctic Circle in Siberia, Mongolia, and northeastern China, east to Hokkaido in northern Japan (where occurs Apr–Nov), Kuril Islands, and (rarely) Kamchatka peninsula. Winters in eastern and

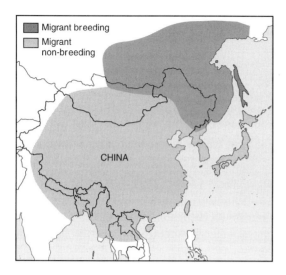

central China, southern Japan, and Korea, south to Vietnam, Myanmar (Burma), Laos, and Thailand. Few birds winter as far west as northern India. Vagrants reach Iran, Jordan, Turkey and Aleutian Islands. Recorded in many European countries, including UK and France; status in these countries complicated by possible escapes from captivity. Can be locally abundant, but probably declining. Population estimates of 100 000– 1 000 000 (Rose and Scott 1997) revised to 500 000–1 000 000 by Miyabayashi and Mundkur (1999) with 500 000 in China, < 3000 in South Korea and 8000 wintering in Japan.

Habitat and general habits

Found in freshwater lakes, rivers, ponds, and inland marshes, often in wooded areas, during breeding season. Frequents coastal lagoons, shallow saltwater bays, and flooded meadows and rice paddies during nonbreeding season. Usually cautious. Dabbles and up-ends in shallow water, grazes on land, and dives well. Generally seen alone or in pairs, except in flocks during nonbreeding season. Mostly feeds on vegetation, green shoots of plants (Dementiev and Gladkov 1952), crop plants including rice, grains and seeds. Also reported to feed on molluscs and aquatic insects (Cheng 1964).

Displays and breeding behaviour

Displays generally similar to those of other dabbling ducks. ♂ performs Grunt-whistle with water flick towards ♀, Introductory shake with head moved in quarter circle downwards, Turn-back-of-head, and Preen-behind-wing. Head-up-tail-up common ♂ display, performed broadside to ♀ and including Head-jerk towards her (Lorenz and Von de Wall 1960). ♀ Inciting consists of alternating Chin-lifts and pointing towards ♂ while uttering two-syllable call. Introductory shake and Preen-behind-wing also performed by ♀, and both sexes Wing-flap during social courtship. Pair members Chin-lift with calls for greeting and aggression towards other pairs. Neck-jerking and lateral Head shakes precede flight, and copulations preceded by mutual Head-pumps (Johnsgard 1965a). Found in pairs or loose groups during breeding season.

Breeding and life cycle

Eggs laid late May–early June in Russia, mainly June in India. Nests on ground among thick grasses, tussocks, swamped shrubbery, or hidden in deadwood; usually near water, but also reported in small bushes about 80 m from water (Dementiev and Gladkov 1952). Eggs white with pinkish yellow tint; 55.8×37.8 $(53–58.5 \times 37.6–41.5)$ $(n = 1$ clutch) (Dementiev and Gladkov 1952) or 56.2×39.65 $(53–58.5 \times 38–41)$ $(n = 21$ eggs) (Phillips 1922–26); weight in captivity 43.1 (38.0–48.5) $(n = 100)$ or 49 (calculated by Schönwetter 1960–66 from measurements of 120 eggs); clutch *c* 7.5 (6–10). Incubation, by ♀ alone, 24–25 days in captivity (Dementiev and Gladkov 1952, Delacour 1954–64). ♂ abandons ♀ during incubation. Ducklings hatched in captivity weighed 27.2 $(n = 14)$. Probably breeds at one year. Little data on hatching and fledging success, growth, survival or longevity.

Conservation and threats

Although reasonably common in some areas, considered to be declining (Perennou *et al.* 1994, Miyabayashi and Mundkur 1999); wintering population of Japan has decreased (Brazil 1991). Hunting pressure for food and feathers, especially in China (del Hoyo *et al.* 1992), and habitat loss due to wetland drainage, will likely continue as primary threats.

Gwenda L. Brewer

Chiloe Wigeon *Anas sibilatrix*

PLATE 15

Anas sibilatrix Poeppig, 1829, in Froriep, Notizen, **25**, col. 10

Talcahuano, Concepción, Chile

Etymology: *sibilatrix* L. means whistling, in reference to ♂ voice. Vernacular name 'Chiloe' comes from Island of Chiloé where birds common; 'wigeon' dates from 1513, refers to Eurasian Wigeon, and is also onomatopoeic in origin.

Other names: Southern, Chilean or South American Wigeon; Black and White Wigeon (Falklands). French: Canard de Chiloé; German: Chilepfeifente; Portuguese: Marreca-oveira; Spanish: Pato or Silbón overo, Pato real.

Variation: no subspecies.

Description

ADULT: only slightly dimorphic. ♂ forehead and face white with small whitish patch behind and below eye. Black head and neck with wide iridescent green band extending from eye to nape. Head rounded with feathers extended at nape. Back, scapulars, and tertials black-edged with white or buff, giving striped appearance. Median and greater coverts white, forming large patch. Secondaries velvet black, with innermost lined white on outer edge. Primaries and tail medium brown to black, with upper and lower tail coverts white. May have rust under tail. Breast white with black bars and may have some rust near belly. Belly white with sides and flanks mottled or solid rusty chestnut. Bill slate blue with prominent black nail and black lower mandible; legs silver grey with darker web; iris brown. ♀ face may be less white, and white wing coverts, black secondaries, and white rump mottled or dusky. Less green on head than ♂ and head shape less chunky.

MOULT: no ♂ eclipse plumage. Uncertain timing of wing and, presumably, of 2 annual body moults in both sexes, but flightless birds noted Jan in Isla Grande (Weller 1975c) and late Nov–early Dec in Rio Negro province, Argentina.

IMMATURE: like adult but with sides barred and little green on head. Immature ♀ has white coverts

more dingy or barred brown, and secondaries more grey than black.

DUCKLING: face noticeably rufous with dark line along top of head. Back dark brown and belly buff. Large white or buff spots on either side of rump, with smaller markings along flanks and in scapular region.

MEASUREMENTS AND WEIGHT: ♂ ($n = 8$) wing, 235–274 (258.6); tail, 77–96 (88.7); bill, 35–38 (36.1); tarsus, 40–43. ♀ ($n = 4$) wing, 240–262 (249.2); tail, 74–88 (81.2); bill, 34–37 (35) (Blake 1977). Weight ♂ ($n = 16$), 934 ± 57; ♀ ($n = 16$), 773 ± 79 (Schlatter *et al.* 1983); fall and winter, ♂ ($n = 5$), 939.0; ♀ ($n = 3$), 828.3; immature ♀ ($n = 2$), 665.0 (Weller 1968b).

Field characters

Length 430–540 mm (del Hoyo *et al.* 1992). Large white forewing, black speculum, pale wing linings, white belly, and white rump distinctive in flight. Chunky body, with head tucked in close on water. Rounded, elongated head shape notable for ♂. Very vocal and may graze on land. Powerful flyer.

Voice

Highly vocal, even at night. Sonograms available for most vocalizations (recorded from captives; Brewer 1997). ♂ utters loud, two-syllable whistled *rakoo*, sometimes preceded by snorts during courtship, when separated from mate, after copulation, and during pair or family Triumph Ceremonies. ♀ gives loud honks during Triumph Ceremony and rolling *errr* as Inciting call. ♀ also gives series of evenly spaced, prolonged honks when prospecting for nest (Persistent Quacking). ♂ and ♀ utter soft chittering calls or honks when feeding and when accompanying broods. ♀ has loud honk for alarm situations, and ♂ sharp rising whistle. Latter call and short whistles (Pic calls) given by ♂ during Bill-flipping bouts. Decrescendo call, series of 2 honks of descending pitch, heard from wild ♀♀ separated from mate and from 2 captive ♀♀ when ducklings died soon after hatch. Ducklings have typical distress and content-ment calls when young (Kear 1968), but ♀ develops high-pitched honks and ♂ trills as they age. These calls and soft peeps given by ducklings during family Triumph Ceremonies.

Range and status

Breeds in pampas and Patagonian region of southern South America, from 34°S, in northern Argentina, Chile, Paraguay, and Uruguay, south to Tierra del Fuego, and Falkland Islands. Has occurred on several sub-antarctic islands including South Georgia and South Orkney (Marchant and Higgins 1990, del Hoyo *et al.* 1992). Generally sedentary, although most southern populations migrate north Mar–Apr. No evidence that population on Falklands regularly leaves islands. Winters to southeastern Brazil and Paraguay, vagrant to Junin in central Peru. Widely distributed and fairly common over much of range. Important staging and moulting areas located on foothill plateaux of southern Andes where large concentrations

Breeding
Migrant non-breeding

(18 900 individuals) found at certain times (Scott and Carbonell 1986). Woods and Woods (1997) recorded 1500–2700 on Falklands. Total population estimated at 100 000 to one million (Wetlands International 2002).

Habitat and general habits

Found in freshwater lakes, marshes, lagoons and occasionally streams or wide rivers. Favours shallow lakes with dense submergents such as *Potamogeton*, *Ruppia*, *Nitella*, *Lileopsis*, and *Zanichella*, or floating carpets of *Myriophyllum* (Weller 1968b, Fjeldså and Krabbe 1990). Selects wetter low-lying parts of East and West Falklands (Woods and Woods 1997), where more shy than South American or Speckled Teal and Crested Duck with which associates. Sometimes grazes on shore in areas with short grass, including family groups (Brewer 1990); often feeds at night. Diet consists primarily of vegetable matter, especially in winter (Weller 1975c); 37 stomachs examined in Chile by Schlatter *et al.* (1983) contained 82.9% *Potentilla anserina* seeds, 5.7% *Triglochim montevidense*, and 3.6% *Polygonum avicular*, with grit in gizzard. Housse (1945) found worms, seeds, larvae and minnows in stomachs of summer birds, including more fish in ducks collected at one lake.

Displays and breeding behaviour

Displays similar to those of other wigeon, although behavioural specializations associated with biparental care and strong family bonds appear more goose-like. Unlike other wigeon, pairbond suspected to be long-term. ♂ courtship and pair-maintenance displays consist of giving *rakoo* calls, Preen-behind-wing, Grunt-whistle, Turn-back-of-head, and Display-shake (Johnsgard 1965a, Brewer 1997). Unpaired ♂♂ also direct courtship displays towards ducklings and attempts to pair with them (Brewer 1991). Pairs and families may perform Triumph Ceremonies when they re-unite or after aggressive encounters, when ♂ gives *rakoo* whistle, ♀ Chin-lifts and Honks, and ducklings Chin-lift and call to greet parents. ♀ Inciting display consists of rapid Chin-lifts and Inciting calls, sometimes alternating with threats. Copulations occur after both sexes perform Head-pumps and ♀ adopts prone posture. After copulation, ♂ adopts alert posture, broadside to ♀, or whistles *rakoo*. Forced extra–pair copulations noted in captivity and in wild, but ♂ defends mate vigorously and effectively. Typical aggressive displays are Open-bill threat, rubbing head repeatedly on back (Head-rubs), side-to-side movement of tail (Tail-wag) and, less commonly, Wings-up posture. Paired ♂♂ associate in small groups when mates laying and incubating, and perform bouts of Bill-flipping (upward flips of bill) accompanied by short whistles, alarm calls, frequent comfort movements, threats, and direct aggression. Pair remain together in nonbreeding season.

Breeding and life cycle

Occurs in scattered pairs or groups during breeding season that starts as early as Aug in north of range. Courtship noted in July in Argentina (Weller 1968b), June–July in Chile, and also during Dec–Feb breeding season in Argentina and Oct–Dec breeding season in central Chile. In Falklands, breeds Sept–Dec (Woods and Woods 1997), and 8 broods hatched 10–25 Dec. Nest hidden in grass, or under shrubs or dry branches. Most nests 10–30 m from shore, although reported between reeds along edge of lake. From 4 nests in Argentina, 28 ivory eggs measured $55.4 \pm 2.1 \times 39.5 \pm 1.0$; for eggs collected in Chile, Johnson (1965) reported 60.7×41.2, and

13 eggs laid in captivity measured 58.0×40.0 ($53.8–61.0 \times 39.9–42.0$) (Phillips 1922–26). Captive laid eggs weighed 50.0 (41.0–59.0) ($n = 100$), larger than other wigeon. Clutch size c 6.5 (5–9) and incubation, by ♀ alone, 24–26 days. Day-old captive ducklings weighed 31.2 ($n = 86$). Brood size for newly hatched ducklings 6.74 ± 2.43 (2–10) ($n = 27$) in Argentina and 8.42 ± 2.24 (5–13) ($n = 19$) in central Chile. Duckling survival to fledging in Patagonian region of Argentina $66.7 \pm 22.4\%$ (33–100%) ($n = 10$ broods). Both parents active in care of brood, with ♂ caring for broods alone when ♀ removed or has disappeared (Brewer 1990). ♀ performs Distraction display in response to threats. Sometimes double brooded in captivity. Breeds at one year in captivity. No information on adult survival nor longevity.

Conservation and threats

Still fairly common. Not considered globally threatened, but likely to be most affected by grazing erosion, lack of protection for breeding areas, American Mink introductions, illegal hunting and elimination of aquatic vegetation by fishermen. Protected from shooting on Falklands since Aug 1999.

Gwenda L. Brewer

Eurasian Wigeon *Anas penelope*
PLATE 15

Anas Penelope Linnaeus, 1758, Syst. Nat., ed.10, p. 126 coasts and swamps of Europe.

Etymology: Penelope was wife to Ulysses, and famous for embroidery; name of duck perhaps refers to beauty of ♂.

Other names: Wigeon, European Wigeon, Whewer. Danish: Pieband; Dutch: Smient; French: Canard siffleur; German: Pfeifente; Icelandic: Rauðhöfðaönd; Japanese: Hidori-gamo.

Variation: no subspecies.

Description

ADULT: dimorphic. ♂ in breeding, or alternate, plumage has chestnut head and neck with yellowish

crown, often with suffuse green-black tipped feathers around eye and throat. Pinkish grey breast, vermiculated grey upperparts and sides. White lowerbreast and belly, extending up to white patch at rear of flanks, contrasting with black around white-grey tail. White upperwing coverts shown in flight and as white band along side when at rest. Elongated scapulars vermiculated grey; speculum dark green edged black; primaries grey-brown; axillaries typically dusky grey. Bill blue-grey with black tip; legs slate grey with dusky webs; iris brown. ♀ neck and head buffish pink-brown, barred and spotted black; mantle and scapulars brown with pink-buff bars and edges. Upperbreast and flanks brown with extensive pink-buff edges. Rest of underparts white with dark marks on undertail coverts. Axillaries greyish; underwing fawn with paler markings; wing coverts grey-brown; speculum blackish with little green. Bill and legs duller grey-blue than ♂.

MOULT: ♂ in eclipse, or basic, plumage rich reddish chestnut, superficially resembling adult ♀, but with upperparts darker, flanks rufous, and contrasting white forewings. ♂♂ moult flight feathers late May–July, ♀♀ late June–early Sept.

IMMATURE: closely resembles adult ♀ with variability in plumage. Belly mottled brown. By 1st winter much like adult, but ♂ does not assume white forewings until 2nd winter; 1st winter ♀ has less obvious whitish tips to wing coverts than adult ♀.

DUCKLING: warm sepia brown and light cinnamon above, darkest on crown. Markings on side of head and along flanks ill defined. Differs from many dabbling ducklings by reduction of markings and rufous hue. Bill grey; legs and feet olive-brown with blackish webbing; iris brown.

MEASUREMENTS AND WEIGHT: ♂ adult wing ($n = 781$), 267, juv (1st winter) ($n = 400$), 260; adult skull ($n = 591$), 86.3, juv ($n = 254$), 85.8; adult tarsus ($n = 18$), 40.1, juv ($n = 24$), 40.3; adult winter weight ($n = 800$), 790, juv ($n = 384$), 712. ♀ adult wing ($n = 473$), 250, juv ($n = 449$), 248; adult skull ($n = 358$), 83.1, juv ($n = 295$), 82.5; adult tarsus ($n = 14$), 38.9, juv ($n = 30$), 38.7; adult winter weight ($n = 481$), 719, juv ($n = 438$), 645; data from WWT ringing stations.

Field characters

Medium-sized (450–510 mm long), short-necked, compact dabbling duck with short grey bill, peaked forehead, pointed tail and narrow wings. ♂ has reddish chestnut head and neck topped with yellowish stripe, pinkish breast, grey back and flanks, white forewing (grey in 1st winter) and belly and black undertail. ♀ has russet-brown head, neck, chest, back and side, and white belly.

Voice

Clear, piercing whistled *whee-OOO* of ♂, uttered both in flight, when on water and when feeding.

Multi-syllable calls *wip . . . wee . . . wip-weu* uttered as threat in disputes. ♀ has low purring or growled *krr*, often given when flushed; lacks quacking quality of other *Anas*. Sonograms of adult call in Cramp and Simmons (1977) and of distress call of duckling in Kear (1968).

Range and status

Breeds between *c* 50° and 75°N across northern Europe and Asia, from Iceland and northern Britain across Scandinavia and northern Russia to Pacific coast. Strongly migratory, leaving breeding ground in late summer to winter across almost whole of temperate zone of Europe and Asia, with concentrations in coastal areas of western Europe, Mediterranean and Black Sea regions, Caspian Sea lowlands, Iraq and Iran east to southern and eastern China and Japan. Occurs in winter along Nile valley as far south as Sudan and Ethiopia, with smaller numbers reaching Kenya and Tanzania. Occasional in west Africa. Regular as vagrants on east and west coasts of North America and, especially Aleutian Islands and Mexico.

No discrete populations identifiable, but 5 main wintering groups probably exist. Likely to be mixing on breeding grounds and at major moulting areas. Population in northwest Europe in winter showed significant upsurge over last 20 years with apparent rate of increase of 7.5% per annum (Rose 1995), but signs that part of Russian breeding population declined at same time, reflected in rapid decline in Black Sea/Mediterranean population. Numbers wintering in west Mediterranean have probably decreased by 45% in last 20 years, while numbers wintering in Black Sea/East Mediterranean may now be less than half those of 1982 (Rose 1995). Population in southwest Asia in winter also decreasing (Scott and Rose 1996). Krivenko (1993) reported slight decline in middle regions of Russia 1972–89, and numbers wintering in Iran apparently decreased by 62% over almost same period (Perennou *et al.* 1994). Winter estimates suggested 1 500 000 in northwest Europe, 300 000 in Black Sea/Mediterranean, 250 000 in southwest Asia/northeast Africa, 250 000 in south Asia (Wetlands International 2002), and 500 000–1 000 000 in eastern Asia (500 000 in China, 10 000 in South

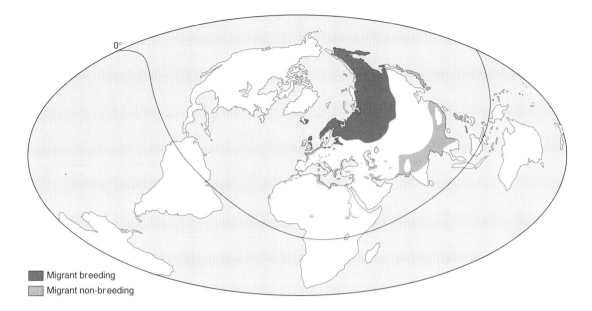

Migrant breeding
Migrant non-breeding

Korea and 160 000 in Japan) (Miyabayashi and Mundkur 1999).

Habitat and general habits

Breeds on shallow freshwater marshes, lakes and lagoons, surrounded by scattered trees or open forest; winters in coastal marshes, freshwater and brackish lagoons, estuaries, bays and other sheltered marine habitats. Consumes almost entirely vegetable diet throughout year, mainly leaves, stems, stolons, bulbils and rhizomes; also some seeds and occasional animal materials. Food obtained either on land by grazing while walking, on water from surface or, less often, under water by immersing head and neck. Gregarious night and daytime feeder (depending on local disturbance and tides). Grazes to greater extent than most other *Anas*, grazing flocks keeping close together in tight packs. ♂♂ generally more vigilant than ♀♀ (Mayhew 1987) but individual vigilance rates decrease with increasing flock size. Length of vigilance by ♂♂ increases with distance from water (Jacobsen and Ugelvik 1994).

♂♂ congregate at important moult gatherings, recorded at many localities in Russia (e.g. Volga Delta, lakes in Urals and upper Pechora), and in Estonia, southern Sweden, Denmark and Iceland. Main departure from breeding and moulting grounds occurs Sept, and main arrival on winter quarters Oct–Nov.

Highly gregarious outside breeding season, tending to form close congregations, often of enormous numbers, on wintering ground. Leaves winter quarters in northwest Europe and Black Sea region in 2nd half Mar and early Apr, but does not arrive on breeding ground in northern Russia before 2nd half May.

Displays and breeding behaviour

Highly gregarious except when nesting. Pair formation generally occurs in winter when ♂♂ compete for mates, several crowding round ♀ on water or land, displaying to her while thwarting one another's approach. In disputes during communal courtship, ♂♂ threaten one another at high intensity by calling and adopting Wings-up display with wing tips crossed and folded wings raised high above back, exposing conspicuous white forewings. Typically, at start of courting bout, ♂ performs Burp display, head raised, with nape and crest feathers erect, and characteristic Whistle-call uttered while body aligned laterally to ♀. ♂♂ threaten while manoeuvring towards ♀. Eventually dominant ♂ in group rushes forward towards ♀ performing Forehead-turning display; ♂ faces ♀ with head erect and held slightly back, crown feather erect and bill pointed down and moved slightly from side to side. ♀ acceptance of particular ♂ indicated by Inciting display when other ♂♂ intrude.

Moves back to breeding areas in small flocks of 25–30. Size of home range variable, some pairs making extensive foraging trips, others rather sedentary—availability of local food supply probably major factor. Extent of territoriality uncertain but ♂ readily defends ♀ against other ♂♂. While ♀ incubates, ♂ remains at 'waiting area' in vicinity, defending this against other ♂♂. Small flocks of 2–6 ♂♂ also observed in breeding area, but status unknown. Monogamous pairbond lasts until soon after clutch initiation, although ♂ may briefly accompany broods (Bannerman 1957–58). Recent studies show that pair members can find one another and re-establish pairbond in winter (Mitchell 1997). ♀ usually tends brood alone, staying until *c* time of fledging.

Absence of many *Anas* displays, combined with frequent hostility between courting ♂♂, gives communal courtship of this, and other wigeon, less ritualized character than similar *Anas*.

Breeding and life cycle

Although much geographical variation in nesting season (e.g. can nest Apr in Scotland), generally lays May–June. Nests usually not far from water in thick cover, well concealed under overhanging vegetation, grass tussock or scrub, in shallow depression, lined with grass, leaves and sometimes twigs with much down added after laying. Eggs bluntly ovate, smooth and cream or pale buff; 55 × 39 (49–60 × 35–42) ($n = 200$) (Schönwetter 1960–66); weight in captivity 41.4 (32–47.5) ($n = 100$); clutch usually 9 ($n = 357$) eggs (Bengtson 1972b); incubated 24–25 days. Will replace lost clutches; 2nd nesting possible. Of 301 eggs laid in Finland, 78% hatched and 34% of young reared to fledging (Hildén 1964a). Hatching success of 551 nests in Iceland 1961–70, averaged 68% (40–81%) with Raven, American Mink and desertion main reasons for failure (Bengtson 1972b). Of 148 Scottish nests, 55% hatched, 44% predated and 1% deserted. Captive day-olds weigh 25.8 ($n = 96$). ♀ leads brood to nursery area where young feed on invertebrates (e.g. chironomids), but swiftly switch to vegetable food. Fledge in 40–45 days.

Will breed in 2nd summer (at one year), sometimes not until 3rd. ♀ known to return to natal area to breed. Adult survival rate *c* 64% (Boyd 1962, Bell and Mitchell 1996). Sex ratio of first winter birds in flocks even, in comparison with unequal adult ratio (123 ♂♂:100 ♀♀), suggesting adult ♀ survival lower than adult ♂. Proportion of young in winter flocks fluctuates annually (21–46%, 1989–96) and this reflected in proportion of shot young in hunters' bag samples. Longevity record of BTO ringed bird 33 years 7 months (Clark *et al.* 2000).

Conservation and threats

Autumn and spring passage sites in Baltic, Belarus and Russia, suggest that important passage sites, where birds are vulnerable, must exist elsewhere on other flyways through Europe *en route* from breeding to wintering ground. Most wintering sites in northwest Europe and Mediterranean region protected, as are known key passage sites; in contrast, while two most important sites in Caspian Basin protected, very few of remaining 38 are.

Appears susceptible to disturbance (e.g. from increasing pressure on freshwater for year-round recreational activity) and pollution. Is quarry throughout range, and substantial numbers shot annually. In UK, is 3rd most abundantly taken quarry species, with annual bag of *c* 60 000 (Harradine 1985).

Carl Mitchell

American Wigeon *Anas americana*
PLATE 15

Anas americana Gmelin, 1789, Syst. Nat., **1**, p. 526
Louisiana and New York

Etymology: *americana* means of America.

Other names: Baldpate. Danish: Amerikansk pibeand; French: Canard siffleur d'Amérique; German: Nordamerikanische Pfeifente; Icelandic: Ljóshöfðaönd; Spanish: Pato chalcuán.

Variation: no subspecies.

Description

ADULT: sexually dimorphic. ♂ in breeding, or alternate, plumage has distinctive whitish forehead and centre of crown, with dark green band extending back from eye to nape, sides of head and neck greyish (greyish white with dark mottling at close quarters). Breast and flanks pinkish brown, with white band in front of black ventral region. Upperparts greyish brown, white wing coverts forming horizontal bar between sides and back. Adult ♂ usually has narrow black band around base of bill. Bill grey; legs blue-grey to dark grey; iris brown. ♀ much like ♀ Eurasian Wigeon, though head greyish, not brown, and breast and flanks brighter and more rufous. Greater coverts paler, difference more obvious in flight than that between adult ♂♂, both with large white patches in front of green and black speculum, with less green in all ages and both sexes of American species. Underwing pale grey, darker on lesser coverts and flight feathers, axillaries and median coverts white.

MOULT: ♂ in basic or eclipse plumage much like Eurasian Wigeon. Palmer (1976) reported alternate plumage of ♂ acquired though fall and retained into following summer, while basic usually follows in late June, and wing moult (21 days flightless) begins late July. In ♀, head and body of basic plumage acquired in spring, wing not moulted until late summer. Bellrose (1980) noted timing varies greatly between individuals.

IMMATURE: both sexes appear much like immature Eurasian Wigeon.

DUCKLING: has less well-defined dark stripes through and below eye than typical of most *Anas*; face largely brown, sometimes tinged with chocolate below eye, which is narrowly ringed yellow. Back and wings dark brown with yellow trailing edges to wing and patches above tail. Throat, breast and underparts duller yellow than most dabbling ducklings. Bill and feet grey at all ages; iris dark brown (Nelson 1993).

MEASUREMENTS AND WEIGHT: (autumn to spring) ♂ (*n* = 12) wing, 256–275 (264); tail, 98–123 (111); culmen, 35–39 (37); tarsus, 37–43 (40); weight 590–1089 (821), in flightless moult 567–794 (674), 1st autumn 318–1134 (794). ♀ (*n* = 12) wing, 236–256 (246); tail, 81–92 (88); culmen, 35–40 (36); tarsus, 37–40 (37); weight, 544–1043 (767), 1st autumn 408–952 (708).

Field characters

Medium-sized dabbling duck, 450–560 mm long, short-necked and compact, with short small bill, peaked forehead, pointed tail and narrow wings. Similar to Eurasian and Chiloe Wigeon, though with longer bill, neck and tail. On water, and in all plumages, has greyish head on brown body (and white belly when seen ashore). Appearance of ♀ Eurasian Wigeon more variable and some may be difficult to distinguish from *americana*. Though range of Chiloe far removed from that of two northern wigeon, is kept in many waterfowl collections in Europe and North America so that escaped birds often occur. In most plumages, white face and greenish grey head sufficient to distinguish them, but hybrids with one or other of northern species have caused confusion (Madge and Burn 1988). Confusingly, small numbers of European Wigeon winter in northeast North America, including recoveries of birds ringed in Iceland, and may now include few breeding in Newfoundland and Labrador, though no confirmed nesting records yet. Some European Wigeon also winter in Alaska. American Wigeon increasingly recorded in Japan (Brazil 1991), where

45–65 seen most winters among large concentrations of Eurasian Wigeon.

Voice

Comparatively noisy. ♂ in courtship display, on water and in flight, utters 3 distinct whistling notes, 2nd higher pitched (louder *wheoo* call of *A. penelope* slurred, not interrupted). Tracheal bulla of ♂ smaller than Eurasian Wigeon and calls correspondingly weaker. Adult ♀ alarm call low growling *krr*. Conversational notes used between members of pair, by ♀ with young and within flocks, not studied in detail. For sonogram see Mowbray (1999).

Range and status

Breeds from US northern plains and intermountain marshes to Alaska. Sparse in eastern North America

40–55°N, though increased in agricultural areas in eastern Canada since 1950. Greatest numbers in Canadian prairies and parklands, extending north to mouth of Mackenzie Delta and North Slope of Alaska, west to shores of Kotzebue Sound and Yukon-Kuskokwim Delta.

Winters chiefly in central valley of California and along Gulf coast, especially in Louisiana, with appreciable, though decreasing, numbers in Pacific Northwest (including British Columbia) and along Atlantic coast from Carolinas to Florida. Few travel as far as Cuba and Belize. Probably many more in Mexico now than formerly, though surveys there incomplete and infrequent in recent years. Alaskan birds winter almost entirely in Pacific coastal states, as do smaller numbers breeding in British Columbia. Many from Mackenzie Basin and Prairie

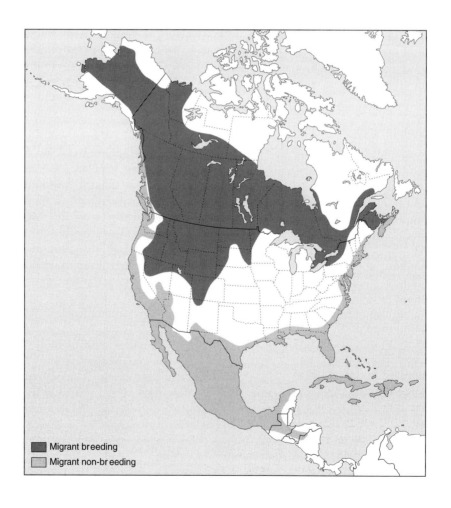

Migrant breeding
Migrant non-breeding

Provinces also winter in Pacific Flyway, but increasing majority move east of south, chiefly through Mississippi Flyway states.

Annual aerial surveys, May–early June, found *c* 3.1 million in 1955–59 and again in 1970–74, peaking at nearly 3.6 million in 1980, decreasing to *c* 2.0 million 1990–94, returning to nearly 2.7 million 1995–97. Greatest reductions occurred in prairies and parklands (1.9 million, 1955–59; 560 000, 1995–97), greatest increase in Alaska (87 000, 1955–59; 890 000, 1995–97; mean density of nesting pairs increasing from 0.37 to 3.76 per km^2). Highest nesting density formerly occurred on Athabasca Delta, but drastically reduced by hydrological changes caused by construction of Bennett Dam, far upstream, from 14.9 pairs per km^2 in 1955–59 to 2.25 in 1990–94. In south of range, average pair densities far lower, though there are island sites where nest densities may be high.

Habitat and general habits

Bill shorter and more pointed than that of most dabbling ducks, with coarser lamellae spacing, so better grazer and poorer at straining food organisms from water. However, probably grazes less than Eurasian Wigeon, taking much food from, or just below, surface of relatively deep and permanent waters. Occurs in wide variety of habitats, in summer from arctic tundra through boreal marshes to prairie potholes, and in winter from coastal saltmarshes in British Columbia to inland wetlands in Arkansas and Tennessee and brackish coastal lagoons around Gulf of Mexico.

Depends much less on seeds than most dabbling ducks, preferring stems and leaves of pondweeds and other aquatic plants, such as Wild Celery *Vallisneria americana* in inland waters and Eelgrass *Zostera* in estuaries. Often collects where coot, Redhead and other diving duck bring up aquatic plants which they steal without difficulty. Do not often up-end for food, as Northern Mallard do readily, and rarely reported diving.

Displays and breeding behaviour

Johnsgard (1965a) found agonistic and sexual behaviour of American and Eurasian Wigeon to be identical, apart from weaker call of ♂ American Wigeon. As in other Anatinae, pre-flight movements include Neck-jerking and lateral Head-shaking. ♀ Decrescendo call often monosyllabic; Inciting call (continually repeated *errr*) accompanied by repeated Chin-lifting towards preferred ♂. Lorenz (1951–53) noted this ceremony in wigeon homologous to that of Gadwall. Threatening movements towards opponent seen occasionally. Highly ritualized Preen-behind-wing probably most important mutual display in developing and maintaining pairbond. ♂♂ have lost any social contact call and depend upon highly specialized courtship whistle for all motivational displays. Lorenz emphasized that lack of social courtship and presence of highly specialized pairbonding distinguish wigeon from other dabbling ducks. Head-pumping precedes copulation, as in other dabbling ducks. After copulation, ♂ assumes erect posture facing ♀, again resembling Gadwall.

Pair formation may begin in winter quarters as early as Nov, but many pairs not formed until breeding area reached in spring. Weller (1965), noting that pairing in ducks seems correlated with development of breeding plumage, suggested late-pairers probably yearlings. Many pairs remain together only until 1st or 2nd week of incubation; yet, as in Eurasian Wigeon, minority remain together after young have hatched.

In prairie pothole region, selects relatively large semi-permanent water bodies (0.2–0.4 ha); in boreal and sub-arctic areas, most often found on small lakes. Nests on islands or in upland sites, usually among trees or extensive clumps of sedge, further from water than other ducks. Territorial behaviour less evident than in Northern Mallard.

Breeding and life cycle

Egg-laying from mid May. Nests in small depressions, lined with grass and weed stems, down light grey with conspicuous white tips. ♂ takes no part. Eggs ovate, creamy white, somewhat glossy; 55.0 ± 2.5 × 38.4 ± 1.4; 100 laid in captivity weighed 38.5 (30.0–49.0); clutch varies with latitude, with reported means 9.5 in Montana, 8.9 on plains and 7.6 in parklands of Alberta, but no concurrent widespread sampling, so extent of, and reasons for, regional and annual variation unknown. Incubation

23–25 days. Nests hard to find, so that few studies involve large samples.

Most breeding studies show low hatching success of 54% (20–75%), varying widely between years and study areas. Re-nesting occurs, though extent unknown. Broods move relatively little, remaining on larger lakes in pothole region. Assessment of losses of young between hatching and fledging made difficult by tendency of broods to aggregate, more often than other dabbling ducks. Most ♀♀ remain with broods until nearly full grown. Weight of duckling at day-old 24 (21–27), at 1 week 54 (42–66), at 5 weeks 433 (359–507); first flight at 37–48 days.

Most probably breed at end of 1st year, although complex sequence of plumages of both sexes suggests that rate of maturing varies. No estimates of adult survival from ring recoveries reported.

Conservation and threats

With wide and ecologically varied breeding and wintering ranges, seems to be adapting successfully to man-made environmental changes. Major population changes encouraged by wetland destruction in prairies and parklands, and by climatic warming in Alaska. While *c* 50% of population used to breed in south of range, only *c* 30% now do so. Formerly, during periods of drought, some overflew prairies and settled in north; when wet conditions returned, so did many wigeon. Yet increased pond numbers in prairies in mid-1990s did not produce rapid return to numbers found in earlier wet periods.

Changes in estimates of numbers shot by licensed hunters driven by rise and fall in numbers of hunters, which peaked in late 1970s, as well as by changes in breeding success and abundance of ducks. In US, mean annual kill 1966–99 was 726 000, ranging from 271 000 in 1988 to 1 068 000 in 1976; in Canada, mean is 92 000 (decreasing almost continuously from 190 000 in 1969 to 35 000 in 1999). In 1967, when combined kill highest (1.22 million), surveyed population in May had been 2.5 million, leading to fall flight of 4.6 million, from which kill was *c* 26%. In 1986, with only 1.74 million in May and 2.9 million in Sept, reported kill was *c* 21%. These levels of kill seem unlikely to be limiting population, with survival *c* 64% for adult and 57% for juvenile ♀♀, and 66% for adult ♂♂.

Hugh Boyd

African Black Duck *Anas sparsa*
PLATE 14

Anas sparsa Eyton 1838, Monogr. Anatidae, p. 142 South Africa

Etymology: *sparsa* L. for speckled.

Other names: Black River Duck. Afrikaans: Swart Eend; French: Canard noir d'Afrique.

Variation: 2 races usually recognized, South African Black Duck *A. s. sparsa* and Ethiopian Black Duck *A. s. leucostigma* Rüppell, 1845; validity of west African *A. s. maclatchyi* Berlioz, 1947 doubtful and considered synonym of *leucostigma* by Livezey (1991).

Description

ADULT: sexes alike. ♂ dark sooty brown. Most evenly brown on belly, but some mottling caused by pale edging to belly feathers; few birds white on chin and neck. Scapulars and uppertail coverts barred white, and tail crossed by 2 rows of white spots. Pattern of spotting individually variable. Wings dark brown above with prominent carpal spurs. Secondary coverts with apical third white, broadly tipped black. Speculum metallic blue-green, tipped black and white. Tertials dark brown, barred white. Underwing coverts brown, broadly tipped white, axillaries white. Bill state grey in southern *sparsa*, pink at base and on undersurface of lower mandible, pink in northern *leucostigma*, nail and culmen ridge black, narrower buff bars and spots on upperparts; legs and feet dull orange with blackish markings; eyes brown.

MOULT: no ♂ eclipse. In southwestern Cape, 2 body moults per year, pre-nuptial (Feb–May and post-nuptial (Oct–Dec); wing moult occurs Oct–Feb.

IMMATURE: similar to adult, but with whitish under-parts. Barring on upperparts and tail buff rather than white.

DUCKLING: black above with 3 pairs of pale yellow spots, buff white below, with white collar on upper breast; chin, throat and foreneck white; face patterned with black and pale yellow lines; whitish eyebrows, black line through eyes, another from bill to ear coverts where is black patch, and third line beneath. Bill black; legs dusky, yellowish in front (Delacour 1954–64).

MEASUREMENTS AND WEIGHT: ♂ ($n = 39$) wing, 241–280 (262); tail ($n = 22$), 100–115 (110); bill, 45–51 (47); tarsus 41–45 (43); weight ($n = 38$), 1086. ♀ ($n = 29$) wing, 229–257 (248); tail ($n = 20$) 90–100 (98); bill, 43–46 (44); tarsus, 39–42 (40); weight ($n = 29$), 914 (Siegfried 1968a, Frost *et al.* 1979).

Field characters

Length 500–550 mm. Dark brown duck with distinctive white or buff markings on upperparts. On water, slightly longer tail and shorter neck give more elongated appearance than Yellow-billed Duck. Bill dark, legs orange. In flight, white axillaries and blue-green speculum with white edges conspicuous.

Voice

♂ call quiet, wheezy whistling *weep* given repeatedly in regular series as contact when separated from mate, and in more rapid series during Mutual Greeting and hostile interactions on water and in flight. ♂ whistle apparently accompanies Grunt-whistle, Head-up-tail-up, and post-copulatory Bridling displays, but grunting sound not recorded. ♀ utters Persistent Quacking as contact call and when flying with mate. Decrescendo call, used as contact with mate, has 5–8 notes. In Mutual Greeting, ♀ gives loud *ga-ga, ga-ga, ga-ga, ga-ga*. When pair prepare to fly, ♂♂ give rapid *peep-peep, peep-peep, peep-peep* or *pepepepepe* while ♀ uses increasingly loud and rapid *ka ka ka ka* (McKinney *et al.* 1978). Sonogram in Maclean (1993).

Range and status

Resident south of Sahara, from Ethiopia in east and south to Cape; isolated population in Gabon and Cameroon. Scarce in Angola and Namibia, rare in west Equatorial Africa, but widely dispersed in suitable habitat in most of range. *sparsa* occurs in southern Africa south of Zimbabwe, but may intergrade with *leucostigma*, which is found in Gabon, Cameroon, Angola, Zaire, east Africa, Sudan and Ethiopia. West African population may be vulnerable, but poorly surveyed. Rose and Scott (1997) suggested 1000–5000 individuals in Gabon, 100 in Guinea Conakry highlands, 1000–5000 in Cameroon highlands, 2000–10 000 in Ethiopian Highlands, 10 000–25 000 in eastern Africa and 20 000–50 000 *sparsa* in southern Africa.

Habitat and general habits

Prefers river habitats, particularly shallow, rock-bottomed streams with fairly rapidly moving water in wooded and mountainous country. Has no morphological specializations for life in fast-water habitats, as do Torrent or Blue Ducks, and at times uses sluggish rivers, stagnant pools, dams and ponds near rivers. Often overlooked in rivers with overhanging banks and tangles where disruptive coloration cryptic. Pairs highly territorial during breeding season, occupying exclusive, actively defended, stretches of river that they patrol daily (Ball *et al.* 1978). Pairbond strong and may be renewed for 2 or more years. Territory defence and pairbonds weaken during nonbreeding season, mates may form temporary liaisons with neighbours during moult, but territorial individuals probably highly sedentary so long as river habitat remains tenable.

Daily activities of territorial pairs involve feeding in favoured sections of pools and riffles, preening and resting on rocks, and moving through territory alert for conspecific intruders. Pairs often fly from one part of territory to another, generally following water course. Pairs and unpaired individuals also make use of other wetlands near river, such as farm dams, as night roost when river levels low, or as refuge when excluded from river by territory-owning pairs.

Feeds mainly by dabbling with bill, head, or head and neck submerged while probing around rocks in riffles, or in mud or among aquatic plants. Adults and ducklings feed in fast-moving and sluggish water. Adults dive for food, such as acorns, at times,

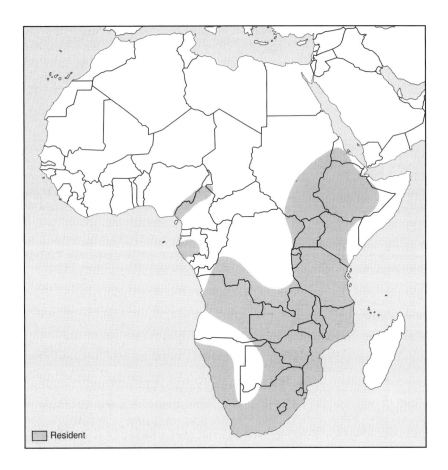

Resident

and ducklings dive frequently. Adults also walk on river bank in search of acorns.

Displays and breeding behaviour

Mallard-like in size, body shape and postures, but lacks social courtship characteristic of most dabbling ducks. Pair formation occurs among resident pairs on river territories when dead partner replaced, or when one partner evicted after fighting, or among non-territorial individuals (Ball *et al.* 1978). Part-time bonds or liaisons form first, and these become full-time pairbond once established on territory.

Prolonged tense swimming manoeuvres, involving several birds, apparently associated with assessment of potential mates. Mutual Greeting frequent when mates affirm pairbond, especially in presence of intruding individuals or pairs. These noisy performances involve repeated up and down head movements by ♀, with bill wide open while she gives double-noted calls. In response, ♂ gives less pronounced downward movements of head, or Bill-dips. Grunt-whistle and Head-up-tail-up displays rarely performed, when single ♂ courts ♀. ♂ directs subtle displays (Head-up, Bill-rub) as well as more overtly aggressive displays (Open-bill-threat, Rush, Neck-biting) towards mate, and ♀ often assumes Prone position apparently as appeasement. Behaviour of adults towards one another reflects high level of aggressiveness evident during fighting over mates and territories, and need for appeasement and bond maintenance between mates. Fighting highly developed and shown by both sexes. During disputes between pairs, ♂ fights ♂ and ♀ fights ♀. Fighting birds grasp one another by back of neck while holding bodies erect on water and vigorously striking repeated blows with wings. Both sexes strike with wing-spurs on carpal joints, and leading edge of wings around spurs often bloody after severe fight. Expulsion flights over territories frequent and vigorous, with clashing wings and loud calling (McKinney *et al.* 1978). Only established territory-holders breed. Territories 200–700 m in length along river.

Breeding and life cycle

Laying dates vary with region; in southwest Cape July–Dec, peak in Sept; Zimbabwe, Zambia May–Aug; Kenya Oct, Dec–Feb, June–July. Nests found in vegetation or brush piles on bank or nearby, with plenty of down added. Eggs glossy, pale yellow; 57.3–65.5 × 40.2–48.8; weight in captivity 68.4 (66.5–71.0) ($n = 5$), larger in proportion to ♀ body weight than most mallard types. Clutch rather small at 5.9 (4–8) eggs ($n = 42$). Incubation, by ♀, 25 days (Brown *et al.* 1982). ♀ alone escorts ducklings during day, but may join mate at night at roost site. Brood ranges primarily on breeding territory. Growth and plumage development of captive ducklings described by Frost *et al.* (1979). No data on age at 1st breeding, breeding success, survival or longevity.

Conservation and threats

No evidence of widespread decline, although local increases and decreases noted. Territorial behaviour produces dispersed populations, and numbers nowhere numerous. Major threats come from destruction of rivers by damming and extraction, although artificial impoundments may be used and are important when rivers dry (Callaghan and Green 1993). Deforestation reported as threat in Kenya.

†Frank McKinney

American Black Duck *Anas rubripes*
PLATE 17

Anas obscura rubripes, Brewster, 1902, *Auk* **19**, p. 184 Lake Umbagog, New Hampshire shore

Etymology: *rubripes* L. means red-footed.

Other names: Black Mallard, Blackie, Redleg. Kortright (1942) listed 34 common names in general and local use for Red-legged Black Duck and Common Black Duck, the 2 subspecies mentioned in AOU Checklist of 1931. French: Canard noir; Spanish: Pato oscuro.

Variation: no subspecies currently recognized; Brewster (1902) suggested 2, nominate and *A. r. tristis* 1909, but differences described reflect those of age classes. Considerable individual variation in plumage, and some geographical variation (birds south of New England have face and necks plain) and clinal differences in size (northern birds larger). Effects of hybridization with Northern Mallard and Mottled Duck unclear (Palmer 1976), but see Longcore *et al.* (2000) and McCracken *et al.* (2001).

Description

ADULT: sexes alike. ♂ in breeding, or alternate, plumage dark sooty brown except for pale head and neck. Buff brown feather margins conspicuous on flanks and uppersides, show as scalloped rich brown pattern against dark feathering in fresh plumage. Tail feathers dark with variable pale edging to outer vanes. Head and neck medium brown to grey-buff with fine dark streaking and dark (sometimes greenish) eyestripe of variable length and boldness. Crown and nape darker, often with green iridescent feathering. Speculum bluish purple, extends distally to include all but last secondary, and shows narrow white bar on trailing edge (sometimes lacking). Bill yellowish, grading to olive at base and with black nail; legs and feet brownish orange to coral red with dark webs; eyes brown. ♀ like ♂ but overall shade lighter. Face and neck more heavily marked (dark on light with more defined eyestripe). Crown and nape more lightly streaked, without greenish washes. Speculum as ♂ but iridescence does not extend onto 2 distal secondaries. Bill variably olive with some dark marks on upper mandible, nail blackish; legs and feet muted fleshy orange with dark webs.

MOULT: basic or eclipse plumage of ♂ much duller, and colour of bare parts becomes muted, generally feathers smaller, without gloss and giving scaled appearance on flanks and sides. Summer basic plumage of ♀ paler 'washed out' version of breeding plumage with shorter broader feathers. Bare parts become darker, and dark bluish or greenish bill saddled with dark markings.

IMMATURE: tail feathers narrow with notched ends. First moult produces adult-like feathering in both sexes; however retained juvenile wing feathers narrower than those of adults with rounded (not squarish) ends.

DUCKLING: closely resembles Northern Mallard or darker version of Mottled Duck. Yellows more orange and undersides dirty neutral colour; eye-stripe heavier, complete and black. Cheek stripe lacking but ear-spot shows. Legs and feet dark (Palmer 1976, Nelson 1993).

MEASUREMENTS AND WEIGHT: ♂ ($n = 377$) wing, 285.0 ± 7.6; culmen, 54.3 ± 2.4; tarsus, 46.2 ± 2.1; adult fall weight ($n = 222$), 960–1640 (1317 ± 130); juv weight ($n = 857$), 825–1755 (1158 ± 113). ♀ ($n = 355$) wing, 268.7 ± 6.9; culmen, 51.1 ± 2.0; tarsus, 43.1 ± 2.3; adult fall weight ($n = 227$), 810–1380 (1090 ± 102); juv weight ($n = 664 \pm 96$), 720–1285 (1016) (Longcore *et al.* 2000).

Field characters

Size (530–610 mm long), shape, proportions and deportment, including flight characteristics, closely resemble Northern Mallard. Plumage much darker than ♀ Mallard (with which Black Duck can be confused) but in good visibility contrast between lighter brown head and brown-black body noticeable. In flight, silvery underwings make flashing contrast with dark body. Flocks usually contain fewer individuals (5–25) than those of much more gregarious Mallard.

Voice

Similar to Mallard, voice of ♀ about one tone lower. Calls associated with courtship display include noisy quacking from ♀, and reedy grunting and clear whistling call from ♂ (Palmer 1976, Longcore *et al.* 2000). No published sonograms.

Range and status

Breeding concentrated in hemlock, white pine and northern hardwood forest region east of longitude 85°W, and occurs as far north as open boreal forest of Québec and Labrador and south to coastal marshes of North Carolina. Coastal marshes and floodplains of rivers principal nesting areas with some inland lakes being of local importance. In summer, ♂♂ disperse widely to moult, and sometimes occur beyond usual breeding range in treeless sub-arctic, prairies and parklands of mid-continent, and cypress swamps and marshes of subtropical south (Rusch *et al.* 1989).

Size of breeding population not determined reliably. Most of breeding range lies outside areas surveyed annually for Northern Mallard and prairie ducks (Rusch *et al.* 1989); however, Spencer (1979) suggested summer population of 1.04 million for Canada, and 200 000 for US.

Winters as far north as available open water and food allow and, in general, population compressed into narrow strips along Atlantic coast and larger river systems of east central interior below ice line (Palmer 1976). Again, accurate counting difficult; many winter in small, widely dispersed groups that cannot be monitored annually. Rose and Scott (1997) suggested 210 000 in Atlantic and 90 000 in Mississippi flyways.

Habitat and general habits

Found on range of fresh, brackish and saltwater biotopes. Essentially of boreal forest zone in summer with most of population occurring in marine habitat in winter. In wintering areas on Atlantic coast from Cape Cod to Newfoundland, essentially maritime, occurring where water remains free of ice, feeding in saltmarsh habitat, exposed flats or in kelp beds depending on tides. From New Jersey south to North Carolina, prefers habitat brackish marshes bordering bays and estuaries but includes some freshwater wetlands inland. In Mississippi valley, diverse freshwater types occupied, particularly flooded woodlands (Palmer 1976).

Diet varies between habitats and determined by availability. Forages by up-ending or dabbling. Diet includes more small animal life than Northern Mallard, resulting in high intakes of long-residual

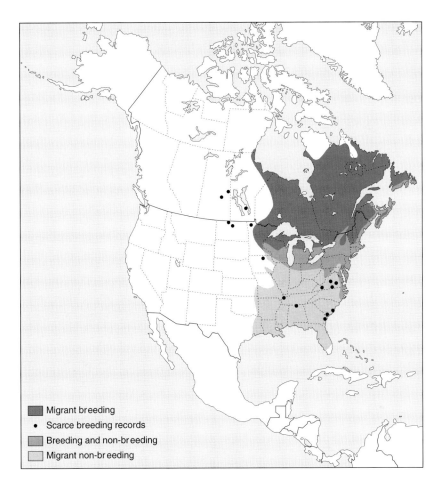

Migrant breeding
• Scarce breeding records
Breeding and non-breeding
Migrant non-breeding

pesticides, effects of which not fully known. In fresh and brackish water, plant foods such as seeds of grasses and sedges, and leaves, stems and root-stalks of aquatic plants predominate. In marine situations, invertebrates become important. During nesting, proportion of invertebrates taken increases for ♂ as well as ♀. Reinecke and Owen (1980) found that crustaceans, insects and molluscs comprised 74% (by dry weight) of summer diet in Maine. Extensive data on diet in Longcore *et al.* (2000).

At end May, ♂♂ begin to congregate in groups of considerable size on estuaries and in tidal marshes for wing moult. By mid Aug, most regain flight capability and begin moving to traditional staging areas prior to autumn migration (Wright 1954). Here joined by ♀♀ and juveniles. Seems indifferent to cold weather, and movements induced by decreasing food availability, disturbance by shooting

and icing of feeding areas (Palmer 1976). Some populations only weakly migratory and show greater fidelity to regional wintering areas than, for example, Northern Mallard (Diefenbach *et al.* 1988). Habitat preferences and tendency to form small flocks reduces extent of association with other ducks (Palmer 1976).

Displays and breeding behaviour

Basic elements of courtship identical to Northern Mallard, including Inciting, Nod-swimming, Down-up, Grunt-whistle, and copulatory behaviour. Displaying begins Aug, reaches sub-climax in late autumn, tails off in mid winter during severe weather but resumes on quiet sunny days and increases in frequency to climax Feb–Mar. Each form of display corresponds to progressive level of courtship intensity, eventually leading to pair formation. Some evidence to suggest re-pairing with former mates, and that homing is behavioural trait of weakly migratory populations (Anderson *et al.* 1992). Pairs arrive on breeding ranges before winter conditions break. Prior to nesting, pairs select 'home-ranges' during daily feeding and 'exercise' forays, and occupy these at earliest opportunity. Copulation becomes increasingly frequent. Territory defence varies, ♂♂ seem most concerned with protecting ♀♀ from advances of others. ♂♂ wait at territories through egg-laying until incubation underway before departing to moulting areas (Palmer 1976).

Adults begin pair formation early Sept and most paired mid Dec. Immatures begin pairing Dec–Jan. Evidence that some pairbonds sustained and monogamous (Palmer 1976, Bellrose 1980); certainly in captivity, bond between some individuals renewed every autumn.

Breeding and life cycle

Dates of nest initiation vary between years and advance from south to north beginning mid Mar in Maryland and Ohio but terminating mid June irrespective of latitude. ♀ selects nest site and, using feet and bill, scrapes base 3–4 days before 1st egg laid. Nest lined with adjacent plant material and, although small amounts of down added after 2–3 eggs laid, most plucked with onset of incubation. Sites diverse and sometimes several km from water. Ground nests placed under cover of grasses, herbs, briers, bushes, small conifers or brush piles in cultivated and wooded uplands above flood zone, or in cavities and crotches of trees in flooded lowlands. In many parts of range, nests on wooded islands (Bellrose 1980). In northern bogs, prefers sedge zones. Egg laid every 24 h; ovate to elliptical ovate, with smooth shells and white, cream or pale buff-green; 59.4 × 43.2 ($n = 82$) (Bent 1923); weight in captivity 54.5 ($n = 17$); clutch 9.3 (7–12) ($n = 1189$). Incubation, by ♀, 26 (23–33) days ($n = 51$) (Stotts and Davies 1960), probably depending on ambient temperatures and nest attentiveness. Captive ducklings weigh on hatching 31.3 (27.3–37.2) ($n = 25$) (Smart 1965b). Nest success 38% ($n = 574$) in Chesapeake Bay area of Maryland (Stotts and Davies 1960) and 49% on St Lawrence Estuary (Reed 1968). Failure occurs due to flooding and disturbance from human activity, and

destruction by reptilian, avian and mammalian egg predators. Raptors, foxes and Raccoons known to prey on incubating ♀♀. Will re-nest up to 3 times if clutches or young broods lost, with older ♀♀ more likely to repeat nesting than yearlings (Bellrose 1980).

Once dry, ducklings led to water by ♀, sometimes walking several km overland. Feed on miscellaneous insects found in or on water, taking increasing amounts of plant food from 3 weeks. Hatch-to-fledging survival rate estimated at 42% on inland breeding areas in Maine, with late hatching ducklings surviving less well than young from early nests (Ringelman and Longcore 1982). Reed (1975) found 32% survival rate of broods in St Lawrence Estuary. Duckling mortality attributable to inclement weather and to predation from Snapping Turtles, American Mink, gulls and crows. During early part of brood rearing, ♀ attentive but, in latter stages, spends increasingly long periods away from brood. Once ducklings capable of flight at 58–63 days, ♀ abandons family to moult flight feathers. ♀♀ can be found in varying stages of wing moult mid July–mid Sept. Young gradually disperse from rearing area once fledged (Bellrose 1980).

Survival rates vary geographically, particularly for young (Krementz *et al.* 1987). Survival rates of birds banded in Canada (1968–81) 54–60% for adults and 35–50% for young (Rusch *et al.* 1989). Adults of both sexes, banded before hunting season, survived at higher rates than did young, with adult ♂ survival higher than adult ♀, and with little difference between sexes of juveniles. Up to 42% of total mortality attributed to hunting (Krementz *et al.* 1987).

Conservation and threats

Long sequence of winter surveys in Mississippi and Atlantic flyways showed sustained decline in numbers, averaging 3% per year since 1950s. As consequence, selected as of priority concern in North American Waterfowl Management Plan. In 1992, just over 200 000 found along Atlantic and 76 000 in Mississippi flyway (US Fish & Wildlife Service 1992). Several causes of decline postulated including habitat alteration and disturbance (such as deforestation of wooded wetlands and contamination of breeding habitat with pesticides and acid rain) concomitant with range expansion of Northern Mallard and mortality due to hunting. Suggested that land clearance, beginning in New England during mid 1800s, opened eastern wetlands to several duck species formerly confined to western US (Heusmann 1974). Eastward range expansion of Northern Mallard, particularly, through natural colonizations and deliberate releases for hunting and recreational purposes, considered proximate cause of decline. Through introgressive hybridization and competitive exclusion from optimum breeding habitat, Northern Mallard appear to be displacing Black Duck from former strongholds (Ankney *et al.* 1987); however, declines not uniform, and evidence of only minor decreases and some increases in eastern part of Canada (Rusch *et al.* 1989). Palmer (1976) noted that, as Mallard appeared to move east, so Black Duck moved west with breeding becoming established in Minnesota and western Ontario. Further details in Longcore *et al.* (2000).

Nigel Jarrett

Northern Mallard *Anas platyrhynchos*
PLATE 17

Anas platyrhynchos Linnaeus, 1758, Syst. Nat., ed. 10, p. 125
Europe

Synonymy: *A. boschas* Linnaeus, 1758, Syst. Nat., ed. 10, p. 127

Etymology: *platyrhynchos* Gr. *platus* means broad, plus *rhunkhos*, bill; *boschas* from *boskas* Gr. for wild duck. Vernacular name came to Britain with the Normans, but origin unknown.

Other names: Common Mallard, Mallard, Wild Duck; plus many names that refer to varieties of domestic Mallard such as Aylesbury, Pekin, Indian Runner, etc. Danish: Gråand; Dutch: Wilde Eend; French: Canard colvert; German: Stockente; Icelandic: Stokkönd; Japanese: Ma-gamo; Spanish: Ánade Real, Pato de collar.

Variation: 2 subspecies recognized, nominate *A. p. platyrhynchos* from Europe, Northern Asia and North America, and *A. p. conboschas* C.L. Brehm, 1831 from Greenland.

For data on extinct Mariana Duck, a mallard hybrid, see Pacific Black Duck account.

Description

ADULT: dimorphic. Nominate ♂ in nuptial, or alternate, plumage has grey body, brown breast, black above and below tail, and iridescent dark green head and white collar. Tail predominantly whitish grey with 4 central feathers black and curled upward. Wings grey brown above with darker flight feathers and creamy underwing coverts. Speculum of both sexes bright purple-blue with narrow black and white borders. Bill yellow, legs and feet orange; eye brown. ♀ in nuptial plumage, mottled pale brown to buff with dark streaks on crown and through eye with noticeable paler supercilium. Wings brown. Bill brown with variable black spotting; legs and feet dull orange. *comboschas* similar in appearance, but larger with proportionately smaller bill.

MOULT: ♂ in post-nuptial, basic, or eclipse plumage similar to ♀ but with blacker crown, darker upperparts and breast, lack of mottling and paler unspotted yellow bill. ♀ post-nuptial (definitive basic) not easily identifiable; has darker crown and mantle, and feathers with narrower buff edges.

IMMATURE: similar to adult ♀, differentiated by fresher darker plumage, with narrowly streaked underparts. Crown and eyestripe black, bill more diffusely orange with no spotting (Harris *et al.* 1993). ♂ develops greener bill, quickly turning yellow. For full description of plumages and patterns of moult, see Palmer (1976) and Drilling *et al.* (2002).

DUCKLING: dark brown above with yellow face, underparts and spots on back and wings. There is dark line through eyes, and dark, rounded patch on ear coverts. Legs dull orange with greyish brown pattern, bill dark with pink tip (nominate and *con-boschas* figured in Nelson 1993).

MEASUREMENTS AND WEIGHT: *platyrhynchos* in Netherlands, ♂ wing (*n* = 13), 272–285 (279); tail (*n* = 14), 80–91(85.8); bill (*n* = 58), 51–61(55.4); tarsus (*n* = 45), 42–48 (45.3). ♀ wing (*n* = 13), 257–273(265); tail (*n* = 12), 81–90 (84.5); bill (*n* = 48), 47–56 (51.8); tarsus (*n* = 37), 41–46 (43.4) (Cramp and Simmons 1977). In England, ♂ wing (*n* = 665), 250–298 (274.8); bill (*n* = 500), 45.6–63.1 (54.6); tarsus (*n* = 500), 40.8–51.0 (45.7). ♀ wing (*n* = 880), 235–280 (258.6); bill (*n* = 500), 45.5–58.9 (51.3); tarsus (*n* = 500), 39.9–48.0 (43.4) (Owen and Montgomery 1978). In US and Canada, ♂ wing (*n* = 12), 273–300 (286); tail, 82–92 (86.7); bill, 47–59 (55.3); tarsus, 45–53 (47.7). ♀ wing (*n* = 12), 256–278 (272); tail, 82–91 (86.4); bill, 48–57 (53.6); tarsus, 41–48 (44.6) (Palmer 1976). In India (no sample size), ♂ wing, 266–292; tail, 80–97; bill, 50–57; tarsus, 40–45. ♀ wing, 232–276; bill, 44–55 (Ali and Ripley 1987). In New Zealand, ♂ wing (*n* = 101), 255–303 (277.7); tail (*n* = 79), 74–103.6 (89.4); bill (*n* = 111), 49.2–61.4 (55.1), tarsus (*n* = 111), 41.9–54 (47.3). ♀ wing (*n* = 99), 242–278 (262.6); tail (*n* = 87), 77.2–104 (90.2); bill (*n* = 101), 47.3–58.7 (51.6); tarsus (*n* = 99), 41.3–49.2 (45.2) (Marchant and Higgins 1990). See also Drilling *et al.* (2002).

comboschas in Greenland, ♂ (*n* = 69) wing, 275–306 (292); bill, 44–51 (46.6). ♀ (*n* = 41) wing, 261–285 (272); bill, 45–52 (48.1) (Cramp and Simmons 1977).

Weight in Czechoslovakia Mar–Apr, ♂ (*n* = 26), 873–1458 (1142), ♀ (*n* = 11), 1003–1270 (1096); Dec ♂ (*n* = 15), 1017–1442 (1216); ♀ (*n* = 14), 921–1320 (1084) (Folk *et al.* 1966, Cramp and Simmons 1977); in Illinois in autumn, ♂ (*n* = 631), 1240; ♀ (*n* = 402), 1080 (Palmer 1976); in India, ♂ (no sample) 1135–1800, ♀ (no sample) 735–1195 (Ali and Ripley 1987); in New Zealand, ♂ (*n* = 68), 993–1412 (1209.5); ♀ (*n* = 86), 792–1403 (1113) (Marchant and Higgins 1990). See also Drilling *et al.* (2002).

Field characters

Probably world's best-known duck, extensively studied, abundant and widespread, used as type by which other dabbling ducks judged. Large (♂ 550–700 mm, ♀ 500–600 mm long), heavy-looking dabbler, regularly seen in variety of wetland habitats. ♂ in nuptial plumage unmistakable, with green head, white collar, brown breast, grey flanks and black undertail area. Post-nuptial (eclipsed) ♂ and ♀ may be mistaken for other Holarctic dabbling ducks, notably Gadwall (smaller, greyer, with white belly and, often narrow, white speculum, bill with orange sides), Northern Pintail (slender body and neck, plain pale head, grey bill and narrow tail), American Black Duck (darker, contrasting head, no pale edges to tail, red feet and legs), Mottled Duck (darker, contrasting head, no pale edges to tail, green speculum with black borders) and, in Australasia, for Pacific Black Duck (dark striped face). Spreads into range of related species; resultant hybridization and introgression, plus regular mixing with domestic strains, leads to presence of many abnormally coloured, patterned and sized birds.

Voice

♂ has nasal *raeb* often given repeatedly, particularly during antagonistic encounters, and whistles given during courtship display. ♀ has variety of calls, notably *quacks* and conversational *queg-queg* call. *Quack* may be loud as in Decrescendo call or repeated as in Persistent Quacking (see McKinney *et al.* 1990a). Inciting and Repulsion calls may be loud. For details of calls, and sonograms, see Abraham (1974), Cramp and Simmons (1977) and Drilling *et al.* (2002); sonogram of sounds recorded from hatching eggs in Kear (1968).

Range and status

Nominate race Holarctic and widespread between Arctic Circle and Tropic of Cancer, scarce in arid areas. Small numbers migrate north to, and breed within, Arctic region and there are wintering populations in Africa (along Nile Valley to Ethiopia and Sudan), Asia (e.g. in India, China, Korea and Japan) and Mexico, Cuba and Bahamas. Recorded and may breed in Azores, Madeira and Canary Islands. Vagrants widely recorded outside main range, e.g. in Hawaii, Mariana, Marshall, Kiribati and Cook Islands (Pratt *et al.* 1987), Macquarie (Marchant and Higgins 1990), Kenya, Nigeria, Mali, Senegal

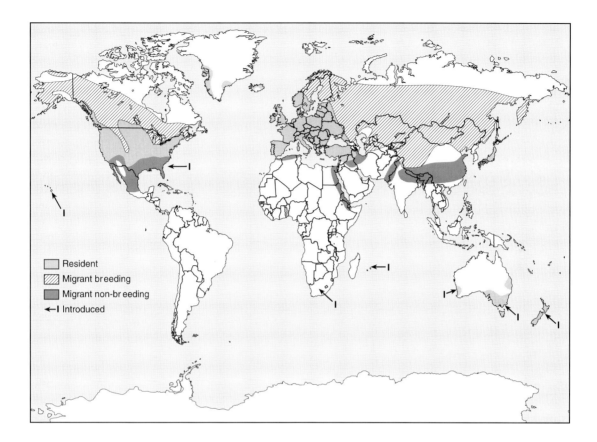

(Dowsett and Forbes-Watson 1993), Gambia (Gore 1990), Panama (Phillips 1922–26), Jamaica, Hispaniola, Puerto Rico, St Croix (Virgin Islands), Cayman and Lesser Antilles (St Barthelemy, Antigua, Guadeloupe, Martinique and Grenadines) (Raffaele *et al.* 1998). Captive reared birds widely released within range to supplement stocks for hunting; this may have distorted local distribution and population densities, as well as affecting other resident ducks.

Introduced to South Africa, Bermuda, southeast and southwest Australia, New Zealand and Mauritius. (see Long 1981, Lever 1987). New Zealand birds have colonized many offshore islands including Chatham, Antipodes, Snares, Auckland and Campbell Islands. Bird ringed in New Zealand was shot in Australia (Heather and Robertson 1996); has also reached Lord Howe and Norfolk Islands (Marchant and Higgins 1990). Generally abundant

throughout range, densities vary locally, often through climatic conditions. Common in Australia and abundant in New Zealand. Some populations declining in east-central Europe, Black Sea and east Mediterranean (Rose 1996) and, more recently, in Great Britain (Musgrove *et al.* 2001). Population estimates include 4 500 000 wintering in northwest Europe, 1 000 000 wintering in western Mediterranean, 2 000 000 in Black Sea/eastern Mediterranean in winter (Scott and Rose 1996, Delany and Scott 2002), 800 000 in southwest Asia, 75 000 in south Asia (Perennou *et al.* 1994), 1 500 000 in eastern Asia (Miyabayashi and Mundkur 1999), 18 000 000 wintering in North America in peak years and 8 000 000 breeding in 1995 (Todd 1996, Drilling *et al.* 2002) and 3 000 000 in New Zealand (Heather and Robertson 1996).

Population of *comboschas* found on Greenland's west coast north to Upernavik, and east coast to

Angmagssalik (Palmer 1976), considered stable at 15 000–30 000 (Rose and Scott 1997).

Domesticated in Europe by Romans and in Asia by Malays; many domestic varieties exist, greatly altered from original in size, colour, shape and behaviour, but ♂ of all retains 4 curly tail feathers (Kear 1990).

Habitat and general habits

Occurs on almost all wetland types within range, preferring shallow water with available cover. Will feed and roost on sea and in brackish waters. Tolerant of humans and will readily colonize urban and artificial environments. Uncommon in fast-flowing rivers. Migratory, may collect in large flocks during winter. Traditionally many birds migrate north after ice and snow melt; however, increasingly resident populations developing in suitable areas. Use of human-influenced environments and release of game-reared birds has changed Mallard habits dramatically in many places.

Large numbers of Icelandic birds winter in British Isles, some birds from northwest Russia and Fenno-Scandia go as far south as Spain. May move along River Danube to winter in Black Sea and further south, 2 birds ringed in Volga delta, Russia, recovered in Egypt (Cramp and Simmons 1977). Winters throughout North America where water kept open, even in Alaska; however, large numbers move south. Dramatic movements recorded, e.g. 3 100 000 on Mississippi Flyway (Bellrose 1980). Migration patterns in southern Asia less well known; wintering birds probably come from further north. Birds ringed in Pakistan recovered in Novosibirsk, Russia (Ali and Ripley 1987). Non-migratory in New Zealand, but disperses widely. Moult migrations and moulting congregations known (Cramp and Simmons 1977).

Feeds predominantly by dabbling in shallows by swimming, walking or up-ending in slightly deeper water. Dives, predominantly when young, but will do so at all ages. Foot paddles to stir up food material, and may feed ashore and even graze. Forages principally in early morning or evening, but will often do so throughout night. Diet varied and includes vegetable and animal material, depending on location and season (Palmer 1976, Cramp and Simmons 1977, Drilling *et al.* 2002).

comboschas probably largely vegetarian during breeding season, moving to coast in winter and switches to mainly animal diet (Palmer 1976).

Displays and behaviour

Well studied (Lorenz 1951–53, Johnsgard 1965a, Palmer 1976, Cramp and Simmons 1977). ♂ uses Drinking as greeting and Preen-behind-wing. Display components include Initial Bill-shake, Head-flick, Tail-shake, Grunt-whistle, Head-up-tail-up, Turn-towards-♀, Nod-swim, Turn-back-of-head, Bridle and Down-up. ♀ may Incite mate or potential mate vigorously and Nod-swim. Display usually given on water in groups of ♂♂ when one or more ♀♀ present. Paired birds and those seeking mates join in display bouts (McKinney 1992). In studies of courting Mallards in North America (Johnsgard 1960c), Grunt-whistle most used display in 1st few months of pair formation, Down-up least frequent; during peak of activity, Down-up most frequent display.

Pre-copulatory behaviour consists of mutual Head-pumping, ♀ becoming prone on water surface if accepting ♂. Post-copulatory display principally Bridle, with single call, Steam, possibly Nod-swim and Turn-back-of-head (Johnson *et al.* 2000). Forced extra-pair copulation common (McKinney *et al.* 1983, McKinney and Evarts 1997), and widely used secondary reproductive strategy.

Typically forms pair during autumn and winter, ♂ and ♀ migrating back to breeding ground together. ♂ generally establishes and defends large area that overlaps with adjoining territories; nest and main foraging zone within or near defended area (Anderson and Titman 1992). ♂ chases intruders, and 3-bird flights common (see Titman 1983). Adaptable, and may vary spacing system depending on habitat; in many artificial situations, ♂ may defend moving territory around ♀ while she is away from nest. Nests may be close and ♂♂ congregate while ♀ incubates. Pairbond lasts until early or mid incubation (McKinney 1965c), ♂ playing no part in brood rearing; however, in urban and other artificial situations, increasingly normal to see ♂ accompanying ♀ and brood.

Breeding and life cycle

Has lengthy breeding season at lower latitudes, more restricted in north. Sometimes, particularly when influenced by human protection of food supply or by genes selected for domestication, nesting and young recorded every month of year.

Nest seeking ♀ often quacks repeatedly; behaviour may attract predators and make them betray presence (McKinney *et al.* 1990a). Nests generally close to water and made from available vegetation, usually grasses; may be on ground, in hollows or holes in trees, or, in urban environments, on buildings. Eggs blunt oval, smooth, grey-green or bluish ('duck egg green'); *platyrhynchos* 56.8 × 41.2 (50−65 × 37−45.5) ($n = 500$) (Schönwetter 1960− 66); weight 51 (42−59) ($n = 200$). Clutch variable, usually 9−13; incubation, by ♀, 27−28 days; hatch weight 34.6 (31.2−38.4) ($n = 20$) 68% of fresh egg weight; fledge in 50−60 days (Palmer 1976, Cramp and Simmons 1977). Breeding data for *comboschas* unrecorded, except eggs laid in captivity 63.4 ($n = 11$).

Of 180 nests in southwest England, 88.7% successful and 82.4% of eggs hatched (Ogilvie 1964). Mean brood size from 80−140 pairs, 1957−62, 6.9 (4.9−7.9); and young reared per successful ♀ 4.7 (3.6−6.4) (Boyd and King 1964). Annual mortality 40−80%, variable by region (see Cramp and Simmons 1977, Bellrose 1980). Half or more of all losses through action of humans. Age at 1st breeding, 1 year, but 6−7 months recorded for both sexes (Cramp and Simmons 1977). May live to 25 years old, record of 29 years (Drilling *et al.* 2002); however, few survive > 5 years (Palmer 1976, Toms and Clark 1998).

Conservation and threats

Regularly seen more as sinner than sinned against. Re-stocking and introduction programmes have led to hybridization with populations of North American mallard types, competition with other species, eutrophication of wetlands, and spread of disease (see Callaghan and Kirby 1996 for review). Decline of Pacific Black Duck or Grey Duck in New Zealand and North American Black Duck may end in extinction of these taxa; Mexican Duck may already be extinct in US (Callaghan and Green 1993). See Drilling *et al.* (2002) for conservation and management.

While range greatly expanded, numbers in decline in many places. Tightening of hunting controls and provision of protected nesting areas needed throughout range in order to maintain status.

Glyn Young

Mottled Duck *Anas fulvigula*
PLATE 17

Anas obscura var. *fulvigula* Ridgway, 1874, Amer. Naturalist, **8**, p. 111
St. John's River, Florida

Etymology: *fulvigula* L. from *fulvus* tawny and *gula* throated.

Other names: Dusky Duck. Florida Mallard, Florida Duck (*fulvigula*). Mottled Mallard, Black Duck, Summer Duck, Mallard Hen (*maculosa*). Spanish: Pato tejano.

Variation: 2 subspecies tentatively recognized, Florida Duck *A. f. fulvigula*, and Mottled Duck *A. f. maculosa* Sennet, 1889; genetic differences between populations detailed in McCracken *et al.* (2001).

Description

ADULT: sexes alike. ♂ body plumage medium to dark fuscous-brown, mottled and streaked with dark brown and black. Retrices show faint shade of grey, while body feathers have relatively broad pale edges. Cheeks and throat buff, and vary from having fine streaking to none. Dark brown supercilium. Usually bluish green speculum not bordered by white, although anterior, narrow white border sometimes occurs. Bill clear yellow with black nail; legs orange; eyes brown. ♀ similar to ♂, but has dull orange-yellow bill with olive markings, also wider buff brown feather edges and overall lighter appearance (Palmer 1976, Bellrose 1980, Moorman and Gray 1994). *fulvigula* adult ♂ has body plumage medium fuscous-brown. Cheeks immaculate buff and speculum ultramarine-violet, but uncertain whether these characters typical. *maculosa* adult ♂ has body plumage dark fuscous-brown. Cheeks finely streaked and speculum cobalt-ultramarine, but again uncertain whether characters typical.

MOULT: no seasonal change in plumage pattern, so no ♂ eclipse.

IMMATURE: similar to ♀ but less strongly marked (Palmer 1976, Bellrose 1980).

DUCKLING: blackish brown above (more olive-brown and dusky yellow than Northern Mallard), and buff-yellow below, with yellow face. Four buff-yellow spots on lateral and anterior part of back, and anterior narrow buff-yellow lines on wings. Dark eyestripe and dark spots on ears. Legs, feet and bill black (Palmer 1976, Nelson 1993).

MEASUREMENTS AND WEIGHT: *fulvigula* ♂ wing ($n = 21$), 237–264 (252.0); culmen, 51.1–57.8 (54.6); tarsus, 42.0–49.1 (45.9); weight ($n = 86$), 876–1241 (1043); *maculosa* ♂ wing ($n = 13$), 248–264 (256.0); culmen, 50.1–63.1 (54.9); tarsus, 43.1–48.2 (45.5). *fulvigula* ♀ wing ($n = 9$), 222–245 (234.0); culmen, 49.1–52.1 (50.4); tarsus ($n = 8$), 44.0–47.0 (45.0); weight ($n = 71$), 699–1151 (934); *maculosa* ♀ wing ($n = 9$), 229–253 (239.0); culmen, 47.8–54.9 (51.7); tarsus, 38.1–46.2 (42.5) (Palmer 1976, Bellrose 1980, Moorman and Gray 1994).

Field characters

Darker and slightly smaller than ♀ Mallard, with essentially plain head and no white on tail. American Black Duck darker with purple speculum (Palmer 1976, Bellrose 1980, Moorman and Gray 1994).

Voice

Vocalizations resemble those of Northern Mallard. ♂ emits low, raspy *raeb*; single *raeb* given as alarm call and 2-note *raeb-raeb* during courtship or as conversational call. Single, sharp whistle given during Head-up-tail-up display. ♀ has loud, raspy, sequenced Decrescendo call, *quack*, which typically consists of 6 notes, 2nd being loudest and highest in pitch. When alarmed, emits 3–4 harsh *quacks*. Also, gives irregularly accented *gagg* during Inciting, and *gaeck-gaeck-gaeck-gaeck* during Repulsion display (Johnsgard 1965a, Paulus 1988a, Moorman and Gray 1994).

Range and status

Eastern subspecies confined to peninsula Florida (US), where largely sedentary, undergoing only local seasonal dispersal. Highest density occurs on prairie wetlands near Lake Okeechobee, agricultural lands south of Okeechobee, and in upper St Johns River marshes (Johnson *et al.* 1992). Western race breeds along coastal Louisiana and Texas, south at least to Tampico in Mexico, and also largely sedentary; however, in winter significant numbers move west and south along Gulf Coast to Mexico, when occurs as far as Veracruz (Palmer 1976, Moorman and Gray 1994). Birds released in South Carolina in 1976 established resident population in vicinity of Delta Santee Wildlife Management Area (Moorman and Gray 1994).

Population in west fluctuates with changing water conditions along Gulf Coast. Favourable conditions can result in early autumn population of 200 000–250 000 individuals. In recent decades has expanded breeding range in US, particularly north, owing to increasing exploitation of rice fields for nesting (Bellrose 1980). Rose and Scott (1997) estimated stable population of 185 000, while McCracken *et al.* (2001) suggested threatened populations of *c* 56 000 in Florida and 500 000–800 000 in Texas and Louisiana.

Habitat and general habits

Inhabits both freshwater and brackish sites, including marshes, pools, ponds, ungrazed fields and rice fields. Offshore islands also utilized where suitable conditions exist. Probably least gregarious of North

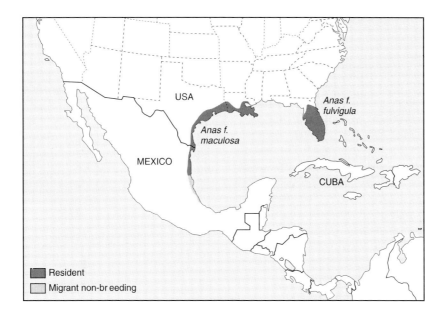

American dabbling ducks. Small flocks (5–25) can be seen in autumn and winter, but only solitary pairs general Feb–July. In Sept–Oct, after post-nuptial moult, large concentrations of up to 3000 *maculosa* noted where food plentiful but, by Nov, these flocks break up into small groups (Bellrose 1980, Johnson *et al.* 1992, Moorman and Gray 1994).

From Sept–Feb, individuals average 43% of day feeding, 36% resting, 7% preening, 7% alert, 6% walking, swimming or flying, and <1% each in courtship and agonistic activities (Paulus 1984b, 1988c). Diet varies between habitats and seasons, but consists mostly of plant matter (seeds of grasses and sedges, and stems, leaves and roots of aquatic plants). Animal food is molluscs, insects (especially chironomids), crustaceans and fish, which can predominate in diet seasonally (e.g. during moult). Microhabitat for foraging is water <300 mm deep, especially among emergent vegetation. Filters substrates and water surface usually by head dipping while sitting on water or standing in shallows (Palmer 1976, Moorman and Gray 1994).

Displays and breeding behaviour

Paulus (1984b) provided description of agonistic behaviour, including Bill-threat, Chase, Bite, Incit-ing, Repulsion and Pursuit Flights. Down-up may act as appeasement gesture by one ♂ towards another (Johnsgard 1965a). Courtship appears identical to Northern Mallard and American Black Duck, and includes Head-shake, Introductory-shake, Inciting, Grunt-whistle, Head-up-tail-up, Nod-swim, Preen-behind-wing, Turn-back-of-head, and Down-up. Copulatory and post-copula-tory displays include Head-pump, Bridling, Nod-swimming, and Turn-back-of-head (Weeks 1969, Palmer 1976, Paulus 1984b, Moorman and Gray 1994).

Seasonally monogamous (bond lasts 3–6 months). Pair formation occurs as early as Aug; number of paired ♀♀ in Louisiana increases through autumn and winter as follows: 21% in Aug, 71% in Sept, 83% in Oct, 84% in Nov, 93% in Dec, 96% in Jan, 100% in Feb (Paulus 1988a).

Breeding and life cycle

Earliest nests initiated Jan, continuing to Aug, with peaks Mar–Apr. Nest lined with vegetation and located on ground amongst dense vegetation. Active nests scattered but can reach density of 3 per ha. Eggs laid daily, and after 5th or 6th egg, nest down appears. Eggs elliptical, dull white to pale olive; $56.5 \pm 0.26 \times 42.4 \pm 0.19$ (54.5–61.4×40.9–44.8) ($n = 32$), or $54.9 \pm 1.8 \times 40.8 \pm 1.0$ ($n = 854$); weight 57 ± 0.5 (52–64) ($n = 32$), or 50.7 ± 3.4 ($n = 854$); clutch of *maculosa* 10.4 (7–14) eggs ($n = 108$), those of *fulvigula* 10.1 (5–13) ($n = 78$). Incubation, by ♀, 26 (24–28) days. During incubation, ♀ spends 83% of time on nest, with recesses averaging 245 min per day ($n = 277$ recesses for 12 ♀♀). Peak hatching late Apr–early May. Newly hatched ducklings weigh 30.7 (27.5–34.6) ($n = 22$). Nest success varies 28% ($n = 108$) to 74% ($n = 93$), with losses mainly attributed to predation by scavengers, and collection by humans. Ducks will, however, re-nest up to 5 times (Beckwith and Hosford 1956, Stieglitz and Wilson 1968, LaHart and Cornwell 1971, Palmer 1976, Bellrose 1980, Stutzenbaker 1988, Moorman and Gray 1994, Johnson *et al.* 2002).

Eggs have 95–96% hatch rate (Stieglitz and Wilson 1968, Stutzenbaker 1988), and duckling survival *c* 50% (95% CI = 0.38–0.66; $n = 21$ broods) (Gray 1993). Ducklings intolerant of salinity > 12 ppt, and probably have slower growth and survival rates in marshes 9–12 ppt *v* marshes < 9 ppt (Moorman *et al.* 1991). Until *c* Day 21, ducklings feed almost exclusively on invertebrates, but then switch to seeds of emergent and aquatic plants (Stutzenbaker 1988). Broods usually break up at 65–70 days of age (Paulus 1984b). Capable of limited escape flights at 45–56 days, and sustained flight at 63–70 days (Stutzenbaker 1988, Moorman *et al.* 1991). ♂ deserts ♀ during incubation and gathers in late July in small groups for post-nuptial moult lasting *c* month. ♀♀ begin slightly later during Aug and tend to remain solitary. By late Sept, virtually all adults have completed moult (Johnson 1973, Palmer 1976, Bellrose 1980).

Record life-span of wild bird 13 years (Stutzenbaker 1988), but average life expectancy of immature ♂ and ♀ 2.5 and 1.4 years respectively (Moorman and Gray 1994). Average annual survival in Florida 0.50 ± 0.047 ($n = 69$) for adult ♀, 0.47 ± 0.096 ($n = 145$) for immature ♀, 0.55 ± 0.064 ($n = 187$) for adult ♂, and 0.91 ± 0.19 ($n = 238$) for immature ♂ (Moorman and Gray 1994).

Conservation and threats

Substantial habitat loss within range due to general development and associated wetland drainage and degradation; e.g. in mid 1970s to mid 1980s, 116 000 ha of palustrine wetland lost within Florida (Frayer and Hefner 1991). Nonetheless, numbers in Florida remained stable 1985–93, and spring and autumn populations estimated at 28 000 and 56 000 respectively (Johnson *et al.* 1992). Small but rapidly growing population of resident, introduced Northern Mallard in Florida increasingly hybridizes with Florida Ducks. These Mallard originate from releases for both ornamental and hunting purposes, although former illegal. Despite serious threat, several hunting reserves in northern Florida continue to release game farm Mallard regularly (Hill 1994, Mazourek and Gray 1994, Callaghan *et al.* 1998). Florida Duck (as *A. f. fulvigula*) listed as Near-threatened by Threatened Waterfowl Specialist Group (2001). About one-third of Florida Ducks taken by hunters every year, which population apparently sustained (Bellrose 1980); however, McCracken *et al.* (2001) felt population under serious threat from growing urbanization, agricultural pressure and hybridization with released Northern Mallard. Texas/Louisiana population also threatened, but hybridization not of immediate concern. Distinct nature of 2 populations (McCracken *et al.* 2001) suggests separate treatment for conservation purposes. Had highest rate of lead shot ingestion (up to 38%; $n = 1233$) of any waterfowl in North America, but high level of vegetable protein in diet probably mitigates against catastrophic losses (Sanderson and Bellrose 1986, Moulton *et al.* 1988, Moorman and Gray 1994). Since 1991, lead shot banned for waterfowl hunting in US.

Des Callaghan

Mexican Duck *Anas diazi*

Anas diazi Ridgway, 1886, Auk **3**, p. 332
San Ysidro, Puebla, Mexico

Etymology: named after Augustín Díaz (1829–93), Mexican geographer and explorer.

Other names: Mexican Mallard, New Mexican Duck, Diaz's Duck. French: Canard fauve; Spanish: Pato triguero, Pato Mexicano, Pato altiplanero.

Variation: no recognized subspecies; however, high degree of variation within range and hybridization with close relatives makes interpretation of relationship with Northern Mallard and Mottled Duck difficult (see Hubbard 1977). Variation within range led to 2 subspecies being recognized in past, *A. diazi diazi* in south, and New Mexican Duck *A. d. novimexicana* Huber, 1920 in north; however, several studies, including Aldrich and Baer (1970), concluded that *novimexicana* invalid. Has undoubtedly hybridized readily with other mallard types, notably with Northern Mallard, thus threatening survival; extensive 'game' releases, in particular, have reduced genetic purity.

Description

ADULT: sexes alike. ♂ recalls ♀ Northern Mallard but darker with blackish tail and tail coverts, and contrasting pale sides of head and neck. Wing darker than ♀ Mallard with speculum more green and white forward edge less distinct and often absent. Bill greenish yellow. ♀ brown and less rufescent than ♂ (Palmer 1976); bill more olive-green with little orange at base and none, or few, dark markings on upper mandible. Undertail coverts dark brown with paler edges, outer tail feathers darker than those of ♀ Mallard (Huey 1961). High degree of individual variation, and hybrids often present within range (see Hubbard 1977 for descriptions of hybrids).

MOULT: no ♂ eclipse.

IMMATURE: plumage more streaked than adult, scapulars shorter, more rounded. All feathering softer than in older stages (Palmer 1976).

DUCKLING: pale, large dorsal spots; eyestripe thin and incomplete. Ear-spot inconspicuous (Delacour 1954–64, Palmer 1976, Nelson 1993).

MEASUREMENTS AND WEIGHT: 6 sites in Mexico, ♂ ($n = 52$) wing, 257–297 (281); weight, 849–1243 (1028); ♀ wing ($n = 46$), 248–277 (261); weight ($n = 48$), 647–1267 (908) (Scott and Reynolds 1984). Northern specimens ('*novimexicana*') ♂ ($n = 18$) wing, 260–289 (273.9), bill, 50.4–56.4 (53.0); tarsus, 40.1–47.4 (44.2); ♀ ($n = 27$) wing, 237–271 (254.7); bill, 47.1–55.1 (51.0); tarsus, 38.3–49.3 (42.6) (Aldrich and Baer 1970). Southern specimens ('*diazi*') ♂ ($n = 13$) wing, 260–282 (269.9); bill, 51.1–55.6 (53.3); tarsus, 43.1–48.4 (46.3); ♀ ($n = 13$) wing, 232–268 (253.4); bill, 45.5–52.7 (50.3); tarsus, 40.2–43.6 (42.0) (Aldrich and Baer 1970). In New Mexico, Mexico (and ♂ from Nebraska) ♂ ($n = 10$) wing, 289–295 (284.5); bill, 52–55 (54); tarsus, 42–50 (46); weight (no details), 960–1060; ♀ ($n = 11$) wing, 158–270 (266.6); bill, 49–55 (52); tarsus, 43–48 (45.5); weight (no details), 815–990 (Palmer 1976).

Field characters

Large dark dabbling duck, 510–560 mm long, resembling ♀ Northern Mallard. Darkish body and paler face noticeable, but never so dark as American Black Duck. Range does not overlap with American Black Duck nor Mottled Duck. Greenish speculum, narrow white bar at leading edge of speculum and little or no white in tail should differentiate from Mallard. Speculum of American Black Duck lacks white borders and that of Mottled Duck often lacks white trailing edge.

Voice

Poorly recorded; presumably as Northern Mallard. No sonogram published.

Range and status

Formerly continuous from southern US to central Mexico, range now fragmented, probably following extensive habitat conversion. In north, breeds

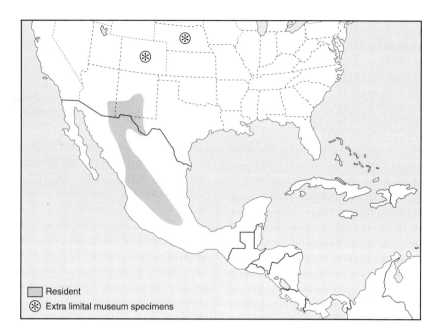

Resident
⊛ Extra limital museum specimens

principally in Rio Grande watershed in New Mexico and Texas, in the Gila watershed in southwest New Mexico and in San Simon Cienega on south Arizona–New Mexico border. In south, in Mexico, breeds mostly in Chihuahua, Durango, Jalisco and Mexico states. Some evidence of migratory movements, notably along Rio Grande Valley (Palmer 1976) and only small numbers recorded in Chihuahua in winter (Bellrose 1980) while numbers increase in Jalisco (Aldrich and Baer 1970). Extralimital records complicated by identification problems and hybrids; museum specimens exist from Nebraska and Colorado.

Status hard to determine. Population in US undoubtedly declined through habitat loss and hybridization, and often considered to be biologically extinct. In Mexico, perhaps less affected by problems of north, 55 000 birds counted in 1978 (Scott and Reynolds 1984); has adapted to artificial habitats well and uses reservoirs, unlike northern population (Scott and Reynolds 1984, Perez-Arteaga *et al.* 2002). Wetlands International (2002) estimated increasing population of 55 500.

Habitat and general habits

Lives principally along rivers with adjacent marsh, and, occasionally, on small lakes. May occur on temporary wetlands in semi-arid areas, and volcanic lake in Mexico. Outside breeding season, wary and rarely forms sizeable flocks. Thousand recorded on lake in Jalisco State, Mexico in Jan 1968 (Aldrich and Baer 1970). Rarely mixes with other ducks.

Feeds in similar way to Northern Mallard. Diet includes green shoots of alfalfa, cattail, roots and seeds of grasses, wheat, rice, corn and freshwater molluscs (Phillips 1922–26, Palmer 1976).

Displays and breeding behaviour

Poorly studied. Johnsgard (1965a) does not detail displays, linking taxa to Mallard. Down-up, Nod-swim, Turn-back-of-head, Incitement and copulatory behaviour observed and considered identical to Northern Mallard (Palmer 1976). Lindsey (1946) recorded egg carrying by nesting ♀♀.

Breeding and life cycle

Poorly studied (see Lindsey 1946). Breeds Apr–June in New Mexico, and probably into Aug in Mexico. Nest made in grass usually close to water. ♀ apparently deserts readily if disturbed. Eggs white, tinged green (Palmer 1976); in New Mexico 56.8 × 41.2 (53.3–59.6 × 40.0–43.2) (*n* = 23) and in Mexico 55.2 × 41.0 (*n* = 71) (Lindsey 1946); weight unrecorded. Clutch 4–9; incubation, by ♀, 26–28 days (Todd 1996). Hatch weight and fledging period unrecorded. No data on breeding success, survival nor on longevity.

Conservation and threats

Future appears bleak in US; widespread habitat modification and influence of invading Northern Mallard may make slide to extinction unstoppable. Censuses required in parts of range to determine numbers, while further studies needed better to understand taxonomy, and to ascertain levels of phenotypic variation in Mexican population. Fifteen sites in Mexico identified as holding > 70% of midwinter counts, 10 of which qualify as Ramsar sites (Perez-Arteaga *et al.* 2002), and conservation action should be concentrated here. Has probably never been maintained well in captivity, and might make good subject for managed captive breeding programme aimed at re-stocking.

Glyn Young

Hawaiian Duck (Koloa) *Anas wyvilliana*
PLATE 17

Anas wyvilliana P. L. Sclater, 1878, Proc. Zool. Soc. London, p. 350
Hawaiian Islands

Etymology: *wyvilliana* after Sir Charles Wyville Thompson (1842–1900), English ornithologist, who led *Challenger* expedition 1873–76.

Other names: Koloa Maoli, Sandwich Islands Duck. French: Canard d'Hawaï; Spanish: Pato Hawaiiense.

Variation: no subspecies; some individual variation, see below.

Description

ADULT: although lacking marked sexual dimorphism, differences sufficiently obvious for field identification. ♂ darker than ♀, tending to chestnut below (more reddish brown plumage) and olive-green bill; head may have flecks or streaks of deep green, similar to ♂ Northern Mallard, some ♂♂ also have upturned central tail feathers (Delacour 1954–64, Yealland 1957, Munro 1960, Greenway 1967, Berger 1981, Pratt *et al.* 1987). Top of head blackish and feathers tipped pale brown with dark metallic green stripe from eyes to nape. Feathers of neck also blackish, mixed with light brown, and those of upperback and interscapular region blackish brown with crescent-shaped and undulated rufous-brown bands. Lowerback, rump, and uppertail coverts brownish black with few brown edges and spots. Inner tertials and greater scapulars brown, greyish in middle and narrowly-edged pale brown; primaries dark greyish brown. Speculum emerald green to metallic purplish blue (lighting in field may enhance blue), bordered behind with black line, in front by white and black lines (Engilis *et al.* 2002, Madge and Burn 1988). Sides of head, neck and throat mottled blackish brown and pale buff-brown. Breast rufous brown, with u-shaped blackish markings, or more or less round spots. Upperbreast and sides more rufous. Abdomen brownish buff, distinctly shaded greyish in oldest specimens. Sides of body pale rufous brown, with longitudinal or v-shaped deep brown markings. Undertail coverts blackish and brownish, and underwing coverts and axillaries white (Phillips 1922–26, Swedberg 1967, Weller 1980, Berger 1981). Bill greyish olive with black nail, legs and feet of ♂ and ♀ described as similar, but varies from dark grey to orange-yellow to scarlet, although scarlet apparently seen only on few adult ♂♂ (Delacour 1954–64, Berger 1981, Pratt *et al.* 1987); eyes brown. ♀ smaller, resembling ♀ Northern Mallard but deeper and redder brown. Blackish brown above with all feathers broadly margined with brownish buff and most with 1–2 zigzag bars across. Primaries dark greyish brown. Speculum emerald green to purplish blue bordered as ♂ but less distinct. Underparts buff-brown, darker on breast, and spotted blackish brown especially along sides of body and on breast. Chin mostly unspotted and reddish, and underwing coverts white but variable, with those near margin sometimes dark brown with pale borders. Some have distinct pale superciliary line. Bill variable, usually dusky but tip may be orange, yellow-orange or grey (Phillips 1922–26, Berger 1981, Pratt *et al.* 1987, Livezey 1993a, Engilis *et al.* 2002).

MOULT: although Yealland (1957) stated that, if ♂ eclipse exists, scarcely discernable from breeding plumage, Delacour (1954–64) and Swedberg (1967) noted eclipse phase, when ♂ resembled ♀ more closely. ♂ bill pattern retained.

IMMATURE: like ♀, or ♂ in eclipse (Phillips 1922–26). Delacour (1954–64) described immature as being slightly duller and more lightly marked than adult. According to Pratt *et al.* (1987), 1st year ♂ has subdued Northern Mallard pattern, with greenish head, black rump and undertail.

DUCKLING: closely resembles Northern Mallard, although smaller, more olive above and buffer and less yellow on belly and on face. Feet darker than most Mallards. Has narrow brown stripe from base of bill through eye to about level of ear (Delacour 1954–64, Nelson 1993).

MEASUREMENTS AND WEIGHT: ♂ ($n = 14$) wing, 233.2 ± 10.3; tail, 78.9 ± 5.9; culmen, 46.3 ± 1.6; tarsus 41.7 ± 1.7; weight ($n = 38$), 628 ± 105. ♀ ($n = 16$) wing 220.8 ± 6.8; tail, 74.4 ± 4.4; culmen, 43.8 ± 1.1; tarsus, 39.9 ± 1.1; weight ($n = 22$), 568 ± 14 (Livezey 1993a).

Field characters

Small mottled brown duck, ♂ 483–508 mm long, ♀ *c* 76 mm shorter (Berger 1981). In Hawaii, identification confused through presence of introduced Northern Mallard, and of hybrids. Both sexes resemble dull, half-size Mallard, with 44% decrease in body mass and in dimensions. Small white eye-ring (characteristic of island endemics) may be present or absent, but never as extensive as in Laysan Duck (Weller 1980, Berger 1981). Several authors noted individual variation in plumage, likely due to age (Rothschild 1893–1900, Phillips 1922–26, Delacour 1954–64, Swedberg 1967), although Perkins (1903) suggested variability indicated hybridization. Phillips (1922–26) thought variation greater in ♀ plumage,

while Delacour (1954–64) indicated ♂♂ showed more individual variation.

Voice

Less vocal than Northern Mallard (Weller 1980). Has voice and calls of Mallard, but higher-pitched (Delacour 1954–64) and less powerful (Phillips 1922–26). ♀ noted to *quack* loudly as rises from water. Munro (1960) stated that ♀ quacks and ♂ hisses, and sounded like domestic duck.

Range and status

Historically found on all Hawaiian Islands, with exception of Lanai and Kahoolawe (Perkins 1903, Berger 1970), and considered common (Phillips 1922–26, Schwartz and Schwartz 1953, Munro 1960). After turn of last century, decline in numbers attributed to drainage of wetlands, indiscriminate hunting, and Small Indian Mongoose introduction (Phillips 1922–26, Berger 1970, US Fish & Wildlife Service 1999); predation by rats, feral cats, pigs and dogs, particularly on eggs and ducklings, and impact of introduced pigs and goats on nesting habitat along Kauai's montane streams, also likely contributed (Schwartz and Schwartz 1953).

No population estimates prior to 1940, and only evidence of former abundance in 1923 when 400 ducks per square mile estimated on Mana Marsh, Kauai (2400 on whole marsh) (Schwartz and Schwartz 1953, US Fish & Wildlife Service 1999). Marsh now extensively drained. Also believed to be fairly common in natural and farmed wetland habitats and that Taro *Colocasia esculenta* (agricultural crop grown in pond-like environments) cultivation initially provided considerable wet agricultural habitat (Swedberg 1967). In addition, cultivation of rice *Oryza sativa* in late 1800s to 1940s continued to provide wetland habitat (US Fish & Wildlife Service 1999). Although decline in flooded agriculture occurred by 1900, there were still *c* 7700 ha of taro and 6500 ha of rice (Bostwick 1982). However, by 1946–47, only 5 ducks per square mile, or 30 birds, reported on Mana Marsh; at same time, estimated population on Oahu < 30, with subsequent observations indicating continual declines due to drainage of swamp and pond areas. Around 1949, considered occasional visitor to island of Hawaii, and presumed

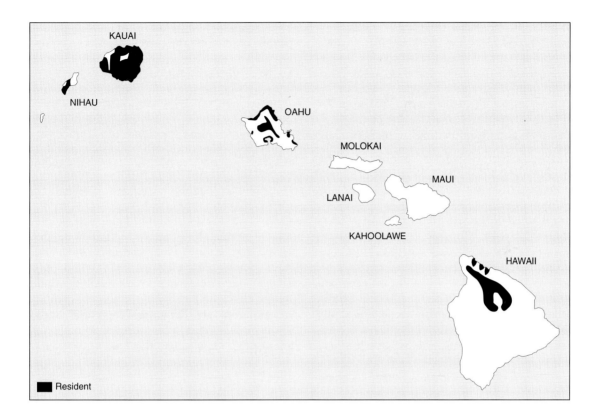

extirpated on Maui and Molokai (Schwartz and Schwartz 1953). By 1960, believed gone from Oahu, when Kaelepulu Pond, their last stronghold, modified as part of housing development; by 1960s, found only on Kauai and probably Niihau (US Fish & Wildlife Service 1999), and by 1953, Schwartz and Schwartz (1953) estimated 500 birds on Kauai derived from sample counts and information from local observers; survey in 1960s yielded *c* 3000 there (Swedberg 1967, Weller 1980).

Declared Federally Endangered in 1967 (US Fish & Wildlife Service 1967). In 1970s and 1980, ducks reared in captivity at Pohakuloa, Hawaii, released on Oahu and Hawaii (Berger 1981, US Fish & Wildlife Service 1999). Waterbird surveys of 1970s and 1980s showed steady increase, although surveys did not cover stream and montane wetlands where main population thought to exist (US Fish & Wildlife Service 1999). Population on Kauai has maintained itself without releases; majority still nest along montane streams and, until recently, it was

believed there were no hybrids (US Fish & Wildlife Service 1999). Recent study of state waterbird surveys indicates hybrids on Kauai as early as 1992. Those sampled for genetic characteristics on Oahu have been Northern Mallard–Koloa hybrids despite plumage characteristics that suggest otherwise (Griffin and Brown 1990). Hybrids with Mallard found also on Maui and may now outnumber pure Koloa; highland population on Hawaii believed genetically pure and isolated from lowland populations of Mallard, but Koloa–Mallard pairs seen in Hilo area (US Fish & Wildlife Service 1999).

Population in state of Hawaii of pure Koloa estimated at *c* 2200 birds, with 2000 on Kauai/Niihau and 200 on Hawaii (Engilis and Pratt 1993, US Fish & Wildlife Service 1999, Engilis *et al.* 2002).

Habitat and general habits

Reported to occur in many types of wetland habitats, and apparently tolerant of varying ecological and climatic conditions (Berger 1970). May have used highland forest bogs (Perkins 1903), freshwater streams up to 2400 m, coastal lagoons (Munro 1960), flooded rice fields, reservoirs, major irrigation ditches and marshy areas (Schwartz and Schwartz 1953). Swedberg (1967) estimated > 90% of those on Kauai lived along upland streams at 300–1200 m. Remainder on Kauai found sparsely below 300 m, occupying many habitats (Schwartz and Schwartz 1953). Weller (1980) reported birds gathered on reservoirs or taro paddies in evening on Kauai, apparently moving from isolated territories where day spent. Nesting on Kauai reported from sea level to 300 m and in areas with annual rainfall varying 89–300 cm (Berger 1970), and along streams and ditches in sugar cane fields and near reservoirs. Artificial wetlands (including taro, lotus, shrimp, and fish ponds) supplement existing habitat and provide important feeding areas (US Fish & Wildlife Service 1999). Prefers freshwater, although not absent from coast in past where suitable ponds existed (Phillips 1922–26).

Although able fliers (Munro 1960, Greenway 1967, Weller 1980), non-migratory (Schwartz and Schwartz 1953, Delacour 1954–64). No evidence of widespread inter-island movement, except between Kauai and Niihau (Engilis and Pratt 1993), and ♀♀ known to nest on islands off Oahu, subsequently leading ducklings back to Oahu (Munro 1960). Thought to show no seasonal movements (Schwartz and Schwartz 1953); however, biannual surveys suggest movement from lowland wetlands to more secluded habitats in summer (US Fish & Wildlife Service 1999). Summer declines in numbers could represent altitudinal movements, dispersal up stream valleys, or reclusive post-breeding moult period (US Fish & Wildlife Service 1999). More information needed on seasonal movements in response to availability of ephemeral and permanent wetland habitats. Ephemeral wetlands believed important, though how utilized beyond foraging unknown (Engilis *et al.* 2002). Daily movements recorded between feeding and roosting areas, but little known of home ranges or territory; Weller (1980) observed 3-bird chases and other courtship flights that he believed suggested strong territorial or ♀ defence.

Usually observed as singles or pairs, rarely in groups of 3–4 (Phillips 1922–26, Schwartz and Schwartz 1953). Currently, no large flocks form at any time, although in past, large post-breeding flocks reported (Wilson and Evans 1890–99, Rothschild 1893–1900, Phillips 1922–26, Schwartz and Schwartz 1953). Described as tame on mountain streams and areas where not harassed (Henshaw 1902, Perkins 1903); however, wary during nesting (Weller 1980).

Shift in diet often characterizes island ducks, particularly towards terrestrial foods (Weller 1980, Livezey 1993a). Feeds on wide range of plants, including green algae, rice, grasses, and seeds and leaf parts of wetland plants; also eats variety of invertebrates, such as earthworms, dragonflies, fresh- and brackish-water snails (Henshaw 1902, Perkins 1903, Phillips 1922–26, Munro 1960, Swedberg 1967, Berger 1981, Livezey 1993a). Forages in wetlands and streams in water 24 cm deep (Engilis *et al.* 2002).

Displays and breeding behaviour

Has nuptial or 3-bird flights; after birds take flight, climb almost vertically to *c* 30 m and chase in small circles. Favoured ♂ usually identified by proximity to ♀, while less favoured ♂ keeps at greater distance from start of flight; he may dive to try and intercept favoured ♂ or follow closely, but is driven off, and selection largely decided before flight taken (Swedberg 1967). Weller (1980) saw Koloa give many typical Northern Mallard displays described by Lorenz (1951–53) and Johnsgard (1965a).

In lowlands of Kauai, pairbond forms Nov–May, and pairs disperse to montane locations to breed, although some may nest in lowland wetlands (US Fish & Wildlife Service 1999).

Breeding and life cycle

Little known. Breeds year-round though mostly in spring (Schwartz and Schwartz 1953); nests or ducklings found every month except Aug. On Kauai, main breeding season Dec–May (Swedberg 1967, Berger 1970). According to Perkins (1903), majority nest Mar–June. Phillips (1922–26) suggested that ♂ and ♀ remain together during nesting and that both rear young. Nesting occurs along streams and ditches in sugar cane fields or near reservoirs; few documented cases of nesting occurring in areas populated by humans, especially where feral cats, dogs and mongooses common (US Fish & Wildlife Service 1999).

Nests well concealed on ground, often in Honohono Grass *Commelina diffusa*, lined with down (Greenway 1967, Berger 1981). Nest 304.8–457.2 mm round by 101.6 mm deep. Eggs white, buff or light tan; short oval; 49.8 × 35.9 (Munro 1960, Weller 1980, Livezey 1993a); weight in captivity 43.1 (33.5–51.5) ($n = 100$); clutch 8.3 (2–10) ($n = 11$) (Swedberg 1967); 2–12 eggs observed on Mokulua Islands but, according to Munro (1960), 8 commonest number. Island endemics tend to have smaller clutches than mainland counterparts (Weller 1980), however, Berger (1981) believed that some recorded small clutches (2–3 eggs) represent observations made before egg-laying completed. Proportionate increase in egg size to body size of endemic island ducks may result in greater energy stores for ducklings (Lack 1968a, 1970, Livezey 1993a); however, Weller (1980) found little evidence that island ducks have greater food reserves than continental forms, and suggested disadvantages to larger eggs, including longer incubation periods (Rahn and Ar 1974, Livezey 1993a). Incubation in captivity 28 days (Berger 1981); captive day-olds weigh 26.5 ($n = 54$). Broods of 4–8 observed (Schwartz and Schwartz 1953). Tail feathers appear at 3 weeks, fledge in 9 weeks (Phillips 1922–26, Berger 1981). Can breed at one year (Berger 1981). No data on breeding success, survival or longevity.

Conservation and threats

Has Endangered status in BirdLife International (2000). Protected by federal and state law. Hybridization with Northern Mallard considered primary threat to recovery (US Fish & Wildlife Service 1999). While allozymic data suggest extensive hybridization on Oahu and near disappearance of Koloa alleles, only slight evidence of hybrids on Kauai (Browne *et al.* 1993). However, recent examination of state-wide waterbird survey data shows increasing numbers of hybrids occurring on Maui, Hawaii and Kauai Predation by introduced and feral animals, damage to watershed stream habitats by introduced ungulates, and loss of habitat also remain threats

(King 1977, US Fish & Wildlife Service 1999). Other introduced animals (Largemouth Bass and Bullfrogs) known to kill ducklings on Kauai (Berger 1970). Population maintained on Kauai indicates role of introduced Small Indian Mongoose in decline, and threat posed to recovery (Schwartz and Schwartz 1953, Swedberg 1967, Berger 1981). It is therefore troubling that there now appears to be an incipient population of mongoose on Kauai based on increasing verified and unverified reports of individual mongoose on the island. Although hunting prohibited since 1939, as late as 1953 illegal poaching considered serious (Schwartz and Schwartz 1953). Disease and environmental contaminants may also play adverse role. Streams periodically poisoned to control aquatic weeds and insects; this likely caused loss of nesting habitat and food supply (Schwartz and Schwartz 1953). Botulism occurs annually, and affects all native and migratory waterfowl (US Fish & Wildlife Service 1999).

Habitat in Hanalei Valley, Kauai, acquired by federal government as National Wildlife Refuge in 1972, and other National Wildlife Refuges established on Oahu and Maui. Captive propagation programme conducted by State of Hawaii 1958–82 (Fisher *et al.* 1969, King 1977, Berger 1981), released 293 on Hawaii and 347 on Oahu. State also released < 12 captive-bred Koloa on Maui in 1989, which established small, breeding population that frequents Kanaha and Kealia Ponds and sugar cane reservoirs in valley portion (US Fish & Wildlife Service 1999). Since 1975, state also conducts semi-annual counts of waterbirds. Proposed conservation measures include acquisition of additional wetland refuges, establishment on other islands, and research to define limiting factors, recovery objectives and to improve management techniques (King 1977). Koloa Recovery Plan also includes removing threat of hybridization by implementing State-wide programme to eliminate Northern Mallard and Mallard-Koloa hybrids (US Fish & Wildlife Service 1999). A Koloa recovery implementation group, including various resource agencies and researchers, was established in 2004 to work on this problem.

Ann P. Marshall

Laysan Duck *Anas laysanensis*

PLATE 17

Anas laysanensis Rothschild, 1892, Bull. Brit. Ornith. Club, **1**, p. 17

Laysan Island

Etymology: *laysanensis* means of Laysan, where type specimen collected in 1891.

Other names: Laysan Teal, Laysan Island Duck. French: Canard de Laysan, Sarcelle de Laysan; Spanish: Pato real de Laysan.

Variation: no subspecies, but individuals somewhat variable, see below.

Description

ADULT: sexes almost alike but dimorphism of bill and leg colour sufficient to distinguish ♂♂ from ♀♀ (Marshall 1989, Moulton and Weller 1984, Warner 1963). Plumage dark reddish brown, heavily mottled dark brown, with prominent white eye-ring. Few ♂♂ have faint green iridescence on head and slightly upturned central tail feathers. Amount of white around eye and on head varies individually and also with age and sex (Marshall 1989, Moulton and Marshall 1996). Older ducks have more white, and few individuals nearly white-headed (Sincock and Kridler 1977, Weller 1980, Pratt *et al.* 1987). Chin and throat dark buff to white, feathers of back and sides with wide dark brown streaks or u-shaped markings bordered by dark buff; crown, nape and cheeks dark brown; underwing whitish. ♂ speculum dark green to velvety black behind with white bar at trailing edge, bill dull green with variable black, sometimes saddle-like, blotches/markings. ♀ tends to have more white around eye than ♂ and back and side feathers more tan brown than reddish brown as ♂; speculum dusky to greenish; bill dull orange with variable black blotching; legs and feet of both sexes orange, paler in ♀; iris brown (Phillips 1922–26, Warner 1963, Berger 1981, Moulton and Weller 1984, Marshall 1989).

MOULT: no seasonal change in plumage; 2 moults of body feathers annually, and single moult of flight feathers after breeding. Pre-juvenile moult complete at 55–65 days. Juvenile plumage moulted late summer or early fall, except that most wing feathers retained until following summer (Palmer 1976, Moulton and Marshall 1996).

IMMATURE: in 1st plumage has small white eye-ring (Sincock and Kridler 1977, Berger 1981) and appears darker brown than in succeeding moults. Impossible to distinguish sex by external appearance until 1st moult. Tail dark, usually with notched feather tips (Marshall 1989, Moulton and Marshall 1996).

DUCKLING: noticeably smaller than Northern Mallard duckling and slightly smaller than Hawaiian Duck or Koloa. Inconspicuous face and dorsal patterns on brownish yellow base colour. Top of head dark, and dark line runs before and behind eye. Rest of face yellow-brown, except for median streak. Chin and throat yellow-buff, mantle dark grey with yellow, back and rump dark, and underparts rich sulphur-yellow. Eyestripe may be poorly marked and large, pale ear-spot may extend forwards towards rictus giving impression of cheek stripe. Bill distinctly spatulate and flat-tipped, maxilla olive-grey with dull yellow egg-tooth, and mandible yellowish pink, with brownish pink nail, paler at tip; toes and tarsus light olive-brown, iris dark greyish brown (Phillips 1922–26, Nelson 1993, Moulton and Marshall 1996).

MEASUREMENTS AND WEIGHT: ♂ ($n = 11$) wing, 203.7 ± 10.9; tail, 74.5 ± 4.1; culmen, 39.4 ± 1.4; tarsus, 37.2 ± 1.4; mid toe, 41.7 ± 1.3. ♀ ($n = 17$) wing, 192.3 ± 6.3; tail, 76.7 ± 5.9; culmen, 37.1 ± 2.0; tarsus, 35.5 ± 0.9; mid toe, 39.3 ± 1.6 (Livezey 1993a). Weight ♂ ($n = 64$), 348–548 (455.9); ♀ ($n = 48$), 365–525 (462.8) (Moulton and Marshall 1996). Weight varies significantly with season and reproductive status; during Mar–May, mean of ♀♀ exceeds ♂♂, which may be < peak due to courtship activities; pre-breeding ♀♀ can weigh >600, presumably due to increased size of ovary and oviduct; June–Aug, pattern reverses, and ♂ generally heavier than ♀. Unpaired tend to be lighter than paired birds, and ♀ with brood lightest adult (Moulton and Weller 1984, Moulton and Marshall 1996).

Field characters

Small, length 380–430mm (Berger 1981); only duck on Laysan Island. Like other island endemics, shows reduction in size from mainland counterparts (Weller 1980). Has undergone 59% decrease in body mass compared to Northern Mallard and, sex for sex, body only 74% that of Koloa; also shows comparable decrease in external dimensions, such as wing length and size of pectoral and pelvic girdles. Skeletal measurements c 77% of Mallard; exception is tarsus, proportionately longer than Mallard, presumably due to terrestrial habits. Has disproportionately long femur and short middle toe, representing enhanced walking habit as well as some loss of ability to swim (Lack 1970, Livezey 1993a).

Voice

Similar to Northern Mallard (Abraham 1974), although elements absent or different; no Persistent Quacking by O, and whistle of o during Grunt-whistle display (in captivity) replaced by high-pitched raehb. Calls accompanying courtship display, including O Inciting, raehb call of o, and Decrescendo call of O, common during pairing in autumn and winter (Johnsgard 1965a, Moulton and Weller 1984, Moulton and Marshall 1996). O and o make soft contact calls when paired, as does O with young. Sonograms of o and O calls in Moulton and Marshall (1996).

Range and status

Until recently, believed to be endemic to Laysan Island, coral atoll 3km long and 370ha, in outer Hawaiian archipelago at c 26°N; exception was Lisianksi Island 225km away (King 1977, Weller 1980, Berger 1981). Some authors (Warner 1963, Caspers 1967) accepted accounts of occurrence on Lisianski described in von Kittlitz (1834), others did not (Ely and Clapp 1973, Clapp and Wirtz 1975, Sincock and Kridler 1977, Moulton and Weller 1984). After 1844, no visitors to Lisianski mentioned ducks, and there was none when ornithological collectors visited in 1891 (Rothschild 1893–1900); however, Olson and Ziegler (1995) found bones that indicated early resident population before arrival of humans, and juvenile metatarsus that indicated breeding. In addition, recent archaeological evidence suggests once widely distributed through Hawaiian archipelago, and resident on Hawaii, Maui, Oahu, Kauai, and Molokai (Olson and Ziegler 1995, Cooper *et al.* 1996). Olson and James (1982) recovered skeletons, including juveniles, from lava tubes on Hawaii and Maui. Late Holocene subfossils found on Molokai, Oahu and Kauai at sea level, also appear

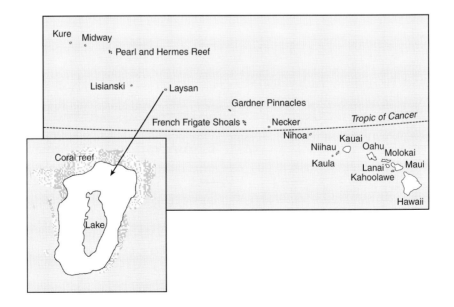

at higher elevations (60–1800m) on Maui and Hawaii in areas that were forested and far from permanent water (Cooper *et al.* 1996). Furthermore, as no apparent osteological differentiation in populations of Laysan and Lisiansky compared with those of Hawaii, northwestern island populations may be of recent origin or supplemented by regular immigrants from main islands (Olson and Ziegler 1995).

Rose and Scott (1997) suggested current wild population of Laysan fluctuates 38–500 individuals. Population in 2001 estimated at 444 ± 181 (Reynolds 2002).

Habitat and general habits

Found in pairs in late autumn, winter and during breeding, and small parties during summer and early autumn before pairing (Moulton and Weller 1984, Marshall 1989). Ripley (1959, 1960) suggested broad, spatulate bill adaptation to insectivorous diet. Feeds, often at night, while walking, dabbling and up-ending in central hypersaline lagoon on brine flies, larvae and adults, noctuid moths, beetles and brine shrimp *Artemia*. Runs through swarms of adult brine flies, moving head from side to side and snapping with bill. Drinks at 2 freshwater seeps at edge of lagoon, but probably has efficient salt-excreting gland (Moulton and Marshall 1996). During the day, ducks generally loaf under vegetation in inner terrestrial zones of island, becoming active around sunset but foraging through night and sunrise around lake and in terrestrial zones (Marshall 1989, Reynolds 2002). Coastal areas rarely used.

Displays and breeding behaviour

Reproductive displays described in captivity by Johnsgard (1965a). Breeding displays similar to those of Northern Mallard, including inciting behaviour, nod-swimming, grunt-whistle, head-up-tail-up, etc. Courtship behaviours occur as long as birds are paired, and ♂♂ tend to be most active maintaining proximity to mate (Moulton and Weller 1984, Marshall 1989). Pairbond breaks after ♀ begins incubating full time (Moulton and Weller 1984, Marshall 1992) and while ♀ that loses clutch or brood may re-pair with original mate, mate-switching from year to year occurs 58% of time (Moulton and Weller 1984). ♂♂ aggressive to one another, but not apparently territorial. Forced extra-pair copulation, at least in captivity, common. Courts and pairs during autumn and winter, extending into early spring.

Breeding and life cycle

Breeds spring and early summer. Egg-laying as early as Feb, but typically Apr–Aug. ♀ selects and builds nest hidden in upland vegetation such as *Eragrostis* and *Cyperus*. Eggs short subelliptical, ivory to light buff; 56.3×38.0 (53.2×37.3–39.3) ($n = 6$) (Moulton and Marshall 1996); weight in captivity 46.7 (34.5–56.0) ($n = 100$), large for size of ♀ at *c* 10% of her body. Clutch 3.8 (3–6) ($n = 13$), eggs laid one per day; incubation, by ♀, 28 days, with recesses of *c* 3 per day (Moulton and Marshall 1996). ♀ may re-lay if eggs lost. Smallest duckling captured on Laysan weighed 18, most newly-hatched young weigh 22–30 (Moulton and Weller 1984); precocial and follow ♀ off nest shortly after hatching (Moulton and Marshall 1996). No paternal care; ♀ broods young during heat of day and at night. Ducklings take same diet as adults and pursue prey in similar manner. Brood mixing common. For wild ducklings, Class I (downy, no feathers) lasts *c* 20 days, Class II (partly feathered) includes *c* next 25 days, and Class III (fully feathered) 45 days, to fully grown flight feathers at 50–60 days (Gollop and Marshall 1954, Moulton and Weller 1984, Marshall 1992, Moulton and Marshall 1996). In captivity, flies at 49 (46–52) days ($n = 8$) (Marshall 1992). Little information on breeding success, but duckling survival low, especially in years with low numbers of brine flies (Marshall 1989, Reynolds 2002); suffers egg predation by Laysan Finch *Telespiza cantans*. Captives breed at one year. No data on adult survival, but ringing recovery shows oldest wild individual 12 years (Moulton and Marshall 1996).

Conservation and threats

Laysan Island occupied for guano-mining 1891–1904, and by 1902 duck population < 100; introduced European Rabbits reduced vegetation further and, by 1912, only 7 ducks remained. With starvation of rabbits in 1924, numbers rose to 33 in 1950 and today fluctuate to 700 at times, although carrying capacity of island *c* 500. Many die of starvation in drought years when brine fly numbers drop, and affected adversely by nematode parasite (Moulton and Marshall 1996). Accidental introductions of rats or mongooses to Laysan Island would be disastrous, and natural disasters could result in extinction on Laysan.

Given Vulnerable status in BirdLife International (2000), and is on US Federal Endangered Species List. Laysan Island now reserve, with access only for scientists and officials. Large population in captivity; although inbred, individuals breed freely when young. US Fish and Wildlife Service and USGS Bio-

logical Resources Division in Hawaii are collaborating on a plan to establish an additional breeding population on Midway Atoll National Wildlife Refuge. The first translocation is planned for Sep 2004 or during 2005. Long-term goals are to increase the number of breeding populations, and to re-establish Laysan Ducks in the main Hawaiian Islands.

Ann P. Marshall

Philippine Duck *Anas luzonica*
PLATE 18

Anas luzonica Fraser, 1839, Proc. Zool. Soc. London, p. 113
Luzon

Etymology: *luzonica* from Luzon, origin of type specimen and northernmost large island in Philippines.

Other names: Philippine Mallard, Little Mallard, Luzon Duck. Spanish: Pato del monte, Papan.

Variation: no subspecies.

Description

ADULT: sexes alike. Dark mousy brown crown and hind neck joining paler mousy brown mantle; lowerback, rump and uppertail coverts distinctly darker. Dark brown eyestripe separated from crown by supercilium matching rusty cinnamon cheeks, throat and sides to neck. Cinnamon suffuses grey-brown upper breast and, much more sparingly, grey belly in some birds, and seems to increase with wear. Wing mousy brown above with axillaries and underwing coverts white; speculum greenish purple with broad black bars above and below; these secondaries tipped white in freshly moulted birds but most white lost from worn plumage. Bill lead blue; legs brownish black; eyes reddish hazel.

MOULT: no ♂ eclipse plumage. All mallard said to moult body feathers twice annually (Delacour 1954–64), but this needs confirmation in many tropical species. Tail feathers moulted Apr, and rectrices Apr–May; flightless ♀ taken in Samar on 29 Apr (Ripley and Rabor 1958, Rand and Rabor 1960) signifying post-breeding moult of flight feathers.

IMMATURE: said to be slightly duller (Delacour 1954–64), but carefully aged material unavailable and reported differences may be more related to moult.

DUCKLING: olive-brown with bright yellow face and neck. Clove-brown of top of head carried down onto neck to form partial collar. Differs from close congeners, not so much in basic pattern as in degree, having no eyestripe in front of eye and reduced white spots on back and sides of rump (Ripley 1951). Jones (1953) rightly remarked that ducklings 'comically resemble their parents in design'.

MEASUREMENTS AND WEIGHT: ♂ wing Negros, ($n = 7$), 235–262 (244.4), Samar, ($n = 6$), 247–255 (249.8); weight Samar ($n = 6$), 906.4, Bohol, 803.5. ♀ wing Negros, ($n = 7$), 225–235 (231.4), Samar, ($n = 7$), 231–238 (233.6); weight Samar Apr ($n = 8$), 778.6, Bohol, 764 in May (Rand 1951, Rand and Rabor 1960).

Field characters

Graceful brownish grey mallard-type with contrasting rufous head and neck marked by dark brown crown, nape and eyestripe; 480–580 mm long. Uniform dark grey bill distinguishes it from Spot-billed Duck, which occurs in small numbers in winter in north of range. Flight rapid like Northern Mallard, glossy green speculum clearly evident; black and white edges to speculum may not be seen in flight; underwing white.

Voice

Like Northern Mallard but ♂ more drawling and ♀ either little harsher (Delacour 1954–64) or squeakier

(Johnsgard 1978). Low *quack* alarm call (Rabor 1977) also uttered in flight (Gonzales and Rees 1988).

Range and status

Resident in most islands of Philippines (Dickinson *et al.* 1991) where suitable habitat exists, but not reported from Palawan, Basilan or Sulu Archipelago. In Luzon in spring, with dry season bringing restricted habitat, flocks of some 200 or more seen at Candaba Swamp, Pampanga, and in Mindoro on saltpans, probably rain-filled after salt harvest, where peak conditions seem to occur Nov–Dec, up to 2000 birds reported (Temme 1976). Straggler reportedly seen at Yonaguni-jima, Nansei Shoto (Ryu Kyus), Japan, in spring 1987 (Brazil 1991) and vagrants in Taiwan. Wetlands International (2002) suggested declining population of <10 000.

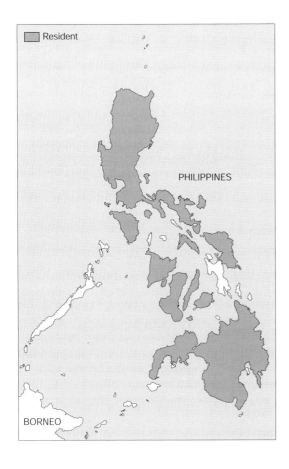

Habitat and general habits

Primary habitat is expanses of shallow freshwater, preferably with marsh vegetation to offer food and cover, but reported on tidal creeks (McGregor 1909), Water Buffalo wallows and small streams in original forest (Rand and Rabor 1960) and saltpans (Temme 1976). Found up to 300–400 m (Rand and Rabor 1960).

Feeds in shallow water. Diet mainly plants, molluscs and crustaceans, but fish and frogs may be taken (Rabor 1977); insects, rice and shoots of young plants also eaten (Gonzales 1983). More active in early morning and evening and during moonlit nights (Gonzales 1983). Usually in pairs or small groups but outside breeding season, especially as seasonal waterbodies dry, large flocks may occur. Shy and nervous, usually flies before approached closely.

Displays and breeding behaviour

Sideways Head-dipping by ♀, characteristic of Northern Mallard, accompanied by weak quacking of intensity and tone of ♀ Gadwall or Northern Pintail sometimes prompting ♂ to swim 'rapidly alongside her in a rather stiffly erect posture' (Ripley 1951). Characteristic and exaggerated Nod-swimming, almost inevitably following Head-up-tail-up display (Delacour 1954–64). ♂♂ also have Independent Nod-swim, Grunt-whistle and Down-up (Johnsgard 1965a).

General behaviour in wild described as identical to Northern Mallard (Temme 1976).

Breeding and life cycle

Enlarged gonads reported Feb in Negros and Mar in Mindoro (Ripley and Rabor 1958). Temme (1976) suggested breeding season Mar–Nov with peak July–Aug, but rainfall patterns in southwest Mindoro not typical of entire range. Nest, illustrated in Temme (1976), well hidden under thick cover of Water Bindweed *Colopogohium muconoides*. Eggs dull unglossed white with brownish tinge and elliptical; 50.7 × 38.5 (*n* = 10) (Temme 1976); in captivity, eggs reported as greenish (Ripley 1951, Delacour 1954–64), but it is not certain that eggs in question are result of cross breeding; weight in captivity 48.4 (40.5–55.0) (*n* = 100) only slighter smaller than Northern Mallard. Clutch size reported as 10, followed by 2nd clutch of 8 (Jones 1953), based on 1st successful captive breeding, confirmed from wild by Temme (1976), who found nest with 10 eggs on 13 July, and reported frequent clutches of 8–10 and occasional ones of 15 or 16. Incubation 25–26 days; day-olds in captivity weigh 30.8 (*n* = 54). Ducklings collected Mar–May, Sept and Dec (Gonzales 1983) and 3-week-old young found early Oct (Temme 1976). No data on breeding success, survival or longevity.

Conservation and threats

Restricted range means concerns regularly expressed about survival. Seems to have been widespread, but usually uncommon, in Philippines throughout 1st half of 20th century, and heavily shot since Second World War (Manuel 1953). Evidence of last 20 years suggests decline. Loss of habitat (e.g. draining of Candaba Swamp in 1990s) and hunting pressure major adverse influences (BirdLife International 2001). Loss of Mangroves also cited but causal linkage unproven. Treated as Vulnerable by BirdLife International (2000).

In captivity, hybrids with Pacific Black Duck reported (Hachisuka 1932), and with Northern Mallard and Spot-billed Duck (Johnsgard 1965a). Todd (1979) expressed concern that tendency to hybridize with related species may render genetically pure stocks rare.

Edward Dickinson

Pacific Black Duck (Grey Duck) *Anas superciliosa*
PLATE 18

Anas superciliosa Gmelin, 1789, Syst. Nat., **1**, p. 537 Dusky Sound, New Zealand.

Etymology: *superciliosa* from L. *superciliaris* meaning eyebrowed.

Other names: Pacific Gray Duck, Brown Duck, Wild Duck, Grey Duck (NZ), Australian or Australasian Black Duck. Australian Aboriginal: Gwoom-nan-na, Mara, Koona, with > 40 other Aboriginal names listed by Marchant and Higgins (1990). Bismarck Archipelago: Mbolom. Celebes: Kiti-balang. Dutch: Wenkbrauweend. Fiji: Ngaloa. French: Canard à sourcils blanc. German: Australische or Australasische Wildente, Augenbrauenente. Maori: He-turvera, Parera, Muamu. New Caledonia: Nia. Pelew Islands: Atababar, Tabarr. Society Islands: Mora. Samoa: Toloa, Doloa. Spanish: Anade cejudo. Tonga: Toloa.

Variation: no subspecies recognized here; however, weak evidence that 3 races exist: nominate *A. s. superciliosa* from New Zealand; *A. s. rogersi* Mathews, 1912 from Australia, New Guinea and Indonesia; and *A. s. pelewensis* Hartlaub and Finsch, 1872 for slightly smaller birds of Pelew and other islands in southwest Pacific. Studies, based on mitochondrial DNA, found no phylogenetic discontinuity between Australian and New Zealand populations (Rhymer *et al.* 1994, 2004), lending support to notion that they are not different races.

Oustalet's or Mariana Duck (also called Marianas Mallard) *A. (platyrhynchos) oustaleti* Salvadori, 1894, formerly resident on Guam, Saipan and Timian, was naturally occurring and unstable hybrid swarm between Northern Mallard and Pacific Black Duck (Yamashina 1948, Marchant and Higgins 1990, Livezey 1991, Threatened Waterfowl Specialist Group 2001), with some birds resembling Mallard and others Pacific Black Duck from the Pelew Islands. Has not been seen since 1980s (Reichel and Glass 1991, Reichel and Lemke 1994), and probably now extinct.

Description

ADULT: sexes alike. Has almost black crown (though browner and usually streaked in ♀), bold off-white superciliary stripe above broad black stripe from bill through eye to above ear. Pale yellow to buff cheeks with fine up-swept malar stripe from gape to below eye. Chin and throat off-white. Most of body grey-brown, boldly scaled by broad buff edging to tips of all feathers of lowerneck, mantle, scapulars and sides of body. Sides and back of neck more streaked, greyer and softly feathered. Lowerback almost black especially in ♂. Large tertials conspicuous on folded wing when duck sitting on water or walking. Tertials of ♂ always unpatterned and dark brown but those of ♀ almost always patterned, providing excellent character to distinguish sexes in field. Tertial patterns of ♀ usually some combination of longitudinal stripes or stripes broken into bars; these ♀ tertial patterns vary between individuals and from moult to moult. Tail grey-brown with outer edges of feathers paler; underparts paler, less scaly and more streaked. Wings uniformly dark grey-brown above with conspicuous green or purple speculum (depending on light angle with some areas looking velvet black) edged fore and aft with black-and-white. Underwing coverts and axillaries white. Bill grey or grey-green with black nail; legs and feet grey-green to dusky orange; eyes dark brown.

MOULT: no eclipse plumage in ♂. Body moult generally continuous in adults but intensity varies; most in fresh plumage and not moulting at start of breeding (July–Aug in southeast Australia). By Sept–Oct in this region, body plumage showing wear and some replacement occurs in most feather tracts. Most active body moult Dec–Mar and, during this time, full wing moult takes place. Flightless period of *c* 3–4 weeks, later in ♀ (usually follows fledging of last brood) than in ♂. By Apr, most adults finish body and wing moult and in fresh plumage; some worn feathers replaced by brief pre-breeding moult in midwinter refreshing plumage. Body, tail and tertial tracts moult independently of wing surfaces and remiges. Tertials replaced at least 3 times annually. Unpatterned dark tertials almost always present on adult ♂ but ♀ sometimes produce unpatterned tertial feathers in post-breeding period; if so, these retained briefly until pre-breeding, when patterned tertial and boldly scalloped plumage typically acquired by all ♀♀.

IMMATURE: has streaked underparts, particularly on breast. Following moult at *c* 3 months, plumage indistinguishable from adult.

DUCKLING: mostly yellowish or dark olive-brown with conspicuous head pattern (like adult) and white underparts. Large white spot either side of rump and white trailing edge to wing stubs extends inwards to form spot either side of lower back. Similar to ducklings of Northern Mallard or Mallard-derived

domestic forms, hybrids and other related mallard types.

MEASUREMENTS AND WEIGHT: in New Zealand and Australia, ♂ wing ($n = 259$), 230–290 (264); tail ($n = 39$), 81–99 (88); bill ($n = 267$), 42–58 (52); tarsus ($n = 139$), 41–52 (45); weight ($n = 401$), 765–1400 (1104). ♀ wing ($n = 303$), 200–285 (251); tail ($n = 46$), 73–95 (86); bill ($n = 322$), 42–59 (50); tarsus ($n = 170$), 39–51 (43); weight ($n = 519$), 600–1400 (1007) (Marchant and Higgins 1990).

Field characters

Large, dark dabbling duck, 540–610 mm long, of Australasian and southwest Pacific region with conspicuously striped head pattern and white underwings seen in flight. Resembles in general behaviour and ecology Northern Mallard but without extreme sexual dimorphism. Within range, only likely to be confused with smaller and slimmer Australasian Shoveler (much larger bill, blue leading edges to upperwings); uniformly dappled dark grey Freckled Duck (distinctive retroussé bill, no wing speculum and pale but not white underwings; long neck and hump-backed flight appearance) and ♀ or ♂ Australian Wood Duck in eclipse (small bill, brown head with less distinct head pattern lacking black eye-stripe, spotted breast and underside, pale grey tertials, white speculum and pale grey upper forewings). Beyond normal range, most like Spot-billed Duck and Philippine Duck, but shows similarities to several other mallard-like ducks.

Voice

Call repertoire similar to that of Northern Mallard. ♂ has loud *raehb* call varying from drawn-out note used when alarmed to more clipped version used for contact and softer hissy version used during close contact. Grunt-whistle call (high-pitched whistle followed by deep resonant grunt) given during display by ♂. Similar high-pitched whistles given with Down-up, Head-up-tail-up and post-copulatory Bridle displays of ♂. ♀ has loud and well-known *quack* uttered in mild alarm and as contact call. Variations include Persistent Quacking used during nest-searching behaviour and sometimes before take-off when call given alternating with pre-flight visual signal, Decrescendo call starting explosively and continuing as series of loud rapidly repeated *quacks* of decreasing amplitude with much variation between individuals, Inciting call harsh and more rapidly delivered quacking used when giving distinctive Inciting signal, and Repulsion even harsher and often used in rhythmic triplets with emphasis on first note *gag-gag-gag, gag-gag-gag* and associated with distinctive Repulsion signal. Other softer quack-like calls given in close conversation, especially to ducklings; these soft calls uttered in response to sounds from ducklings in egg before hatching. Soft calls also given when close to partner. Calls of ducklings similar to those of Northern Mallard. Full range of calls developed within 6 months of hatching. For details and sonograms see Marchant and Higgins (1990).

Range and status

Widely distributed throughout Australia, New Guinea and islands of Indonesian archipelago as far as southern Sumatra, Celebes (Sulawesi) and Halmahera; also found in New Caledonia, New Zealand and most southwest Pacific islands east to Rupa Island and north to Solomon Islands, New Hebrides, Fiji, Tonga and Samoa (Phillips 1922–26, Holyoak 1980, Marchant and Higgins 1990). Occurs on many offshore and oceanic islands including sub-antarctic islands to south. In New Zealand, now widely hybridized with introduced Northern Mallard and these hybrids disperse to islands nearby, such as Lord Howe, Norfolk and Macquarie (Marchant and Higgins 1990). Population in Australia estimated to be at least 500 000 but may be more than million at times (based on data in Marchant and Higgins 1990, Kingsford *et al.* 1999). Steady decline in numbers found in eastern Australia from mid 1980s to 1999 shown to be significant long-term trend (Kingsford *et al.* 1999, 2000).

Habitat and general habits

Present on many different wetlands, having broad habitat tolerance. In Australia, most commonly seen duck in many areas, though not always most abundant. Often found on deep vegetated swamps, shallow seasonal swamps and rivers and creeks running through timbered or open country. Generally less common on saline habitats, though sometimes, specially in dry seasons, will use estuaries, coastal

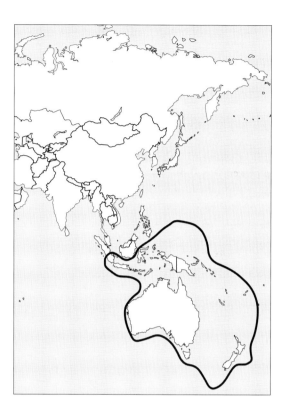

lagoons, saltmarshes, tidal parts of rivers and sheltered inshore waters. In New Zealand, habitat requirements similar and widely distributed, occurring on variety of wetlands including those in mountain or densely forested regions. Less common in agricultural and settled areas of New Zealand where introduced Northern Mallard and hybrids with Mallard dominate. Often resorts to more productive and accessible marine habitats on sub-antarctic islands (Marchant and Higgins 1990).

Feeds mostly on plant material, particularly seeds of aquatics and waterside vegetation but animal matter probably underestimated. Dabbles at surface (suzzling), along edge of water or on exposed muds and, in deeper water, will up-end to reach submerged plants or filter bottom muds; will also graze ashore. Generally loafs on water or ashore and typically seen sitting on fallen timber, stumps, low branches or posts. Often found in loose groups save for close company of established pairs and also family groups often stay together for some time after ducklings fledged. Feeds mostly during early part of night and again at dawn but loafing often occurs for time before dawn and increasingly during morning, and is most common behaviour during early afternoon (Marchant and Higgins 1990).

Considered sedentary on more permanent waters but known to be capable of dispersive movements. Occurs on ephemeral wetlands inland following rain and will disperse widely again as wetlands dry (details in Marchant and Higgins 1990). Has reached New Zealand from Australia. Capable of extensive movements within Australia, especially as consequence of severe drought when known to make long ocean crossings to many scattered islands within southwest Pacific region.

Displays and breeding behaviour

Social displays similar to those of most mallard-like ducks; detailed information in Marchant and Higgins (1990). Signals mostly directed towards establishing and maintaining pairbond and asserting dominance. Pre-flight signal typical, with head raised rapidly in repeated jerky movements, usually irregular. When rising from water, initial wing-beat is onto surface; lift-off can be explosive and near vertical when suddenly alarmed.

Adults defend small surrounding space, and breeding ♀ extends area to include space occupied by brood, especially when attending recently hatched ducklings. Adult ♂ defensive towards other ♂♂ near nest site of partner. Body posture of hostile or dominant ♂ distinctive, with head held high and wings folded high at 'elbow' on back, presenting maximum lateral profile and revealing conspicuous immaculate tertial region. Forward Threats and Chases used in hostile encounters by and between both sexes. ♂ has noisy *raehb-raehb* display when ♂♂ challenge one another or when ♂ attempts to drive another away; these encounters become especially noisy when several ♂♂ involved, resulting in *raehb-raehb* Palavers. Hostile Wing-flaps, given on water in upright posture and non-vocal, used by aggressive ♂♂ to assert dominance. Typically ♂ gives 3 sharp, deliberate flaps with audible swishing noise of pinions followed by exaggerated lateral tail wags on settling. Other attention-seeking postures by ♂ include Jump-flights and Heavy Landings. Down-up display accompanied by whistle used in hostile disputes between ♂♂. Adult ♀ gives Inciting display, accom-

panied by harsh repetitive sound, to urge preferred ♂ to direct attention towards intruder (usually another ♂) and goad him into driving off perceived threat. Repulsion display of ♀ is posture with feathers raised and fluffed out, head tilted upwards and withdrawn between shoulders. This 'hackles raised' bristly posture is accompanied by loud repetitive call with bill wide open, and given from early in laying period, but especially from incubating ♀ briefly off nest and by ♀ guarding brood of young ducklings.

Fighting takes form of skirmish in which birds lock together while attempting to grasp one another at wing or neck. Usually results in chase, with one taking flight and being, temporarily, driven off. Hostile encounters between rival ♂♂ lead to short Pursuit-flights. Hostile encounters between ♂ near his partner's nest site and intruding pair leads to 3-bird flight in which defending ♂ directs attention towards ♀ of intruding pair in order to drive them away. Other ♂♂ may join these flights, but chasing ♂ soon breaks off pursuit and returns to resume guard. When pressed, will dive to escape. Reacts by mobbing ground predators in similar way to many other wildfowl. Only ♀ has Injury-feigning display to distract attention from brood.

Pair formation involves repertoire of stereotyped postures performed during complex encounters in communal display. These occur in bouts of intense activity interspersed by periods of strategic manoeuvring. Individuals join and leave displaying groups. Many events lead to courtship display, not least of which are seasonal climate and availability of unpaired birds. Sure stimulant to display is presence of ♀, particularly if she solicits courtship. Preliminary postures given by ♂ in courtship include Head-flick, Head-shake and Introductory Shake. These postures are followed, as intensity of display increases, by sequence Grunt-Whistle, then Head-up-tail-up, Nod-swim, Turn-back-of-head and finally Leading-away if attention of ♀ obtained. Sequence may break but never given in different order, except that Grunt-whistles can be independent and repeated, as can Nod-swim following assertive *raehb* calling when head of ♂ held high and beak opened widely with each note. Independent Bridle not often given. Down-up display contests between ♂♂ occur at any time within these bouts of courtship. ♀ elicits courtship bouts by performing Nod-swims or Inciting.

Pairbond may be reinforced by courtship encounters, and pairbond recognition signalled by subtle postures such as Preen-behind-wing and Preen-dorsally, both displays given most often by ♂. Soft conversation calls used to maintain contact between pair or members of family. ♀ can draw attention to herself by Persistent Quacking and loud Decrescendo call. ♂ has visual signals and much less penetrating *raehb* call to attract attention or to indicate distant recognition of partner. Greeting signalled by both sexes by using Forward-stretch and soft calling.

Copulation only occurs on water following mutual Head-pumping; after mounting, ♂ performs Bridle then Nod-swims in semi-circle about ♀ before both bathe, Wing-flap, and usually Preen-behind-wing. Sustained monogamous pairbond, probably lifelong. Solitary nesters.

Breeding and life cycle

Seasonal breeding for up to 5 months duration and in southeastern Australia, nesting July–Dec, but sometimes into Feb. Season similar in New Zealand, but few data from elsewhere within range. ♀ chooses nest during searching behaviour, often accompanied by ♂ who rarely inspects site closely. Site usually in tree hollow, but sometimes old nests of other waterbirds and, less commonly, on ground concealed in vegetation; will use nest-boxes. Nest fashioned from material immediately surrounding; copious grey down plucked and added from time of laying penultimate egg and addition of down may occur into incubation. Eggs elliptical, smooth and fine textured, glossy and greasy, more or less lustrous and pale cream (Campbell 1901, North 1901–14); 58×41 $(51–63 \times 37–45)$ ($n = 188$ from 21 clutches) (Frith 1982); clutch 9 (7–12) eggs ($n = 60$), any >12 likely laid by more than one ♀, but no evidence of dump nesting as ♀ strategy (Marchant and Higgins 1990). Small clutches suggest incomplete laying, and most not incubated. ♀ lays at daily intervals, usually in early morning. Incubation, by ♀, 29 (26–32) days (from 37 closely observed nests) (Marchant and Higgins 1990). ♂ remains near, at

least early in incubation and often throughout. ♀ usually takes 2 recesses, one at dawn and other in late afternoon, and rarely leaves at other times; daily time off clutch usually <2 h. Guarding ♂ loafs between recesses and closely accompanies ♀ when she leaves. ♀ tends to sit uninterrupted during last 2 days before hatch. Re-laying can occur 2 weeks after premature loss of brood, and within 8 weeks following successfully reared brood. Two broods often reared in season and one record of ♀ laying 3rd clutch after rearing 2 broods in season (Marchant and Higgins 1990). Ducklings leave nest site permanently as soon as dry, usually early in morning. Descent from elevated site is by falling ('parachuting') and, contrary to oft quoted myth, ♀ never carries ducklings to ground. No paternal care, but loose association with ♀ and brood often evident. ♂ not aggressive to any brood, but tolerated close only by ♀ partner, and other ♂♂ vigorously repelled. Ducklings respond only to visual and vocal signals by ♀ parent, and ♀ can discriminate own brood efficiently, although confusion occurs when recently hatched or very young ducklings become disorientated. Such ducklings attempt to join any brood of roughly same age and, in these circumstances, brood ♀ may recognize and mercilessly attack and even kill 'orphans'. ♀ defensive of brood and remains close until they fledge. Frightened ducklings seek hiding place and freeze even when well grown. Capable of flight at 58 (52–66) days ($n = 13$). Pair will re-unite following brood dispersal or sometimes before fledging if succeeding clutch to be laid. Brood usually independent soon after fledging but sometimes remain close to parents, especially if parents not engaged in further breeding activity. Few data on breeding success; in one study *c* 40% of clutches (21 from 4 seasons) successfully incubated, and 5 ducklings (1–9) per brood on average reached flying stage. Sixty percent of total brood losses occurred within 1st 10 days (Marchant and Higgins 1990). Pairbond often formed at *c* 6 months, and capable of breeding in 1st year. No recent analysis of data on adult survival but several banded birds known to be alive >10 years after marking. Most young have life expectancy of *c* 15 months (Frith 1982).

Conservation and threats

Abundant and widely distributed, with no immediate threats to survival. Australian population often exceeds million, and estimates of 80 000–150 000 made for numbers in New Zealand (Rose and Scott 1997). However, in New Zealand, occurrence of widespread hybridization with introduced Northern Mallard and other feral Mallard derivatives of concern; few Pacific Black Duck populations in New Zealand remain unaffected, and listed (as New Zealand Grey Duck *A. s. superciliosa*) by Threatened Waterfowl Specialist Group (2001) as Endangered. Similar occurrence of hybridization in Australia mostly confined to urban area where domestic ducks common; however, Australian Black Duck (as *A. s. rogersi*) and Lesser Grey Duck *A. s. pelewensis* both considered Near-threatened by Threatened Waterfowl Specialist Group (2001). Other populations within south-west Pacific little studied, but many seem to be in small numbers; probable that such island groups augmented by dispersal of birds from core population in Australia. Dispersal of hybrids from New Zealand, particularly to neighbouring islands, is increasing worry.

Peter Fullagar

Spot-billed Duck *Anas poecilorhyncha*
PLATE 18

Anas poecilorhyncha J. R. Forster, 1781, Indian Zoology, p. 23, pl. 13, fig. 1
Ceylon

Etymology: *poecilorhyncha* Gr. for bill *rhunkhos* that is spotted *poikilos*.

Other names: *poecilorhyncha* and *haringtoni* known as Spotbill, Spot-billed Grey Duck, Grey Duck, *zonorhyncha* as Eastern Spot-billed or Yellow-billed Duck, Zone-billed Duck, Dusky Mallard, Eastern Grey Duck, Yellow-nib. Burmese: Vume-be, Rtaubay; French: Canard à bec orange; German: Fleckschnabel Ente, Buntschnabel Ente or for *zonorhyncha* Gelbschnabel Ente; Hindi: Garam-pai, Bata, Gugral; Japanese: Karu-gamo; Nepal: Naddun; Manipur: Kara; Sind: Hunjar.

Variation: 3 subspecies recognized, Indian Spotbill *A. p. poecilorhyncha*, Burmese Spotbill *A. p. haringtoni* Oates, 1907 and Chinese Spotbill *A. p. zonorhyncha* Swinhoe, 1866.

Description

ADULT: sexes alike. Plumage, in general, resembles that of Pacific Black Duck, except that body markings much more prominent with underparts of nominate race and *haringtoni* having broad white edges to all feathers creating bold scaly effect. Body plumage of *zonorhyncha* closer in appearance to that of Pacific Black Duck. Head pattern similar to Pacific Black Duck but more streaked, has much less boldly defined eyestripe, and lacks clear lower stripe across cheek diagnostic of Pacific Black Duck. Faint cheek-bar present in *zonorhyncha* but is smudgy and small compared with sharply defined cheekstripe of Pacific Black Duck. Black crowns from forehead to back of head (more streaked in ♀), off-white superciliary stripe above thick black stripe from bill through eye, decreasing rapidly in width behind eye. Cheeks pale cream almost white, with numerous fine dark spots and streaks. In *zonorhyncha*, there is broad but smudgy malar stripe from gape towards eye. Chin and throat off-white. Most of body dark grey, boldly scaled by broad cream to off-white edging to all feathers of lower neck, breast, mantle, scapulars, and sides of body. Sides and back of neck pale grey, finely streaked and softly feathered. Lower back almost black, especially in ♂ where velvety black. Large tertials conspicuous on folded wing when duck sitting on water or walking. Tertials have prominent white outer vanes except in *zonorhyncha* in which only outer edge of vane broadly margined white. White on tertials of ♀ seems less extensive and smudged with smoky markings but character requires confirmation. Tail black-brown with outer edges of feathers paler. Underparts paler, less scaly and more streaked. Vent and undertail brown to black. Wings uniformly dark grey-brown above with conspicuous satiny green or purple speculum (depending on light angle with some areas of speculum also looking velvety black) broadly edged fore and aft with black-and-white. Underwing coverts and axillaries white. Bill of both sexes black with diagnostic broad yellow tip and black nail, yellow to orange area at base of bill of ♂ becomes swollen and red in breeding condition but much less obvious in ♀, and not found in *zonorhyncha*; legs and feet dull orange; eyes brown.

MOULT: no eclipse plumage in ♂. No published information on timing of wing or body moults.

IMMATURE: duller than adult, with breast and flank markings smaller and appearing as neat rows of small spots. Red bill spot absent.

DUCKLING: almost identical in colour and pattern to downy ducklings of Pacific Black Duck.

MEASUREMENTS AND WEIGHT: few published data and most sources do not give sample size and provenance; following mostly from Phillips (1922–26) and Johnsgard (1978). ♂ *poecilorhyncha* wing, 248–269; bill 52–55; tarsus, 46–48; ♂ *haringtoni* wing, 245–268 (Madge and Burn 1988); ♂ *zonorhyncha* wing, 263–293; bill, 50–55; tarsus, 43–49. ♀ *haringtoni* wing, 237–255 (Madge and Burn 1988); ♀ *zonorhyncha* wing, 255–262; bill, 45–49; tarsus, 42–44. Weight ♂ *poecilorhyncha*, 1230–1500; ♀ 790–1360. ♂ *zonorhyncha* (*n* = 13), 1156 (1000–340); ♀ (*n* = 2), 750 and 980 (Shaw 1936).

Field characters

Large, 580–630 mm long, heavily built duck, with strongly patterned plumage and bright yellow tip to bill. Only similar duck in range is Northern Mallard, from which differs in being strikingly variegated black-and-white, with spotted bill and, especially in ♂, large white areas on tertials. Pale head, neck and foreparts contrasting with black rear distinctive in flight.

Voice

No detailed descriptions, but vocalizations similar to Northern Mallard; ♀ *quack* said to be more sonorous than Mallard (Baker 1921, Johnsgard 1965a, Ali and Ripley 1987). Call repertoire probably not different from that described for Pacific Black Duck, further studies needed. No published sonograms. Duckling calls resemble those of Mallard.

Range and status

poecilorhyncha occurs on Indian sub-continent south to Sri Lanka and east to Bangladesh, Assam and Manipur. *haringtoni* found in Myanmar (Burma) and nearby southern China to Vietnam, also likely to be race found through Laos, most of Cambodia and extreme south Vietnam. Originally described as occurring in basin of Irrawaddy River in Myanmar, but boundaries with nominate form to west, and partially migratory race *zonorhyncha* to east and north, unclear and extent of overlaps need investigation. *zonorhyncha* widespread through most of China north to Manchuria, Mongolia and southern parts of eastern Siberia to Korea and Japan. Northern population in China, Mongolia and eastern Russia migratory, moving south in winter and said to reach as far as Cambodia and Thailand. Vagrant to Alaskan islands, and to north Philippines.

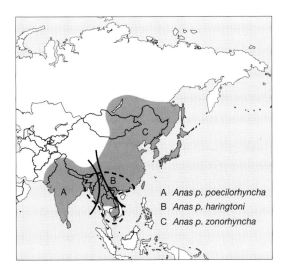

A *Anas p. poecilorhyncha*
B *Anas p. haringtoni*
C *Anas p. zonorhyncha*

Miyabayashi and Mundkur (1999) gave estimates of 50 000–100 000 for *poecilorhycha* in southern Asia, 800 000–1 000 000 for *zonorhyncha* in eastern Asia, and 100 000–1 000 000 for *haringtoni* in southeastern Asia, including 23 500 on Poyang Lake in China in winter of 1988–89.

Habitat and general habits

Said to favour shallow freshwater lakes and marshes with extensive emergent vegetation, less frequent on rivers (Phillips 1922–26, Madge and Burn 1988), and presumably there are ecological differences with Northern Mallard as they do not mingle to any extent in zone of sympatry (Johnsgard 1965a). Baker (1921) also regarded *poecilorhyncha* as selecting only freshwater and rarely tidal or brackish water, although *zonorhyncha* certainly occurs in coastal habitats (Brazil 1991). Habits seem like those of Northern Mallard or Pacific Black Duck, but almost nothing recorded on feeding or diets. Some anecdotal data given in Baker (1921) suggested only that diet typical of dabbling ducks. Regarded as less social than others, often found in pairs or small flocks, rarely as many as 100.

Displays and breeding behaviour

Display said to resemble Northern Mallard (Johnsgard 1965a); needs examination and comparison with Pacific Black Duck. Pairbond probably long-term as in Pacific Black Duck, as ♂ remains close to ♀ on nest and with brood (see Baker 1921, 1935, Phillips 1922–26). Injury feigning by ♀ as in Mallard (Baker 1921).

Breeding and life cycle

Probably nests most often on ground but may use elevated sites (Phillips 1922–26, Baker 1935). Down never present as thick mass in nest of *poecilorhyncha* but nest well lined with down in *haringtoni* and *zonorhyncha*; when present, down indistinguishable from that of Northern Mallard (Baker 1921, 1935, Ali and Ripley 1987). Eggs short elliptical, devoid of gloss or only slightly glossy, white or greyish white; also described as like those of Mallard but more grey-buff and less grey-green (Baker 1935). Sample 100 eggs of *poecilorhyncha* 56.0 × 42.3 (50–60 × 37–44); 80 of *zonorhyncha* 55.5 × 41.6 (51.0–57.3 × 39.7–43.6), while 27 of *haringtoni* slightly smaller at 53 × 40 (49–61 × 39–44) (Baker 1935, Schönwetter 1960–66, Ali and Ripley 1987); calculated weights, 57 for *poecilorhyncha*, 55 for *zonorhyncha* and 50 for *haringtoni* (Schönwetter 1960–66). Breeding season of *poecilorhyncha* mostly July–Sept (Baker 1935) but laying occurs at other times and circumstantial evidence (Baker 1921, 1935) suggests that successive clutches laid as in Pacific Black Duck. Breeding season of *haringtoni* probably similar, but *zonorhyncha* nests Apr–July (Ali and Ripley 1987, Brazil 1991). Clutch of *poecilorhyncha* 6.4 (3–10) ($n = 14$) (Hume and Marshall 1879–81), with maximum of 14 (Phillips 1922–26). No accurate records of incubation but said to be 24 days (Baker 1935) or *c* 28 days (Phillips 1922–26, Todd 1996). Duckling weights of *poecilorhyncha* in captivity 32.3 ($n = 15$) (Smart 1965b) or 28.4 ($n = 27$). No data on growth and development of young or period of dependence, but said to fledge in 49–56 days (Todd 1996). No information on breeding success, survival nor longevity.

Conservation and threats

Widespread and numerous; not globally threatened, and likely to have world population in excess of million. In Japan, only common duck breeding in rice field areas in summer (Brazil 1991, del Hoyo *et al.* 1992). Distribution, movements and related taxonomic questions require further study.

Peter Fullagar

Yellow-billed Duck *Anas undulata*
PLATE 17

Anas undulata Dubois, 1839, Ornith. Gallerie, **1**, p. 119, pl. 77
Cape of Good Hope

Etymology: *undulatus* L. for wavy, presumably referring to fine patterning of feathers. *rueppelli* after Wilhelm Ruppell (1794–1884), German zoologist and collector.

Other names: Yellowbill Duck. Afrikaans: Geelbekeend.

Variation: 2 subspecies recognized, nominate African Yellowbill *A. u. undulata*, from Uganda to Cape, and Abyssinian Yellowbill *A. u. rueppelli* Blyth, 1855 from northern Kenya to Ethiopia.

Description

ADULT: sexes alike, although ♂ slightly larger than ♀, with more gentle slope to forehead (Day 1977). Pale edges to grey feathers give scaled appearance; head and upperneck darker than body. In flight, whitish underwings and blue-green speculum seen. ♂ may have dark, slightly elongated tips to central tail feathers. Bill bright yellow with black nail and extended black triangle from base of upper mandible, stretching beyond nostrils; legs and feet yellowish to grey; eyes reddish brown. *rueppelli* said to be darker brown than nominate race, with narrower pale margins to feathers, deeper yellow bill and bluer speculum.

MOULT: not fully understood; no eclipse plumage in ♂. Post-nuptial moult includes full body moult and flightless period that lasts about 4 weeks. Freshly moulted feathers have yellowy buff margins, becoming greyer after few weeks.

IMMATURE: duller than adult, head may be slate grey. Pale feather margins are narrower.

DUCKLING: mallard-like with dark upperparts and yellowy underparts. Face quite yellow and yellow shows on sides of bill at few days of age.

MEASUREMENTS AND WEIGHT: *undulata* in Transvaal, ♂ ($n = 100$) wing, 245–289 (268); tail, 90–109 (100); bill, 46–56 (52); tarsus, 39–51 (45); weight ($n = 7839$), 533–1310 (965). ♀ ($n = 100$) wing, 229–273 (252); tail, 86–108 (97); bill, 44–54 (49); tarsus, 39–48 (43); weight ($n = 6080$), 600–1123 (823) (Day 1977, Dean and Skead 1979).

Field characters

Large, elegant, uniformly grey dabbling duck of open water, 510–630 mm long. Long, slender neck, slightly bulbous head and bright yellow bill distinguish this African mallard; however, subspecies cannot be separated with confidence in field.

Voice

Typical mallard calls. *Raeb* call of ♂ more whistle than that of other mallards. Sonogram in Maclean (1993).

Range and status

Widespread in southern and eastern Africa from Lake Tana and Blue Nile, Ethiopia, and Sudan to Cape. Parts of population nomadic, moving with availability of seasonal wetlands. Recorded to 4000 m in Ethiopia. Furthest recoveries 1007 and 2224 km (SAFRING) from ringing site, although most movements <1000 km (Oatley and Prŷs-Jones 1986).

Outside main range, recorded in Nigeria, and Cameroon (6 records). Records from suitable habitat on Adamawa Plateau, Cameroon, and nearby wetlands may suggest resident there (Robertson 1992, Young and Robertson 2001). Cameroon birds not identified confidently to race (2 considered to be *rueppelli*). May be abundant in some areas, although numbers fluctuate; commonest duck on many wetlands. Population difficult to estimate because of semi-nomadic habit. Status of *rueppelli* unclear; commonly recorded in Ethiopia 1966–85 (Wilson 1993), and over 300 birds present at Lake Bilate, Ethiopia in Nov 1994 (Scott and Rose 1996). In 2002, Wetlands International estimated 20 000–60 000 in eastern Africa, >100 000 in southern Africa and 20 000–50 000 *rueppelli* in northern east Africa.

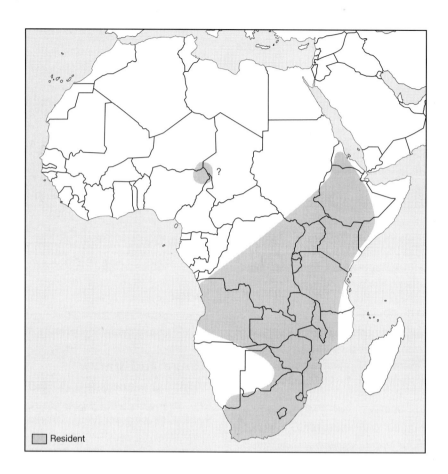

Resident

Habitat and general habits

Uses variety of wetlands, including marshes, lakes, dams and estuaries with marginal vegetation. Less frequently found in rivers or salt-pans. Quickly utilizes flooded grasslands amid arid areas, large flocks developing. Flocks up to 5000 may gather while moulting or during drought (Maclean 1997c).

Feeds principally by dabbling in shallows but will up-end and come ashore to forage. May feed nocturnally. Diet principally vegetable matter, mostly seeds of aquatic plants, and feeds on grain after harvest.

Displays and behaviour

Poorly studied. Performs typical mallard displays (Rowan 1963, Brown *et al.* 1982). In captive birds, Down-up most commonly recorded group courtship. Grunt-whistle, Head-up-tail-up and Down-up significantly longer than in Northern Mallard, allowing ♂ to exhibit thin neck and speculum. Independent Nod-swimming observed in both sexes and Nod-swimming recorded in 47% (*n* = 14) of Down-ups analyzed in 2 captive flocks, as well as component of Head-up-tail-up (Young 1999). Post-copulatory display consists of Bridle with call, Steam and Turn-back-of-head. Use of Nod-swim not fully recorded (Johnson *et al.* 2000).

Not territorial when nesting. Pairs remain together during breeding season and may stay paired for more than one season. Forced extra-pair copulation recorded but may be uncommon.

Breeding and life cycle

Breeds throughout year. Nomadic over large parts of range and breeding controlled by rainfall. Exploits temporary wetlands and maximum invertebrate availability in order to rear young (Rowan 1963). May be more sedentary in north of range, breeding July–Dec in Ethiopia (Brown *et al.* 1982). Disperses following breeding, with flocks of > 1000 on suitable waters.

Nests made in dense vegetation on ground, usually close to water (Rowan 1963). Eggs of *undulata* ovate, smooth, creamy yellow or buff; 55 × 41.5 (51–60 × 37–46) (*n* = 268) (Maclean 1993); weight in captivity 44–62 (54) (*n* = 80); clutch 7.8 (4–12) (*n* = 35) (Rowan 1963). Incubation, by ♀ alone, 26–29 days (Brown *et al.* 1982). Hatch weight in captivity 32.4 (26–40) (*n* = 37) or 32.7 (*n* = 47). Fledge in 68 days (Maclean 1993). Probably breed at one year. No data on growth, breeding success, survival nor on longevity.

Conservation and threats

Maintenance of suitable habitat, especially temporary wetlands, and control of hunting and pollution within range, will keep current population levels. Not considered threatened, and has adapted well to agricultural and urban situations. Hybridization with introduced Northern Mallard reported in South Africa and, although restricted to urban areas, may pose future threat. Eradication of Mallard will prevent problems that have occurred elsewhere.

Glyn Young

Meller's Duck *Anas melleri*
PLATE 17

Anas melleri P.L. Sclater, 1865, Proc. Zool. Soc. London (1864), p. 487, pl. 34
Madagascar (Analamazotra)

Etymology: named for Charles James Meller (1836–69), botanist (visited Africa with David Livingstone), who collected 2 specimens in 1862, which he identified as Red-billed Pintail.

Other names: none in English. French: Canard de Meller; Malagasy: Angaka.

Variation: no subspecies.

Description

ADULT: sexes alike. ♂ slightly larger than ♀ and large skull gives appearance that ♂ has longer bill than ♀. Body brown; speculum green, bordered white. Two central tail feathers of ♂ tipped black and usually slightly longer than buff-tipped feathers of ♀ (Young 1991). ♂ has longer feathers on flanks and, discernible in hand, on crown. Bill blue-grey with black nail; legs and feet orange-brown; eyes dark brown.

MOULT: not fully understood; no eclipse ♂ plumage. Post-nuptial moult includes full body moult and flightless period of *c* one month. Prenuptial moult takes place over several months.

IMMATURE: similar to adult, feather margins may appear brighter, giving 'fresher' appearance.

DUCKLING: like Northern Mallard; however, facial markings differ, dark patch on ear coverts more elongated. As duckling grows, large bill becomes increasingly distinctive.

MEASUREMENTS AND WEIGHT: captive, plus 11 wild birds, ♂ wing (*n* = 62), 245–275 (263); bill (*n* = 60), 56–66 (61); skull (*n* = 61), 114–127 (121.5); tarsus (*n* = 20), 41–50 (43); weight (*n* = 19), 883–1240 (1010). ♀ wing (*n* = 61), 235–265 (250); bill (*n* = 65), 54–61 (57); skull (*n* = 66), 106–120 (113); tarsus (*n* = 15), 38–49 (43); weight (*n* = 21), 832–1140 (911) (Young 1991). ♂ tail 100–102 (Delacour 1954–64).

Field characters

Large, 650 mm long, uniform brown, monochromatic dabbling duck of open water, superficially resembling ♀ Northern Mallard but with longer, greyer bill. Only mallard in Madagascar. Pale underwing contrasts with dark body in flight. Dark appearance, long neck and bill unmistakable; however, confusion has occurred with recently fledged Comb Duck. Latter species brown before 1st moult but shows some white. In recent years, Northern Mallard established in Mauritius.

Voice

Typical mallard calls. ♀'s *quack* higher than Northern Mallard, and *raeb* call of ♂ has 3 notes (Lorenz 1951–53). No sonogram published.

Range and status

Endemic to Madagascar, introduced to Réunion (unsuccessfully) and Mauritius (Mascarene Islands) around 1850 (Meinhertzhagen 1912). Since deforestation of much of Madagascar's Central Plateau, breeds predominantly along eastern edge, possibly to coast, e.g. observed in Pangalanes canal. Found to 2000 m and probably above, and on isolated massifs at Andringitra and Kalambatritra (Langrand 1990, Projet ZICOMA 1999). Largest numbers recorded at Lake Alaotra where nests in small numbers, and flocks of nonbreeders collect. Occasional records from 'unsuitable' areas of Central Plateau and west coast lakes probably evidence of post-breeding dispersal. Virtually extinct in Mauritius, and may only survive through release of captive birds (Safford 1995). Rose and Scott (1997) suggested declining population of 2000–5000.

Habitat and general habits

Freshwater, lakes, rivers and marshland often in forested areas. Preferred habitat, now highly degraded, probably slow-moving streams and rivers of eastern drainage. Many thousands of streams and small rivers have eroded narrow floodplains through forested uplands. These streams fringed by narrow permanent marsh, ducks spacing in pairs along watercourses. May occur in fast-flowing rivers. Birds often collect on open water or in marshes, occasionally in large flocks when feeding, e.g. 160 with Glossy Ibis *Plegadis falcinellus* at Lake Alaotra, or when roosting during day, e.g. 260 together at Alaotra (Young and Smith 1989). Nocturnal activity recorded regularly. Feeds predominately by dabbling in mud or by up-ending; however may come ashore to forage. Diet poorly known, aquatic vegetation including water-lilies and invertebrates, particularly molluscs, eaten. Captive birds eat variety of food, including fish, emerging aquatic chironomid flies, filamentous algae and grass.

Displays and behaviour

Does not possess Down-up display in courtship repertoire; Grunt-whistle most used display in group courtship. Grunt-whistle and Head-up-tail-up take significantly longer than those of Northern Mallard, allowing monochromatic Meller's to show long neck and speculum to good effect (Young 1999). Independent Nod-swimming exhibited by both sexes (Young 1999). Post-copulatory display consists of Bridle with call, Steam, Nod-swim and Turn-back-of-head (Johnson *et al.* 2000).

Defends well-demarcated territory aggressively, breeding along narrow streams and rivers and channels within marshes. Pairs probably only meet at territory's end or when overflying adjacent pair. Captive flock held territories after onset of egg-laying. Paired ♂ remains within territory when ♀ incubating; does not associate with other ♂♂ and repels aggressively all conspecific intruders, concentrating attack on ♀ if pair enters territory. Forced extra-pair copulation rare, as paired ♀ always defended and probably is not reproductive strategy (Young 1995a). Fighting ♂ attempts to grab, with bill, back of opponent's neck and hit with wings. Well-matched ♂♂ may chase one another in circles.

Pairs remain together throughout incubation; however, ♂ not present with broods observed in Madagascar. Pairs may come together for consecutive breeding seasons.

Breeding and life cycle

Long nesting season, with records in Madagascar July–Apr, timing probably determined by rainfall. Nests and young observed Madagascar in Jan 2000 at onset of late eastern wet season. Other details from captivity; nests on or near ground; eggs ovate, smooth,

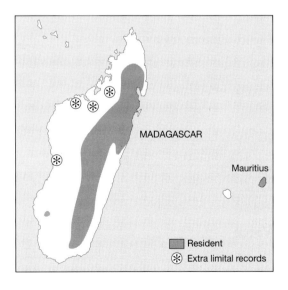

MADAGASCAR

Mauritius

☐ Resident
⊛ Extra limital records

dull white; 56.5×40.5 $(48.2–64.4 \times 30.8–44.0)$ $(n = 902)$; Delacour (1954–64) gave 59×42 with no details; weight 52.6 (40.0–64.0) $(n = 232)$; clutch 8.15 (5–13) (mode 9) $(n = 28)$ (Young 1994); incubation, by ♀, 26–28 days (Young 1988); hatch weight 30.8 (23–42) $(n = 93)$. Two broods of > 12 recently hatched ducklings seen at Alaotra. Fledge in captivity at 11 weeks, and breed at one year. No data on breeding success in wild, adult survival nor longevity.

Conservation and threats

Population declined (Langrand 1990, Young 1996b) due to indiscriminate subsistence hunting, habitat loss and pollution throughout Madagascan range. Introduced large fish, e.g. Largemouth Bass and Snakehead *Ophicephalus striatus*, may have led to desertion of some wetland areas.

Control of hunting through implementation of existing regulations, and development of protected areas that include reasonable numbers of nesting ducks, would go long way towards protection. Listed as Endangered in BirdLife International (2000), continued reduction in numbers and possible further development of Lake Alaotra may push towards extinction. Healthy *ex situ* captive population exists; 230 birds reared at Jersey Zoo (Durrell Wildlife Conservation Trust) from 13 wild-caught Madagascan birds 1994–2001.

Glyn Young

Blue-winged Teal *Anas discors*
PLATE 20

Anas discors Linnaeus, 1766, Syst. Nat., ed. 12, **1**, p. 205
North America = Carolina
Etymology: *discors* L. for different, unlike or discordant.
Other names: Bluewing, Mexican Duck, Summer Teal, Teal, White-faced Teal. French: Sarcelle à ailles bleues; Spanish: Cerceta aliazul clara.
Variation: 2 races sometimes suggested, Prairie or Western Blue-winged Teal *A. d. discors* breeding west of Appalachian Mountains, and Atlantic Blue-winged Teal *A. d. orphna* Stewart and Aldrich, 1956 breeding along Atlantic Seaboard from southern Canada to North Carolina.

Description

ADULT: dimorphic. ♂ in breeding or alternate plumage, head and neck steel-blue with white facial crescent between bill and eye. Crown, forehead, chin, and border of crescent black. Body brownish, sides brownish red, tan belly with dark brown spots. Tail black or brownish black, sides of rump in front of tail white. Light blue upperwing coverts. Green speculum on wing, white stripe on either side of speculum but only stripe between speculum and blue shoulder obvious. Bill blue-black and almost as long as head; feet and legs dull yellow to yellow-orange; eyes brown. ♀ forehead, crown, and nape dusky; also dusky stripe through eye. Remainder of head and neck pale with fine streaks. Body mottled brown, dark brown back, pale or white belly with brown tinge and dark blotches. Light blue upperwing coverts, not so bright as ♂. Green speculum darker or duller than ♂, white stripe absent or not as obvious as ♂. Tail grey or olive-brown, sides of rump in front of tail white. Bill dusky with yellow edges and black spots, lighter oval area at base; feet and legs duller yellow than ♂; eyes brown. (See also Rohwer et al. 2002.)

MOULT: ♂ in basic or eclipse plumage similar to ♀, but sides of head dull and may be more streaked.

IMMATURE: ♂ similar to ♀, but more heavily streaked on breast and belly. ♂ has brighter metallic green on speculum and more prominent white stripe than ♀.

DUCKLING: down yellow with olive-brown pattern. Narrow yellow forehead; thin, dark, usually complete greyish brown eyestripe; long, dark ear-spot. Bill greyish olive-brown with wide nail; feet greyish yellow or dull orange-yellow with dark greyish brown pattern; eyes brown (Nelson 1993).

MEASUREMENTS AND WEIGHT: ♂ wing ($n = 50$), 187; weight ($n = 35$), 318–544 (463). ♀ wing ($n = 31$) 180; weight ($n = 129$), 227–500 (377) (modified from Bellrose 1980). ♂ wing 180–196; culmen, 38–44. ♀ wing, 175–192; culmen, 38–40 (Johnsgard 1978). ♂ tarsus, 42–44. ♀ tarsus 39–42 (Phillips 1922–26).

Field characters

Fast-flying small dabbling duck, 370–415 mm long. Large blue patch on wing distinctive in flight but not visible when sitting or swimming. Cinnamon Teal similar in size and has blue wing patch, but ♂ much ruddier in colour and lacks white facial crescent. Northern Shoveler also has blue wing patch, but larger, with distinct spoon-shaped bill. Wing patch brighter blue than in Garganey. Breast and belly appear brownish in flight, but white in American Green-winged Teal. On water, white facial crescent against blue-grey head and white rump patches in front of black tail distinguish ♂. ♀ very similar to Cinnamon (and other) Teal, but Cinnamon Teal has more shoveler-like bill.

Voice

Less vocal than most ducks, even when displaying. ♂ has single call, usually thin, high-pitched whistling note *tseee*, repeated calls (series of quiet, clear whistles) given during pair formation and Decrescendo call, whistled note followed by series of shorter, quieter, low-pitched notes. ♀ during breeding season gives short series of loud repeated *quacks* especially in evening, and long series of loud *quacks* during days immediately before egg-laying, very rapid series of notes higher-pitched and quieter than Mallard's during Inciting, single loud *quack* followed by number of quieter rapid notes during Repulsion display, and very quiet rapid notes when returning to nest or incubating. Decrescendo call usually one long note followed by variable number of short notes (McKinney 1970). See Miller (1976) for sonograms of ♀ calls.

Ducklings give Soft calls consisting of 3–4 syllables of same or slightly ascending pitch, repeated in bouts of 3 or more. Feeding calls similar to Soft call, but lower in pitch and with fewer syllables. Short calls (2 syllables accented on 2nd) precede Whistle of Distress, series of 6 or more well-spaced notes that rise in pitch and volume, followed by steady piping (Nelson 1993).

Range and status

Breeds in central North America, most abundantly in central prairie provinces and states, also in Alaska, and across southern part of Canada from British Columbia to Québec, Nova Scotia and Newfoundland. In contiguous US, breeds in California, Oregon, and Washington on Pacific coast, across northern and central states, and in New England south to North Carolina on Atlantic coast. Breeds as far south as Arizona, New Mexico, Oklahoma, Texas, and Louisiana, and occasionally in Alabama and central Florida.

Breeding and winter ranges hardly overlap. Migrates long distances to winter primarily in Central and South America. Abundant in Mexico and as far south as Panama, Colombia, and Venezuela. Recorded over most of South America, including few records from Chile, Argentina, and Uruguay. Some winter in southern US, including coastal Texas, Louisiana, Florida, and South Carolina, with few reported in Arkansas, Mississippi, Alabama, Georgia, North Carolina, Missouri, Tennessee, Oklahoma and New Mexico. Also reported wintering in Cuba, Bahama Islands, Haiti, Dominican Republic and Puerto Rico; vagrants recorded in Europe. Wetlands International (2002) suggested population of 6 100 000.

Habitat and general habits

Highly sociable. May be found in flocks from early fall through spring migration. Also associates with other ducks, including American Green-winged Teal, North American Black Duck, Northern Pintail, Northern Shoveler, Cinnamon Teal, and American Coot *Fulica americana*. May form small, tight flocks in flight. Flight relatively fast and

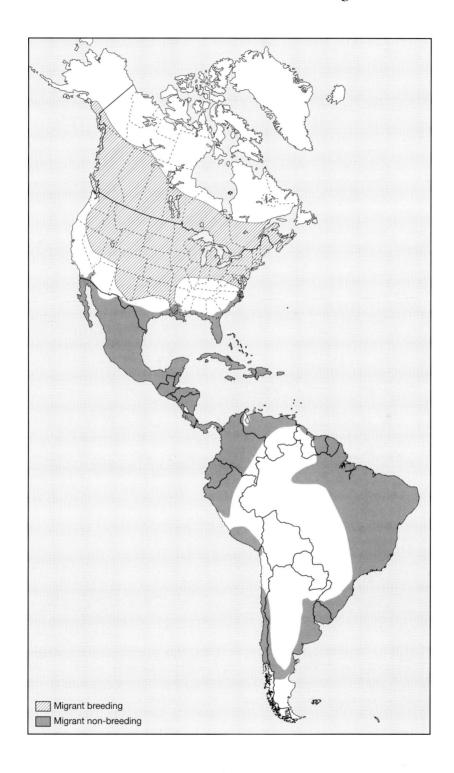

Migrant breeding
Migrant non-breeding

characterized by frequent changes of direction. Preferred breeding habitats shallow ponds, lakes and marshes in prairie grasslands, also found in wetlands in boreal and deciduous forests and coastal wetlands, including brackish marshes. Wintering habitats more diverse, and include shallow subtropical or tropical wetlands of fresh, brackish or saltwater.

Prefers to feed in shallow water. Predominantly surface feeders; may occasionally up-end but rarely dive. Diet consists of plant and animal matter, and may vary from 70% plant material (Mabbott 1920) to over 90% animal matter (Swanson *et al.* 1974). During spring, slightly higher proportion of diet is animal matter. Plant material mainly seeds of grasses *Panicum, Chaetochloa, Zizania aquatica, Homalocenchrus oryzoides, Oryza sativa, Monanthochloe littoralis*, and sedges *Cyperus, Eleocharis, Fimbristylis, Scirpus, Cladium effusum, Carex*, but also includes vegetative parts of pondweeds and algae *Potamogeton, Ruppia maritima, Najas flexilis, N. maritima, Zannichellia palustris, Polygonum, Chara, Lemna* (Johnsgard 1975, Palmer 1976, Bellrose 1980). Depending on type of wetland, animal foods consist mainly of molluscs, principally snails Lymnaeidae, Planorbidae, Physidae, as well as insects (Diptera, Coleoptera, Trichoptera, Heteroptera, Homoptera, Odonata and others), crustaceans (Amphipoda, Decapoda, Ostracoda, Copepoda, Cladocera and others), and few arachnids, hydrachnids and fish (Mabbott 1920, Swanson *et al.* 1974).

Displays and breeding behaviour

Seasonally monogamous. During courtship, ♂ performs short Jump-flights towards ♀, apparently to attract her attention. Ritualized feeding and comfort movements basis for many ♂ courtship displays on water (Mock-feeding, Tipping-up, Head-dipping, Shaking and Preening). Turn-back-of-head and Mock-feeding, also called Lateral-dabbling, common ♂ courtship displays. ♀♀ also perform ritualized Shaking, Preening and Mock-feeding. During pair formation, ♀ Incites beside mate or prospective mates, she Chin-lifts while Head-pumping, uttering rapid series of calls, and directs threatening movements towards another duck, usually ♂ to which ♀ is not paired.

♀ may also Incite toward other ducks when brood present, even though ♂ is not. ♂♂ respond to ♀ Inciting by Chin-lifting and Turn-back-of-head. Mates perform mutual Chin-lifting when coming together after period of separation. Copulation preceded by mutual Head-pumping; ♂ grasps ♀'s nape as he mounts, and may utter quiet calls while treading. After dismounting, ♂ orients himself broadside to ♀, extends neck, points bill downwards, and gives single whistle or Decrescendo call.

Although forms large flocks on wintering grounds, intolerant of other pairs during breeding season. ♂ response varies from mild rushes across water at both ♂♂ and ♀♀ to vigorous aerial pursuits and fights on water. ♂♂ may also perform Hostile Pumping—fast head movements with bill pointed slightly upward accompanied by peeping calls. ♀ performs Inciting or Repulsion (hunched posture with ruffled feathers) and Repulsion call once brood hatched and pairbond broken.

♀♀ sometimes produce Distraction display (feigning injury by flapping over ground or water) when flushed from nest or brood. New pairbond formed annually in winter, during migration northwards, and on breeding grounds.

Breeding and life cycle

One of last dabbling ducks to nest in spring, *c* month later than Northern Mallard and Northern Pintail. Nest initiation begins late Apr or early May; with peak initiation mid May, latest mid July. Nests dispersed and preferred sites dry with grass cover, within 400 m of water. ♀ forms shallow bowl on ground; as laying progresses, she adds grass, other vegetation and down. One egg laid per day, usually in morning. Eggs smooth, slightly glossy, creamy tan; 46.6×33.4 ($43.2–49.5 \times 31.3–36.2$) ($n = 120$) (Schönwetter 1960–66) with calculated fresh weight of 29.0; in captivity weigh 25.8 ($n = 72$); clutch 10–11 (6–15); average for later nests smaller at 7–9 eggs. ♀ may attempt re-nesting (not necessarily with same ♂) if clutch lost. ♀ incubates 23–24 (21–27) days; hatching synchronous, weight of captive day-olds 15.7 (10.5–20.4) ($n = 73$) (Smart 1965b) or 16.0 ($n = 55$). Hatching success ranges

21–60%. Nests and eggs destroyed primarily by skunks, foxes, Coyote *Canis latrans*, weasels *Mustela*, American Mink, American Badger *Taxidea taxus*, Raccoons, crows and Magpies *Pica pica*. Flooding, mowing, and grazing by cattle also contribute to nest losses.

Pairbond weakens and ♂♂ depart about 2 weeks into incubation. ♀ broods and cares for young until fledging. Young precocial, and able to feed themselves and travel distance to water soon after

hatching. Fledge at 39–40 (35–49) days. Fledging success *c* 55–77%. Adult mortality ranges 41–68% annually. Both sexes generally breed as yearlings.

Conservation and threats

Cultivation has reduced the amount of prairie pothole habitat in North America, but still abundant. Not globally threatened.

Susan Evarts

Cinnamon Teal *Anas cyanoptera*
PLATE 20

Anas cyanoptera Vieillot, 1816, Nouveau Dictionnaire d'Hist. Nat., nouv. éd., **5**, p. 104
Rio de la Plata and Buenos Aires

Etymology: *cyanoptera* Gr. *kuanos* means dark blue, plus *pteron* wing.

Other names: Red Teal, Red-breasted Teal. French: Sarcelle cannelle; Spanish: Cerceta aliazul café, Pato colorado.

Variation: 5 subspecies recognized (Snyder and Lumsden 1951, Palmer 1976, Gammonley 1996). Northern Cinnamon Teal *A. c. septentrionalium* Snyder and Lumsden, 1951 breeds in western North America from southern Canada to central and western Mexico. 4 other races breed in South America: Argentine Cinnamon Teal *A. c. cyanoptera*; Tropical Cinnamon Teal *A. c. tropica* Snyder and Lumsden, 1951; Andean Cinnamon Teal *A. c. orinomus* Oberholser, 1906; and Borrero's Cinnamon Teal *A. c. borreroi* Snyder and Lumsden, 1951. Information below for *septentrionalium* unless stated otherwise.

Description

ADULT: dimorphic. ♂ *septentrionalium* in breeding or alternate plumage has head, neck, sides, flanks, and belly reddish brown to rich chestnut. Head from bill to crown, chin, throat, and back of neck black. Most also have black on lower abdomen. Black undertail coverts. Back, rump, uppertail coverts, and tail brownish black. Mantle has dark bars. Upperwing coverts blue. Metallic green speculum on wing with narrow tan trailing edge. Bill black, slightly spatulate; legs

and feet yellow to orange with dusky webs; eyes yellow-orange to scarlet. ♀ much like ♀ Blue-Winged Teal, body mottled brown; individual colouring ranges from rather pale to moderately dark. Dark streaking on head and neck; chin and throat white to buff. Breast tan, belly whitish with darker blotches or streaks. Blue upperwing coverts. Dark green speculum (duller than ♂). Bill slaty, slightly spatulate; legs and feet dull yellow with dusky webs; eyes hazel. *septentrionalium* smaller than *cyanoptera*, pronounced sexual dimorphism (♂ larger); ♂ redder in colour than other subspecies and lacks spots on breast, sides and belly, ♀ varies in colour from pale to dark. *cyanoptera* ♂ has dark chestnut coloration with black spots on breast, sides, and belly, ♀ lighter in colour than *borreroi*. *tropica*, smallest subspecies, has sexes almost equal in size, ♂ usually dark with brownish black belly and black spots on breast, sides and flanks, ♀ dark. *orinomus*, largest subspecies with longer bill, ♂ lighter with little or no dark coloration on belly, ♀ more heavily streaked. *borreroi* ♂ similar to *cyanoptera* but darker in colour with more black spots on breast, sides and flanks, ♀ darker than ♀ *cyanoptera*.

MOULT: eclipsed ♂ similar to adult ♀, but body more reddish brown, eye red and speculum brighter green.

IMMATURE: ♂ similar to adult ♀ except for red eye (by age 8 weeks) and brighter green speculum, and may be more heavily streaked, especially on underparts.

DUCKLING: greenish yellow with bright olive-brown pattern. Narrow yellow forehead; thin, dark, usually incomplete brownish eyestripe; long, dark ear-spot. Bill grey or olive grey, longer than Blue-winged Teal, nail narrower than Blue-winged Teal; feet dull yellow or light olive-brown with less conspicuous dark greyish brown pattern; eyes greyish brown (Nelson 1993).

MEASUREMENTS AND WEIGHT: ♂ ($n = 44$) wing, 180–202 (191); tail, 62–78 (70); culmen, 41–49 (44.2); tarsus, 32–38 (35.1); weight, 315–450 (383). ♀ ($n = 69$) wing, 170–192 (182); tail, 62–76 (68); culmen, 40–47 (42.9); tarsus, 30–38 (32.5); weight, 265–470 (372) (Gammonley 1996; see also for measurements of South American races).

Field characters

Small, 360–430 mm long, dabbling duck; flight fast and characterized by frequent changes of direction. Large blue patch on wing visible during flight. ♂ easily distinguishable during breeding season by chestnut head and body. Similar in size to Blue-Winged Teal but absence of white on body, more spatulate bill, and red eye distinguish ♂ Cinnamon Teal. ♀ nearly indistinguishable from ♀ Blue-Winged Teal, but body slightly redder, bill slightly longer and wider at tip, and facial markings less defined.

Voice

Less vocal than other dabbling ducks, and quieter than Blue-Winged Teal. ♂ has single call, quiet *rrar*; repeated calls, series of single or double notes given during pair formation; rapid series of rattling, three-syllabled *rrar* notes given during hostile pumping. ♀ utters quick repeated notes (rippling chatter) during Inciting display, harsher and more rattling than ♀ Blue-Winged Teal; during Repulsion display gives single loud *quack* followed by series of quieter rapid notes. Decrescendo call usually one long note followed by variable number of short notes that have hoarse, rattling quality (McKinney 1970).

Ducklings give Soft calls consisting of 3–4 syllables of same or slightly ascending pitch, repeated in bouts of 3 or more. Feeding calls similar to Soft call, but lower in pitch and with fewer syllables. Short calls (2 syllables accented on 2nd) precede Whistle

of Distress, series of 6 or more well-spaced notes that rise in pitch and volume, followed by steady, often 2-syllabled, piping (Nelson 1993).

Range and status

septentrionalium breeds in western North America, most abundantly west of Rocky Mountains, especially in Great Basin of Nevada and marshes near Great Salt Lake in Utah. Breeds as far north as southern British Columbia, southern Alberta, and perhaps southern Saskatchewan in Canada, and as far east as Montana, Wyoming, Colorado, New Mexico, and northwest Texas. Rare in Great Plains. Breeds as far south as Baja California, and Jalisco and Tamaulipas in central Mexico. Winters in southwestern states (primarily California, Arizona, New Mexico, and south Texas) and south through Mexico, Central America, and occasionally Colombia and Venezuela.

cyanoptera breeds at low altitudes from southern Peru, Paraguay, southern Brazil and Uruguay to Tierra del Fuego and, rarely, Falkland Islands, *tropica* below 1000 m in Cauca Valley of Colombia and in lower parts of the Cauca and Magdalena drainages (Delacour 1954–64, Johnsgard 1978), *orinomus* at high altitudes in Puna from southern Peru and Bolivia to Argentina and Chile, and *borreroi* in moist highlands of Colombian Andes at 1000–3600 m but limits of range poorly known.

Estimates in Wetlands International (2002) suggest stable population of 260 000 for *septentrionalium*, probably one of least abundant dabbling ducks in North America (although may be locally common); <10 000 for *tropica*, 10 000–100 000 for *orinomus* and <250 for *borreroi*. Rose and Scott (1997) earlier estimated 25 000–100 000 for *cyanoptera*.

Habitat and general habits

Most commonly found in pairs or small groups. May form larger flocks during migration. Also associates with other species, including American Green-winged Teal, Blue-winged Teal, Gadwall, and Northern Shoveler in North America and Red Shoveler and South American (Speckled) Teal in South America. Preferred breeding habitats shallow freshwater or brackish wetlands with emergent vegetation, also found in alkaline habitats. Wintering birds select habitats similar to those used during breeding.

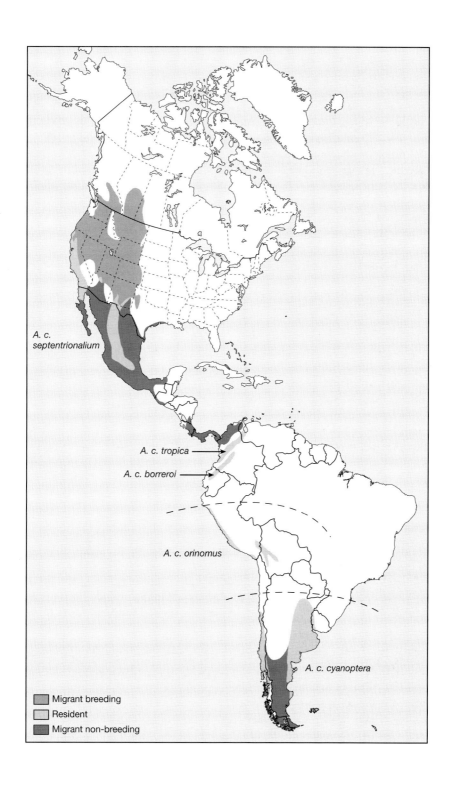

A. c.
septentrionalium

A. c. tropica

A. c. borreroi

A. c. orinomus

A. c. cyanoptera

Migrant breeding
Resident
Migrant non-breeding

Feeds in shallow water, predominantly at surface; may occasionally up-end, but rarely dives. Social feeding also occurs. Diet consists of seeds, aquatic vegetation, aquatic and semi-terrestrial insects, snails and zooplankton (Gammonley 1996). Amount of animal matter in diet varies (8.8–89.3%) with location, sex and season. During breeding, invertebrates form higher proportion of diet, especially of ♀. Animal food items consist mainly of chironomids and other dipterans, cladocerans, corixids, coleopterans, gastropods and odonates. Plant material mainly seeds of *Scirpus*, *Polygonum*, *Ruppia maritima*, *Zannichellia palustris*, *Echinochloa* and *Stipa* (Thorn and Zwank 1993, Hohman and Ankney 1994, Gammonley 1995a).

Displays and breeding behaviour

Seasonally monogamous. During courtship, ♂♂ perform short Jump-flights towards ♀, apparently to attract her attention. Ritualized feeding and comfort movements basis for many ♂ courtship displays on water (Mock-feeding, Tipping-up, Head-dipping, Shaking and Preening). Turn-back-of-head and Mock-feeding, also called Lateral-dabbling, common ♂ courtship displays. ♀ also performs ritualized Shaking, Preening and Mock-feeding. During pair formation, ♀♀ Incite beside their mates or prospective mates. In this display, ♀ Chin-lifts while Head-pumping, utters rapid series of calls, and directs threatening movements toward another duck, usually ♂ to which ♀ is not paired. ♀ may also Incite towards other ducks with her brood present, even though ♂ is not. ♂♂ respond to ♀ Inciting by performing Chin-lifting and Turn-back-of-head. Copulation preceded by mutual Head-pumping by both sexes. ♂ grasps ♀'s nape and mounts. After dismounting, he orients himself broadside to ♀, extends his neck, points bill down, and gives single call.

♂♂ intolerant of other pairs during breeding season. ♂ responses may vary from mild rushes across water at both ♂♂ and ♀♀, to aerial pursuits and fights on water. ♂♂ may also perform Hostile Pumping—fast head movements with bill pointed slightly upward accompanied by loud calls. ♀ uses Inciting or Repulsion (hunched posture with ruffled feathers) once brood has hatched and pairbond broken. ♀♀ sometimes perform Distraction display (feigning injury by flapping over ground or water) when flushed from nest or brood. New pairbond formed every year in winter, during migration northwards, and on breeding ground.

Breeding and life cycle

Nests dispersed, but less so than Blue-winged Teal. Preferred nesting sites dry, with dense grass or other low vegetation for cover, and close (usually < 50 m, often < 10 m) to water. Nest initiation late Apr–late May, peak initiation from mid May–mid June, may continue until late July. ♀ forms shallow bowl on ground and, as laying progresses, adds grass, other vegetation, and down. Lays one egg per day, usually in morning. Eggs smooth, slightly glossy, and creamy white to pale buff; 47.7 × 34.7 (44–54 × 32–39) (*n* = 120) (Schönwetter 1960–66) with calculated fresh weight of 32; weight in captivity 27.2 (*n* = 83); eggs of *cyanoptera* in captivity weigh 29.1 (*n* = 22); clutch 9–10 (4–16), mid season clutches appear larger than early or late ones. ♀♀ may attempt re-nesting (not necessarily with same ♂) if clutch lost. ♀ incubates 24–25 (21–25) days. At hatching, captive *septentrionalium* ducklings weigh 18.5 (*n* = 31); hatching synchronous, and success of eggs hatched ranges 43–97%. Percentage of nests where at least one egg hatched 12–80%. Nests and eggs destroyed primarily by predators including California Gull *Larus californicus*, Raven, Common American Crow *Corvus brachyrhynchos*, Bald Eagle, Black-billed Magpie *P. p. hudsonia*, skunks, Brown Rat, Raccoon, Coyote, American Mink, weasels and Opossum *Didelphis marsupialis*.

Pairbond weakens and ♂ departs *c* 3 weeks into incubation. ♀ broods and cares for young until fledging. Young precocial, and able to feed themselves and travel to water soon after hatching; fledge in *c* 7 weeks. Estimated 4.5–6.9 young per brood survive to Class III (Gollop and Marshall 1954, Gammonley 1996). Annual adult survival rates not well known, one study estimated 2nd year survival of 46% (Kozlik 1972). Both sexes generally breed as yearlings.

Conservation and threats

Populations of *septentrionalium* appear stable, but diversion, degradation and disturbance of water sources have reduced amount of available habitat. Some small South American populations may be declining, and research is needed. Borrero's Cinnamon Teal regarded as Critically Endangered, and Tropical Cinnamon Teal as Endangered, by Threatened Waterfowl Specialist Group (2003).

Susan Evarts

Cape Shoveler *Anas smithii*
PLATE 21

Spatula smithii Hartert, 1891, Kat. Vogelsammlung Mus. Senckenberg. Naturforschendegesell. Frankfurt, p. 231
Cape Province

Etymology: named after Sir Andrew Smith (1797–1872), first Director of Cape Town Museum.

Other names: Cape Shoveller, South African Shoveler, Smith's Shoveler. Afrikaans: Kaapse Slopeend.

Variation: no subspecies.

Description

ADULT: dimorphic. ♂ has pale grey head which contrasts with dark bill and body, slightly smaller ♀ has paler bill, and head contrasting less with browner body. Blue forewing, typical of all shovelers, may be seen in resting birds and obvious in flight. Fore-edge of speculum separated from forewing by white band. ♂ bill black; feet and legs yellow, orange-yellow in breeding season; eyes yellow. ♀ forewing and speculum less distinct and white band may be missing. Underwing pale brown. Bill dark brown; legs and feet greyish yellow; eye dark brown.

MOULT: unique amongst African and Malagasy *Anas* in having no ♂ eclipse plumage and being permanently dichromatic. Moult cycle not fully understood; however, assumed to have two body moults annually. Movements recorded prior to wing moult.

IMMATURE: resembles adult ♀. Young ♂ becomes identifiable as wing coloration develops.

DUCKLING: buff-olive upperparts, darker over crown and nape. Yellow underparts and orange-buff face with dark eyestripe. Broad yellow lines on back near wings and tail (Brown *et al.* 1982).

MEASUREMENTS AND WEIGHT: ♂ (*n* = 42) wing, 222–253 (238.6); tail, 63–98 (76.4); bill, 54.5–65 (57.7); tarsus, 30–43 (40.4). ♀ (*n* = 32) wing, 208–248 (227.4); tail, 61–83 (71.7); bill, 52–64 (56.8); tarsus, 33–41 (37.8) (Maclean 1993). Weight in western Transvaal, ♂ (*n* = 27), 522–680 (603); ♀ (*n* = 24), 492–665 (572) (Brown *et al.* 1982); in southwest Cape, ♂ (*n* = 32), 548–830 (688); ♀ (*n* = 26), 476–691 (597.8) (Siegfried 1965c).

Field characters

Only *Anas* breeding in region that nests seasonally, and undertakes seasonal migration (Siegfried 1965c, 1974a). Medium-sized duck, 530 mm long, sits quite low in water, often with large, spatulate, dark bill pointing downwards. Contrast of ♂ pale head with dark body and bill obvious. In flight, heavy bill and pale blue forewing distinctive. Northern Shoveler winter in Africa and may be inseparable in juvenile ♂ and ♀ plumages; ranges, however, overlap rarely.

Voice

♂ has loud *rrar*, and faster *rararararara*. ♀ *quacks* and has Decresendo call. Other calls may be produced during courtship display. Sonograms of adult in Maclean (1993) and distress call of young in Kear (1968).

Range and status

Restricted to Southern Africa from Cape to southwest Angola, northern Namibia, Botswana and southwest Zimbabwe. Absent from northern Transvaal and Mozambique except, rarely, at southern border. Some undergo regular, probably seasonal migration-like movements, birds ringed in South Africa recovered in Namibia, 1680 km away (Brown *et al.* 1982); some inland populations may be nomadic.

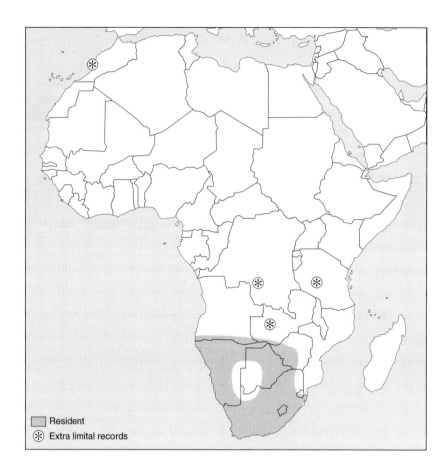

Resident

⊛ Extra limital records

Vagrant to Zambia, Zaire and Tanzania; there are few, probably erroneous, records from North Africa, Ethiopia and Kenya (Brown *et al.* 1982). Pair near Agadir, Morocco, Apr 1978 may have escaped from captivity, but single bird at same site Mar 2004.

Considered common in southwest Cape and Transvaal but may be less so in other parts of range. Nomadic habits of some populations make estimate of numbers difficult, although no obvious signs of decline. Adapts well to artificial waters and numbers increased in southwestern Cape Province and in Zimbabwe (Scott and Rose 1996, Maclean 1997f). Rose and Scott (1997) estimated population of 20 000–50 000.

Habitat and general habits

Frequents shallow lakes and marshes, especially following flooding. Will feed in estuaries, lagoons, salt-pans and highly alkaline waters. Not found on deep lakes nor on fast-flowing water.

Usually in small groups outside breeding season, only rarely in larger numbers although up to 600 recorded. Does not mix with other species. May feed throughout day and night, only coming ashore to loaf and sleep.

Feeds by dabbling in shallow water, often with head immersed, and rarely by up-ending. Feeds cooperatively, as do all shovelers, 2–7 birds swimming in circle feeding on aquatic organisms stirred up and concentrated by bow wave of bird ahead. Diet mainly aquatic invertebrates and tadpoles, some plant material taken (Siegfried 1965c).

Displays and behaviour

Display simple and typical of shovelers. ♂ Burps, with head level and neck outstretched. Chin-lifting used frequently. Mock-feeding with ♂ treading water, spreading flank feathers and, often, Belching may end with Up-ending or Tipping. Display Jump-flights recorded, ♂ Burping before flying up to nearby ♀ where he Mock-feeds or Turns-back-of-head. During Jump-flight, wing feathers may be ruffled making fluttering sound and exposing coloured forewing and speculum. In courting groups, ♂ constantly jostles for best position, through swimming and Jump-flights, to attract chosen ♀ (Johnsgard 1965a, Siegfried 1965c, McKinney 1970, Brown *et al.* 1982). Post-copulatory display consists of Wing-up-bill-down, with call, and Erect-facing (Johnson *et al.* 2000).

Pairs arrive to breed already paired, and often remain together throughout incubation and brood rearing, ♂ accompanying ♀ and young (Siegfried 1974a) and strongly defending moving territory around her.

Breeding and life cycle

Nesting recorded all months of year, and may be dependent on increased rainfall in some parts of range. In Transvaal, breeds throughout year with peak July–Sept (Maclean 1997f). Many, however, apparently more seasonal, showing, for example, marked Aug–Dec peak in southwestern Cape Province, with only few breeding records in other months (Maclean 1997f). Nests built in vegetation near water, preferred sites close to food source. Eggs ovate, smooth cream with occasional green tinge; 53.4×38.7 $(48.4–59.5 \times 36.6–41.1)$ ($n = 350$), weight in captivity 38 (34–43.5) ($n = 85$); clutch (no sample size) 9.36 (5–12); incubation, by ♀ alone, 27–28 days (Siegfried 1965c). Hatch weight in captivity 23.3 ($n = 37$); fledge in 56–63 days (Siegfried 1965c). Probably breeds at one year. No data on nesting success, survival nor longevity.

Conservation and threats

Protection of habitat, especially ephemeral wetlands, and controls on hunting needed; however, seasonal movements and biology must be better understood if sensible conservation strategy to be developed.

Glyn Young

Red Shoveler *Anas platalea*
PLATE 21

Anas platalea Vieillot, 1816, Nouv. Dict. Hist. Nat., **5**, p. 157
Paraguay

Etymology: *platalea* is L. for the spoonbill.

Other names: Argentine Shoveler, South American Shoveler, Blue-winged Shoveler. French: Canard spatule; German: Fuchslöffelente; Portuguese: Marreca-colhereira; Spanish: Pato cuchara.

Variation: no subspecies.

Description

ADULT: dimorphic. ♂ in breeding or alternate plumage has head pale buff with fine black stippling concentrated on crown. Chin and throat almost white. Body rufescent cinnamon to deep reddish chestnut below, profusely marked with black oval spots. Elongated, black scapulars with white streaks along shaft. Lower back, rump, and middle of tail black, with creamy white edge on tail and white side patch near rump. Outer rectrices brown and tail long and pointed. Primaries brownish black with white shafts. Upperwing coverts blue, with white tips on upper coverts forming prominent bar. Speculum bright iridescent green. White wing linings. Large, spatulate black bill; feet grey to yellow to orange; iris white to light yellow. ♀ head and underparts buff and more or less spotted brown. Throat white. Back and tail dark brown with buff feather edges, with creamy white edge on tail. Wings like ♂ but upperwing coverts duller and white bar reduced. Speculum blackish with little or no green. Spatulate bill browner; feet grey to yellowish; iris dark brown.

MOULT: ♂ lacks eclipse plumage, but after breeding season, worn feathers lighter and greyer on head, mantle, and breast. Little information on timing of wing and body moults of both sexes, but large assemblages of flightless birds form Nov–Feb in southern Argentina (Fjeldså and Krabbe 1986).

IMMATURE: like ♀ but greyer upperwing coverts and belly less distinctively spotted. Speculum brighter in ♂.

DUCKLING: dark brown with cinnamon and yellow markings and underparts.

MEASUREMENTS AND WEIGHT: ♂ (*n* = 6) wing, 206–221 (212); tail, 92–98 (95.8); bill, 81–84 (82.2); tarsus, 34–38; weight in fall and winter (*n* = 10), 608.3. ♀ (*n* = 7) wing, 200–206 (203.6); tail, 81–91 (87.7); bill, 60–81 (76); weight (*n* = 7), 522.6, immature (*n* = 3), 543.0 (Weller 1968b, Blake 1977).

Field characters

Length 450–560 mm. Bill shape distinctive for both sexes. Tends to sit with head tucked, and tail noticeably long. Light head in contrast to reddish body of ♂, light head and darker brown body of ♀. In flight, white wing linings and pale blue forewings with white border towards green speculum notable. Conspicuous white side patch on rump of ♂.

Voice

Only few quiet calls noted, and little information available for wild birds. ♂ gives low rattle or sputtering sound when accompanying ♀, and hollow *tooka-tooka-tuk-tuk* in courtship, as alarm call, and as introduction to Mock-feeding displays (Johnsgard 1965a, 1978). ♂ also has deeper *tuk tuk* call in flight. ♀ gives harsh *quack* when disturbed, and rasping *whrrt* or *rrr* when Inciting (Johnsgard 1965a, 1978). No published sonograms.

Range and status

Found in southern South America from southern Peru, Bolivia, southeastern Brazil and Paraguay south to Tierra del Fuego. Accidental in Falkland Islands where 10 records of up to 12 birds noted during breeding season 1985–92 (Woods and Woods 1997). Generally found below 3400 m except for strays, but small resident populations

Resident and partially migratory

found in highlands of Puno and Cuzco regions of Peru. Moults in tens of thousands on plateaux of Patagonia region in southern Argentina at 700–1200 m (Fjeldså and Krabbe 1986). Partially migratory, with more southern breeders wintering in northern end of range. Fairly common and widespread. Large concentrations (4000–5000) in Argentina at Laguna Mar Chiquita, Córdoba province (Nores and Yzurieta 1980) and around 20 000 near Meseta de Stroebel, Santa Cruz province (Fjeldså and Krabbe 1986). Population estimates range 100 000–1 000 000 (Wetlands International 2002).

Habitat and general habits

Inhabits shallow ponds, lakes, and marshes, including brackish coastal lagoons. Prefers areas where water weeds cover surface, but also turbid alkaline lakes with dense zooplankton. Generally seen in pairs or small groups, but in large congregations when moulting. Poor walker. Filters water and mud by dabbling, head-dipping and up-ending; rarely makes short dives. Feeds on seeds and other parts of aquatic plants, and plankton-sized aquatic invertebrates. In winter in Chile, Housse (1945) found diet consisted of vegetable matter, larvae, worms, insects, molluscs and small frogs.

Displays and breeding behaviour

Displays appear similar to other blue-winged ducks, but little information for wild birds. Head-shaking occurs as pre-flight display. In courtship, ♂ and ♀ make short Jump-flights, with ♂ giving short *tuk* calls near ♀ on landing. ♂ Preen-behind-wing, Mock-feeding (Johnsgard 1965a), and display in which ♂ gives Head-shake then rises out of water also seen in courtship. ♂ noted to court ♀ with brood. Both sexes lift heads up and down as aggressive display. Copulations preceded by mutual Head-pumps, and ♂ utters short call with neck extended vertically, then turns to face bathing ♀ after copulation (Johnsgard 1965a). ♀ Inciting consists of stretching neck and lifting head up and down, with soft *rrr* call. Courtship noted Nov–Dec in Argentina following Sept–Nov breeding season (Weller 1968b).

Breeding and life cycle

Fairly gregarious during breeding season, which begins Sept–Oct. Nests on ground built of twigs, aquatic plants, dry grass, and reeds in dry areas near lakes or in swampy vegetation (Housse 1945, Johnson 1965). Eggs oval, smooth and dull white with rosy-yellow tint; 59–64 × 37–39 ($n = 8$) and 49–60 × 37–38 ($n = 7$) (Housse 1945), or 54.0 × 39.0 (49.3–58.3 × 33.3–44.3) $n = 12$ (Schönwetter 1960–66); weight in captivity 37.3 (27.5–46.5) ($n = 100$); clutch reported as 5–8, and incubation in captivity, by ♀ alone, 25 days. Captive day-olds weighed 22.6 ($n = 9$) and, at 21 days, 3 averaged 202. Brood size of recently hatched ducklings 5.7 ± 2.3 (2–10) ($n = 15$) in Argentina and Chile. ♂ sometimes seen with ♀ and brood, but appears not to provide parental care (McKinney and Brewer 1989). Probably breeds at one year. No data on breeding success, survival nor longevity.

Conservation and threats

Fairly common. Hunted in some areas, and likely to suffer from contamination of wetlands in areas overstocked with domestic animals.

Gwenda L. Brewer

Australasian Shoveler *Anas rhynchotis*
PLATE 21

Anas Rhychotis Latham, 1801, Index Ornith., Suppl., p. 70
New South Wales
   Etymology: *rhynchotis* from Gr. *rhunkhos* for bill, in reference to distinctive shape.
   Other names: Australian, New Holland or New Zealand Shovel(l)er; Blue-winged or Southern Shovel(l)er; Blue-wing, Shovelbill, Spoonbill or Shovel-nosed Duck, Stinker, Widgeon. Australian Aboriginal: Bar-doo-ngoo-ba, Bardunguba, Kalperi, Motang, Tauanda, Wanu, Wudjug; Dutch: Australische Slobeend; French: Canard bridé; German:

Halbmond-Löffelente; Maori: Kuruwhengi; Spanish: Cuchara Australiano.
   Variation: 2 subspecies claimed, nominate *A. r. rhynchotis* in Australia, and *A. r. variegata* Gould, 1856 in New Zealand. *A. r. variegata* not supported on present evidence and not different in size from nominate population (Marchant and Higgins 1990). Poor distinguishing features depend on quality of adult ♂ alternate plumage; differences difficult to substantiate when comparing fully coloured Australian ♂ with similar New Zealand ♂, breeding and moulting under different daylight regime.

Likely that emigrants from Australia often reach New Zealand.

Description

ADULT: dimorphic. ♂ in breeding, or alternate, plumage has blue-grey head, slightly glossed green with variable crescent-like white patch before eye. Crown and throat almost black and variable amounts of fine streaking visible on heads of most individuals. Underparts dark grey and scaly on breast; reddish brown to chestnut on sides and belly which boldly mottling dark brown; conspicuous white patch present at rear of each flank. Rest of upperbody dark shading to black on upper and lower tail coverts with dark brown tail slightly paler on outer edges. At rest, lanceolate scapulars with white shaft streaks droop from uppersides of body. In flight, pale blue upper forewing distinctive with bright green speculum separated by broad white border more obvious towards middle of wing. Underwing lining white. Bill grey-black; legs and feet bright orange; eyes bright yellow. ♀ dull speckled and mottled brown with dark brown eyes and brownish orange legs and feet. In flight, wing pattern of ♀ similar to that of ♂ but forewing greyer and speculum browner with less iridescent green.

MOULT: ♂ basic plumage during eclipse resembles ♀ but eye colour remains distinguishing character. ♂ plumage variable and often drab with most features described being less well defined and colourful. Head pattern and size of white flank patch most obviously variable. No critical information on moults but pattern probably follows that found for other *Anas*, particularly those of same region (Pacific Black Duck and Chestnut Teal).

IMMATURE: resembles ♀ except feathers of lower-neck and breast streaked not blotched and general colour warmer.

DUCKLINGS: as other shovelers. Crown, hind-neck and upper body dark brown, cheeks and underparts pale yellow. Yellow spot on each side of rump and yellow patches on trailing edges of wing pads. Broad yellow supercilium with dark eyestripe from bill to back of head and dark ear patch. Bill mostly dark grey and legs and feet dark brown.

MEASUREMENTS AND WEIGHT: *rhynchotis* ♂ wing ($n = 74$), 210–261 (239); tail ($n = 15$), 68–85 (79); bill ($n = 72$), 56–67 (61); tarsus ($n = 16$), 36–39 (38); weight ($n = 76$), 570–852 (667). ♀ wing ($n = 102$), 210–297 (238); tail ($n = 9$), 73–80 (76); bill ($n = 69$), 57–62 (60); tarsus ($n = 8$), 32–38 (35); weight ($n = 70$), 545–745 (665) (Marchant and Higgins 1990).

Field characters

Typical shoveler. Dark-coloured slim duck of medium size, 460–530 mm long, with massive bill, not easily mistaken for any other duck within normal range except for similar-looking vagrant Northern Shoveler. Pink-eared Duck has proportionally massive bill but of different shape, much smaller and has distinctive black-and-white zebra-like pattern over most of underside.

Voice

Generally silent but calls not well known. Courting ♂ has distinctive double note *club-it* call, repeated persistently or in rapid series. Decrescendo call of ♀, like that of other ♀ shovelers, series of sharp *quacks*; first note longer, louder and insistent, followed by 7–10 or more hurried syllables that have general downward inflection and become increasingly shorter—*quaaag, gak-gak-gak-gak-gak-ga-ga*. Further details, including sonograms, in Marchant and Higgins (1990).

Range and status

Endemic to Australia and New Zealand. Range disjunct, with populations in Western Australia mostly restricted to southwest and coastal areas north to about Gascoyne River. In southeastern Australia most concentrations occur in south of South Australia and in Victoria and southern New South Wales; occurs more sparingly to central coastal Queensland. Also widespread in Tasmania. In New Zealand found on both main islands.

In Australia, range extends well inland following flooding with breeding records as far as 30°S in

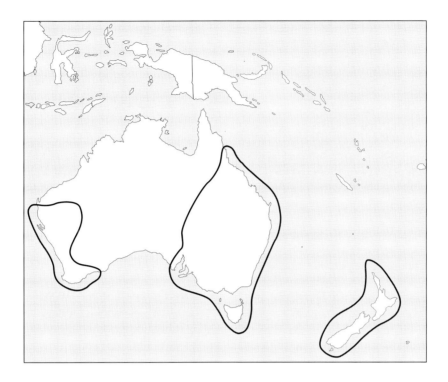

east and 26°S in west. Breeding distribution restricted by need for suitable cover near water for ground-nesting. May have declined in numbers this century (Blakers *et al.* 1984, Marchant and Higgins 1990). Indices of abundance in east Australia 1983–92, obtained from aerial surveys during Oct, give low figure of 16 000 and high near 200 000 (Marchant and Higgins 1990, Kingsford *et al.* 1999, 2000). At times probably confined almost entirely to dune lakes in southeastern South Australia, wetlands at confluence of Murrumbidgee and Lachlan Rivers, or wetlands on floodplains of Paroo River and Cuttaburra Channels in north central New South Wales (Marchant and Higgins 1990). In West Australia, summer counts in southwest during 1986–88 produced 2300–4500 birds (Marchant and Higgins 1990). Population of New Zealand thought stable or increasing at 100 000–150 000 individuals (Marchant and Higgins 1990), although Wetlands International (2002) put it at 10 000–100 000. World population probably varies 100 000–300 000.

Habitat and general habits

Favours large freshwater wetlands where filter feeds in shallow open water and in soft muds. Less commonly found on estuarine or inshore waters, brackish or saline lakes (Marchant and Higgins 1990). Strains water or mud and often swims quickly with bill submerged. Sometimes up-ends and occasionally dives when bottom filtering probably occurs. Diet seems mostly animal matter with some seeds; see Marchant and Higgins (1990) for further details.

Displays and breeding behaviour

Pre-flight signal involves Head-shaking and vertical Head-thrusting from erect posture without calling. Courtship like that of other shovelers. Hostile-pumping with rapid up and down action of head used by ♂ and ♀; in ♂, used with call as threat to other ♂♂, but in ♀, used to attract and initiate display from ♂, possibly without associated call. During courtship bouts, ♂♂ assemble near ♀ and perform 2 main displays.

Several minor signals, mostly involving ritualized Preening and Bathing by ♂, occur as preliminary signals. Most attention seeking is stiffly executed Wing-flap by ♂. He then starts Jump-flights and most often these lead to Pursuit-flights. Courting parties of ♂♂ follow ♀ who continues to attract attention by Hostile-pumping. In Jump-flight, ♂ performs typical pre-flight signals then suddenly rises from water to fly stiffly away from ♀ before splashing down and quickly swimming back to group; often flights semi-circular, repeated many times and by different ♂♂. Pale upper-wing area and speculum revealed prominently during display. Eventually, ♀ will take off followed by several ♂♂ in Pursuit-flight. With ♀ leading, group twists and turns while gradually gaining height as birds circle. Usually ♂♂ detach one by one and drop away leaving single ♂ with ♀; pair set wings and drop at some distance from where they took off. Pair selection seems based on these contests. Copulation probably similar to other shovelers.

No information on nature of pairbond but probably monogamous and without ♂ parental care. Persistence of pairbond unknown.

Breeding and life cycle

Solitary nester on ground often at some distance from water and well-concealed in vegetation. Pair together when nest site searching. Season in Australia generally starts Aug and continues until end of year or sometimes beyond; inland populations occasionally breed in other months following erratic rainfall. In New Zealand, most laying Oct– Nov. Eggs elliptical or roundish oval, close-grained, smooth and glossy, light creamy white, faintly tinged blue-green (Marchant and Higgins 1990); 54 × 37 (51–57 × 36–40) ($n = 120$) (Frith 1982); no wild weights available, in captivity, 22 eggs of Australian birds weighed 38.9 and New Zealand ones averaged 42.1 ($n = 41$). Clutch size poorly known in Australia but probably 9–11, in New Zealand 9.3 (5–11) ($n = 26$). Incubation 24–25 days. Captive New Zealand day-olds weighed 25.9 ($n = 16$). Incubation and brood rearing by ♀ alone. Fledge in 8 weeks. Probably breed at one year. Breeding success, survival and longevity unknown.

Conservation and threats

Population in New Zealand possibly stable but in Australia may be less common than early last century. Steady decline in numbers in eastern Australia occurred mid 1980s-99, and this shown to be significant long-term trend (Kingsford *et al.* 1999, 2000). Despite lack of information, still relatively numerous and no immediate concern about survival. In past, hunting regulations employed to reduce numbers taken in Australia. Still important game species in New Zealand.

Peter Fullagar

Northern Shoveler *Anas clypeata*
PLATE 21

Anas clypeata Linnaeus, 1758, Syst. Nat., ed. 10, p. 124 coasts of Europe

Etymology: *clypeatus* L. for shield, in reference to shape of bill.

Other names: Common or European Shoveler, Shoveller. Danish: Skeand; French: Canard souchet; German: Löffelente; Icelandic: Skeiðönd; Japanese: Hashibiro-gamo; Spanish: Pato cuchara, Pato cucharón.

Variation: no subspecies.

Description

ADULT: dimorphic. ♂ in breeding or alternate plumage has iridescent green head except for brownish black crown, to back and rump; chestnut belly and black undertail coverts contrasting markedly with white of neck and breast, axillaries, underwing and strip between belly and undertail. Elongated scapulars pale blue, dull green, black and white; forewing pale blue; speculum bright green with white secondary coverts. Bill grey-black; legs orange-red; eyes yellow to orange. ♀ in breeding plumage, whole head and body brown (much like ♀ of other dabbling ducks) but all paler areas and feather edges cinnamon-pink to pink-buff. Bill olive-grey or dark brown with yellow to orange cutting edges and base; legs orange-red; eyes brown or yellow.

MOULT: ♂ eclipse resembles dark ♀, but more uniformly and redder brown; retains blue forewing and green speculum. ♀ in nonbreeding plumage, brown with paler feather edges, greyer head and neck, and darker forehead and crown. ♂ moults primaries early May–early June and ♀ *c* month later.

IMMATURE: resembles adult ♀ nonbreeding, but upperparts more uniform and underparts more streaked. Wings of ♂ brighter and those of ♀ duller (median and lesser coverts grey-brown and speculum sometimes absent).

DUCKLING: above blackish brown, lighter with buff-brown shafts on anterior back; side of head and dorsal and lateral spots, cream-buff with varying strong cinnamon tones; throat cinnamon, with breast straw yellow, grading to whitish on crissum; dark eye line and large ear-spot which may extend across cheek. Bill deep grey with vinaceous nail, reddish cast on side and buff-yellow on lower mandible; legs and feet blackish brown with orange-yellow sides; iris brown. Expansion of sub-terminal portion of bill pronounced in newly hatched ducklings and larger young have remarkably long bills (Nelson 1993).

MEASUREMENTS AND WEIGHT: ♂ adult wing ($n = 38$), 247, juv (1st winter) wing ($n = 66$), 238; adult skull ($n = 17$), 117.3, juv skull ($n = 26$), 116.7; adult tarsus ($n = 7$), 37.3, juv tarsus ($n = 23$), 37.5; adult winter weight ($n = 36$), 636, juv winter weight ($n = 66$), 598. ♀ adult wing ($n = 24$), 230, juv wing ($n = 46$), 228; adult skull ($n = 6$), 109.1, juv skull ($n = 14$), 108.4; adult tarsus ($n = 5$), 35.4, juv tarsus ($n = 9$), 36.6; adult winter weight ($n = 23$), 577, juv winter weight ($n = 46$), 555, data from WWT ringing stations. ♂ adult wing ($n = 27$), 244, juv wing ($n = 41$), 235; tarsus ($n = 48$), 37.2. ♀ adult wing ($n = 18$), 230; juv wing ($n = 29$), 222; tarsus ($n = 39$), 36.0 (Cramp and Simmons 1977).

Field characters

Large bill most diagnostic feature, usually angled downward 30–40° in flight and at rest. Bill not much longer than head, but breadth and spoon-shaped tip make it unique among Palearctic wildfowl. In flight, blue forewing conspicuous against brown primaries and, in ♂, black back contrasts with broad white braces; below from head to tail, distinctive pattern of green-white-red-white-black.

Voice

Relatively silent. During display period, ♂ utters repeated, hollow *took-a* call; additionally noisy wing rattling accompanies take-off during courtship flight. ♀ has variety of low quacking calls, including short descending series of *quacks* typical of genus, but only of 4–5 syllables. Sonograms of ♂ and ♀ calls in Cramp and Simmons (1977).

Range and status

Highly cosmopolitan northern duck. Holarctic, with wide breeding range generally 40–60°N, across North America and northern Eurasia. Strongly migratory in north of range, may be sedentary or dispersive further south. Generally winters 20–40°N, in temperate lowlands and northern tropics, south to western and eastern Africa, Arabian Peninsula, central America, India, and southeast Asia.

Nests in greatest abundance across mixed prairies of North America (densities 1.7–2.9 pairs per km^2, Bellrose 1980) but also occurs in parklands (0.88 to 2.5 pairs per km^2, Bellrose 1980). Numbers decrease in short-grass and long-grass prairie zones and Rocky Mountain marshes from central British Columbia to southern Colorado. Large numbers also breed in western US south to California. Breeding numbers declined (18% in 1955–89) in most important area, Canadian prairie/parklands, although increased over same period in other parts of North American range (e.g. Alaska). In America, winters over much of southern US, with up to 260 000 in California, about half of which winter in San Joaquin Valley, and 235 000 in Louisiana, about two-

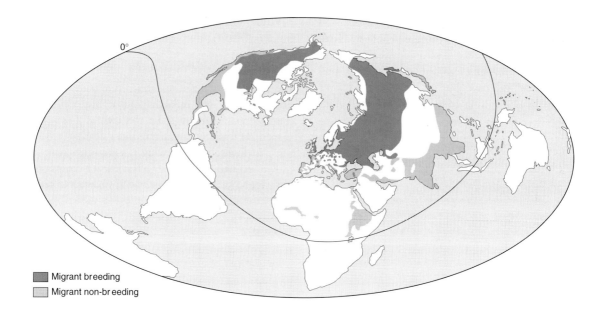

Migrant breeding
Migrant non-breeding

thirds of which winter in coastal marshes between Marsh Island and Sabine Lake (Bellrose 1980). Others continue to Mexico (*c* 260 000), along Atlantic coast of America, Cuba and other parts of the West Indies. Have shown 1.1% decline per annum in wintering numbers in North America 1967–86 (Boyd 1990), perhaps reflecting decline in breeding mentioned above. Continental numbers estimated at *c* 2.6 million (Rose and Scott 1997). Current North American/Mexican winter population estimated at 3.5 million, and old world population estimated at 1.5–2 million (Wetlands International 2002).

In Eurasia, avoids arctic areas but breeds north to Iceland (where rare), sparingly in southwest and southern Europe, with main breeding range from British Isles east across central Europe and Asia to Kamchatka, south to Mongolia and southern central Asia. Separation of populations difficult since almost continuous wintering range at Mediterranean levels across Atlantic coasts to east Asia. Winter estimates suggest 40 000 in northwest Europe, 450 000 in Black Sea/Mediterranean/West Africa, 400 000 in southwest Asia/east Africa (Wetlands International 2002). Also estimated are 100 000–1 000 000 wintering in southern Asia and 500 000–1 000 000 in eastern and southeastern Asia (Miyabayashi and Mundkur 1999)

including 500 000 in China, 7000 in South Korea and 23 000 in Japan. Northwest European population appears stable over past 20 years, although migrates further south in harsh winters, and this tends to complicate pattern (Rose 1995). Major concentration in east Mediterranean inadequately covered and no determination of trends possible, but increase in numbers wintering in west Mediterranean (Rose 1995). Trends in numbers wintering in southwest Asia/northeast Africa unknown; however, Krivenko (1993) reported sharp decline in west and central Siberia 1972–89.

Habitat and general habits

Sociable ducks of freshwater lakes and marshes, preferably well vegetated but muddy shores in open country. Also winters on brackish lagoons and tidal mudflats. Although occurring in small numbers through taiga into tundra zone, main haunts in temperate open woodland, grassland and steppe regions. Copious floating vegetation tolerated if enough patches of open water and abundant surface plankton present. Attracted by sewage farms, rice fields and other artificial waters (e.g. overflow river lakes in Mississippi River basin) bordered by vegetation.

In deep water, apparently feeds on surface plankton (steady stream of water taken in at bill tip and ejected at base, strained through lamellae). Groups frequently observed feeding in tight rotating circles (head to tail), stirring up water surface. Because of microscopic size and fast digestibility, plankton does not show up adequately in food habit studies based on gizzard contents. In shallow water, usually feeds by partially or totally immersing head, moving slowly with neck stretched forward, bill sweeping from side to side. About 25% of diet macroscopic animal life, particularly small molluscs, insects and larvae. Marshes and vegetated lakes contribute seeds of bulrushes and pondweeds. ♂ may stay with ♀ during moult, or may undertake moult migration to favoured moulting areas (e.g. Volga Delta).

Displays and breeding behaviour

Gregarious, except when nesting, most likely to congregate when feeding. Flocks often show unbalanced sex ratio; thus, often excess of ♂♂ in The Netherlands rising to over 80% in autumn and winter. In America, hunting records 1966–73 showed 66% ♂♂ in adult sample and 52% ♂♂ in 1st winter (Bellrose 1980), whilst flock scans during spring showed composition of 60% ♂♂ (Bellrose *et al.* 1961). Increasingly consists of pairs as season progresses but, as with other species that acquire nuptial plumage late in season, does not establish pairbond until winter. In spring, courtship of ♀ by group of ♂♂ common (Johnsgard 1965a). As time for nesting draws near, each pair increasingly becomes confined to specific area. Home range consists of 'waiting area', several peripheral ponds and nest site.

Monogamous pairbond probably of seasonal duration. Poston (1969) considered pairbond still weak on arrival on breeding ground in southwest Alberta. ♂♂ vary length of time spent with mate after incubation begins; some desert on 1st day, others stay for 2 weeks or more, and few faithful until hatching (Oring 1964). Presence of territorial ♂ in suitable breeding habitat often belies presence of nesting ♀. Promiscuous tendencies on part of ♂♂ weak, and rape of other ♀♀ rare (McKinney 1970), although some harassment suffered by ♀ when off nest from territorial and unpaired ♂♂. Polyandry

reportedly common (Millais 1902), but this not substantiated in recent studies.

Breeding and life cycle

Regularly returns to same nesting area. Laying starts early–mid May in northern Russia (Cramp and Simmons 1977). At Delta Marsh, Manitoba, 42% of ♀♀ marked on nest returned subsequent year (Sowls 1955). In view of annual mortality, this homing rate may represent all those alive. Unpaired ♂♂ may also return to same breeding area, and likely that paired ♂♂ follow spouse to breeding area of ♀♀. Such site fidelity increases susceptibility to habitat loss.

May spend 6–8 days selecting nest site and constructing nest, usually scrape on ground lined with grass and down. When grass cover unavailable, uses hayfields, meadows and, rarely, bulrush marshes. Most nests 25–75 m from waiting areas. Eggs laid almost every day; bluntly elliptical ovate, olive-buff to pale green-grey; 52 × 37 (unknown sample, Bellrose 1980) in North America, 52 × 37 (48–57 × 35–40) (n = 275, Schönwetter 1960–66) in Europe; weight 40 (35–43) (n = 27, Cramp and Simmons 1977) or 38.6 (33.5–44.0) (n = 100) in captivity. Average clutch 9.4 (5–14) (n = 585) (Bellrose 1980) in North America, and 9–11 (6–14) (Cramp and Simmons 1977) in Europe. Single brood, but will replace lost clutch (21% of 33 marked ♀♀ re-nested at Delta Marsh, Manitoba, Sowls 1955). Incubation 22–23 days (Cramp and Simmons 1977). Has relatively high nesting success, studies in North America indicated 59% of 575 nests hatched. In Europe, of 451 eggs laid in Finland in 3 years, 74% hatched and 17.5% reared to fledging (Hildén 1964a); in Scotland, of 26 clutches, 54% hatched, 42% predated and 4% deserted (Cramp and Simmons 1977). Bellrose (1980) reported on 295 successful nests, 0.68 of an egg per nest failed to hatch, of which 25% infertile and 75% contained dead embryos.

Only ♀ tends young, leading them from nest to pond used earlier as 'waiting area'. Newly hatched ducklings in captivity weighed 25.1 (n = 29). Mean brood size at hatching of 8.7 young (unknown sample) reduced to 6.8 for Class I age group (n = 259) representing considerable loss during 1st few days after hatching (see Gollop and Marshall 1954 for definitions). Class II broods numbered 6.5 ducklings ($n = 151$) and Class III broods contained 5.9 ($n = 80$), 22% loss of those leaving nest. Fledging takes minimum of 36 days in Alaska, and most fledge in 52–66 days in Manitoba (Bellrose 1980).

Most breed when 1 year old. Information on survival scanty. Immatures from small sample ringed in Minnesota had annual survival rate of 29%, adults 39% (Lee *et al.* 1964); while, in Britain, adults showed survival rate of 56–63% (Boyd 1962, Wainwright 1967). Longevity record of BTO ringed bird 13 years 7 months (Toms and Clark 1998).

Conservation and threats

Throughout northwest European range, numbers show period of stability after steady growth in 1960–70s (Rose 1995). Breeding attempts in Britain and Ireland have, however, declined during same period, with 12% reduction attributed to habitat loss in 10 km squares where breeding recorded 1968–72 and 1988–91 (Mitchell 1993). Lack of consistent count data does not permit determination of trends from other Eurasian wintering areas, and adequate surveillance remains priority here. Most major key sites in Africa and west Eurasia protected. Over 60 keys sites in northwest Europe (supporting 30–40% of that population), 43 key wintering sites in Mediterranean/west Africa and 42 in southwest Asia/northeast Africa, protected. Few key passage sites known for last 2 populations, but Manych-Godlio lakes north of Caucasus Mountains recorded being used simultaneously by 555 000 in spring (Scott and Rose 1996); if true, most birds from both these wintering populations may be present. Adequate safeguards for all internationally important sites needed. Quarry species through most of world range but, apparently partly because of poor flavour, rarely taken in large numbers, e.g. only 36 000 killed annually in US and Canada 1983–86 (Boyd 1988).

Carl Mitchell

Madagascar Teal *Anas bernieri*
PLATE 16

Querquedula Bernieri 'J. Verr.' Hartlaub, 1860, Journ. Ornith., **8**, p. 173
Madagascar

Etymology: named after Chevalier J.A. Bernier, collector in Madagascar 1831–34.

Other names: Bernier's Teal. French: Sarcelle de Bernier; Malagasy: Mireha.

Variation: no subspecies.

Description

ADULT: sexes similar, ♂ having steeper forehead than ♀, feature discernible in field (Young *et al.* 1997). Body uniform brown, darker centres to feathers giving fine spotted appearance, not discernible at distance. Speculum black with broad white fore-band and smaller white trailing edge. Underwing grey with white axillaries. Bill reddish; legs grey-brown; eye large, bright and chestnut-brown. Previous descriptions suggest chestnut plumage, and plates often, erroneously, give dark cap to both sexes (Madge and Burn 1988). Bill of ♀ grey when breeding.

MOULT: no ♂ eclipse plumage. Wing and tail moult after breeding on secure well-vegetated lakes, e.g. Antsamaka, where flightless adults caught and ringed June 1997, and May and June 1998–2000. Captive birds flightless for 3 weeks during post-nuptial moult.

IMMATURE: greyer than adult, spotting on feathers more marked.

DUCKLING: dark grey upperparts and whitish grey underparts give shelduckling-like pied appearance. Darker areas more extensive than on Grey Teal, and thick white line runs from above wing to vent. Bill pinky grey (Young and Brayshaw 2004).

MEASUREMENTS AND WEIGHT: from Bemamba, July–Oct 1993 and 1995 ♂ ($n = 7$) wing, 205–216 (209); bill, 34–40 (36); skull, 79–84.5 (82); weight, 320–405 (382). ♀ ($n = 2$) wing, 199–203; bill, 35.6–38.8; skull, 78.9–81.5; weight, 365–385 (Young *et al.* 1997). From Antsamaka, May–June 1999 and

2000, in wing moult ♂ (*n* = 83) bill, 33.6–48.7 (37.9); skull, 77.2–89.7 (82.3); weight (*n* = 104) 330–450 (385). ♀ (*n* = 66) bill, 32.2–47.9 (35.5); skull, 73.7–81.5 (77.8); weight (*n* = 75), 290–420 (351.5). Captive ♂ wing (*n* = 41), 205–220 (213); bill (*n* = 7), 33.5–37.5 (34.75); skull (*n* = 41) 79.7–84.9 (82.6); weight (*n* = 39), 325–420 (387). Captive ♀ wing (*n* = 50), 188–217 (205.6); bill (*n* = 10), 33–36 (33.7); skull (*n* = 52) 76.5–81.7 (79.2); weight (*n* = 49), 270–408 (361). Tarsus (unsexed) 30–38 (Madge and Burn 1988); tail ♂ 83–91 (Delacour 1954–56).

Field characters

Length 400 mm. Small size, uniform colour, wading habits and long neck characteristic and unmistakable. Seldom swims and feeds by wading in shallows; rarely flocks. On wing, distinctive black speculum and adjoining white bands unique among waterfowl. Among grey teal, upper and underwing patterns differ between species, and eye of Madagascar Teal darker (Young *et al.* 1997).

Voice

Poorly recorded; can be vocal. ♂ calls include short, quiet, multi-syllabic whistles, reminiscent of Fulvous Whistling-Duck. ♀ has sharp, harsh croaking *quack* and soft clucking; Incitement and Decrescendo calls may be loud. No sonograms published.

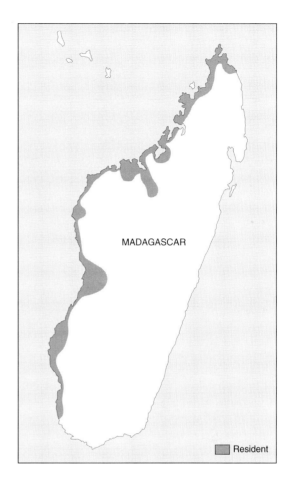

MADAGASCAR

☐ Resident

Range and status

Endemic to Madagascar, and declining. Found predominantly on west coast, historic record from Lake Alaotra doubtful (Langrand 1985). Subfossil record suggests more widespread (Langrand and Goodman 1995) before arrival of humans. Rarely seen until few found on lakes north of Ambereny in 1970 (Salvan 1970). Lakes Masama and Bemamba surveyed shortly after discovery, with 120 found at Bemamba (Scott and Lubbock 1974, Young *et al.* 1993). Small numbers recorded from many west coast lakes, rivers and in mangrove, with majority seen between Antsalova and Morondava, particularly at Lakes Bemamba and Antsamaka, and at Beroboka-nord; population of 100–500 estimated from this region in 1993 (Safford 1993). Most sightings made during west coast dry season (Mar–Nov) when not nesting, probably because researchers prefer to visit then.

Outside Antsalova–Morondava area, seen in 1990s at many locations along coastal zone: at Lake Tsimanampetsotsa, on sand-bars in Tsiribihina, Betsiboka and Mahavavy estuaries and in Baly and Bombetoka Bays. Also seen inland of Mahajanga, at artificial lake, Amboromalandy, and at Lake Ampotaka, 5 km further south, and at Lake Ambondromofehy. All sightings from western domain; recent observations south of Vohimar and in Lokia Bay on northeast coast, still from this domain. Largest concentrations recorded in Betsiboka estuary and Bombetoka Bay in dry season—e.g. 81 in June 1995 (Thorstrom and Rabarisoa 1996)—and at Lake Antsamaka when moulting—e.g. 101 caught and ringed May–June 1998, and 115 May–June 2000. Wetlands International (2002) suggested total population of 1500–2500.

Habitat and general habits

Forced from shallow wetlands by spread of rice cultivation, now found during west-coast dry season (Mar–Nov) in saline areas, shallow lakes, exposed sand-bars in river estuaries and mangrove. Shuns aquatic vegetation, floating plants and marshy lake edges during dry season, preferring exposed areas of shallow water. Active dabblers, almost constantly moving forwards in shallow water. In July at Bemamba, foraging took up 80% of daylight hours, followed by short rests during heat of day, with foraging again on moonlit nights; 68% of feeding while wading in shallows, shelduck-like (Green *et al.* 1994), but will swim and up-end. Ducklings and immatures dive for food.

Seen occasionally with Fulvous Whistling-duck, and may forage in shallows with waders such as Black-winged Stilt *Himantopus himantopus*. Surveys suggest similar dry season requirements to flamingos, especially within lake systems (Safford 1993). Diet known only of moulting birds at Antsamaka in June (Razafindrahanta 1999); faeces contained remains of terrestrial and aquatic insects (Hymenoptera, Coleoptera, Homoptera, Diptera and Hemiptera) with seeds of Cyperaceae, Nymphaeaceae, Ceratophyllaceae, and leaves and stems of monocotyledons.

Breeds in mangrove and flooded forest during wet season (Dec–Mar). As breeding lakes dry, moves to coast, estuaries and shallow lakes still holding water (e.g. Bemamba); not truly nomadic. In dry years, moves to coast after nesting. Flightless birds hide in aquatic vegetation if threatened.

Displays and breeding behaviour

High degree of aggression during dry season by pairs within small flocks at Lake Bemamba; 97% of attacks were on conspecifics (Green *et al.* 1994). Head-pumping display, recorded in wild birds (Green *et al.* 1994), similar to that of Brown Teal and Grey Teal. Behaviour observed from captive ♂♂ (Young 2002) includes Head-shake, Head-roll, Head-throw-swim, Burp, Grunt-whistle and Head-up-tail-up. Chin-lift and Down-up, common displays of Grey Teal, not seen. Lateral Incitement by captive ♀ recorded. Copulation followed by Bridling, as in Grey Teal; however, also exhibits Nod-swim and Turn-back-of-head.

Breeding and life cycle

Breeding occurs during west-coast wet season (Dec–Mar) in forested wetlands, especially mangroves when water levels highest; majority of west-coast wildfowl breed at same period. Nesting unrecorded until Mar 1997 when pairs found in mangrove forest at Lake Ambaratamaty, and adjacent wetlands of Ambereny region. Nests located annually since, with further site in mangrove at Ampasindava, northwestern Madagascar, in 1998 (Halleux 1998). Copulation seen in July (Green *et al.* 1994), pairs probably remaining together during dry season. Territory vigorously defended around nest site by both sexes; conspecifics and some other species chased away. Captives chased White-backed Duck underwater. ♂ remains close to nesting ♀ through incubation, and accompanies brood.

Nests in holes in Mangrove *Avicennia marina* trees. Eggs smooth, elliptical, pale fawn to yellow-buff, may be stained; in captivity 46.1 × 34.7 (40.6–51.4 × 32.3–37.6) ($n = 262$); weight 29.4 (27.3–32.4) ($n = 22$); laid in Madagascar, 44.1 × 32.4 (43.3–45.0 × 31.6–33.1) ($n = 3$); clutch in captivity 6.7 (3–9) ($n = 38$) (Young *et al.* 2001). Incubation in captivity, by ♀, 27–28 days; hatch weight 18.4 (13.5–24.1) ($n = 79$); fledge in 6.5–7 weeks. Breeds in captivity at one year. No data from wild on breeding success, survival nor longevity.

Conservation and threats

Declined in places through natural aridification before arrival of humans < 2000 years ago (Goodman and Rakotozafy 1997). Threatened through conversion of shallow wetlands to rice production since 14th century, becoming restricted to areas of west coast too saline for rice growing.

Given Endangered status by BirdLife International (2000). Full protection and establishment of reserves within remaining areas of suitable wetland on west coast required. Use of nestboxes may maximize breeding potential within protected areas. Further surveys essential to establish parameters of habitat and reproductive cycle at, e.g. Lake Bemamba, where most observations made. Bemamba may prove less important for survival, whereas coastal mangrove, estuaries and breeding areas must be protected.

Problems of hunting lessened in recent years as travel and ammunition became expensive; however, sport hunters from overseas still encouraged, and may be significant threat (*contra* Young *et al.* 1993); education on local species and their status non-existent. Probably not trapped by subsistence hunters using snares, slingshot and dogs during dry season, as lives in open areas; however, vulnerable when nesting, since eggs harvested from all tree-hole nesting species. Adults, trapped when nesting or moulting, reputed to be popular food, and suitable habitat, particularly mangrove, accessible from towns, heavily utilized by human population. Trapping at moulting sites may be major cause of decline. Ducklings captured and reared for eating. Drought has forced humans to move to new areas of Madagascar and, with habitat modification occurring along west coast, last part of range under threat of conversion to rice cultivation.

Three ♂♂ captured in 1993, and 2 pairs in 1995, as part of breeding programme at Jersey Zoo (Durrell Wildlife Conservation Trust). First eggs laid June 1998, and 177 young hatched by 2001.

Glyn Young

Indonesian Teal *Anas gibberifrons*
PLATE 16

Anas (Mareca) gibberifrons S. Müller, 1842, Verh. Nat. Geschiedenis Nederlandsche Overzeesche Bezittingen, Land-Volkenkunde, p. 159
Celebes (Sulawesi)

Etymology: *gibberis* L. means hump and *frons* brow, in reference to bulging forehead.

Other names: Sunda Teal, East Indian Grey Teal, Oceanic Teal, Indonesian Gray Teal. Indonesian: Itik kelabu.

Variation: no subspecies. Here considered resident grey teal population of Indonesian islands; see Ripley (1942) for measurements and drawings of grey teal foreheads.

Description

ADULT: sexes similar, ♂ may have larger, more prominent forehead. Similar to Grey Teal but darker, more russet, with distinctive bulbous forehead. Speculum black with white area on leading edge; terminal band narrow and buff. Both sexes have obvious iridescence, usually appearing bronze, on 7th–10th secondaries, probably narrower in ♀. Underwing coverts black. Other details of plumage as Grey Teal. Bill blue-grey; iris red.

MOULT: no ♂ eclipse; timing of body and wing moults unknown. Outside breeding season, eye appears dark brown.

IMMATURE: similar to adult, spotting finer, giving dark 'clean' appearance.

DUCKLING: brownish above with grey underparts. Black cap; face, cheeks, chin and breast to legs brown with dark line behind eye and dark spot over ear. Prominent pale spot either side of rump (Young and Brayshaw 2004).

MEASUREMENTS AND WEIGHT: ♂ wing ($n = 19$), 178–205 (193); tail ($n = 19$), 67–90 (83); bill ($n = 19$), 34–39 (37); tarsus ($n = 17$), 29–38 (34); weight ($n = 6$), 300–450 (402). ♀ wing ($n = 12$), 175–199 (184); tail ($n = 12$), 61–82 (73); bill ($n = 12$), 32–37 (35); tarsus ($n = 11$), 29–35 (32); weight ($n = 5$), 360–455 (403) from specimens measured at Bogor Museum (by late G. F. van Tets).

Field characters

Head shape unmistakable (see Fullagar 1992) and differs from any similar duck. Lack of bulbous forehead of Grey Teal of Australia suggests Indonesian Teal sedentary within tropics. Wing pattern, especially speculum, should make identification simple, except for presence in region of Grey Teal. Care necessary in identification of flying birds unless head shape obvious. Note that Chestnut Teal recorded in Papua New Guinea. Duckling readily distinguished from Grey

Teal duckling (Young and Brayshaw 2004). Function of bulbous forehead unknown; arises early in embryonic development, and is enlargement of frontal bones of skull to form 2 sinuses separated by thin septum. Sinuses not like those of other dabbling ducks (Ripley 1942), and unlikely to be related to salt extraction by super-orbital glands, although feeds in saline water, as do all grey teal.

Voice

Generally quiet, but not well studied. ♀ has harsh quacking Decrescendo and softer clucking calls. ♂ whistles rarely and has sharp Burp often given on land. No sound recordings known.

Range and status

Constant confusion with Grey Teal has complicated observation. Range thought to be Java, Bali, Lombok, Borneo (Pulau Jawa, Kalimantan), Celebes (Sulawesi, including Salayar, Muna, Buton and Sula), Lesser Sunda Islands including Sumba, Flores, Timor and Wetar. Recorded in Sumatra but not known to breed. Grey Teal rarely breeds in far northern Australia; however, disperses widely, sometimes in large numbers, and found regularly within presumed range of Indonesian Teal (see Young 1996a for distribution of grey teal group in Asia). Nothing known of interaction, but hybridization suspected.

Close relationship with Grey Teal has, unfortunately, left Asian endemic under-recorded. Little known of biology, as largely ignored even by ornithologists, seemingly content with view that birds in Indonesia are same as better-studied Australian duck. Wetlands International (2002) suggested stable population of 10 000–100 000.

Habitat and general habits

Found in marshes, ponds and rivers. Although poorly recorded, large concentrations probably occur in mangrove swamps. Diet presumably similar to Grey Teal; may feed in mangrove areas.

Displays and breeding behaviour

Little known. Grunt-whistle recorded, no down-up seen in captivity.

Breeding and life cycle

Little known. All data from captivity; nests on ground and in boxes; eggs smooth, elliptical and white; 49.25 × 35.8 (44.4–54.0 × 33.4–38.8) ($n = 109$); weight unrecorded; clutch 8.3 (6–11); incubation 26–28 days, by ♀ alone. Hatch weight 19.4 (17.1–21.4) ($n = 3$); fledge in c 7–8 weeks. Probably

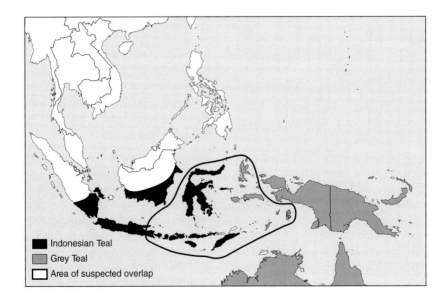

Indonesian Teal
Grey Teal
Area of suspected overlap

mature at one year. No data on breeding success, adult survival or longevity.

Conservation and threats

All ducks widely hunted in Indonesia, and Indonesian Teal found in markets, apparently even in Jakarta. Widespread deforestation, burning and other habitat modification undoubtedly affects numbers, as they do other endemic wildlife of region. Insufficient information to determine conservation needs. Studies required to determine distribution and status, and to investigate feeding habits, social behaviour and breeding biology.

Peter Fullagar and Glyn Young

Grey Teal *Anas gracilis*

Anas gracilis Buller, 1869, Ibis, p. 41
Manawatu River, North Island, New Zealand.

Etymology: *gracilis* L. for slender.

Other names: Gray Teal, Australasian Gray Teal, Mountain, Slender or Wood Teal. Australian Aboriginal: Calyung, Chin-bijee, Googagoora, Nimon, Quall-yuan, Wang-anner; Dutch: Grijze Taling; French: Sarcelle grise; German: Weisskehlente; Maori: Tete, Tete moroiti, Pohoriki; Spanish: Cerceta grís.

Variation: no subspecies. Here treated as highly mobile, often widely dispersive, teal of Australia, including Rennell Island Teal *A. g. remissa* Ripley, 1942 and Australian Grey Teal *A. g. rogersi* Mathews, 1912 (also called *A. g. mathewsi* Phillips, 1923). Presence in New Zealand doubtless supported by occasional invasion across Tasman Sea; occurrence on other remote islands (e.g. Solomon's) evidence of such dispersal.

Description

ADULT: sexes similar but ♂ slightly larger than ♀. Whole body plumage of adult ♂ uniformly grey with indistinct scaly or mottled pattern formed by pale edging to most feathers. Head faintly streaked and noticeably darker on crown graduating to much paler on face. Chin and upperthroat distinctly pale creamy white. Breast noticeably spotty. Plumage pattern of wings identical to Chestnut Teal. Upperwing dark brown with prominent white wedge, diminishing inwards, along leading edge of black speculum and narrow white tips on trailing edge. Oval patch of bronze-green across inner speculum. Underwing brown with black-brown leading edge and conspicuous white axillaries and central under coverts. Bill blue-grey, darker on ridge; legs and feet dull grey; eyes bright crimson. ♀ entirely similar to ♂, with no plumage feature providing means of distinguishing them.

MOULT: no ♂ eclipse plumage and no seasonal differences in plumage except by wear. Moult of body feathers continuous, including tertials, but wing quills and tail shed once annually during complete post-breeding plumage change. In breeding pairs, flightless moult earlier in ♂ than ♀. Plumage of both sexes duller by midsummer. Although moult detectable in most tracts throughout year, greatest intensity occurs post-breeding; however, both sexes undergo another major replacement of body plumage in autumn or early winter ahead of breeding season. Occasionally delays moult, depending on environmental conditions such as prolonged wet season.

IMMATURE: like adult but lower neck and breast heavily and uniformly streaked longitudinally rather than spotted. Eyes dull brown until completion of post-juvenile moult, sometimes for longer. Complete post-juvenile body moult, as in Chestnut Teal, at *c* 14–17 weeks including replacement of tail (when notched juvenile feathers lost) but not wings. This moult occurs in 1st autumn or early winter after which plumage identical to adult.

DUCKLING: dull grey-brown above and off-white below, similar to ducklings of Chestnut Teal but paler. Chin white but face warmer brown with dark stripe through eye and less distinct stripe below and behind eye usually visible as small patch at ear. Trailing edges of wing pads off-white and small white patches either side of rump. Bill dark blue-grey; legs and feet blue-grey; eyes dark brown (Young and Brayshaw 2004).

MEASUREMENTS AND WEIGHT: ♂ wing (*n* = 209), 175–220 (205); tail (*n* = 8), 81–97 (88); bill (*n* = 210), 32–43 (37); tarsus (*n* = 12), 33–37 (35); weight (*n* = 210), 395–670 (507). ♀ wing (*n* = 148), 164–243 (198); tail (*n* = 6), 77–89 (82); bill (*n* = 148), 32–39 (36); tarsus (*n* = 11), 31–36 (34); weight (*n* = 138), 350–602 (474) (Marchant and Higgins 1990).

Field characters

Small drab grey slender duck, 370–470 mm long, most likely to be confused with Chestnut Teal. Head often held high on slender but short neck with prominent rising forehead and long nape feathers that increase size of head when raised. When in pairs, greater body length and higher posture of head of ♂ usually noticeable. Best distinction of sex is voice and behaviour. Body plumage of Chestnut Teal ♀ much warmer and darker toned than Grey Teal. Head of Chestnut Teal ♀ darker, more obviously streaked and lacking clear pale chin characteristic of Grey Teal. In both species, plumage may become worn or heavily iron-stained making identification more difficult. Characteristic calls and ♂ behaviour foolproof way to distinguish ♂ Grey Teal from ♀ Chestnut Teal. Hybrids between Grey and Chestnut Teal rare, but can cause difficulties, especially with ♀ hybrids. Most ♂ hybrids look like eclipsed ♂ Chestnut Teal; darker crown with signs of green, some chestnut feathering to underbody and at least shadow of pale patch at rear of flank. Hybrid ♂♂ remain almost unchanged in this dull plumage, unlike true eclipse of ♂ Chestnut Teal which is transient.

Voice

Repertoire identical to that of Chestnut Teal. Details and sonograms of adult calls in Frith (1982) and Marchant and Higgins (1990).

Range and status

Most widespread and abundant duck in Australia. Endemic to Australia, vagrant elsewhere in region

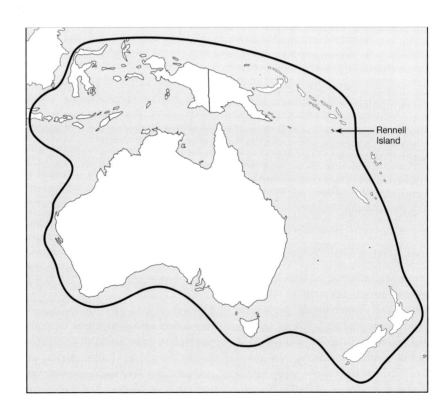

and occasional dispersal leads to establishment of local breeding populations as, for instance, in New Zealand. Similar occurrences no doubt explain presence until recently in Solomons (Rennell Island), where possibly became extinct following mining operations and introduction of *Tilapia* fish into only freshwater lake (Kear and Williams 1978). After particularly favourable conditions in Australia, numbers increase greatly with inevitable massive dispersal to nearby regions. Vagrants reported widely after these events in Indonesia, South Moluccas, Timor and New Guinea region. Occasionally reaches sub-antarctic and oceanic islands, e.g. Lord Howe Island and Macquarie Island. Sub-fossil remains found in New Caledonia (Balouet and Olson 1989).

Measures of abundance complicated by erratic dispersal and mobility, making comprehensive survey difficult. Suggested that population of 4 000–10 000 in southwestern Australia undertakes regular seasonal migrations between winter and spring breeding areas in interior and summer refuges on southwest coast (Gentilli and Bekle 1983). Population of Australia estimated at least 1.7 million but may be as high as 4.2 million and possibly > 5 million at times (Marchant and Higgins 1990, Kingsford *et al.* 1999, 2000). Wet-season concentrations of nonbreeders occur in Northern Territory most years occasionally numbering as many as 50 000 in Alligator Rivers region (Morton *et al.* 1990b). Steady decline in numbers in eastern Australia from mid 1980s to 1999 shown to be significant long-term trend (Kingsford *et al.* 1999). New Zealand population increasing; estimated at < 20 000 in 1970s (Mills 1976) and at 25 000–100 000 two decades later (Rose and Scott 1997).

Habitat and general habits

In Australia found on almost any wetland. Breeding largely restricted to southeast and east below 20°S but many utilize inland swamps during breeding season, although coastal breeding within range of Chestnut Teal far from uncommon. Essentially like Chestnut Teal, feeds by filtering surface of water or soft muds, and up-ends in shallow water, occasionally diving. Food mostly invertebrate but some

studies biased by sampling method emphasizing vegetative material persistent in gizzards. For details of diet see Marchant and Higgins (1990).

Displays and breeding behaviour

Comparative studies by Prawiradilaga (1985) confirmed behavioural repertoire of Grey Teal essentially identical to that of Chestnut Teal (see that account, and also Marchant and Higgins 1990). Sustained or long-term monogamous pairbond general, with no evidence of sustained polygamy or strategic promiscuous matings.

Breeding and life cycle

Like Chestnut Teal and no significant differences observed. Nests solitarily and usually in hollows of trees along watercourses or flooded areas. Opportunistic character of breeding overemphasized (e.g. Frith 1982), whereas laying period should be described more properly as seasonal (for detail see Marchant and Higgins 1990). Over most of breeding range, i.e. south of summer rainfall areas of tropics and sub-tropics, nests June–Feb, but breeding can occur in other months following exceptional rainfall and flooding. Breeding later in north Australia but relatively uncommon above 25°S. In New Zealand nests Sept–Nov.

No nest constructed except from materials at site but copious pale grey 'sticky' down added from *c* time of laying penultimate egg. Site chosen by pair in nest-searching behaviour when ♂ accompanies ♀ during inspection of possible cavities. Eggs elliptical, fine textured, smooth and almost lustreless, cream or light creamy white; 50 × 36 (49–58 × 35–42) ($n = 126$) (Frith 1982); laid at daily intervals in early morning; weight in captivity 34.3 ($n = 81$); clutch 8.9 (4–17); larger clutches (up to 32 eggs reported) due to dump laying by additional ♀ or ♀♀. ♂ continues to guard site through incubation, remaining close and accompanying ♀ during recesses from nest. ♀ usually leaves 3 times, early morning, noon and late afternoon, and remains off eggs for *c* 1 h daily. Laying of 2nd clutch starts around time of fledging of 1st brood, but earliest recorded was 32 days after hatch. Replacement clutch usually started within 3 weeks of loss of earlier clutch or brood. Incubation, by ♀ alone, 28 ± 2 days. Captive day-old ducklings weigh 23.0 (*n* = 39). Details of incubation and brood-rearing routines summarized in Marchant and Higgins (1990). Young capable of flight at *c* 55 days. Some information on breeding success given in Marchant and Higgins (1990) but few quantitative studies reported.

Pairs commonly rear 2 broods a season, but unlikely to rear more except during specially prolonged floods. Many pairs lay several clutches if broods lost. Close parental care of ducklings by both parents. Broods may remain in close association with parents for some weeks after gaining flight. Pair formation usually occurs in 1st winter and both sexes capable of breeding at one year. Limited data on survival and longevity; studies in New Zealand found higher survival of juveniles post-fledging for heavier than lighter-weight ducklings, and almost complete turnover of population every 4 years (Mills 1976).

Conservation and threats

Most widespread of waterfowl in Australia and one of most abundant. New Zealand population (and other regional isolates) derives from periodic emigration from Australia. These spectacular dispersal movements follow good breeding seasons, particularly with major flooding inland; widespread dispersal occurs as consequence of inevitable drying of inland wetlands. Increasing in numbers in New Zealand, where nestbox schemes employed successfully (McFadden 1983), but trend in eastern Australia 1986–99 shows steady decline with no exceptional high peaks. Protected from hunting in New Zealand (although some shot accidentally); is major game species in States or Territories of Australia where duck hunting still permitted.

Peter Fullagar

Andaman Teal *Anas albogularis*

Mareca albogularis Hume, 1873, Stray Feathers, **1**, p. 303
Andaman Islands.

Etymology: *albogularis* L. *albus* means white, *gula* is throat.

Other names: Gibbery, Mangrove Teal, Oceanic Teal. German: Andamenenente.

Variation: no subspecies; however, racial differentiation (larger amount of white on head), of *A. a. leucopareus* J.H. Fleming, 1911 from northern and central islands of archipelago, suggested but unconfirmed.

Description

ADULT: sexes similar. Like Grey Teal but darker with warmer grey tones on body. Unlike Grey Teal, crown more uniformly black and has white eye-ring, sometimes with other irregular areas of white on face, chin and fore-neck. Forehead slightly swollen (Delacour 1954–64) but not so bulbous as that of Indonesian Teal. Speculum like that of Grey Teal but 1st secondary almost white on outer edge and wing band slightly wider and darker buff. Some individuals have pinkish margins on lower mandible, otherwise bill like Grey Teal (Phillips 1922–26).

MOULT: no ♂ eclipse plumage. Nothing reported on timing of moults.

IMMATURE: no information.

DUCKLING: like that of Grey Teal, grey-brown above with duller underparts. Facial pattern varies (Young and Brayshaw 2004).

MEASUREMENTS AND WEIGHT: ♂ wing, 199–205; tail, 79–81; tarsus, 35–37; culmen, 34–36; weight, 400. ♀ wing, 197–205; culmen, 34–35; weight, 340 (Hume and Marshall 1879–81, Delacour 1954–64).

Field characters

No similar duck in Andamans.

Voice

No description or recordings but repertoire said to resemble Grey Teal (Delacour 1954–64); see Phillips (1922–26) for further references.

Range and status

Endemic to Andaman group of islands in Bay of Bengal. Present from North Andaman to Little Andaman in south (Vijayan 1996); not found in Nicobar Islands. Vagrant once on coast of Myanmar (Burma). Information on distribution and status provided by Vijayan (1996); survey concluded population of 500–700, but Wetlands International (2002) suggested declining population of 500–1000.

Habitat and general habits

Reported from coastal mangrove swamps and wherever there are freshwater lagoons. Also found in paddy-fields. Said to use creeks and dyke-intersected marshes somewhat inland during breeding season following start of monsoon in June (Phillips 1922–26). Information in Phillips (1922–26) suggested that habits resemble those of Grey Teal.

Displays and breeding behaviour

Nothing known. Displays like those of related species (Delacour 1954–64)

Breeding and life cycle

Almost nothing described, making comparisons with related species impossible. Breeding starts early July (Phillips 1922–26), nests in tree hollows or on ground, clutch reported as 10 (Phillips 1922–26) but probably smaller. Eggs cream and devoid of gloss; 49.0×36.3 ($47.3–51.2 \times 35.7–37.3$) ($n = 10$) with calculated weight of 36 (Schönwetter 1960–66), large for size of $\female$. Both parents care for brood.

Conservation and threats

Confined to Andaman Islands, and likely to be particularly vulnerable. Without more ecological information, impossible to assess conservation needs. Not listed as Endangered by BirdLife International (2000) because of uncertainty over racial status, but designated as Vulnerable by Green (1992b) and Endangered (as *A. gibberifrons albogularis*) by Threatened Waterfowl Specialist Group (2003). Bred at London Zoo in 1905 (Delacour 1954–64) and at Slimbridge in 1982 (2 ducklings reared) but no current *ex situ* captive flock exists.

Peter Fullagar

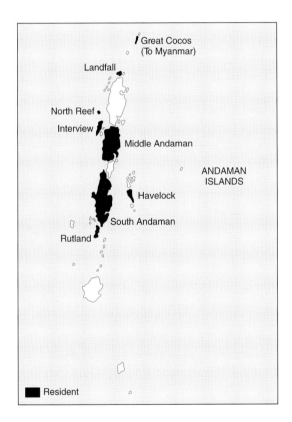

Map legend: ■ Resident

Map labels: Great Cocos (To Myanmar), Landfall, North Reef, Interview, Middle Andaman, ANDAMAN ISLANDS, Havelock, South Andaman, Rutland

---

Chestnut Teal *Anas castanea*
Plate 16

Mareca castanea Eyton, 1838, Monogr. Anatidae, p. 119, pl. 22
New South Wales

Etymology: *castanea* L. for chestnut-coloured.
Other names: Chestnut-breasted, Black, Brown, Green-headed or Red Teal. Australian Aboriginal:

Bener, Calyung, Gnwool-ye-nug-ger-rang, Guldaba, Gun-timar, Naap, Ngwol-yi-naggirang, Yamuru; Dutch: Kastanje Taling; French: Sarcelle rousse; German: Kastaneinente; Spanish: Cerceta castaña.

Variation: no subspecies.

Description

ADULT: dimorphic. ♂ in breeding, or alternate, plumage has head iridescent bottle green with bronzed or black appearance in some lights and slightly crested nape. Back dark brown, rump and tail black. Underside rich chestnut from breast to vent with prominent dark blotches on flanks. Upperwing dark brown with prominent white wedge, diminishing inwards, along leading edge of black speculum and narrow white tips on trailing edge. Oval patch of bronze-green across inner speculum. Underwing brown with black-brown leading edge and conspicuous white axillaries and central undercoverts. Bill blue-grey, darker on ridge; legs and feet grey; eye crimson. ♀ streaked and scalloped dark brown, generally with richer tone to body than Grey Teal but less obvious pale chin region and head appearing more streaked; distinction not easily made without observing behaviour. ♀ often has slight chestnut tone to plumage of underparts and shades of green particularly in dark brown of crown. Wing of ♀ as ♂. Both sexes have bright claret red eyes.

MOULT: ♂ in eclipse, or basic, plumage almost like ♀ but head darker, smudge of white usually remains near vent and darker undertail coverts usually evident. Moult of body feathers continuous, including tertials, but wing and tail feathers shed once annually in complete post-breeding plumage change. Successfully breeding ♂ frequently acquires full eclipse during brood-tending stage, often with delayed wing moult. ♂ continues to breed in eclipse and delays return to alternate plumage until breeding finishes that season. Brightest ♂ alternate plumage seen in late winter or early spring following another replacement of most body feathers starting early winter. ♂ plumage much duller by midsummer with white side patch then less distinct. ♀ undergoes similar moults with major replacement of body plumage in winter, before laying, and another complete moult, including wings and tail, post-breeding.

IMMATURE: like ♀ except paler with breast and belly streaked not blotched. Eye dull brown becoming gradually red-brown. Moult at about 14 weeks to 1st adult plumage.

DUCKLING: dark brown above, pale grey below with whitish spots on trailing edges of wing pads and, conspicuously, on both sides of rump. Head has 2 dark brown stripes across pale grey face, one through eye, other below (Young and Brayshaw 2004). See also Grey Teal.

MEASUREMENTS AND WEIGHT: ♂ wing ($n = 9$), 211–227 (218); tail ($n = 6$), 88–97 (91); bill ($n = 9$), 37–43 (41); tarsus ($n = 9$), 36–40 (38); weight ($n = 67$), 562–816 (683). ♀ wing ($n = 4$), 195–212 (203); tail, no data; bill ($n = 4$), 37–40 (38); tarsus ($n = 4$), 36–38 (36); weight ($n = 50$), 505–766 (593) (Marchant and Higgins 1990).

Field characters

Small and compact dabbling duck, 380–460 mm long, in all ways similar in structure and behaviour to Grey Teal, with which often seen. From Grey Teal differs in colourful alternate plumage of ♂ with dark green head and chestnut underparts, but ♀♀ very similar. ♂ Grey Teal easily recognized by voice and ♂ behaviour from ♀ Chestnut Teal. Grey Teal looks paler with greyish tones to plumage rather than brown. Chin area and upper throat almost always clear creamy white in Grey Teal and more distinct than in ♀ or juvenile Chestnut Teal. Fully coloured ♂ Australasian Shoveler only duck superficially similar in pattern to ♂ Chestnut Teal in same region. See also Brown Teal. Wild hybrids with Grey Teal not well known but certainly occur; resulting ♂ like eclipsed Chestnut Teal. Many hybrids known from captivity (see Marchant and Higgins 1990).

Voice

Calls almost constantly, at least at low levels, in social contact. Frequently noisy in flocks, especially during bouts of social display and in flight. Most characteristic calls loud laughing Decrescendo chuckles of ♀ and clear, sharp whistled *gedee-oo* Burp calls of ♂. Wide range of signal-specific calls given but none shared by sexes, and no differences from repertoire of Grey Teal. Grey Teal's Burp slightly higher pitch than Chestnut Teal's, but individual variation considerable in most calls of both sexes; consequently no easy ways to separate species on voice alone. Sonogram of adult call in Frith (1982).

Range and status

Endemic to Australia with disjunct distribution. Common in southeast, especially in Tasmania, but in west restricted to far southwest of continent. Abundant in coastal areas, particularly in southeast of South Australia and most abundant duck throughout Victoria and Tasmania (Marchant and Higgins 1990). Generally much less common inland of Great Divide in eastern Australia, with scattered occurrences in more arid regions of New South Wales and southeast Queensland. Restricted to wetter coastal areas in southwest. Vagrant elsewhere on continent, also to south New Guinea and Lord Howe Island.

In southwest may number 1000 (Marchant and Higgins 1990). In 1983, counts in southeast Australia suggested population of 21 000 mostly occurring in Victoria (> 16 500), but numbers in Tasmania at that time underestimated (Norman and Brown 1988). Grey Teal outnumbers Chestnut Teal by factor of 8:1 (Norman and Brown 1988).

Habitat and general habits

Occurs widely on many types of terrestrial and estuarine wetland but most often found on lower reaches of rivers, inlets, saltmarshes, coastal lagoons, mangrove swamps, saltpans and salt lakes, and uses large coastal wetlands as post-breeding or drought refuge. Feeds by filtering at water surface or in soft muds and up-ending in shallows, particularly along edges of wetlands or over sand or mudflats, occasionally diving. Food mostly invertebrate but some studies biased by sampling method emphasizing vegetative material persisting in gizzard. For details of diet see Marchant and Higgins (1990).

Displays and breeding behaviour

Seen in pairs throughout year, gregarious when not breeding, forming small groups and, at times, large flocks. Feeds in pairs or family parties in breeding season. Loafs on water or hauls out on log, stump, fallen branch or along shoreline, head tucked in

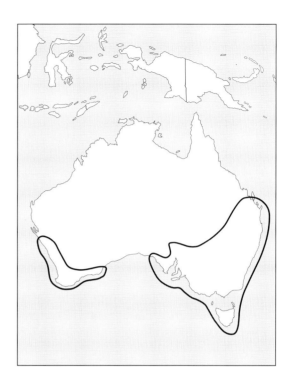

scapulars or withdrawn onto shoulders. Flight fast; walks readily on land with near horizontal carriage.

No nonbreeding territory held. Monogamous pairbond, often for life. No conclusive evidence of sustained polygamous bonds nor strategic promiscuous matings. Usually pair formation occurs rapidly in young birds in 1st autumn and winter. Displays conspicuous and noisy. Behaviour typical of *Anas* dabbling ducks. No pursuit flights. Wing-flap and lateral Tail-wag assertive signals. Bill-dips usually precede or punctuate other displays. Pre-flight signal, without vocalization, given by both sexes using rapid upward jerking of head. Main threat signal Chin-lift, mostly given by ♂, accompanied by chittering call. Individual distance maintained by Forward-stretch. Will lunge, jab and fight. Synchronous swimming sometimes seen near nest site in breeding season when ♂♂ twist and turn in unison on water; these parallel swimming activities indicative of fierce boundary dispute. ♂ especially aggressive to conspecifics near nest at laying, and during early incubation. Social display between ♂♂ often involves much Chin-lifting and typical Down-up display accompanied by whistle like that in Burp. Conspicuous identity signal of ♂ is Burp delivered with head elevated, feathers of crown and nape often raised forming larger head profile, bill wide open and pointed slightly downwards when sharp call given during slight forward nod-like jerk of head. Inciting signal of paired ♀ to her partner involves usual sideways pointing and harsh rattling call followed by Head-high posture. This signal most often directed against intruding ♂ or another pair; also used during pair formation, and Inciting call with pointing can occur in flight. Even harsher version of rattle given in Repulsion posture by ♀ if threatened when leaving nest or during brood rearing.

Hostile attacks take form of pursuits on water and, less often, on land. Established ♂, or ♂ accompanied by ♀, directs attack at ♀ of intruding pair. ♂ attack sometimes leads to fights in which ♀ grasped or forced underwater; ♀ may resort to diving in effort to retreat. Most often ♀ responds with loud Inciting and Repulsion calls and takes wing, frequently leading to 3-bird flight in which hostile ♂ chases pair away from area, concentrating effort on ♀ but eventually pulling out and returning to area near nest site or partner. Other ♂♂ sometimes join these hostile pursuits.

Pair formation occurs on water. ♂ advertises with Burp and ♀ with Decrescendo call. Ritualized display used in pair formation, pairbond maintenance and pairbond testing. Sequence highly predictable; bouts of display often switch between heterosexual activities and ♂ to ♂ contests, with jostling for optimum position with respect to ♀♀. Synchronized Down-up and Chin-lifting signals prominent in asserting ♂ dominance. Bouts of pair-bonding display by ♂♂ start in presence of ♀. ♂♂ begin by performing random Head-shakes, Head-rolls and Introductory-shakes without calls, leading to Grunt-whistle where bill dipped into water as body arches upwards, bill flicking sideways to throw out beads of water with body brought almost to vertical and head tucked in to bring bill against breast before regaining normal posture. Explosive high-pitched whistle followed by deep resonant grunt given at height of posture. ♂♂ then perform part or whole of stereotyped sequence: Head-up-tail-up, Turn-towards-♀ on giving clear whistle,

Head-throw-swim, Turn-back-of-head, then Lead-away with Turn-back-of-head. Head-throw-swim combines Bridle with single Nod-swim. Independent Bridles also given by ♂♂ accompanied by clear whistle. During Turn-back-of-head, ♂ swims away from party sometimes switching head from side to side leading ♀. She performs repeated Head-throw-swims among or past ♂♂, accompanied by conversational notes and loud Decrescendo calls. Display eventually leads to pairs breaking away from group, with ♀ using Inciting signal to reinforce attachment to ♂.

Social contact between pair maintained by constant soft calls and Forward-greeting signal. Preen-behind-wing often used when pair unite after separation. Mutual pre-copulatory Head-pumping leads to ♀ adopting flattened posture on water and ♂ mounting. ♂ Bridles post-copulation and Wing-flaps; both preen and ♀ invariably bathes, ♂ less often. Copulation can occur well before egg-laying, and most display seems independent of imminent breeding activity. Details of displays in Prawiradi-laga (1985) and Marchant and Higgins (1990).

Breeding and life cycle

Generally uses tree hollows for nest site but ground-nesting occurs in absence of cavities. Site chosen by pair in searching behaviour when ♂ accompanies ♀ during inspection of possible location. Breeding generally seasonal with prolonged activity in favourable conditions leading to laying of several successive clutches. Will lay at any time conditions become favourable, usually following rainfall with flooding after drought but, particularly, when several months or longer have passed without possibility of breeding. Eggs elliptical, chalky becoming polished and greasy, rich light cream often stained; 52×37 ($35–57 \times 35–41$) ($n = 366$) (Frith 1982); weight 44 ($n = 18$) (Marchant and Higgins 1990); laid daily in early morning; clutch usually 7–10. Replacement laying occurs after loss of eggs or young, and may rear 2 broods in succession. Incubation by ♀ from completion of clutch and plucking of copious down to form bulk of nest. ♂ continues to guard site throughout incubation, remaining close and accompanying ♀ during recesses. ♀ usually leaves nest 3 times, early morning, noon and late afternoon, and remains off eggs for *c* 1 h daily. Incubation probably as Grey Teal at 28 ± 2 days. Weight of day-old 27 (21–34) (*n* = 231) (Marchant and Higgins 1990) or 64% of fresh egg (Williams *et al.* 1991).

Following departure from nest, brood defended vigorously by both parents. Young fly at 60–80 days. Some broods successfully tended by ♂ alone from early stages, when ♀ presumed dead. Occasionally, ♀ may lay 2nd clutch before independence and departure of 1st brood. Ducklings then tended almost entirely by ♂ from start of renewed incubation, and ♀ seen with them only during brief recesses. Brood dispersal usually gradual, but both sexes acquire adult body plumage in < 4 months and capable of breeding in 1st year. Further information on aspects of breeding, with references, in Marchant and Higgins (1990).

Conservation and threats

Widespread and abundant. Remains an important game species in Victoria and Tasmania but hunting not immediate threat to survival. Loss of much coastal wetland area more serious where increase in development at coast, and settlement by humans usually leads to reduction in suitable habitat. Although no measures of abundance for Tasmania, population in Australia estimated to be at least 45 000 and may be as high as 250 000 (based on data in Marchant and Higgins 1990, Kingsford *et al.* 1999, 2000). Occurred in high numbers in southeast Australia in 1984 and again in 1991, but has not shown any long-term trends over period from early 1980s to 1999 (Kingsford *et al.* 1999).

Peter Fullagar

Brown Teal *Anas chlorotis*
PLATE 16

Anas chlorotis G. R. Gray, 1845, in Richardson and J. E. Gray (eds), Voyage Erebus and Terror, **1**, Birds, p. 15, pl. 20
New Zealand

Etymology: *chlorotis* Gr. *khloros* meaning green, plus *otos* ear, referring to green iridescence on side of ♂'s head.

Other names: Brown Duck. Maori: Pateke.

Variation: Mathews (1937) differentiated North Island (*chlorotis*) from South Island (*peculiaris*) claiming shorter wings for South Island birds. Claim not investigated.

Description

ADULT: dimorphic. ♂ in breeding, or alternate, plumage has head and neck iridescent green, face brown, narrow white eye-ring, occasionally indistinct pale band at front and side of lower neck. Entire body dark brown with flank feathers barred light and dark brown, breast dark chestnut, abdomen light brown. Undertail black with white patch at base of tail. Upperwing brown with indistinct green speculum having trailing narrow white bar, underwing brown tending to be mottled with white near base. Bill black; legs and feet dark grey; eye black. ♀ uniformly dark brown with light edge to feathers giving overall mottled appearance. Lowerbreast and abdomen pale brown. Conspicuous white eye-ring. Wings, eye, bill and legs as ♂.

MOULT: ♂ seasonally dimorphic and, in eclipse, lacks green iridescence on head, breast darkly mottled, flank feathers without barring and white tail patch indistinct. Annual wing moult of breeders takes place on nesting sites after breeding. Nonbreeding birds moult at flock sites, commonly Oct–Nov.

IMMATURE: similar to ♀ but uniformly darker until post-juvenile moult. Body and breast feathers have broad buff edging to otherwise dark feathers giving strongly mottled appearance. ♂ and ♀ indistinguishable.

DUCKLING: back and head brown-black with greenish sheen. Pale stripe through eye. White-fawn on underparts. Small pale brown spots on rump.

MEASUREMENTS AND WEIGHT: from live birds ♂ (*n* = 30) wing, 200–228 (212); tail, 85–101 (93); bill, 41.7–47.0 (44.1); tarsus, 40.4–46.6 (44.5); weight in breeding season ($n = 30$), 610–860 (720), nonbreeding ($n = 159$) (586 ± 61). ♀ ($n = 30$) wing, 182–213 (197); tail, 74–92 (82); bill, 39.4–44.0 (41.5); tarsus, 37.3–44.0 (41.3); weight in breeding season ($n = 30$), 580–860 (696), nonbreeding ($n = 171$) (530 ± 81).

Field characters

Small (480 mm long) dark brown duck whose wings cross high on back, and whose elongate body distinguishes it from New Zealand Scaup.

Voice

♂ has 2 distinctive high-pitched calls, *Krick*-whistle and Burp. *Krick*-whistle is wheezy, 2-syllabled *mmn-yea* given when disturbed, during hostile encounters in flock, and during social courtship. Burp is typical of many teal being bell-like *pop* given mostly during social courtship. ♀ has high-pitched Decrescendo call of up to 7 syllables, rasping Inciting call during social interactions in flocks, and raucous growl also heard mostly in social interactions. Soft contact call given while feeding with mate or when accompanying young. Sonogram in Marchant and Higgins (1990).

Range and status

Formerly widespread throughout New Zealand's 3 main islands, many nearshore islands, and on Chatham Island. Now confined to New Zealand's fourth-largest island, Great Barrier (population declining, presently 800–1000), to 3 nearshore islands (not exceeding 10 pairs on each) and to small coastal region within northern North Island (population declining, presently c 300). Formerly extensive Fiordland (southern South Island) population effectively extinct with scattered remnant birds hybridizing with either Pacific Black Duck or invading introduced Northern Mallard.

Habitat and general habits

Prior to human settlement of New Zealand (1000 years bp), common about lakes and slow-flowing waterways, and widespread and common throughout lowland forest of North and South Islands (Atkinson and Millener 1991, Worthy and Holdaway 1994). In middle of 19th century, following European settlement, reported to be common in swamp forest and occluded lowland

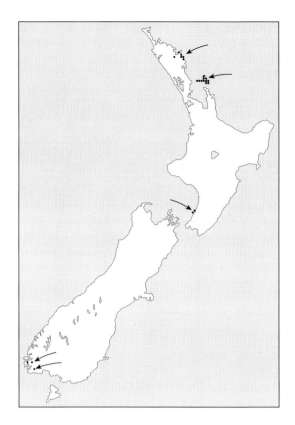

wetlands (Buller 1888), but declining elsewhere. Present-day habitat within predominantly agricultural environment. Overgrown stock ponds, sections of small watercourses still retaining overhanging riparian vegetation and canopy, and small densely vegetated swamps used as breeding sites. During summer and through most of nonbreeding period, large segment of each local population assembles at traditional flock site, usually a secluded location near freshwater–saltwater interface on small river or stream. Summer flocks comprise adults whose breeding sites uninhabitable during dry period and juveniles. Highly sedentary, generally remaining within or close to catchment. Even on Great Barrier Island, where principal concentrations are < 10 km apart, little evidence of interchange (Dumbell 1987).

Generally crepuscular to nocturnal in habit, feeding on land and in dense swamp vegetation under cover of darkness. Food includes seeds, grasses, insects and worms, and birds dabble for long periods in muddy areas to extract edible organic material. On Great Barrier Island, some birds visible during daytime feeding in estuarine areas on crustaceans and small bivalves (Weller 1974, Dumbell 1986).

Displays and breeding behaviour

♂ courtship displays similar to Chestnut Teal (Johnsgard 1965a, Marchant and Higgins 1990) and include Bridling, Introductory Shake, Grunt-whistle, *Krick*-whistle, Burp, and Nod-swim. Head-up-tail-up and Down-up absent. ♀ displays include Nod-swim and Inciting. Pre-copulatory behaviour involves mutual Head-pumping. Group courtship of ♀ by several ♂♂ seen in summer flocks. Solitary ♂♂ will attempt to acquire ♀ and breeding site by direct attack on ♂ of breeding pair on territory.

Pairs remain year-round in exclusive territories whenever sites remain wet during summer. Other pairs vacate territories seasonally and return to them when autumn water levels permit. Territories contain abundant escape cover, feeding, nesting and brood-rearing sites. Pairs occupying streams in agricultural areas use riparian vegetation as daytime protective cover but feed at night up to 500–600 m distant in wet or swampy paddocks.

Breeding and life cycle

Broods recorded all months except Apr and May. Most nesting July–Sept. Nest site commonly on ground beneath *Carex* or *Cyperus* clump near water; also in long grass, *Typha* stand and fern clumps near water. Nest bowl woven from adjacent grasses and lined with down. Eggs pale fawn; 60.1×43.1 ($56.7–66.4 \times 38.8–45.9$) ($n = 88$); weight 60.8 ($55.9–66.8$) ($n = 24$); clutch 5.9 (3–9) ($n = 47$). In captivity, eggs laid daily. One clutch per season, although 2nd clutches in 10% of pairs in one

Northland study. Incubation by ♀ only. ♂ remains close and joins mate during nest relief. Incubation period in captivity 27–30 days (Reid and Roderick 1973), 29–30 in wild. Day-old captive ducklings weigh 39.8 ($n = 26$). Both parents attend young throughout fledging period of 60–70 days (Reid and Roderick (1973), 50–55 day fledging period reported in captivity. Brood rearing confined to breeding territory which ♂ defends vigorously. Young physically evicted from territory by ♂ soon after fledging and at weight equivalent to adult non-breeding weight. Breeding occurs in 1st year of life.

Contrasting productivity data from Great Barrier Island (GBI, Dumbell 1987) and Northland (Nld) populations: per breeding pair to fledging 0.9 (GBI, $n = 27$)—2.0 (Nld, $n = 81$). Annual adult survival 0.63 (GBI, $n = 90$) −0.33 (Nld, $n = 92$); 1st year survival 0.1 (Nld, $n = 51$). Has lived to 24 years in captivity.

Conservation and threats

Conservation status Endangered (BirdLife International 2000). Over 60% decline in Northland population 1988–98 suggests extinction on New Zealand mainland imminent. Extremely vulnerable to introduced mammalian predation (especially feral cats, dogs and mustelids) while swamp and riparian habitats profoundly affected by intensive cattle grazing. Little chance of recovery on mainland other than in small protected areas subjected to permanent predator control. Great Barrier Island presently lacks mustelids and has limited pastoralism, but expanding human settlement and household pets. Protected by law since 1924.

Murray Williams

Auckland Island Teal *Anas aucklandica*

Nesonetta aucklandica G.R. Gray, 1844, Gen. Birds, **3**, p. 627, pl. 169, fig. 4
Auckland Islands
    Etymology: named after islands where found.
    Other names: Auckland Islands Flightless Teal (or Duck).

Variation: no subspecies.

Description

ADULT: dimorphic. ♂ in breeding, or alternate, plumage similar to Brown Teal but generally darker. Head and neck dark brown with trace of green iridescence on nape. Conspicuous white eye-ring. Entire body dark brown with flank feathers conspicuously barred light and dark brown. Breast dark chestnut, abdomen lighter brown feathers in both areas spotted with black tips. Undertail black with smudgy whitish patch at base of tail. Upperwing brown, speculum indistinct green with white trailing edge, underwing mottled brown. Bill, legs and feet dark grey; eye dark brown. ♀ similar to Brown Teal but slightly darker. Uniformly dark brown but lighter abdomen. Conspicuous white eye-ring. Wings, eye, bill, legs and feet as ♂.

MOULT: ♂ in eclipse similar to alternate plumage but dark head lacks iridescence, breast dull chestnut, no barring of flank feathers and little indication of tail spot. Annual wing moult occurs on breeding territories after breeding, during ♂ eclipse.

IMMATURE: generally indistinguishable from ♀.

DUCKLING: as Brown Teal.

MEASUREMENTS AND WEIGHT: from live birds. ♂ (*n* = 33) wing, 128–152 (141); tail, 66–89 (77); bill, 36.8–42.0 (39.7); tarsus, 34.6–38.1 (36.3); weight in breeding season (*n* = 11), 500–620 (560), nonbreeding (*n* = 38) (551 ± 38). ♀ (*n* = 30) wing, 105–137 (126); tail, 51–79 (67); bill, 34.0–38.5 (36.6); tarsus, 30.8–35.5 (33.4); weight in breeding season (*n* = 8), 420–560 (480), nonbreeding (*n* = 30) (409 ± 32).

Field characters

Small, dark brown, flightless duck with conspicuously short wings, found on seashore among kelp, and in streams of Auckland Islands.

Voice

♂ has *Krick*-whistle (*Trill* of Weller 1975a) and Burp call as Brown Teal, both given in defence of territory. ♀ calls as Brown Teal. Duckling calls like those of Brown Teal. No published sonograms.

Range and status

Endemic to Auckland Islands, occurring on all substantial islands of group except main Auckland Island where exterminated by introduced mammals.

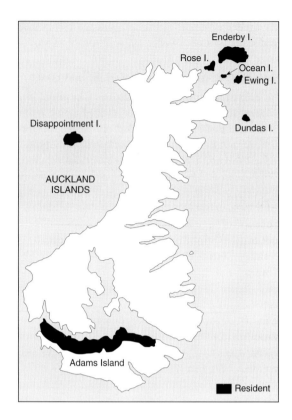

Total population previously underestimated (Williams 1986, Marchant and Higgins 1990) due to difficulty of detection in grassland habitat; probably > 1500.

Habitat and general habits

In coastal sub-antarctic *Poa foliosa* tussock grassland communities, generally preferring damper locations containing megaherb *Stilbocarpa polaris* and *Carex* sedges. Also along peaty streams in *Metrosideris* forest near coastal edge. Coastal grassland adjacent to protected shorelines favoured where storm-cast algae collects and rots. On Ewing Island, some pairs live within *Olearia* forest. On Disappointment Island, major seabird and albatross breeding site, lives without access to coastal edge.

Generally crepuscular to nocturnal but enjoys daytime sunning in protected locations and, during breeding season, ♂♂ with shoreline territories rest conspicuously at water's edge during daytime. Seeks daytime protection under dense vegetative cover, in petrel burrows or rock crevices. Predominantly carnivorous diet including small marine invertebrates, terrestrial amphipods, insect larvae and small molluscs (Weller 1975a). Dabbles in peaty ooze.

Adult population dispersed in territories year-round; fledglings live furtively and solitarily amongst territories (Williams 1995). Flocking rare and confined to shoreline locations where algal windrows offer abundant food, and protected roosting sites available. Flock birds identified as both adults and juveniles (Weller 1975a, Williams 1995).

Displays and breeding behaviour

Social courtship not observed and probably does not occur. Overtly hostile displays (Open-bill threat, rushes, chases) characterize autumn social interactions on Ewing Island. Behaviour in captivity similar (Williams *et al.* 1991). Only territorial pairs attempt breeding. All feeding, nesting and brood rearing confined to territory. Territory size on Ewing Island varies, 1000–3700 m^2 in grassland, 200–550 m^2 for coastal grassland/shoreline (Williams 1995). Territorial defence extremely vigorous.

Breeding and life cycle

Eggs laid from late Oct, first broods early Dec. Young broods still present Mar–Apr suggesting second laying peak, perhaps of initially failed breeders, in Feb (Williams 1995). Nests on ground amongst dense vegetation such as fern, tussock or sedge. Nest bowl of adjacent vegetation with modest down lining. Nesting sites re-used. Eggs pale fawn; $64.8 \pm 2.3 \times 44.8 \pm 1.1$ (59.0–71.4 × 42.4–47.6) ($n = 99$); weight (by calculation) 71.2, larger than Brown Teal or Campbell Island Teal (Williams 1995); clutch 3.4 ± 1.0 (1–6) ($n = 45$), smaller than Brown Teal. Incubation by ♀ alone; ♂ remains close and guards ♀ while feeding during nest relief. Incubation in wild exceeds 30 days (Williams 1995), and is 30–35 days ($n = 4$) in captivity (Williams *et al.* 1991). Day-olds weigh 48.1 ($n = 3$), 64% of fresh egg weight (Williams *et al.* 1991). Almost all nests successful.

Both parents attend and defend young throughout 'fledging' period of 60–70 days. Ducklings reach average adult ♀ nonbreeding weight in 60 days. Brood rearing confined to territory and nest site used as main daytime refuge. Brood survival poor with most broods reduced to singleton within 10 days of hatching. Ewing Island population 1991–92 (Williams 1995); mean brood size at hatching 3.4, estimated 14% duckling survival to 'fledging', mean extant brood size at 'fledging' 1.6; up to 66% of pairs fail to raise young. No data on post-fledging or adult survival. Both sexes breed at one year in captivity.

Conservation and threats

Population considered stable and at carrying capacity of island. Listed as Vulnerable in BirdLife International (2000); however, presence on 6 pest-free islands confers considerable security. Auckland Island will be focus of mammal (pig, cat) eradication programme over next decade which will allow return of teal to all former range. Auckland Islands are national nature reserves without human settlement.

Murray Williams

Campbell Island Teal *Anas nesiotis*
PLATE 16

Xenonetta nesiotis J.H. Fleming, 1935, Occas. Papers Roy. Ontario Mus. Zool., no. 1, p. 1
Campbell Island
    Etymology: *nesiotis* Gr. for islander.
    Other names: Campbell Island Flightless Teal.
    Variation: no subspecies.

Description

ADULT: dimorphic. ♂ in breeding, or alternate, plumage similar to Auckland Island Teal but smaller and darker. Head and neck dark sepia with strong green iridescence. Entire body dark sepia with green iridescence on back, dark chestnut on breast, abdomen lighter. Rest of plumage as for Auckland Island Teal but white tail spot more obvious. Bill, legs, feet steely grey; eye dark brown surrounded by conspicuous white ring. ♀ uniformly dark brown with paler abdomen. White eye-ring conspicuous, otherwise similar to ♂ eclipse. Darkest and smallest ♀ of 3 New Zealand teals.

MOULT: ♂ eclipse plumage similar to alternate but iridescence generally lacking on head and less intense on back. Feathers on shoulders and flank greatly reduced vermiculation and tail spot becomes indistinct. Eye-ring becomes pale fawn. Timing of moults uncertain.

IMMATURE: similar to ♀ but slightly darker and more uniformly dark all over. Sexes indistinguishable.

DUCKLING: as Brown Teal.

MEASUREMENTS AND WEIGHT: wild specimens, ♂ (*n* = 7) wing, 128–138 (132); tail, 76–96 (89); bill, 36.6–39.6 (38.1); tarsus, 32.2–37.0 (34.0); weight in field (*n* = 9), 290–500 (371 ± 56). ♀ (*n* = 5) wing, 114–125 (118); tail, 63–74 (72); bill, 33.4–35.9 (34.4); tarsus, 29.8–32.4 (31.1); weight (*n* = 4), 280–365 (310 ± 31).

Field characters

Small, dark brown, flightless duck with conspicuously short wings in grassland or on sea at Campbell Island.

Voice

As for Auckland Island Teal

Range and status

Endemic to Campbell Island and associated islets. Presumed to have occurred on Campbell Island (no authentic records), but exterminated by rats following island's discovery by sealers in 1810. Restricted to Dent Island (23 ha), 3 km from western coast of Campbell Island (Figure 9.27). Total population 60–100 (Goudswaard 1991, McClelland 1993), unlikely to exceed 25 pairs (Williams and Robertson 1996).

First specimen collected 1886 but not recognized until 1935 (Fleming 1935). Second specimen taken 1944 from rocks on Campbell Island immediately opposite Dent Island. Not seen again until encountered on Dent Island in 1975 (Robertson 1976, Williams and Robertson 1996).

Habitat and general habits

Restricted to *Poa foliosa* tussock grassland on lower eastern slopes of Dent Island where appears to

9.27 Dent ('tooth') Island, 23 ha in extent, 3 km off western shore of Campbell Island, and home to the tiny remaining population of endemic teal.

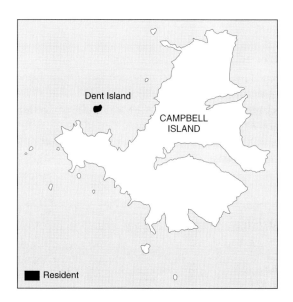

favour moister shallow gullies amongst tussocks, ferns and megaherb *Stilbocarpa polaris*. Makes extensive use of petrel burrows, moving beneath tussock canopy along petrel-induced pathways between tussock bases. Probably occupied wider range of habitats when on Campbell Island similar to Auckland Island Teal (Williams and Robertson 1996).

Little known of general habits. Appears dispersed as territorial pairs in Dec, Feb and June suggesting year-round territoriality like Auckland Island Teal. Both sexes respond vocally to calls of other teal and approach and chase territory intruders. ♂♂ may use prominent rocks as territory viewing sites. Birds encountered sun-basking beneath *Stilbocarpa* and emerging from cover to feed in exposed areas only at or after dusk. Diet unknown but probably dominated by amphipods and insects. Holes made by probes in peat adjacent to seepage channels on lower island slopes considered to be teal feeding sign.

Displays and breeding behaviour

Not known from wild. In captivity, most ♂ social interactions involve hostile displays (Open-bill threat, rushes, chases) and attempted mountings of ♀, while ♀♀ chase and fight one another and incite ♂♂ to do so. ♂ has Trill call described for Auckland Island Teal; ♀ has high-pitched Decrescendo call. In captivity, pairs strongly territorial with 2 pairs seldom managing to establish exclusive space in single large aviary.

Breeding and life cycle

Not known from wild (Dent Island). In captivity, eggs, laid Oct–Jan at 3 day intervals, pale fawn; $62.1 \pm 2.5 \times 42.8 \pm 1.2$ $(57.5–66.8 \times 40.4–44.9)$ $(n = 67)$; weigh 61.6 $(n = 14)$ or calculated at 65.4 $(n = 20)$. In captivity, wild-caught ♀ has laid, producing consecutive clutches of 3 and 4 eggs in each of 2 years. Mean size of 21 clutches laid in captivity 3.8 ± 1.1, similar to Auckland Island Teal. Incubation, by ♀, 30–34 days. Day-old weight calculated as 39–42. Adult weight and wing length attained by Day 63. Both sexes can breed at one year. No data from wild on breeding success, survival nor longevity.

Conservation and threats

Listed as Critically Endangered by BirdLife International (2000), but has survived solely on Dent Island for at least past 150 years. Population extremely vulnerable should rats reach Dent from Campbell Island. New Zealand's Department of Conservation has active captive breeding programme (Gummer and Williams 1999) having raised (by 1999) 52 birds from initial wild-caught stock of 11 (7 ♂, 4 ♀). Two introductions, each of 12 birds, made to Codfish Island in 1999 and 2000 to provide, temporarily, 2nd wild population, and breeding confirmed. Rats were eradicated from Campbell Island during programme initiated in 2001, and population will be re-established in 2004 using captive-raised birds and translocations from Codfish Island.

Murray Williams

White-cheeked Pintail *Anas bahamensis*
PLATE 19

Anas bahamensis Linnaeus, 1758, Syst. Nat., ed. 10, p. 124
Bahama Islands

Etymology: *bahamensis* means of the Bahamas. Vernacular name 'pintail' dates from Pennant's *British Zoology* of 1768, and referred to Northern Pintail.

Other names: Bahama Pintail, Duck or Teal, White-jaws, White-faced Duck. French: Canard des Bahamas; Spanish: Pato quijada colorado, Pato de la orilla.

Variation: 3 subspecies recognized, Lesser White-cheeked Pintail *A. b. bahamensis* from northern South America and West Indies, Greater White-cheeked Pintail *A. b. rubrirostris* Vieillot, 1816 from southern South America, and Galapagos Pintail *A. b. galapagensis* Ridgeway, 1889 restricted to Galapagos Islands.

Description

ADULT: sexes alike. ♂ crown and back of neck dark mottled brown, cheeks, chin and upper foreneck white. Breast, underparts and sides light brown with black spotting. Upperbody plumage medium brown. Tertials elongated and pointed, dark brown with buff fringes. Secondaries with iridescent green speculum, followed by narrow black sub-terminal border, and wide buff terminal band. Uppertail and undertail coverts and pointed tail pale buff. Bill dark bluish grey with brilliant red spot at base; legs and feet dark grey; eyes red to red-brown. ♀ smaller with shorter tail; brown plumage on crown and back paler; bill spot smaller and less colourful (orange-red to red). *rubrirostris* larger and slightly brighter than *bahamensis*; *galapagensis* smaller, greyer plumage, white face not sharply demarcated from brown crown.

MOULT: similar plumage worn year-round by both sexes (i.e. no dull eclipse plumage during wing moult of ♂). Moult patterns not studied in detail, but in Bahama Islands population, most (*n* = 229) captured during winter and spring undergoing body moult. During wing moult (May–Aug), uses ponds with heavy vegetative cover and remains out of sight much of time. If disturbed, hides in shoreline vegetation instead of flushing. Secretive nature of birds during wing moult may account for reported disappearance or decline in numbers during some seasons. Unpaired ♂♂ and nonbreeding pairs moult wings earlier than breeding pairs, and pair members may remain together while moulting (Sorenson 1992).

IMMATURE: similar to ♀ but duller. Brown plumage on crown and back paler than adult with greyish wash. Bill spot pale orange to orange-red; tail lacks distinctive point; eyes brown.

DUCKLING: brightly coloured, with face, neck and broad superciliary band vivid yellow; conspicuous blackish line from eye to nape hardly indicated in front of eye; cap and upperparts dark brown with 2 whitish lines on sides of back; upperparts pale yellow. Bill bluish grey with pink wash at base indicating red patch of adult (Delacour 1954–64).

MEASUREMENTS AND WEIGHT: *bahamensis* ♂ (*n* = 68) wing, 201–232 (220); tail, 98–139 (124); culmen, 34–49 (45); tarsus, 35–42 (39); weight, 440–630 (526). ♀ (*n* = 50) wing, 189–220 (207); tail, 84–121 (108); culmen, 39–47 (42); tarsus, 35–40 (37); weight, 395–650 (502). Early breeding season weights for ♂ and ♀ average *c* 10 g heavier than averages given here; all data from Paradise Island, Bahamas population. *rubrirostris* ♂ wing, 225–231, weight (*n* = 7), 710; ♀ wing, 219–221; weight (*n* = 4) 670 (Delacour 1954–64, Weller 1968b). *galapagensis* ♂ wing, 190–215; culmen, 40–45; ♀ wing, 180–202; culmen, 37–43 (Delacour 1954–64).

Field characters

White cheek patches and throat contrasting with dark brown crown and red bill-spot distinctive;

410–510 mm long. Unlikely to be confused with any other dabbling ducks within range. Leucistic form of *rubrirostris* common in captivity, and sometimes escapes (Madge and Burn 1988).

Voice

♂ utters rising *bzzzzzz* sound during Burp display given in courtship, when alarmed, and as contact call to mate. Loud 2-note whistle given while performing Down-up display. ♀ *quacks*, has 4–8 syllable Decrescendo call (given when separated from mate), and vocalizes with series of *rrr-rrr rrr-rrr* notes during Inciting, and whinnying notes during Repulsion display. Also has low *purr* as contact call to mate. Ducklings have peeping calls typical of dabbling ducks.

Range and status

Range of *bahamensis* encompasses most islands of West Indies, including Bahama Islands, Greater

Anas b. bahamensis
Anas b. galapagensis
Anas b. rubrirostris

Antilles (Cuba, Hispaniola, and Puerto Rico), Lesser Antilles, and Netherlands Antilles, and northern South America (Columbia, Venezuela, Guianas, and northern Brazil). *rubrirostris* found in southern South America including southern Brazil, east Bolivia, Paraguay, Uruguay, north Argentina, Ecuador, Peru, and north Chile.

Wetlands International (2002) estimated numbers of 75 000 for *bahamensis*, 2000–5000 for *galapagensis* and 100 000–1 000 000 for *rubrirostris*.

Habitat and general habits

Occupies shallow fresh, brackish and saltwater ponds and lagoons, mangrove swamps and marshes, tidal creeks and estuaries. In Great Abaco Island, Bahamas, found in 'the Marls', expansive shallow tidewater region, dotted with mangrove-covered clayey flats and small ponds surrounded by tall, dense mangrove vegetation. Also inhabits reservoirs and waste-stabilization ponds (sewage lagoons). In Cuba, makes extensive use of rice plantations. Salinity of saltwater ponds in Bahamas ranged from 61–252 ppt (1.7–7.2 times as salty as seawater). Following heavy rainfall, freshwater lens temporarily layered on top of saltwater provides fresh drinking water. *galapagensis* also found in salt lagoons and ponds, as well as in temporary or permanent freshwater ponds.

Gregarious, usually found in small flocks during nonbreeding season, larger flocks numbering > 100 birds occasionally observed. During breeding season, pairs disperse and defend territories, nonbreeders may remain in small flocks. Some birds associate as pairs year-round. Extent of movements between islands difficult to assess, but movement patterns apparently variable throughout range; populations on some islands either sedentary or subject to small-scale wandering in response to water and food availability (e.g. Bahama Islands population, where 229 birds marked and studied 1984–91, and counted through 1993, most remained in area and utilized ponds from one of 3 adjacent islands—New Providence, Paradise and Rose Island—for 2–8 years while some disappeared for periods of 1–3 years, but then returned). Other populations may undergo short-distance seasonal migrations. *rubrirostris* probably migratory in southern part of range (Delacour 1954–64).

Food habits not studied in detail, but diet likely consists of both animal and vegetable matter. Dominant invertebrate taxa sampled in areas where Bahama Islands population feeds include shorefly larvae (ephydrids), brine shrimp, water boatman (corixids) in saltwater ponds, and scuds *Gammarus*, aquatic nematodes, midge larvae (chironomids) and water boatman in brackish ponds. Sieves from benthos by dabbling, up-ending or feeding with head under in shallow water. Feeds on brine shrimp and brine fly larvae in water column by swimming along, rapidly dipping bill and grabbing at food items. Birds observed eating brine flies, occasionally present on hypersaline pond shorelines, by running through swarm and snapping them out of air. Invertebrate hatches in saline ponds follow periods of heavy rainfall; local movements reflect use of these ephemeral food resources (Sorenson 1990, 1992). Numbers also fluctuated greatly in 19 ponds surveyed in Virgin Islands, presumably reflecting changes in food availability (Norton *et al.* 1986). Diet of nonbreeding population in Surinam consisted largely of seeds of aquatic vegetation (primarily Wigeon Grass *Ruppia maritima*); invertebrates recorded included gastropods, corixids and dipterans (Spaans *et al.* 1978). Stomachs of 8 adults collected in Puerto Rico contained seeds of Wigeon Grass (16.25%), foliage and anteridia of *Chara* (83.75%). Two ducklings ate seeds of foxtail grass *Chaetochloa*, Wild Millet *Echinochloa crus-galli* and panic grass *Panicum* 94%, miscellaneous seeds 2.5%, and animal matter 3.5% (water boatman, water creeper *Pelocoris* and snails) (Wetmore 1916). Animal matter in latter two studies probably underestimated because analysis of food items not restricted to oesophageal contents (inclusion of stomach contents inflates importance of seeds in diet because invertebrates rapidly digested, Swanson *et al.* 1979).

Displays and breeding behaviour

Social courtship may occur year-round but most frequent and intense during winter and early spring. Typically, 2–10 ♂♂ surround 1–4 ♀♀ on water and, while jockeying and jostling for position, perform Burps and Down-ups as major courtship displays. Down-up preceded by Introductory-shake and typically performed broadside to target ♀, followed by

Turn-towards-♀ with head and body. Two-note whistle of Down-up and splashing caused by chasing among ♂♂ attracts other ♂♂ to courting party. ♀ sometimes gives low, descending 2-note *quack* during ♂ social courtship, often at moment of ♂ display (called Gasping by Lorenz 1951–53). ♂–♂ aggression (Pecks, Open-bill-threats, Swim-offs, Chases, Fights, Parallel-swims/Flights) frequent during social courtship. Down-up display also used as threat signal to rival ♂♂ (McKinney *et al.* 1990b); ♂ performs Down-up broadside to target ♂, and Turn-towards-♂ and other aggressive behaviour typically follows. Rival ♂♂ often exchange series of broadside Down-ups with no turns. Both paired and unpaired birds participate in social courtship, but unpaired ♂♂ court most actively. Older ♂♂ more successful at pairing than yearlings. Skewed sex ratio (1.45 ♂:1 ♀) gives ♀ opportunity to choose from amongst competing ♂♂. ♀ indicates preference for one ♂ and rejection of others with Inciting display. Paired ♂ may Lead ♀ from courting party with Turn-back-of-head. Mate switches and temporary liaisons common prior to and throughout breeding season. Pair courtship displays include Burp, Down-up, Head-pumping, Belly-preen, Preen-behind-wing and Mutual-drinking. Before copulation, ♂ initiates Head-pumping, ♀ usually joins in, then adopts prone posture; ♂ performs post-copulatory Bridling while dismounting (accompanied by whistle) and ♀ bathes. Territorial ♂ evicts intruding ♂♂ with Chases (on water or aerial) and Swim-offs. During Swim-offs, aggressor has head-low, bill-down posture, object of aggression adopts bill-up posture. Rival ♂♂ on neighbouring territories frequently exchange broadside Down-ups and engage in Parallel-swims at territory boundary.

Most birds pair monogamously but low level of polygyny occurs (4–9% of paired ♂♂ obtain 2 mates). Polygynous ♂♂ particularly effective at mate-guarding during breeding season, important to ♀ breeding success. Before breeding, pairs disperse from flocks, ♂♂ become increasingly aggressive and intolerant of other ♂♂ near mate. Although individual behaviour variable, on average ♂ establishes territory 17 days before 1st egg laid and defends it until Day 21 of incubation. Throughout pre-laying, laying and incubation periods, ♂ guards mate from courtship, harassment and forced extra-pair copulation attempts by other ♂♂. FEPC attempts by paired ♂♂ common, and ♂♂ have specialized tactics for finding fertile ♀♀ and achieving FEPCs. Aggressiveness by paired ♂♂ most intense during mate's fertile period when ♂ guards paternity. Although some ♂♂ continue to associate with, court, and guard their mate for part of brood-rearing period, only ♀ cares for ducklings. Courtship of ♀ tending brood common. Both long-term pairbonds and mate changes between years recorded. In long-term study of Bahama Islands population (1985–91), of 66 pairs in which both mates marked, 20 pairs (30%) were intact following year, 15 pairs (23%) divorced, one member of 22 pairs (33%) had new mate but other mate not seen, ♂ of 2 pairs (3%) unpaired but other mate not seen, and both members of 7 pairs (11%) not found in following year. Alternatively, 57% (20/35) of marked pairs, with option of maintaining bond for 2 years (i.e. mate still alive), did so, while 43% (15/35) divorced. Pairbonds lasting 2 ($n = 14$), 3 ($n = 6$), and 4 ($n = 1$) years documented; mate retention in 2nd year not related to breeding success in 1st (Sorenson 1990, 1992, 1994a, 1994b). ♂♂ of Bahama Islands population defended territories on Paradise Island ponds, ♀♀ nested on Salt Cay located 1.4 km north, but returned to mate's territory to feed and preen during incubation recesses.

Breeding and life cycle

Mild climate throughout much of range allows extended breeding season and/or breeding occurs opportunistically in response to irregular rainfall. Northern Bahama Islands have extended but seasonal breeding, nests initiated Feb–June, depending on rainfall. In southern Bahamas (Inagua) and islands extending south and east, breeding more irregular and again correlated with rainfall. In Puerto Rico, nest initiations peak Apr and July, but nests found every month; in Virgin Islands, Apr–Nov (Norton *et al.* 1986), Trinidad/Tobago Aug–Nov (ffrench 1973), Venezuela July–Dec (de Schauensee and Phelps 1978) and, in Surinam, May–Oct (Haverschmidt 1968). *rubrirostris* nests in austral spring (Oct–Nov) in Argentina (Phillips 1922–26), Apr–Aug in Equador (Marchant 1958, 1960). *galapagensis* nests year-round whenever conditions suitable (Phillips 1922–26, Harris 1974).

Nests on offshore cays common in West Indies. Bahama population nests on ground concealed underneath low (<1 m) vegetation (*Rachicallis americana, Casasia clusiifolia, Borichia arborescens, Jacquinia keyensis, Suriana maritima* and *Conocarpus erectus*). Nest bowl scraped from leaf litter or sand covering limestone rock, lined with dead leaves and down. Nests in Virgin Islands recorded in *Oplonia spinosa, Caesalpinia bonduc* and *Sesuvium portulacastrum* (Meier *et al.* 1989). In Marls of Abaco, one breeding pair per 15–20 ha mangrove island (McKinney and Bruggers 1983). Nests in mangrove areas placed in grass among mangrove roots. At Humacao Wildlife Reserve in Puerto Rico, nests found over water in grass clumps *Cyperus* growing out of old palm stumps. Eggs buff, shell smooth; 52.3×37.7 (49.0–57.1×34.6–39.3) ($n = 19$ clutches); those of captive *rubrirostris* weigh 36.9 (32.0–42.5) ($n = 100$); clutch 8.2 (6–10) ($n = 16$ nests, Bahama Islands population); clutch of 11 also documented (Marchant 1960). Re-nesting may occur if nest destroyed by predator; one instance of double brooding documented (♀ successfully fledged brood, then laid 2nd clutch a month later). Incubation, by ♀ only, 25–26 days. ♂ typically accompanies ♀ to nest area during prospecting and laying, may also escort her back to nest after daily incubation recess. ♀♀ nesting on offshore cays lead day-old ducklings across ocean back to island with pond habitat. ♂ may occasionally escort ♀ and brood, but parental care by ♀ only. Incubating and brood-tending ♀ reacts to courting ♂ other than mate with aggression and Repulsion display. Of 23 nests, at least one duckling hatched in 14 nests, 2 were abandoned and 7 destroyed by rats. Captive day-old *rubrirostris* weigh 21.7 (17.0–27.5) ($n = 100$). Mean brood size at hatching 5.9 ± 2.7 ($n = 14$ nests). First flight at 45–60 days old. Young sometimes continue to associate with mother after fledging. Brood amalgamation (crèching) occasionally occurs. Of 35 birds marked as ducklings, juveniles or yearlings, 22 known to remain in natal area for >1 years, 2 known to disperse to islands located 55 and 160 km away. Both sexes may reproduce in 1st year. Mean annual adult survival rate for ♂♂ 0.75 ± 0.19, for ♀♀ 0.74 ± 0.3. Of 229 birds marked over 8 years, 6, 4, and 1 individuals known to have lived at least 6, 7, and 8 years, respectively. Nonbreeding common; 31% (19–50%) of marked ♀♀ apparently made no attempt to breed (Sorenson 1990, 1992, Sorenson *et al.* 1992).

Conservation and threats

bahamensis subspecies formerly abundant throughout West Indies archipelago (Allen 1905, Phillips 1922–26), now rare or uncommon on most islands (although with advent of rice farming in 1960s, numbers increased substantially in Cuba). Population declines likely caused by excessive hunting and poaching, and nest predation by introduced rats, Small Indian Mongoose, Raccoon, feral cats and pigs, and land crabs. In Bahamas, where fully protected, poaching widespread and birds common only on islands with extensive areas of inaccessible habitat such as Abaco, Andros and Great Inagua (McKinney and Bruggers 1983). Loss of habitat of concern as coastal areas, ponds, and large expanses of mangrove swamp destroyed for use by expanding human population. Isolation and small population size makes *galapagensis* race particularly vulnerable to natural catastrophes and/or disease (Kear and Williams 1978) and listed by Threatened Waterfowl Specialist Group (2003) as Endangered. Populations of small West Indian islands at risk from hurricanes or hunting and poaching; recolonization may not occur, or take many years, if populations on neighbouring islands sedentary. Entire range needs close monitoring, and legal protection from hunting provided if warranted. Sanctuaries also required to protect crucial habitat. Study of inter-island movements of marked birds fitted with radio-transmitters would provide information on habitats utilized during year and on ability to recolonize. Reintroduction programmes may be warranted on islands where occurred historically.

Lisa G. Sorenson

Red-billed Pintail *Anas erythrorhyncha*
PLATE 19

Anas erythrorhyncha Gmelin, 1789, Syst. Nat., **1**, p. 517
Cape of Good Hope

Etymology: Gr. *eruthros*, red, and *rhunkhos*, bill, referring to bill colour of both sexes.

Other names: Red-billed Teal, Red-billed Duck. Afrikaans: Rooibekeend; French: Canard à bec rouge; Malagasy: Menamolotra.

Variation: no subspecies.

Description

ADULT: sexes alike. Greyish with dark cap and nape, and pale, occasionally white, cheeks and face. Body feathers have pale margins giving scaled appearance, underparts darker than breast, neck and body. Tail not noticeably long. Underwing dark; speculum broad and cream with thin dark band on leading edge. Bill bright pinkish red, with black at base of upper mandible; legs dark grey; eyes brown.

MOULT: no ♂ eclipse. ♂ in breeding condition may become brighter, and more prominently scaled so almost dimorphic during breeding season (Bell 1996).

IMMATURE: similar to adult, little duller with pink bill.

DUCKLING: dark brown above, pale yellow below. Cheek very yellow giving distinctive pale face. Eyestripe well defined and circles eye, yellow supercilium and dark patch on ear coverts.

MEASUREMENTS AND WEIGHT: in Transvaal, ♂ (*n* = 100) wing, 210–238 (226); tail, 75–95 (84); bill, 34–51 (45); tarsus, 34–43 (40); weight, 345–954 (591). ♀ (*n* = 100) wing, 204–228 (218); tail, 73–93 (83); bill, 38–46 (42); tarsus, 32–42 (38); weight (*n* =1177), 338–955 (544) (Day 1977, Dean and Skead 1979).

Field characters

Medium-sized duck of open water, 430–480 mm long. Red bill and contrasting dark cap and pale cheeks unmistakable. At distance, or in poor light, can be confused with smaller dumpier Hottentot Teal which has buff cheeks and blue bill. In flight, creamy speculum obvious; however, in Madagascar, can be confused at dusk or in haze with white speculum of Madagascar Teal.

Voice

Generally quiet. ♂ gives soft whistle-like *whizzt* and ♀ sharp *quack*. During courtship, birds more vocal (Brown *et al.* 1982). Sonogram in Maclean (1993).

Range and status

Widespread in southern and eastern Africa from Ethiopia and Sudan to Cape and throughout Madagascar. May be sedentary, with some populations semi-nomadic and moving as conditions change at favoured wetlands. There may be little or no movement between eastern and southern African populations (Scott and Rose 1996). Limited breeding data from Madagascar suggests some movement between there and mainland Africa. Heavily dependent upon rainfall in arid regions. Absent in western areas of southern Africa but moves north along Angolan coast; movements up to 1800 km (Brown *et al.* 1982) and 2191 km (SAFRING) recorded. Vagrant at Ma'agan Mikael, Israel (June–July 1968). Common to abundant, and most common duck in many parts of range including Madagascar where, although declining through habitat modification, populations remain reasonably high. Moves widely within southern Africa, over 5% of recoveries more than 1000 km from ringing site (Oatley and Prŷs-Jones 1986). Rose and Scott (1997) estimated population of 500 000–1 000 000 in southern Africa, 100 000–300 000 in eastern Africa and a decreasing 15 000–25 000 in Madagascar.

Habitat and general habits

Frequents open shallow lakes, marshes, dams and flooded fields. Forages amongst submerged and floating vegetation as well as at lake edges and on shore; feeds also in rice fields. In Madagascar, found in marshes, lakes and in small rivers. Collects in large flocks, up to many thousands, outside breeding season and readily associates with other ducks.

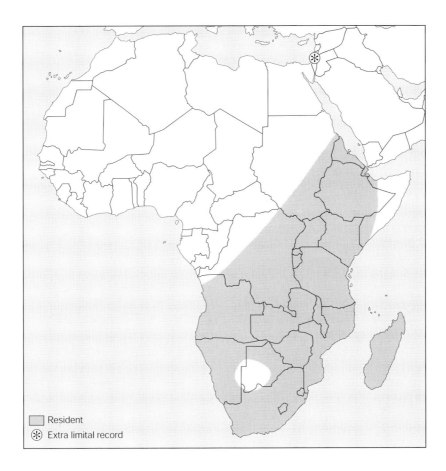

Resident

⊛ Extra limital record

Feeds by dabbling or up-ending, grazing in shallows or on land. Often nocturnal, especially when feeding on arable crops. Diet aquatic plants, seeds, tubers and invertebrates. Breeding and post-breeding birds examined on Nyl River floodplain, South Africa, in 1993 (Petrie 1996) had fed principally on seeds of *Panicum schinzii*. While may feed on animal matter at times, Petrie (1996) found able to reproduce on only small amounts of invertebrates. Adaptation to breeding on low invertebrate/high *Panicum* diet allows nesting in semi-arid lands and during drought years when wetlands scarce. See Woodall (1979) for details of diet.

Displays and breeding behaviour

Well studied and undemonstrative. ♂♂ have reduced pintail displays; only Burp may be used in which ♂ sitting on water, thrusts head upwards and backwards with bill held horizontally or slightly down uttering rapid *geeeee* call. Unlike other pintail, call only given as head moves upwards. ♂ also Turns-back-of-head while Leading Inciting ♀. Preen-behind-wing recorded (Lorenz 1951–53, Johnsgard 1965a). Post-copulatiory display consists of Bridle with single call, possibly followed by Burp (Johnson *et al.* 2000). Not strongly territorial; however, ♂ may accompany and defend mate while rearing brood.

Breeding and life cycle

Breeding recorded in all months, apparently stimulated by changing water levels, when large numbers move to breeding areas. In southern Africa, breeds predominantly Oct–May, varying with region, and June–Jan (Aug–Oct peak) in western Cape Province (Maclean 1997e). In east Africa, breeds Jan–Aug (Brown *et al.* 1982). Broods found in eastern Madagascar in Jan 2000 at onset of wet season. In stable wetlands, may nest throughout year; in areas of instability, as water levels drop, breeding ceases and pairs disperse.

Nests on ground in waterside vegetation, always close to water's edge. Eggs ovate, smooth buff or cream (Brown *et al.* 1982); 50.0 × 37.5 (44.2–54.6 × 32.0–41.7) ($n = 124$) (Maclean 1993); weight in southern Africa 38 (36–40) ($n = 20$) (Maclean 1993) or, in captivity, 37.5 ($n = 41$); clutch in southern Africa 10 (5–12) (Brown *et al.* 1982). Incubation by

♀ alone 25–28 days (Maclean 1993). Hatch weight in captivity 23.5 ($n = 36$). Fledge in 56 days (Maclean 1993). Probably breeds at one year. No data on breeding success, survival nor longevity.

Conservation and threats

Protection of wetlands and strict controls on hunting will maintain high numbers.

Glyn Young

South Georgia Pintail *Anas georgica georgica*
PLATE 19

Anas georgica Gmelin, 1789, Syst. Nat., **1**, p. 516 'Georgia Australi America'

Etymology: *georgica* from island of South Georgia, 1300 km east of Falkland Islands in south Atlantic Ocean, where type specimen taken.

Other names: South Georgia Teal, South Georgian Pintail.

Variation: subspecies of Brown Pintail; see that account, page 593.

Description

ADULT: slightly dimorphic. ♂ has rufous crown flecked black, sides of head buff or grey-brown. Neck lighter, becoming grey or greyish white on throat, with thick sprinkling of small brown central spots on feathers. Dorsal surface predominantly brown, upperback buff-brown; all feathers with dark centres and wide, distinct paler margins. Tertials olive-brown with central longitudinal velvety black stripe, chiefly on inner web. Wing coverts buff-grey, with darker shaft streaks, distal row buff, succeeded on secondaries by velvety black speculum with faint green lustre, and buff terminal band. Primaries and tail grey-brown, central feathers elongate with rufous margins; usually 16 tail feathers, but variable 14–16. Chest more rufous than back. Belly sometimes similar, but almost white in most birds. Underwing coverts and axillaries grey-brown, longer members with whitish tips and more or less white sprinkling. Bill, nail and distal borders of maxilla black, remainder of bill tip slaty blue, sides of maxilla deep lemon yellow, becoming

greenish where blends with blue tip; legs and feet greyish olive-green, joints and webs darker, with patches of greenish yellow on legs; iris dark brown. ♀ similar, but with mid dark brown speculum showing only suggestion of velvety black distally; band formed by tips of secondaries likewise more buff, and velvety black stripes on tertials less conspicuous (Murphy 1936). Bill less strikingly marked, sides of maxilla yellowish green. During breeding season, many ♀♀ have bald patch on crown due to ♂ biting feathers at copulation.

MOULT: little seasonal variation in plumage. Adults flightless during synchronized moult at end of breeding season. Three, located after nightfall among tussock grass and captured Feb, had recently dropped primaries. Most birds flightless Mar, and rarely seen in daylight; moulting 1st generation captives also hide during day. Most birds flying again Apr. Body moult underway by Dec in ♂, but delayed until after brood rearing in ♀.

IMMATURE: resembles ♀.

DUCKLING: dark brown but guard hairs ginger, giving rufous appearance. Longitudinal fawn stripe extends each side of midline from wings to tail. Trailing edge of wings also fawn, showing transverse line from longitudinal stripe to edge of body. Head has broad dark brown stripe from crown rearwards. Face fawn or pale brown, with dark brown stripe leading posteriorly from eye. Dark cheek patch or short stripe occurs around ear. Breast fawn, belly cream. Bill grey, sides becoming greenish with age; legs and feet pale grey.

MEASUREMENTS AND WEIGHT: ♂ (*n* = 18) wing, 219–235 (225); head, 81.1–86.9 (84.7); exposed culmen, 33.3–36 (34.8); bill width (*n* = 4), 16.4–17.4; mass, 540–655 (597). Skins (Murphy 1936) (*n* = 8); tail, 93–104 (100); tarsus, 35.5–39 (37); mid toe and claw, 45–51 (48). ♀ (*n* = 6) wing, 206–221 (213); head, 77.5–81.9 (78.9); exposed culmen 32.1–33.9 (32.9); bill width (*n* = 3), 16–18; mass, 460–495 (475). Skins (Murphy 1936) (*n* = 4) tail, 85–93 (89); tarsus, 35–36 (35.9); mid toe and claw, 46–49 (48.0).

Field characters

Brown duck, ♂ 415–445, ♀ 390–415 mm long, whose newly moulted and juvenile birds dappled due to contrast between dark brown centres and buff-brown edges of most body feathers. Appearance more uniform and greyer as plumage wears. Conspecific with Brown Pintail of South America and Falkland Islands, but smaller and darker with reduced extremities giving stockier appearance, and less brilliant speculum (Delacour 1954–64, Weller 1975b). Duckling darker than Brown Pintail. Speckled Teal (race of South American Teal), only other duck on South Georgia, smaller, much paler, with brilliant green speculum.

Voice

Main vocalization and display of ♂ Burp-whistle involving wheezy, hollow-sounding *geeeeegeeeee* with shorter, but concurrent *twer-dip* that sounds double-noted (Lorenz 1951–53, Weller 1975b) but appears as 3 notes on sonograms. Main ♀ call is short *quack*, sometimes repeated.

Range and status

Endemic to South Georgia where common and widespread. Breeds in all coastal Tussock *Poa flabellata* habitats; survey (Prince and Poncet 1996) showed breeding in 29.7% of 5 km² surveyed and presence in further 17.6%. No precise figures on population but > 2000 individuals estimated on

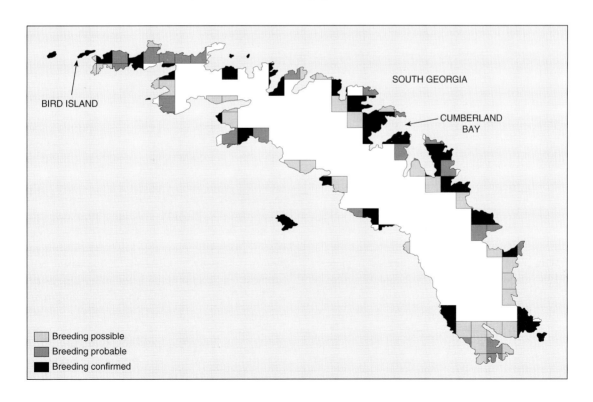

BIRD ISLAND

SOUTH GEORGIA

CUMBERLAND BAY

▢ Breeding possible
▨ Breeding probable
■ Breeding confirmed

basis of local counts and widespread distribution. Counts at Bird Island Apr–May usually find 120, with maximum 250 in Oct 1983. Counts in Cumberland Bay indicate similar numbers, suggesting that most fjords on northern side contain 50–150 birds by end of breeding season.

Habitat and general habits

Predominantly intertidal feeder for most of year as freshwater freezes and snow blankets land. Even in summer, streams and ponds away from coastal zone rarely used; normally seen on shoreline or in habitats within 100 m of it. During Nov–Dec, Weller (1975b) observed birds spending *c* 60% of time in tussock ponds and 17% on seashore and in fjords; presence on sea probably influenced by tides. Gut contents from 6 specimens and analyses of 50 faecal pellets during breeding season indicated diet of fairy shrimp *Branchinecta gaini*, amphipods, small range of other freshwater invertebrates including dipterans and snails, plus marine algae. Feeds by up-ending or by stretching head and neck underwater. Dives regularly; mean submersion time in ponds 450–700 mm deep, 8.1 (6–11) sec ($n = 23$) (Weller 1975b). On Bird Island, grazes on marine algae and Antarctic Starwort *Callitriche antarctica*. Sometimes feeds on and around Antarctic Fur Seal *Arctocephalus gazella* carcasses. Also feeds downstream of carcasses being scavenged by giant petrels *Macronectes* and skuas, often in close proximity to these potential predators. Forages actively at night, often loafing in middle of day. Forms small, loose groups when foraging, but flocks of 10–20 (up to 40) occur on ponds used for bathing and resting. Birds come and go from such ponds in small groups throughout day.

Displays and breeding behaviour

Weller (1975b) indicated pattern of display similar to Northern Pintail (Lorenz 1951–53, Johnsgard 1965a, Smith 1968), including Chin-lifting by both sexes. Grunt-whistle less common than Burp-whistle and occurs only during intense courtship. Single and paired ♀♀ often give Repulsion gesture and associated rasping call when approached by sexually active ♂. When pressed, ♀ may go ashore or take flight, often followed by several ♂♂. On such flights, climbs to 100 m and flies several km. Communal display of ♂ includes Bill-dip followed immediately by Head-up-tail-up and Kick, accompanied by brief whistle.

Breeding and life cycle

Earliest observation of breeding activity was of pair copulating at Bird Island on 16 Oct 1988. Nests with eggs seen Dec–Mar; broods from 24 Nov (Weller 1975b) to 15 Mar (von der Steinen 1890). Dec–Jan probably peak hatching months, and later broods likely derive from replacement clutches. Nest constructed of grasses forming deep bowl, normally situated off ground in dense vegetation such as tussock clump. Down added with penultimate egg. Eggs rounded ovate and light buff, laid on alternate days; in captivity $55.6 \pm 2.3 \times 39.6 \pm 1.2$ (50.5–67.0×36.6–42.8) ($n = 105$); mass 46.2 ± 3.8 (37.0–55.5) ($n = 29$) but some eggs partially incubated; dimensions of two wild clutches in middle of range. Mean clutch in captivity 4.9 ± 1.4 (3–9), mode 5 ($n = 66$); wild clutches consistent, perhaps slightly smaller (half clutch size of Brown Pintail). Clutch replacement common in captives, with up to 3 nests per season at intervals of 16–22 days between egg loss and re-laying (Martin 2002). Incubating ♀ leaves nest for 10–20 min, usually accompanied by ♂; all 3 wild observations made during evening, when ♀♀ characteristically restless and active, calling frequently. Incubation in captivity 25.9 ± 1.1 (24–28) days ($n = 15$) (Martin 2002). ♀ apparently rears ducklings unaided, and may be harassed by other ♀♀. Captive ♂♂ may fertilize 2 or more ♀♀ and attempt to mate with other duck species.

Most obvious predator is Antarctic Skua *C. a. lonnbergi* which frequently pursues any duck in flight but seems to ignore bird on ground or on water. Pintail wings occasionally found at skua middens, but this rare even at Bird Island where population of skuas > 400 pairs at average density of pair per ha. Nevertheless, behaviour of duck (hiding during daylight and during moult, and extreme wariness of ♀♀ and broods) indicates predation as strong influence, and ever-present skua as great threat.

Breeding success, age at breeding and longevity in wild unknown. Captive birds frequently breed successfully in 1st year and commonly survive 5–8 years, with annual breeding.

Conservation and threats

Murphy (1916) stated that duck, which has tameness typical of island birds, suffered severely at hands of whalers who shot them for eating at every opportunity. In Nov 1912, Murphy saw 6 birds in Cumberland Bay and considered himself fortunate; visiting same bay today, at least 150 birds would be counted. As Murphy (1916) correctly observed, whalers were restricted in overland movement by nature of terrain, with many glaciers and mountains, and impact of shooting local rather than widespread.

Currently listed as Near-threatened by Threatened Waterfowl Specialist Group (2003), but now fully protected and population likely to be stable or expanding rather than declining. Despite presence of introduced Brown Rats on northern coastline, no evidence that duck suffers extreme predation at nest or on young; appears able to breed successfully in areas frequented by rats (Martin 2002). Breeds well in captivity (Martin 2002).

Tony Martin and †Peter Prince

Brown Pintail *Anas georgica spinicauda*
PLATE 19

Anas spinicauda Vieillot, 1816, Nouv. Dict. Hist. Nat., nouv. éd., **5**, p. 135
Buenos Aires

Etymology: *spinicauda* L. *spina* means thorn, plus *cauda* tail.

Other names: Chilean Pintail, Yellow-billed Pintail. Portuguese: Marreca-parda (Brazil); Spanish: Pato jergón grande (Chile), Pato maicero (Argentina).

Variation: 3 subspecies recognized: *A. g. georgica* Gmelin, 1789, from South Georgia (here treated separately, see page 590), Niceforo's Pintail *A. g. niceforoi* Wetmore and Borrero, 1946 from central Columbia (extinct) and Brown Pintail *A. g. spinicauda* from southern South America and Falkland Islands.

Description

ADULT: sexes alike. Uniform pale brown, darker scaled back may contrast with greyer neck. Speculum green; 2 central tail feathers project beyond surrounding feathers. Bill bright yellow with pale blue sub-terminal band and black central ridge; legs and feet dark grey; iris brown. Two races in continental South America larger than South Georgian race; *niceforoi* reported to look darker than larger *spinicauda* with less pointed tail and longer, less upturned bill (Delacour 1954–64); *georgica*, smallest and darkest race, usually has 16 tail feathers compared to 14 in *spinicauda*.

MOULT: 2 moults of body feathers assumed but no seasonal variation in plumage, and no ♂ eclipse. Wing moult follows breeding.

IMMATURE: resembles adult, duller with breast streaked rather than spotted.

DUCKLING: upperparts, head, neck and sides of breast dark brown; markings on back and wings, throat, breast and abdomen dull yellowish buff; face markings reduced to ill-defined pale lines above and behind eyes (Delacour 1954–64).

MEASUREMENTS AND WEIGHT: *spinicauda* (no sample size) ♂ wing, 230–260; bill, 40–43; tarsus, 40–42; tail, 140–148. ♀ wing, 212–240; bill, 40–41; *niceforoi* (no sample size) ♂ wing, 226–230; bill, 52–54; tarsus, 39–41. ♀ wing, 226–230; bill, 50; tarsus, 41 (Delacour 1954–64). Weight *spinicauda* in Argentina (no range given) ♂ ($n = 74$), 776; ♀ ($n = 34$), 705 (Weller 1968b).

Field characters

Medium-sized, elegant-looking, long-necked, surface-feeding duck, 500–600 mm long. Uniform pale brown plumage, long neck and yellow bill distinctive. Speckled Teal, race of South American Teal, which also has yellow bill, markedly smaller with greyer plumage and dark head. No other South American duck within range could be confused.

Voice

Generally quiet; ♂ has loud Burp, and variety of whistles heard particularly in flight. ♀ has quacking calls, including Decrescendo, similar to Northern Pintail. No sonogram published.

Range and status

Found in southern and western South America, including Andean slopes. *spinicauda* widespread from southern Columbia, Nariño and Putumayo Departments (Hilty and Brown 1986) in west, and from southeastern Brazil, São Paulo and Rio Grande do Sul, and Paraguay in east. Common throughout Uruguay, Argentina and Chile as far south as Tierra del Fuego; southernmost populations migratory, flying north after breeding. Arrives Tierra del Fuego Aug–Sept, leaving Mar–Apr. Exact movements unknown, may be migratory through most of range (Weller 1968b). Resident in Falkland Islands but uncommon (Woods 1988). Stragglers reach Antarctica with records from King George Island, South Georgia (two individuals in company with resident subspecies), South Orkney and South Shetland Islands and Antarctic Peninsular (Marchant and Higgins 1990, Prince and Croxall 1996, Todd 1996). Considered rare in northern parts of range and abundant further south; however, surveys show possibly serious declines, particularly in Argentina (Antas *et al.* 1996). Rose and Scott (1997) estimated population of 100 000–1 000 000.

niceforoi was endemic to eastern Andes of Columbia, in Cundinamarca and Boyaca, particularly Lake Tota; one record from Cauca valley (Fjeldså and Krabbe 1990). Described in 1946, considered extinct in Cundinamarca in 1948 and at Lake Tota by mid 1950s (Young *et al.* 1996). Over-hunting and wetland drainage thought likely causes for decline. Exotic trout introduced into these wetlands, but probably after extinction of *niceforoi*.

Habitat and general habits

Freshwater lakes, marshes, flooded fields and rivers. Gregarious outside breeding season, large flocks may roost and feed together, often in sea, in sheltered bays. Regularly feeds in open, dry fields, and during night. In north of range, altitudinal movements

recorded, birds moving to feed on swampy areas of Andean Plateau, 4000 m and above. Typically feeds by dabbling and up-ending but will dive. Diet mostly vegetarian, particularly seeds of aquatic plants, including water milfoil *Myriophyllum* (Phillips 1922–26). Some invertebrates eaten, including molluscs.

Displays and breeding behaviour

Behaviour similar to Northern Pintail (Johnsgard 1965a). ♂ active, and may display in groups throughout year. Group courtship often initiated by 'restless' ♀ (Delacour 1954–64). ♂ frequently Burps, and follows with repeated Grunt-whistles. Head feathers erected during display, giving appearance of dramatically enlarged head (Lorenz 1951–53). No Head-up-tail-up nor Down-up; ♂ may Turn-back-of-head, and Leads Inciting ♀.

Few remain paired throughout year, with ♂ attending brood; however, in more southerly populations, ♂ more likely to desert mate and brood, especially at time of wing moult (Weller 1968b, McKinney and Brewer 1989).

Breeding and life cycle

Little studied in wild. Nesting takes place in austral spring, Oct–Dec, in most regions, Sept–Dec in Falklands. Breeding season may be longer in north, with 2 peaks to reproductive activity, e.g. in Mar–Apr and Oct–Nov in Columbia (Hilty and Brown 1986). Timing probably influenced by local wetland conditions.

Nests on ground in long grass, usually close to water. Eggs cream; 52.4×37.5 ($49–56 \times 35–40$) ($n = 40$) (Schönwetter 1960–66), or 53.9×37.1 ($51.1–57.3 \times 35.5–38.4$) ($n = 22$) (Goodall *et al.* 1951); weight in captivity 39.0 ($n = 60$). Clutch in Patagonia 8 ($n = 11$) (Phillips 1922–26), 6–12 (Delacour 1954–64); incubation, by ♀ alone, 26 days. Hatch weight in captivity 25.4 ($n = 66$); fledging period unrecorded. Brood size of recently hatched ducklings 5.6 ± 2.2 (1–10) ($n = 34$) in Argentina and Chile. Breeds at one year in captivity. No data on breeding success, survival nor longevity, except that one captive lived 23 years (Mitchell 1911).

Conservation and threats

Remains reasonably common throughout most of range, and may be most common duck in South America. Wetland management, sensible hunting practices, maintenance of refuges, particularly in arid areas and during dry years essential. Coordinated protection by all range states should allow this popular duck to maintain present status and, perhaps, to regain former numbers.

Glyn Young

Northern Pintail *Anas acuta*
PLATE 19

Anas acuta Linnaeus, 1758, Syst. Nat., ed. 10, p. 126
Europe

Etymology: *acuta* L. sharp-pointed, in reference to pointed tail feathers.

Other names: Pintail. Danish: Spidsand; French: Canard pilet; German: Spiessente; Icelandic: Grafönd; Japanese: Onaga-gamo; Spanish: Pato golondrino.

Variation: no subspecies recognized. Pairbond seasonal, pairs being formed away from breeding areas where birds of differing summer provenance mix. This dispersive nature, and ability to colonize new habitat opportunistically, have ensured homogeneous genetic diversity and corresponding mixing, with no morphological differences over wide range.

Description

ADULT: dimorphic. ♂ in breeding, or alternate, plumage has nape, throat and head chocolate-brown with contrasting white stripe up side of neck. Much of upperparts and flanks finely vermiculated grey. Lower front to neck, breast and central underparts white. Ventral yellow-buff flags to both sides. Undertail and uppertail coverts black. Two central elongated tail feathers slender black with pale grey edging extending beyond normal length, similarly marked remaining tail feathers. Underwing grey, darker on coverts. Upperwing primaries brownish grey, coverts greyish brown, buff edging to greater coverts. Speculum metallic green to bronze, becoming black inwards, with black sub-terminal band and broad white trailing edges. Central elongate tertials and scapulars grey with contrasting black central stripes. Bill blue-grey with central black stripe in all plumages, nail and edges black; legs grey, webs blackish; iris brown, occasionally yellowish. ♀ head and neck greyish brown finely flecked and mottled. Neck and lower underparts all slightly paler, finely mottled. Flanks more brownish with black sub-terminal band giving heavy crescent-shaped markings along sides of body. Upperparts brownish grey marked with black sub-terminally presenting scalloped effect. Underwing grey. Upperwing grey-brown with pale edging to greater coverts giving whitish line above speculum. Speculum bronze-brown, with broad white trailing edge. Bill duller than ♂, culmen less markedly dark; legs and eye as ♂.

MOULT: in eclipse, or basic, plumage ♂ resembles adult ♀ but retains heavier markings on head, grey elongate tertials, heavily marked speculum and dark centre to tail. Does not show broad buff edges to body feathers characteristic of ♀, and bill remains blue-grey.

IMMATURE: ♂ similar to breeding ♀, but with dark, almost brown crown, mottled buff, off-white streaked dark brown on head and neck, upperpart and flank feathers dark brown, edged with narrow fringes of grey-buff and white. Tail feathers notched, sepia brown, edged buff. Feathers narrower than adults, with less square tips characteristic of juveniles. Wing like adult ♂, but white secondary and greater covert tips narrower, lesser and median coverts dull grey-brown, narrowly edged white. Tertials and coverts shorter, duller and less ornate. ♀ rather as juvenile ♂, but unbarred mantle characteristic; wing as adult ♀ but speculum dark grey-brown, lacking gloss, narrower white tips to secondaries and greater coverts, especially broken and thinner on innermost feathers.

DUCKLING: crown, eyestripe, hind neck and back pale sepia or reddish. Underparts, streaks over and below eye, on rear of wing, linear arrangement of spots on flanks, and rump white. Bill and legs olive-grey or bluish. Proportionally longer tarsi than Northern Mallard (Nelson 1993).

MEASUREMENTS AND WEIGHT: in Europe, ♂ adult wing ($n = 20$), 275; juv (1st winter) wing ($n = 35$), 266; adult tarsus ($n = 40$), 42.6; adult weight ($n = 183$), 851. ♀ adult wing ($n = 12$), 260; juv wing ($n = 20$), 248; adult tarsus ($n = 30$), 41.0; adult weight ($n = 68$), 735.3 (Cramp and Simmons 1977). In North America, ♂ adult wing ($n = 45$), 271.8; juv wing ($n = 30$), 266.7; adult weight ($n = 390$), 1031; juv weight ($n = 760$), 954. ♀ adult wing ($n = 27$), 256.5; juv wing ($n = 31$), 248.9; adult weight ($n = 166$), 871; juv weight ($n = 526$), 803 (Bellrose 1980).

Field characters

Slight, slender ducks borne upon long narrow wings, making flight silhouette almost gull-like. Although medium-sized among dabbling ducks, 510–560 mm long, long neck and tail make it longer overall than Northern Mallard which weighs quarter as much again. Best identified by greyish appearance of plumage, proportionally small rounded head, long neck and slender appearance. White breast of ♂ conspicuous among resting ducks.

Voice

♂ has monosyllabic extended *geeeee* call, ♀ makes series of low *quacks*, rather like Northern Mallard, but quieter. Sonogram of ♂ Burp in Cramp and Simmons (1977). Calls of ducklings similar to Northern Mallard; for details see Smith (1968).

Range and status

Extends over more of northern hemisphere than any other waterfowl species. In North America, nests throughout Alaska and central Canadian Arctic south to Great Lakes, central Kansas, southern Colorado into New Mexico and southern California (Bellrose 1980). In favourable arctic habitat, breeding densities reach 5.0 pairs per km^2, and 8.8 pairs per km^2 in the Mackenzie Delta (Bellrose 1980). Mean prairie densities of 4.0 pairs km^{-2} range from 9.3 pairs per km^2 (Alberta) to 2.8 pairs per km^2 (South Dakota, Bellrose 1980). Boreal forests, parkland and short-grass prairie regions support lower densities.

Strongly migratory throughout northern range, although some populations sedentary. Small numbers remain in Aleutian Islands and Alaskan panhandle throughout winter, but generally North American populations winter south of 40°N, in greatest numbers in Californian Central Valley and coastal marshes of Mexico and Louisiana. Winters south into West Indies, Central and northern South America and even on Pacific Ocean islands, including Hawaii and Marshall Islands (Bellrose 1980). North American population numbered 9.6 million during 1955–56, declining to 3.2 million by 1962 after sustained drought in prairie region affected habitat availability. Numbers recovered to 5.9 million by 1969 and remained at 5.6 million through 1970s; however, fell to 2 million by 1988 (US Fish & Wildlife Service/Canadian Wildlife Service 1992) as result of habitat loss and degradation, overexploitation and climate.

In Old World, breeds throughout Siberia, Russia, Scandinavian peninsula, as well as locally in Iceland and Greenland, nesting south to North Africa, Hungary and Turkey in west and Kamchatka and

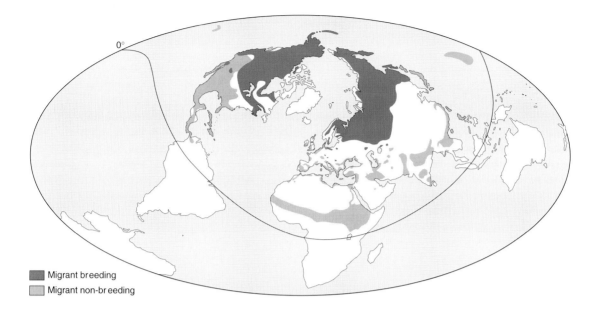

Migrant breeding
Migrant non-breeding

Sakhalin in east (Cramp and Simmons 1977). Few published nesting densities, but 2.4–2.7 pairs per km^2 occur in Fennoscandia (Haapanen and Nilsson 1979). Winters as far south as Philippines, Borneo, Malaysia, India, Pakistan, southwest Asia, throughout southern and western Europe and south into central Africa (Cramp and Simmons 1977). Third most common dabbling duck in Japan in winter (after Northern Mallard and Spot-billed Duck) (Brazil 1991). Winter estimates suggest 1 200 000 in west Africa where numbers thought stable over past 30 years (Rose 1995, Rose and Scott 1997). Some 60 000 winter in northwest Europe where evidence of decline in recent years. Population of 300 000 in Black Sea/eastern Mediterranean declining at 6.4% per annum (Rose 1995). Some 700 000 winter in southwest Asia and east Africa, but count coverage insufficient to provide details of population trends (Rose and Scott 1997). Numbers wintering in southern and eastern Asia not well monitored, but 90 000–120 000 pass through Kamchatka Peninsula in spring, with 50 000 recorded from Moroshech-naya River alone (Gerasimov and Gerasimov 1995a). Regional total currently thought to number 100 000 in southern Asia and 500 000–1 000 000 in eastern and southeastern Asia (Miyabayashi and Mundkur 1999), with suggestions of declines in recent years (Rose and Scott 1997).

Habitat and general habits

Occurs in productive freshwater, brackish and saline wetlands, usually with shallow water to facilitate dabbling and up-ending for winter food, predominantly vegetable, mainly storage organs, especially seeds. Invertebrates increasingly taken prior to spring migration (Miller 1986, 1987). Characteristically found in relatively few large coastal congregations within Europe, half population found at just 13 sites, *c* 50% in Britain (Monval and Pirot 1989). Susceptible to cold, showing increased recovery distances from point of capture and increase in recovery rates during severe weather (Ridgill and Fox 1990). Winter body condition (as measured by body mass, fat depots and gizzard mass) relates to food availability (Smith and Sheeley 1993a).

In North America, distribution more general and range of habitats exploited far wider (Bellrose 1980). Ringing studies show strong winter-site fidelity (Hestbeck 1993a), in contrast to opportunist nature in summer, exploiting ephemeral wetlands, and over-flying regularly used wetlands during dry seasons. Birds associating on wintering areas, therefore, represent more stable population units than breeding-ground affiliations. Hence, local overexploitation in winter may depress long-term viability of population units and management on winter grounds may be most effective in restoring declining population trends in some areas. Restrictive hunting regulations during 1959–61 in Pacific Flyway of North America may have helped increase ♂ survival during period of low population levels (Hestbeck 1993b).

May congregate at large moulting areas in North America and Russia, to which at least some individuals show site fidelity (Dementiev and Gladkov 1952, Anderson and Sterling 1974). Omnivorous during moult (Krapu 1974b), but abundant protein-rich food availability may enhance speed of moult (Smith and Sheeley 1993b).

Displays and breeding behaviour

Display described by Lorenz (1951–53), Johnsgard (1965a) and Smith (1968). Inciting by ♀ accompanied by less pointing bill movements than in mallards, call softer and Decresendo call shorter and not so loud. Preen-behind-wing common ♀ display, but Nod-swim does not occur. In ♂♂, Burp frequent; replacing Introductory Shake of mallards and accompanied by *gee* call rather than *raeb*. ♂♂ crowd around courted ♀ and Burp repeatedly before performing Grunt-whistle followed by Head-up-tail-up (as in all green-winged teal) and then by turning bill to ♀. ♂♂ often Turn-back-of-head after Burping and do so while Leading Inciting ♀. Pre-copulatory display consists of Mutual Head-pumping.

Breeding behaviour induced by changes in daylength, egg-laying being brought on by long daylength in artificial situations (Bluhm 1992). Pair formation occurs relatively early in season because large size and stored reserves enable nesting soon after arrival on breeding areas. ♂♂ defend ♀♀ rather than territories, presumably because of patchy and ephemeral nature of spring food supply (Oring and Sayler 1992).

Dispersed nature of pairs in spring, and subsequent nest sites, means little aggressive behaviour, mates not closely defended and ♂♂ may be highly mobile, leading to frequent display and forced copulations, not normally broken up by attendant ♂ (Smith 1968, McKinney 1973). In North America, selects wide diversity of breeding habitat, responding quickly to newly created habitats in way only explained by emigration (Hochbaum and Bossenmaier 1972); hence, moves into sub-Arctic and Arctic in response to

prairie droughts restricting breeding ground (Smith 1970), North American birds even reaching Siberia in some dry seasons (Henny 1973). ♂ even less philopatric to breeding areas than ♀ (Sowls 1955, Derrickson 1977), and young ♀ less so than older ones (Lokemoen *et al.* 1990).

Breeding and life cycle

Nests shortly after arrival on breeding ground, ♀♀ having stored fat reserves for reproduction (Krapu 1974a); however, because of differences in spring thaw and water-level conditions, 1st egg dates may vary by up to 14 days (Sowls 1955). Date of nest initiation ranged from 9 Mar in California to 12 May in Alaska (Krapu *et al.* 2002). Older experienced ♀♀ lay earlier and larger clutches than younger, less experienced ones (Duncan 1987a). ♀ diet largely (77–99%) invertebrates during laying period (Krapu 1974a), with burst in availability of fairy shrimps (Anostraca) dominating diet, especially in years when seasonal ephemeral wetlands abundant. Later, ♀♀ feed upon chironomids, gastropods and earthworms (forced to surface by high water-tables) when Anostraca no longer available (Krapu 1974a, 1974b).

Nests in cover, rushes, grass or low scrub, may be close to wetland, but can be more than 1 km from water. Not normally colonial, but can nest 2–3 m apart. ♀♀ less likely to desert than ♀ Northern Mallard (Sowls 1955). Eggs ovate, off-white to yellowish green; 55 × 39 (48–60 × 36–42) (*n* = 75) (Cramp and Simmons 1977) in Czechoslovakia and 53.6 × 38.2 (unknown sample) (Bellrose 1980) in North America; weigh 43 (37–50) (*n* = 28) (Cramp and Simmons 1977); clutch 7–9 (6–12) in Europe (Cramp and Simmons 1977) and 7.76 (3–14) (*n* = 1276) in North America (Bellrose 1980). Single brood, will replace lost clutch; incubated by ♀ for 22–23 days (Bellrose 1980). Captive ducklings weigh 26.1 (*n* = 47) on hatching. Growth and plumage development described in Blais *et al.* (2001).

Recorded nest success 32.3–67.0% (Bellrose 1980), with 53% mortality amongst ducklings in 1st 2 weeks of life, 73% to fledging (Duncan 1986b). Highly susceptible to Red Fox predation, but as shows little inclination to nest on islands, provision of island nesting sites has little effect on breeding output (Sargeant *et al*. 1984). Bellrose (1980) gave mean brood size on hatching as 6.86, falling to 5.89 for Class I (see Gollop and Marshall 1954 for definitions) broods ($n = 1342$), 5.63 for Class II broods ($n = 1599$) and 5.22 for Class III broods ($n = 1312$). Late nesting ♀♀ may delay completion of moult until arrival on wintering grounds (Hohman *et al*. 1992). First-year survival (♂ 56%, ♀ 51%) less than adults (♂ 63–81%, ♀ 42–77%) (Reinecker 1987, Hestbeck 1993b). May breed in 1st year, though some not until 2nd (Cramp and Simmons 1977). Longevity record of BTO ringed bird 15 years 11 months (Toms and Clark 1998).

Conservation and threats

In Western Europe, highly aggregated coastal winter distribution at relatively few sites and recent reduction in numbers give cause for concern. Habitat loss and overexploitation identified in action plan for Europe. Continued pressure for industrial land claim in coastal areas problematic. Little known about breeding biology in Palearctic and studies here should be future priority. In North America, population continues to decline in spite of conservation measures; loss of prairie pothole habitat, potentially worsened in recent years by drought and in future years from predicted global climate change, has had drastic effect. Clutches laid early now have reduced hatching rate, and species limited capacity to re-nest in late spring on prairie breeding grounds probably contributes to decline (Krapu *et al*. 2002).

Tony Fox

Eaton's Pintail *Anas eatoni*
PLATE 19

Querquedula eatoni Sharpe, 1875, Ibis, p. 328 Kerguelen Island

Etymology: named after Rev A.E. Eaton (1845–1929), English naturalist and explorer who took part in Transit of Venus Expedition of 1874–75.

Other names: Indian Ocean Pintail, Kerguelen Pintail, Southern Pintail. French: Canard d'Eaton.

Variation: 2 subspecies recognized, Kerguelen Pintail *A. e. eatoni*, and Crozet Island Pintail *A. e. drygalskii* Reichenow, 1904.

Description

ADULT: sexes nearly alike. ♂ in breeding plumage lacks full breeding plumage of Northern Pintail ♂ and closely resembles ♀; plumage rather uniform and reddish brown; buff and cinnamon underparts. Around 1% of ♂♂ attain some brighter plumage characteristics, including hints of brown head and white neck stripe, but generally only distinguished from ♀ by brighter speculum and slightly elongate central tail feathers. Bill blue-grey with black stripe along culmen; legs dark grey; eyes yellowish brown. ♀ like small, dark reddish Northern Pintail ♀, with duller brown speculum; bill duller than ♂ with black culmen less clear (Marchant and Higgins 1990).

drygalskii poorly differentiated from *eatoni*, but underparts less conspicuously barred, wings and bill shorter, but tarsi and culmen longer (Weller 1980).

MOULT: 2 annual moults of body feathers and single wing moult. Seasonal change in ♂ plumage much less marked than in Northern Pintail (Weller 1980), merely losing vermiculations; ♂ in eclipse May–Nov, when resembles ♀ except for speculum (Delacour 1954–64). Post-breeding wing moult lasts Apr–July (Stahl *et al*. 1984).

IMMATURE: like ♀ but more streaked below, ♂ soon showing brighter speculum (Delacour 1954–64).

DUCKLING: like that of Northern Pintail but smaller, paler, and spots on back and wings reddish buff, not white. Breast and underparts more strongly tinged rufous; face also rufous, not white, and less distinctly marked; dark line through eye conspicuous, but lower line missing or reduced to short streak near nape (Delacour 1954–64). Brownish colour matches peaty soil (Weller 1980).

MEASUREMENTS AND WEIGHT: *eatoni* ♂ wing ($n = 20$), 233.6 ± 1.32; tail ($n = 19$), 105.2 ± 3.87; culmen

($n = 19$), 33.7 ± 0.34; tarsus ($n = 19$), 35.1 ± 0.19. ♀ ($n = 9$) wing, 203.4 ± 1.50; tail, 85.2 ± 0.86; culmen, 31.0 ± 0.13; tarsus, 32.5 ± 0.49. *drygalskii* ♂ wing ($n = 17$), 212.0 ± 1.61; tail ($n = 9$), 99.8 ± 1.36; culmen ($n = 18$), 34.5 ± 0.34; tarsus ($n = 18$), 36.4 ± 0.25. ♀ ($n = 5$) wing, 202.2 ± 1.02; tail, 81.2 ± 2.24; culmen, 31.8 ± 0.48; tarsus, 34.2 ± 0.34 (Weller 1980); weight, 450 (Lack 1970).

Field characters

Smaller and stockier than Northern Pintail, 350–400 mm long, with bill comparatively small and short. Only duck, other than introduced Northern Mallard, on islands of Kerguelen, Crozet, St Paul and Amsterdam.

Voice

Both sexes resemble Northern Pintail, but slightly higher-pitched and quiet (Marchant and Higgins 1990). Duckling calls soft, even when lost, perhaps due to threat from aerial predators (Weller 1980). Sonograms in Stahl *et al.* (1984).

Range and status

eatoni endemic to Kerguelen Island (6675 km²) and archipelago in southern Indian Ocean 3800 km from Africa at *c* 50°S, and introduced to nearby St Paul and Amsterdam Islands, where may not persist due to predation. *drygalskii* occurs on 5 vegetated Crozet Islands (Possession, East, Pig, Penguin and Apostle Islands), 1100 km west of Kerguelen and 2528 km from Africa.

Numbers of *eatoni* probably 45 000–60 000, and decreasing, while those of *drygalskii* remained at 1000–1350 during 1966–84 (Green 1992b), with 80 on East Island, 200 on Possession Island and 200 on Penguin Island (Stahl *et al.* 1984), and estimated at 1800–2100 by Wetlands International (2002). Buffard (1995) estimated 150–200 on Ile du Port. Introduced feral cats almost eradicated population of Pig Island where 1–5 breeding pairs probably depend on regular immigration from Apostle Island (Green 1992b).

Habitat and general habits

Frequents freshwater ponds as well as sheltered coastal bays in winter; takes animal items such as crustaceans and moist soil invertebrates, as well as seeds, from wallows of Elephant Seal *Mirounga leonina*. Feeds diurnally in small groups and gathers in larger numbers at night to roost (Buffard 1995); may feed at night during wing moult. Runs with ease, perches on rocks and boulders, and flies strongly (Delacour 1954–64) rising vertically from land and

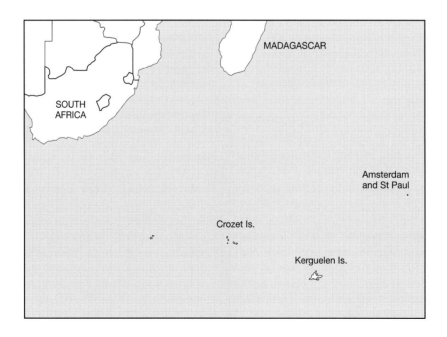

water. Small size enables diving without using wings, in manner of true diving duck (Johnsgard 1965a).

Sedentary; little movement recorded between islands of Kerguelen and Crozet.

Displays and breeding behaviour

All ♂ courtship displays of Northern Pintail present, including Burping and Grunt-whistle, with associated Head-up-tail-up, although tail not normally lifted so far. ♂ leads Inciting ♀ by Turning-back-of-head with vigour typical of Northern Pintail (Johnsgard 1965a). Courtship display Sept–Nov, and 3-bird flights noted (Falla 1937). Gregarious for much of year, except spring, when mostly in pairs (Stahl *et al.* 1984).

Breeding and life cycle

Lays Nov–Feb, often moving inland up to *c* 500 m asl; nests far apart, and built in tussock and grass, or rocky clefts, near water and lined with moss and down (Delacour 1954–64). Eggs pale olive green; 53.6 × 37.8 (52–56 × 36–39) (*n* = 5) (Falla 1937); weigh in captivity 40.1 (*n* = 24), slightly smaller than Northern Pintail, although ♀ much smaller; clutch, mode of 5 (2–6) (Weller 1980). Incubation by ♀, length unrecorded. Young mostly hatch Feb; captive day-olds weigh 25.7 (*n* = 10). Cared for by ♀, who gives Distraction display; probably reared on freshwater but abandoned early (Delacour 1954–64), forming large gatherings while still flightless (Buffard 1995). Antarctic Skua natural predator, and ducklings secretive and retiring as result. Adults escape predation during wing moult on riverbanks, under Kerguelen Cabbage *Pringlea antiscorbutica*, or

in caves. No data on growth. Clutches of 3.9 eggs reduced to broods of 3.2 soon after hatching, and 1.8 towards independence at *c* Day 20 (Stahl *et al.* 1984). Likely to nest at one year. No information on adult survival nor longevity.

Conservation and threats

Adults tame like many island birds (Delacour 1954–64). At one time much hunted by sealers and scientific expeditions. Since establishment of base on main island of Kerguelen in 1950, 200–300 shot May–Oct every year, allegedly without impact on population size (Marchant and Higgins 1990). Feral cats, introduced in 1956 to control rats and mice, have now spread, despite eradication attempts, and may be serious threat if petrels, present staple diet, reach low levels. Main Island of Kerguelen unprotected (Scott and Rose 1996). Introduced rabbits on Ile du Port have destroyed vegetation and forced ducks to moult in caves (Buffard 1995).

Only Apostle, Penguin and East Island of Crozet group free of cats and rats, and last supports *c* 60% of population of *drygalskii* (Scott and Rose 1996); they are within Specially Protected Area. At least 34 pintail introduced from Kerguelen to Amsterdam Island, 1600 km northeast but, although breeding occurred, group disappeared probably due to predation by cats and rats (Jouventin *et al.* 1988, Green 1992b). Species classified as Vulnerable by BirdLife International (2000); Crozet Islands race listed as Endangered by Threatened Waterfowl Specialist Group (2003) and Kerguelen race as Vulnerable.

Janet Kear

Garganey *Anas querquedula*
PLATE 20

Anas Querquedula Linnaeus, 1758, Syst. Nat., ed 10, p. 126
Europe

Etymology: *querquedula* L. for type of small duck. Common name said to be onomatopoeic, its root echoing call of ♂.

Other names: Garganey Teal, Cricket Bird. Dutch: Zomertaling; French: Sarcelle d'été; German: Knäkente; Hindi: Chaitua.

Variation: no subspecies.

Description

ADULT: dimorphic. ♂ in breeding, or alternate, plumage has white stripe curving from in front of and above eye, down nape and contrasting with black-brown forehead and crown, foreneck golden brown flecked white, elongated and drooping scapulars, striped grey, dark green and black-and-white.

Mantle to uppertail coverts black-brown with feathers edged and barred pale. Tail brown with grey bloom, feathers edged white. Undertail white with dark brown bars and spots. Breast and sides of upper mantle pink-brown barred black, sharply divided from vermiculated greyish flanks and white belly. Chin and throat with black patches. Forewing pale blue-grey, underwing with dark leading edge. Speculum dull green edged white. Bill lead-grey and black; legs dull grey; eyes brown. ♀ brown with lighter feather edges and white lower breast and belly. Bill greenish grey; eyes umber-brown; foot olive-grey or grey with darker webs.

MOULT: in eclipse, or basic, plumage, ♂ resembles ♀ but brighter, belly and throat whiter, and retains adult wing character (more colourful upperwing than ♀); begins early or mid-July and completed early Aug. In adult post-nuptial moult, flight feathers shed simultaneously and birds flightless 3–4 weeks (♂ mid June-mid Aug and ♀ 1 month later). Body feathers moulted late May–July by ♂ and later, after young independent, by ♀. Adult pre-nuptial moult partial (head, body, tail and tertials), starts slowly after renewal of flight feathers, finishing in winter quarters Nov–early Mar (Ginn and Melville 1983, Baker 1993).

IMMATURE: ♂ and ♀ like adult ♀, but underparts more finely streaked and spotted.

DUCKLING: brown above with face and underparts paler yellowish brown. Two dark lines run almost parallel from bill to back of head, one through eye, other below it.

MEASUREMENTS AND WEIGHT: from France (*n* = 525): ♂ adult wing, 185–211 (198); juv, 180–207 (196). ♀ adult wing, 177–201 (188); juv, 175–200 (188) (Girard 1996). Cramp and Simmons (1977) reported similar measurements from The Netherlands: ♂ adult bill, 37–43 (40); juv, 35–42.5 (38); ♀ adult, 37–42 (38.7); juv, 35–39 (37). Both sexes skull length, 75–82 (Brown *et al.* 1987); ♂ adult tarsus, 30–34 (31.4); juv, 29–33 (31); ♀ adult tarsus, 29–32 (31); juv, 28–31 (30). ♂ adult weight (*n* = 110), 260–520 (368), juv (*n* = 126), 230–480 (359); ♀ adult weight (*n* = 122), 240–585 (335); juv (*n* = 115), 200–660 (348). Cramp and Simmons (1977) had

similar weights from different areas, 250–600 for ♂ adults and 250–550 for ♀ adults, and Dunning (1993) gave 326 as mean body mass. In France, Girard (1996) showed significant increase in weight mid July–end Sept, before autumn migration.

Field characters

Small duck, 370–410 mm long. ♂ best identified by white eyestripe, contrasting with dark brown head. In flight, ♂ seen from below has dark breast contrasting boldly with light coloured belly. Blue forewing with white band behind characteristic. ♀ similar to ♀ Eurasian Teal, but paler, with longer bill, whiter throat, more distinct dark eyestripe and lighter supercilium; in flight, greyish forewing and indistinct greenish brown speculum obvious; from below, has dark leading edge to wing. Baikal Teal ♀ has more buff on lower face and white loral spot. Blue-winged and Cinnamon Teal ♀♀ have blue rather than greyish forewings. Facial pattern similar to ♀ Northern Mallard, but Garganey smaller. Confusingly, hybrids sometimes occur with European Wigeon, Eurasian Teal and Pintail.

Voice

Neither sex very vocal outside breeding season. ♂ has harsh rattling or crackling note given in Burp display, ♀ low *quack*. Sonograms in Cramp and Simmons (1977) and Pearce (2000). Calls of ducklings described in Cramp and Simmons (1977).

Range and status

Breeds between *c* 42–65°N, from west Europe to Asiatic coast. In winter, European countries deserted except for few Mediterranean sites where some birds shot throughout season (Girard 1996). Like Northern Pintail, flies beyond Sahara, wintering south of desert, in inundation zones beside Senegal and Niger Rivers and around Lake Chad. In Eastern Africa, small numbers winter in Zambia and Malawi; vagrant to South Africa (Brown *et al.* 1982). Lacks site fidelity when selecting wintering ground, moving considerable distances during single winter in relation to changing flood levels and, in different years, may switch between wetlands as far apart as India and Africa (Alerstam 1990). Probably most travelled of all ducks.

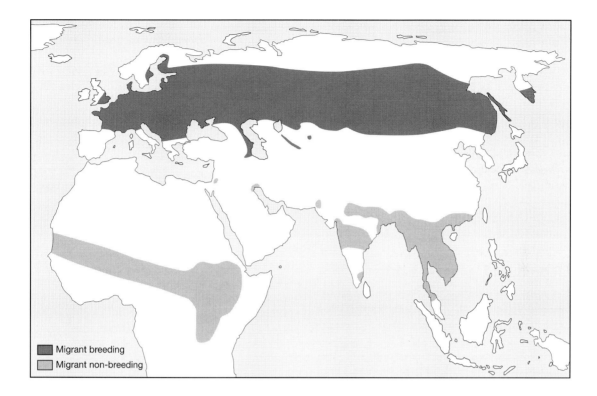

Migrant breeding
Migrant non-breeding

Tucker and Heath (1994) estimated population of Europe at 640 000–1 100 000 pairs, 90% in Russia, and felt that number of breeding pairs in western Europe fell in last 20–30 years. However, del Hoyo *et al.* (1992) considered bird common to abundant throughout range, and west European breeding numbers not varying significantly. Probable that natural shyness, nuptial displays occurring on distant breeding grounds (Girard 1994), difficulties of ♀ identification, wide dispersal of pairs and fluctuation in level of shallow pools after spring flooding (Elkins 1983, Perennou 1991) all make population trends difficult to assess. Outside Russia, where breeding population (580 000 pairs) may be decreasing, with largest concentrations in Ukraine (*c* 300 000), east and central Siberia (*c* 100 000) and western Siberia (*c* 30 000) (Fokin *et al.* 2000); former seems stable, latter may be decreasing slightly (Tucker and Heath 1994). In other countries with smaller populations, large declines in The Netherlands (1250–1750) (Teixeira 1979, SOVON 1987) and smaller decreases in Poland (2500–4000), Lithuania (3000–5000), Germany (4000), Estonia (2000) and Latvia (1000–2000) (Bauer and Thielcke 1982, Rheinwald 1982, Nicolai

1993, Leibak *et al.* 1994, Tucker and Heath 1994, Zalakevicius 1995) and stable or fluctuating trends in Finland (3000) and Hungary (1300–1500) (Koskimies 1989, Gorman 1996). For countries with breeding pairs estimated at < 1000, numbers seem stable in Denmark, Moldova, Croatia and Italy (Dybbro 1976, 1985, Meriggi 1983, Brichetti *et al.* 1984, Tucker and Heath 1994) but falling in Sweden, France and Belgium (Yésou and Trolliet 1983, Maes and Voet 1988, Girard 1994); where numbers are small or irregular, as in UK with 120 pairs 1989–2000, trends stable, fluctuating or in slight decline (Schifferli *et al.* 1980, Muntaner *et al.* 1983, Szijj 1983, Schmitz *in* Bertelsen and Simonsen 1986, Hutchinson 1989, Rufino 1989, Walasz and Mielczarek 1992, Gibbons *et al.* 1993, Tucker and Heath 1994, Storkersen 1994, Ogilvie and RBBP 2002).

Occasionally more complete counts permit better estimation of numbers wintering in Africa. Ogilvie (1975a) wrote 'half a million is probably on the low side and 1–2 million may be nearer the mark'. At end of 1980s, Monval and Pirot (1989) estimated *c* 2 000 000 for west Africa and some 500 000 for East Africa, and Trolliet *et al.* (2002) estimated at end of 1990s–start of 2000s >1.5 million for West Africa. Asian numbers largely unknown; Perennou and Mundkhur (1992) suggested 200 000 individuals, while Miyabayashi and Mundkur (1999), following Rose and Scott (1997) and Perennou *et al.* (1994), estimated 250 000 wintering in southern Asia and 100 000–1 000 000 in east and southeastern Asia. Recoveries of ringed birds show, in eastern breeding area, mixture of birds that migrate west via Europe to West Africa and those that migrate south to winter in India (Cramp and Simmons 1977). Vagrant to Indian Ocean (Seychelles, Reúnion, Rodrigues), Pacific Ocean (Palau, Mariana, Hawaii), New Guinea, Christmas Island; regular in Australia.

Habitat and general habits

In winter, prefers fresh to brackish water with partially submerged and developed vegetation in which to shelter (Dodman and Taylor 1995). In breeding season, occurs in open lowland areas including steppe, forest-steppe, extensive wetlands and farmland. Nest sites found around lakes fringed by vegetation, as well as in wide deforested river valleys and extensive fens.

Feeds mainly at night (Cramp and Simmons 1977, Roux *et al.* 1978), but will by day if not disturbed (Martin 1993). Omnivorous, consuming plant and animal items, mainly when swimming with head submerged, rarely up-ending. In spring, molluscs important with smaller quantities of insects and crustaceans (ostracods, phyllopods, etc). In summer, diet consists mainly of vegetative parts of aquatic plants, such as hornwort *Ceratophyllum* and naiad *Najas*, plus insects and crustaceans. In autumn, shifts to plant-dominated diet, including seeds of pondweeds, smartweeds, sedges and dock *Rumex* (Johnsgard 1978). During winter, feeds mainly on seeds of wild rice and grass ingested from water few cm deep. In late winter, when large areas dry out, eats seeds on dry riverside beds (Alerstam 1990). Duckling diet almost exclusively animal.

Displays and breeding behaviour

Pair formation begins in winter. Many ♀♀ paired by Sept–Oct, suggesting substantial renewal of pairbond by older individuals (Johnsgard 1978); however,

some ♀♀ arrive on breeding grounds unpaired, and Gorman (1996) mentioned pursuits by several ♂♂ during spring in Hungary. ♂ commonly uses Burp and Burp call, Belly-preen and Swimming-shake (Pearce 2000). In courtship, ♂ has display unique among dabbling ducks, Laying-head-back, similar to Head-throw of diving ducks; in most elaborate form, head thrown back so that front of crown touches lower back and bill points skywards. May be used in courtship and ♂–♂ interactions (Pearce 2000).

Amongst wildfowl, only entirely summer visitor to Europe. Spring migration begins mid Feb in southern Europe (Spain, France, Italy, Greece) and peaks end Mar and Apr–May. Return movements begin July–Aug. Generally last birds noted end Sept–Oct (Bauer and Glutz 1968–69, Cramp and Simmons 1977, Goodman and Meininger 1989). Warm anticyclonic conditions selected for migration (Elkins 1983). In spring, migration seems routed largely over Italy, Balkan Peninsula and other parts of Mediterranean region, where winter rains create many suitable wetlands; these wet areas may explain why lower numbers pass through northwest Europe in spring than in autumn (Finlayson 1992). Gregarious in African wintering quarters and widely dispersed during breeding season. Does not show high philopatry (Impekoven 1964).

Breeding and life cycle

Amongst last waterfowl migrants to arrive on breeding ground, typically appearing in small flocks of paired individuals who soon establish nesting territories (Johnsgard 1978). Generally breeds at low altitude, up to 662 m (Bauer and Glutz 1968– 69) but, in France, breeds in some uncommon areas at moderate altitudes of 1200 m and more (Salasse 1979, Roche 1988). Breeding staggered over 4-month period Apr–July. Promiscuity unrecorded so pair densities generally low, although Leibak *et al.* (1994) recorded densities in Estonia at 6–7 pairs per km^2. Strong territorial defence, with intense and frequent boundary disputes between ♂ and ♂, and ♂ and ♀ of intruding pairs. Threats, aerial chases and circular fighting used in defence of well-defined breeding area (Anderson and Titman 1992).

Main laying period early May. Nests located up to 150 m from water and built by ♀, depression lined with plant material, down and some feathers (Harrison 1975), frequently hidden under rushes or tall grass (Johnsgard 1978). Average nest 20 cm round and 8–10 cm deep (Ogilvie 1975a). Eggs elliptical to short subelliptical, smooth, warm buff without greenish tints (Harrison 1975) or light straw (Ogilvie 1975a); 45.3×33.0 (40–50×30–36) ($n = 170$) (Schönwetter 1960–66); calculated weight 27; laid daily; clutch 8 or 9 (6–14) eggs; incubation, by ♀ alone, begins on completion of clutch, and lasts 21–23 days (Harrison 1975). Pairbond lasts through incubation. Hatching synchronous. Ducklings seen from mid May (Britain) or late May (in northeast) to July; precocial, weighing 16–18 (Fjeldså 1977). Study of chronology of hatching shows 6.2 (1–11) young per brood in France. Brood, tended by ♀, fledge in 38 days (Fjeldså 1977). No data on replacement clutches, though possibly occur (Cramp and Simmons 1977). ♂♂, and unsuccessful ♀♀, leave incubating ♀♀ and fly to suitable moulting site such as Volga Delta (Alerstam 1990).

Sexually mature at 1 year (Ogilvie 1975a). Oldest BTO ringed bird 14 years 6 months (Toms and Clark 1998). As in other dabbling ducks, adult survival higher for ♂ than ♀.

Conservation and threats

Actions for conservation and restoration of populations underway in some European countries (Anon. 1992). Problems encountered are destruction of nests during early mowing of meadows and increased human disturbance, lead poisoning (Holzinger 1987), botulism during hot summers (Reichholf 1983), drainage and intensive grassland management in some breeding areas (Tucker and Heath 1994), hunting in Europe where $> 500\,000$ shot annually especially in southern Russia, Ukraine (where makes up 30% of bag in Dnieper valley), France (15 000 a year) (Trolliet 1986), Poland (Rutschke 1990) and Africa. Also threatened by habitat destruction on wintering ground (del Hoyo *et al.*1992).

Olivier Girard

Baikal Teal *Anas formosa*
PLATE 15

Anas formosa Georgi, 1775, Bemerkungen Reise Russischen Reich, p. 168
Irkutsk and Lake Baykal.

Etymology: vernacular name refers to Lake Baikal, source of type specimen. *formosa* L. means beautiful.

Other names: Formosa Teal, Spectacled Teal, Clucking Teal. French: Sarcelle élégante, Sarcelle formose; Japanese: Tomoe-gamo; Korean: Kachang-Ori.

Variation: no subspecies.

Description

ADULT: dimorphic. ♂ head in breeding, or alternate, plumage has striking combination of yellow, green, black-and-white. Most eye-catching is white supercilium stretching to nape, and curving black line dropping like inky tear from eye to throat. Upperparts generally dull brown, with long rufous and white-fringed scapulars. Underparts at rest show strongly pinkish breast, white-vertical breast stripe and grey flanks. Bill dark grey; legs and feet grey to yellowish; iris brown. ♀ similar to Eurasian Teal, but more contrastingly grey-faced and warm breasted with greater contrast in face pattern. Face has pale loral spot encircled with dark border, and dark eyestripe; often shows dark and pale mark across lower cheek. Bill, feet and eye as ♂.

MOULT: two body moults annually. Breeding plumage worn Oct–July, but some not fully coloured until end of year (Delacour 1954–64). ♂ in eclipse, or basic, plumage resembles ♀, but rather richer rufous, and often shows dark tear-drop of breeding plumage (for more details see Palmer 1976).

IMMATURE: resembles ♀, but facial pattern less defined, and browner rather than rufous tones (Madge and Burn 1988). ♂ perhaps show paler bills towards base.

DUCKLING: rather distinctive. Dark brown and yellow, like Eurasian Teal, but light areas of head vivid yellowish and no dark cheek strip (Palmer 1976).

MEASUREMENTS AND WEIGHT: ♂ ($n = 12$) wing, 203–225 (211); tail, 74–87 (77.6); bill, 38–40 (38.7); tarsus, 36–39 (37); weight, 360–520 (437). ♀ ($n = 12$) wing, 201–214 (206.5); tail, 74–83 (78); bill, 36–38 (37); tarsus, 33–38 (35.7); weight ($n = 8$), 402–505 (431) (Shaw 1936, Palmer 1976).

Field characters

Asian teal, with all dark bill, distinctive upperwing pattern with rufous brown leading edge to greenish black speculum, and broad white trailing edge to secondaries. Compact-looking, 390–430 mm long, somewhat recalling medium-sized alcid in flight, in that appears fuller-bodied and shorter-necked than other ducks of region. Distinguished from Eurasian Teal in flight by differences in patterning of speculum, by more contrasting (whiter) axillaries and, in ♀, by generally yellower tones. Behaviour good identification pointer: tends to be highly gregarious, with flock sizes regularly of 20 000–100 000 in favoured localities. Possibly in response to hunting pressure, typically spends day loafing in huge rafts at lake centre or in wet reedbed, and feeds in large groups, mainly at night, in rice fields; therefore often seen as large yellowy-brown 'island' in lake centre during day or in spectacular flight to feeding area in evening. Smaller groups sometimes mixed with Eurasian Teal or Northern Mallard.

Voice

Often rather quiet in mid winter, though flocks when roosting emit low rumbling noise, reminiscent of distant busy roadway. Vocalizations given by flock of over e.g. 300 000 in still weather barely audible more than 500 m away. Closer up on occasion in autumn and apparently, in spring especially, can be heard giving incessant deep chukling *wot-wot-wot,* (occasionally given in flight), while ♀♀ have low *quack* or *kweck* and soft repeated Inciting *geg-geg* (Johnsgard 1965a, Palmer 1976, Madge and Burn 1988, pers. obs). Decrescendo call of ♀ infrequent, consisting of long note followed by *c* 5 shorter descending ones. No published sonograms, and no information on duckling calls.

Range and Status

Largely confined to East Asia, with vagrants occurring south to Mongolia and India, east to North America (chiefly Alaska but south to California), and west to Europe's Iberian peninsula (Palmer 1976, Cramp and Simmons 1977, Harper 1996).

Breeds across eastern Siberia, from Yenisey Valley eastwards to Cape Shmidt on Chukotka peninsula, western Anadyr basin, northern Kamchatka and Sea of Okhotsk coast. Formerly extended north to Arctic Ocean, excluding northern Taymyr peninsula, but including Arctic Ocean islands of Bolshoy Lyakhovskiy and Stolbovoy. Over much of huge range seems somewhat local, with concentrations centred on basins of major river systems (Madge and Burn 1988). No recent records from western breeding range around Ob, Yensie and Taz (Green 1992b). Details of past and present distribution in BirdLife International (2001).

Considered always rare on migration in coastal wetlands of Russian Maritimes. Recorded more commonly on Middle and Lower Amur on southward migration, and especially during spring migration at Khanka Lake on Russian–Chinese border, where 86 000 birds recently counted, and in Daubikhe River Valley (Shibaev *et al.* 1992). In China in early 20th century, was locally abundant in Yangtze basin (see, for example, Guan 1963) and Fujian (see Cheng 1941) and presumably elsewhere, but in past 2 decades, no reports made of very large concentrations. Starts arriving in South Korea, where presently largely confined in winter, in mid September, with largest numbers from Nov–Mar: 210 000 in 1999; 300 000–400 000 in winter 2001–2002, > 400 000 2002–2004, including single flock of 400 000 in Nov 2003), with lesser numbers in China's Yangtze River valley (*c* 20 000) and in Japan, where < 10 000 in 1980, 2756 in 1987, 1912 in 1988 (Brazil 1991) and only 700 on average winters 1992–97 (Miyabayashsi and Mundkur 1999).

Habitat and general habits

Strongly migratory, taking different routes in spring and autumn. Pairs arrive in breeding areas late Apr–May, and present in wintering areas especially

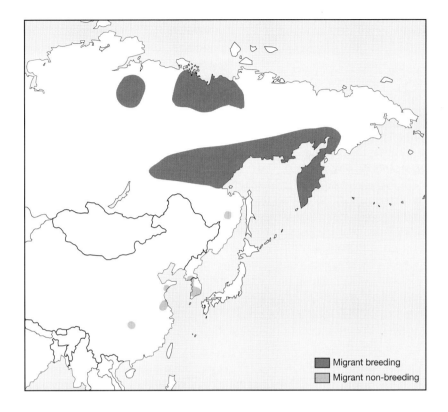

Migrant breeding
Migrant non-breeding

mid Nov–late Feb or early Mar. On migration recorded in variety of wetlands, occasionally including estuaries and on sea. Favourite stopover sites of Khanka Lake and Daubikhe River Valley are only extensive rice-growing areas in Siberia and far eastern Russia, where remain for month or more (Shibaev *et al.* 1992). Considered largely nomadic in South Korea in winter, moving southwards through favoured wetlands in response to freezing of lakes and availability of food. Some possibly continue on to wetlands 500 km to southwest in Yangtze River valley. In South Korea (where discovered wintering in 1984), prefers large lakes surrounded by rice fields. Roosts in dense, effectively single-species concentrations during day, and flies in shorebird-like clouds or lines to wet or dry rice fields to feed on spilt rice grain in late evening and at night (Allport *et al.* 1991). Evening flights often involve elaborate 'aerial ballet' with swirling flocks circling still-roosting birds in ever higher and wider circles—apparently part of a decision-making process as the flock tends to feed in different areas each night. Although flock usually leaves roost as single unit, this breaks up into smaller groups

rapidly. Many return to daytime roost before first light; almost all before sunrise. Returning and night-flying flocks lack whistling sound in wings, but often betrayed by a snapping sound, presumably made by wings pulled tight and rigid. When roosting largely inactive until mid-afternoon, unless disturbed. Small groups (30–300 birds) form tight groups in flight, swarming around and in front of potential predators, leading them away from main flock. Behaviour most often used against patrolling Mongolian Gulls *Larus cachinnans mongolicus*, but also against Hen Harrier *Circus cyaneus*, and species as large as Black Stork *Ciconia nigra* that stray over roost. Single flock of 400 000 in Nov 2003 was roosting next to and in wet reedbeds on reclamation lake (Gocheonnam, Haenam) adjacent to extensive rice fields. Rarely dabbles in mud in shallow freshwater wetlands of South Korea and Japan, though occasionally takes seeds from surface of water, sometimes dislodged by active tugging of reeds.

Analyses of stomach contents collected in South Korea and Russia reveals seed diet of spilt rice, soybeans, grains of *Echinochloa orizoides* (common weed of Russian rice fields) (Shibaev *et al.* 1992), and seeds of wild cereals and herbs such as *Panicum grus-galli*, *Trifolium* and *Polygonum aviculare* (Polivanova 1971). Occasionally takes variety of aquatic animal life, including water snails and other invertebrates (Cheng 1979, Zhuge 1990). By time of spring migration north, has gained thick layer of body fat (Vorobyev 1954).

Displays and breeding behaviour

At least some pairs appear to form in November, before onset of colder weather. Pairing apparently coincidental with Chin-lifting by males, and by Chasing and Ritualized Bathing. ♂ and ♀ drop heavily into water, even swimming beneath surface for 1–3 seconds, before standing up in water, with exaggerated wing-flapping, exposing white of belly and on underwings, followed by chase flight. Breeding largely initiated after departure from wintering areas. Inciting by ♀ conspicuous and Gadwall-like, alternating threat with Chin-lifting and repeated *geg-geg-geg* call as ♂ displays. ♂ has Burp, consisting of lifting of head and erection of small crest with *ruk-ruk* call, often followed by Drinking. In Leading Inciting ♀, ♂ Turns-back-of-head with tail held high. ♂ threatens with Bill-tilting display that shows off black throat markings. ♂ lacks typical *Anas* Grunt-whistle, Bridling, Down-up and Head-up-tail-up (Johnsgard 1965a). Many apparently start pairing in early winter.

Breeding and life cycle

Limited information. Nests in tussocks by swampy pools in taiga and in delta-type wetlands at tundra edge. Egg-laying from end May south of Arctic Circle (Labutin and Perfilyev 1991) or 1st week of June to mid June in northernmost areas (Mikhel 1935, Vorobyev 1963). Eggs pale greyish green; 48.2 × 34.3 (45–52.5 × 32.0–38.0) (*n* = 30); calculated weight 31 (Schönwetter 1960–66); clutch in Khroma-Indigirka area of Yakutia 6.9 (4–10) eggs (*n* = 29). Incubation, by ♀ alone, probably 24 days. Eggs begin to hatch central Yakutia 21 June, and ducklings fly by 1st week of Aug (Krechmar *et al.* 1978). ♂ leaves incubating ♀, and moults locally or elsewhere. Probably breeds at one year. No data on breeding success, adult survival nor longevity.

Conservation and threats

Hunting widely considered responsible for very significant decline in latter half of 20th century, although pesticide spraying in Russian rice fields might have contributed (Shibaev *et al.* 1992). Was considered by La Touche (1925–34) commonest duck in northeast Asia, and was numerous on migration in 19th and first half of 20th centuries in eastern Siberia (Przewalski 1877–78, Shulpin 1936, Vorobyev 1954). Catastrophically reduced in numbers through intensive hunting in eastern Siberia, China, and most especially in Japan; for example, 3 men with throw-nets took 50 000 birds in 20 days on pond in Japan in 1947 (Austin and Kuroda 1953, Green 1992b). As result, was thought to number only 20 000–40 000 individuals in 1980s (Anon 1993). Subsequently, increased observer activity and creation of new wintering habitat as lakes and rice fields by reclamation of extensive west-coast tidal-flats in South Korea since mid 1980s (Moores 1996) has led to significant increase in known population. Probable that some of reported increase is real, and not result of shift to South Korea from unknown wintering areas in China.

Considered globally Vulnerable (BirdLife International 2000, 2001), and target species for special conservation action under Asia-Pacific Waterbird Conservation Strategy 2001–2005 (Anon 2001). Potential breeding areas have, according to anecdotal evidence, suffered extensive degradation or loss, while regularly (and increasingly) found in the bags of hunters in far north of breeding range (Syroechkovski and Zockler 1997). In winter, hunting remains problem but, more significantly, feeding and roosting areas largely artificial and intensively used by humans. Following wetland reclamation, resulting reservoirs and rice fields (favoured in South Korea, at least, where main wintering concentrations not officially protected) become increasingly surrounded by roads, buildings and telegraph wires, and attract increasing numbers of sightseers who contribute to increased disturbance. Predation of at least sick birds by Mongolian Gull recorded. Overcrowding of waterbirds at increasingly polluted roosting lakes led, in Nov 2000, to outbreak of avian cholera that killed at least 10 000 Baikal Teal at Cheonsu Bay, South Korea.

Nial Moores

Eurasian Teal *Anas crecca*
PLATE 16

Anas Crecca Linnaeus, 1758, Syst. Nat., ed. 10, p. 126
Europe

American Green-winged Teal *Anas carolinensis*
PLATE 16

Anas carolinensis Gmelin, 1789, Syst. Nat., **1**, p. 533
Carolina to Hudson Bay = South Carolina

Etymology: *crecca* from Swedish *kricka* from call of ♂; *carolinensis* 'duck from Carolina'. Common name 'teal' recorded as early as 1314, and imitates sounds of birds feeding.

Other names: Common Teal, Eurasian Green-winged Teal. Danish: Krikand; French: Sarcelle d'hiver, Sarcelle à ailes vertes; German: Krickente; Icelandic: Urtönd; Japanese: Ko-gamo; Spanish: Cerceta alioscura.

Variation: 2 species, separated (by BOU) mainly on basis of cytochrome *b* and ND2 mitochondrial gene DNA sequences; analysis showed high divergence (5.8%), similar to genetic difference between Northern Mallard and Northern Pintail. *A. crecca* has 2 subspecies, nominate Eurasian Teal, and Aleutian Teal *A. c. nimia* Friedmann, 1948 which is sedentary and restricted to Aleutian Islands, although regularly reported from British Columbia. Johnson and Sorenson (1999) found *crecca* and *nimia* identical using molecular systematic.

Description

ADULT: dimorphic. European *A. crecca* ♂ in breeding, or alternate, plumage has head cinnamon red-brown, with broad decurving green stripe through eye to nape, edged by buff line that extends to base of bill. Flanks and back vermiculated grey-white, appearing uniform grey at distance. Buff-cream breast heavily spotted black, belly and underside almost white. Black-bordered triangle of cream-yellow undertail conspicuous. Mid grey wing coverts tipped buff-brown, metallic black-green speculum edged by 2 pale lines, white-tinged buff above, thinner and paler below. Underwing predominantly pale, mostly white. Bill dark grey with fine black spots and striations, may become olive-green or even yellowish at base in moult; legs grey-blue or olive-grey, usually with darker webs; iris warm dark brown. ♀ neck and head grey-buff-brown, with dark crown and stripe from bill base through eye. Neck and cheeks striated, lighter then crown and body. Back and rump slightly darker, but less mottled than back and flanks. Breast and belly light, almost white. Wing coverts browner than ♂, lesser and median coverts with light margins, outer greater coverts tipped white, inner ones buff. Scapulars long, wide with square tip. Generally larger extent of black to green on speculum than adult ♂. Bill dark grey-olive, usually with orange-yellow lower base to upper mandible, speckled black (never present on ♂); legs blue-grey or olive-grey with darker webs; iris brown. Race *nimia* claimed slightly larger than nominate (Bellrose 1980), which it closely resembles.

North American *A. carolinensis* differs from European bird described above mainly in plumage of adult ♂. Shows prominent white vertical line from waterline on grey flanks and lacks horizontal white stripes of Eurasian species. Also lacks cream-buff line extending from bill above green eye-patch to back of head. ♀ can often be distinguished from *A. crecca* by richer cinnamon colour at leading edge of wing speculum (see Sangster *et al.* 2001). Some apparent hybrids reported in Europe with prominent vertical and horizontal lines to flanks and intermediate head patterns.

MOULT: eclipsed ♂ resembles ♀ in both species, but darker and more uniform, less distinct dark eye-stripe. Eclipse, or basic, plumage of short duration, Aug–Sept, but much of plumage may be retained into Nov in some individuals. Several different eclipse plumage morphs distinguished on mantle feather patterns. ♀ basic plumage similar to alternate or breeding. For fuller description of plumages and moult sequences of both species, see Palmer (1976), Cramp and Simmons (1977) and Johnson (1995).

IMMATURE: ♂ resembles heavily barred adult ♀, but with dusky streaks on underparts, scapulars narrow with pointed tip. Upperwing coverts more dull and brown than in adult ♂. Tertials short and narrow, dark sepia with outer web greyer, narrowly edged white. Notched tail feathers distinctive, but may be moulted as early as Sept. Bill pale horn colour at tip and base, otherwise greyish like adult; feet and iris as adult. ♀ body plumage like immature ♂, but wing as adult ♀. Tertials like immature ♂, grey edges to lesser and median coverts. Restricted metallic green to speculum. Otherwise as immature ♂.

DUCKLING: like South American Teal, with prominent dark eye and cheek stripes. Bill dark grey with flesh-coloured edge to base; feet blue-grey with darker webs. Nelson (1993) figured and described ducklings of *A. carolinensis* and *A. crecca nimia*.

MEASUREMENTS AND WEIGHT: *A. crecca* ♂ adult wing ($n = 1001$), 187.0; juv (1st winter) wing ($n = 3582$), 184.2; adult skull ($n = 325$), 81.6; juv skull ($n = 891$), 81.2; adult tarsus ($n = 326$), 31.1; juv tarsus ($n = 886$), 31.0; adult winter weight ($n = 999$), 320.4; juv winter weight ($n = 3577$), 303.6. ♀ adult wing ($n = 499$), 178.8; juv wing ($n = 2295$), 177.3; adult skull ($n = 205$), 77.4; juv skull ($n = 557$), 77.2; adult tarsus ($n = 205$), 30.0; juv tarsus ($n = 557$), 30.0; adult winter weight ($n = 498$), 290.6; juv winter weight ($n = 2295$), 280.4. Data from WWT Ringing Station at Abberton Reservoir, southeast England (Fox *et al.* 1992). *A. c. nimia* in Amchitka, June, weight ♂ ($n = 15$), 310–440 (392); ♀ ($n = 4$), 338–418 (378) (Palmer 1976).

A. carolinensis ♂ adult wing ($n = 86$), 185.4; juv wing ($n = 66$), 182.2; adult weight ($n = 113$) 322.1; juv weight ($n = 332$), 326.6. ♀ adult wing ($n = 51$), 177.8; juv wing ($n = 71$), 175.3; adult weight ($n = 79$), 308.5; juv weight ($n = 265$), 290.1 (Bellrose 1980). Further weights in Johnson (1995).

Field characters

Small dabbling ducks, 340–380 mm long, fast-flying, often abundant, but equally encountered singly or in small groups on small waterbodies. In flight, pale belly and white edged speculum distinctive, fast wing-beats like diving ducks, but wings and body longer in proportions. Will twist in flight like flock of waders. Small size distinguishes from all but Garganey, from which differs in grey (not blue) forewings.

Voice

♂ has distinctive and obvious 2-syllabic whistle; ♀ *quacks*, but note shorter and higher pitched than Northern Mallard. Sonograms of ♂ *krick-et* call and *quack* of *A. crecca* in Cramp and Simmons (1977) and of *A. carolinensis* in Johnson (1995). Little data on calls of ducklings.

Range and status

Breeds throughout middle latitudes of northern hemisphere, from tundra through to steppes and even desert fringes. Strongly migratory in northern parts of range; some largely sedentary.

A. crecca breeds in Old World in continuous band from Japan, China and Russian eastern Asia right through Russia to Mediterranean and eastern Europe across to Britain, Ireland and Iceland. Scott and Rose (1996) considered no discrete populations identifiable in Western Eurasia; however, birds from eastern part winter in Japan and eastern China with some 400 000 in Indian sub-continent and other parts of south Asia (Rose and Scott 1997) and 600 000–1 000 000 wintering in eastern and southeastern Asia (Miyabayashi and Mundkur 1999). Estimated 1.5 million winter in southwest Asia and northeast Africa, apparently originating in western Siberia (Perennou *et al.* 1994, Scott and Rose 1996). Teal wintering in Black Sea, Mediterranean and West Africa thought to originate in western Siberia, west and central Russia, Ukraine and eastern Europe, numbering some 1 050 000 with stable population trends (Scott and Rose 1996). Northwest Europe wintering population concentrated on The Netherlands, France, Britain,

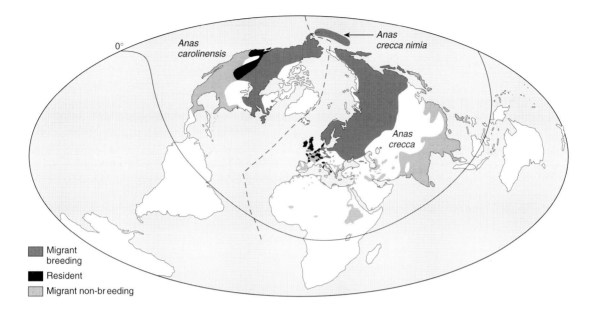

Migrant breeding

Resident

Migrant non-breeding

Ireland and Spain, numbering 400 000 individuals and stable (Scott and Rose 1996). Non-migratory *nimia* estimated at < 10 000 (Rose and Scott 1997).

A. carolinensis nests in greatest abundance in Yukon Flats in North America (densities of 2.1 pairs per km^2), but in parts of coastal Alaska and arctic Canada densities vary 1.4–0.3 pairs per km^2, generally highest in association with major river deltas (Bellrose 1980). Densities also high in Canadian Parkland areas (highest in Alberta 2.1 pairs per km^2) and, while numbers high on Prairies, densities relatively low (1.4–0.2 pairs per km^2) (Bellrose 1980). Smaller numbers nest as far south as Kansas and even New Mexico. Winters over most of North America, from Alaska and Newfoundland, extending into South America. More than half winter in Mississippi Flyway, vast majority in coastal marshes and rice fields of Louisiana. In Pacific Flyway, most winter in California, others in Washington and Oregon (Bellrose 1980). Frequent winter vagrant to Ireland, Britain and continental Europe. Numbers considered stable in recent decades, at an estimated 2.9 million birds (Wetlands International 2002).

Habitat and general habits

Both species typically feed in shallow water, in freshwater, brackish and intertidal marine wetlands.

In winter, prefers marsh and lake habitats with high productivity, shallow sheltered waters with abundant vegetation, brackish lagoons with abundant submergent vegetation and estuarine waters. Consumes wide variety of food, generally of small particle size sieved from substrate using finely spaced lamellae (Pöysä 1983, Nudds and Bowlby 1984). In winter, seeds of sedges, grasses, emergent and submerged macrophytes often predominate (e.g. Cramp and Simmons 1977, Bellrose 1980) but will feed on agricultural waste, such as cereals and rice (Sell 1979, Quinlan and Baldassarre 1984). In summer, takes aquatic insects, larvae, molluscs and crustaceans (Danell and Sjöberg 1982). Considered opportunistic (Nummi 1993), feeding in waters generally less than 8 cm deep (Pöysä 1983, 1985, 1991, Gaston 1992). For details of diet of *A. carolinensis*, see Johnson (1995). In many studied situations, forage predominantly at night during hunting season (Tamisier 1976, Euliss and Harris 1987), but by day during breeding season (Danell and Sjöberg 1982).

In North America and Europe, ♂♂ move to moulting congregations away from breeding ♀♀ once incubation commences (Oring 1964, Kortegaard 1974). During moult, primary feathers grow 4.8 mm per day, and weight loss demonstrated (Sjöberg 1988b), presumably related to 35% increase in energy consumption, as measured by oxygen uptake in resting state (Guozhen and Hongfa 1986).

nimia said to feed in tidal pools and sheltered marine waters in winter (Palmer 1976).

Displays and breeding behaviour

Displays apparently similar in both species, but Laurie-Ahlberg and McKinney (1979) found differences in Nod-swim between captive *A. crecca* and *A. carolinensis*. Nod-swimming, and its association with Grunt-whistle, much reduced in *A. crecca*, although function in both species seems to be appeasement. Communal courtship and pair formation conspicuous from Aug. Early courtship often involves pre-copulatory display, even early in pair formation. ♂ display similar to Speckled Teal race of South American Teal and includes, in addition to Nod-swim and Grunt-whistle, Turn-towards ♀, Bill-up, Down-up, Turn-back-of-head, Bridling, Bill-dip and Preen-behind-wing. Most display occurs on water, and Jump flights common (see Johnsgard 1965a, McKinney 1965a, McKinney and Stolen 1982 and Johnson 1995 for details). Pairbond lasts until soon after clutch initiation. Breeding behaviour little studied, since nests hard to find and birds secretive. ♀ generally considered to select nest site in attendance with ♂.

Breeding and life cycle

No apparent differences between *A. crecca* and *A. carolinensis*, possibly because none has been looked for. Breeds Apr–July, later in north of range (Cramp and Simmons 1977, Bellrose 1980, Fox 1986). ♀ lays from 2nd summer (Bellrose 1980), shows low rates of philopatry (14%, Lokemoen *et al.* 1990), and little evidence of opportunistic responses to variable wetland conditions (Johnson and Grier 1988). Hence, may not breed in prairie drought years (Smith 1971, Stoudt 1971).

Nests on ground, usually amongst available vegetation, especially dense grass, but also in dwarf scrub and under bushes, typically close to water, rarely more than 100 m away (Bellrose 1980, Fox 1986). In Britain and Ireland, *A. crecca* favours oligotrophic waters (Fox *et al.* 1989), but will nest anywhere with dense emergent vegetation and abundant duckling food. Nesting densities of *A. carolinensis* generally low, rarely breeding within 1 m of one another (Bellrose 1980).

Eggs bluntly ovate, creamy white; 45×33 ($42–50 \times 31–36$) ($n = 250$) (Schönwetter 1960–66); weigh 29 (25–31) ($n = 19$) (Cramp and Simmons 1977) for *A. crecca*, and 45.8×34.2 (unknown sample) (Bellrose 1980) for *A. carolinensis*; clutch usually 8–11 (7–15) for *A. crecca* (Cramp and Simmons 1977), 5–16 for *A. carolinensis* (Bellrose 1980). Single brooded (but will replace lost clutch), incubation 21–23 days (Cramp and Simmons 1977, Bellrose 1980). Day-old *A. carolinensis* weigh 16.0–16.5 ($n = 3$) (Smart 1965b) or 15.1 ($n = 5$) (Nelson 1993). ♀ leads brood to nursery areas where young initially feed on invertebrates (Sugden 1973). Bellrose (1980) cited mean brood size of *A. carolinensis* at hatching as 7.0 ($n = 177$) reduced to 5.7 for Class II age group ($n = 214$) and to 5.4 for Class III age group ($n = 128$) (see Gollop and Marshall 1954). Fledging takes *c* 34–35 days, fastest of all dabbling ducks (Bellrose 1980). Birds breed in 1st year.

Adult *A. carolinensis* survival varies 0.33–0.69 (Martin *et al.* 1979, Chu *et al.* 1995, Krementz *et al.* 1997), with maximum life span 20 years 6 months (Johnson 1995). In Europe, survival estimates of *A. crecca* vary 0.35–0.71 (Boyd 1957, 1962, Gitay *et al.* 1990, Bell and Mitchell 1996), with maximum life span of 25 years 7 months (Toms and Clark 1998). Being small, both species more vulnerable to severe weather than other dabbling ducks, high winds reducing condition and uric acid levels (Bennett and Bolen 1978). In western Europe, analysis of count data and recovery information showed large numbers of *A. crecca* moving from Britain south and west into France and Spain where recovery rates exceed levels in normal winters (Ridgill and Fox 1990). ♀♀ exhibit higher levels of stress than ♂♂ and generally move further (Bennett and Bolen 1978, Ridgill and Fox 1990); however, majority of birds wintering in Camargue remained in area < 10 days, suggesting high levels of turnover (Pradel *et al.* 1997), hence probably mobile in winter irrespective of conditions. Winter weight dynamics characterized by build up of fat reserves from low levels in Sept on arrival at wintering grounds, to highest levels in Dec (Baldassarre *et al.* 1986, Fox *et al.* 1992).

Lipid content and body mass declines thereafter, independent of restrictions imposed by weather and food, suggesting adaptive weight loss rather than consequence of winter conditions (Baldassarre *et al.* 1986).

Conservation and threats

Little known currently of status of *A. crecca* in eastern Palearctic, and continues to show local breeding declines, as in Britain, with decreasing numbers and contraction of range. Maintenance of breeding in lowland wetlands (threatened by habitat loss and modification) and in upland areas (where loss of habitat is linked to afforestation and other land-use change) remains important priority for preservation of local biodiversity. On wintering grounds, adequate site safeguard well established, but due attention must be paid to protecting wetlands that function as refuges only during periods of severe weather.

A. carolinensis shows stable or slightly increasing population trends, unlike most other North American wildfowl, although reason unclear (Johnston 1995).

Tony Fox

South American Teal *Anas flavirostris*
PLATE 16

Anas flavirostris Vieillot, 1816, Nouv. Dict. Hist. Nat., nouv. éd., **5**, p. 107
Buenos Aires, Argentina

Etymology: *flavirostris* L. *flavus* means golden-yellow, plus *rostris* billed.

Other names: Andean Teal, Chilean Teal, Merida Teal, Sharp-winged Teal, Speckled Teal (Falkland Islands and South Georgia), Yellow-billed Teal. Brazil: Marreca-pardinha; French: Sarcelle à bec jaune; German: Andenente; Spanish: Pato barcino, (Argentina), Pato jergón chico (Chile).

Variation: 4 subspecies recognized here: Speckled Teal *A. f. flavirostris*; Sharp-winged Teal *A. f. oxyptera* Meyen, 1834; Merida Teal *A. f. altipetens* Conover, 1941; and Andean Teal *A. f. andium* P.L. Sclater and Salvin, 1873. Andean Teal often treated as separate species *A. andium*. Livezey (1997b), on morphological and behavioural grounds, considered *altipetens* and *andium* races of Andean Teal, and *flavirostris* and *oxyptera* races of Yellow-billed Teal. *A. flavirostris* may have evolved from American Green-winged Teal ancestors colonizing South America from northern hemisphere (Johnson and Sorenson 1999).

Description

ADULT: sexes alike. ♂ head and neck light grey or buff, heavily speckled or vermiculated with black. Feathers extend out towards crown, giving head large, rounded appearance. Upperparts black and brownish, with lighter margins surrounding dark feather centres. Tertials long and pointed, with tawny buff margins. Belly and sides grey to light grey (especially *oxyptera*), with dark spots on breast. Grey-brown uppertail coverts and tail. Wings grey-brown upper coverts and dark remiges. Speculum velvet black and metallic green, bordered with narrow rufescent band in front and buff or white band on trailing edge. Bill yellow with dark culmen and dark tip (*flavirostris*), dull yellow (*oxyptera*), or blue-grey to dark grey (*altipetens* and *andium*); feet grey with lighter web; iris brown. ♀ similar to ♂ but head shape not so distinctive; scalloped pattern of dark on side feathers and breast rather than spotting; bill not so bright (*flavirostris*).

oxyptera subspecies has more slender dull yellow bill with dark ridge; pale bodied (head looks dark), with small black spots on light brown back and light grey flanks. *altipetens* darker with blue-grey bill; narrow light feather margins above and breast coarsely spotted. *andium* very dark with longer slate grey or lead blue bill; also has narrow light feather margins above and breast coarsely spotted, with dark markings reaching back further along flanks.

MOULT: no ♂ eclipse plumage. Flightless birds noted Jan in Isla Grande (Weller 1975c) and Rio

Negro province, Argentina, and late Nov in Cordoba and Rio Negro provinces, Argentina.

IMMATURE: upperparts obscurely mottled, with black spots vaguely outlined. Bill yellowish after 2 weeks of age (*flavirostris*).

DUCKLING: dark brown with yellow spotting near rump and shoulders (more white in Andean subspecies). Broad dark band on yellowish cheeks with light supercilium. Underparts yellowish white with brown band on upperbreast (*flavirostris*).

MEASUREMENTS AND WEIGHT: *flavirostris* ♂ ($n = 180$) wing 176.5–209 (196.5); culmen, 28.7–38 (34.2); tarsus, 31.3–42.2 (35.9). ♀ ($n = 96$) wing, 175–212 (189.2); culmen, 29.7–36 (33.2); tarsus, 29.4–40 (34.9) (Port 1998a). Tail measurements ♂ ($n = 8$), 60–80 (72.4), ♀ ($n = 5$), 56–67 (63.2) (Blake 1977), or ♂ ($n = 42$) 70–101 (83.6), ♀ ($n = 22$) 65–88 (74.5). *altipetens* ♂ ($n = 8$) wing, 217–229 (224.6); tail, 90–100 (95.5); culmen, 40–42 (40.8). ♀ ($n = 7$) wing, 205–218 (210.7); tail, 75–86 (81.5); culmen, 35–40 (37.2); tarsus, 34 (Blake 1977). *andium* ♂ ($n = 5$) wing, 225–240 (233); tail, 90–115 (101.4); culmen, 39–42 (39.8); tarsus, 37–38. ♀ ($n = 5$) wing, 216–242 (230.4); tail, 87–100 (92); culmen, 37–40 (37.8) (Blake 1977). *oxyptera* ♂ ($n = 6$) wing, 207–224; tail, 75–95 (86); culmen, 33–37 (35.1); tarsus, 36–38. ♀ ($n = 2$) wing, 201, 209; tail, 82, 84; culmen, 32, 34 (Blake 1977). Weight ♂ ($n = 182$), 411.5; ♀ ($n = 96$), 387.3 (*flavirostris* early spring; Port 1998a). ♂ ($n = 17$), 429.1; ♀ ($n = 5$), 394.6; juv ♀ ($n = 5$), 388.2 (*flavirostris* fall and winter; Weller 1968b). ♂ ($n = 12$), 465; ♀ ($n = 6$), 423 (*flavirostris* winter; Schlatter *et al.* 1983). ♂ ($n = 1$), 484 (*andium*; Botero *et al.* 1993).

Field characters

Small, 350–450 mm long. Yellow-billed races resemble Brown Pintail, but smaller, head tucked towards body and squarish. Darker head notable, especially in Andean subspecies. Pale wing linings, black speculum, with metallic green bordered by tawny in front and white or buff at rear edge, distinctive in flight. Flight swift and erratic; very active and frequently social, recalling American Green-winged Teal.

Voice

Described by Standen (1976, 1980), but no sonogram available. ♂ gives loud, single syllable *krick* whistle during Burp display, as alarm call and when separated from mate. Similar short whistle used by ♂ during Bridle and Grunt-whistle displays. Gives chittering calls during Point display, and series of soft, meow-like calls when agitated. ♀ has loud *quack* when alarmed, or when separated from mate or brood; her Inciting call consists of grating *rraak*, and Decrescendo call has 5–12 syllables (Johnsgard 1965a).

Range and status

Lowland race *flavirostris* occurs in southern third of South America, with southern populations migrating north to Paraguay, Uruguay, and southern Brazil in winter; tends to be widespread and fairly common over much of range; breeds from southeastern Brazil south to Tierra del Fuego, Falkland Islands, and South Georgia. *andium* found in central and western cordilleras of Andes (Colombia and Ecuador), occurring seldom below 3500 m and up to snow line; sparsely distributed throughout range, and some populations may show altitudinal migrations. Density estimate for *andium* in southern Ecuador (Cajas National Park) 4.26–6.43 per km². *altipetens* found at 3200–4300 m (seasonally down to 2600 m) in northern Andes of Venezuela (Merida, Tachira, and Trujillo provinces) and Colombia (eastern cordilleras south to Bogota), where scarce. *oxyptera* generally occurs at 2500–4500 m throughout highland areas from Catamarca (northern Argentina) to Cajamarca (northern Peru), descending to Pacific lowlands along Lluta and Huasco rivers, northern Chile, and in south Peru in July–Oct (Fjeldså and Krabbe 1990); also found in highlands of northwest Argentina and Bolivia, and in valleys and coastal areas of rivers crossing northern desert of Peru and Chile. Widely scattered but common in some areas.

Wetlands International (2002) suggested > 1 million for *flavirostris* in mainland South America, and Woods and Woods (1997) 6000–11 000 pairs, or total population of 18 000–33 000, in Falklands; Wetlands International (2002) further estimated 25 000–100 000 for *oxyptera* and, for both *andium* and *altipetens*, declining populations of $< 20 000$.

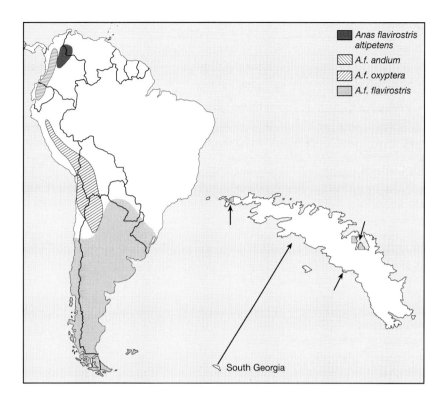

Legend:
- *Anas flavirostris altipetens*
- *A.f. andium*
- *A.f. oxyptera*
- *A.f. flavirostris*

South Georgia

Habitat and general habits

Found in variety of freshwater lakes, streams, and marshes, and on coast, especially in winter. Nominate lowland race shows tendency to perch and nest in trees when available, and inhabits marshes, small lakes and streams. In high-altitude areas, found in muddy estuaries, bogs with ponds and creeks, small acidic lakes, rivers, and sometimes along steep, rocky lake shores. Feeds by up-ending, surface feeding, filtering through mud and debris, and occasionally diving. Diet consists of variety of small prey items, seeds, and fruits. In winter, Schlatter *et al.* (1983), found 79% *Potentilla anserina* and 6.4% *Trifolium*; by dry weight 72.6% *Potentilla anserina*, 5.9% *Ranunculus* in stomachs of *flavirostris* (*n* = 17). By contrast, in 6 stomachs of young and 3 of adult *flavirostris* in summer, Weller (1972) found mostly cladocerans (*Bosmina*), but also midge larvae, insects, fish eggs, amphipods and seeds.

Displays and breeding behaviour

Displays similar to other dabbling ducks, especially other green-winged Teal, but pairbond long-term and extra-pair courtship common, at least in nominate race (Port 1998b). Generally monogamous, but bigamy noted in captive nominates (McKinney 1985). Forced extra-pair offspring common in one population (10 of 15 broods with > 1 extra-pair offspring). Intraspecific brood parasitism also detected in 8 of 15 broods. Displays described for *flavirostris* by Standen (1976, 1980). Active social courtship. ♂ courtship and pair maintenance consist of Grunt-whistle, Head-up-look-at, Burp, Point, Shake, Bridle, and Turn-back-of-head. Aggressive displays include swim or walk-off, Nod-swim and Nod-walk, and use of courtship displays (Grunt-whistle, Bridle) as aggressive signals (McKinney *et al.* 1990b). Some displays (Head-up-look-at, Nod-swim) may be commoner in *oxyptera* than in *flavirostris* (Von de Wall 1963). ♀ Inciting display consists of stretching head out, then withdrawing it while calling. ♀♀ also perform Head-up-look-at (infrequently) and Point. Copulation occurs after ♂ and ♀ pump their heads and ♀ adopts prone posture. Bridling performed by ♂ as post-copulatory display. Forced extra-pair copulations noted in captivity and in wild for *flavi-*

rostris and *oxyptera* races, with variable ♂ defence. Paired ♂ *flavirostris* defends arboreal nests from other ♂♂ and ♀♀ of other pairs (Port and McKinney 2001), and intolerance of other pairs on same wetlands noted for *andium* with broods (Botero *et al.* 1993). Parental care by both parents noted in Andean races (Botero *et al.* 1993), and appears more variable in lowland race *flavirostris* (McKinney and Brewer 1989) where it can also be common (Port 1998b). Both ♂ and ♀ perform Distraction display, and ♂ may even protect extra-pair ducklings (Port 2000). Ducklings only few days old will perform Point as greeting (Von de Wall 1963). Nests solitarily or small groups, but *flavirostris* can be very concentrated in areas with arboreal nests (Port and Brewer 2004). Actively court throughout year, and pairs noted in fall and winter.

Breeding and life cycle

Breeding Oct–Mar for *andium* and *oxyptera* (Weller 1968b, Fjeldså and Krabbe 1990), Aug–Dec for *altipetens* (de Schauensee and Phelps 1978), and Aug–Jan for *flavirostris* (Johnson 1965, Port and McKinney 2001). Possibly extra clutches June–July in Peru for *oxyptera*. All subspecies nest on ground in grassy areas near water in some parts of range. Cavity nesting noted for *oxyptera* in banks or rocky outcrops (Johnson 1965) and ground burrows of woodpeckers (Nores and Yzurieta 1980); use of abandoned chambers in compound nests of Monk Parakeets *Myiopsitta monachus* and other tree sites well documented for *flavirostris* in Argentina (Gibson 1920, Hudson 1920, Aramburu 1990, Port and Brewer 2004). Eggs in 2 nests of *andium* in Colombia measured 57.3 × 39.6 (*n* = 10) (Botero *et al.* 1993); in Chile, Johnson (1965) reported egg size for *oxyptera* as 59.9 × 38.3; in captivity, 44 eggs of *oxyptera* weighed 40.9. For *flavirostris*, Port (1998a) found 149 eggs measured 52.1 ± 2.0 × 36.0 ± 0.9, mass 34.8 ± 2.4 (*n* = 7) and laying interval 1–2.4 days (*n* = 37); in captivity, 71 eggs of *flavirostris* weighed 36.5. Clutch 5–8; for 63 nests in Buenos Aires province, Port (1998a) reported 7.67 ± 2.1 (5–13) eggs, with one clutch of 18 eggs where 2 ♀♀ laid in same cavity. Incubation 29.6 ± 2.4 (25–35) days (*n* = 29) (Port 1998a). Captive day-old *flavirostris* weighed 22.1 (*n* = 65), and *oxyptera* 24.0 (*n* = 9). Nest success 42.9% (*n* = 77) for *flavirostris* (Port 1998a). Fledge in 6–7 weeks. Breed in 1st year. Sex ratio ♂:♀ 1.48:1 in Buenos Aires province, with site fidelity high (♀ 63.0%, ♂ 56.3%; 80% of marked paired ♂ returned) (Port 1998a). Pairbond long-term, documented to 6 years, with 89.4% mate fidelity (Port 1998b). ♂ generally accompanies ♀ and brood, but can be variable. No data on adult survival.

Conservation and threats

Currently listed as Vulnerable (*altipetens*) and Near-threatened (*andium*) by Threatened Waterfowl Specialist Group (2003) due to scarcity and limited range, but *flavirostris* and *oxyptera* common and widespread. Egg collecting, erosion from overgrazing, development, and illegal hunting identified as main threats (Callaghan and Green 1993).

Gwenda L. Brewer and Jeff Port

Versicolor Teal *Anas versicolor*
PLATE 20

Anas versicolor Vieillot, 1816, Nouv. Dict. Hist. Nat., nouv. éd., **5**, p. 109
Paraguay

Etymology: *versicolor* L. means many coloured; *puna* means of the puna.

Other names: Gray Teal, Pampa Teal, Puna Teal, Silver Teal. French: Sarcelle versicolore, Sarcelle bariolée; Spanish: Pato capuchino, Cerceta versicolor.

Variation: 3 races recognized: Northern Silver Teal *A. v. versicolor*; Southern Silver Teal *A. v. fretensis* King, 1831; and Puna Teal *A. v. puna* Tschudi, 1844; Puna Teal often regarded as separate species (e.g. Livezey 1991, Johnson and Sorenson 1999).

Description

ADULT: sexes similar. ♂ head blackish brown cap above eyes, sharply separated from pale buff cheeks.

Neck and breast buff with small black spots that increase in size and become vertical bars on flanks. Rump and tail coverts covered with fine vermiculations of black and white. Upperwing coverts dull slaty blue; greater secondary coverts tipped white. Speculum iridescent green, with narrow black and white bars posteriorly. Underwing grey-banded. Bill pale blue with black nail and black culmen stripe, and (except in *puna*) yellowish spot below and behind nostrils; legs and feet greyish; eyes brown. ♀ similar to ♂ but less distinctly barred on flanks and with slightly less colourful speculum and bill.

versicolor smallest and palest of races, *fretensis* similar but slightly larger and plumage darker; *puna* much larger than others, bill relatively longer and lacking yellow.

MOULT: no ♂ eclipse. No information on timing of wing or body moults.

IMMATURE: similar to ♀ but duller, with less contrasting head pattern.

DUCKLING: blackish brown above, pairs of white spots on wings and sides, and greyish white below; sides of head conspicuously marked, broad black eyestripe joining black nape slightly divided by thin whitish line near ear, and thin brown line encircling cheeks and ear coverts; bill thick and heavy, greyish blue and, in *versicolor*, with indication of yellow spot. *puna* ducklings larger, with larger bill, lighter brown above, thinner dark streak through eye and no brown line around cheeks (Delacour 1954–64).

MEASUREMENTS AND WEIGHT: *versicolor* ♂ (*n* = 10) wing, 183–195 (188); tail, 65–72 (69); bill, 37–41 (39); tarsus, ♂ 30–32. ♀ (*n* = 10) wing, 178–191 (183); tail, 64–76 (69); bill, 35–40 (37). *fretensis* ♂ (*n* = 10) wing, 190–205 (203); tail, 60–76 (68); bill, 41–45 (42). ♀ (*n* = 5) wing, 188–211 (199); tail, 66–72 (70); bill, 38–44 (42). *puna* ♂ (*n* = 8) wing, 215–235 (224); tail, 72–90 (81); bill, 47–53 (50); tarsus, 33–36. ♀ (*n* = 7) wing, 212–221 (217); tail, 77–88 (79); bill, 44–47 (45) (Blake 1977). Weight *versicolor* 442–473; *c* 550 for *puna* (del Hoyo *et al.* 1992); *versicolor* ♂ (*n* = 10), 442; ♀ (*n* = 3), 373 (Weller 1968b); *puna* ♂ 546–560 (Koepcke and Koepcke 1963).

Field characters

Length 380–430 mm *versicolor/fretensis*; 480–510 mm *puna*. Small black cap with creamy buff cheeks, vertical barring on flanks, and blue bill with black central ridge and yellow spot below nares distinguish *versicolor/fretensis* races; *puna* larger, with longer bill lacking yellow spot. In flight, green speculum with white edges fore and aft distinctive. ♂ calls quiet, audible only at close range. Adults usually swim with head resting on, shoulders giving rather dumpy appearance (Johnsgard 1965a).

Voice

versicolor ♂ quiet *buzz* accompanies Burp, like sound of winding watch. Quiet, continuous rattle also heard during Nod-swim. Series of quiet alarm calls with similar buzzing noise given by ♂ escorting his ♀ and ducklings. ♀ gives loud Persistent Quacking in pre-breeding phase. ♀ Decrescendo call can include long sound followed by 8–15 shorter notes.

puna heard to give Decrescendo call with 4–5 weaker notes (Johnsgard 1965a, McKinney and Brewer 1989, McKinney *et al.* 1990a). Other calls of *puna* race may differ. Fjeldså and Krabbe (1990) reported low chatting *hueer, pt pt pt . . .*, mechanic *trrrrr* (rising pitch) and *dr-r-r . . .* Alarmed low *whr* and *errr*.

Range and status

Lowland races *versicolor* and *fretensis* occur in southern third of South America, *versicolor* breeds from southern Brazil, Uruguay, Paraguay and Bolivia south to central Argentina and migrates to Bolivia, Paraguay and Brazil during winter, while *fretensis* breeds in central Chile and central Argentina south to Tierra del Fuego and Falkland Islands. Both races migrate northwards in winter, but *fretensis* resident in Falkland Islands. Widespread and locally abundant, especially in pampas marshes. *puna* resident in Andes from central Peru south to extreme northwestern Argentina, and common. Wetlands International (2002) suggested stable populations of 25 000–100 000 for *versicolor* and *fretensis*, and 100 000–1 000 000 for *puna*.

Anas versicolor
versicolor

A. v. puna

A. v. fretensis

Habitat and general habits

Prefers shallow freshwater lakes and marshes with emergent vegetation in open country. Tame and generally quiet marsh-dwelling bird, showing no inclination to perch on trees. Feeds on seeds, aquatic plants, and invertebrates, by surface dabbling, head-dipping and up-ending. *puna* prefers open, weakly alkaline lakes with much submergent or floating vegetation, normally feeding offshore, on floating vegetation, especially *Chara* (Fjeldså and Krabbe 1990). Flight swift and generally low over marsh.

Pairs disperse, and ♂ territorial during breeding season. ♂ regularly accompanies ♀ and brood, and pairbond may be maintained during post-breeding wing moult; at least some pairbonds long-term (Weller 1968b, McKinney and Brewer 1989). May occur in large flocks when not breeding.

Displays and breeding behaviour

Courtship repertoire not elaborate, most displays subtle and inconspicuous. ♂ Burp frequent, involving slow raising of head (tilted slightly towards ♀) and slight raising of tail with quiet *buzz*. Burp may be preceded or followed by Head-shake. ♂ also directs Preen-behind-wing (may be preceded by ritualized Drink), Lateral-dabble, Shake, and Turn-back-of-head displays to ♀. Chains of ♂ displays common, e.g. Head-shake + Lateral-dabble + Burp + Lateral-dabble + Turn-back-of-head. ♂ also performs Nod-swim (repeated back and forward movement of head while swimming) while giving quiet continuous rattle. Johnsgard (1965a) recorded ♂ giving Chin-lift in hostile situations. ♀ Inciting reminiscent of blue-winged ducks, involving Chin-lifting alternating with threat. Copulation preceded by Head-pumping by ♀ and ♂; initial ♂ post-copulatory display Wings-up-bill-down followed by Erect-facing towards ♀ (Johnson *et al.* 2000).

Territorial ♂ chases other pairs in 3-bird Flights, then returns to original waiting site. Paired ♂ also pursues other ♀♀ and performs forced extra-pair copulations. Otherwise ♂ contributes to care of ducklings by being attentive, spending time with head high in vigilant posture. ♂ also behaves aggressively towards other ducks in vicinity. Families often feed in aquatic vegetation and retreat into emergent cover when alarmed.

Breeding and life cycle

Not thoroughly studied in wild. Laying dates vary with region, mainly Oct–Nov in south, Sept–Mar in Peru (del Hoyo *et al.* 1992); *puna* Sept–Mar and July, probably peaking July (Fjeldså and Krabbe 1990). Nests on ground in vegetation or in reed beds. *puna* reported to nest in tall grass, sometimes away from water (Delacour 1954–64) and often in small congregations on islands or in reed marshes (Fjeldså and Krabbe 1990). Eggs measure, for *versicolor* 49.0×34.4 $(47.0–51.8 \times 32.6–36.8)$ $(n = 10)$ and *puna* 56.8×39.0 $(52–63 \times 37–42)$ $(n = 40)$ (Schönwetter 1960–66); weight in captivity for *versicolor* 31.5 $(26.0–38.0)(n = 100)$ and *puna* 44.4 $(n = 66)$. Clutch size 8 (6–10) for *versicolor* (del Hoyo *et al.* 1992) and 5–6 for *puna* (Delacour

1954–64). Incubation in captivity 25 days (Jones 1946). Captive ducklings of *versicolor* weigh 18.0 on hatching (*n* = 53) and those of *puna* average 24.7 (*n* = 22). Probably breed at one year.

Growth rates, breeding success, adult survival and longevity unknown.

Conservation and threats

Not considered threatened, although subject to some hunting pressure (del Hoyo *et al.* 1992). All races reported common to abundant.

†Frank McKinney

Hottentot Teal *Anas hottentota*
PLATE 20

Anas punctata Burchell, 1822
Querquedula hottentota Eyton, 1838, Monogr. Anatidae, p. 129
western coast of South Africa, near Orange River, Cape Province

Etymology: the Hottentots are nomadic pastoral people of southern Africa.

Other names: none in English. Afrikaans: Gevlekte Eend; French: Sarcelle Hottentote; Malagasy: Kazazaka.

Variation: no subspecies; Hottentot Teal of Madagascar once separated as distinct race, *A. h. delacouri* Neumann, 1932 but no longer recognized.

Description

ADULT: sexes rather similar. Plumage brownish with dark cap and nape, buff cheeks and throat. Upperparts dark brown with paler edges to feathers, back and rump blackish; underparts paler with dark brown spots on neck and breast. Upperwing dark, glossed green and blue with green speculum that has sub-terminal black and white bands; underwing pale with white axillaries. Blue bill has black ridge along upper mandible; legs and feet dark bluish grey; iris brown. Sexes often considered difficult to separate; however, ♂ has pale unspotted fawn flanks and fine vermiculations on feathering between flanks and tail, while ♀ has spots from breast to tail (Young and McCann 2002). ♂ has prominent pale lines in centre of scapulars and secondaries iridescent green while those of ♀ mainly brown. Clark (1965a) noted green invisible on closed wing of ♀.

MOULT: poorly understood; no identified ♂ eclipse plumage, but breeding ♂ much brighter than ♀ and breast spots more pronounced (Bell 1996b).

IMMATURE: less distinctly marked, few spots.

DUCKLING: greyish brown upperparts, yellowish grey below. Pale cheeks with pinky buff wash and grey-brown ear-spot.

MEASUREMENTS AND WEIGHT: in southern Africa (sexes combined *n* = 37), wing, 147–157 (151.4); tail, 55–66 (59.5); bill, 32–42 (36.8); tarsus, 22–29 (26.1) (Maclean 1993). ♂ Lake Bemamba, Madagascar, in May 1994, *n* = 1) wing, 152; bill, 36.7; weight, 280. Weight southern Africa, ♂ (*n* = 1), 288 (Maclean 1993), ♀ (*n* = 3), 216–282 (243) (Brown *et al.* 1982).

Field characters

Length 330–350 mm. Very small, quiet, often inconspicuous duck. Dark cap, buff cheeks and blue bill identify it. Red-billed Pintail larger, paler, with whiter cheeks and red bill. Confusion may occur with distant birds in haze and poor light. In flight, small size, fast flight and dark speculum separate from Red-billed Pintail.

Voice

Both sexes make series of clicking notes, given as harsh *ke-ke-ke* when disturbed, when flying, or within flock (Brown *et al.* 1982), or in much softer form, as *tok-tok-tok-tok-tok* of courting ♂ during Burp. ♀ has harsh *quack* and Decrescendo call. Sonograms of ♂ and ♀ calls, including Burp and Decrescendo, in Pearce (1999) and of Burp in Maclean (1993).

Range and status

Widespread throughout eastern and southern Africa from Ethiopia to eastern Cape, scarce in western southern Africa in Namibia and southern Angola. Occurs throughout Madagascar, where more numerous in west. Isolated population exists in equatorial Africa in northern Nigeria, Niger, Cameroon and Chad. Rarely gathers in large flocks, and unobtrusive, often crepuscular and nocturnal habits make counting difficult. Apparently still reasonably common through much of range, including Madagascar, where can be most common duck at Lake Alaotra. There may be cause for concern over rarely seen west African population; only 2 recorded (in Niger in Jan 1995) in recent African Waterfowl Census. Has adapted well to artificial wetlands in southern Africa and may be increasing there (Maclean 1997d). Wetlands International (2002) estimated decreasing 1000–5000 in Chad, stable 25 000–100 000 in east and southern Africa and declining population of 5000–10 000 in Madagascar.

Habitat and general habits

Mostly crepuscular. Frequents shallow, freshwater marshes and lakes, feeding at muddy edges, and amongst aquatic vegetation including water-lilies. Often associated with bulrushes *Typha* (Maclean 1997d). Will feed on land and in flooded fields, rice paddies, and in waterside areas heavily disturbed by wild ungulates and cattle. During daytime often sleeps on open water or in quiet backwaters of marsh, but may come ashore to sleep or loaf. Even outside breeding season, usually found in small groups, large flocks rare. Regularly associates with other ducks including Red-billed Pintail and

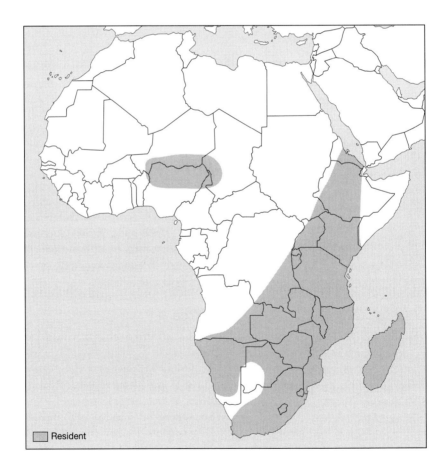

Resident

African Pygmy-geese. Feeds by dabbling, swimming or on foot, in shallows or in deeper, well-vegetated areas. Diet mostly seeds and fruits, predominately vegetable matter; however, may take aquatic invertebrates almost exclusively if super-abundant.

Displays and breeding behaviour

Fairly undemonstrative during courtship; display described in Johnsgard (1965a), Clark (1971) and Pearce (1999). Burp most obvious ♂ display, used in courtship and during hostile interactions between ♂♂. In Burp, neck stretched upwards and 5 *tok* notes given when head is straight. Burp almost invariably followed by drinking. Repeated-Burps also used, starting as typical Burp, ♂ crown feathers flattened after 1st *tok* call; while head held high, ♂ gives soft *tok* calls and repeats typical Burp. Sequence may be repeated several times, each inter-Burp including soft calls. ♂ may turn head during display. Wing-flapping, Drinking, Both-wing-stretch (upwards), Swimming-shake and Lateral Dabbling also recorded. ♂ Turns-back-of-head rarely to Inciting ♀. One of group of courting ♂♂ may threaten chosen ♀ and chase her into air, displaying upon settling with further threats, Burps and Wing-flaps, often leading to further flights. Copulation preceded by mutual Head-pumping and, after dismounting, ♂ may give brief Wings-up-bill-down, often with quiet repeated *tok* calls, followed by Erect-broadside, and may Turn-head-to-face ♀ and Turn-back-of-head (Pearce 1999, Johnson *et al.* 2000).

Not territorial, some pairs stay together for long periods; ♂ may accompany mate while brood rearing.

Breeding and life cycle

Nesting recorded all months of year, probably controlled by rainfall in many parts of range, but more sedentary than most African ducks, breeding in stable wetlands.

Nests in vegetation, often above water in drowned trees, *Phragmites* or Papyrus clumps. Nest built from surrounding vegetation. Eggs ovate, smooth cream or yellowish buff; in southern Africa 44 × 32.4 (41–48 × 31–35.5) ($n = 45$) (Maclean 1993); in Zimbabwe 44 × 32.5 (41–48 × 31–34) ($n = 26$) (Thomas and Condy 1965); in captivity 45.1 × 33.0 (41.6–48.1 × 30.4–34.8) ($n = 46$); weight 28 (26–30) ($n = 7$) (Brown *et al.* 1982), or 24.8 (23.0–26.5) ($n = 13$); clutch in southern Africa 7.2 (6–9) ($n = 9$). Incubation, by ♀, 25–27 days. Hatch weight in captivity 15.9 ($n = 11$); fledge in 60–65 days (Maclean 1993). No data on breeding success, survival or longevity.

Conservation and threats

Protection of wetlands and waterside vegetation, and control of hunting will maintain populations.

Glyn Young

The pochards and scaup (diving ducks)

Only three diving ducks—the Tufted Duck, Common Pochard and Greater Scaup—were known to Linneaus, and appear in his ordering of the natural world, the *Systema Naturae* of 1758 and 1761; the rest were described scientifically by more recent authorities, sometimes in remarkable ways. The male Pink-headed Duck was first described by John Latham in 1790 apparently from a watercolour painting brought back to London from India by a Lady Impey, whose husband was Chief Justice in Calcutta in the 1770s and kept an aviary of native birds there.

The North American Ring-necked Duck owes its discovery to the body of a drake displayed for sale in a London market in March 1801, and received its common and specific names because, when its head hangs down, a chestnut coloured ring around its neck is obvious—it isn't all that clear at most other times. The bird was a vagrant that had crossed the Atlantic Ocean only to meet its end in Lincolnshire.

Pochards are better adapted than the dabblers for water living and, like them, tend to be vegetarian. To some extent, they occupy the same ecological niche as the swans, but dive for their plant food rather than reaching for it with a long neck. They have legs placed far back on the body, large feet and a lobed hind toe (Figure 9.28), and are generally associated with freshwater rather than marine habitats (although the Greater and Lesser Scaup also go to sea).

As in migratory dabbling ducks, the pairbond between male and female is usually seasonal, lasting only until incubation starts. Again, there are two annual moults of body feathers and, in general, the sexes look different for part of the year, with the male being the more conspicuous. However, the breeding (or alternate) plumages of male diving ducks tend not to be complex, and certainly there is no species with a particularly resplendent male—unless we count the pink and chocolate of the extinct Pink-headed Duck. A shiny speculum is not present on the wing (although pale wing bars and stripes on the secondaries are), and iridescent colouring is restricted to the heads of a few.

Diving ducks normally nest at ground level, and often build a floating structure, the females fashioning a base for their nest from emergent vegetation. Egg-laying tends to be later than in dabbling ducks in the same environment, as they need to wait for aquatic vegetation to grow; thus, they are particularly affected by summer droughts and by drainage. The habit of laying in floating nests reduces predation by mammals such as foxes, and stranded nests left high and dry by receding water are frequently abandoned. Egg thieves that hunt from above, such as crows, are defeated by camouflage and by an overhead screening of reed and grass stems pulled down and arranged around and by the sitting bird. Eggs are fairly large and clutches small; they hatch after 23–28 days and, as in all ducks, incubation is shortest in small species that lay at high latitudes, and longest in larger ones nesting near the tropics. Many female ducks occasionally lay in the nests of others. In diving ducks, especially the North American Redhead, this behaviour may be common enough to influence the biology of a local population. The habit of dump nesting is more likely to occur if there is a shortage of nest sites and an increasing population. A clutch too large to incubate adequately can result.

The phenomenon of an unequal sex ratio is acute in certain pochards where females are heavily outnumbered. The imbalance in sexes in the population may be because the female is more vulnerable when she is nesting and rearing young, or more susceptible to being shot by hunters, or to feeding competition between the sexes.

Many northern pochards are a favourite quarry for hunters and wildfowlers, especially in North America, where 200 000 Redhead can be shot in a season. Birds come in to roost on a low flightpath and seem to be particularly easy to attract onto models of their own kind. Drainage of wetlands for farming, especially pothole areas, has deprived them of breeding habitat. In general, northern diving ducks have not done well from human agricultural activities; because feeding on dry land is not the northern diving ducks' normal regime, they usually ignore harvested grain and potato fields unless these are flooded. However, some have benefited from the human need for large town reservoirs, and for sand and gravel extraction (see Chapter 8). The introduction of the Zebra Mussel *Dreissena polymorpha* into many of these freshwaters, from the Baltic into western Europe (it was first noticed in London's Commercial Docks in 1824) and then to America, has done wonders for winter feeding opportunities of a few adaptable species. Sadly, two members of the tribe have probably become extinct during the last century (BirdLife International 2000): the Pink-headed Duck, and the Madagascar Pochard, which, in 1894, was the most recent member of the tribe to be described.

9.28 A pochard diving.

Janet Kear

Taxonomy

The pochards or diving ducks, tribe Aythyini, seem related closely to the dabbling ducks (Anatini), with a more distant connection to the seaducks (Mergini) (Delacour 1954–64, Johnsgard 1961e, Woolfenden 1961, Brush 1976, Bottjer 1983, Madsen *et al.* 1988), although Livezey (1996c) found that relationships among tribes within the Anatinae could not be determined. The tribe is composed of 17 modern species which Livezey (1996a, 1997b) split into three subtribes: Marmaronetteae (Marbled Teal), Rhodonessina (narrow-billed pochards), and Aythyeae (broad-billed pochards). They are distributed across the world, although species diversity is clearly highest in the north, and particularly in the temperate regions of the Palearctic (Figure 9.29). Livezey (1996a) suggested that the tribe was limited originally to the northern hemisphere (perhaps the Palearctic), with three or four subsequent transequatorial radiations that gave rise to the southern species.

The earliest fossil assigned to the tribe is *Aythya arvernensis*, uncovered from lower Miocene (possibly late Oligocene) beds in France (Brodkorb 1964). The earliest fossil record of the Redhead (Delacour 1954–64) comes from the Pleistocene of California (Miller 1925) and Oregon (Shufeldt 1913); later fossils are known from Florida (McCoy 1963) and Texas (Brodkorb 1964). The frequency of interspecific hybridization is relatively high within the group, and many hybrids with dabbling ducks have been recorded (Johnsgard 1960a, Gillham *et al.* 1966, Scherer and Hilsberg 1982).

The pochards are a reasonably homogenous group, sharing a number of features. These include significant specialization for diving, moderately heavy wing loadings, loss or great reduction in frequency of Decrescendo calling by females, and the absence or rudimentary occurrence of pre-copulatory Head-pumping (Johnsgard 1960b, 1961a, 1961e, 1962, 1965a, Livezey 1996a). Courtship display is less variable than in the dabbling ducks. Head-throws, in

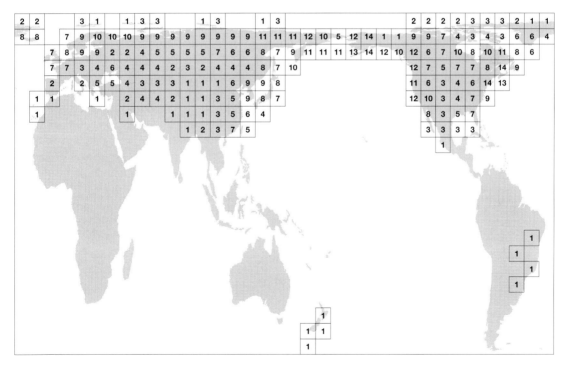

9.29 Species diversity of pochards (Aythyini) that survived into the Holocene. The number of species that occur (or occurred) within each grid-cell is indicated.

which the male raises his head, sometimes so that his bill points to the sky, and then lays it back on his rump are common. Males may use Preen-behind-wing displays, and rub their quills in order to produce a rattling sound, and sexual differences in eye colour are important in courtship—the bright iris of the male can be expanded and contracted to startling effect.

The Marbled Teal shows a number of dabbling duck characteristics and has been included within the Anatini tribe by some authors (Phillips 1922–26, Delacour and Mayr 1945, Delacour 1954–64, Brush 1976). In many ways, it is intermediate between the Anatini and Aythyini, but seems to be closest to the latter (Johnsgard 1961a, 1961c, 1961e, 1978, Livezey 1986a, 1996a, 1997b).

Since the provisional placement of the little known Pink-headed Duck as an aberrant dabbling duck (Delacour and Mayr 1945, Delacour 1954–64), subsequent studies have shown many similarities to the pochards (Johnsgard 1961a, 1961c, 1962, Woolfenden 1961, Humphrey and Ripley 1962, Brush 1976, Livezey 1986a, 1996a). Humphrey and Ripley (1962) suggested descent from a marine diving duck that responded adaptively to long-term changes in the ecology of the Ganges area during Tertiary times, evolving gradually to become a surface feeder on freshwater. Livezey (1996a, 1997b) recognized a relationship between the Pink-headed Duck and Red-crested Pochard, and concluded that they formed a sister group to the other two narrow-billed pochards, the Rosybill and Southern Pochard. He put the last two in a genus *Metopiana*.

The remaining Aythyini were placed in the true or broad-billed pochards by Livezey (1996a, 1997b) and split into three subgenera, *Aristonetta* (redheads), *Nyroca* (white-eyes), and *Aythya* (scaup). The three redheads—Common Pochard, Redhead and Canvasback—he felt deserved distinct recognition within the genus *Aristonetta* (Livezey 1997b). The Common Pochard is usually considered sister to the Canvasback (Delacour and Mayr 1945, Delacour 1954–64, Johnsgard 1961c, 1965a, 1978, 1979), although, with marginal support from his data, Livezey (1996a, 1997b) concluded that the Common Pochard and Redhead were sister species.

The white-eyed ducks comprise a distinct clade of four species (Hardhead, Madagascar Pochard, Ferruginous Duck and Baer's Pochard). The relationship between them remains inadequately resolved, although a close relationship between Ferruginous Duck and Baer's Pochard is well established (Delacour and Mayr 1945, Delacour 1954–64, Johnsgard 1961a, 1978, Livezey 1996a, 1997b).

The last group, the scaups, is composed of five species: New Zealand Scaup, Ring-necked Duck, Tufted Duck, and Greater and Lesser Scaups. A close relationship between the Ring-necked Duck and Tufted Duck is inferred frequently (Salvadori 1895, Peters 1931, Boetticher 1952, Delacour 1954–64, Livezey 1996a, 1997b); however, Johnsgard (1961a) suggested that the Ringneck was closer to the three red-headed pochards on the basis of similarities in downy plumage, male trachea and courtship behaviour.

DNA data (Harshman 1996, Johnson and Sorenson 1998, Sorenson *et al.* 1999) have suggested that several other species, usually assigned to other groups, may be related to the pochards, such as the White-winged Duck, Blue-winged Goose and Hartlaub's Duck.

Des Callaghan

Marbled Teal *Marmaronetta angustirostris*
PLATE 21

Anas angustirostris Ménétriés, 1832, Cat. Raisonné Objets Zool. Recueillis Voyage Caucase, p. 58 Lenkoran, Azerbaijan

Marmaronetta Reichenbach, 1853

Etymology: *marmaronetta* from Gr. *marmaros* meaning marble plus *netta* duck; *angustirostris* L. *angustus* narrow, *rostris* billed.

Other names: Marbled Duck. French: Sarcelle marbrée; Spanish: Cerceta pardilla.

Variation: no subspecies described; although several isolated populations exist, there are no studies of morphological or genetic variation.

Description

ADULT: sexes alike. ♂ generally grey-brown, noticeably spotted with pale cream feather centres and contrasting dark grey-brown edges. Slightly darker above than below, with broad dark eye-patch extending to nape; rest of head and neck finely streaked and pale whitish cheeks. Nape feathers elongated to form pendant shaggy crest. Forehead feathers also elongated to form slight crest. Primaries pale silver-grey, secondaries pale brown fading into grey-brown tips; tail partly tipped white. In flight, no distinct pattern apart from paler secondaries. Legs and feet variable from blackish to olive green to yellow; bill in breeding season gloss black with narrow blue band behind nail, along cutting edge and lateral base of upper mandible; in nonbreeding season, glossy shine lost, and blue band fades to pale grey. ♀ similar to ♂ but slightly smaller, bill shorter (Green 2000b), crest smaller or absent and head rounder profile. Eye-patch less extensive, crown lighter and cheeks dirtier white. Scapulars and back feathers (below mantle) lighter and less contrasting, tips of primaries blacker and less silvery. Bill in breeding season matt black with olive green patch of variable size at base of upper mandible; nonbreeding, olive green often fades to greyish.

MOULT: no ♂ eclipse, although 2 annual body moults assumed.

IMMATURE: generally resembles adult, but newly fledged juveniles distinctive due to thinner and lower profile, uniform, matt black bills and relatively dark but unspotted back. Eye-patch more subtle, and upperwing coverts clearly darker in flight; however, strongly contrasting marbled body acquired within 18 days of fledging. Within 5 months, ♂ acquires blue band around base of upper mandible and ♀ grey basal patch. Streaking on breast finer and more regular.

DUCKLING: like Northern Mallard but upperparts darker, with light patches ill-defined and absent on wing. Longer down on upperparts, streak over eye, cheeks, chin and throat cinnamon-buff rather than yellow. Chest grey-buff; underparts pale grey, sometimes suffused cream-yellow (Cramp and Simmons 1977).

MEASUREMENTS AND WEIGHT: Spanish skins (age unknown, $n = 10$ for ♂ and ♀): ♂ wing, 194–210 (202); tail, 65–76 (70); bill, 43.2–47.3 (45.0); tarsus, 33.6–37.8 (36.2). ♀ wing, 192–202 (197); tail, 59–74 (67); bill, 40.5–44.0 (42.5); tarsus, 34.2–37.8 (36.1). Wild hatched but captive reared juveniles, Valencia ($n = 10$ for ♂ and ♀): ♂ wing, 199–210 (205); tail, 64–70 (67); bill, 44–48.3 (46.1); tarsus, 36.3–41.3 (38.6). ♀ wing, 194–205 (200); tail, 66–71 (68); bill, 42.2–45.5 (43.6); tarsus, 36.3–40.3 (37.9). Captive reared adults, Seville: ♂ wing ($n = 11$), 205–212 (208); bill, 41.6–46.2 (43.8); tarsus, 37.2–41.7 (39.3). ♀ wing ($n = 14$), 198–206 (202); bill, 39.9–43.3 (41.8); tarsus, 34.1–39.5 (37.2). Wild adults, Seville: ♂ wing ($n = 3$), 210–216 (214); bill, 43.9–46.0 (45.1); tarsus, 38.1–41.2 (39.7). ♀ wing ($n = 2$), 201–203 (202); bill, 41.7–42.2 (42.0); tarsus, 35.7–38.7 (37.2). Weight: wild hatched but captive reared juveniles, Valencia, Sept ($n = 10$ for ♂ and ♀): ♂ 391–458 (420), ♀ 367–438 (402). Captive reared adults, Seville: ♂ ($n = 11$, [Sept 7, Nov 4]) 360–413 (380), ♀ ($n = 14$ [Sept 6, Nov 5, July 3]) 327–380 (353). Captive reared adults, Slimbridge (Dec, Chisholm and

Leigh-Hunt 1996): ♂ (*n* = 16) 350–435 (407), ♀ 345–435 (384). Wild adults, Seville: ♂ (*n* = 3) 415–510 (465), ♀ (*n* = 2) 375–469 (422).

Field characters

Small (390–420 mm long) duck with no speculum, likely to be confused only with ♀ Eurasian Teal, Garganey, Pintail and Red-crested Pochard. Eye-patch and marbled pattern distinctive and even more striking at distance. Tail relatively long and rises above back when on water (distinctive feature in silhouette). Quiet in flight, always flies low, with slower wing-beats than Eurasian Teal. Eye-patch of ♀ Red-crested Pochard continues over crown, and flight feathers contrast more with forewing.

Voice

Relatively silent. ♂ produces nasal call (sonogram in Cramp and Simmons 1977) as head touches back in Head-jerk display used in courtship and as alarm call when guarding brood. Call described as *eeeep* and reminds one of call of Marsh Harrier *Circus aeruginosus*. ♀ occasionally does Head-jerk and produces similar call. When flushed, juveniles emit monosyllabic *deee-ee* alarm call with slight increase in frequency towards end, total duration of *c* 0.4 sec and interval between calls of *c* 0.4 sec.

Range and status

Fragmented range and rapidly declining population in Mediterranean region, southwest and central Asia and West Africa, including Canary and Cape Verde Islands. Formerly one of most abundant ducks in some parts of range, but badly affected by wetland loss and degradation and, recently, by drainage of Iraqi marshes where most of remaining world population may have bred (Green 1993a, 1996). World wintering population estimated at 14 000–26 000 (Wetlands International 2002).

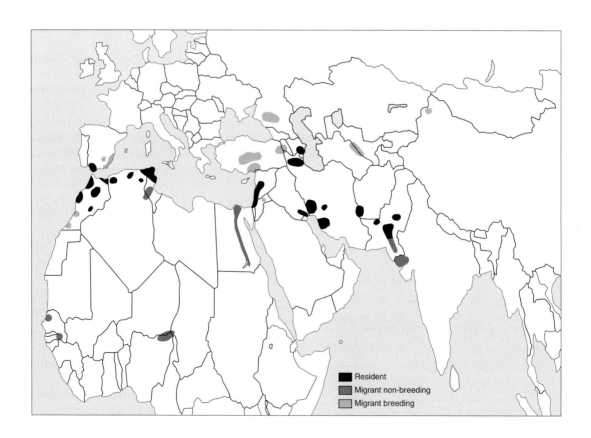

Resident
Migrant non-breeding
Migrant breeding

Habitat and general habits

Dependent on shallow habitats rich in emergent and submergent vegetation (Green 1993a, 1998a, 2000c, Navarro and Robledano 1995), apparently preferring brackish, seasonal or semi-permanent wetlands (Green 2000c). Gregarious and non-aggressive, often forming large monospecific flocks post-breeding and in winter. More dispersed in breeding season, but paired birds often mix with conspecifics. In ecological terms, dabbling duck feeding mainly in top 20 cm of surface layer (Green 1998c). Feeds mainly nocturnally in autumn–winter, when flocks often fly from daytime roosts (with dense emergent vegetation) to more exposed, shallow feeding sites at dusk. Less than 2% of daytime spent feeding Nov–Mar in Sidi Bou Ghaba, Morocco and Doñana, Spain (Green and El Hamzaoui 2000). More day-active at other times of year.

Historical data on diet limited and imprecise but demonstrates omnivory (Cramp and Simmons 1977, Green 1993a). Report from last century that fed largely on ant-lions *Myrmeleon* (Phillips 1922–26) seems unlikely. Recent information (Green 2000c, Green and Selva 2000) shows variation between sites and seasons. In Feb in Sidi Bou Ghaba, Morocco, faeces contained mainly adult chironomids (98%) with traces of coleopterans, spiders and *Salicornia* seeds. In July in Turkey, adult faeces contained mainly seeds of Cyperaceae—*Scirpus* (= *Schoenoplectus*) *litoralis* and *Scirpus maritimus*—and small coleopterans, dipterans, hemipterans (corixids) and ostracods (Green and Selva 2000). Diving rarely observed but in July in Turkey, ducklings and juveniles seen diving to take *Chara* (Green 1998b). In late July in Doñana, Spain, ducklings seen picking spiders off dead *Arthrocnemum* stalks. In Aug and Nov in Doñana, Spain and Oct in Sidi Moussa, Morocco, adult faeces rich in *Ruppia* seeds taken from sediments. In May at Sidi Moussa, proportion of *Ruppia* seeds reduced whereas those of invertebrates (especially corixids) and *Ranunculus* seeds much higher.

Volumetric content of several stomachs analysed in Alicante, Spain: one adult in June dominated by chironomid larvae (68%) and pupae (15%) with smaller amounts of other dipterans (Ceratopogonidae, Ephydridae), coleopterans (Hydrophilidae), Odonata, plecopterans, trichopterans, ostracods, amphipods (gammarids), isopods (Sphaeromatidae) and seeds (Chenopodiaceae, Zannichelliaceae, Umbelliferae, Polygonaceae and Compositae). Three adults in Oct contained seeds of Graminaeae, Leguminosae, Cyperaceae, *Potamogeton pectinatus*, *Ruppia* and Ranunculaceae. Thirty stomachs collected Sept–Nov 1997 dominated by *Scirpus litoralis* seeds ingested from water surface. One newly emerged duckling in June full of chironomid adults (90%) with small quantities of ants, aphids, spiders and seeds of *Suaeda*. Except for ducklings, less dependent on invertebrates and more on seeds than many north temperate ducks (Green and Sánchez 2003).

Displays and breeding behaviour

Previously described in some detail in captivity (Cramp and Simmons 1977). Recent field studies (Navarro and Robledano 1995) less detailed but generally confirm captive observations. Four displays regularly seen in mixed groups of 2–15 courting birds autumn-spring: Neck-stretch-Head-jerk with crest erected, head raised vertically extending neck fully, head held momentarily then jerked backwards and downwards quickly onto back, opening bill and calling at same time; Neck-stretch Only with head raised vertically as before, head held stationary with neck fully extended, then slowly lowered vertically to starting point; Head-jerk Only with head jerked backwards and downwards quickly onto back whilst calling, but without initial neck stretch, this may be Neck-stretch-Head-shake of Cramp and Simmons (1977); Sneak with head and neck stretched horizontally over water. At breeding sites, ♂♂ recorded flying in tight vertical spiral, then dropping back, but significance of display unknown. Birds in Head-up alert posture also often seen to Head-jerk, particularly those attending broods (Green 1997). Preflight Chin-lifting observed, as is display resembling Bridling of dabbling ducks.

Breeding and life cycle

Apparently adapted to maximize reproductive output when suitable breeding conditions available in ephemeral wetlands (i.e. *r* strategist), causing major population fluctuations in relation to variation in rainfall (Green *et al.* 1999b, Green 2000c). Monogamous, pairing mainly Mar–Apr. Pairing begins in winter but completed on breeding sites. In mid Feb, in Sidi Bou Ghaba, Morocco, 5% of birds paired, increasing to 35% mid Mar (Green and El Hamzaoui 2000). Small number of birds already paired Oct.

Nests recorded 13 Apr–26 June. Broods recorded ($n = 193$, all ages combined) 15 Apr–12 Sept (20 June). Nests later than sympatric ducks, and breeds later in more northerly parts of range (Green 1998c). Median hatching date 20 June ($n = 101$) in Andalusia (Green 1998c). Owing to population declines, usually now nests at low density but formerly observed in close proximity (Hawkes 1970). Intraspecific nest parasitism common and up to 24 eggs found per nest (Green 1998c); old unconfirmed report of large communal nests with up to 100 eggs in Andalusia (Valverde 1964). Nests in variety of habitats both above water (e.g. in *Typha* stands) and on dry land (e.g. in clumps of *Arthrocnemum* or *Suaeda* and even in roofs of reed huts—Hawkes 1970); built by ♀, lined with down and dried vegetation.

Eggs ovate, pale straw; 46 × 34 (42–51 × 32–36) ($n = 100$) (Cramp and Simmons 1977); weight in captivity 29.4 (25.5–34.5) ($n = 100$); complete clutches in Andalusia 13.3 (9–20) ($n = 17$), with earlier clutches larger (Green 1998c); mean size of apparently unparasitized clutches 11.8 (Green 1998c). Incubation, by ♀, 25–27 days (captivity). Weight of 100 captive ducklings at hatching 17.5 (14.0–22.0); on Day 4 ($n = 3$) 20.5–21.0. Brood size much larger than sympatric ducks (Green *et al.* 1999b), decreasing from 10.9 (6–14) ($n = 8$) in 1st week to 8.5 (4–13) ($n = 8$) when fully feathered (Green 1998c). Brood amalgamation occasional (Green 1998c, Green *et al.* 1999b). Fledge in 50–54 days (captive). Age classes of young (captive, Vanhoof 1996): Class I Days 1–17, Class IIa 18–27, IIb 28–35, IIc 36–41, Class III 42–50 (see Gollop and Marshall 1954 for definitions). Evidence that some ♂♂ remain with ♀ and brood to fledging (Green 1997). ♂ may act as guard, closely monitoring and often flying around potential sources of danger (Green 1997). Reports that ♂♂ flock together after deserting ♀♀ when egg-laying starts (Cramp and Simmons 1977) erroneous; however, most ♂♂ seem to leave ♀♀ after hatching.

Peregrine and other falcons take adults, and Marsh Harriers and Black Kites *Milvus migrans* probably important predators of ducklings (Green 1993a, Navarro and Robledano 1995). In Spain, high rates of nest predation by Red Foxes, raptors, crows, Brown Rats and Eurasian Badger *Meles meles* (Navarro and Robledano 1995, Green 1998c).

Age at 1st breeding (captive and wild) 1 year. Oldest captive ♂ and ♀ 12 years old; of 8 birds of known age ringed in Spain and recovered (7 when shot), 2 were in 1st calendar year, 3 in 2nd, 2 in 3rd and 1 in 4th.

Conservation and threats

Badly affected by continuing destruction of seasonal wetlands within range, and poorly adapted to exploit permanent wetlands (e.g. reservoirs) that replace them (Green 1993a, 1996, 2000c). Problems of sedimentation and changes in hydrology cause many former breeding sites to dry before this late nester can complete breeding. Population crashes occur during droughts (Green and Navarro 1997). Even in years of high rainfall, bottlenecks tend to occur in post-breeding period, when seasonal wetlands dry out before winter rains arrive (Green 2000c). Serious water-quality problems can occur at this time, and combination of poisoning from organophosphate insecticides, botulism, salmonella and lead poisoning killed hundreds (most of local population) in Alicante in autumn 1997 and again in summer 1999. In former times of abundance, was popular quarry with hunters (Valverde 1964, Green 1993a, Navarro and Robledano 1995). Despite widespread legal protection, hunting still severe problem in many areas, as easy to shoot and hunters often ignore protected status (Navarro and Robledano 1995, Green 1996). Globally threatened, classified as Vulnerable by BirdLife International (2000, 2001).

Andy J. Green

Pink-headed Duck *Rhodonessa caryophyllacea*

Anas caryophyllacea Latham, 1790, Index Ornith., p. 866

India (Oudh). A painting, commissioned in Calcutta *c* 1775 and now in Liverpool Museum, may have been Latham's type (Fisher and Kear 2002).

Rhodonessa Reichenbach, 1853

Etymology: *rhodon* Gr. for rose and *nessa* duck; *caryophyllacea* L. name of family that contains pinks and carnations.

Other names: none in English. Hindi: Lal sira.

Variation: no subspecies.

Description

ADULT: dimorphic. ♂ had narrow bill, long thin neck, fairly long legs, thick body and short tail (Figure 9.30). Head somewhat tufted at back. Bill, head and neck rose pink, except for blackish line on forehead and black band from chin to breast, broadening at foreneck; rest of plumage brownish black, mantle, scapulars, and breast finely lined pale pink; edge of wing pinkish white; outer secondaries pale fawn or salmon with white tips, tertiaries glossy chocolate brown. Bill pink, with unfeathered area of soft skin around distal part; legs reddish black; iris bright red. ♀ similar, but pink on head and neck whitish, dull and tinged fawn, particularly deep on crown, nape and hind neck; no black line on throat and foreneck; rest of plumage duller and less dark. Legs brown; iris brownish orange (Delacour 1954–64). Foot of adult *Anas*-like with hind toe only slightly lobed, unlike most pochards (Humphrey and Ripley 1962).

MOULT: no data; probably 2 annual body moults and one post-breeding wing moult, but no ♂ eclipse plumage, unlike Red-crested Pochard.

IMMATURE: similar to adult but paler, neck and head fawn with rosy tinge.

DUCKLING: unknown.

MEASUREMENTS AND WEIGHTS: ♂ wing, 250–282; tail, 106–131; culmen, 50–56; tarsus, 38–40; weight

9.30 The male of the extinct Pink-headed Duck.

($n = 5$), 794–993 (874). ♀ wing, 250–260; weight ($n = 1$), 879 (Hume and Marshall 1879–81, Delacour 1954–64, Ali 1960).

Field characters

Length 600 mm. Confused at times with much commoner Red-crested Pochard, had peculiar upright stance and unique colour combination of pink and chocolate. In flight, pale pink underwing contrasted with dark body (Madge and Burn 1988). Recorded singly or in pairs, sometimes in company of other waterfowl.

Voice

Windpipe bulla of ♂ resembles that of pochards, and has enlarged tracheal tube (Johnsgard 1961c, Humphrey and Ripley 1962). ♂ had wheezy whistle, and mellow 2-syllabled call with metallic ring *wugh* (Finn 1909). ♀ said to quack.

Range and status

Resident in northeast India and Bangladesh. More than 2 centuries ago, may have been abundant in floodplains, reedbeds and swamps of plains of Lower Ganges and Brahmaputra rivers. Probably extinct since late 1930s or 1940s. Salim Ali (1960) listed 71 skins in museums, mainly shot in Bihar, Orissa and western Assam; other specimens have come to light since, and there may be more, some unrecognized, in

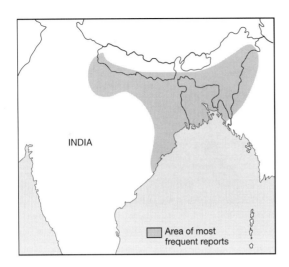

INDIA

☐ Area of most frequent reports

private hands (Fuller 2001). ♂ trachea exists in British Museum.

Habitat and general habits

Swampy grass jungles. In cold weather, Nov–Mar, observed in flocks of 6–30 or even 40 in lagoons adjoining large rivers. Fed mainly on surface, but could also dive for waterweeds and molluscs. Rarely perched on trees. Sedentary or partially migratory (Delacour 1954–64). Latham (1824) reported was often kept in captivity and became 'tolerably familiar'.

Displays and breeding behaviour

♂♂ displayed socially, puffing out short head feathers, with neck shortened, resting on back, then stretching neck upward while calling (Finn 1909, Johnsgard 1965a), presumably comparable to Head-throw of other diving duck. Not aggressive in captivity, so possibly not territorial nester. Latham described it as living in pairs, but Shillingford (*in* Ali 1960) said paired in Apr, nested during May, and that eggs found June–July.

Breeding and life cycle

Reported to nest no more than 460 m from water. Nest circular, well built of dry grass and few feathers, *c* 230 mm in diameter, 100–125 deep and with walls 75–100 thick without any special lining; hidden in tuft of tall grass, and hard to find (Ali 1960). Eggs unusual, almost spherical, stone white and lacking 'soapy' texture characteristic of ducks' eggs (Walters 1998). Six in British Museum measure 45.9 × 42.0 (43.3–47.0 × 40.6–44.2) (Walters 1998), for which Schönwetter (1960–66) calculated fresh weight of 45 (round eggs are particularly strong, and typically laid by birds that nest in holes or that hatch asynchronously—neither feature apparently applicable here). Clutch size 5–10, with likely average of 9. Incubation unrecorded. Both sexes found near nest. ♀ with eggs or ducklings reported to give loud quacks and typical Distraction display—fluttered about, dragging herself when approached, flopping as if injured, but finally flew off perfectly (Shillingford *in* Ali 1960). Growth and development of young unknown; fledging probably took 2 months (Ali 1960). Age at 1st breeding, productivity, and survival unknown; individuals lived for > 12 years in captivity.

Reasons for extinction

Although listed as Critically Endangered by BirdLife International (2000, 2001), almost certainly extinct due to drainage schemes and spread of human populations into range and, latterly, because of unrestrained collecting and hunting, despite being poor sport (Fooks 1947, Fuller 2001). Up to 12 or so live ducks offered for sale in Calcutta's bird market most winters 1890–1910 (Ali 1960); ironically, was officially protected only in 1956 after last individual probably dead. Held in captivity in India and Europe, but never bred. Sightings continue to be reported, but most records seem due to confusion with Red-crested Pochard.

Janet Kear

Red-crested Pochard *Netta rufina*
PLATE 22

Anas rufina Pallas, 1773, Reise Verschiedene Provinzen Russischen Reichs, **2**, p. 713
Caspian Sea and lakes of the Tartarian Desert
Netta Kaup, 1829

Etymology: *rufina* L. for 'a representation of gold' presumably in reference to ♂ head colour.

Other names: Red-crested Duck. French: Nette rousse; Spanish: Pato colorado; Dutch: Kroonend.

Variation: no subspecies.

Description

ADULT: dimorphic. ♂ in breeding, or alternate, plumage has dark chestnut head grading to rusty gold above and behind eye. Short, rounded crest. Black nape, underparts, rump and back with prominent white flanks and shoulder crescent. Tail dark grey. Dull grey-brown mantle, scapulars and folded wings extend to barring on upperflanks. Almost full length of upperwing white, constrasting with brown forewing. Bill pale red, eye and legs red. ♀ has chocolate brown cap extending down nape. Pale grey patch over lores, ear coverts and foreneck; rest of upperparts dull brown. Underparts also rather uniform brown, paler than upperparts, especially on vent. Bill dark grey with pink at tip and cutting edges; legs and toes pink, webs blackish; eyes brown.

MOULT: ♂ eclipse similar to adult ♀ but red bill and eye retained, and generally darker appearance.

IMMATURE: young ♂ assumes dull version of adult appearance by end of 1st winter. ♀ similar to adult, with black-brown bill.

DUCKLING: crown, eyestripe, hindneck and upperparts dark brown, with yellowish spots on and behind wings and at sides of rump. Face and underparts dull yellowish.

MEASUREMENTS AND WEIGHT: ♂ wing (*n* = 16), 255–273 (264); tail (*n* = 15), 67–76 (70.6); bill (*n* = 25), 45–52 (48.2); tarsus (*n* = 25), 42–47 (44.1). ♀ wing (*n* = 14), 251–275 (260); tail (*n* = 15), 62–74 (68.4); bill (*n* = 26), 42–50 (46.6); tarsus (*n* = 26), 40–45 (42.2). Weight ♂ Feb in southwest Caspian (*n* = ?), 900–1170 (1135); Mar, Kazakhstan (*n* = 17), 990–1300 (1130); May–Sept, Russia, Holland (*n* = 8), 1020–1347 (1167); Oct, Kazakhstan (*n* = 11), 1200–1420 (1320). ♀ Feb in southwest Caspian (*n* = ?), 830–1320 (967); Mar, Kazakhstan (*n* = 12), 1000–1200 (1100); May–Sept, Russia, Holland (*n* = 9), 1020–1300 (1146); Oct, Kazakhstan (*n* = 6), 1100–1400 (1220) (Cramp and Simmons 1977).

Field characters

Large, distinctive duck, 530–570 mm long, with no similar species. ♀ superficially resembles ♀ Common Scoter, which is smaller and darker, with more prominent, swollen bill and longer tail. Swims high on water, with long-necked, big-headed appearance. Takes off with pattering run, revealing broad wings with striking pattern of white or off-white primaries and secondaries (narrowly tipped blackish) and distinctively white underwings. ♂ in flight shows, in addition, narrow white leading edges to wings, and oval white flank patches contrasting with black underparts. Feeding and breeding behaviour intermediate between diving and dabbling ducks.

Voice

Rather silent except during courtship. ♂ has rasping wheeze and ♀ grating *kurr*. Sonograms in Cramp and Simmons (1977). Downy young utter weak, low-pitched trilling and shrill piping.

Range and status

Main breeding range from Black Sea lowlands and Turkey, eastwards across central Asia to northwest China and west Mongolia. European breeding population considerably smaller and more scattered, occupying small lakes with emergent vegetation, and wetlands (especially river deltas) of northwest Mediterranean, from south

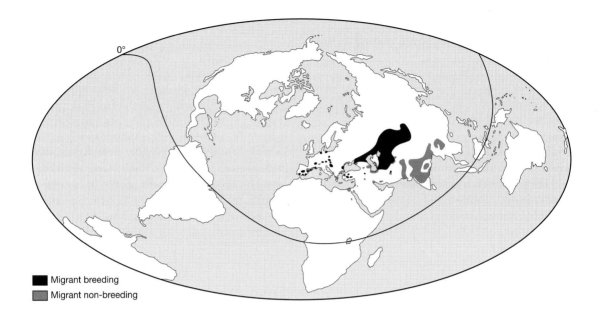

Migrant breeding
Migrant non-breeding

and east Spain and southern France, through isolated pockets of central Europe to The Netherlands and Denmark. Asiatic birds winter around Black and Caspian Seas, throughout Indian subcontinent east to Myanmar (Burma), with small numbers occurring also in Egypt and Middle East. European birds winter widely in Mediterranean basin (where some French and Spanish birds sedentary) and north to central Europe. Small English population of captive origin, breeds mostly in one area dispersing more widely in winter.

Winter population estimates for southwest and central Europe, 50 000; southeast Europe, 20 000–43 500; southwest Asia, 250 000; south Asia 25 000–100 000 (Wetlands International 2002). Eastern shores of Caspian perhaps most important single wintering area. European breeding population declined in 19th century to isolated pockets of central Europe. Central European wintering population, most of which occurs on Swiss lakes, increased by >50% annually 1987–96 (Delany *et al.* 1999). Increase continues, and 23 000 counted in Switzerland Nov 2002 (Keller and Burkhardt 2004). Early stages of increase in Central Europe reflected redistribution of birds formerly wintering in west Mediterranean (Keller 2000).

Habitat and general habits

Prefers deep, reed-fringed lakes and rivers, saline and alkaline lagoons. Feeds principally on aquatic vegetation, especially oogonia of green algal stonewort. Generally diurnal, feeding most actively during early morning and evening. Diving (as deep as 13.7 m) and dabbling predominate in feeding repertoire, which also includes up-ending and head-dipping (Cramp and Simmons 1977). Individuals in flocks tend to use same feeding method. Small invertebrate and vertebrate animals also occasionally taken, perhaps accidentally.

Displays and breeding behaviour

Pair formation occurs in (often large) wintering flocks, though can be delayed by biased sex ratios in these flocks. Monogamous, seasonal pairbond more similar to *Anas* than *Aythya* ducks, with ♂ accompanying ♀ until brood hatches, and ♂ also indulging in *Anas*-type promiscuous aerial chases.

Ritual behaviour well developed. Three main threat displays recognized, often associated with communal courtship in spring: Forward display (both sexes)—neck stretched horizontally above water with bill open; Downward sneeze—♂ draws head into neck and bill vertically downward into water while uttering Sneeze call; and Attack-intent—♂ holds head low and thrust forwards whilst uttering threat call.

In communal courtship, 5–20 displaying ♂♂ gather round one or more ♀♀ indulging in secondary displays, including Head-pumping, Ceremonial drinking, Upward-shake, and Head-flick leading to Sideways-sneeze, in which ♂ withdraws neck, lowers head in direction of ♀ with quick lateral movement, then jerks crown towards her while uttering Sneeze-call. Major displays follow, including Sideways-sneeze and ceremonial Leading, in which ♂ Leads ♀ while performing Turn-back-of-head with fully erect crest. ♀ responds by threatening or evading rejected ♂ and repeatedly turning in Neck-stretch posture away and towards favoured ♂.

Courtship behaviour of ♂ includes courtship feeding—he brings weed to surface which she accepts—(Johnsgard 1965a) and Ceremonial-drinking. Pre-copulatory displays include *Anas*-like Head-pumping, Bill-dipping and Preen-behind-wing.

Breeding and life cycle

Most pairs start breeding early May; in southern Russia may begin mid May. Nests near water at ground level in dense vegetation; diameter 28–45 cm and cup 10–20 cm deep, lined with leaves and down, built by ♀ using materials within reach. Usually well dispersed, but sometimes as close as 30 m. Eggs pale stone when fresh; 58 × 42 (53–62 × 39–45) (*n* = 150) (Schönwetter 1960–66); weight in captivity 56 (47–69) (*n* = 101); clutch 8–10 (6–14), egg dumping frequent, up to 39 eggs reported (Hellebrekers and Voous 1964). Single brood. Incubation, by ♀, 26–28 days. Hatching synchronous, young precocial and nidifugous; weight of captive day-olds 31.2 (*n* = 96). Parent–young bond stronger than in *Aythya*, lasting at least 11 weeks. ♀ broods young when small and may dive to bring up algal food for them. Fledge in 45–50 days. Breeds 1st at one year, though some not until 2.

Breeding success and adult survival rate unknown; oldest ringed bird was 7 years 2 months (Rydzewski 1974).

Conservation and threats

Main threats hunting and pressure on habitat, e.g. in Mediterranean wetlands. Land-use changes in central Asia, particularly in basins of Aral and Caspian Seas, affecting crucial habitats. Popular in captivity, where egg dumping habit may increase likelihood of escape and inadvertent introduction; this may explain records in Japan and Australia, growing population in UK, and perhaps other isolated northwest European populations.

Simon Delany

Rosybill *Netta peposaca*
PLATE 22

Anas peposaca Vieillot, 1816, Nouv. Dict. Hist. Nat., nouv. éd., **5**, p. 132
Paraguay and Buenos Aires, Argentina
　Etymology: *peposaca* is Paraguayan name for Rosybill.
　Other names: Rosy-billed Pochard, Great Duck, Peposaca Duck. Portuguese (Brazil): Marrecão; Spanish: Pato Negro (Chile); Pato Picazo (Argentina).
　Variation: no subspecies.

Description

ADULT: dimorphic. ♂ head, neck and breast black, with former glossed purple. Upperparts black, finely spotted white or grey, and belly and flanks vermiculated black-and-white (appearing grey). Undertail coverts white, and wing coverts sooty brown with darker tips tinged green. Secondaries and primaries mainly white with black tips, and underwing white. Bill rosy pink with black nail and large crimson knob at base; legs and feet yellow; iris red to yellowish orange. ♀ rufous to fuscous brown overall. Crown and mantle darker brown, grading to white on chin and throat. Breast and upperparts darker brown, and belly whitish. Undertail coverts and secondaries white. Bill dark bluish grey with black nail, and only slight swelling at base; legs orange to yellowish grey; iris brown.

MOULT: no ♂ eclipse plumage (Weller 1968b). No data on timing of wing or body moults.

IMMATURE: similar to ♀, but browner underparts.

DUCKLING: pale, buffy brown above, and bright yellow below.

MEASUREMENTS AND WEIGHT: ♂ (*n* = 8) wing, 216–247 (241); exposed culmen, 59–65 (62.4); tail, 60–69 (63.7); tarsus, 41–45; weight (*n* = 6), 1182. ♀ (*n* = 7) wing, 225–245 (236); exposed culmen, 55–60 (57.9); tail, 62–76 (66.4); weight (*n* = 5), 1004 (Delacour 1954–64, Weller 1968b, Blake 1977).

Field characters

Unmistakable; large-headed, stocky pochard, with high bill; 530–570 mm long. In flight, white underwing and prominent white wing bar on upper secondaries (becoming cream on primaries) separate from Southern Pochard.

Voice

Johnsgard (1965a) noted 2 ♀ calls associated with agonistic and sexual behaviour, harsh *krrrr* emitted when Inciting (described *errrr* by Steinbacher 1960), and Decrescendo-like call of 3–4 syllables, rarely emitted. He also noted 3 ♂ calls associated with agonistic and sexual behaviour, low, guttural *krrrr* given with Sneak display, and faint *wheee-ow* associated with Head-throw and Kinked-neck displays, and soft whirring sound, which may result from compression of body plumage, but seems homologous to Coughing call of *Aythya*. No information on calls of ducklings.

Range and status

Partial migrant found from east Bolivia and southern Brazil, south to Tierra del Fuego. In Bolivia, known only from Santa Cruz Province (Remsen and Taylor 1989), while occurs across Paraguay, but rare generally (Hayes 1995). In Brazil, restricted to south where, in Rio Grande do Sul Province, described as scarce to common in summer, and common to abundant in winter (Belton 1984).

Resident

Breeding also likely in São Paulo Province (Sick 1993), which would be most northern known breeding ground. In north and central Argentina, remains locally common, and has expanded range in south to Tierra del Fuego, where 'not uncommon' (Fjeldså and Krabbe 1990). Common in Uruguay, where is one of most frequently counted ducks (Carp 1991). Also occurs in central Chile, and expanded range in south (Fjeldså and Krabbe 1990).

Seems no significant decline in numbers, and in south of range apparently increasing and expanding (Fjeldså and Krabbe 1990). Large flocks, some of several thousand, frequent during nonbreeding season (Belton 1984, del Hoyo *et al.* 1992). Movements poorly understood, although obviously connected with dry periods (Phillips 1922–26, Weller 1968b, Belton 1984, Madge and Burn 1988). Numbers in Rio Grande do Sul (southeast Brazil) vastly augmented during winter, reaching peak quite late (Aug–Sept); ringing data suggest some of these birds nest in northern Argentina (Belton 1984). Total number probably > 1 000 000 (Wetlands International 2002).

Habitat and general habits

Usually found in small groups in lowland marshes, ponds and lakes with dense macrophyte growth; however, also feeds frequently in rice fields (Belton 1984) and, on migration, found on 'weedy ponds' up to 1000 m in Patagonia (Fjeldså and Krabbe 1990). During moult, larger, open waterbodies frequented and, during nonbreeding season, large flocks gather. Feeds mostly by dabbling, head-dipping, up-ending and grazing (in flooded fields), and dives infrequently. Diet poorly known, but seems essentially vegetarian, including seeds, roots, vegetative parts of aquatic macrophytes, grasses and sedges (Delacour 1954–64, Weller 1968b, Fjeldså and Krabbe 1990, del Hoyo *et al*. 1992).

Displays and breeding behaviour

Agonistic and sexual behaviour of ♀ includes conspicuous Preen-behind-wing and same form of highly ritualized Drinking as ♂. Sneak also performed by ♀ and ♂ (Steinbacher 1960, Johnsgard 1965a). Drinking conspicuous display of ♂♂, and replaces normal drinking, occurring whenever 2 birds meet, regardless of sex. Highly exaggerated Sneak also seen, while Head-throw performed infrequently. Preen-behind-wing common. ♂♂ swim ahead of Inciting ♀ while Turning-back-of-head to them and holding head feathers depressed (Steinbacher 1960, see Johnsgard 1965a for description of display).

Breeding and life cycle

Limited data. Breeding season occurs mainly during austral spring and summer, with broods noted Apr in Brazil (Belton 1984). Nest built on ground from herbaceous matter, over water or at edge, and under cover of dense vegetation (Phillips 1922–26, Delacour 1954–63). Eggs cream to greenish grey; 55 × 42 (Delacour 1954–64); 100 laid in captivity weighed 55.5 (43.5–64.0). Clutch size usually 10; incubation 27–29 days (Phillips 1922–26) and ♂ does not participate in brood care. Newly-hatched ducklings in captivity weighed 32.8 ($n = 48$). No information on growth, breeding success or survival.

Conservation and threats

No specific conservation projects in place. In parts of range, e.g. in Argentina and southern Brazil, is common quarry (Weller 1968b, Belton 1984, Sick 1993). Owing to claims of damage in rice fields, also persecuted, e.g. in Brazil where control encouraged by head bounty (Sick 1993). Poison used in some rice-growing areas, and illegal control during breeding season (Belton 1984).

Des Callaghan

Southern Pochard *Netta erythrophthalma*
PLATE 22

Anas erythrophthalma Wied, 1832, Beitr. Naturgeschichte Brasilien, **4**, p. 929
Lagoa do Braço, Villa de Belmonte, eastern Brazil
    Etymology: *erthrophthalma* Gr. for red-eyed.
    Other names: Red-eyed or Brown Pochard, African or South African Pochard (*brunnea*), South American Pochard (*erythrophthalma*). Afrikaans: Bruineed; Portuguese: Paturi-preta (Brazil); Spanish: Pato morado.
    Variation: 2 subspecies recognized, *N. e. erythrophthalma* of South America and *N. e. brunnea* Eyton, 1838 of Africa.

Description

ADULT: dimorphic. ♂ in breeding plumage has head and neck purplish black merging with glossy black breast, while rest of body nearly uniform dark brown, mantle being olive-brown and abdomen and undertail coverts grading to fulvous. Tail dark brown and upperwing surface olive-brown, except for broad white bar; bases of secondaries have brown tips. Bill bluish grey with black nail; legs and feet bluish grey and blackish; iris red. ♀ differs from ♂ in having head, crown, hindneck and nape medium brown, grading to umber on cheeks, whitish markings at base of mandible and maxilla, and broad, whitish crescent shape behind eye. Upperparts olive-brown vermiculated buff-brown, while flanks more fulvous. Underparts dull brown, but undertail coverts mottled white. Bill dark slate grey; iris brown (Delacour 1954–64, Johnsgard 1978). Adult ♂ *erythrophthalma* predominantly dark chestnut brown (Fjeldså and Krabbe 1990), ♂ of *brunnea* paler (Delacour 1954–64).

MOULT: no ♂ eclipse (Brown *et al.* 1982). In southwest Cape, South Africa, wing moult occurs after influx from north Aug–Sept, and birds flightless for *c* 31 days (Brown *et al.* 1982). Elsewhere in Africa, particularly near equator, timing of wing moult unclear, while great variation in South America (Antas and Resende 1983).

IMMATURE: paler than adult ♀ with facial markings less pronounced and ill-defined. Immature ♂ darker on lower neck, chest and abdomen (Delacour 1954–64, Johnsgard 1978).

DUCKLING: upperparts, crown, flank patch above thigh, and sides of chest and thighs sepia brown with strong olive tinge. Faint brown streak across ear coverts, while forehead, sides of head and rest of underparts pale sulphur yellow. Bill pinkish grey; legs and feet dark olive-grey; eye pale grey (Delacour 1954–64).

MEASUREMENTS AND WEIGHT: *erythrophthalma* ♂ wing (*n* = 13) (219); culmen, 42–45; tarsus, 37–41. ♀ wing (*n* = 6) (207); culmen, 41–44 (Delacour 1954–64, Gómez-Dallmeier and Cringan 1990). *brunnea* ♂ wing (*n* = 24), 202–228 (217.5); tail (*n* = 28), 52–66 (59.0); culmen (*n* = 32), 40–48 (44.0); tarsus (*n* = 32), 35–44 (39.6); weight (*n* = 577), 592–1010 (799). ♀ wing (*n* = 23), 201–221 (208.9); tail (*n* = 31), 52–68 (56.5); culmen (*n* = 32), 38–49 (43.3); tarsus (*n* = 32), 36–44 (39.6); weight (*n* = 463), 484–1018 (763) (Middlemiss 1958, Dean and Skead 1979).

Field characters

Length 480–510 mm. In flight, wings appear set well back on body, and white wing bar extends almost full span. In Africa, ♀ most easily confused with ♀ Maccoa, but can be separated by facial markings, since latter has horizontal white facial streaks (Brown *et al.* 1982). In South America, ♂ lacks whitish flanks of Lesser Scaup, while white facial markings of ♀ Lesser Scaup confined to area around bill. ♀ Rosybill completely lacks white facial markings (Hilty and Brown 1986, Gómez-Dallmeier and Cringan 1990).

Voice

♀ emits nasal *krrrrow* with downward inflection, frequently repeated, also threatening *quarrrk*. ♂ utters soft, almost hissing, vibrant *quack* and, in flight, *prerr . . . prerr . . . prerr*. In display, ♂ emits deep and low croaking *phreeeooo* associated with Head-throw, soft 3–4 noted call during Sneak, and mechanical *eerooow* in courtship. ♀ gives harsh *rrrr-rrrr* when Inciting (Johnsgard 1978, Brown *et al.* 1982). Sonogram of ♀ call in Maclean (1993), and of distress call of duckling in Kear (1968).

Range and status

In Africa occurs widely in south and east; not known to breed north of central Kenya and western Uganda, though common as migrant in Ethiopia north to Eritrea (Britton 1980) and as occasional straggler to Somalia (Ash and Miskell 1983). Common to locally abundant in most range countries (depending on season) and flocks of 1000–7500 regular (Benson *et al.* 1971, Urban and Brown 1971, Benson and Benson 1977, Britton 1980, Brown *et al.* 1982, Ash and Miskell 1983, Newman 1989, Sinclair *et al.* 1993). Tentative population estimate of *brunnea* 30 000–70 000 individuals (Wetlands International 2002).

In South America, generally localized and has disappeared from many areas. Still known from north and west Venezuela, Peru, northwest Argentina and central and eastern Brazil, and historic records from northen Chile, Ecuador and Trinidad; only recent record in Colombia is single ♀ near Bogotá in 1977 (Koepcke 1964, King 1977, Kear and Williams 1978, Antas and Resende 1983, Hilty and Brown 1986, Scott and Carbonell 1986, Narosky and Yzurieta 1987, Fjeldså and Krabbe 1990, Gómez-Dallmeier

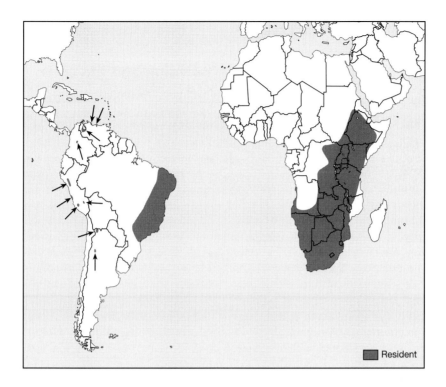

Resident

and Cringan 1990, Bertonatti *et al.* 1991, Canevari *et al.* 1991, Green 1992b, Sick 1993). In Peru, listed in Red Data Book and occurs in just 2 protected areas (Pulido 1991); in Venezuela, population estimated at 5000–10 000 individuals (Gómez-Dallmeier and Cringan 1990), although records suggest this too high. Recent increase in Brazil, and range extended west to central plateau, but remains localized (Antas and Resende 1983, Bertonatti *et al.* 1991, Green 1992b, Sick 1993). In 1992, 1000 counted at Sobradinho Lake, Bahia State, Brazil (Blanco and Canevari 1993). Western South American population of *erythrophthalma* estimated at < 2500 and, in east, at 10 000–25 000 (Wetlands International 2002).

Habitat and general habits

Occurs on most still freshwaters with abundant submergent vegetation (shallow to deep, large to small, permanent or temporary, and with or without emergent vegetation) (Brown *et al.* 1982, Fjeldså and Krabbe 1990). Has recently colonized reservoirs

on central plateau of Brazil (Antas and Resende 1983) and is known on rice farms in Venezuela (Gómez-Dallmeier and Cringan 1990). Recorded from sea level to *c* 2400 m in Africa and to *c* 3650 m in South America (Brown *et al.* 1982, Fjeldså and Krabbe 1990).

In Africa, significant numbers of southern breeding birds move north in dry season to Zimbabwe, Zambia, Malawi, Botswana, southern Mozambique and Kenya (Brown *et al.* 1982), and marked influx in some regions with onset of rains (Brickell 1988). In South America, movements poorly known, although seasonal movements probably occur within Brazil (Antas and Resende 1983). Although usually encountered in pairs or small parties, large numbers of moulting birds and juveniles frequently congregate. Active during early morning and evening, spending most of day resting ashore or on water. Feeds mainly during daylight, although sometimes at night, mostly by diving, up-ending and dabbling on water surface (Brown *et al.* 1982, Hilty and Brown 1986, Fjeldså and Krabbe 1990).

Frequently found among flocks of other species (Brickell 1988).

Diet consists primarily of seeds of aquatic vegetation (including rice), although some vegetative parts and aquatic invertebrates also consumed (Middlemiss 1958, Clancey 1967, Schulten 1974, Brown *et al.* 1982, Gómez-Dallmeier and Cringan 1990).

Displays and breeding behaviour

Inciting is primary ♀ display, in which head is thrown up and forwards to fullest extension of neck and then withdrawn (accompanied by call). Courtship display of ♂ includes head being withdrawn into shoulders with bill held horizontal, accompanied by call. Same call uttered when ♂ raises feathers on crown to form peak and lifts head slowly and returns it to original position before neck fully extended. Latter display performed by ♂♂ in courting groups to which ♀♀ do not seem to react. Other displays include typical Head-throw (with accompanying call) when head is rolled from withdrawn position back in line with body until back of head touches mantle. Sneak (also with accompanying call) includes ♂ slightly extending head and neck towards ♀. Display Preen also often performed by ♂, and he often reacts to Inciting by swimming ahead of ♀ and Turning-back-of-head toward her while depressing his crown feathers. Courtship flights conspicuous and last 3–5 minutes, and may be preceded by ♂ rushing aggressively at ♀. Both birds perform slight Head-pumping movements before copulation, while ♂ also Bill-dips and Dorsal-preens. Single call uttered by ♂ after treading; he then swims rapidly away in Bill-down posture with feathers on head peaked (Clark 1966, Johnsgard 1965a, 1978, Brown *et al.* 1982).

Timing of pair formation unclear, but pairbond presumably temporary and monogamous (Johnsgard 1978). In Africa, adult ♂♂ outnumber ♀♀ by 1.4:1 in most flocks, while juvenile ♂♂ outnumber ♀♀ by 1.6:1 (Skead and Dean 1977).

Breeding and life cycle

Nesting occurs throughout year (Brickell 1988), but more frequent during rainy season. Basin-shaped nest (17.5–28 cm across and 10–23 cm deep) constructed of plant material and lined with variable amounts of grey-fawn down. Usually located in tall vegetation, either above water in emergent vegetation or along bank, although sometimes away from water in tall grass. Eggs equally rounded at both ends, creamy white to light brown with pinkish tinge, smooth but with small pitting and slightly glossed; 56.3×43.7 (50.8–59.6×40.1–46.5) ($n = 42$); weight 59 ($n = 19$) (Schönwetter 1960–66, Clancey 1967, Brown *et al.* 1982); clutch 6.7 (5–15) ($n = 103$). Incubation by ♀, probably for 23–26 days (Johnsgard 1978, Brickell 1988), though one estimate of 20–21 days (Clancey 1967). During incubation, ♂ usually deserts and begins to moult, although occasionally present during brood rearing (Middlemiss 1958, Brickell 1988). Fledge in 7–8 weeks (Brickell 1988), and known to mature during 1st year (Delacour 1954–64). Predators undocumented. No information on breeding success, adult survival nor longevity.

Conservation and threats

South American race listed as Near-threatened by Threatened Waterfowl Specialist Group (2003). Reasons for large decline in western South America unclear, but siltation caused by soil erosion probably degrades favoured rich macrophyte waterbodies (Fjeldså and Krabbe 1990). In Africa, local numbers probably decreasing through loss of wetlands for agriculture (del Hoyo *et al.* 1992) and use of gill nets, but also increasing due to use of reservoirs.

Des Callaghan

Canvasback *Aythya valisineria*

PLATE 23

Anas valisineria Wilson, 1814, Amer. Ornith., **8**, p. 103, pl. 70, fig. 5.
eastern United States
Aythya Boie, 1822

Etymology: *valisineria* after A. de Vallisnera (1661–1730), for whom wild celery *Vallisneria* named. Vernacular name from white sides and back of ♂, with vermiculations resembling canvas fabric.

Other names: none in English. French: Morillon à dos blanc; Spanish: Pato Coacoxtle (Mexico).

Variation: no subspecies.

Description

ADULT: dimorphic. ♂ in breeding, or alternate, plumage blackish on crown and near base of bill grading into reddish chestnut on remainder of head and neck. Breast, upperback, rump, and vent areas black. Flanks and scapulars white with fine dusky vermiculations. Belly white. Tail brownish slate. Primaries brown-grey darkened near tips; secondaries and tertials pearly grey with increasingly dense white flecking towards tips grading into solid white edging. Greater upperwing coverts grey (secondaries) or brownish black (primaries) with amount of white flecking near tips increasing with age. Remaining wing coverts white with dusky vermiculations above and unvermiculated below. Bill black; feet and legs slate; eyes red. ♀ head and neck cinnamon, darkest on crown and nape and palest on chin, throat, ventral neck, and along eyeline. Breast and upperback brown. Flank pale brownish grey. Belly white. Back and scapulars greyish, greyish brown with extensive white vermiculations. Rump, vent, and tail dusky brown. Primaries brown-grey darkened towards tips with white edging on tips of tertials and proximal secondaries. Upperwing coverts, especially marginals, darker than ♂ with amount of white flecking near tips increasing with age (Serie *et al.* 1983b). Bill, feet and legs as ♂; eyes brown. (See also Mowbray 2002.)

MOULT: in ♂, upperparts duller in basic than in alternate plumage. Head and neck brown. Breast, upper back, rump, and vent areas brownish black. Flanks and scapulars greyish, densely vermiculated dusky on white. In ♀, basic similar to alternate, but back dusky brown, head and neck pale brown, and flank brown with some buff mottling. Moult evident in ♂ from cessation of breeding in late May (initiation of pre-basic) until arrival on wintering areas in early Dec (completion of pre-alternate), peaks during wing moult (late July–early Sept) (Lovvorn and Barzen 1988, Thompson and Drobney 1995). ♀ pre-basic moult, begun during spring migration (Mar), continues after arrival on nesting areas until onset of incubation and completed Aug–Sept when remiges replaced (Hochbaum 1944, Lovvorn and Barzen 1988). Alternate plumage acquired late summer (Aug) to early winter (Dec) (Palmer 1976).

IMMATURE: resembles definitive basic of ♀, but head, neck, and breast darker, and flanks without mottling. First and definitive alternate body plumages similar in ♂. In ♀, head, neck, and back uniformly darker in 1st than in definitive alternate plumage. Immature ♀ lacks white feathers on nape.

DUCKLING: colour and pattern similar to other pochards. Olive-brown on forehead, crown, nape and back contrasting with yellow on remainder of head and neck. Contrast intermediate to paler Redhead and darker Ring-necked ducklings. As in other pochards with yellow base colour, prominent shoulder and rump spots continuous with yellow underparts (breast, belly and undertail) (Nelson 1993). Partial light eye-ring evident in many ducklings (Dzubin 1959). Narrow nail and long and narrow bill relative to other *Aythya*. Bill, leg and foot colour variable; bill brown to slate; feet grey to yellow often with orange on sides of toes and webbing; iris dark brown.

MEASUREMENTS AND WEIGHT: ♂ adult wing ($n = 74$), 228–248 (237 ± 4); tail ($n = 305$), 48–69 (58 ± 2.8); keel, 93.1–112.5 (101.0 ± 2.7); tarsal bone, 41.5–47.5 (44.6 ± 1.1); maximum bill width, 20.1–23.4 (22.3 ± 0.5); bill, 58.7–69.0 (64.5 ± 1.6); weight ($n = 305$), 810–1658 (maxima: fall staging [Oct–Nov $n = 965$] 1497 ± 115; minima: wing moult [Aug $n = 27$] 1183 ± 99). ♀ adult wing ($n = 86$), 221–235 (228 ± 3); tail ($n = 256$), 47–70 (59 ± 4.1); keel ($n = 254$), 90.8–106.0 (97.4 ± 3.2); tarsal bone ($n = 256$), 39.8–46.0 (43.1 ± 1.1); bill width ($n = 255$), 20.1–23.2 (21.8 ± 0.6); bill ($n = 255$), 57.5–68.0 (61.4 ± 1.6); weight ($n = 256$), 740–1630 (maxima: pre-laying to laying [May $n = 29$] 1418 ± 99; minima: incubation [June $n = 8$] 1117 ± 147) (Serie and Sharp 1989, Barzen and Serie 1990, Thompson 1992).

Field characters

Medium-sized diving duck, 475–565 mm long, with long tapering bill and sloping forehead giving head distinctive wedge-shaped profile. Long stout neck evident when in flight and alert on water. Most similar to Common Pochard, but distribution not overlapping and bill lacks conspicuous broad, pale band. Distinguished from Redhead primarily on basis of head profile, absence of pale bill markings, and white back and flanks (♂ only). Although ♂ Greater and Lesser Scaup also may appear to have white backs, they are smaller, have rounded (*v* sloping) foreheads, and sit higher in water.

Voice

♂ Kink-neck call *ick ick cu-oo* given during Head-throw or with short forward thrust of head while neck arched slightly backwards and head held low to breast (Hochbaum 1944). Inconspicuous coughing *hfff* uttered by ♂ while in Neck-stretch posture. When alarmed or in flight during nesting season (e.g. courtship flights or returning from egg-laying or incubation bout), ♀ emits coarse, high-pitched growl *whaaa-aaa-aaa-aa-aa-a-a-a*. Low guttural purring or short repeated call *kuck kuck* uttered by ♀ while Neck-stretching, Inciting, or attending young. Aggression sometimes preceded by *rrr-rrr-rrr* (♂) or *kuck-kuck-kuck* (♀) (Alexander 1980b).

Vocal repertoire of 7-day-old ducklings includes 4 call types: twitter, trill, peep and shriek. Physical characteristics of calls (sonograms and power specral sections), context of calling and duckling

responses described by Kostow (1981); twitter and trill short range signals, peep and shriek carry longer distances. Peeps emitted more frequently when caller isolated from siblings and out of range of soft calls. Playback of trills attracted brood mates, but ducklings unresponsive to twitters. Kostow (1981) proposed that ducklings responded to audible twitters by maintaining distance to caller and twittered in reply; trills produced when twitters became faint and served to attract brood mates. Peeps emitted when twitters and trills inaudible, and served to attract ♀ and siblings.

Range and status

Breeds in prairie, parkland, and sub-arctic wetlands of north central US (northwestern Iowa and western Minnesota to Dakotas and northern Montana), western Canada (southern Manitoba to central British Columbia to Yukon and Northwest Territories) to Alaska, and isolated sites in western US. Winters in coastal North America (New York to South Carolina, Gulf of Mexico, and San Francisco Bay) and some inland sites in southeastern US and central Mexico. Vagrant to Iceland, UK, Germany, Hawaii and Marshall Islands. Sexual differences in winter distribution with ♂♂ at higher latitudes (Nichols and Haramis 1980a).

Population status 1955–95, breeding population indices for traditional survey area gave 353 700–770 600 and averaged 542 800 birds (US Fish & Wildlife Service, Office of Migratory Bird Management). Decade averages 629 900 in 1950s, 530 600 in 1960s, 541 900 in 1970s, 510 200 in 1980s and 546 700 in 1990s. Population declined 0.6% per year 1955–93, but increased to record high (770 600) in 1995.

Habitat and general habits

Preferred habitats have abundant below-ground plant foods (i.e. tubers, roots, rhizomes or turions—dormant vegetative buds) or benthic invertebrates. In summer (Apr–July), breeders use shallow wetlands of varying permanence (seasonal to permanent flooding) with dense stands of emergent and submersed plants. Post-breeding ♂♂ concentrate during wing moult (July–Aug) on large wetlands in parkland and boreal forest regions of west central

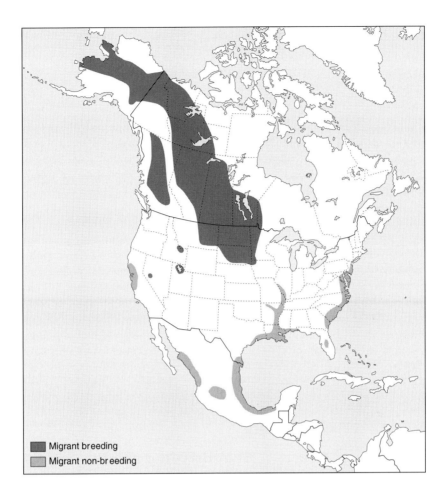

Migrant breeding
Migrant non-breeding

Canada. Migrants stage in spring (Mar–Apr) and fall (Oct–Nov) on prairie marshes, northern lakes, and rivers. Coastal bays, estuaries, and some inland lakes and rivers used in winter (Nov–Feb). ♀ preference for smaller waterbodies at some wintering sites (Nichols and Haramis 1980a).

Behaviourally and morphologically specialized for feeding on submerged plant parts and benthic invertebrates. Feeds almost exclusively by diving. Food selection by sexes similar except possibly during nesting season (May–July). Moulting and staging birds eat >93% plant material (80–100% Fennel-leaf Pondweed *Potamogeton pectinatus* tubers, rootstalk, seeds and stems) (Thompson 1992). Fall migrants also feed almost exclusively (99%) on plant material (43% Wild Celery winterbuds and 56% Stiff Arrowhead *Sagittaria rigida*) (Korschgen

et al. 1988), but diet may consist of mostly animal foods (snails, clams, and benthic insects) at some stopover sites (Thompson 1973). In Gulf of Mexico region, diets contain >80% below-ground plant parts of Chufa Flatsedge *Cyperus esculentus*, arrowheads, or American Bulrush *Scirpus americana*, but diets of birds wintering elsewhere variable. In San Francisco Bay and along Atlantic coast, bivalve molluscs *Macoma* eaten in estuarine habitats whereas plant foods consumed by birds using inland wetlands (Alexander 1980a, Perry and Uhler 1982, Lovvorn 1987, White *et al.* 1988). Food habits in Chesapeake Bay changed during past 30 years from diet consisting partly of plant foods (Wild Celery and Fennel-leaf Pondweed tubers) to one comprised almost entirely of animal material (Stewart 1962). Shift attributed to declines in abundance of submersed vegetation in Chesapeake Bay and corresponds to reduction in use of Chesapeake Bay and increased numbers of wintering birds in brackish coastal North Carolina (Lovvorn 1989a). Animal food (benthic invertebrates) consumption increased in spring migrants (29–44%) and in ♀♀ during ovarian follicle growth (51–78%), incubation (68–78%) and brood rearing (88%) (Noyes and Jarvis 1985, Korschgen *et al.* 1988, Austin *et al.* 1990). Duckling diets composed 85–94% of animal material, especially gastropod snails, caddisflies, chironomids and damselfly immatures (Bartonek and Hickey 1969a, Jarvis and Noyes 1986).

Migratory throughout range, staging Oct–Nov and arriving on wintering areas Nov–Dec; departing wintering areas Feb–Mar and arriving on breeding grounds Apr–May (Bellrose 1980). Moult migration probably more traditional and extensive in ♂ than ♀ (Hohman *et al.* 1992). Movements in winter limited in Gulf of Mexico region (Hohman *et al.* 1993, 1995a), but more extensive along Atlantic coast, where ice cover occasionally restricts foraging (Lovvorn 1989a). Daily movements change seasonally in relation to reproductive and moult status, habitat, food availability, tide, development of young and disturbance.

Time-activity budgets, best quantified for non-breeding period, vary seasonally and geographically. Resting (29–49%), feeding (13–39%), and comfort movements (15–27%) major diurnal activities of moulting and staging birds; resting maximal and feeding minimal while birds flightless (Thompson 1992). Fall migrants rest 35% time and spend 15–19% time each in feeding, locomotory, or comfort activities (Takekawa 1987). Wintering birds rest 30–50% of day with variable time allocated to other activities (Alexander 1980a, Lovvorn 1989b, Hohman and Rave 1990, Howerter 1990). Courtship (5–13%) and feeding (36–40%) increased in spring migrants (Mar–Apr) (Lovvorn 1989b). Nonbreeding birds often active at night (Thornberg 1973, Hohman *et al.* 1990a, Howerter 1990). Sexual differences in winter distribution, location within flocks, and habitat use attributed to ♂ dominance of ♀ (Nichols and Haramis 1980a, Alexander 1987). High levels of aggression and stable dominance hierarchies observed in coastal South Carolina (Alexander 1987) less evident elsewhere and appear unrelated to nutrition of subordinates (Hohman 1993).

Nonbreeders, especially ♂♂, highly social and concentrate at moulting, staging, or wintering sites where preferred foods abundant. Breeding densities lowest in dry prairie and boreal forest (< 0.1 birds per km^2) and highest in prairie pothole region of southwestern Manitoba and some sub-arctic river deltas (> 4 per km^2) (Bellrose 1980).

Displays and breeding behaviour

Performance of reproductive and agonistic behaviour similar to other *Aythya* (Johnsgard 1965a). Mutual displays include Neck-stretch, Drinking or Bill-dip, and post-copulatory swim in Bill-down posture. ♂ courtship behaviour consists of Head-throw and Turn-back-of-head (Johnsgard 1965a). ♀ Inciting consists of Head-pumping with bill brought down oriented towards intruder. Agonistic displays range in intensity from Head-pump to Bill-on-breast to Pushing (breast to breast) to Sneak to chasing and fighting (biting, bill jabs, and wing-beating) (Alexander 1980b).

Breeding and life cycle

Pairbonds formed during spring migration (Mar–Apr) remain intact until early incubation (Hochbaum 1944). ♀ strongly philopatric to natal areas. Return rates in southwestern Manitoba average 21% for 1st year and 69% for after-1st-year ♀♀ and < 10% for ♂♂ (Rohwer and Anderson 1988, Serie *et al.* 1992). ♀♀ and perhaps some ♂♂ breed in 1st year, but participation variable among years (Serie *et al.* 1992). First nests initiated late Apr–late May (peak mid May); re-nests, late May–early July (Stoudt 1982). Arrival and nest initiation later in 1st year than in older ♀♀ (Serie *et al.* 1992). Nests located in semipermanent wetlands with dense stands of flooded (0–91 cm) emergent vegetation; constructed of residual vegetation within reach of bowl (Stoudt 1982). Eggs greyish olive; 62.2 × 43.7 (56.5–66.8 × 38.8–45.8) (*n* = 88) (Bent 1923); weight 68 ± 3.1 (*n* = 12) (Barzen and Serie 1990); clutch 8.2 ± 2.2 (2–16) (*n* = 133), declines seasonally at 0.1 egg per day (Stoudt 1982, Serie *et al*. 1992). Intra- and interspecific (99% Redhead and 1% Ruddy Duck) nest parasitism common with no apparent effect on clutch size, nest or hen success, or hatchability (Serie *et al*. 1992). Rates of intraspecific nest parasitism >36% frequency ($n = 179$), 2.4 (1–10) ($n = 64$) parasitic eggs per nest (Sorenson 1993); interspecific 63% (0–86%) ($n = 134$) frequency, 3.2 parasitic eggs/nest (Serie *et al*. 1992). Hatchability 78–80% (Stoudt 1982, Serie *et al*. 1992, Sorenson 1993). Incubation 24 days (23–29) at 92% constancy (Hochbaum 1944). In southwestern Manitoba, nest success similar 1961–72 (21–62%) and 1974–80 (17–60%) and in parasitized and nonparasitized nests (52%), but differs in wet and dry years (54–60% *v* 17%) (Stoudt 1982, Serie *et al*. 1992). Major causes of nest loss mammalian, especially American Mink and Raccoon, and Common American Crow predation (Stoudt 1982). Hen success for 1st year 52% ($n = 29$); after-1st-year 59% ($n = 91$) (Serie *et al*. 1992). Hatchlings from incubator weighed 41.4 ± 0.52 (Lightbody and Ankney 1984); day-olds weighed 44.7 ± 0.5 (Dzubin 1959). Brood rearing (♀ only), attendant for 14–63 days (Hochbaum 1944). Contour feathers appear at 21–28 days, fledge in 63–77 days (Hochbaum 1944). Juvenile survival to 63 days: brood 88 (83–93)% ($n = 342$); duckling 2.7–62.3% ($n = 342$) (Leonard *et al*. 1996). Adult annual survival, ♂♂ 0.70–0.82, ♀♀ 0.56–69 (Nichols and Haramis 1980b). Survival rates greater in Pacific than in Atlantic flyway (Nichols and Haramis 1980b) and positively related to body mass in early winter (Haramis *et al*. 1986). High winter survival of ♀♀ in Chesapeake Bay (83–100%) (Haramis *et al*. 1993) and coastal Louisiana (>95%) (Hohman *et al*. 1993), but immature survival reduced in inland Louisiana (57–92%) because of hunting, and mortality associated with ingestion of lead shot pellets (Hohman *et al*. 1995a). In captivity, has lived 19 years (Johnsgard 1968a).

Conservation and threats

Sources of variation in population size not well understood, but habitat loss and degradation, low rates of recruitment, highly skewed sex ratio favouring ♂♂ (2.0–2.5:1.0), and reduced survival during 1st year considered important constraints on population growth (Hohman *et al*. 1995b). Although highly traditional in use of habitat, nonbreeding distribution changed dramatically since 1950s. Use of traditional migrational staging areas in north central US declined during 1950s and 1960s when use of navigation pools on upper Mississippi River increased (Serie *et al*. 1983a). Shift in habitat use by migrants related to degradation of traditional habitats caused by siltation, pollution, eutrophication, and introduced fish species and establishment of preferred foods (Wild Celery and fingernail clams *Sphaerium*) in navigation pools. Recent increases in use of some formerly important sites (e.g. Lake Christina, Minnesota, Lake St Clair, Ontario and Lake Erie) associated with improved water quality and increased production of submersed aquatic plants, especially Wild Celery (Hohman *et al*. 1995b). In 1950s, 79% wintered in Atlantic or Pacific flyways, but proportion of continental population wintering in Central and Mississippi flyways increased from 21% in 1955–69 to 44% in 1987–92 as result of declines in Chesapeake Bay and San Francisco Bay and increases in Gulf of Mexico region. Important conservation issues include high rate of wetland loss in prairie region (Dahl 1990), loss of estuarine habitat caused by coastal development, degradation in water quality contributing to reduced production of submersed aquatic plants (Haramis 1991b), introduction of exotics, high rate of lead shot ingestion (Havera *et al*. 1992b, Hohman *et al*. 1990b), exposure to high concentration of contaminants in estuarine and riverine systems (Miles and Ohlendorf 1993), vulnerability to hunting and disturbance related to navigation and recreation (Korschgen *et al*. 1985).

William L. Hohman

Redhead *Aythya americana*
PLATE 23

Fuligula americana Eyton, 1838, Monogr. Anatidae, p. 155

North America

Etymology: 'of America'.

Other names: French: Canard à tête-rouge, Milouin à tête-rouge, Morillon à tête-rouge, Canard violon (south Louisiana, Canada), Milouin américain, Fuligule à tête-rouge (Europe); German: Rotkopfente; Spanish: Pato cabeza roja, Guayareja, Cabeza colorado (Mexico).

Variation: no subspecies. Has hybridized in wild with Canvasback (Haramis 1982), Greater and Lesser Scaup, and Ring-necked Duck (Johnsgard 1960a).

Description

ADULT: dimorphic. ♂ in breeding, or alternate, plumage has head and upperneck chestnut red; lowerneck and chest black; back and sides dark grey (actually white with fine black vermiculations); belly white; tail and tail coverts blackish, paler terminally. Wings dusky grey; primaries brownish grey, darker near tips and on outer webs; secondaries pearl grey, darker near white rear border. Tertials grey, usually taper to a rounded point, some well vermiculated; greater tertial coverts broad, smoothly rounded and flecked or vermiculated; middle and lesser coverts broadly rounded, vermiculated to lightly flecked. Bill pale blue separated from black tip by faint white band; feet and legs grey; eyes yellowish orange. ♀ head and neck yellowish brown, darker on crown, paler at base of bill and behind eye; pale eye-ring; scattered white feathers common on back of head; chest brown; back and sides dark greyish brown, sometimes flecked white; belly white; tail and tail coverts greyish brown, sometimes whiter terminally. Wings brownish grey; primaries brownish grey, darker near tips and on outer webs; secondaries pearl grey, slightly darker near white rear border. Tertials grey, usually taper to a rounded point, without flecking or vermiculation; greater tertial coverts broad, smoothly rounded, without flecking or vermiculation; middle and lesser coverts broadly rounded and

entirely plain to faintly flecked near tips. Bill pale blue separated from black tip by faint white band; feet and legs grey; eyes brown or yellowish brown (Kortright 1942, Weller 1957, Palmer 1976, Carney 1992).

MOULT: ♂ in eclipse, or basic, plumage July–Sept, head and neck browner, breast mottled, back and rump blotched brown, iris dull yellow-orange, bill darker; flightless during wing moult (3 weeks or more). Pre-basic moult late July–early Aug, pre-alternate moult late Aug–Sept. ♀ partial pre-basic moult (i.e. head, body, and innermost wing feathers) in spring (Mar–Apr) and completion (wing and tail) Aug–Sept (flightless during wing moult); pre-alternate moult (head, body, and innermost wing feathers) Aug–Oct; alternate plumage worn through winter, basic in summer; alternate plumage more grey, basic more brown; incubation patch present during nesting (Kortright 1942, Weller 1957, 1970, Palmer 1976).

IMMATURE: ♂ 1st winter plumage less brilliant than adult, head iridescence and vermiculation on flank and scapulars subdued; line of demarcation between black breast and white belly often less distinct; head chestnut, but pale fuscous to blackish brown in some. Tertials usually frayed to sharp, ragged point, without flecking or vermiculation; greater tertial coverts appear narrow and usually have ragged, pointed tips; middle and lesser coverts conspicuously flecked to barely flecked, often narrow somewhat towards tips, with tips notched. Greater secondary covert 12 or 6 with white bar on tip (absent in adult); alula 2 or primary covert 2 without white flecking (present in adult). ♀ undertail coverts in 1st winter usually show pattern of speckled buff brown on white background (*v* brownish olive patches on white in adult); scapulars without white frosting; back of head lacks scattered white feathers. Tertials usually frayed to sharp, ragged point, without flecking or vermiculation; greater tertial coverts appear narrow and usually have ragged, pointed tips; middle and lesser coverts entirely plain (i.e. without flecking), often narrow somewhat towards tip, with tips notched. Greater secondary covert 12, or more distal coverts, with indication of white barring on tip (absent in adult); greater secondary coverts without white flecking (present in adult); greater secondary covert 12 more tapered (*v* somewhat squared in adult) and < 12 mm in width (Dane and Johnson 1975, Carney 1992, Sayler 1995). Weller (1957, 1970) and Palmer (1976) review ♂, ♀, adult and juvenal basic and alternate plumages within framework of moult cycle.

DUCKLING: plumage completely downy, lighter-coloured than other diving ducks; variable from cream and brownish olive to darker brown, light forehead and usually slightly darker upperparts. Leg and bill colour varies with plumage. Posterior margin of nostril *c* quarter distant from lores to bill tip (nail). Most of bright colour fades within 5–8 days in wild (Weller 1957, 1970, Palmer 1976).

MEASUREMENTS AND WEIGHT: data from winter, Gulf of Mexico coast (Texas, Louisiana, Florida; *n* = 3464), live and dead specimens; measurements taken as in Dzubin and Cooch (1992). ♂ flat wing chord (*n* = 2131), 210–256 (233); sternum (*n* = 2067), 81–117 (98); culmen (*n* = 2094), 41–62 (48); tarsus (*n* = 2091), 44–60 (51); body mass (*n* = 2175), 730–1500 (1071). ♀ wing (*n* = 1255), 206–243 (224); sternum (*n* = 1247), 76–109 (93); culmen (*n* = 1253), 40–57 (46); tarsus (*n* = 1247), 42–59 (49); body mass (*n* = 1289), 630–1360 (972). All sex and age groups arrive on wintering grounds in lean condition and increase body mass and lipids through winter. Body mass means for non-wintering birds in Weller (1957) for spring migration ♂ (*n* = 1157) 1110; ♀ (*n* = 485) 990, pre-moult ♂ (*n* = 33) 940; ♀ (*n* = 71) 910, early moult ♂ (*n* = 10) 960; ♀ (*n* = 41) 880), post-moult ♂ (*n* = 51) 1220; ♀ (*n* = 19) 1110, and fall migration ♂ (*n* = 40) 990; ♀ (*n* = 52) 910.

Field characters

On water, large duck (♂ 440–543, ♀ 415–515 mm long), ♂ with dark head (red at closer range), black chest, grey body, and black hindquarters, and ♀ with brown upperparts. Resembles other North American *Aythya* with feet set back on body, dull wing stripe (uppersurface of secondaries), relatively short wings, and tendency to ride low in water. Canvasback ♂ also has red head (darker than Redhead), but can be distinguished on basis of size (Redhead smaller, body not elongated), head shape (Redhead has puffy, round, high-arched head with abrupt forehead; Canvasback forehead slopes), and darker coloration in both ♂ and ♀ Redheads (Canvasback ♂ shows white mid-body). Distinguished from Greater and Lesser Scaup and from Ring-necked Duck on size (Redhead larger), body coloration (♂ scaup show white mid-body, ♂ Ring-necked Duck has white crescent anterior to bend in wing; ♀ scaup and Ring-necked Duck appear darker than Redhead), and head coloration (♂ red hues for Redhead and Canvasback, greens and purples for scaup and Ring-necked Duck; ♀ scaup show white face patch, Ring-necked Duck white eye-ring; ♂ and ♀ Ring-necked Duck white ring on bill). Common Pochard range does not overlap with Redhead, but accidentals can be distinguished from Redhead by Pochard's dark bill at base and tip, with grey in centre, more sloping head and bill shape (intermediate between Redhead and Canvasback), red eye, lighter sides and back, and grey stripe along trailing edge of wing in flight. Redhead in winter in large flocks, usually in hundreds or thousands; groups may have as few as 5–10 individuals, but flocks with tens of thousands not uncommon, especially in coastal Texas, Mexico, and Florida (Michot 2000). In flight, Redhead has rapid, shallow wing-beat. Scaup have deeper wing-beat; scaup and Canvasback fly at greater speeds than Redhead, but Redhead flies faster than most other ducks (Palmer 1976, Bellrose 1980). White belly in contrast to black breast apparent on both ♂ and ♀ Redhead in flight, similar to other *Aythya*. Redhead in flight shorter and darker, and flight more erratic than Canvasback (Kortright 1942).

Voice

♂ in spring and during courtship has cat-like *meow*, guttural *purr* and, sometimes, *qua-qua*. ♀ in courtship utters *quek*, *que-e-ek* and soft low *err*. In rising from water, ♀ makes loud, clear *squak* (Bent 1923, Kortright 1942, Weller 1967d, Palmer 1976). In winter,

♂ has faint *zoom-zoom*, especially at night on coastal ponds. Sonogram of distress call of duckling in Kear (1968). Sonogram of adult ♂ and ♀ in Woodin and Michot (2002).

Range and status

Breeds in North America from Alaska to Mexico, and from Pacific coastal states east to Lake Ontario and New Brunswick (Weller 1964d), but most nest in prairies, parklands, and boreal forests of northern US and southern Canada (70–75%), and in alkaline marshes of Great Basin in Intermountain West of US (20–25%) (Weller 1964d, Bellrose 1980, Bailey and Titman 1984, Woodin and Michot 2002). Post-breeding sites, used primarily by adults during wing moult, located in large lakes of central and northern Manitoba and Saskatchewan (Weller 1964d, Bellrose

1980). Winter range extends through eastern, southern, and western US, into Central America, with most of population wintering in estuarine seagrass beds along coast of Gulf of Mexico in Florida (Apalachee Bay), Louisiana (Chandeleur Sound), Texas (Laguna Madre and associated bays), and Mexico (Laguna Madre de Tamaulipas) (Weller 1964d, Michot 2000). Slight southward shift in wintering distribution over past 40 years. Between 1955 and 1973, proportion of continental population wintering along Gulf of Mexico coast averaged 84% (75–87%), whereas 1978–94 was 92% (83–97%). Over same periods, proportion wintering along Atlantic Coast decreased 9% to 3% (4–16% to 1–7%; calculated from US Fish & Wildlife Service Mid-winter Waterfowl Inventory and Special Redhead Survey data [Michot 2000]). Habitat deterioration

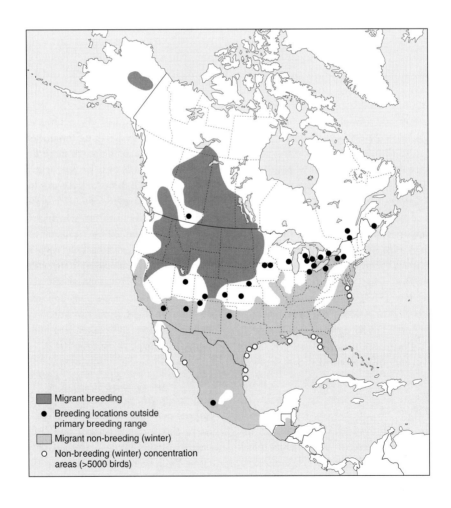

Migrant breeding

● Breeding locations outside primary breeding range

Migrant non-breeding (winter)

○ Non-breeding (winter) concentration areas (>5000 birds)

and decline of submersed aquatic vegetation in Chesapeake Bay and other Atlantic Coast estuaries may account for shift (Haramis 1991a, Perry and Deller 1995, 1996). Vagrants recorded Greenland, Iceland, UK, Siberia, Hawaii, Japan and Guam (Woodin and Michot 2002).

Numbers in North America show no significant linear change 1955–94, based on wintering ($P = 0.63$) and breeding ($P = 0.57$) survey estimates (calculated from US Fish & Wildlife Service Midwinter Waterfowl Inventory, Special Redhead Survey, and from Dubovsky *et al.* 1994). Estimates from breeding and wintering grounds differ somewhat, but correlated ($P = 0.01$, $r^2 = 0.16$). Winter estimates show more fluctuations, 299 200–1 406 500 birds (mean = 724 400). Breeding estimates range 323 300–828 700 (mean = 601 300).

Habitat and general habits

On breeding ground, prefers seasonally, semipermanently and permanently flooded wetlands, and nests constructed over water in emergent vegetation, primarily *Schoenoplectus acutus* and *Typha* (Low 1945, Weller 1964d, Michot *et al.* 1979, Woodin 1987). Although in prairie region, sometimes uses small (< 0.4 ha) and intermediate-sized (0.4–4.0 ha) potholes, prefers larger (> 4.0 ha) wetlands for nesting; in other nesting regions (e.g. Canadian parklands, Great Basin), nests in marshes associated with wetland basins that are tens to hundreds ha in size (Williams and Nelson 1943, Stewart and Kantrud 1973, 1974, Kantrud and Stewart 1977, Michot *et al.* 1979, Woodin 1987). Broods use small ponds and large open water areas, usually within 3 km of nest sites, until flight attained (Bellrose 1980, Yerkes 2000). During post-breeding and moulting periods, congregates on large lakes rimmed with emergent vegetation and feeds on submersed aquatic plants and invertebrates (Bergman 1973, Bailey and Titman 1984).

Based on studies conducted in Manitoba, North Dakota, Wisconsin, and Nevada, diet on breeding and post-breeding grounds *c* 60% (14–100%) plant and *c* 40% (0–86%) animal matter (Bartonek and Hickey 1969a, Bergman 1973, Bailey and Titman 1984, Noyes and Jarvis 1985, Jarvis and Noyes 1986, Woodin and Swanson 1989, Kenow and Rusch 1996). Pattern generally true for adult ♂♂,

for juveniles of both sexes, and for adult ♀♀ during pre-laying and post-laying periods; during laying, ♀♀ consume more animal matter (*c* 75%). Plant food primarily submersed vegetation (45% of total food; e.g. *Chara* [33%], *Potamogeton* [10%]) and seeds of emergent marsh plants (12% of total; e.g. *Scirpus* [9%]), whereas animal food primarily insects (31% of total; e.g. larvae of dipteran chironomids [16%] and trichopterans [11%]).

Winters almost exclusively in shallow coastal seagrass ecosystems. Major wintering areas along Gulf Coast dominated by subtropical seagrass meadows. Shoalgrass *Halodule wrightii*, Turtlegrass *Thalassia testudinum*, and Manateegrass *Syringodium filiforme* predominant in those areas, and feeds almost entirely on rhizomes of *Halodule wrightii*. Laguna Madre of Texas and Laguna Madre de Tamaulipas are hypersaline (> 35 ppt) lagoon systems, dominated by *Halodule wrightii*, and ponds adjacent to lagoon shorelines provide nearby source of freshwater used frequently by birds feeding in lagoons (Saunders and Saunders 1981, Woodin 1994, Adair *et al.* 1996, Michot 2000, Skoruppa and Woodin 2000). In other seagrass beds, where salinities are at or below that of seawater (Murden *et al.* 1997, Michot 2000), do not use supplemental freshwater. Generally feed by dipping and tipping in shallow (< 1 m) water close to shore, often during low tide, although occasionally dive in deeper waters (1–3 m) several km from shoreline (Mitchell 1992, Michot and Nault 1993, Michot and Chadwick 1994, Michot *et al.* 1994a, Mitchell *et al.* 1994, Woodin 1996, Custer *et al.* 1997, Woodin and Michot 1997, 2004, Michot 2000).

In estuarine habitat (seagrass meadows), spends 33–57% of diurnal time budgets resting, 23–46% feeding, 3–11% (rarely 32%) swimming, and 7–14% in comfort movements and other behaviour. On ponds adjacent to Laguna Madre spends 33–78% of time resting, 8–35% (rarely < 1%) drinking, 8–20% swimming, and 8–24% in comfort and other behaviour (Mitchell *et al.* 1992, Woodin 1994, 1996, Adair *et al.* 1996, Michot *et al.* 1997). Fed almost exclusively in estuarine sites and drank almost exclusively in ponds, where spent average of *c* 62 min/day (Moore 1991). In estuarine sites fed by dipping (13–58%), up-ending (25–37%), diving (16–37%) or gleaning (< 1–25%; Mitchell *et al.* 1992, Woodin and Michot 1997, 2004).

Diet on wintering ground consists 76–96% of plant and 4–30% animal material (Stieglitz 1966, McMahan 1970, Cornelius 1977, Saunders and Saunders 1981, Perry and Uhler 1982, Michot and Nault 1993, Woodin 1996, Michot and Woodin 1997, 2004, Michot and Reynolds 2000). Predominant food seagrass *Halodule wrightii* (74–100%) with rhizomes constituting 96% of *Halodule* biomass, remainder being leaves, shoots, seeds and roots. Other seagrass species consumed by only 5% of birds collected (<2% of diet; Michot and Woodin 1997, 2004). Most animals in winter diet molluscs, primarily small (<1 cm) snails (38 species) and clams (10 species). Percentage of animal and plant matter in diet in Louisiana and Texas did not differ due to age, sex, month or location (Michot and Woodin 1997, 2004). Where *Halodule* absent (e.g. Chesapeake Bay) consumed other submersed vegetation (e.g. *Potamogeton*, *Zostera*, *Najas*, *Ruppia*; Stewart 1962).

Displays and breeding behaviour

♀ usually initiates pair's flight from water, preceded by series of repeated Chin-lifts. Aggressive encounters initiated when one bird approaches another directly with head held low and head feathers compressed. Bill may be slightly opened, and low, soft calls uttered. More intense agonistic behaviour characterized by rapid approach with open bill, culminating in pecking and direct attack. Aggression may escalate to aerial chasing.

Shares patterns of courtship and display with other *Aythya*. Courting behaviour begins at low levels in winter, and increases in frequency and intensity during northward spring migration. Inciting by ♀ characterized by repeated lowering of bill, which is then raised and pointed back towards side, while she utters low *err* sometimes referred to as soft growl. Inciting, accompanied by vocalization, may be repeated. ♀ may join mate in mutual Neck-stretching, with breasts touching, throat of ♂ appearing swollen. Both sexes also Preen-behind-wing to expose pale wing stripe. ♂ may Turn-back-of-head following Inciting by ♀; this display characterized by ♂ swimming in front and moving bill laterally back and forth (showing both sides of head) and depressing crown feathers. Kinked-neck display of ♂ given with head and neck drawn back,

throat area enlarged, and pupil contracted while catlike *meow* emitted. Identical call given during exaggerated Head-throw, ♂ extending head and neck backwards to touch lower back and rump. Paired ♀ may become focus of several unpaired ♂♂, which (with paired ♂) form compact display group. Paired birds within group remain close, while mutual Neck-stretching, Inciting and aggressiveness by ♀, and Kinked-neck and Head-throw by ♂♂, common. ♀ may be pursued underwater or in air by courting ♂♂. Forced copulation attempts reported but apparently uncommon. Paired ♂ during aerial pursuit may briefly pull tail of ♀; ♂ may also give *meow* call during aerial chase involving ♀ and another ♂. Bill-dipping (by ♂ or both sexes) and mutual preening precede copulation in water. Post-copulatory display by ♂ may involve Kinked-neck with *meow* call; both birds then swim away Bill-down, preen and bathe (Johnsgard 1965a, McKinney 1965b, Weller 1965, 1967d, McKinney *et al.* 1983).

After selection of site, and construction of nest, ♀ lays; ♂ selects small wetland area where activity centred while awaiting return of ♀ from nest. No true territory or territorial behaviour evident; however, ♂ defends ♀ against advances of unpaired ♂♂ (Hochbaum 1944, Low 1945). Pairs usually avoid one another without overt aggression.

Breeding and life cycle

Classic descriptions of breeding phenology and ecology provided by Hochbaum (1944) and Low (1945). Has monogamous breeding system in which ♀ forms new pairbond with different ♂ every year. Pairing begins mid-winter, with courtship and pair formation accelerating rapidly during northward migration Mar–Apr. Generally migrates north in small flocks of <25 birds (Low 1945), sometimes associated with Lesser Scaup, Canvasback and Ring-necked Duck. All ♀♀ probably paired during breeding season, but some yearlings likely do not nest, especially in years with poor water conditions. Nesting in prairie pothole region initiated early May, with attempts persisting through late July. Nesting initiated in Intermountain Region (between Rockies and Sierras) from *c* 1 May–mid July. ♀♀ may attempt to renest if 1st nest or clutch destroyed (Alliston 1979). Study of marked ♀♀ in Manitoba found 74% of yearling ♀♀ and 92% of adults returned to same nesting site following year (Arnold *et al.* 2002).

Classic overview of parasitic behaviour in Weller (1959). Intraspecific egg parasitism very common (Weller 1959, Lokemoen 1966). ♀♀ exhibit 3 laying strategies (Weller 1959, M.D. Sorenson 1991): those electing 'normal' laying deposit and incubate eggs in nest of own construction; semiparasitic ♀♀ parasitize nests of other ducks before laying and incubating own clutch; completely parasitic ♀♀ lay in nests of other duck, and do not attempt own nest. ♀ apparently chooses laying strategy to maximize fecundity in prevailing environmental conditions (M.D. Sorenson 1991). Nests parasitized frequently (Hochbaum 1944) in areas with high numbers of Redhead and low numbers of Canvasback; Canvasback reproductive success significantly reduced by interspecific egg parasitism (Sugden 1980, Leonard *et al.* 1996). Other species victimized include Northern Mallard, Northern Pintail, Gadwall, American Wigeon, Northern Shoveler, Blue-winged Teal, Cinnamon Teal, Lesser Scaup, and Ruddy Duck (Joyner 1976, Giroux 1981b); clutch size and nest success of some dabbling ducks depressed by Redhead egg parasitism (Joyner 1976, Lokemoen 1991). Species other than ducks occasionally parasitized, e.g. American Bittern *Botaurus lentiginosus*, Sora Rail *Porzana carolina*, American Coot and harrier. In turn, Redhead nests parasitized by Fulvous Whistling-duck, Mallard, Gadwall, Northern Shoveler, Blue-winged Teal, Cinnamon Teal, Northern Pintail, Canvasback and Ruddy Duck (Weller 1959). Extremely high levels of intraspecific parasitism can lead to dump nesting, in which large number of ♀♀ parasitize single Redhead nest, and frequency increases with rapidly changing water levels (Low 1945). Dumping can generate such large clutches that incubation becomes physically impossible. Clutch in dump nests 19–87 eggs.

Nest site usually selected in dense stand of emergent vegetation (but near open water) in large or small wetland (Low 1945), although nests in western US occasionally placed on islands or on dry land (Hammond and Mann 1956, McKnight

1974). ♀ solely responsible for nest construction of dried vegetation (usually *Typha*, Hardstem Bulrush *Scirpus acutus*, *Phragmites australis*, or *Carex*) from previous growing season. ♀ bends plants downward to construct open nest bowl (*c* 150 mm above water surface) covered by protective cupola of vegetation. Down and feathers added at end of laying and during incubation. Most nests include ramp constructed of dried vegetation. Water depth at site varies widely (15–120 cm).

Eggs smooth, glossy, creamy white or rarely brownish buff, elliptical to subelliptical; 60×43 (Low 1945); mean mass 65 (Mallary and Weatherhead 1990). Egg laid per day, although sometimes day skipped. Clutch size notoriously difficult to determine because of parasitism; unparasitized nests *c* 9–10 (7–14) (Weller 1959, Zammuto 1986). ♀ incubates alone; most ♂♂ abandon mates during 1st days of incubation and form large post-breeding congregations prior to moulting (Hochbaum 1944, Bergman 1973). Incubation 23–24 days; reports of incubation periods as high as 29 days undoubtedly biased by parasitism (Sorenson 1991, Yerkes 1998). Egg success low in some years (50%) because parasitism leads to abandonment; in extreme cases, egg success reduced to *c* 10% (Lokemoen 1966, Michot *et al.* 1979). Nest success highly variable, with reported rate 50% (15–85%); variation mirrors pattern for most prairie-nesting ducks in North America. Most nest failures caused by desertion due to parasitism, abandonment because of rapidly rising or receding water levels, and predation (Low 1945, Lokemoen 1966).

Successful eggs hatch within several hours. Body mass of newly hatched ducklings 37 ± 4.0 (Southwick 1953); ducklings remain in nest for few hours (reportedly up to 30 h). Imprinting by ducklings on ♀ dependent on visual, not auditory, cues (Mattson and Evans 1974). Soon after hatching, ♀ leads ducklings to brood-rearing pond (usually larger than nesting pond). Average brood size at hatching *c* 8 ducklings, and at fledging *c* 4. ♂ deserts ♀ late June–July and migrates (often northwards) to post-breeding lakes to moult. ♀ remains with brood until ducklings 6–8 weeks old, then deserts for moult migration July–Aug. Brood often remains together after departure of ♀, and unattended broods may merge. Most ducklings fledge at 8–11 weeks (Hochbaum 1944, Weller 1957, Smart 1965a), when body mass about 700 g. Weller (1957) and Lightbody (1985) described growth in detail. Production ranges 1.3–2.7 flying young per ♀ per year (Bellrose 1980). Longevity known to be 21 years in wild (Clapp *et al.* 1982) and 16 years in captivity.

Conservation and threats

Numbers probably little affected by humans until about 1900; by then, continued year-round shooting and increased commercial market hunting widely believed to be killing excessive numbers of ducks (Linduska 1964), including Redheads. Public concern led to passage of *Migratory Bird Treaty Act* of 1918, which outlawed market hunting in US and Canada. Legal daily bag limits for Redheads, however, remained high (25 birds) through 1920s (Reeves 1976).

Beginning in 1929 and persisting until late 1930s, severe drought gripped much of Great Plains, including prairie pothole region of US and Canada. Prolonged drought had devastating impact on all prairie-nesting duck populations (Hawkins *et al.* 1984). Decline was exacerbated by agricultural development on prairie breeding grounds and by excessive hunting pressure. Crisis in 1930s for North American ducks led to series of responses which were subsequently to have profound effects on conservation programmes for Redheads and others. These included passage of key US conservation legislation (*Migratory Bird Hunting Stamp Act* of 1934, *Fish and Wildlife Coordination Act* of 1934, and *Federal Aid in Wildlife Restoration Act* of 1937), establishment of Ducks Unlimited (1937) and Ducks Unlimited (Canada) (1938), implementation of restrictive hunting regulations beginning in 1930 (reduced bag limits and cessation of hunting over bait or with live decoys), and use of the first aerial surveys to estimate duck populations in 1931 (Linduska 1964, Hawkins *et al.* 1984).

By 1950s, extensive network of survey routes established for conducting annual aerial surveys for estimating populations of prairie-nesting ducks (Hawkins *et al.* 1984). Annual estimates of Redhead breeding population size vary widely among years (Wilkins *et al.* 2000). Earlier studies

(Hochbaum 1946) had considered Redhead breeding population to be out of synchrony with that of other species of prairie-nesting ducks. Analysis of more recent data (Dubovsky *et al.* 1994), however, has shown that breeding Redhead numbers are in synchrony with American Wigeon, Blue-winged Teal, scaup, and Northern Pintail, but out of synchrony with Northern Mallard, Gadwall, American Green-winged Teal, Northern Shoveler, and Canvasback. Redhead breeding population in recent decades (1955–94) has been relatively stable (Michot 2000). An increase is evident from 1995–2000 (Wilkins *et al.* 2000), but that probably temporary and consequence primarily of temporarily improved wetland conditions during wet phase of climatic cycle (Swanson and Meyer 1977, Lynch 1984).

Can suffer high annual mortality, with mortality rate of 1st year birds frequently reported to exceed 75% (Hickey 1952, Brakhage 1953, Weller and Ward 1959, Rienecker 1968). Adult mortality rates typically estimated at 40–55% (Hickey 1952, Weller and Ward 1959, Rienecker 1968). Geis and Crissey (1969) concluded that restrictive harvest regulations (i.e. reduced bag limits and shorter or closed hunting seasons) reduced annual mortality of adults to 21%, although Rienecker (1968) reported no significant reduction in mortality of juveniles during years with closed hunting seasons. Hunting regulations affect numbers harvested; closed seasons result in < 20 000 being shot (Reeves 1976), while more liberal hunting regulations in some hunting seasons lead to harvests of > 200 000. No known widespread mortality problems from contamination by trace elements, organochlorines, hydrocarbons, or cholinesterase inhibitors (Gamble and Woodin 1993, Michot *et al.* 1994b), or from parasitic infections (Michot *et al.* 1995), diseases or lead poisoning.

Major concern on breeding ground is continued conflict between need to conserve habitat for nesting ducks on one hand, and pressure from farming industry to convert wetlands to croplands on other. Drainage and filling of wetlands is continuing issue in prairie pothole region of north-central US and south-central Canada (Dahl 1990). Secondary issue on breeding grounds of prairie pothole region is increased predation pressure (Johnson and

Sargeant 1977, Sargeant *et al.* 1984), especially during dry conditions (Lokemoen 1966). Continuation of landscape-level land retirement programmes in pothole region and development of ecologically sustainable agriculture offer greatest promise for conserving breeding habitat and restoring reproductive success in North America (Nelson and Connolly 1996).

Important conservation issues on winter range are preservation of *Halodule* meadows and of ponds along coasts of southern Texas, US, and northern Tamaulipas, Mexico (Woodin 1996). Evidence that numbers could be limited by food resources in winter (Mitchell *et al.* 1994, Michot 1997), and documented decline in seagrasses in Gulf of Mexico

(Handley 1995, Onuf 1995), are worrying. Loss of *Halodule wrightii* in Laguna Madre of Texas of particular concern (Quammen and Onuf 1993, Onuf 1996). Further reduction in *Halodule*, primary winter food, could lead ultimately to population decline. Grazing intensity could limit *Halodule* recovery (Mitchell *et al.* 1994) in some areas. Availability of freshwater and low salinity wetlands along coast also important conservation issue on winter range; Redheads depend on these wetlands for drinking (Woodin 1994, Adair *et al.* 1996), especially when Laguna Madre becomes hypersaline during drought periods.

Thomas C. Michot and Marc C. Woodin

Common Pochard *Aythya ferina*
PLATE 23

Anas ferina Linnaeus, 1758, Syst. Nat., ed. 10, p. 126 Europe

Etymology: *ferina* from L. for wild or game, in reference to eating qualities. Common name derives from 'poker' and refers to feeding behaviour.

Other names: Eurasian or Northern Pochard, Red-headed Diver. Danish: Taffeland; French: Fuligule milouin; German Tafelente; Icelandic: Skutulönd; Japanese: Hoshi-hajiro; Spanish: Porrón común.

Variation: no subspecies

Description

ADULT: dimorphic. ♂ in breeding or alternate plumage has head rufous chestnut. Breast, upper mantle, undertail coverts, tail and rump blackish. Almost whole of rest of body vermiculate grey, darker on upperwing coverts. Flight feathers paler more uniform silver-grey, darkening along tips of primaries and outer secondaries. Underwing almost white. Legs and feet bluish grey; bill dark grey, with black tip and broad sub-terminal pale grey band; iris bright orange-red. ♀ head dull brown, with pale grey eyestripe, patches on throat, lores and cheeks, although pattern varies considerably. Much of body

uniform greyish brown, darker above. Wing as ♂, but browner. Bill dull grey to blackish, thick black tip and broad sub-terminal pale grey band; iris warm brown.

MOULT: in eclipse or basic plumage, ♂ resembles ♀ but body always greyer, lacks defined facial pattern, breast contrasting darker.

IMMATURE: ♂ may take more than one season to attain adult plumage, but not well understood. Generally similar to adult ♀, but head duller, lacking eyestripe, pale grey or white vermiculations usually visible on some body feathers, notched tail feathers before these regrown. Mantle, chest and flanks dark grey, feathers edged pale. In subsequent years, increasingly resembles full adult ♂, but vermiculation on wing takes some years to develop. ♀ like juvenile ♂, but mantle, scapulars and tertials uniform grey-brown with olive edging. Wing coverts uniform brown-grey, tips of secondaries unflecked white.

DUCKLING: predominantly brown above with yellowish streaks over eyes, rear upper edges and below wings, sides of back and rump. Underparts yellow, fading white under vent and tail.

MEASUREMENTS AND WEIGHT: ♂ adult wing (*n* = 19), 212–223 (217), juv (*n* = 41), 202–220 (213) ; adult tarsus (*n* = 52) 37–42 (39.5); winter weight (*n* = 119), 585–1240 (849). ♀ adult wing (*n* = 22), 200–216 (206), juv (*n* = 23)185–215 (206); adult tarsus (*n* = 47), 36–41 (38.8); winter weight (*n* = 202), 467–1090 (807) (Cramp and Simmons 1977).

Field characters

Medium-sized, freshwater diving duck, 420–490 mm in length. Short, stocky body slopes to stumpy tail. Steep forehead and relatively long bill emphasize peak to crown. Adult ♂ red head and uniform grey body only confusable with American *Aythya* ♂ counterparts, and ♂ Northern Wigeon, which lacks black breast, has yellow forehead, lateral white stripe and white/black undertail patch. Head and bill shape distinguish ♀-type plumages from all other species. In flight, relatively long neck, bulbous head and stubby tail end distinguish from other diving ducks. Canvasback ♂ has all dark bill, Redhead ♂ has yellow iris and darker grey back. ♀ harder to distinguish

from American *Aythya*, but long bill and steep forehead of Canvasback unmistakable, ♀ Pochard greyer and less warm brown than ♀ Redhead.

Voice

♂♂ generally silent, display includes wheezy whistles in summer. ♀ utters soft growl when flushed. Sonogram of ♀ calls in Cramp and Simmons (1977). Ducklings utter contact calls in groups of 2–4 notes; distress calls higher and faster than *Anas* of same age and size.

Range and status

Breeds in steppes 40–60°N, east as far as 120°E, including Lake Baikal, western Mongolia, western China, Aral, Caspian and Black Seas. Extends into some parts of boreal region in low breeding densities, but last century consolidated distribution in western parts of Europe in oceanic climates. In 19th century, spread westwards into Sweden, Finland, Denmark and The Netherlands; early last century, colonized Britain, much of central Europe and France, latterly extending into much of Germany, Belgium and Iberia. This expansion linked to drying of shallow breeding lakes in central Asia (Cramp and Simmons 1977), but more recent

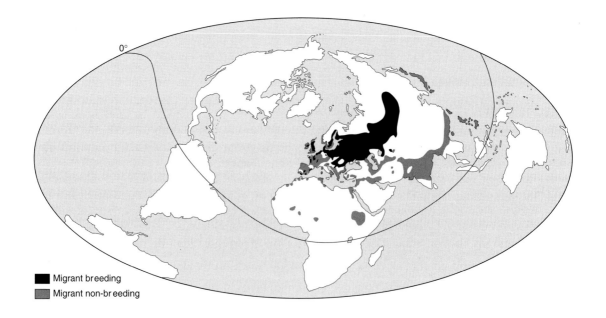

■ Migrant breeding
■ Migrant non-breeding

expansions likely linked to increasing provision of artificial habitats in breeding and wintering areas in form of flooded mineral extraction pits, reservoirs, fishponds, etc., and to eutrophication of waters (Fox and Salmon 1989). Quick to take advantage of new feeding opportunities, feeds on Zebra Mussels where mollusc has colonized new habitats (Suter and Schifferli 1988, Meile 1991). Isolated breeding groups exist in Japan, Manchuria, Tibet, Afghanistan, Transcaucasia, central Turkey and in Iceland. Nests in well-vegetated eutrophic to neutral, but generally base-rich, waters with abundant emergent fringing vegetation.

Common throughout western Europe, winter numbers here swollen by breeders from further north and east. This population numbers 350 000 but experienced 30% decline in numbers over last 20 years (Rose 1995, Rose and Scott 1997). Winters generally further south than Tufted Duck on range of habitats, from oligotrophic upland waters to lowland eutrophic lakes, shallow brackish bays and saltwater. Vagrant in western Alaska (Aleutian and Pribilof Islands), Africa south to Tanzania and Cameroons, Zaire and Gambia.

Important wintering areas occur in central Europe, especially on large subalpine lakes that remain ice-free even in harsh winters and may represent cold weather refuges for northwest European birds in hard weather (Ridgill and Fox 1990). May suffer mass starvation mortality during late cold spells when food reserves depleted (Suter and van Eerden 1992). Numbers in this region remain stable in contrast to 70% declines since 1970s in numbers wintering in western Mediterranean (Rose and Scott 1994, Rose 1995). Also signs of decline in eastern Mediterranean, Black Sea and Sea of Azov, although count coverage insufficient to confirm this. Overall Black Sea/Mediterranean element of population estimated to comprise 1 000 000 birds and declining overall (Rose and Scott 1997).

Rose and Scott (1997) estimated populations of southwest Asia wintering mostly in Syria, Iraq, Iran at 350 000 (but trends unknown) and those in south Asia at 100 000–1 000 000, with 90 000 in Pakistan alone and large numbers in northern India (numbers stable). Eastern breeders thought to winter in southeast and east Asia and number between 600 000 and 1 000 000 (trend unknown) distributed between Japanese waters, Philippines, China and Vietnam (Rose and Scott 1994, Miyabayashi and Mundkur 1999); with 500 000 in China, 30 000 in South Korea and 170 000 in Japan. However, regular recoveries of birds marked in winter in Britain and found east to 150°E show this last population to have considerable flexibility in migration strategy. Most British-ringed Pochard originate from Baltic republics and Russia, supplemented by German and Finnish breeders.

Habitat and general habits

Bottom-feeding divers requiring extensive open water with abundant submerged plant and/or animal food. In winter can be crepuscular and often feeds by night, frequently far from safe daytime roosts. Plant material taken includes seeds, rhizomes, buds, shoots and tubers, but frequently feeds on *Chara*, although *Potamogeton*, *Myriophyllum* and *Ceratophyllum* also (Olney 1968, Bezzel 1969, Cramp and Simmons 1977). May have suffered local changes in abundance as consequence of eutrophication altering lakes from clear-water macrophyte-dominated to phytoplankton-dominated systems. Chironomid larvae important at sites lacking macrophytes (e.g. Galhoff 1987), feeding distribution relating to chironomid abundance (Phillips 1991). In lakes and coastal areas in winter, may associate with sewage outfalls, where abundant *Tubifex* and other species taken (Galhoff 1987). Ironically, improvements to changes in sewage discharges in Firth of Forth, Scotland, led to decline of major wintering concentrations there (Campbell 1984, Fox and Salmon 1989). Sensitive to disturbance, especially hunting (Meile 1991) and waterborne recreation (Fox *et al.* 1993). Sexually dimorphic in feeding habits, ♂♂ said to dive in deeper areas than ♀♀ (Bezzel 1969); ♂♂ generally dominant in agonistic interactions, leading to displacement of ♀♀ in time and/or space from food-rich sites (Choudhury and Black 1992) and perhaps explaining north–south cline of decreasing ♂:♀ ratio (Owen and Dix 1986, Carbone and Owen 1995). ♀♀ and ducklings apparently feed on chironomid and caddis larvae during summer (Dementiev and Gladkov 1952), but diet little studied.

Moult gatherings of up to 50 000 ♂♂ common in western Europe (Cramp and Simmons 1977) and Russia, where between-year fidelity to moult sites demonstrated by ringing recoveries (Dementiev and Gladkov 1952).

Displays and breeding behaviour

Nuptial display starts in late winter and continues through spring migration, ♀ being courted by several attendant ♂♂. Copulation may occur during these communal courtships, prior to establishment of pairs. Courtship flights commence in late spring, originating from communal courtship. Pair-based courtship little known, but pairbond maintained until start of incubation (see Johnsgard 1965a, Cramp and Simmons 1977).

Breeding and life cycle

Arrives relatively late at eastern breeding areas (Dementiev and Gladkov 1952) and almost certainly accumulates fat and protein stores *en route*.

Breeds on base-enriched waters, even saline, brackish and soda lakes, occasionally along sheltered coastal bays. Nests close to water, rarely more than 10 m from water's edge, often on platforms built above surface (e.g. 77% over water, 16% on islets but 7% on dry land of 380 Czech nests, Cramp and Simmons 1977). Sensitive to changes in water level as result, with years of high or low water affecting reproductive output (Dementiev and Gladkov 1952). Nest shallow cup of reed stems and other plant material lined with down.

In study of Czech fish ponds, 66% of ♀♀ nested successfully, 18% unsuccessfully and remainder did not attempt to breed; however, large differences existed between years, with drought reducing breeding proportions to less than one-third when water levels low (Fiala 1988).

Eggs broad oval, green-grey; 62 × 44 (56–68 × 39–47) (*n* = 300) (Schönwetter 1960–66); weight 65 (55–74) (*n* = 57) (Cramp and Simmons 1977). Clutch 8–10 (4–22, but > 15 probably result of dumping), mean 9.5 (6–14) (*n* = 142, Germany) or 8.1 (3–13) (*n* = 307, Czechoslovakia) quoted by Cramp and Simmons from specific studies. Clutch size declines with time of laying; replaced if lost (45% in one study) but generally single brooded, incubated for 25 (24–28) days (Cramp and Simmons 1977). May be parasitized by Red-crested Pochard (Amat 1982, 1985). Captive ducklings weigh 37.2 (*n* = 45) on hatching. Average brood size 7.1 at hatch from 1st clutch, repeat clutches 6.0, giving rise to 4.4 fledged young per successful pair (4.6 in Czech study, Fiala 1988), 1.8 for all pairs (Cramp and Simmons 1977). Fledge in 50–55 days (Cramp and Simmons 1977). No data on adult survival.

Breeds at one year, although some not until 2. Oldest BTO-ringed bird 22 years (Clark *et al.* 2002); lived in captivity for 20 years, and fertile for entire period (Johnsgard 1968a).

Conservation and threats

Considered sensitive to disturbance during breeding period, as well as having distinctive habitat requirements so vulnerable to environmental change. On wintering grounds, may have lost suitable habitat as result of recent eutrophication, as on Norfolk Broads in England. Here, eutrophication processes resulted in development of phytoplankton-dominated aquatic systems which made previously clear but relatively base-rich waters opaque, which in turn has profound effect on bottom flora of *Chara* upon which Pochard feed; however, wintering Pochard also feed on chironomid larvae which may benefit from elevation of organic matter levels in even quite polluted aquatic systems. Consequently proved adaptable in responding to, for instance, food-processing factory waste discharge outfalls as dietary source. Adequate site safeguard network to protect internationally important wintering, moulting and breeding areas remains priority.

Tony Fox

Hardhead *Aythya australis*
PLATE 23

Nyroca australis Eyton, 1838, Monogr. Anatidae, p. 160 (ex Gould)
Australia = New South Wales

Etymology: *australis* means southern or Australian. Common name has uncertain origin; in use since 1913 (*cf* Hardhead alternate name for Ruddy Duck).

Other names: Australian White-eyed Pochard, White-eyed Duck, White-eye, White-wings, Widgeon, Barwing, Brownhead, Copperhead, Coppertop. Australian Aboriginal: Bubbuloo, Buel-bun-bun-loot, Djared, E-ro-to, Er-roo-doo, Errudo, Garrut, Irodu, Punkerri; Dutch: Australise Witoogeend; French: Fuligule austral; German: Tasmanmoorente; Maori: Karakahia; Spanish: Porrón Australiano.

Variation: no subspecies; treated as highly mobile and widely dispersive, crossing Tasman Sea to New Zealand occasionally; also found on New Caledonia and other more remote islands (e.g. Banks Island). So-called Banks Island Hardhead, *A. a. extima* Mayr, 1940, *A. a. papuana* Ripley, 1964 from Irian Jaya and *A. a. ledeboeri* Bartels and Franck, 1938 from Java included here within nominate *A. a. australis*.

Description

ADULT: dimorphic mainly in eye colour. ♂ in breeding plumage rich chestnut brown, specially on head and breast where plumage almost glossy; flanks, back and tail duller reddish brown; undertail white and central region of underparts white. Underwing white with narrow border of brown. Eye white; bill dark grey with conspicuously pale blue-grey band across tip contrasting with black nail; legs and feet brownish grey. ♀ like ♂ but much duller with no gloss and eye brown. Bill pattern similar to ♂ but noticeably duller.

MOULT: ♂ eclipse plumage undoubtedly occurs if only briefly. Almost no critical observations of moults (see Marchant and Higgins 1990) but assumed to follow pattern of other *Aythya*.

IMMATURE: resembles ♀ but paler, especially on chin and throat and generally more mottled on underparts. Difficult to separate in field.

DUCKLING: distinctive with almost unmarked yellow cheeks and face; underparts bright yellow contrasting with dark crown and remaining upperparts. Trailing edges of wing-pads broadly striped pale yellow, and large pale patch each side of rump.

MEASUREMENTS AND WEIGHT: ♂ wing (*n* = 99), 183–243 (215); tail (*n* = 13), 54–62 (58); bill (*n* = 14), 43–47 (45); tarsus (*n* = 13), 38–42 (40); weight (*n* = 105), 525–1100 (902). ♀ wing (*n* = 88), 186–234 (217); tail (*n* = 11), 55–67 (60); bill (*n* = 12), 39–45 (42); tarsus (*n* = 12), 35–40 (39); weight (*n* = 88), 530–1060 (838) (Marchant and Higgins 1990).

Field characters

Dark brown diving duck, 420–590 mm long, with conspicuous white undertail. In flight has broad white longitudinal stripe on upperwing with white underwing and large white belly patch. Dark plumage, white eye (of ♂) and bill pattern distinctive. Diving behaviour makes confusion possible only with Blue-billed Duck in normal range, but white undertail and different shape of Hardhead useful features. Ashore, outline of resting Hardhead, at distance, can be mistaken for Freckled Duck because pale belly often visible on Freckled Duck and extreme upright postures, adopted by both when loafing, are similar.

Voice

Generally silent, mostly vocal during courtship. ♂ call soft wheezy whistle and *whirrrr* given during advertizing display. Main call of ♀ loud, harsh rattle, often given in flight. For more details and sonogram, see Marchant and Higgins (1990). Sonograms of contact and distress calls of ducklings in Kear (1968).

Range and status

Endemic to Australia. Widespread throughout continent; regular but scarce in Tasmania (Marchant and Higgins 1990); only white-eyed diving duck

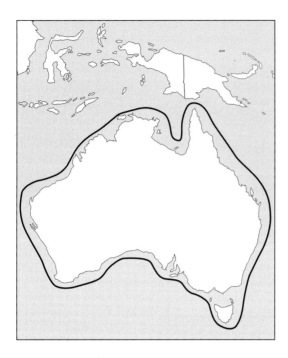

not to appear on list of threatened birds (BirdLife International 2000). Following favourable season, wide dispersal may result in individuals reaching New Zealand, New Guinea, Indonesia, New Caledonia and several islands in southwest Pacific where breeding has sometimes followed, but colonies thus established seem not to survive (Blakers *et al.* 1984). Breeding distribution in Australia widespread, with possibility that large numbers use floodplains of interior during favourable times in same way as Freckled Duck; these occurrences not clearly understood.

Owing to wide distribution, no assessment of population satisfactory and counts from southwest of continent and Victoria only concern portions of range; however, indices of abundance for large area of eastern Australia 1983–92, obtained from aerial surveys during Oct, gave average population estimate of 170 000 with peak numbers ranging up to 620 000 (Marchant and Higgins 1990, Kingsford *et al.* 1999). These surveys found large concentrations at Lakes Moondarra and Galilee, west and central Queensland, shallow wetlands in southeast South Australia and wetlands at confluence of Murrumbidgee and Lachlan Rivers. Other reports suggest that, at widely scattered localities, concentrations sometimes

approach 100 000 (Marchant and Higgins 1990); populations may vary between wide extremes and, as with Freckled Duck, be largest following infrequent major floods of regions of inland eastern Australia.

Habitat and general habits

Generally requires wetlands with deep water and mature development providing abundant bottom dwelling food. Uncommon on saline wetlands, but occasionally found on coastal freshwater lagoons, salt lakes, mangrove swamps and inshore waters (Marchant and Higgins 1990).

Diet mostly aquatic animals, in particular mussels and freshwater shellfish. Food obtained by diving, birds leaping forward and submerging with little surface disturbance. Swims underwater using feet for propulsion and sieving for prey with bill on bottom. Will occasionally dabble in waterside mud, up-end and strip seeds from aquatic plants. Rarely feeds in pastures or other croplands. Further details in Marchant and Higgins (1990) but available information probably biased by reliance on gizzard contents.

Displays and breeding behaviour

No detailed studies. Has silent Pre-flight signal indicated by repeated upward flicking of bill with neck stretched upright. Courtship display similar to that of other *Aythya*. Kinked-neck and Head-throw most obvious ♂ displays. Kinked-neck involves soft wheezy buzzing call following sudden horizontal distortion rearwards in middle of neck with head in exaggerated upright posture. It often follows Sneak in which head thrust low and forwards pointing at opponent. In Head-throw, ♂ suddenly thrusts head back towards tail pointing bill upwards; often head tilted or twisted sideways presenting face to ♀, and call similar to that of Kinked-neck display given. In courting parties, with several ♂♂ gathered around ♀, Kinked-neck used between ♂♂, and also by ♂♂ towards ♀ as they manoeuvre about her. In Inciting by ♀, head thrust towards adversary with rattling call. ♀ will join ♂ in Head-high and ♂ adopts typical Turn-back-of-Head posture attempting to lead ♀ away. According to Johnsgard (1965a), ♀ also performs Head-throw with hoarse call (presumably rattle) and, occasionally, Kinked-neck. During copulation, ♂ alternates slight Head-pumping movements with mock Dorsal-preen and Bill-dip before mounting when ♀ adopts receptive posture. Post-copulation, ♂ performs Kinked-neck, then swims away Bill-down while ♀ bathes (Johnsgard 1965a). Information on pairbond inadequate but probably seasonal monogamy or sequential or successive polygamy.

Breeding and life cycle

No detailed studies and little useful reported information. Seem to be solitary breeders, nesting in thick vegetation, mostly over water. Breeding season undefined but probably Aug–Dec; however, intensive breeding activity likely follows major rainfall and flooding inland. Incubation by ♀, who alone rears brood. Eggs elliptical, fine grained, glossy and creamy-white, largest of white-eyed pochards; 57 × 42 (49–65 × 37–45) (*n* = 105) (Frith 1982); in captivity weigh 50.4 (*n* = 99). No information on laying interval. Clutch size not properly quantified but *c* 10.5 (9–13), with larger clutches due to dump laying. Incubation period not properly determined but claimed 25 days (Frith 1982), 30–32 days (Marchant and Higgins 1990) or 27 in captivity. Newly hatched captive young weigh 29.5 (21.0–40.0) (*n* = 100). No data on brood care and maturation of young, nor on breeding success, survival and longevity.

Conservation and threats

Widespread and of no immediate conservation concern; world population *c* 200 000–700 000, possibly more after floods in inland Australia. In eastern Australia, has shown no long-term trends from early 1980s to 1999 but numbers peaked in 1984, 1991–92 and 1996 (Kingsford *et al.* 1999, 2000). Populations in New Guinea, New Caledonia, New Zealand and elsewhere on other islands within this region no doubt constantly supported by immigrants from Australia. No evidence at present that any group can be considered isolated endemic population.

Peter Fullagar

Madagascar Pochard *Aythya innotata*
PLATE 23

Nyroca innotata Salvadori, 1894, Bull. Brit. Ornith. Club, **4**, p. 2
Betsileo, Madagascar

Etymology: L. *innotatus* means unremarkable and refers to duck's drab and unassuming nature.

Other names: Madagascar White-eyed Pochard. French: Fuligule de Madagascar; Malagasy: Onjy, Fotsy Maso.

Variation: no subspecies.

Description

ADULT: dimorphic mainly in eye colour. ♂ in breeding plumage dark brown with white underparts. Both sexes have conspicuous white wing bar. ♀ similar but overall plumage drabber. Bill lead grey with black nail; legs and feet grey; iris white in ♂, dark brown in ♀.

MOULT: ♂ in eclipse resembles ♀ but retains white iris.

IMMATURE: resembles ♀, but browner. ♂ quickly develops grey iris that becomes white later in 1st year (Delacour 1954–64).

DUCKLING: dark brown above, yellow face and underparts. Specimens held at British Museum (Wilmé 1994).

MEASUREMENTS: ♂ wing, 190–201; tail, 54–58; bill, 46–49; tarsus, 28–33. ♀ wing, 188–195; bill, 44–46 (Delacour 1954–64). No weights recorded.

Field characters

Length 460 mm. Only pochard of Malagasy region. White iris of ♂, white wing bar and need to run across water to take off, distinguish from other Madagascan wildfowl. Secretive and often solitary, remaining in floating vegetation. Note recent record of Ferruginous Duck in Seychelles (Skerrett 1999).

Voice

Not recorded, likened to Redhead (Delacour 1954–64). No sonogram published.

Range and status

Endemic to Madagascar. Distribution restricted to area of Lake Alaotra, with only occasional records away (Wilmé 1993, 1994). Recorded in 1970 at Lake Ambohibao near Antananarivo (Salvan 1970). Common at Alaotra in 1929 (Delacour 1954–64) and 1935 (Webb 1936). Not seen at Alaotra after 1960, nor anywhere after 1970 despite several thorough searches (Wilmé 1994). ♂ captured alive at Alaotra in 1991 (Wilmé 1993); however, none seen since. Extreme habitat degradation and introduction of exotic fish into many lakes, most notably herbivorous species, e.g. *Tilapia* and carnivorous Largemouth Bass, considered main causes for rapid decline (Young and Smith 1989). Severe pollution and lake drainage may prevent Alaotra from recovering.

Habitat and general habits

Found in well vegetated areas, particularly quiet pools covered by water-lily within extensive marsh at Lake Alaotra's southern end. Not known to flock or associate with other ducks.

Feeds by diving; diet unknown, probably includes seeds of aquatic plants such as water-lilies, and invertebrates.

Displays and behaviour

Displays not recorded, probably similar to other white-eyed pochards (Johnsgard 1965a).

Breeding and life cycle

Little information. Assumed to breed Oct–Jan (Delacour 1954–64). Nest unknown, eggs ovate, buff white; 55×40; weight unrecorded; clutch 6–8 (given erroneously as 2 by Milon *et al.* 1973 and Langrand 1990, probably referring to incomplete clutch); incubation, by ♀ alone, 26–28 days; all data from captivity (Delacour 1954–64). Fledging period, breeding success, adult survival and longevity unrecorded.

Conservation and threats

Protection of lakes, especially satellite lakes to Alaotra, essential. Hunting and all human activities should be prevented, including introduction of exotic fish. Areas of Lake Alaotra should also be protected.

Once bred successfully in several European collections; none survives today. May be extinct; considered by BirdLife International (2000) to have Critically Endangered status.

Glyn Young

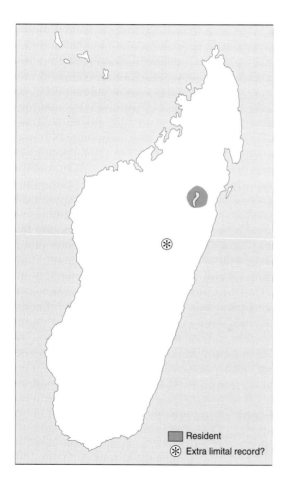

Resident
⊛ Extra limital record?

Ferruginous Duck *Aythya nyroca*
PLATE 23

Anas nyroca Güldenstädt, 1770, Novi Commentarii Acad. Sci. Imp. Petropolitanae, **14** (1769), p. 403 southern Russia

Etymology: *nyroca* from Russian *nyrok* for a duck.

Other names: Common White-eye, Ferruginous White-eyed Pochard. French: Fuligule nyroca; Hindi: Kurchiya; Spanish: Porrón pardo.

Variation: no subspecies.

Description

ADULT: dimorphic, particularly in eye colour. ♂ in breeding plumage reddish chestnut head, neck and breast, and slightly paler flanks. Belly and undertail white, and upperparts and tail blackish brown. Primary and secondary coverts blackish brown. White wing bar extends across secondaries and into primaries, and black tips to secondaries and primaries form terminal band. Underwing mainly white, with black posterior edge. Bill slate grey with black nail; legs and feet blackish grey; eye white. ♀ similar to ♂, though duller and browner overall with white feathering at base of bill, and brown eyes.

MOULT: ♂ eclipse resembles ♀, but retains white eye and white undertail. ♂ undergoes complete, post-breeding, flightless moult June–Aug, and ♀ likewise, but 4–6 weeks later. Partial, autumn–winter moult undertaken also, which often overlaps with post-breeding moult (Cramp and Simmons 1977, Vinicombe 2000). Moult movements poorly understood, but large flocks of moulting individuals gather regularly in several larger deltas of eastern Europe (e.g. Volga, Dnestr and Danube, *contra* Cramp and Simmons 1977).

IMMATURE: similar to ♀, but only slight reddish tinge to plumage and more uniform colour overall. Belly mottled brown and white, and undertail grey-buff (Vinicombe 2000).

DUCKLING: blackish brown above and yellow below. Sides of head and superorbital region bright yellow with no distinct dark facial markings.

MEASUREMENTS AND WEIGHT: ♂ wing ($n = 31$), 180–196 (188); culmen ($n = 58$), 38–43 (40.3); tail ($n = 31$), 50–60 (54.0); tarsus ($n = 58$), 31–35 (32.7); weight ($n = 5$), 470–730 (589). ♀ wing ($n = 8$), 178–185 (182); culmen ($n = 28$), 36–40 (38.2); tail ($n = 8$), 50–55 (52.7); tarsus ($n = 29$), 30–34 (32.2); weight ($n = 5$), 464–727 (558) (Cramp and Simmons 1977).

Field characters

Length 380–420 mm, relatively small, chestnut brown diving duck, with flat forehead and rather high crown. Conspicuous white undertail and wing bar characteristic in flight (Vinicombe 2000).

Voice

Similar to other *Aythya*, with calls of ♀ louder and harsher than ♂. Generally rather silent, with calls mainly associated with courtship. Three ♂ courtship calls recognized by Steinbacher (1960), quiet soft *weck*, louder hoarse *wück* or *wückwück*, and loud *witt*. *wück* given during Kinked-neck and Sneak displays, also accompanies Head-throw according to Johnsgard (1965a) who described it as *wheeoooo*, and identified 4th call, high-pitched *WEE-whew* (Coughing Call). Sonogram in Cramp and Simmons (1977) seems closest to *wück* call, and consists of rapid chatter of brief, harsh, slightly metallic but muffled *chk* notes, audible only at close range and delivered at *c* 6 notes per sec for up to 3 sec (Cramp and Simmons 1977). Steinbacher (1960) identified 2 ♀ calls *gek* or *dii*, and *err*. Latter given during ♀ version of Kinked-neck display; *gek* presumably Inciting call, described as *gak-gak-gak* by Johnsgard (1965a), who distinguished another call, *gaaak*, associated with ♀ version of Head-throw. Duckling distress calls more rapid than Pochard, but at same frequency.

Flight call loud, harsh, growling or croaking *aark* repeated at *c* 2 notes per sec (Cramp and Simmons 1977).

Range and status

Breeding range extends east from western Europe to western China (Sinkiang and northern Szechuan)

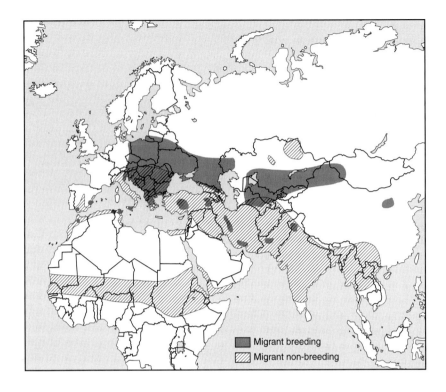

Migrant breeding
Migrant non-breeding

and western Mongolia, and north from Iran to Lithuania to *c* 54°N. Europe comprises *c* half breeding range (Tucker and Heath 1994). Southern breeding areas overlap with winter range which extends east from west Africa to southeast Asia and north from sub-Saharan Africa to southern Europe. Breeding range in Europe concentrated in eastern and central areas, with smaller numbers in north, west and south. Key winter areas poorly known, but seem to include Niger Basin wetlands of Mali, Chad Basin, northern Nile Basin wetlands of Sudan, coastal wetlands of Egypt and Israel, Indus Basin of Pakistan and northwest India and Brahmaputra River Valley wetlands of northeast India (Tucker and Heath 1994, Scott and Rose 1996). Recent surveys have found large numbers, perhaps into tens of thousands, in Inner Mongolia, and is apparently common on Tibetan Plateau, China and in winter in India, Bangladesh, Myanmar (Burma) and Thailand (BirdLife International 2000). About 13 records annually in England in early winter (Vinicombe 2000); vagrants recorded Seychelles.

Now globally near-threatened, although once described as 'one of the most plentiful [Anatidae] species over a great part of its range' (Phillips 1922–26). Has declined severely in population size and range in many countries, but particularly in Europe; e.g. in Dniestr-Dniepr region of Ukraine and Moldova, where population estimated at 65 000 pairs in late 1960s (Isakov 1970), but currently totals 4500–6300 pairs (90% decline). Also, numbers breeding in Spain declined from *c* 500 pairs earlier last century to verge of extinction (0–4 pairs annually). At present, *c* 13 000–24 000 pairs in Europe (Threatened Waterfowl Specialist Group in prep.), suggesting midwinter world population of 40 000–100 000 individuals; census data outside Europe poor, but 10 000 estimated for eastern Eurasia (Miyabayashi and Mundkur 1999). Large margins of error attached to estimates, owing to secretive behaviour, choice of densely vegetated wetlands, and identification problems when present in mixed *Aythya* flocks. Also, almost all census data collected *ad hoc*, either as part of general waterbird monitoring programmes or casual observations, particularly in east of range.

Habitat and general habits

Generally less gregarious than other western Palearctic diving ducks with which often mixes during nonbreeding season; differs in using shallower, more densely vegetated habitats and generally avoids open areas. Habitat more in common with some sympatric dabbling than diving ducks (Green 1998a).

Chiefly migratory, although some southern birds remain in breeding areas year-round (Scott and Rose 1996). Movements poorly understood since ringing data sparse, and little known of migration routes. Most European birds seem to winter in Africa and Middle East, though substantial numbers (10 000–50 000) remain in southern Europe, particularly in milder years (Threatened Waterfowl Specialist Group in prep.).

Concentrated in lowland, continental middle latitudes, extending to high altitudes only sporadically. During breeding, prefers fairly shallow expanses of water, rich in submergent and floating vegetation, fringed by dense stands of emergent plants (large river deltas often support substantial breeding numbers). In some areas, salt lakes (saline, brackish, or alkaline) commonly used for breeding, e.g. in Hungary (Sterbetz 1969), Romania (Kiss *et al.* 1984) and Turkey (Green 1998a). In central and eastern Europe, extensively managed fishponds important breeding habitat (Radovic *et al.* 1998). During nonbreeding season, habitat choice similar, although coastal waters, inland seas and large, open lagoons also frequented (Cramp and Simmons 1977, Amat and Soriguer 1982).

Diet omnivorous, but plant material predominates in stomach contents. Chiefly seeds and other parts of aquatic plants, such as *Potamogeton, Ceratophyllum, Scirpus* and *Carex*, and macro-algae such as *Chara* taken. However, animal material can predominate locally, and includes invertebrates such as chironomids, snails and beetles, and also frequently small fish (typically 2–7 cm) and frogs (Phillips 1922–26, Dementiev and Gladkov 1952, Sterbetz 1969, Cramp and Simmons 1977, Amat and Soriguer 1982, Kiss *et al.* 1984, Paspaleva *et al.*

1984, Ponyi 1994, Dvorak *et al.* 1996, Patrikeev 1996). Areas of shallow water (30–100 cm) close to dense littoral vegetation favoured feeding sites. Food taken by dabbling at surface, when swimming with head submerged or up-ending, and by diving (Sterbetz 1969, Cramp and Simmons 1977, Amat and Soriguer 1982, Dvorak *et al.* 1996, Green 1998a).

Displays and breeding behaviour

Little studied except in captivity (Steinbacher 1960, Johnsgard 1965a, Cramp and Simmons 1977). ♂ has Courtship-intent posture, with head moderately raised and crown feathers erected. Also, frequently depresses tail sharply into water so white under-tail coverts show triangular patch on each side. Courtship displays include Head-throw, Kinked-neck, and Sneak, accompanied by main courtship call. Head-throw preceded by Head-shake and probably Head-flick. Courtship display immediately followed by Neck-stretch. At times, neck enlarged both during full Sneak and Neck-stretch. Coughing display frequent, whereby ♂ rapidly flicks up tips of wing while Coughing. Pre-copulatory display of ♂ consists of repeated Bill-dipping and Preen-dorsally.

Breeding and life cycle

Monogamous pairbond of seasonal duration, breeding late relative to most other European ducks. Pairs form late, Jan on, and most birds arrive on breeding grounds in pairs. Arrival occurs from early Mar in southern Europe (Handrinos and Acriotis 1997, Radović *et al.* 1998) to early Apr and into May further north (Dementiev and Gladkov 1952, Cramp and Simmons 1977). Nest located on ground close to water, or over water in dense reeds and other aquatic vegetation. In Danube Delta, nests in cavities near base of flooded willow trees. Occasionally nests within gull colonies, as at Milicz fishponds in Poland (Stawarczyk 1995). Eggs 53 × 38 (48–60 × 35–43) ($n = 160$) (Cramp and Simmons 1977, Kiss 1980); weight in captivity 35.7 (31–41) ($n = 82$); clutch 7–10 (6–14), with larger clutches probably containing dumped eggs. Incubation begins as early as Feb in southern Europe, and as late as June in north. Ducklings hatch in 25–28 days and weigh, in captivity, 21.8 ($n = 97$); brood size in Croatia 6.8 (1–14) ($n = 85$) (Radović et al.1998). Young cared for by ♀ (♂ leaves during incubation); fledge in 55–60 days, and become independent at or just before fledging (June–Sept, depending on latitude). Individuals sexually mature at one year (Dementiev and Gladkov 1952, Cramp and Simmons 1977). No information on breeding success, adult survival nor longevity.

Departure from breeding localities begins Sept and peaks Oct (Dementiev and Gladkov 1952, Cramp and Simmons 1977, Handrinos and Acriotis 1997, Radović et al.1998).

Conservation and threats

Listed as Near-threatened by BirdLife International (2000). Together with habitat degradation, loss of wetland habitat from human developments probably most significant factor in decline. In particular, canalization of rivers and flood defence works have caused loss of many floodplain wetlands, most of which were prime habitat. To small extent, this compensated by creation of extensively managed fishponds, e.g. on Danube Floodplain in Bulgaria. Degradation of extensively managed fishponds by

abandonment (causing succession to scrub) or intensification (causing reversion to open water with little or no plant growth) in many European countries has had serious effects; e.g. *c* 60% breed currently on fishponds in Romania, where > 50% of fishponds have been abandoned since 1989 (Threatened Waterfowl Specialist Group in prep.). Introduction and stocking of Grass Carp *Ctenopharyngodon idella* has probably seriously degraded habitat, since introduction of fish usually causes substantial reductions in macrophyte biomass and corresponding declines in animals dependent on these plant communities (Bain 1993).

Hunting also major threat; large numbers (1500–2500) shot currently on autumn passage through Volga delta, while on wintering grounds in Sudan (and perhaps elsewhere) is frequent quarry of foreign hunters (Threatened Waterfowl Specialist Group in prep.). Protected in many countries, but illegal hunting and accidental shooting owing to confusion with other ducks, particularly Tufted Duck and Common Pochard, widespread problem (Hecker 1994, Tucker and Heath 1994).

Des Callaghan and Andy J. Green

Baer's Pochard *Aythya baeri*
PLATE 23

Anas (Fuligula) Baeri Radde, 1863, Reisen Süden Ost-Sibirien, **2**, p. 376, pl. 15
middle Amur Valley, eastern Siberia

Etymology: *baeri* after K.E. von Baer (1792–1876), explorer of Siberia.

Other names: Asiatic, Eastern or Siberian White-eyed Pochard, Baer's Diver, Baer's Scaup, Baer's White-eye. Japanese: Aka-hajiro.

Variation: no subspecies.

Description

ADULT: dimorphic, mainly in eye colour. ♂ in breeding plumage, glossy, greenish black head with white chin spot grading into rich rufous chestnut chest. White lower flanks sharply delimited from chest, while upper and posterior parts of flanks barred reddish brown. Upperparts dark brown to

chestnut brown (with obscure cinnamon vermiculations on mantle); lowerparts including undertail coverts white. Uppertail coverts and lower back black, while upperwing surface brown, except for white wing bar and posterior black border formed mainly by secondaries. Base of primaries grey, forming extension to wing bar. Bill slate grey with lighter tip and black nail; legs and feet lead grey (with darker webs); iris white. ♀ superficially resembles ♂, but has dull brown head and chest, brown iris and subtle pale brown patch between bill and eyes.

MOULT: eclipsed plumage ♂ resembles ♀, but retains white (or nearly white) iris, more vividly coloured chest and lacks pale brown patch between eyes and bill. Little known of moult cycle, but ♂♂

seen early Aug in nuptial plumage (Nechaev and Gluschenko 1993).

IMMATURE: as adult ♀, but has russet brown abdomen.

DUCKLING: similar to Greater Scaup, but crown slightly darker and area behind vent lighter (Palmer 1976).

MEASUREMENTS AND WEIGHT: ♂ (*n* = 9) wing, 206–215 (212); tail, 54–64 (59.3); culmen, 44–46 (45); tarsus, 36–37 (36.4); weight, *c* 880 (Palmer 1976). ♀ (*n* = 7) wing, 196–209 (201); tail, 57–60 (58.5); culmen, 40–45 (43); tarsus, 34–36 (34.6); weight, *c* 680 (Palmer 1976).

Field characters

Dark coloration and large white wing bar characteristic in flight (Dementiev and Gladkov 1952). Length 410–460 mm. Only white-eyed pochard with iridescent colouring on head and, perhaps, only confused on wintering grounds in western parts of range where overlaps with smaller and more chestnut-coloured Ferruginous Duck (Johnsgard 1978).

Voice

Said to resemble Common Pochard, and expressed as *kek-kek-kek* and *kook-kirr-kirr* (Smythies 1986). Johnsgard (1978) noted that ♀ utters coarse *gaaaak* call. No information on calls of young.

Range and status

Breeds in eastern Russia (Upper and Middle Primorye, and Primorye Krai) and northeast China including Hong Kong, and probably in North Korea and eastern Mongolia. Bulk of population winters in east China, but smaller numbers winter from Japan and South Korea, south to Thailand (and possibly northern Cambodia) and west to northeast India (occurring on passage in Nepal) (Nowak 1970, Palmer 1976, Chalmers 1986, Smythies 1986, Ali and Ripley 1987, Scott 1989, Brazil 1991, Choudhury 1991, Inskipp and Inskipp 1991, Nechaev and Gluschenko 1993, Thompson *et al.* 1993, Collar *et al.* 1994, Perennou *et al.* 1994). Recorded in North America (Palmer 1976). Old

CHINA

Migrant breeding
Migrant non-breeding

UK records considered hybrids (Gillham *et al.* 1966).

Fluctuating numbers and sparse information make long-term trends in population size difficult to estimate, but numbers seem to have declined sharply during last century, possibly more marked during past 2 decades (Kolosov 1983, Ler *et al.* 1989, Hu and Cui 1990, Brazil 1991, Williams *et al.* 1992, Nechaev and Gluschenko 1993, Collar *et al.* 1994). Numbers breeding at Khanka Lake vary according to water level, with reduced numbers during low levels, although reasons unclear (Nechaev and Gluschenko 1993). In southern parts of wintering range, numbers greater during colder winters (Dementiev and Gladkov 1952). Most recent population estimate > 10 000 individuals, with counts in early 1990s exceeding 1500 birds at 2 sites in China, Qing Dao and Jiangsu Coast (Perennou *et al.* 1994, Miyabayashi and Mundkur 1999). Upper limit of 20 000 individuals seems reasonable (Wetlands International 2002).

Habitat and general habits

Breeds around lakes and in marshes with ample emergent vegetation, favouring open habitat. In winter occurs in similar habitat, but also on brackish lagoons, estuaries and reservoirs. Usually encountered in small groups during nonbreeding season, often with other ducks, but large flocks occasionally reported. Single pairs or small loose groups usual in breeding season (Dementiev and Gladkov 1952, Smythies 1986, Ler *et al.* 1989, Brazil 1991, Nechaev and Gluschenko 1993, Perennou *et al.* 1994, Collar *et al.* 1994).

Diet poorly known, but includes both plant and animal material, probably obtained principally by diving (Johnsgard 1978). Rice important food in some areas (Nechaev and Gluschenko 1993), and Dementiev and Gladkov (1952) noted consumption of small frogs.

Displays and breeding behaviour

♀ has harsh Inciting call; performs Head-throw and Preen-behind-wing at preferred ♂. Repeated Kinked-neck most frequent ♂ display, and includes exaggerated neck movements and harsh *krraaaa* call. Often ♂ also stretches head and neck over water in Sneak, followed immediately by *krraaaa* call. This call also accompanies ♂ Head-throw. Display preening of white wing bar commonly performed by both sexes, often mutually, and ♂ response to ♀ Inciting includes swimming ahead of ♀ and Turn-back-of-head (Johnsgard 1965a, 1978). During display, ♂ contracts pupil, creating white flash (of iris), with head in rapid motion (Palmer 1976). Copulatory behaviour similar to other pochards, but preceded by slight Head-pumping by ♂, in addition to mutual Bill-dipping and Dorsal-preening by both sexes. After treading, usual call and Bill-down display performed by ♂. Many displays shared with Hardhead (Johnsgard 1965a, 1978).

Breeding and life cycle

Arrives on breeding ground in pairs, mostly during Apr, but as early as mid Mar and as late as mid May.

Nest scrape on ground amongst dense cover or within gull colony, and lined with vegetation and down. Nest bowl 168 mm (155–180) by 85 mm (55–120) deep ($n = 3$). Laying usually starts late May–early June; eggs in captivity cream; 51 × 38; weight 39.3 ($n = 44$); clutch 10.2 (9–13) ($n = 5$) (Dementiev and Gladkov 1952, Nechaev and Gluschenko 1993); 27 days incubation (Johnstone 1970); newly hatched ducklings weigh 24.2 ($n = 48$). Little known of rearing of young but, on Khanka Lake, broods seen until 19 Aug (Dementiev and Gladkov 1952). Autumn migration Sept–Oct (Brazil 1991, Nechaev and Gluschenko 1993). No data on breeding success, adult survival nor longevity.

Conservation and threats

Principal threats seem to be overhunting and habitat degradation, particularly from drainage and rice cultivation. Disturbance may be significant locally (Kolosov 1983, Ler *et al.* 1989, Hu and Cui 1990, Green 1992b, Nechaev and Gluschenko 1993). Little direct conservation action has been taken. Fully protected from hunting in Russia, although confusion with Tufted Duck known to cause hunting mortality at Khanka Lake (Nechaev and Gluschenko 1993). In 1991, nature reserve established covering most of breeding area around Khanka Lake (Nechaev and Gluschenko 1993), while there are proposals for giving principal site in Thailand (Bueng Boraphet) Ramsar designation; this site threatened with drainage (Green 1992b). Given Vulnerable status by BirdLife International (2000).

Des Callaghan

New Zealand Scaup *Aythya novaeseelandiae*
PLATE 24

Anas novae Seelandiae Gmelin, 1789, Syst. Nat., **1**, p. 541
Dusky Sound, South Island, New Zealand

Etymology: *novaeseelandiae* means 'of New Zealand'. Scaup derives from *skalp* meaning mussel-bed, and refers to diet of Greater Scaup.

Other names: Black Teal. Maori: Papango.

Variation: no recognized subspecies, but differentiation of North and South Island (*A. n. maui*) birds suggested by Mathews (1937) who claimed darker plumage and longer wings for South Island residents. Claim not investigated.

Description

ADULT: dimorphic. ♂ in breeding or alternate plumage has uppersurface black with green or purple iridescence strongest on head. Undersurface brownish black, lower breast and belly mottled brownish white. Upperwing black with conspicuous broad white band on secondaries; underwing mottled brownish white. Bill bluish black with black nail; legs and feet black; eye yellow. ♀ upper surface dark brown, rump almost black. Under surface dark brown, lower breast and belly mottled brownish white. Upperwing dark brown with white band in centre of secondaries; underwing mottled brownish white. White patch at bill base most conspicuous in breeding season. Bill brownish black; legs and feet dark brown; eye brown.

MOULT: no ♂ eclipse.

IMMATURE: resembles ♀. ♂ identifiable *c* 6 months after fledging.

DUCKLING: pale brown above, buff-white below. Four obscure cream spots at wing and rump. Eye brown, bill brown, legs and feet grey-brown.

MEASUREMENTS AND WEIGHT: ♂ from skins (*n* = 23) bill, 35.6–42.1 (38.7); tarsus, 31.9–39.8 (35.4); wing, 179–196 (187); tail, 51–62 (56); weight in wild (*n* = 11), 630–760 (695). ♀ from skins (*n* = 4) bill, 35.2–39.9 (37.9); tarsus, 33.2–35.8 (34.4); wing, 178–197 (185); tail, 52–61 (57); weight in wild (*n* = 15), 530–700 (600).

Field characters

Small (400–460 mm long) and dark with rounded profile on water. Patters along surface at take off, generally flies low over water with rapid wing-beats and upper white wing bar conspicuous. Dives to feed.

Voice

Little studied. Generally quiet with calls mostly associated with display. ♂ gives soft whistle-like *whe* in singles, doubles or multiples depending upon display.

♀ has high-pitched *errrr* during social courtship and trill *whirr whirr* as alarm call to ducklings.

Range and status

Endemic to North and South Islands. Subfossil remains on Chatham Islands. Widespread until late last century when suffered heavy exploitation by hunters and, especially, from agricultural development. In South Island retreated to large glacial lakes on eastern flanks of Southern Alps; in North Island disappeared from most lowland lakes and remained common only on central volcanic lakes near Taupo and Rotorua. Since late 1950s, has slowly expanded, initially by colonizing hydroelectric dams on Waikato River. Slowly expanding from protected lowland locations in North Island where releases of captive-reared birds provided initial colonists. South Island population still restricted to alpine lakes and protected lakes on western coast. Probably < 10 000 individuals.

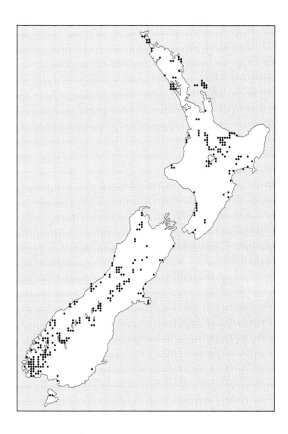

Habitat and general habits

Regarded as inhabitant of large and deep lakes but this probably artifact of recent restricted distribution. Presently inhabits some shallow coastal dune lakes (Northland, Manawatu), volcanic lakes of varying trophic status in central North Island, high-altitude glacial lakes (South Island), lowland peat lakes (West Coast) and hydro-lakes. Rarely seen on flowing water although this apparently well used last century (Buller 1888). Estuarine and brackish waters not presently colonized.

Regarded as sedentary, although no confirming studies. Winter congregations suggest local movement away from summer breeding areas but whether these are local flocks or birds moving from one wetland to another is unknown. Flocks also persist through breeding season and are thought to comprise nonbreeders and mostly ♂♂.

Daily activity pattern little known. Thought to feed in late afternoon and at dusk and not at night but this needs confirmation. Foods obtained mostly by diving and include chironomid larvae, probable variety of other aquatic insects, gastropods and tips of aquatic vegetation. May also eat zooplankton as flocks reported dabbling intensively at surface.

Displays and breeding behaviour

Similar to other *Aythya* ducks (Johnsgard 1965a) and includes Coughing, Nod-swim, Head-throw, Kinked-neck and Sneak (Marchant and Higgins 1990). ♀ responds to courting ♂ with Inciting display and call, ♂ then performs Turn-back-of-head. Pre-copulatory behaviour includes mutual Bill-dipping and Preen-dorsal displays.

Breeding and life cycle

Breeding starts rarely before Oct and may extend into Feb. Most laying late Oct–Nov, with ducklings mostly seen Dec–Jan. Variety of sites used mostly in dense cover near water, often partly enclosed above, and on islands wherever available. May be isolated from other scaup or within loose colony (especially on islands). Nest bowl simple and includes grasses and reeds within reach of site. Eggs elliptical, smooth textured, creamy white to mocha brown; $63.1 \pm 1.2 \times 44.7 \pm 07.3$ (59.3–75.1×41.6–46.6) ($n = 83$); weight 70.5 ± 4.0 (59.5–81.0) ($n = 216$) (Stokes 1991), large for size of ♀; clutch 6.5 (4–8) ($n = 22$); where birds nest close together and evidence of dumping 7.9 ± 2.5 (2–13) ($n = 49$). In captivity, eggs laid c 1.4 days apart (Reid and Roderick 1973), in wild mean interval 29 ± 12.3 h ($n = 89$) (Stokes 1991). Incubation, by ♀ only, in captivity 29–31 days (Reid and Roderick 1973), in wild 30.6 ± 1.3 days ($n = 13$) (Stokes 1991). Captive ducklings weigh 43.8 ($n = 95$) on hatching.

Ducklings attended by ♀; brooded in nest for 24 h and observed feeding and diving soon after reaching water. Although broods may amalgamate, ♀ remains close to young, and true crèches (mixed broods attended by single) not observed. Fledging period in captivity 75 days (Reid and Roderick 1973) but, in wild, juvenile plumage assumed in 7–8 weeks (Stokes 1991). Productivity sometimes extremely low with 2.5% ($n = 286$) and 4.4% ($n = 163$) survival of ducklings to fledging in consecutive years (Stokes 1991). Breeding thought to occur in 2nd year but unconfirmed in field; some captive ♀♀ lay in 1st year. No adult survival and longevity data.

Conservation and threats

Protected by law. Possibly threatened on account of population size and limited geographic range. Capable of recolonizing much of former range but may need to be placed into key lowland areas to permit dispersal. Greatest threat to range expansion probably from hunters who fail to identify properly their quarry.

Murray Williams

Ring-necked Duck *Aythya collaris*
PLATE 23

Anas collaris Donovan, 1809, Brit. Birds, **6**, pl. 147 and text

Lincolnshire, England, specimen found in Leadenhall market, London

Etymology: *collaris* L. for neck, in reference to chestnut collar of ♂.

Other names: Ring-billed Duck, Ringbill, Ring-necked Scaup. French: Morillon à collier; Spanish (Mexico): Talalactli, Pato piquianillado.

Variation: no subspecies, and no geographic variation in measurements.

Description

ADULT: dimorphic. ♂ in breeding, or alternate, plumage has head, neck, breast, scapular, and back regions black with purple-green sheen. Dark chestnut collar incomplete dorsally. Belly white. Flanks finely vermiculated dusky on white (greyish) contrasting with white (unvermiculated) in front of wing. Tail and associated coverts black without iridescence. Remiges brown-grey (primaries) to pearly grey (secondaries and tertials) darkened towards tips with white edging on tips of tertials and proximal secondaries. Wing coverts blackish with green sheen above and pale grey below. Bill slate with wide white band behind black tip and edges of upper mandible and nares narrowly white; feet and legs olive-grey; eye yellow-orange. ♀ head and neck mottled dusky to brown on buffy white, darkest on crown and nape and palest near base of bill, throat, ventral neck, and around eye. Variable number of white flecks on nape increasing with age (Hohman and Cypher 1986). Breast and flank brown. Belly (feathers with buffy white tips and dusky brown base) pale with variable mottling. Back, scapulars, and tail and associated coverts dark brown. Wing coverts dark brown above and pale grey below. Bill dark slate with faint white band; feet, legs, and remiges as ♂; eye olive-brown.

MOULT: upperparts duller (dusky-dark brown *v* glossy black) in ♂ basic, or eclipsed, plumage than in alternate. Crown shortened. Flanks brownish grey, thus contrast with upperparts reduced. White bill markings faded. ♀ basic plumage similar to alternate, but extent of pale areas in head and neck somewhat reduced and less clearly defined. Extensive dark mottling on belly. Breast and flank reddish brown. Moult of both sexes most intense during period of remigial moult (Aug) and also elevated during winter (Dec–Jan) (Hohman and Crawford 1995). Moult reduced during spring (Mar) and fall (Oct) migrations. Whereas moult remains at low levels in ♂ throughout breeding season, ♀♀ initiate pre-basic moult after arrival on breeding areas (Apr) and moult intensively until onset of incubation (June).

IMMATURE: aspect before 1st pre-alternate moult resembles definitive basic of ♀, but head, neck, and breast darker and belly paler. Sexual difference in eye colour evident after appearance of contour feathers. Greater amount of white coloration on breast (♂) or belly (♀) in 1st alternate than in definitive alternate plumage. Compared to adult, immature ♀ has reduced facial mottling and no flecking on nape.

DUCKLING: dark olive-brown on crown, nape and back sharply contrasting with yellow on remainder of head and neck and especially large sholder and rump spots continuous with yellow underparts (breast, belly and undertail). Oval nail narrow relative to other *Aythya*, wide yellow forehead, and feet with contrasing olive-grey and yellow markings also distinctive. Iris dark brown (Nelson 1993).

MEASUREMENTS AND WEIGHT: adult ♂ wing ($n = 200$), 191–220 (206 ± 5); tail ($n = 43$), 50–63 (58 ± 2.3); keel ($n = 296$), 80.4–92.1 (86.3 ± 2.3); tarsus ($n = 237$), 40.5–46.8 (43.8 ± 1.2); maximum bill width ($n = 296$), 20.8–24.8 (22.7 ± 0.8); bill ($n = 264$), 46.0–52.2 (49.1 ± 1.2); weight ($n = 624$), 542–910 (maxima: fall staging [Sept–Oct $n = 10$] 820 ± 73; minima: wing moult [Aug $n = 71$] 667 ± 45). Adult ♀ wing ($n = 196$), 178–210 (196 ± 5); tail

($n = 59$), 50–63 (57 ± 2.4); keel ($n = 217$), 78.2–89.6 (82.5 ± 2.1); tarsus ($n = 214$), 40.0–45.9 (43.0 ± 1.0); bill width ($n = 217$), 20.7–23.6 (22.1 ± 0.6); bill ($n = 158$), 44.5–50.2 (47.1 ± 1.1); weight ($n = 685$), 490–894 (maxima: pre-laying-laying [May–June $n = 23$] 780 ± 52; minima: brood rearing [July $n = 96$] 580 ± 48) (Hohman *et al.* 1988).

Field characters

Small-bodied diving duck, 385–455 mm long, initially confused with Tufted Duck (Brewer 1854). Although superficially resembling scaup, ♂ distinguished on basis of blackish upperparts contrasting with pale grey flanks especially white in front of wing, short crest giving head angular (*v* rounded) profile, distinctive white bill markings, and uniformly dark upperwings lacking speculum. ♀ brownish with white eye-ring, short crest, bill with faint white band, upperwings darkish and lacking speculum, and pale region near base of bill less clearly defined than in scaups. ♀ most closely resembles Redhead, but smaller, with eye-ring.

Voice

No published sonograms of adult or duckling calls. ♂ Kinked-neck call *wow* emitted during Neck-stretch or Head-throw softer and weaker than that of other *Aythya*. Short whistling Cough or chirp frequent during social display. When alarmed or in flight during nesting season (e.g. returning from egg-laying or incubation bout), ♀ gives short, high-pitched growling *burrr*. Soft

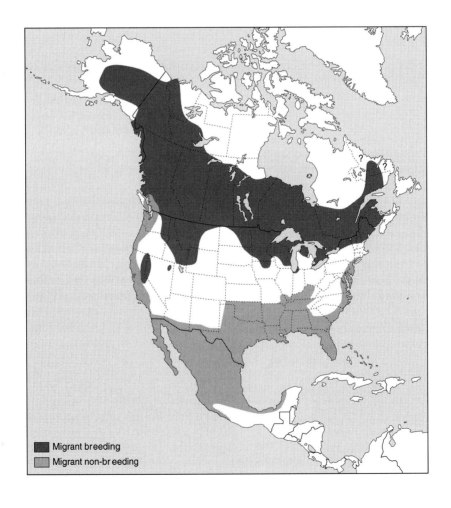

Migrant breeding
Migrant non-breeding

purring growl emitted during courtship display, when curious, or gathering brood (Mendall 1958). Alarm call, given to brood, short soft *cut-cut-cut*. No detailed information on calls of young; vocalizations of *Aythya* and *Anas* ducklings similar in form, accent and syllables, but lower-pitched and slower, with more harmonics (Kear 1968, Nelson 1993, Wilson 2002).

Range and status

Breeds in boreal forest, parkland, and, to lesser extent, prairie regions of northern US (Maine through Great Lakes to Dakotas and northern Montana) and southern Canada (Maritimes to central British Columbia) to Alaska; also western US (California to Washington). Expansion east of Great Lakes occurred after 1930s (Mendall 1958, Koons and Rotella 2003). Winters primarily inland along Gulf of Mexico from Florida to Yucatan; also, inland along Atlantic and Pacific coasts of United States, some Caribbean islands, and central Mexico to Panama. Few seen most winters in UK, especially since 1970s, with 35 counted in 1980; presence now annual (bird ringed Canada found Powys, Wales, in 1967, and ♂ ringed WWT, Slimbridge in 1977, shot 2 months later in Greenland), and recorded at many other European locations from Iceland and Portugal to Austria and Azores. Increase in visits to Europe coincided with range expansion in North America.

Between 1955 and 1995, breeding population indices for traditional survey area ranged 160 800-1 286 600 and averaged 563 100 birds (US Fish & Wildlife Service, Office of Migratory Bird Management). Decade averages rose from 334 100 in 1950s, 458 700 in 1960s, 508 100 in 1970s, 676 800 in 1980s to 923 100 in 1990s. Population estimates for eastern survey region (1990–95) ranged 96 400–250 300 (US Fish & Wildlife Service). Wetlands International (2002) gave total population figure of 1 220 000. Sexual differences in winter distribution with ♂♂ at higher latitudes (Alexander 1983); ♂♂ outnumber ♀♀ 1.6:1 (Bellrose *et al.* 1961).

Habitat and general habits

During summer and winter, prefers shallow (< 2 m), freshwater wetlands with abundant emergent and submersed or floating plants. Migrants use shallow lakes with dense stands of emergents or submergents and temporally flooded areas (e.g. floodplains). Rarely found on wetlands with salinity > 5 ppt. Noted for rapid occupancy of newly created nesting (Beaver ponds, Beard 1953), migrational staging (Upper Mississippi River navigation pools, Korschgen 1989) and wintering habitats (aquacultural ponds, Christopher *et al.* 1988). Differential use of habitat by sexes at some wintering sites (Bergan and Smith 1989). Shifts from traditional winter habitats to open water lakes related to proliferation of Hydrilla *Hydrilla verticillata*, non-native submersed aquatic plant that forms dense mats (Johnson and Montalbano 1984).

Feeds principally by means of shallow dives, but also up-ending, dabbling, and snapping. Food selection by sexes similar, except possibly during nesting season (Eberhardt and Riggs 1995). Feeding opportunistic, strongly influenced by availability, and more generalized than other *Aythya* (Desgranges and Darveau 1985, Hohman 1985). Diet omnivorous with prey size ranging from < 0.1 mm (oogonia of *Chara*) to 50 mm (leeches, Hirudinea). Animal food consumption greatest in downy young (98%) and attending ♀♀ (92%), but also may be elevated during other reproductive periods (25–81%; Hohman 1985, Eberhardt and Riggs 1995), fall migration (Thompson 1973) or winter (43%, Hoppe *et al.* 1986). Important animal foods benthic (annelid leeches, chironomid midges, snails and clams) or associated with vegetation (dragonflies, caddisflies) but not free-swimming. Otherwise, diet composed largely of vegetative material, especially seeds of submersed *Potamogeton* and floating aquatic plants (Watershield *Brasenia schreberi*, Fragrant Water-lily *Nymphaea odorata*, yellow water-lily *Nuphar*) and annuals (Wildrice *Zizania aquatica*, Reed Canary Grass *Phalaris arundinacea*) and tubers (Fennel-leaf Pondweed, arrowheads, Hydrilla, and Chufa Flatsedge).

Migratory throughout range, staging Sept–Oct and arriving on wintering areas Nov; departing wintering areas Feb–Mar and arriving on breeding grounds Apr–May. Moult migration by ♂♂, but participation by ♀♀ variable (Hohman *et al.* 1992). Dispersal distances of fledged young before fall migration also variable. Movements during winter sometimes extensive. Daily movements change seasonally in relation to reproductive and moult status, habitat, development of young, and disturbance.

Feeding (20–55%) and resting (14–43%) major winter activities; courtship rare ($<1\%$) (Hohman 1984a). Wintering birds generally inactive at night (Jeske 1985, Bergan *et al.* 1989). ♂♂ reportedly dominant to ♀♀ and adults dominant to immatures (Alexander 1987). Although intensive fighting observed (Titman and Seymour 1976), intraspecific aggression rare in winter and dominance relations appear unrelated to nutrition of subordinates (Hohman and Weller 1994). Feeding dominant activity of nesting ♀♀: up to 19 h per day during laying and 57% time during incubation recesses (Hohman 1985, 1986a). ♂♂ attending mates, and ♀♀ rearing broods, mostly vigilant. Ducklings spend 41% time feeding, 31% resting, and 21% in comfort activities (Maxson and Pace 1992). During wing moult, $>50\%$ time spent performing comfort movements and resting. Pre-migrants spend 53% time engaged in comfort and locomotory activities.

Nonbreeders dispersed in small flocks (6–12) throughout most of range, but may be concentrated at fall staging areas and non-traditional wintering sites with abundant foods (e.g. wild rice or Hydrilla). Widely dispersed at low densities during nesting season (0.03–3.6 birds/km², Bellrose 1980).

Displays and breeding behaviour

Reproductive and agonistic behaviour similar to other *Aythya* (Johnsgard 1965a). Mutual displays include Neck-stretch, Drinking or Bill-dip, and post-copulatory swim in Bill-down posture. ♂ pre-copulatory behaviour consists of Head-throw, Nod-swim, and Preen-behind-wing. ♀ Inciting stereotypic. Agonistic displays range in intensity from Bill-on-breast to Pushing (breast to breast) to Sneak to chasing and fighting (biting, bill jabs, and wing-beating) (Titman and Seymour 1976).

Pairbond forms during spring migration (Mar–Apr) and remains intact until early incubation.

Breeding and life cycle

♀ philopatric to natal area (Mendall 1958). Return rates in Minnesota 15% for 1st year and 53% for after-1st-year ♀♀. Although ♂ and ♀ breed in 1st year, participation variable among years (Hohman 1984b, 1986b). Nesting phenology similar across range. Initiation of 1st nests, early May–mid June (peak 20 May–10 June); re-nests, late May–early July (Mendall 1958). Nests in flooded sedge (Koons and Rotella 2003) or mixed sedge-herbaceous vegetation or sedge-shrub stands (least preferred) (Townsend 1966, Sarvis 1972); constructed of residual vegetation within reach of bowl. Eggs olive-buff; 55.6×39.9 ($n = 88$) (Sarvis 1972); fresh weight 48.3 (Hohman 1984b); clutch in 1st nests 9 (6–14) ($n = 423$); re-nests 7 (5–9) ($n = 48$) (Mendall 1958). Hatchability 90% (McAuley and Longcore 1989). Incubation, by ♀, 26–27 days (25–29) ($n = 37$) at 85% constancy. Nest success in Maine, Michigan and Saskatchewan before 1970 64–70% ($n = 473$, Mendall 1958; $n = 49$, Townsend 1966; $n = 36$ Sarvis 1972); Maine 1983–85 ($n = 32$) 38% (McAuley and Longcore 1989). Causes of nest failure predation by American Mink, Raccoon and corvids (67–80%), flooding (16–24%) and desertion (5%) (Mendall 1958, McAuley and Longcore 1989). Parental care by ♀, who attends 21–56 days (Mendall 1958, Hohman 1984b, 1986a). Contour feathers appear Days 15–16; fledge at Days 49–56 (Mendall 1958). Juvenile survival to 45 days: brood 0.77 ($n = 64$); duckling 0.37 ($n = 381$) (McAuley and Longcore 1988). Ducklings <25 days of age survive at lower rate (0.975/day) than older ones (0.982/day) (McAuley and Longcore 1988). Annual survival of adult ♂♂ 0.63–0.69, ♀♀ 0.48–0.58 (Conroy and Eberhardt 1983).

Conservation and threats

Continental population considered stable or increasing but may be declining or distribution may be shifting at some locations (Conroy and Eberhardt 1983, Montalbano *et al.* 1985). Population stability or increases attributed to use of permanently flooded wetlands outside agricultural region for nesting, ability to pioneer into new areas, and adaptability to changing habitat conditions (Montalbano *et al.* 1985). Important conservation issues include acidification of northern wetlands, loss of freshwater habitats in southeastern US caused by coastal erosion, sea level rise, subsidence, urbanization and commercial (e.g. oil and gas) development, degradation of water quality contributing to reduced production of submersed aquatic plants, introductions of exotic species, high rates of lead shot ingestion, exposure to high concentrations of contaminants in riverine systems, disturbances related to navigation and recreation, chemical control of vegetation and fish stocking.

William L. Hohman

Tufted Duck *Aythya fuligula*
PLATE 24

Anas Fuligula Linnaeus, 1758, Syst. Nat., ed. 10, p. 128
Europe

Etymology: *fuligula* L. means sooty throated. Vernacular name first used by Ray in 1678.

Other names: Blue-neb, Tufted Pochard or Scaup, Tufty. Danish: Troldand; French: Fuligule morillon; German: Reiherente; Icelandic: Skúfönd; Japanese: Kinkuro-hajiro; Spanish: Porrón moñudo.

Variation: no subspecies.

Description

ADULT: dimorphic and ♂ slightly larger than ♀. ♂ in breeding plumage has black head (glossed purple), breast and upperparts (glossed green with faint vermiculations), white flanks. Wing coverts sometimes minutely speckled near tip. Long drooping crest at back of head. Relatively short blue-grey bill with broad black nail and small white band at base of nail; feet grey-blue with darker webs; eyes yellow. In flight, wings black with broad white stripe along entire width, less well defined on primaries. White underwing and white belly. ♀ generally dark brown with lighter brown flanks. Lesser and median coverts black-brown, often almost as black as ♂, sometimes speckled white. Pale feather edges on flanks and breast give barred effect. Belly whitish, mottled brown. Some individuals have whitish undertail coverts, especially during autumn, although most are brown. Short occipital crest. Often shows white around base of bill. Pattern in flight similar to that of adult ♂ with black areas dark brown. Bill greyer than adult ♂; feet greenish grey; eyes yellow.

MOULT: in eclipse or basic plumage, ♂ resembles adult ♀ but with yellow eye, darker plumage on head, breast and upperparts (brown-black); sides and flanks pale brown showing some vermiculations, lacks white around base of bill and has whiter underparts. Little or no crest. ♂ moults flight feathers late June–early Sept, and flightless for 2–3 weeks.

IMMATURE: ♂ has darker sides to head and foreneck with whitish flecking on mantle and scapulars; becomes increasingly like adult ♂ from Dec onwards but with duller iris, greyer flanks and narrower flight and tail feathers. Adult plumage fully attained by 1st summer.

DUCKLING: sooty brown above, paler below, with indistinct facial markings. At fledging, resembles adult ♀.

MEASUREMENTS AND WEIGHT: measurements from The Netherlands—Rijkinstitut voor Natuurheheer, Arnhem and Zoölogisch Museum (Institut voor Taxonomisches Zoölogie), Amsterdam—except culmen from Johnsgard (1965a). ♂ wing ($n = $ 46), 198–215 (206); tail ($n = 44$), 49–58 (54); culmen (38–42); bill ($n = 66$), 37–44 (40); tarsus ($n = 40$), 34–37 (36); weight Dec–Mar, Switzerland (Bauer and Glutz 1968–69) ($n = 92$), 600–1020 (813), Jan, Switzerland (Kestenholz 1994) ($n = 27$), 765–1015 (868). ♀ wing ($n = 40$), 193–205 (199); tail ($n = 39$), 48–57 (53); culmen (38–41); bill ($n = 73$), 36–41 (39); tarsus ($n = 40$), 32–37 (35); weight Dec–Mar ($n = 58$), 560–930 (718), Jan ($n = 5$), 730–815 (778).

Field characters

Small compact diving duck with rounded forehead, flattish crown, characteristic drooping crest and short, flattish bill. Length 400–470 mm. Distinctive rounded head shape and bill pattern particularly useful in identification (Madge and Burn 1988). Birds in eclipse and in transitional stages can be confused with Ring-necked Duck; ♀ Tufted Ducks in these plumages often show whitish foreflanks; however, flank border line of Ring-neck distinctly S-shaped, and birds shorter tailed and longer bodied. Tufted Ducks also lack distinctive head shape and bill pattern of Ring-necked Duck. ♀ often shows white at base of bill recalling scaups, or white undertail coverts recalling Ferruginous Duck or Baer's Pochard. ♀ Ferruginous Duck has particularly obvious white undertail coverts and, along with Baer's Pochard, has distinctive crown which peaks in middle and lacks crest. In addition, eye of ♀ Ferruginous Duck dark brown compared to yellow-orange of Tufted Duck.

Greater Scaup far larger, more bulky, relatively longer bill with less black at tip, and larger head with smoothly rounded crown lacking crest. ♂ Greater Scaup has grey not black mantle and ♀ shows distinct pale oval ear-patch on sides of head. Separation from Lesser Scaup more problematic. Plumage of Lesser Scaup similar to that of Greater Scaup. Prominent raised area at back of Lesser Scaup crown gives higher profile than Tufted Duck. Lesser Scaup bill broader and white patches at base of bill always distinct and clean. Furthermore, breast, mantle and scapulars of Lesser Scaup almost uniform with flanks, contrasting markedly with head. At close range, flanks and scapulars of all scaup show indistinct grey 'frosting', feature lacking on Tufted Duck. Juvenile Tufted Duck often lacks crest, is lighter in colour than ♀, and requires careful scrutiny.

Voice

Generally silent outside courtship period. Non-vocal sounds include whistling of wings in flight and rattling of bill against flight feathers in Preen-behind-wing display. Adult ♂ utters quiet courtship call *buck buck buck* of varying intensity, often introduced by single loud *buck*. Also produces mellow *whee oo* during Head-throw and Kinked-neck display, and whistled *wha wa whew*. Outside breeding season, gives whistle somewhat reminiscent of Eurasian Wigeon. Also utters soft *kack* and *rr* sounds. During courtship, ♀ utters 3 recognized calls: *quack*, *karr*, and *gack*. Guttural *bre bre bre* given in flight. ♀ leading young may give accented *grr grr grr orr arr arr* when disturbed, but otherwise utters rather soft call (Bauer and Glutz 1968–69, Johnsgard 1965a). Sonograms in Cramp and Simmons (1977). Distress calls of young similar to Ferruginous ducklings.

Range and status

Widespread, breeding from Atlantic to Pacific, from 45–70°N, across entire Palearctic region in boreal, temperate and steppe climatic zones.

Five, almost discrete, wintering populations identified (Rose and Scott 1997). Northwest European population, estimated at 1 000 000, breeds in Iceland, Fennoscandia, Baltic region and Russia, highly migratory, moving southwards to join resident birds in Baltic and North Sea and around Atlantic coast during winter. In hard winters, many birds may leave Baltic to bolster numbers in The Netherlands, Britain and Ireland (Durinck *et al.* 1994). Population that winters in central Europe, Black Sea and Mediterranean (600 000) originates from breeding grounds in Russia and northwestern Siberia (Monval and Pirot 1989). Third population, breeding in western Siberia and southwest Asia and wintering in northeast Africa, estimated at 200 000. In eastern Asia, breeds widely across Siberia to Russian far east and winters in southern, southeastern and eastern Asia. Central and southern Asian population estimated at 100 000–1 000 000. East and southeast Asian population estimated at 500 000–1 000 000; of these, *c* 500 000 overwinter in China, 10 000 in south Korea and 80 000 in Japan (Miyabayashi and Mundkur 1999).

Regularly seen in North America, on Atlantic and Pacific coasts; also recorded as vagrant in many African countries south to Tanzania.

Habitat and general habits

Lowland breeder of natural freshwater lakes, reservoirs, ponds and mineral extraction pits with abundant marginal and emergent vegetation (Bengtson 1971b). Favours islands for nesting. Has preference for eutrophic waters 3–5 m deep but adapts to waters of different trophic status. Avoids lakes

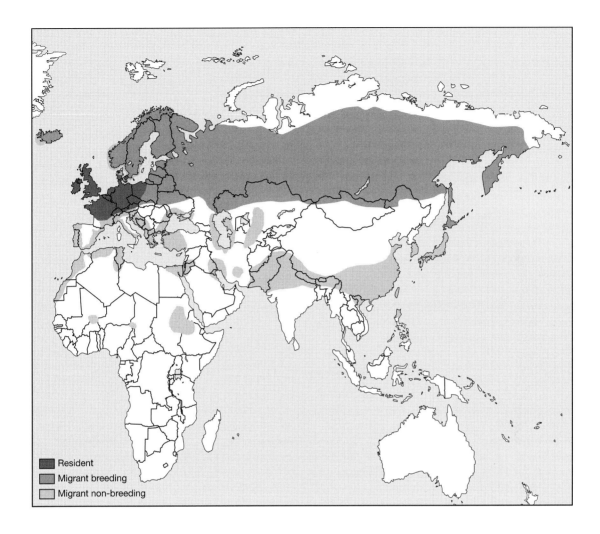

Resident
Migrant breeding
Migrant non-breeding

deeper than 15 m. Also breeds along quiet stretches of rivers. In winter, selects large freshwater bodies but may occur on brackish inland seas and sheltered coastal locations. Omnivorous, with adult diet composed of items collected from dives to bottom. Will also take invertebrates from emergent vegetation and from water surface and occasionally up-ends. Comes ashore to feed on grain and may take food from humans. Great variation in diet according to locality, year and season largely dependent on availability and abundance of food. In coastal areas, chiefly molluscs taken (Madsen 1954) and, inland, mainly animal material including molluscs, crustaceans, and insects, although plants form major part of diet in some areas (Campbell 1947, Olney

1963). Has taken advantage of spread of Zebra Mussels which flourish in European freshwaters (Olney 1963). Large proportion of diet inland composed of molluscs in Japan and Ireland (Winfield and Winfield 1994a, Oka *et al.* 1999). Ducklings take most food items from surface; newly hatched ones take seeds and adult insects, older ducklings take *Limnaea* snails, other molluscs and chironomid larvae (Lees and Street 1974, Hill and Ellis 1984). Forages day and night and may spend up to 61% of daylight feeding (Nilsson 1970, Folk 1971). Limited capacity to store food in gut and long digestive pauses suggest large proportion of winter activity budget spent feeding (DeLeeuw 1999). Mean dive duration 20 sec (Folk 1971);

inter-dive interval increases with increasing dive time to point where relatively longer period needed on surface for recovery (Nilsson 1972). Selectivity for small mussels increases with diving depth (DeLeeuw and van Eerden 1992). At low temperatures, foraging rate increases as more food required to balance higher heat loss (Nilsson 1972). Experimentally shown that dive duration shorter in low temperatures and larger food items taken and ingested at water surface (DeLeeuw *et al.* 1999), suggesting that cost of crushing shells increased in favour of reducing diving cost in cold weather.

Highly gregarious in winter, with flocks of many thousands (Scott and Rose 1996). Moult migrations occur in some areas, with moulting flocks reaching peak late July. Autumn migration begins Sept and breeding areas deserted late Sept-early Oct. Spring migration begins late Feb and birds on breeding grounds late Apr; however, most northerly breeders do not return until mid May.

Displays and breeding behaviour

Courtship behaviour begins early. ♀ often courted by more than 10 ♂♂ that parade around her in alert posture. Single ♂♂ adopt courtship-intent posture with neck sunk in shoulders; neck enlarged and pupil contracts to increase intensity of yellow in eye (Millais 1913). Secondary displays of ♂ include Head-shake, frequent Head-flicks, and Upward-shakes. Head-throw and Kinked-neck displays accompanied by courtship calls. Head-throw rapid and preceded by Head-shakes and Head-flicks. These behaviours often followed by Bill-dipping and Preen-behind-wing. Neck-stretch display with thickened neck and raised crest often performed silently in front of ♀. Coughing display also frequent, ♂ giving Coughing Call whilst flicking tail and wings. In final display, ♂ nods head while swimming, ceremonially leads ♀ by swimming in front of her giving Turn-back-of-head with head feathers strongly depressed. ♀ will also perform Head-throw and Nod-head, frequently Bill-dip and often dive (Johnsgard 1965a, McKinney 1965c).

Copulation initiated by ♂. Pre-copulatory display consists mainly of repeated preening by ♂ with some Peening-behind-wing and occasional Bill-dipping. ♀ may respond with similar behaviour before assuming copulatory posture. Post-copulation, ♂ immediately performs Kinked-neck display and swims away, calling, in characteristic Bill-down posture.

In flocks, generally peaceful but give aggressive rushes over water with head lowered and neck extended. ♀ Incites ♂ by calling while alternating between lateral threatening movements and assumption of Neck-stretch posture with Chin-lifting. Rape attempts rare. Within flocks, Chin-lifting used as pre-flight signal (Johnsgard 1965a).

Breeding and life cycle

Nests built on ground or in water, generally in vegetation tussocks or under bushes (Thomas 1980, Hill 1984). First eggs laid Iceland *c* 25 May. Will also nest in open, but then usually within colonies of gulls or terns that offer protection from predators (Newton and Campbell 1975, Väänänen 2000). Not colonial, but hundreds often nest at same site. Nests regularly dispersed 7–11 m apart; denser within gull colonies, 2–3 m apart (Newton and Campbell 1975). Usually within 20 m of water (Thomas 1980) unless on islands where may occur 150 m from water. Nests constructed in depression and lined with vegetation and down, diameter 20–25 cm, cup depth 7–10 cm. ♀ builds using material within reach and shapes cup by rotating body. Eggs greenish grey, 59 × 41 (53–66 × 38–46) ($n = 300$) (Schönwetter 1960–66), weight 53 (46–65) ($n = 58$); clutch 9.5 (8–16) (Hildén 1964a, Havlín 1966a, Hori 1966, Newton and Campbell 1975). Interspeciifc and intraspecific egg dumping frequent (Hildén 1964a, Newton and Campbell 1975). Incubation 24 (23–28) days, by ♀, begins on clutch completion. Young precocial and nidifugous and cared for by ♀; weight at hatching 35 (30–43) ($n = 100$). Fledge in 45–50 days. During pre-fledging period of linear development, ducklings in captivity increased mass by *c* 11 g per day (Kear 1970a). ♀ deserts juveniles 29–42 days after hatching. Single-brooded.

In Czechoslovakia, nest failures caused by desertion as result of disturbance, flooding and predation (Havlín 1966b). Breeding success varies between years but published figures suggest approximately 68% of nests successful and 11–15% of young fledge (Hildén 1964a, Havlín 1966b, Hill 1982). Nest success related, in part, to nutrient reserves of

♀ during egg-laying and incubation, due to reliance on endogenous reserves during incubation (Blums *et al.* 1997). Eggs and ducklings taken by avian and mammalian predators (Hildén 1964a, Havlín 1966b, Newton and Campbell 1975); chilling further cause of duckling mortality (Koskimies and Lahti 1964). Can breed in 1st year yet majority begin in 2nd (Blums *et al.* 1996).

Life expectancy 1.7 years and mean annual mortality of adults ringed in northwest Europe 46% (Cramp and Simmons 1977). Oldest BTO ringed bird 17 years 9 months (Toms and Clark 1998).

Conservation and threats

One of few *Aythya* to have increased in numbers and distribution in western Eurasia over recent decades. Has expanded rapidly in breeding range since 1950s, coinciding with spread of introduced Zebra Mussel which occurs in freshwater; numbers positively correlated with Zebra Mussel densities in Switzerland (Burla and Ribi 1998). High mussel densities in some areas may increase winter survival. Colonization also bolstered by freshwater eutrophication and increase in artificial waterbodies, increasing abundance of invertebrate biomass, plant growth and potential nesting habitat.

Agricultural intensification may reduce available breeding habitat, and breeding success be reduced through disturbance caused by increasing recreational activities at inland waterbodies. Falling water levels due to construction of dams, sedimentation, organic pollution and inorganic effluents attributed to recent declines in wintering numbers at Burdur Gölü in Turkey (Green *et al.* 1996). Fish stocking reduces breeding success and can lower overwintering numbers as fish compete for available food supplies (Phillips 1992, Giles 1994, Winfield and Winfield 1994b). Although quarry in most of range, hunting mortality at present level appears sustainable.

James A. Robinson

Greater Scaup *Aythya marila*
PLATE 24

Anas Marila Linnaeus, 1761, Fauna Svecica, ed. 2, p. 39
Lapland

Etymology: *marile* Gr. means charcoal embers, and refers to grey back of ♂.

Other names: Greater Scaup used mainly in North America, but also Bluebill and Broadbill; Scaup in Europe. Pacific Scaup sometimes referred to as *A. m. mariloides* race and European Scaup as *A. m. marila*. Danish: Bjergand; French: Fuligule milouinan; German: Bergente; Icelandic: Duggönd; Japanese: Suzugamo; Spanish: Pato-boludo Mayor (Mexico).

Variation: 2 subspecies, *A. m. marila* found throughout Europe and western Asia, *A. m. mariloides* Vigors, 1839 in eastern Asia and North America. *A. m. nearctica* Stejneger, 1885 is merged in *A. m. mariloides*.

Description

ADULT: dimorphic. ♂ in breeding or alternate plumage, head and neck black with green gloss, sometimes purple. Breast, upper mantle, rump, tail-coverts (upper and under) also black or blackish. Lower mantle and scapulars vermiculated white and black giving greyish appearance. Sides and belly white with feint greyish vermiculations. Upperwing coverts black with brownish tinge, speckled white; broad white band along secondaries and most of primaries. Underwing and axillaries whitish becoming lighter towards trailing edge. Iris golden yellow. ♀ in winter dull brownish with clear white patches surrounding bill base and on side of bill, both becoming more obvious as brownish feather tips wear. Usually some white vermiculations on mantle, scapulars and along flanks; latter noticeably lighter brown than upperparts. Wing browner than ♂, lacks speckled white. In summer, vermiculations absent and white patches obscured because of fresh brown-tipped feathers. Iris also becomes paler yellow and sometimes grey; bill leaden grey. Subspecies similar in size; in *mariloides*, vermiculations coarser and usually underside of only 6 primaries white, not all or most as in *marila* (Palmer 1976, Kessel *et al.* 2002).

MOULT: similar to Tufted Duck. Adult ♀ moults body and tertials Mar, wings mid–late summer (some Sept–Nov, Joensen 1973), and tail Apr–Sept (Baker 1993). Also partial body moult Aug–Nov. In ♂, body moult (eclipse) starts later than in ♀, late May–early July; flight feathers drop simultaneously so that flightless for 3–4 weeks June–Sept. Unlike juvenile ♀ Tufted duck, apparently moults only once in autumn (Billard and Humphrey 1972). Eclipsed ♂ in basic plumage, unlike most other ducks, similar to full adult plumaged ♂ except that black parts more brownish, white flanks contain brown streaks and hint of white on feathers around bill base; bill also duller.

IMMATURE: resembles adult ♀ with less white around bill base. Cheeks, front of neck and sides paler, especially in ♀. Little vermiculation on ♂ and none on ♀. By Oct, assumes some adult features, more so by Apr but does not gain full plumage until 2nd year. Bare parts darker than adult.

DUCKLING: upperparts generally olive-brown, sometimes with feint shoulder spots; underparts pale yellowish, greying breast band; wing patches and rump spots inconspicuous; head darker than back but pale yellowish cheeks; eyestripe often large in front of eye, and small or thin behind; irides olive grey becoming paler; tarsus grey-green becoming paler; bill base, yellow-orange getting darker (Nelson 1993).

MEASUREMENTS AND WEIGHT: from Cramp and Simmons (1977) for *marila* skins, ♂ wing (*n* = 45), 219–237 (227); tail (*n* = 45), 52–61 (56.3); bill (*n* = 46), 41–47 (44.0); tarsus (*n* = 56), 38–42 (39.9); toe (*n* = 58), 61–72 (65.9); weight (*n* = 17), 972–1372 (1219). ♀ wing (*n* = 35), 211–225 (217); tail (*n* = 34), 51–60 (55.7); bill (*n* = 36), 40–45 (42.9); tarsus (*n* = 45), 37–41 (38.6); toe (*n* = 40), 61–68 (64.3); weight (*n* = 12), 1037–1312 (1183). Measurements of *mariloides* in Palmer (1976).

Field characters

Medium-sized diving-duck, 400–510 mm long, bulky in appearance with blue, broad bill on rounded head showing little neck. At distance, could be confused with Redhead; at close range can be confused only with Lesser Scaup or Tufted Duck. Lesser Scaup smaller, less bulky, more curved back (Greater's is almost flat) and more buoyant on water. Vermiculations on Lesser Scaup noticeably darker grey in field and alternating lines of black and white much broader. Head more purplish, not green as Greater Scaup, has distinct bump on rear of crown, and flanks greyer. In flight, white band on upperwing does not, or barely, extends into primaries. Hybrids with other *Aythya* cause problems of separation (see Gillham *et al.* 1966, Harris *et al.* 1993). ♂ Tufted Duck looks similar to ♂ Greater Scaup but smaller, has black back and usually obvious crest on back of head. ♀ and immature Greater Scaup can be confused easily with ♀ Lesser Scaup and Tufted Duck. Lesser Scaup lacks white ear patch in all plumages but general structure and wing pattern best distinguishing features. ♀ Tufty darker brown; sometimes has white feathers around bill base but never so extensive as scaup; again, general structure best separator.

Separation of duckling from Lesser Scaup difficult but generally darker bodied, always larger (body and bill) at given age, less contrasting facial markings; can be separated with 90% certainty using morphometrics (Nelson 1993).

Voice

Generally silent in nonbreeding season. ♂ has 2 main calls often linked with courtship, soft dove-like *kucku* given during Head-throw and Kinked-neck displays (Millais 1913, Steinbacher 1960) and rapid whistling *week-week-whew* sound (Johnsgard 1965a) made during Cough display. ♀ calls more complex and nondescript, described by Millais (1913), Steinbacher (1960) and Johnsgard (1965a). Sonogram of ♂ and ♀ calls in Cramp and Simmons (1977).

Range and status

Nominate race breeds from Iceland across northern Scandinavia and Russia to River Lena halfway across Siberia; winters primarily in northwest Europe and Black and Caspian Seas, probably further east, and to some extent in Mediterranean. Winter population estimate for northwest Europe, 310 000 birds, thought to be accurate. Numbers wintering in

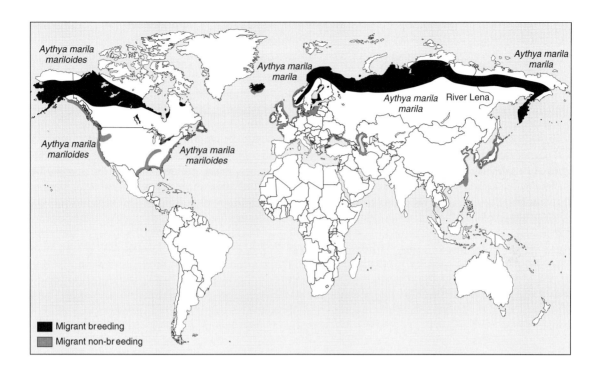

Black, Caspian and Mediterranean Seas unknown but rough estimate of 50 000 has increased to equally rough 200 000 birds (Rose and Scott 1997) suggesting population of *c* 500 000 for this race. Degree of movement between east and west European birds unknown. Icelandic Greater Scaup mix with European and Russian birds in winter off mainland Europe and evidence of Icelandic birds subsequently breeding in Russia. Isolation of Icelandic birds, and dependence on British Isles in winter, felt by some to be sufficient reason to treat as separate population. Vagrant to North Africa, Greece, Iraq, Malta, Cyprus, Azores, Marianas Islands, West Indies and Hawaii.

In North America and eastern Asia, population estimates confounded by lack of information and/or enormous difficulty in separating Greater from Lesser Scaup in both winter and summer over large areas. No recent estimates but Johnsgard (1975) stated North American population *c* 750 000 individuals. Widespread and common visitor to Japan in winter (Brazil 1991). Based on little information, Scott and Rose (1997) put eastern Asia population in range 100 000–1 000 000; Miyabayashi and Mundkur (1999) revised this to 200 000–400 000, with 5000

wintering in China, 20 000–30 000 in South Korea and 170 000 in Japan.

There is, likewise, little information on trends in numbers, except locally in parts of Europe. In Britain and Ireland, small wintering population of *c* 11 000 has fluctuated greatly over last 30 years, accompanied by shifts in distribution thought associated with changing temporary food sources (Kirby *et al.* 1993). Elsewhere in Europe, increases and decreases recorded with no overall pattern (Tucker and Heath 1994); same true of breeding populations in Europe and Russia. Information from breeding population in Iceland suggest numbers at Lake Mývatn decreased greatly 1949–76 (Garðarsson 1979).

Habitat and general habits

Breeds by freshwater lakes, pools and rivers in tundra regions and moorland. Highly gregarious in nonbreeding season, often found in large rafts, predominantly in shallow coastal waters, especially estuaries, but also on large lakes. Awkward on land but readily rests on sandbanks in inaccessible areas, especially at low tide. Flies infrequently, rising from water with difficulty, but flies rapidly in closeknit flocks. Not shy but often overlooked by observers. Migratory throughout most of range. More ♂♂ winter further north than ♀♀.

Feeds in shallow water, sometimes dabbling or up-ending, diving in water less than 6 m deep, but frequently 2 m. On Solway, most often seen feeding at edge of rising tide, diving in shallow water (< 1 m) and nearly always < *c* 3 m. Feeding patterns probably affected by tides and nocturnal feeding suspected to occur, sometimes in response to daytime disturbance (Nilsson 1969). Omnivorous, diet variable according to location and time of year; in winter, shellfish preferred food, especially mussels, cockles *Cardium*, and clams *Macoma*. In Denmark, cockles, periwinkles *Littorina*, Dogwhelk *Nassa reticulata*, laver shells *Hydrobia*, and Blue Mussel *Mytilus edulis*, especially, accounted for up to 95% of diet by volume. Molluscs also important in brackish waters but mainly *Hydrobia*; crustaceans *Gammarus*, plant material (seeds, e.g. from pondweeds *Potamogeton*) significant (Madsen 1954). Baltic Clam *Macoma balthica* and cockle *Cardium lamarckii* important in Sweden (Nilsson 1969). In former USSR (Dementiev and Gladkov 1952), Rybinsk Reservoir, molluscs made up 31.5% volume, 24% aquatic insects, 33% plant roots and 10.5% seeds. In Caspian sea, fed entirely on either *Cardium edule* or mussels *Mytilaster lineatus* in 2 different areas. On freshwater Lough Neagh, Northern Ireland, diet dominated by chironomids (Winfield and Winfield 1994a). In semi-natural conditions (The Netherlands), daily consumption of Zebra Mussels was 2–3 times body weight; feeding activity typically involved short bouts of number of dives until oesophagus and gizzard full, followed by longer pauses (5–10 min) for digestive purposes (DeLeeuw 1999).

Summer diet differs; most detailed information from Lake Mývatn, Iceland, where chironimid larvae, stickleback *Gasterosteus* eggs and molluscs eaten, relative amounts varying between sexes, years and season (Bengtson 1971a, Garðarsson 1979). On Pechora Delta, Western Siberia, plant leaves, mainly from *Potamogeton* (Dementiev and Gladkov 1952), found as main item in stomachs of 10 animals. In Sweden, pea-shell *Pisidium*, insect larvae and *Gammarus* taken (Bauer and Glutz 1968–69).

In some areas, readily adapts to new and changing food sources. Most recently, prolific Zebra Mussel colonizing parts of Great Lakes of North America from Europe, now forms important part of diet (Hamilton and Ankney 1994). Recorded exploiting human-related food sources; in Scotland, fed on grain from outfall pipes at breweries and distilleries and at sewage pipes where presumably high densities of invertebrates accumulate (Campbell 1984). Evidence that birds exploit blue cockles rejected by cockle dredging in Scotland (Quinn *et al.* 1996b), and fish thrown from boats in harbours in US (Christmas 1960).

Displays and breeding behaviour

Communal courtship between several ♂♂ and single ♀ common in late winter and spring. In Courtship-intent posture, hunched ♂ swims with smoothed feathers on rounded head. Major displays include Head-throw and Kinked-neck accompanied by crooning call, inconspicuous Sneak and Coughing. Many secondary displays recorded. ♀ Incites ♂ by orientating bill away from ♂. Courtship flights common. Pair courtship incorporates much of above activity but also Preen-behind-wing by both sexes. Pre-copulatory behaviour consists mainly of repeated Preen-behind-wing and Bill-dips while ♀ adopts prone posture. Copulation initiated by ♂ who performs Kinked-neck display while calling and swimming away with Bill-down. ♀ swims briefly in same manner and bathes (see Johnsgard 1965a, Bengtson 1968 for further details).

Breeding and life cycle

Monogamous, but pairbond only of seasonal duration. Pair forms any time from late winter. Nest both solitarily and colonially, sometimes among gulls and terns (Hildén 1964a). Laying in Arctic, dependent on thaw, late May-early June. Nest built by ♀ on ground, sometimes in shallow water and normally well concealed in tussocks. Eggs olive-grey, blunt and ovate, laid one per day; dimensions on Yukon Delta, Alaska (Flint and Grand 1999) 63.52×43.28 ($n = 3937$); in captivity, mean weight 64.8 ($n = 56$). In Finland, clutch size 10 (7–14) (Hildén 1964a); 2 or more ♀♀ laying in same nest common in Iceland where 1st clutches contain

9.7 eggs (Bengtson 1972b). Incubation, by ♀ alone, 26–28 days and starts on completion of clutch. ♂ usually deserts midway through incubation. Young precocial and nidifugous and, in captivity, weigh 38.5 (*n* = 14). Small crèches sometimes seen. Fledge in 40–45 days by which time juveniles independent. Hatching success in Finland averaged 77% of eggs laid over 3 years and 6.5% of young reared to fledging, but high variation noted between years (Hildén 1964a). Breeds in captivity sometimes in 1st and usually in 2nd year; not proven in wild. Mean annual adult mortality of Icelandic birds estimated at 52% (Boyd 1962); longevity record of BTO ringed bird 8 years 5 months (Toms and Clark 1998).

Conservation and threats

Main threat susceptibility to oil pollution when moulting and in winter. In Caspian Sea, thought to be less numerous than previously because of oil pollution. Also may be susceptible to accumulation of high levels of organochlorine contaminants (Perkins and Barclay 1997) which may have management consequences, perhaps even by affecting thermal properties of plumage as suggested for Lesser Scaup (Stephenson 1997). Use as biomonitors of metal contamination advocated in US federal reserves (Cohen *et al.* 2000). Legal protection required for most important areas and control of oil exploration and transport, both terrestrially in Arctic and by sea elsewhere. Hunting legal in 7 countries of European Union, where 8000 shot annually in 1980s (Bertelsen and Simonsen 1986)—the majority (>80%) in Denmark where seaduck hunting in decline. By early 1990s, numbers shot in Denmark *c* 1000–3000 (Madsen *et al.* 1996b) and currently remain at this level. In Europe, winter populations considered to have unfavourable conservation status, although threats localized. Not threatened worldwide (Collar *et al.* 1994).

John L. Quinn

Lesser Scaup *Aythya affinis*
PLATE 24

Fuligula affinis Eyton, 1838, Monogr. Anatidae, p. 157

North America

Etymology: *affinis* L. for related or allied, presumably in reference to Greater Scaup.

Other names: Little Bluebill, Broadbill (also used for Greater Scaup), Dosgris. French: Petit morillon; Spanish: Pato boludo chico.

Variation: no subspecies nor geographical variation in measurements.

Description

ADULT: dimorphic. ♂ in breeding or alternate plumage head black with purplish sheen; neck, breast and upper mantle black; flanks and belly white; lower mantle grey flecked and ventral region black. In flight, white wing stripe extends across secondaries, primaries greyish brown. Bill slaty blue; feet and legs grey with darker webs; eye brilliant yellow. ♀ fuscous to chocolate brown with white patch of varying size at base of bill; upper parts darker, wing coverts flecked grey but otherwise as ♂. Bill dark grey; feet and legs as ♂; eye colour varies with age from olive-brown to olive or brownish yellow (Trauger 1974).

MOULT: basic or eclipse plumage of ♂ similar to ♀ but more mottled and lacking face patch. Basic plumage of ♀ similar to alternate plumage, but face patch less distinct than in alternate. ♂ moults into basic plumage late June–Aug, with heaviest moulting July–Aug, quickly followed by pre-alternate moult, completed Sept–Oct. ♀ moults into basic plumage early Mar–Apr, and into alternate plumage Aug–Sept. In both sexes, greatest moult intensity occurs during wing moult in late summer.

IMMATURE: before first pre-alternate moult resembles adult ♀ definitive basic plumage, but white face patch less clearly defined; scapular feathers plain, and underparts paler and browner. Eyes in ♂ yellow, in ♀ brownish or greyish olive.

DUCKLING: upperparts dark olive, with inconspicuous dorsal pattern; lowerparts pale yellow-buff, darker at side and undertail. Head buff-brownish olive with bright to buff-yellow cheek and throat; dark eyestripe well defined in front of eye and contrasting with often bright yellow lores; post-ocular stripe and pale eye-ring usually well marked. Bill of Lesser Scaup smaller, more slender at base and with smaller nail than Greater Scaup. Bill blackish, iris dark olive or brownish grey shifting toward greenish yellow.

MEASUREMENTS AND WEIGHT: from breeding birds in Manitoba; see Austin *et al.* (1998) for summary of other locations and periods of life cycle. ♂ ($n = 40$) tail, 47–59 (52.3 ± 0.4); wing, 193–226 (204.8 ± 1.1); keel, 79.2–89.8 (84.1 ± 0.4); bill, 47–54 (50.0 ± 0.3); tarsus, 30.3–37.5 (35.1 ± 0.2). ♀ ($n = 47$) tail, 48–56 (52.0 ± 0.3); wing, 184–205 (195.3 ± 0.6); keel, 76.4–88.3 (82.4 ± 0.4); bill, 46–54 (49.7 ± 0.2); tarsus, 32.0–36.8 (34.3 ± 0.2). Weight data from winter (Louisiana), spring (Illinois, Minnesota), and fall migration (Minnesota), and southern breeding area (Manitoba); see Austin *et al.* (1998); ♂ ($n = 1718$) 546–1156 (maxima: fall staging [Oct, $n = 38$] 959.0 ± 17.8; minima: breeding season [May–Jul, $n = 40$] 721.3 ± 11.3 and winter [Jan, $n = 28$] 721.4 ± 8.8), ♀ ($n = 1252$) 517–1037 (maxima: fall staging [Oct, $n = 36$] 868.1 ± 16.6; minima: spring staging [Mar, $n = 22$] 647.5 ± 16.1).

Field characters

Small-bodied (380–430 mm long) diving duck difficult to distinguish in field from larger Greater Scaup. ♂ has purplish gloss on head and higher profile in comparison to greenish gloss and low, rounded head profile of Greater Scaup ♂. Nail at tip of upper mandible noticeably and proportionally smaller in Lesser Scaup; most readily observed in field in ♂. In flight, white wing stripe of Greater Scaup typically extends from secondaries onto inner 6 primaries, whereas white typically extends only across secondaries and cuts off sharply at primaries of Lesser Scaup. ♀♀ cannot easily be separated at distance except by wing pattern.

Ring-necked Duck readily distinguished from Lesser Scaup by peaked head profile, white ring at base of bill, and grey wing stripe; ♂ has dark back, and white crescent between black breast and grey sides, ♀ has white eye-ring and paler face. Tufted Duck has round head with distinct crest and darker back in both sexes. Redhead ♀ has rounder head, paler throat, heavy black nail on bill, and grey wing stripe.

Voice

♂ generally silent, but gives soft calls during courtship, when leading Inciting mate during interactions with other conspecifics, and during post-copulatory display; ♀ louder and more vocal. Coughing call, frequently uttered by ♂♂ in display groups, single whistled *whew*; Kinked-neck and Head-throw calls of ♂ faint *whee-ooo*. ♀ makes repeated low *arrr* calls while Inciting during interactions with unpaired ♂♂ and other pairs (Johnsgard 1965a). ♀ gives louder repeated series of *purrr* calls during pre-laying and early laying when disturbed by potential mammalian predator (dog, fox); these calls generally given while 'tolling' to predator (i.e. swimming close with head and neck extended maximally upwards) or rarely while circling in flight around predator.

Range and status

Breeds in open boreal forest and forest tundra of Alaska east to Québec, and south in parkland and prairie regions of eastern Oregon, Idaho, north Montana, North and east South Dakota, and northwest Minnesota. Breeding-pair densities in central Canada highest in prairie parkland (north-central Alberta and southwest Manitoba), and lowest in southeast Alberta prairie grassland and boreal forest (Vermeer 1972). One of most common breeding wildfowl in boreal forest of interior Alaska, Yukon, and Northwest Territories (Trauger 1971, Nudds and Cole 1991). Breeding-pair survey in May (Smith 1995) records largest percentage of breeding scaup (Greater and Lesser combined), on average, in Boreal Forest Region of Alaska and Canada (68%); smaller percentages recorded in Prairie-Parklands of US and Canada (25%) and Tundra Region of Alaska (7%). Winters primarily along Louisiana (Harmon 1962) and Florida Gulf Coasts (Chamberlain 1960), Lake Okeechobee, Florida (Turnbull *et al.* 1986), and Pacific and Gulf Coasts of Mexico, specifically coastal lagoons of Tamaulipas and Veracruz and Campeche and Yucatan (Saunders and Saunders 1981, Baldassarre *et al.* 1989).

Largest percentages of wintering scaup recorded, on average, in Mississippi (42%) and Atlantic flyways (41%); smaller percentages in Pacific (10%) and Central flyways (7%) (Austin *et al.* 1998). Also common in Pacific Northwest, upper midwest, and upper Atlantic coasts of US. Regular winter visitors farther south than other *Aythya*, to Central and South America and Caribbean (Botero and Rusch 1988); also occurs in Hawaii and other Caribbean and Pacific islands. Occasionally reported in Greenland (Bent 1923), Britain (Holian and Forley 1992), and on Canary Islands and The Netherlands; presently, 16 confirmed observations in western Palearctic (Clarke *et al.* 1995).

No long-term changes in breeding or wintering distribution into new range or abandonment of existing ranges. Breeding populations declined in southern portion of range, e.g. North Dakota (Bent 1923, Stewart 1975), Minnesota (Roberts 1932) and in Manitoba (Hochbaum 1944). Numbers using migration routes in river valleys of Illinois, Indiana, and on Mississippi River declined (Bellrose *et al.* 1979, Mumford and Keller 1984, Korschgen 1989). Continental population of Lesser and Greater Scaup combined (hereafter referred to simply as scaup), estimated from May Breeding Survey (Smith 1995), averaged 5 512 445 ± 147 090 during 1955–95, with high of 7 996 967 in 1972 and low of 4 080 149 in 1993. Lesser Scaup estimated to comprise 89% of combined continental population of scaup (*cf* Bellrose 1980, see Austin *et al.* 1998). Numbers of scaup wintering in US, estimated from Midwinter Survey (US Fish & Wildlife Service), averaged 1 344 205 ± 77 497 during 1955–95, with high of 2 806 249 in 1963 and low of 679 938 in 1983.

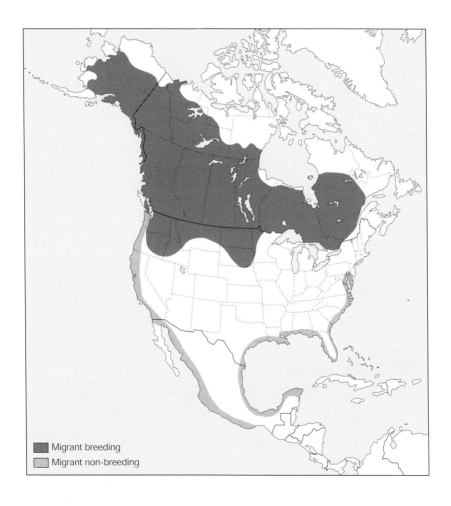

Migrant breeding
Migrant non-breeding

Breeding populations since have declined further to an average of 3 650 000 in 2001–03 (USFWS).

Continental population of breeding scaup exhibits no long-term trend (1955–95), despite large yearly fluctuations. More recently (1975–95), combined continental breeding population declined at rate of 128 635 birds a year; declines were 44 501 birds per year in Prairie-Parklands and 85 643 birds per year in Boreal Forest, whereas population in Tundra Region was stable (Austin *et al.* 1998). Numbers of scaup wintering in US declined at annual rate of 21 409 during 1955–95; declines in Mississippi Flyway, where few Greater Scaup winter, largely responsible for this negative trend (Austin *et al.* 1998). Continental population probably influenced primarily by variation in recruitment rates; annual survival of ♀♀ appears relatively high based on re-sighting of marked adults and ducklings (Afton 1984), and harvest rates relatively low (mean < 5%). ♀♀ exhibit low reproductive rate compared to other ducks, and reproductive success strongly age dependent (Trauger 1971, Afton 1984). Recruitment declines during dry years in Prairie-Parklands due to poor nest success and nonbreeding by 1 and 2-year-old ♀♀ (Rogers 1959, 1964, Afton 1984). Recruitment apparently declined recently in Boreal Forest (Nudds and Cole 1991), but little known of factors affecting recruitment in region (Austin *et al.* 1998).

Habitat and general habits

Breeds in association with fresh to moderately brackish, seasonal and semipermanent wetlands and lakes with abundant emergent plants; some use shallow river impoundments with deep marsh emergents. Fall migrants typically found on larger semipermanent and permanent wetlands and lakes, such as along Great Lakes (Bookhout *et al.* 1989) and large impounded portions of rivers (> 3000 ha) in Minnesota, Wisconsin and Iowa (Korschgen 1989); along coasts, found on large wetlands, lakes, reservoirs, and fresh to brackish estuaries. Spring migrants use smaller wetlands and marshes. Most moulting concentrations found on large boreal forest lakes. Wintering birds mainly use lakes, reservoirs, and fresh to brackish coastal bays and estuaries of south Atlantic and Gulf Coasts (Chabreck *et al.* 1989, Johnson and Montalbano 1989). During severe weather may move to more saline waters; more common in such saline habitats than other diving ducks except Redhead and Greater Scaup. Distribution during migration and winter generally not closely related to distribution of aquatic plant foods as in herbivorous diving ducks.

Feeds primarily by diving. Diet mainly carnivorous and variable, with aquatic invertebrates such as insects, crustaceans, and molluscs dominating. Seeds and vegetative parts of aquatic plants important in certain geographic areas. Diets similar for ♂ and ♀, and for adult and flying immatures (Bartonek and Murdy 1970, Afton and Hier 1991, Afton *et al.* 1991, Custer and Custer 1996).

During spring and summer, adults and ducklings forage in open water zone of shallow lakes (< 3 m deep; Dirschl 1969, Hammell 1973, Siegfried 1976b, van Horn 1991). Amphipods, midges (Diptera), and leeches (Hirudinea) dominant foods; aquatic plant seeds and molluscs important components in some months (Bartonek and Hickey 1969a, Dirschl 1969, Bartonek and Murdy 1970, Afton and Hier 1991). Diet of juveniles dominated by amphipods (49% total volume), molluscs (39%) and midges (8%) (Bartonek and Hickey 1969b); amphipods appear to increase in importance for older ducklings (Sudgen 1973). Fledged juveniles consume primarily amphipods similar to adults collected in same breeding area. Post-breeding ♀♀ in southwest Manitoba consume primarily amphipods, leeches, and chironomids.

Diets during migration generally > 75% animal material. During spring migration through Minnesota, amphipods comprise 33% (of total dry weight) of diet, with snails (Planorbidae and Valvatidae) contributing another 32% (Afton *et al.* 1991). During fall migration through Minnesota, amphipods comprise 55% (of total dry weight) of diet; snails and fingernail clams *Sphaerium* together comprise 15%, and 3 species of fish another 10% (Afton *et al.* 1991). Along Mississippi River in Iowa, fingernail clams dominate (> 95% of food items; Thompson 1973). While migrating through Lake Erie and Lake St. Clair, diet is 92% Zebra Mussel (aggregate % number; Custer and Custer 1996) introduced from central Europe and now at high densities (Leach 1993). In Klamath Basin of northern California, chironomids (44% by volume) and ostracods (18%) form major portion of diet (Gammonley and Heitmeyer 1990).

During winter, feeds mainly on open waters of Gulf of Mexico and on coastal bays, marshes, and inland lakes of southeastern US. Specific components of winter food vary geographically and often reflect local abundance. In most coastal areas, diet dominated by molluscs and benthic invertebrates (Harmon 1962, Hoppe *et al.* 1986, Jones and Drobney 1986, Afton *et al.* 1991). In contrast, along Columbia River in Oregon and Washington, diet mostly vegetative parts of *Elodea* and *Potamogeton*, and plant seeds from 6 aquatic species (Thompson *et al.* 1988).

Migratory throughout range, staging Sept–Oct and arriving on winter areas Nov–Dec, among latest migrants in North America. Depart winter areas late Feb–Mar, arriving on breeding grounds May. Moult migration by ♂♂ but participation by ♀ variable and little studied.

Feeding and resting common behaviours during spring migration; time-budgets of sexes similar and time spent feeding greater during day than night. During pre-laying and laying, ♀♀ spend more time feeding than mates for 1st nest and re-nests, and during day and night; ♂♂ spend more time alert than ♀ during same periods. ♂♂ spend considerable time alert during early incubation when mates are on nests and while with their mates during incubation recesses. Feeding and comfort movements most frequent behaviour of ♀ during incubation recesses. Time spent alert by brood hens high, declining as ducklings grow older; time spent in locomotion by brood hens increases with duckling age, whereas other behaviours do not vary much. Premoulting adults spend most time resting, feeding, locomoting, and in comfort movements. Feeding, resting, and comfort behaviour comprise largest time of moulting ♂ and ♀. During fall migration, feeding and resting are most common behaviours; time spent feeding by juveniles greater than that of adults of both sexes (Austin *et al.* 1998).

Breeding pairs have relatively small, highly overlapping home ranges (Afton 1983, 1984) and share loafing sites. Pre-nesting pairs may tolerate other individuals or pairs within 1–2 m (Hammell 1973), but paired ♂♂ more aggressive and maintain greater inter-pair distances when mates laying. Individuals maintain greater distances between conspecifics on wintering areas than on major northern fall migration areas.

Displays and breeding behaviour

Monogamous, but mate changes common on breeding areas prior to egg-laying. Mate switches occur after extensive fighting among ♂♂. Trios (2 ♂♂ and ♀; novice ♂ and pair of Hochbaum 1944; see also Trauger 1971) result when displaced mate follows his former ♀ and new mate for extended periods. Performance of displays, vocalizations, and agonistic behaviour similar to other *Aythya* (Johnsgard 1965a).

On breeding grounds, paired ♂♂ Turn-back-of-head to Inciting mates (i.e. ♀♀ perform Neck-stretching and Chin-lifting) in interactions with other pairs and unmated ♂♂ (Johnsgard 1965a). Cough most common ♂ display, wing and tail flicked while giving *whew* whistle. Kinked-neck call given with little head movement. Head-throw preceded by preliminary Head-shake and associated with *whee-ooo* call. While performing Turn-back-of-Head towards Inciting ♀, head feathers of ♂ depressed to produce low profile. Preen-behind-wing frequent, often mutual with mate. Paired ♂♂ frequently direct forced copulations at fertilizable, often older ♀♀ (Afton 1985).

On southern breeding areas, mid Apr–early June, sex ratios average 60–68% ♂ (Ellig 1955, Bellrose *et al.* 1961). Segregation by sex generally not observed on wintering areas (Bergan and Smith 1989); however, greater proportion of adult ♂♂ occurs in flocks on Gulf of Mexico than in coastal Louisiana marshes.

Breeding and life cycle

Pairbond formed Mar–Apr during spring migration and maintained until mid or late incubation. One of latest North American ducks to pair, with most pairing occurring quickly during late spring migration (Apr–early May). Less than 10% paired Dec–Jan, 12–17% paired Feb–Mar, and 56% Mar–Apr (Weller 1965); 60% paired in northwest Minnesota late Apr (Austin *et al.* 1998), 68% of ♂♂ and 99.8% of ♀♀ paired by early May on Delta Marsh, Manitoba (Siegfried 1974c); all ♀♀ paired by mid May in southwest Manitoba (Austin *et al.* 1998). Adult ♀♀ philopatric to natal areas—66% of 68 marked adult ♀♀ in Manitoba (Afton *in* Johnson and Grier 1988), and 20% of 330 banded ♀♀ in Northwest Territories, returned to breed (Trauger 1971). Fidelity by ♂ low (6–9%; Trauger 1971,

Afton *in* Johnson and Grier 1988). Fidelity to natal area by yearlings higher for ♀ than ♂ (12% *v* 0% of marked yearlings, respectively, banded in Northwest Territories; Trauger 1971; 49% *v* 4% in Manitoba; Afton *in* Johnson and Grier 1988).

Both ♂ and ♀ can breed at 1 year of age, but some ♂♂ probably do not because of excess in population. Most nonbreeding ♀♀ are 1 and 2 years old (Afton 1984). Most pairs breed in wet years but proportion of nonbreeding pairs varies with ♀ age and water conditions (Rogers 1964, Afton 1984). ♀♀ 3 years and older make one breeding attempt a year under most conditions (Afton 1984). Nesting more synchronous over large geographic range than in other ducks. Peak nesting period in most areas during June (Murdy 1964, Vermeer 1968, Hammell 1973, Hines 1977, Stewart 1975, Afton 1984). Mean date of nest initiation of first nests later for year-old ♀♀ than for older ♀♀ (20 June *v* 12–15 June) (Afton 1984). Most nests located on or near land in tall vegetative cover, sometimes in upland far from water. In Prairie Pothole Region, usually situated in tall vegetation in wet-meadow zones of prairie ponds and lakes, native prairie tracts, hayfields, along ditch banks, on islands, and occasionally in growing grain. In Northwest Territories, nests typically concealed in dense, tussocky sedge, within 1 m of open water, with abundant lateral and overhead cover. Commonly nests on islands, at times at high densities (Long 1970, Vermeer 1968, Brown 1987).

Eggs pale olive or greenish buff to dark olive-buff, smooth and slightly glossy; elliptical to nearly oval; 57.0 × 39.4 (*n* = 145) (Gehrman 1951); clutch mostly 8–10 (6–14) eggs, in late nests (most likely re-nests) smaller than early nests (10.2–10.6 for nests initiated < 30 June *v* 8.5 for later nests in southern Alberta; Keith 1961). Eggs lost to infertility or embryo death < 10% (Miller and Collins 1954, Vermeer 1968). Nest success varies among years, areas and habitats, largely due to differential predation. In Prairie-Grasslands, nest success ranged 8.2% (Giroux 1981a) to 90% (Aufforth *et al.* 1990) and averaged 37.3% (*n* = 1185) (Ellig 1955, Keith 1961, Stoudt 1971, Giroux 1981a, Holm 1984, Aufforth *et al.* 1990, Northern Prairie Wildlife Research Center unpubl. data; all nest success values expressed as Mayfield nest success or Discrete Green estimator, see Johnson

1979). Nest success in Prairie-Parklands averaged 29.5% (*n* = 613) (Kalmbach 1937, Kiel 1953, Smith 1953, 1955, Rogers 1964, Vermeer 1968, Hammell 1973, Hines 1977, Sankowski and Joynt 1992, Northern Prairie Wildlife Research Center unpubl. data). In Boreal Forest, nest success averaged 29.4% in Alaska (*n* = 29) and 67.7% in Northwest Territories (*n* = 21). Nest success low in Washington (10%, *n* = 56) (Gehrman 1951). On islands in Prairies, nest success averaged 31.0% (*n* = 565) (Leitch 1952, Keith 1961, Long 1970, Hammell 1973, Brown 1987). Proportion of ♀♀ re-nesting after loss of 1st nest does not vary with age or among years (overall mean of 16.4%, *n* = 73) but tends to be lower in year-olds and to increase with improving water conditions (Afton 1984).

Most unsuccessful nests lost to American Mink, Raccoon, Red Fox, Skunk *M. mephitis*, Common American Crow, Ring-billed *Larus delawarensis* and California Gulls, and American Badger (Keith 1961, Vermeer 1968, Hammell 1973, Afton 1984). In agricultural areas, some nests lost to farming operations (Afton 1984). Young smaller than Greater Scaup and Mallard ducklings of same age. Day-old ducklings in Alberta averaged 29.8 ± 0.22 (26.0–34.2) (*n* = 51 from 6 broods) (Nelson 1993). Rectrices and side feathers come in first, followed by scapular area, breast and belly, rump and back, head and neck, and lastly mantle; remiges emerge *c* Day 29–33. Shafts of primaries begin to clear *c* Day 49 (Lightbody and Ankney 1984); flight attained *c* Day 47–61 (Gollop and Marshall 1954, Schneider 1965). Hen attends brood 2–5 weeks, usually abandons as young fly. Crèching, or amalgamation of several broods, occurs frequently in areas with high nest success, relatively synchronous hatching, high brood densities and limited suitable habitat (Hines 1977, Afton 1993). Amalgamated broods often consist of several age classes and may include > 100 ducklings and up to 6 ♀♀; typically 15–40 ducklings with 2–3 ♀♀ (Hines 1977, Campbell *et al.* 1990).

Some 67.5 ± 4.9% of ducklings within broods survive 3 weeks (*n* = 39 broods) (Afton 1984). Annual estimated mortality rate for birds banded during summer before 1962 averaged 71% of immatures and 32% for adult ♂♂ (Smith 1963).

Annual estimated mortality for those banded during winter and early spring (1941–62) averaged 47.5% for adult ♂♂ and 53.7% for adult ♀♀. Overall apparent survival of yearling and after-2nd-year ♀♀ was 0.57 on Manitoba and Saskatchewan breeding sites (Rotella *et al.* 2003).

Conservation and threats

Highly regarded game species in north-central and eastern US and in central Canada; less preferred elsewhere. US harvest averaged $341\,523 \pm 29\,523$ for 1961–94, with high of 686 752 in 1977 and low of 93 327 in 1962 (Austin *et al.* 1998). Largest percentages taken in Mississippi Flyway (62%), primarily in Minnesota, Louisiana, and Michigan; smaller percentages in Central (16%), Atlantic (13%) and Pacific Flyway (9%). Harvest declined in all flyways since late 1970s, primarily due to decreasing numbers of scaup and hunters, and more restrictive hunting regulations since 1988.

Investigations into life history and ecology limited by remoteness of core breeding area in northern Boreal Forests and northern Parklands; most knowledge based on studies in southern portion of breeding range. Further information needed on factors influencing recruitment and survival rates, particularly in northern regions where populations declining and information least available. Investigations also needed into relationships of wetland and weather conditions during spring migration to subsequent recruitment; specifically, does drought in prairie pothole region during spring migration affect nutrient reserves, migration, and annual recruitment?

Knowledge of population size and trends confounded by inability to separate Lesser from Greater Scaup in breeding and wintering survey data, and by potential biases in May Breeding Survey (Austin *et al.* 1998). Separate estimates of Lesser and Greater Scaup in May Breeding Survey and Midwinter Survey needed to clarify population status of both species. Potential biases in May Breeding Survey (e.g. possible double-counting during cold late springs) need investigation and correction. Similarly, Midwinter surveys need to be improved for coverage and accuracy.

Conditions along fall migration routes and on wintering grounds have changed greatly over past 50 years, mainly due to human activity affecting water quality and food resources. Most significant are recent explosion of Zebra Mussels in Great Lakes and major rivers, which provide enhanced food resources for migrating and wintering scaup, and industrial thermal pollution, allowing scaup to winter farther north. How these changes have affected migration, hunting pressure and mortality, and winter condition of Lesser Scaup poorly understood. Investigations need to compare fall and winter survival rates between those Lesser Scaup that now migrate through Great Lakes *v* more traditional river migration routes. Comparisons of overwinter survival and prebreeding condition of scaup that winter in Great Lakes and other northern sites *v* traditional southern sites also needed to assess cross-seasonal influences.

Habitat degradation important in altering migration routes and use of breeding and wintering areas of Lesser Scaup, particularly in Illinois and Mississippi River Valleys. Declines probably due to disappearance of food resources such as fingernail clams whose demise coincided with increased pollution, sedimentation, and altered water levels on Illinois River (Mills *et al.* 1966, Bellrose *et al.* 1979). Disturbance to migrant flocks also may be important (Korschgen *et al.* 1985, Havera *et al.* 1992a). Wetlands along Lake Erie and Detroit River have suffered siltation, landfill, exotic plant introduction, and water-level controls (Bookhout *et al.* 1989). Drainage of wetlands and conversion to agriculture in Prairie Grassland and Parkland regions have decreased quality and quantity of habitat used during spring migration and breeding (Higgins 1977, Rakowski and Chabot 1983, Turner *et al.* 1987). Habitat degradation and loss from draining, dredging, levee construction, and altered water flow and salinity of concern in southern coastal marshes of Louisiana and Florida (Chabreck *et al.* 1989, Johnson and Montalbano 1989). In Boreal Forest Region of Northwest Territories, extensive new mining developments threaten breeding habitat.

Jane E. Austin, Christine M. Custer
and Alan D. Afton

The seaducks

The seaducks consist of the scoters, goldeneyes and mergansers and the closely related eiders. They are predominantly a northern hemisphere group— only the extinct Auckland Islands Merganser and the critically endangered Brazilian Merganser come from south of the Equator. They are often saltwater divers that are sexually dimorphic in plumage, voice and display, and they take (unlike most dabbling and diving ducks) at least two years to reach breeding age. They are fish and shellfish eaters that do not cast a pellet of bones or shells, as some other seabirds do, but pass them straight through the gut, squeezing out and digesting the flesh as the meal goes down. They need no extra grit; the muscular gizzard grinds sufficiently powerfully to crush the shells against one another. Seaducks are generally silent, except during display, when the male tends to whistle and the female to growl.

Some seaducks are tree-hole nesters, and have claws that are prominent and sharp for clinging to bark, as have their ducklings since they will need to climb up inside the nest before launching themselves from the opening towards the ground. The behaviour of the newly hatched young is adaptive as well. They cannot fly, so must act appropriately to a 10 m drop. The possibility that they jump had often been doubted—there are many tales of ducklings being carried in their parents' bills, on their backs, or between their legs—but, in fact, they do leap into the unknown and, being light in weight and covered with down, tend to come to no harm. This poses the question whether they hatch without any fear of heights. Research on ducklings taken from the nest with less than 24 hours' experience of the world found that their responses depended on where the species normally hatched. Ducklings that hatch on the ground will not jump off an apparently deep 'cliff', while those, such as Goldeneye and Bufflehead, that see the light of day in holes in trees will select shallow or deep drops at random; however, hole-hatching ducklings do not react as if they could not tell the difference between deep and shallow; they ran off on the shallow side of the test apparatus and launched themselves with a little jump on the deep one—just as they must

when leaving a tree hole (Kear 1967b). The ability to see and avoid a sharp drop aids survival but, clearly, it would be unhelpful if a seaduck hatched with such a fear of heights that it failed to join its mother at the bottom of the tree. It does not positively prefer to fall; if it did it might hurl itself over every cliff it met. Further experiments showed that a disinclination to jump into a chasm is acquired gradually and that, by two weeks of age, even ducklings of hole-hatching parents stay clear of deep drops.

Young seaducks are capable of diving as day-olds and are well insulated, with a layer of body fat beneath the skin and a dense downy coat. The Long-tailed Duck is reported to have three annual moults of body feathers, and both sexes have more than the normal two plumage changes; research may show that some other marine divers replace their feathers more frequently than dabbling ducks.

The eiders, because of their habit of diving with half-spread wings, lobed hind toes, and marine environment, are usually placed with the other seaducks. They are unusual in that when the male loses his beautiful breeding plumage after the young have hatched, and before moulting his wing feathers, he adopts a drab colouring that is not particularly like that of the female. He tends to be blackish rather than brown, and is still readily sexed even in eclipse. However, like most drakes with a nonbreeding plumage, he takes no part in parental care. There are four species of eider, one of which has six races, and an extinct relative, the Labrador Duck, which provides a link with the scoters. All are arctic or subarctic in distribution, marine in winter and shoreline nesters. They are bulky birds and are the ecological equivalent, to some extent, of the steamer-ducks of the southern hemisphere. Young females lay later, have smaller clutches and are lighter in weight at the start of incubation than older birds which are, as a consequence, more successful. The ducklings are dark and lack patterning, and it has been suggested that this is related to the heat-absorbing properties of brown and black—useful for young birds hatching in the chilly Arctic. They leave their downy nest within a day of hatching and go straight to sea, swimming, diving and feeding themselves from the start; the ducklings seldom go ashore, are almost never brooded, but can maintain their body heat and survive external temperatures of $-10°C$ for a while. Only in Steller's Eider, which is different from the rest in a number of ways, is there an iridescent speculum on the wings.

The displays of male eiders are as elaborate as their plumage, and the cooing sounds that they make are heard throughout the Arctic in spring. Most eiders show a tendency to nest colonially and this is particularly apparent on islands, or where man has provided protection from predators. The ducks, escorted by their drakes, come ashore to prospect for nesting sites in shallow depressions on the ground. As in the diving ducks, the sex ratio is biased in favour of males, so mate protection is important until it is too late in the season for a female to be fertilized by another drake. The beautifully camouflaged female sits on her nest for almost a month, not eating and losing one-third of her body weight. She barely moves until a predator approaches too closely, since movement destroys the effect of the camouflage but, if a potential thief does make her fly, she often defecates over the eggs as she springs away. The gut contents of a starving duck have an odour that is quite appalling and, while the droppings are wet, the smell may deter a dog or a fox. After hatching, young eiders tend to crèche in large groups in the company of one or two females which give alarm calls if danger threatens; all ducklings respond by freezing or diving, not just those of the mother concerned.

Janet Kear

Taxonomy

Most authors consider that the seaducks, tribe Mergini, comprise a discrete group, sharing a number of characteristics such as diving habit, primary reliance on animal prey, moderately heavy wing-loadings, rapid flight, predominantly diurnal activity patterns, age at maturity of two or more years, and feather proteins (Weller 1964b, 1964c, Kear 1970, Raikow 1973, Brush 1976, McNeil *et al.* 1992, Livezey 1993, 1995c). However, Patton and Avise (1986) suggested that some members of the group (e.g. *Melanitta* and *Clangula*) are only distantly related, and that a comprehensive genetic

investigation is necessary. The distribution of the group is almost limited to the northern hemisphere, with diversity highest in the north Pacific and west Atlantic (Figure 9.31).

The earliest fossil assigned to the group is *Mergus miscellus*, described by Alvarez and Olson (1978) from the middle Miocene of Virginia, US; however, Livezey and Martin (1988) questioned the generic affinities of *M. miscellus* and suggested that it may not even belong within the seaducks. Other fossil Mergini are mostly of Pleistocene age or younger (Brodkorb 1964, Howard 1964a), except *Bucephala ossivallis* which was collected from late Miocene beds in Florida, US (Becker 1987). Although comparatively rare, hybrids between species and genera within and outside the tribe (with Aythyini and Anatini) have been documented (Johnsgard 1960b, Scherer and Hilsberg 1982, Livezey 1995c).

Relationships of the tribe among ducks are controversial. Livezey (1986, 1996c) found them to be related to the stifftails, but support was weak. Madsen *et al.* (1988) found them closest to the shelducks. Donne-Goussé *et al.* (2002) found them, again with weak support, closest to a clade consisting of the dabblers and pochards. This question needs further investigation. Donne-Goussé *et al.* (2002) also reported the surprising result that the Ringed Teal, generally considered a dabbler, is instead a seaduck, and this too is in need of further confirmation.

The tribe can be split into three subtribes: Somaterina (eiders), the extinct Chendytina, and Mergina (typical seaducks). The eiders constitute a discrete group of birds and, unlike other Mergini, their ducklings retain the supraorbital stripe typical of dabbling ducks (Livezey 1986). Indeed, they are considered by some authors to be closest to the dabbling ducks (Anatini) with separate tribal ranking (Somateriini) (Humphrey 1958a, Delacour 1959, Brush 1976, Cramp and Simmons 1977).

Steller's Eider was included within the greater eiders *Somateria* by Delacour and Mayr (1945), where it is sister to the King Eider and Common Eider complex (Humphrey 1958a, Johnsgard 1964b, Livezey 1995c) and, although sometimes separated in the genus *Lampronetta* (Brandt 1847, AOU 1957), its affinity to the other eiders is clear (AOU 1983). The Common Eider group is split into six taxa, traditionally considered subspecies, and Livezey (1995c) has

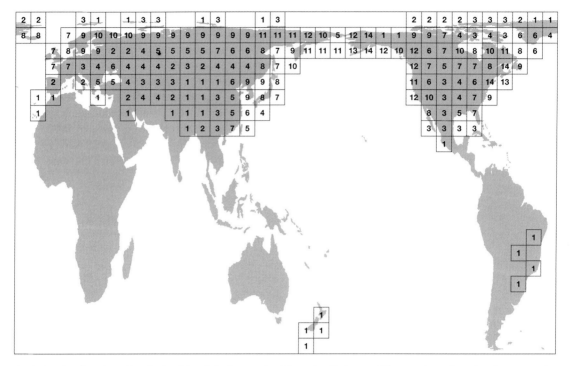

9.31 Species diversity of seaducks (Mergini) that survived into the Holocene. The number of species that occur (or occurred) within each grid-cell is indicated.

partitioned the complex into four 'operational units': those of northwest Europe including the comparatively small *faeroeensis; borealis* of arctic North Atlantic; *dresseri* of Atlantic North America including *sedentaria;* and *v-nigrum* of the North Pacific.

The extinct subtribe Chendytina included at least two species, *Chendytes lawi* and *C. milleri*, that were endemic to the Pacific seaboard of the US (Howard 1955). They were flightless birds, similar in size to the Common Eider, and possessed a strikingly eider-like bill; the two known species were specialized for diving and may have fed on benthic invertebrates (Livezey 1993). *Chendytes* probably nested on offshore islands and became extinct no earlier than 4000 years ago, probably owing to predation by aboriginal humans (Morejohn 1976, Livezey 1993).

Livezey (1995c) considered Harlequin Duck a sister to the remaining seaducks, but Delacour and Mayr (1945) placed it following the scoters. The remaining seaducks, exclusive of the eiders, *Chendytes* and the Harlequin, can be split into two main groups: the Labrador Duck plus the scoters,

and the rest (Livezey 1995c). Some workers have placed Labrador Duck after the scoters but before Long-tailed Duck (Humphrey and Butsch 1958), or as a genus allied to the eiders (Zusi and Bentz 1978).

Within the scoters, species limits are resolved poorly. The Common Scoter may be split into the nominate Eurasian form and the American form, while the Velvet Scoter is split sometimes into the nominate form of Europe and west Asia, and an east Asia/American form (Livezey 1995c). The Common Scoter is sister to the Surf Scoter and the Velvet Scoter (Livezey 1995c) which, examination of morphological characteristics suggested, are more closely related to one another.

A close relationship between the goldeneyes and mergansers is recognized (Delacour and Mayr 1945, Boetticher 1952, Delacour 1959, Myers 1959, Johnsgard 1960d, 1961a, 1978, Brush 1976, Livezey 1986, 1995c), although Patton and Avise (1986) found the goldeneyes to be related more closely to the pochards (Aythyini). The affinities of the Smew are somewhat uncertain; it has been placed between the goldeneyes and mergansers (Peters 1931, Woolfenden 1961, AOU 1983, Livezey 1986), or merged within the mergansers (Delacour and Mayr 1945, Boetticher 1952, Delacour 1959, Johnsgard 1960a, 1961a, 1965a, 1978, 1979). Hybrids between Smew and Goldeneye are relatively frequent in the wild (Phillips 1925, Ball 1934, Gray 1958, Johnsgard 1978), and an analysis by Livezey (1995c) suggested that the relationship is a near one. Within the goldeneyes, it is generally considered that the Bufflehead is sister to the typical goldeneyes (*B. clangula* and *B. islandica*) (Delacour and Mayr 1945, Livezey 1995c). Erskine (1972a) suggested its differentiation, before the Pliocene, from ancestral *Bucephala* soon after divergence from the ancestors of mergansers and scoters.

Among the mergansers, Livezey (1995c) thought Hooded Merganser to be the sister of the other mergansers, although Johnsgard (1961f) argued that it was closest to the goldeneyes. The placement of Hooded Merganser in the monospecific genus *Lophodytes* was confirmed by Livezey (1995c) through analysis of skeletal, tracheal, natal and definitive plumage characters. The two southern mergansers live, or lived, in widely separate locations (New Zealand and outlying islands, and central South America) (Bartmann 1988, Kear and Scarlett 1970). They are unique in that the sexes are alike, they are non-migratory and have (or had) protracted pairbonds (Livezey 1987). Despite superficial similarities, it seems likely that they originated from independent dispersal events from the north, which makes them a remarkable example of convergent evolution (Livezey 1989b, 1995c). The Auckland Islands Merganser was an isolated species that probably diverged from other mergansers immediately after the Hooded Merganser and, with the Brazilian Merganser, is a member of a basal group of small-bodied southern-hemisphere mergansers (Livezey 1989b). The Red-breasted Merganser is the nearest relative (Livezey 1995c) of the rare Scaly-sided Merganser of Asia.

Des Callaghan

Steller's Eider *Polysticta stelleri*
PLATE 26

Anas Stelleri Pallas, 1769, Spicilegia Zool., fasc. 6, p. 35, pl. 5
Kamchatka
Polysticta Eyton, 1836

Etymology: *Polysticta* Gr. for much spotted; *stelleri* after G.M. Steller (1709–46), German naturalist who took part in Bering's expedition to Alaska in 1740. 'Eider' comes from Æðar, the Icelandic name for the Common Eider.

Other names: Little Eider, Siberian Eider. French and Spanish: Eider de Steller.

Variation: no subspecies or geographical variation.

Description

ADULT: dimorphic. ♂ in breeding or alternate plumage has head white, with green feathers on lores and forehead and small green tufts on sides of crown stemming from black spots. Black chin, throat, eye-patch and broad neck collar connecting black upper mantle and centre of back. Lower sides of mantle and forward scapulars white, rear scapulars and tertials marked with purple and white. Rest of upperparts black. Neck below collar and upper flank edges white, merging with buff chest, forebelly, and flanks. Black spot on side of chest (not always visible). Rest of underparts dark, becoming black-brown under tail. Upperwing coverts white, primary coverts and primaries blackish. Secondaries iridescent purple-blue, with broad white tips. Underwing white, with greyer flight feathers. Bill, legs and feet, blue-grey; iris red-brown. ♀ uniformly reddish brown with dark feather centres apparent only on upperparts; head slightly lighter rufous brown with pale buff eye-ring. Upperwing dark reddish brown with broad whitish tips to greater coverts and secondaries. Secondaries otherwise similar to ♂, but less bright, only innermost strongly glossed purple-blue, outers dull brown. Underwing similar to ♂ but dusky mottling along leading edge. Bill, legs and feet, blue-grey; iris brown.

MOULT: ♂ eclipse blackish with head and neck greyish brown and upper breast barred brown; lasts late June–late Sept.

IMMATURE: resembles adult but duller, lacking warm reddish tones except on lower underparts. Wing as ♀ but secondaries dull and white border lines narrower or absent. Young ♂ has slightly curved tertials rather than straight as on young ♀. During 1st winter, pale buff and whitish feathers appear on head and breast of young ♂ who, by 2nd winter, is nearly in full plumage.

DUCKLING: uniform dark brown; above and on side of head and body warm sepia brown, blackish brown on wing pad and posterior back, buff band eye-ring continues as cinnamon band above ear and similar colour occurs on chin; hind neck may be light brown; throat fawn; breast greyer; belly light buff to grey. Bill grey with lighter nail; legs and feet olive-grey with yellowish nails and edges of webbing (Nelson 1993).

MEASUREMENTS AND WEIGHT: western population, ♂ wing adult ($n = 45$), 220; juv (1st winter) ($n = 2$), 203; bill adult ($n = 48$), 38.6; juv ($n = 2$), 37.8; tarsus adult ($n = 23$), 39.7; juv ($n = 2$), 40.0; midwinter weight adult ($n = 10$), 850. ♀ wing adult ($n = 39$), 217; juv ($n = 32$), 210; bill adult ($n = 37$), 40.2; juv ($n = 3$), 38.6; tarsus adult ($n = 23$), 39.7; juv ($n = 3$), 37.3; midwinter weight adult ($n = 13$), 838. Eastern population, adult, ♂ wing ($n = 50$), 223; bill ($n = 46$), 39.9; tarsus ($n = 41$), 37.9; Sept weight ($n = 100$), 690–1010 (848). Adult ♀ wing ($n = 35$), 219; bill ($n = 33$), 40.2; tarsus ($n = 26$), 38.8; Sept weight ($n = 100$), 700–970 (834).

Field characters

Smallest (430–470 mm long), least bulky and most *Anas*-like of eiders. Small size, relatively flat crown and head and bill proportions recall dabbling duck (see photographs in Blomdahl *et al.* 2002). Breeding ♂ shows white head with dark eye and nape patches and collar, rusty or rufous underparts contrasting with black ventral region and black and white upperparts. Flight fast and direct, like Common Goldeneye. ♀♀ and immatures generally brown with pale underwings.

Voice

♂ relatively silent compared with other eiders. Soft growling threat note and, in display, very low growled croon. ♀ more vocal uttering various low barking, growling or hoarse whistling cries, that resemble Eurasian Wigeon (Witherby *et al.* 1939). No published sonograms.

Range and status

Breeds in arctic zone of Siberia from Yamal Peninsula to Kolyma Delta. Majority of breeding pairs found east of Khatanga River (72°N, 102°E) concentrated in large river deltas (e.g. Lena and Indigirka Deltas). Khatanga River suggested as dividing point between birds migrating east to north Pacific wintering quarters and west to north Europe based on recoveries of rings during moult at Izembek Lagoon (Kertell 1991). Small breeding population remains in Barrow, Alaska, and scattered observations (including breeding records) for North Slope of Alaska indicate highly dispersed, irregular breeding population there. In western Palearctic, few breeding records from Kola Peninsula and White Sea (Nygård *et al.* 1995).

Flocks of summering nonbreeders, probably subadult, known from entire breeding and wintering range. Primary Palearctic moulting locations generally unknown, although flocks recorded from northern Norway, Yamal coast and in polynias near breeding sites in east Siberia. Moult occurs at Izembeck Lagoon and Nelson Lagoon, Alaska. Subadults first to moult followed by adult ♂♂, then supposed failed and/or nonbreeding ♀♀. Breeding ♀♀ thought to moult later in autumn.

Recent population estimates derive mainly from winter or spring counts; however, 128 800 counted in mid 1990s on eastern arctic coast of Russia during breeding season, mostly between Indigirka River Delta to Yana River delta (Hodges and Eldridge 2001). In western Palearctic, wintering birds almost exclusively confined to Varangerfjord (Norway), Kola Peninsula (Russia), Saaremaa Island (Estonia) and Palanga coast (Lithuania). Occurrence and increasing numbers in Baltic Sea appears to be recent phenomenon. Wintering birds of Pacific region concentrated at Komandorski and Kuril Islands (Russia), in small numbers in northern Japan, in Aleutian Islands, along Alaska Peninsula and inshore waters along Gulf of Alaska, US.

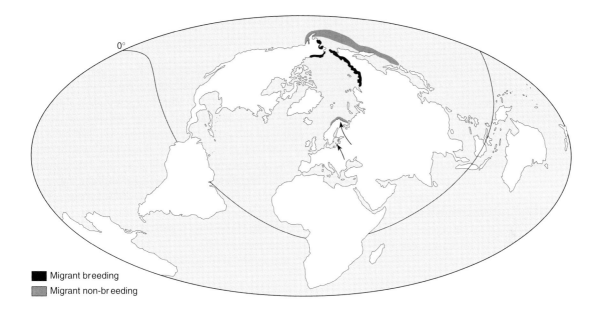

■ Migrant breeding
▨ Migrant non-breeding

World population perhaps decreased by *c* 50% over last 40 years. Pihl (1997) estimated some 220 000 individuals (Europe, *c* 40 000; East Asia, *c* 30 000; North America, *c* 150 000) from *c* 400 000–500 000 in 1960s. From annual spring surveys in southwestern Alaska, Larned (2001) reported estimates of 137 900 in 1992 to 69 000 in 2000, an apparent 6.1% yearly decline.

Habitat and general habits

Sociable, often in large flocks throughout year. Largest gatherings may exceed 50 000 and found during moult gatherings and in spring. Pair formation occurs in late spring and birds arrive on breeding grounds (on Lena Delta) from early June with mass influxes from middle of June. Unlike other eiders, may move several km inland for nesting, normally among pools of different shape and size that characterize flat coastal belt within open tundra zone. Favoured nesting habitat in Lena Delta and Barrow area moss-lichen polygonal tundra. In both areas, nests in territories of breeding Pomarine Skuas *Stercorarius pomarinus* for protection. Successful breeding associated with high densities of lemmings. ♂♂ leave ♀♀ at start of incubation; moult areas may be as far as 3000 km from breeding ground.

In winter, birds concentrate in small number of high-latitude coastal areas, usually feeding in water few m deep, though occasionally up to 10 m (Petersen 1980, Nygård *et al.* 1995). In Norway, select gently sloping coastal profiles and most feed within 200 m of coast (Fox and Mitchell 1997). Favour rocky bays and headlands and shallow sites where freshwater streams enter sea. In Alaska and northeast Siberia during breeding season, stomach contents by volume 45% crustaceans mostly amphipods, 19% molluscs mostly bivalves (especially *Mytilus edulis*), 13% insects commonly found on tundra freshwater ponds particularly chironomid and caddisfly (trichopteran) larvae, 3% annelid worms, 3% scutellid, 2% small fish and 13% plant material (Cottam 1939). In Siberia, extensive feeding on chironomids and tipulids in June; same items reported for breeding ♀♀ in Barrow in June 1991 (Quakenbush *et al.* 1995). Amphipods, bivalves and *Balanus* recorded (Portenko 1972) in summer diet. Feeding ecology during moult at Nelson Lagoon, Alaska, studied May–Oct (Petersen 1980); fed at low tide irrespective of time of day. Diving took 80% of feeding time and up-ending 20%; diet consisted mainly of molluscs and crustaceans with no difference between age and sex classes. In winter in Europe, food items included molluscs (especially bivalves such as *Mytilus edulis* and *Modiolula phase-olina*), crustaceans and polychaetes (Petraitis 1991, Mitchell *et al.* 1996, Bustnes *et al.* 2000). In Norway, diurnal cyclical feeding seen through most of tide cycle, roosting only occurring at high tide. At Vadsø harbour, Norway, fed by diving offshore on ebb and flow tides, resorting to algal beds (to glean gastropods?) when exposed on falling tide, and fed by dabbling on sandy mud beach substrate at low tide (Fox and Mitchell 1997). Diurnal feeding also reported from Sweden (Högström 1977).

Displays and breeding behaviour

In wintering and moulting areas, extremely sociable in most activities. Forms densely packed rafts when feeding, often with precisely synchronized diving. Flocks take flight easily and frequently, especially when disturbed by birds of prey or large gulls (Fox and Mitchell 1996). ♂♂ aggressive in courting parties, encounters between pairs and situations involving pair and unmated ♂ (for full descriptions of displays, see McKinney 1965d).

Breeding and life cycle

Spring departure from winter quarters from late Apr (Lithuania), through May (Estonia, Gulf of Finland). In Varangerfjord, most birds depart in May, although small flocks may stay through summer (Henriksen and Lund 1994). In East Asia, spring migration starts Mar, peaking, in Kamchatka, in May, while in Alaska, starts Apr peaking early May (Larned *et al.* 1994). Uncertain when those that winter in Europe reach breeding areas; birds wintering in Asia and Alaska arrive early June with mass influxes noted from mid June.

Nests on open tundra, or among willows and birch, usually not far from water (polynias or small lake) often in small colonies. Largest colony on Sagastyr Island, Lena Delta in 1993, had 63 nests. Deep nest usually lined with lichens that offer protection from permafrost, with grass and down on top. Eggs blunt ovate, light olive or olive-buff, laid *c* daily; 60.1 × 41.3 ($n = 344$) from Lena Delta; weight 57 ($n = 23$). Clutch 6.1 (5–8) eggs ($n = 32$). Single brood but will replace lost clutch; replacement clutch 3.9 (3–6) eggs ($n = 6$). Incubation 26–27 days. Ducklings hatch from mid July. Brood size after hatching 4.9 (2–6) ducklings ($n = 10$), reduced to 3.8 (1–6, $n = 5$) before autumn migration. In 1993–95, nest success zero in years with low lemming densities, all clutches predated during incubation (Solovieva *et al.* 1998). In Alaska, annual survival rate estimated at 75% for nonbreeding ♀♀. This not lower than stable or declining population of Common Eiders in North America (Reed 1975), but much lower than stable or increasing Common Eider population in temperate Europe with annual survival rates of 86–90% (Swennen 1991). Few studies carried out and, consequently, nothing known of recruitment. Solovieva *et al.* (1998) found indications on Lena Delta that some birds do not attempt nesting or are predated in years with low lemming densities; at Barrow, Alaska, do not attempt to breed in such years.

Conservation and threats

Spring hunting on, or adjacent to, breeding ground occurs in Siberia, and illegal hunting reported in Lena Delta where estimated 1500 shot every year and, in addition, wounding may cause no breeding of > 1000 potential pairs. In North America, subsistence hunting not allowed. Effect of illegal hunting at any time thought to be low although, as numbers decline, may become more significant. Much pristine arctic habitat subject to 'various types of development and disturbance' (Hodges and Eldrige 1995) although with unknown effect. Habitat loss occurs through prospecting for, and exploitation of, natural resources such as oil and gas that pose future threat although current impact hard to assess. Increased traffic of large tankers carrying oil from arctic areas imposes risk of contamination after spills. Further human habitation in remote areas of arctic Siberia and Alaska has increased range and numbers of some large gulls and Ravens, leading to greater risk of predation. Fishing with nets takes place in 3 major wintering areas in Europe and Steller's Eiders have been drowned in these nets (Fox *et al.* 1997).

Reasons behind apparent steady decline in world population unknown. Relatively long-lived, but sensitive to changes in adult survival; may be unable to maintain healthy population unless factors causing adult mortality and level of predation on eggs and hatchlings are reduced.

Carl Mitchell and Stefan Pihl

Spectacled Eider *Somateria fischeri*
PLATE 25

Fuligula (Lampronetta) Fischeri Brandt, 1847, Fuligu-lam (Lampronettam) Fischeri Novam Rossicarum Avium Speciem, p. 18, pl. 1
St Michael, Alaska (in Norton Sound on west coast)
Somateria Leach, 1819

Etymology: type collected during explora-tion (1840s) of western Alaska for St Petersburg Academy of Science, and named after physician and illustrator Gotthelf Fischer de Waldheim (1771–1853).

Other names: Fischer's Eider; Yupic, western Alaska: Kow'uk, Ung'u; Inupiat, northern Alaska: Qavaasuk, Tuutalluk; Yakut, Siberian Eskimo: Dulkiya; Chukot; Siberian Eskimo: Lile'kel; Russ-ian: Ochkovaya Gaga.

Variation: no subspecies. Affinities to other eiders (Humphrey 1958a, Johnsgard 1964a, AOU 1983). Three ♂♂ observed with grey V-marks on throat, similar to King and Pacific race of Common Eider, suggest hybridization or common genetic link (Dau 1975).

Description

ADULT: dimorphic. ♂ in alternate or breeding plumage has green crown and nape with long, slop-ing forehead, large, distinctive white spectacles, charcoal chest and belly and white back. Bill yellow-orange, vivid near base, pale nail; legs and feet pale yellow and webs dusky. Blue iris ring present in both sexes. ♀ brown and heavily marked with darker brown bars; brown spectacle corresponds in size to that of ♂. Head and neck pale brown, streaked black and lighter than upper breast and back. Lower breast and abdomen dark brown with little or no barring. Legs and feet dull olive-brown (Portenko 1952, Palmer 1976, Skakuj 1990, Petersen *et al.* 2000).

MOULT: eclipse (basic) plumage ♂ distinct in 1st and 2nd years (Petersen *et al.* 2000). ♂ eclipsed through Sept (Nelson 1887). Basic I wing coverts dark barred, primaries dull brown as in immature, head and nape buff–grey streaked with black and white-based feathers. Spectacle grey tipped white, throat white, underparts buffy brown to blackish grey. Basic II wing coverts brown-grey with less white than definitive, tertials grey. Head pale grey to olive, underparts similar to Basic I. Underparts barred blackish brown. Definitive primaries dull brownish black, middle primary coverts mixed white and smoke grey, remainder of upperwing white, tertials white. Dusky grey underparts with upper breast, sides and flanks barred buff-brown. Spectacles pale grey and remainder of head slaty grey-brown. Upperparts dark brownish olive to blackish grey.

IMMATURE: sexes similar to 1st pre-alternate moult, often differing in scapular barring with ♂ parallel and ♀ acute (Portenko 1952). By Oct, ♂ identified by grey and white-tipped nape, head and throat and some adult blackish grey tail feathers. First and 2nd year ♀ lighter brown mottling with less distinct body-wide barring, spectacle less dis-tinct, bill more grey than blue-grey of adult. Grey bill of 1st winter ♀ becomes bluish grey in yearling. Legs and feet as adult ♀.

DUCKLING: distinctive spectacle present at hatch (Nelson 1964, 1993). Upperparts dark brown and underparts lighter cream-brown. Flank and facial contour feathers appear at 3 weeks and full juvenile plumage by 5–6 weeks with last down on rump and nape. Bill to fledging, greyish brown; legs and feet uniform dark brown. Blue iris distinct by first fall.

MEASUREMENTS AND WEIGHT: ♂ wing ($n = 19$), 251.0 ± 6.0 (SE) mm (236–264); tail ($n = 18$), 79.2 ± 11.4 (61–88); culmen ($n = 19$), 24.0 ± 1.6 (20.1–27.3); tarsus ($n = 19$), 59.1 ± 4.9 (51.0–63.3); middle toe ($n = 16$), 68.2 ± 3.9 (65.0–72.0). ♀ wing ($n = 16$), 246.8 ± 18.2 (229–261); tail ($n = 14$), 76.5 ± 8.5 (69–83); culmen ($n = 16$), 27.1 ± 3.4 (24.5–30.9); tarsus ($n = 17$), 57.4 ± 2.8 (51.0–60.0); middle toe ($n = 16$), 64.9 ± 6.3 (61.5–74.0). ♂ weight in spring 1494 g (1275–1750) ($n = 53$) and of ♀ 1623 (1300–1850) ($n = 11$). In early summer, ♂ weight declines to 1417 (1325–1540) ($n = 11$) and to 1247 in ♀ (1125–1450) ($n = 15$).

Field characters

Bulky sea ducks, length: ♂ 525 and ♀ 500, ♂ with striking black and white plumage. ♂ similar to Common Eider, with white neck, back and wings. Black precedes from tail to mid-central portion of back in Spectacled Eider and to lower back in Common Eider; and secondary coverts and tertials white in both. Slate-black belly and breast approaches base of neck, while Common Eider has black belly and white breast. Crown and cape pale green in adult ♂ Spectacled Eider, and black in Common Eider. King Eider also has white neck but black back and only white secondary wing coverts. Bill colour yellow-orange in adult ♂ Spectacled and Common Eider and reddish orange in King Eider. ♀ brown and heavily barred as in Common and King eiders, similar to latter in size, differs from both primarily in head plumage and bill size.

Voice

Not detected in ♂. ♀ has 2 calls during breeding season; when disturbed, uses repetitive guttural croak as alarm, and repetitive clucking *buckBUCK-buck-BUCK-buckBUCK* as greeting and for summoning ducklings. Ducklings utter 2-syllable whistle, similar in rate to ♀'s clucking. Whistling purr heard from older ducklings in captivity and, within 2 months, whistle becomes clucking call of ♀.

Range and status

Holarctic breeder primarily within narrow (<30 km) discontinuous band of subarctic coastal habitat and from 70 to 120 km inland in Arctic Alaska and Russia (Portenko 1972, Dau and Kistchinski 1977, Petersen *et al.* 2000). In Alaska, nested along west, northwest and north coast from Nushagak Peninsula to Yukon Territory border in Canada; also on St Lawrence Island in Bering Sea (Fay 1961). In Russia, nests from Chukotsk Peninsula west to Lena River Delta and Novosibirski Islands with centre of abundance Chaun Gulf and Kolyma, Indigirka and Yana River deltas (Buturlin 1910, Dementiev and Gladkov 1952, Portenko 1972, Kistchinski 1973). Centre of abundance in Alaska, once Yukon-Kuskokwim Delta, now in Arctic from Cape Simpson to

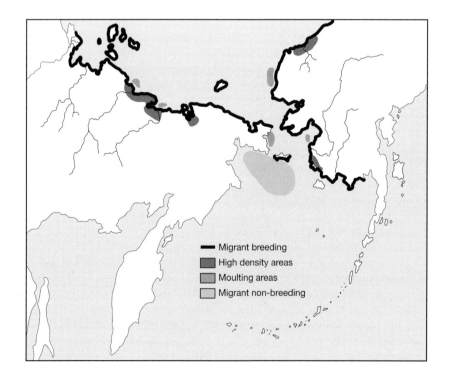

■ Migrant breeding
■ High density areas
■ Moulting areas
■ Migrant non-breeding

Sagavanirktok River; no longer breeds at extremes of historic range, and numbers declined dramatically (Stehn *et al.* 1993, Ely *et al.* 1994, TERA 1995). In northwest Alaska, was less common, now rare or absent (Bailey 1948, Kessel 1989).

Range in 8–10 month nonbreeding season (Dau and Kistchinski 1977) confirmed by satellite telemetry (Petersen *et al.* 1995, 1999). Moult migrations of adult ♂♂ and nonbreeders centred near Bering Strait, and moult takes place in offshore areas from southern Chukchi Sea and Chukotsk Peninsula south to Norton Sound and northern Bering Sea (Nelson 1887, Dau and Kistchinski 1977, Petersen *et al.* 1999), possibly coinciding with summer and fall range of subadults. Winter range within polynias of northern Bering Sea (Dau and Kistchinski 1977, Petersen *et al.* 1999, J. Brueggeman pers. comm.).

Estimates based on winter surveys of polynias in north-central Bering Sea suggest dense concentration of at least 333 000 birds, possibly most of world population (Petersen *et al.* 1999). Other Bering Sea polynias may be used (McRoy *et al.* 1971, Everett *et al.* 1989), especially in Gulf of Anadyr and south of Chukotsk Peninsula (Bogoslovskaya and Votrogov 1981, Konyukhov 1998), and require investigation. Dau and Kistchinski (1977) suggested breeding of 80 000–120 000 pairs in early 1970s; estimates suggest 47 700–70 000 pairs on Yukon-Kuskokwim Delta, 3000 pairs in arctic Alaska, and 30 000–40 000 pairs in Russia. Aerial surveys of arctic Alaska, since 1992 indicate about 4000 pairs (USFWS 1996). Stehn *et al.* (1993) document 20-year decline of over 96% on Yukon-Kuskokwim Delta to *c* 1721 pairs in 1992. From 1992–95, surveys indicated the decline in this area may have stabilized (US Fish and Wildlife Service 1996) and since 1996 the population increasing at nearly 8% a year. Historic estimates put Russian breeding population at larger than 60 000–80 000 individuals (Dau and Kistchinski 1977), with current minimum exceeding 140 000 (Hodges and Eldridge 2002). In Arctic, annual variation in breeding due to climatic influences on habitat availability, makes trend estimation difficult. Long-term studies lacking in Russia; however, near Prudhoe Bay, Alaska, breeding probably declined by *c* 80% since 1981 (Warnock and Troy 1992, TERA 1995).

Habitat and general habits

In Subarctic, nesting restricted to low, wet sedge and grass marshes with numerous small, shallow waterbodies. These subarctic vegetated intertidal habitats are occasionally inundated during tidal storm surges (Hanson 1961, King and Dau 1981). Storm surges infrequent in Arctic due to shallower coastal waters and smaller tide ranges (Reimnitz and Maurer 1979). In Arctic, most nesting in large river deltas, polygonized coastal plains and inland near large lakes and dryer uplands (Dementiev and Gladkov 1952, Kistchinski and Flint 1974, Derksen *et al.* 1981, TERA 1995). Spends 8–10 months in Bering and Chukchi seas (Dau and Kistchinski 1977, Petersen *et al.* 1995, 1999).

Diet during nonbreeding season in marine environment indicates reliance on benthic invertebrates, primarily *Macoma* clams and gastropods (snails) (Petersen *et al.* 1998). Stomach contents of adults and juveniles indicate 50–70% animal food in summer and 100% of adult winter diet. Clams 80% and snails 20% comprise spring marine diet. In summer, feeding in ponds or lakes on insects and insect larvae, especially Trichopterae which were most important animal food for young, seeds (*Potamogeton* and *Hippurus*) and plant material (Cottam 1939, Dau 1974, Kistchinski and Flint 1974, Kondratev and Zadorina 1992, Petersen *et al.* 1998).

Displays and breeding behaviour

Courtship display, from arrival in nesting areas through nest initiation, described by Johnsgard (1964b) and Palmer (1976). When alarmed, guttural croak and injury feigning by ♀ distracts predators from nest or brood, ducklings respond by diving or hiding. Head-nodding and clucking of ♀ greets mate, brood and other ♀♀; call also summons ducklings who respond with similar corresponding calls and head movements (Dau 1974, Kistchinski and Flint 1974).

Breeding and life cycle

Small flocks of pairs arrive in subarctic breeding areas mid May and at arctic sites early June (Dau 1974, Kistchinski and Flint 1974, Kondratyev and Zadorina 1992). Sex ratios equal during spring migration and subadults rarely seen (Dau and

Kistchinski 1977). Arrive from northwest on Yukon-Kuskokwim Delta from wintering or unknown spring staging areas in north-central Bering Sea. Subarctic nesting occurs in vegetated intertidal habitat, with estimated 98% within 20 km coastal fringe (Dau and Kistchinski 1977, King and Dau 1981). In arctic Russia, highest nesting densities occur near coastline but few birds to 120 km inland (Dau and Kistchinski 1977). On Indigirka Delta in Russian Arctic, estimated 84% of nests within 50 km of sea (Kistchinski and Flint 1974).

Nest sites available by 3rd week of May (Subarctic) or 2nd week of June (Arctic) and most (> 80%) selected by 1st week of June (Subarctic) or 3rd week of June (Arctic) (Dau 1974, Kistchinski and Flint 1974, Warnock and Troy 1992). Dau (1974) found 7.2 days on average from arrival to 1st nest, and 12 days to peak nesting. In arctic habitats, climate may delay nesting up to 20 days or preclude altogether. ♂ takes no part in site selection or construction, and departs shortly after incubation begins (Dau 1974, Kistchinski and Flint 1974). In Subarctic, nests dispersed on average 179 m apart (5–604, $n = 214$) with only occasional clumping (Johnsgard 1964a, Dau 1974, Strang 1976). Preferred sites along shorelines or on peninsulas or islands in small ponds, average 2.1 m from water (0.2–192, $n = 214$) with few (11%, $n = 23$ nests) more than 2 m away (Dau 1974). Nesting densities averaging 4.4/km² in 1970s declined significantly in the 1980s and 1990s in Subarctic (Dau and Kistchinski 1977, Ely et al. 1994). In Arctic, nests at densities of 1.0 to 4.7/km² (Kistchinski and Flint 1974, Derksen et al. 1981). A decline in density indicated in arctic Alaska (TERA 1995). ♀♀ often nest semi-colonially with gulls or terns (Kistchinski and Flint 1974). On Yukon-Kuskokwim Delta, compete with other species, especially geese, for island sites (Dau 1974). Most nests (41%) on pond shorelines or small islands (36%) and peninsulas (23%). Island sites that have higher elevation from water (15.2 ± 1.8 cm, $n = 70$) and earlier availability favoured by geese, and ♀♀ often displaced by more dominant species. ♀♀ either construct new nest depressions or rehabilitate old ones. Dau (1974) found 35% of nests in bowls used previous years by eiders (31%) or geese (40%). Clipped grasses, sedges (2.5 cm thick) and down line nest. Down normally deposited from midway through laying into incubation. Average nest dimensions ($n = 214$) 5.1 cm (depth), 14.0 cm (inside diameter), and 24.1 cm (outside). Maintenance of down and nest material continues through incubation often in conjunction with egg-turning. On Yukon-Kuskokwim Delta, sedges and grasses predominate in and around nests; nest material consists of top 5.0–7.5 cm of vegetation within 0.3 m of nest which lowers height of cover to 10–20 cm (Dau 1974).

One egg laid per day, and incubation begins with last or penultimate egg (Dau 1974). In Subarctic, clutch averages 4.7 eggs (1965–76, 1–8, $n = 412$) or 5.1 (1986–92, 1–9, $n = 263$) (Stehn et al. 1993); in Arctic, 4.5–5.6 ($n = 179$) (Kistchinski and Flint 1974, Krechmar 1991, Kondratev and Zadorina 1992). In Subarctic, delayed nesting may result in smaller clutch, but not in complete nesting failure (Dau 1976, Dau and Mickelson 1979) while, in arctic habitats, delayed nesting may reduce clutch size or cause nonbreeding (Kistchinski and Flint 1974). Eggs measure ($n = 682$) 67.9 ± 2.9 × 45.3 ± 1.4 (44.6–77.3 × 31.1–48.6) with fresh weight ($n = 209$) 71 ± 2. Incubation lasts 23–24 days (Dau 1974, Kondratev and Zadorina 1992), and eggs hatch 25 June–5 July in Subarctic and up to 2 weeks later in Arctic (Dau 1974, Kistchinski and Flint 1974, TERA 1995). ♀ attentiveness increases during hatching process which is completed in 27 h (13–47, $n = 21$ nests); for individual duckling, hatching takes c 10 h.

Clutch size and hatching success lower in years when breeding delayed (Dau 1974, 1976). Nest location also affects success due to differing rate of exposure to predation. Mammalian predators in Subarctic, Arctic and Red Foxes and American Mink, prey primarily on peninsular and shoreline nests, while gulls and skuas affect all sites. Incubating ♀♀ attentive but, when disturbed, deter predators by defecating on eggs and feigning injury. Infertile eggs rare, accounting for less than 1% in early 1970s (Dau 1974) but increased to at least 5% recently (Grand and Flint 1997, Grand et al. 1998) possibly due to lead toxicity (Franson et al. 1995). Nesting success on Yukon-Kuskokwim averaged 71% (50–91, $n = 217$ nests) 1969–73 (Dau 1974) and 48% (18–76, $n = 263$ nests in early 1990s (Grand and Flint 1997). Data on hatching success few or lacking for Arctic; however, Kistchinski and Flint (1974) suggest that 10–15% of ♀♀ breeding on Indigirka River delta in 1971 successfully incubated clutch, and that proximity to nests of large gulls and abundant lemmings important factors increasing success. Early nests and larger clutches most successful (Dau 1974, 1976, Grand and Flint 1997).

♀♀ brood newly hatched ducklings for *c* 12 h prior to leaving nest; ducklings weigh 49 ± 5 (44–54, *n* = 38) at hatch and are brooded for up to 4 weeks. They feed immediately, with no assistance from ♀, are agile, moving effectively on land or water feeding primarily on aquatic insects taken from pond surfaces or adjacent wet meadows. First feathers appear at *c* 3 weeks and most down lost by 7 weeks. Fledging occurs at *c* day 50. Brood rearing in freshwater habitats within 100 m of nest site and rarely up to 2.4 km away (Dau 1974, Kistchinski and Flint 1974, Derksen *et al.* 1981, TERA 1995). Dau (1974) estimated duckling survival on Yukon-Kuskokwim Delta at 83.3% and an average loss of 0.7 ducklings per brood by fledging. Recent estimates suggest 34% survive to 30 days and brood mixing seen in 18.4% of cases (*n* = 38 broods) (Flint and Grand 1997). Sexes fledge at identical weights, ♂ 965 ± 113 (850–1075, *n* = 17) and ♀ 965 ± 110 (750–1125, *n* = 19). After fledging, ♀ and brood move from freshwater to marine habitat (Stehn *et al.* 1993). Heavy loads of helminth parasites, plus changes in foraging behaviour, food habits and salt balance, may result in high mortality as evidenced by low numbers of subadults seen subsequently in breeding areas (Dau 1974, 1978, Schiller 1954, 1955). Coccidiosis, helminths and avian cholera identified as important causes of death in Common Eiders (Reed and Cousineau 1967, Persson *et al.* 1974, Korschgen *et al.* 1978, Mendenhall and Milne 1985).

Adult ♂♂ undergo moult migration to Bering and Chukchi Seas late June–early July (Dau and Kistchinski 1977, Petersen *et al.* 1995). Successful breeding adult ♀♀ depart breeding areas with young late Aug–early Sept, and are at moulting sites in Norton Sound and elsewhere mid Sept–mid Oct. All appear to move to wintering locations in Nov (Petersen *et al.* 1995, 1999). Timing of flightless period uncertain.

♀ may first breed in 2nd year, ♂ in 3rd or 4th year when definitive breeding plumage acquired (Portenko 1952, Palmer 1976, Skakuj 1990, Petersen *et al.* 2000). Return of one of 143 marked ducklings as yearling to Yukon-Kuskokwim Delta breeding area, and none as breeder 3–7 years later,

indicates low survival or dispersal (Dau 1974). Breeding propensity and longevity of ♂ and ♀ poorly known; however, return rate of 6 marked breeding ♀♀ one (50%), 4 (33%) and 5 (17%) years after marking suggests high site fidelity and gives preliminary index of adult survival. Female survival rates varied from 44% to 78% depending on exposure to lead (Grand *et al.* 1998). Three ♀♀ monitored over 6 years nested 211 m (107–376) from initial site, 2 returned to breed during 4 years (> 7 years old) and one for 5 years (> 8 years old) (Dau 1974).

Conservation and threats

Relationships to marine habitats uncertain. Climate, oceanography and biological resources in moulting, staging and wintering habitats and interspecific competition requires study (Hood and Kelley 1974, Brower *et al.* 1977, Sayles 1979, Hood and Calder 1981, Grebmeier and Cooper 1995). Peterson and Douglas (2004) suggest population trends related to winter ice and climate, but not to changes in benthic community. Because little data exist on breeding population in arctic Russia, difficult to identify trends and manage this threatened species (USFWS 1996).

Coastal tundra breeding habitat predominately unaltered, but parts developed for mining, oil and gas production with potential threats such as contamination, wetland in-fill, and disturbance from aircraft, road and foot traffic. Increasing petroleum extraction in both onshore and offshore areas of Russia and Alaska could impact significant portions of range including major river deltas. Shipping of petroleum products through the few concentrated marine moulting and wintering habitats is of concern because of potential spills. Seasonally restricted shipping and establishment of marine sanctuaries necessary to protect moulting and wintering areas. Unconfirmed reports of toxic waste dumping, potentially radioactive, in Arctic Ocean and Bering Sea, could cause substantial adverse impacts on eiders and their marine habitats. Surface and subsurface mining activities occur in Russian Arctic which could adversely affect eiders (Tichotsky 1991). Mining also takes place in Alaska and potentially toxic waste products and other pollutants could be released directly or via river systems. Increasing use of off-road vehicles has caused significant adverse alterations of some nesting habitat.

Lead contamination throughout nesting range threatens survival of adults and young (Franson *et al.* 1995, Grand *et al.* 1998). Substantial, persistent amounts of spent lead shot occurs on the Yukon-Kuskokwim Delta (Flint 1998) and possibly other breeding areas. Hunting tradition of increasing and mobile rural population in Alaska (Raveling 1984) along with legalizing expanded hunting seasons may significantly increase shooting mortality. Similar increase in hunting may be occurring in Russia (E.E. Syroechkovskiy, Jr pers. comm.). Ban of lead shot for all hunting in Alaska being proposed and like effort necessary in Russia.

On Yukon-Kuskokwim Delta, larger predator populations since the 1980s undoubtedly increased mortality (Stehn *et al.* 1993). Increasing mammalian and avian predation, primarily large gulls, due partly to anthropogenic factors. Predatory gulls increasing annually at an estimated 5% on the Yukon-Kuskokwim Delta and 4% in arctic Alaska. Eiders displaced from preferred nesting sites by dominant species have greater exposure of eggs and young to increasing predator populations (Dau 1974).

Highly gregarious nature in restricted habitats of Bering and Chukchi seas (Petersen *et al.* 1995, 1999) may result in competition for food resources (Stehn *et al.* 1993) or increased mortality in severe winters (Peterson and Douglas 2004). Stehn *et al.* (1993) hypothesized that Pacific Walrus *Odobenus rosmarus*, which also occurs in southern Chukchi and northern Bering Seas, may have tripled in numbers 1960–80 (Fay *et al.* 1989) and affected food resources adversely when Spectacled Eiders on Yukon-Kuskokwim were in decline. Eiders may also compete for invertebrates with Grey Whales *Eschrichtius robustus* (Rice and Wolman 1971, Kessel 1989). Commercial fishing occurs in Bering and Chukchi Seas; data are lacking to show if direct or indirect mortality is occurring. Populations, and hence commercial harvest, of finfish and crab have changed in Bering Sea which may have affected eiders (Stehn *et al.* 1993). There are no reports of entanglement in drift nets; however, eiders have hit lighted boats at night. Indirect effects of fishing in Bering Sea, such as bottom trawling, could impact benthic invertebrate fauna.

Hunting in US prohibited since 1991; however, shooting and egg gathering by native peoples continues in breeding areas and during migration. Most harvest in Alaska occurs on Yukon-Kuskokwim Delta (Klein 1966, King and Derksen 1986) and, to lesser extent, during migration in northern Alaska (Johnson 1971, Thompson and Person 1963) and at St Lawrence Island. Some 'tens of thousands' of eiders apparently shot every year in Yakutkia and Chukotka, with take of Spectacled Eiders on Indigirka River Delta estimated at > 4000.

C.P. Dau and †A.A. Kistchinski

King Eider *Somateria spectabilis*
PLATE 25

Anas spectabilis Linnaeus, 1758, Syst. Nat., ed. 10, p. 123 Canada, Sweden

Etymology: *spectabilis* from L. for remarkable or showy. Called King in Europe from 1785 when the occasional vagrant ♂ in a group of Common Eiders stood out in spectacular fashion.

Other names: none in English. Danish: Kongeederfugl; French: Eider à tête grise; German: Prachteiderente; Icelandic: Æðarkóngur; Spanish: Eider real.

Variation: no subspecies nor geographical variation.

Description

ADULT: dimorphic. ♂ in breeding plumage has crown and nape pale blue-grey, with greenish cheeks separated by narrow black and white lines. Upperparts, body and tail black except for prominent white patches at sides of tail base. Throat white, marked with black V, chest whitish suffused pink. Tertial feathers form small, black, sickle-shaped points raised above either side of centre of back. In flight, upperwing black with constrasting white patch on coverts; underwing shows more extensive white to anterior. Bill deep orange-red with prominent yellow-orange frontal shield, edged black; legs and feet dull orange; eye yellow. ♀ rufous-brown, tending to cinnamon-brown on head and neck. Fine black streaks on head and neck, bolder blackish chevron markings on upperparts and flanks. Eye-ring pale buff, extending back and down as pale eyestripe. Small pale buff spot at base of bill. Upperwings dark brown with thin white stripe formed by tips of greater secondary coverts; underwing paler. Bill grey; legs and feet greenish grey; eye dull yellow.

MOULT: eclipsed ♂ overall dark brownish black, white on upperwing retained. Few white feathers often, but not invariably, present on breast and back. Bill and frontal lobe duller. Acquired from mid July, with return to full breeding plumage Sept–Nov.

IMMATURE: grey-brown overall, ♂ gradually acquiring white on breast and rump from late autumn, simultaneously becoming darker above. Succession of plumages through 1st and 2nd years, with full adult plumage attained in 3rd year. Lobe apparent in 2nd year.

DUCKLING: upperparts, centre of chin, breast and sides pale grey; sides of head buff-yellow with dark line from eye to nape; chin and underparts off-white. Bill, legs and feet grey-brown, bill lobes present; eye brown.

MEASUREMENTS AND WEIGHT: ♂ wing ($n = 15$), 266–293 (277); tail ($n = 12$), 79–87 (82.8); bill ($n = 17$), 27–34 (30.9); tarsus ($n = 17$), 44–50 (46.5); weight in June ($n = 39$), 1367–1954 (1655). ♀ wing ($n = 7$), 256–276 (270); tail ($n = 7$), 76–83 (79.2); bill ($n = 10$), 31–35 (32.6); tarsus ($n = 10$) 44–48 (45.5); weight in June ($n = 139$), 1213–1923 (1569) (Cramp and Simmons 1977).

Field characters

At distance, adult ♂ only eider with white breast and black rear half; close-up, head shape and colouring distinctive. Length 550–630 mm. Adult ♀ and juvenile similar to Common Eider but slightly smaller with number of distinguishing features, mostly visible at fairly short range, e.g. gape line through pale area at base of bill upturned (less obvious and straight in Common Eider), lobes of bill smaller and with feathering less far down bill, head less triangular, flank markings more angular and less barred, in some ♀♀ short tertial points show on back (Blomdahl *et al.* 2002). Eclipsed ♂ smaller than Common Eider, with less white on upperwing, shorter bill and distinct bulge on forehead.

Voice

♂ coos with tremulous dove-like *croo-croo-croo* or *hoo-hoo-hoo*; also has sharp *kwack* call. ♀ responds to displaying ♂♂ with low *gug-gug* or *gog-gog*; also grunts and growls, especially when alarmed. Calls of ducklings similar to Common Eider. Sonogram of ♂ and ♀ calls in Cramp and Simmons (1977).

Range and status

Breeds in circumpolar high Arctic. In North America, from northwest Alaska east throughout virtually all islands of Canadian Arctic and south down northwest coasts of Hudson Bay and in scattered localities in Ungava peninsula. Breeds on coasts of northern half of west and east Greenland, Svalbard, and irregularly and in small numbers in northern Scandinavia. Russian range extends from Kanin peninsula eastwards to Chukot peninsula and most arctic islands. Winters mainly on or near coasts south of breeding range, in southern Alaska and Aleutian Islands, rarely south to California, Labrador and Newfoundland south to Virginia, southwestern Greenland, eastern Iceland, northern Scandinavia and Kola peninsula, and Kamchatka peninsula.

About 200 000–260 000 individuals nested in west Canadian Arctic in early 1990s and 10 000–35 000 on Alaskan arctic coastal plain. Eastern Canadian Arctic population estimated at 280 000 in 1989, based on winter counts. Breeding population of East Greenland, northern Europe and western Siberia estimated at 300 000 individuals (Rose and Scott 1997), but Greenland's wintering birds seriously threatened by overexploitation (Hansen 2002). No available counts of central Siberian breeding population; Hodges and Eldridge (2001) counted 55 800 on eastern arctic coast of Russia in mid 1990s.

Habitat and general habits

Breeds beside tundra pools, in marshes and occasionally dry tundra, near coast and up to 50 km,

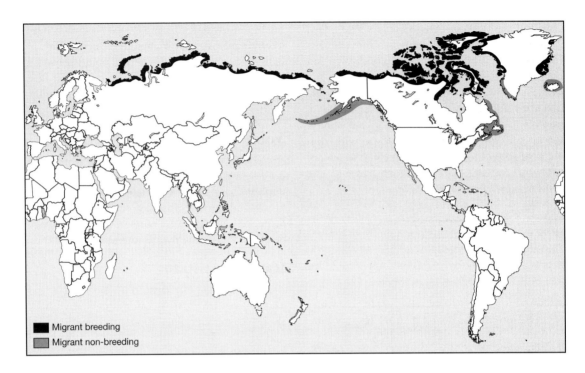

■ Migrant breeding
▨ Migrant non-breeding

rarely 100 km, inland; sometimes nests near Long-tailed Skuas *Stercorarius longicaudus* (Blomqvist and Elander 1988), or Snowy Owls in lemming years on Taymyr Peninsula (Summers *et al.* 1994). Brood rearing in shallow waters with emergent vegetation, initially mainly fresh, but most broods end on salt water where fledging takes place, ♀♀ and broods moving overland. Movement to salt water necessary as freezing of inland freshwaters may occur before young fledge. Moulting areas generally in sheltered fjords and bays with high densities of benthic fauna. Winter on coastal areas with shallow water, offshore in deeper waters, and also close to edge of sea ice.

Feeding in sea almost exclusively by diving, but in freshwater will, as well as diving, indulge in variety of methods depending on water depth, including up-ending, head-dipping, sieving and probing. Diving, often by groups of birds acting synchronously, usually involves foraging on bottom in water from few to 15–25 m deep, exceptionally to 55 m. Wings often partially opened as bird dives from surface, but not used under water. When mean depth 204 m ($n = 192$), most dives last more than 90 sec (Bustnes and Lonne 1997). Marine prey mainly molluscs, crustaceans and echinoderms. In summer, crustaceans and invertebrate larvae, together with some vegetable matter, e.g. sedges and other water plants (Palmer 1976, Cramp and Simmons 1977, Bustnes and Erikstad 1988).

Displays and breeding behaviour

♂♂ indulge in communal courtship display, accompanied by *coo*-ing calls. Commonest display Pushing with head pushed forward and up, exposing chin, performed in series accompanied by calls. Also Wing-flapping while rearing in water, and Reaching, with head down and rear lifted from water. Tertial points often erected during display. Chasing, involving just ♂♂, occurs on land and water. ♀ Incites, accompanied by *gog-gog* call.

Pairbond seasonal and mainly monogamous although ♂ may mate with more than one ♀. Pairs formed before arrival on nesting grounds, and ♂ remains until start of incubation.

Breeding and life cycle

Arrives at Queen Maud Gulf Bird Sanctuary in central Canadian Arctic 4–9 June and median nest initiation 14–22 June (Kellett and Alisauskas 2000). Nest density low, e.g. 1.2 nests per km² (Suydam 2000); built by ♀, little more than hollow formed by turning body, plus down. Eggs olive or olive-buff, 67 × 45 (71–78 × 41–49) (*n* = 200) (Cramp and Simmons 1977), with variation across range (Suydam 2000); weight 67 (62.7–70.9) (*n* = 16) (Summers *et al.* 1994). Clutch 4–5 (3–7); rare nests with more eggs involve 2 ♀♀. Eggs laid one per day. Single brood. Incubation begins shortly before last egg laid, by ♀ only, who may not leave nest for some days at start of incubation, probably daily for short periods thereafter. She may lose 30% of body weight during 23 (22–24) days of incubation (Kellett and Alisauskas 2000). Hatching success 89% (*n* = 202) (Kellett and Alisauskas 2000). Weight of wild-hatched ducklings 46.72 ± 4.01 (*n* = 33). Young precocial and nidifugous, tended by ♀ for up to 50 days, crèching in some areas. Gulls and skuas main duckling predators. Larger eggs produced hatchlings larger in mass and structural size (Anderson and Alisauskas 2002). Anderson and Alisauskas

(2001) suggested that, where predation and food shortage constrain survival, ducklings hatching from large eggs have advantage over those from small ones since speed, endurance and feeding rate (in captivity) correlated positively with egg and body size. Fledge in *c* 50–60 days, becoming independent at same time or soon after. Relatively long-lived; adult ♀ annual survival 79% (Kellett and Alisauskas 2000). Age of 1st breeding 3 years.

Conservation and threats

Both Canadian populations thought to have declined significantly for reasons unknown, although considerable variation in breeding success caused by adverse weather may contribute. Current levels of subsistence hunting in Greenland probably unsustainable, and 10–20% of winter population killed annually (Hansen 2002). Threats from oil spills and other pollution, or from deterioration of habitat, not considered serious (Suydam 2000).

Malcolm Ogilvie

Common Eider *Somateria mollissima*
PLATE 25

Anas mollissima Linnaeus, 1758, Syst. Nat., ed. 10, p. 124
northern Europe

Etymology: *mollissima* means very soft, from L. *mollis* soft.

Other names: Eider, Eider Duck. Danish: Ederfugl; French: Eider à duvet; German: Eiderente; Icelandic: Æður (Æðarfugl).

Variation: 6 subspecies recognized here: *S. m. mollissima*; Faeroes Eider *S. m. faeroeensis* C.L. Brehm, 1831; Northern Eider *S. m. borealis* C.L. Brehm, 1824; Dresser's Eider *dresseri* Sharpe, 1871; Hudson Bay Eider *S. m. sedentaria* Snyder, 1941; and Pacific Eider *S. m. v-nigrum* G.R. Gray, 1856. Seventh race *S. m. islandica* C.L. Brehm, 1830 included in *borealis*.

Description

ADULT: dimorphic. ♂ nominate *mollissima* in breeding plumage has black crown, variably divided by white streak from centre to nape. Rest of head and neck white, with pale green patches on nape and rear of cheeks. Upperparts white, plus scapulars, tertials and round patches either side of rump. Rump and tail black. Breast white, tinged rosy pink, fading with wear. Rest of underparts black. Forewing white, all flight feathers black; underwing pale grey and white. Bill olive-grey with pale yellow at tip and at base where lobes or horns extend towards eyes, tapering to narrow rounded ends; feathering extends nearly to nostrils and ends in blunt points; legs and feet grey-green; eyes brown. ♀ overall warm brown, barred black, paler on head and neck, which are streaked black; pale eye-ring and faint eyestripe. In flight, two thin white wing bars either side dark brown, sometimes purplish, speculum; underwing coverts pale. Bill olive-grey, with frontal lobes as ♀; legs and feet olive-grey; eye brown. Subspecific variation mainly involves body size, size and shape of bill lobes, bill colour, amount of green on head, presence of V on throat of ♂, and breeding plumage colour of ♀. *faeroeensis* is *c* 10% smaller than nominate, including bill; lobes much shorter and coming to sharp point; bill and lobes dark olive-grey lacking any yellowish hue; ♀ darker overall and more heavily barred darker brown. *borealis* varies in size across range from smaller than nominate to similar. Lobes short and narrow, coming to point and feathering not reaching nostrils; bill of ♂ orange-yellow, lobes variable from orange-yellow to olive; ♀ tending more rufous brown. *dresseri* similar in size to nominate; lobes long and untapering, broadly rounded, ending close to eye; feathering on bill pointed and ending beneath nostrils; bill and lobes of ♂ orange-yellow; ♀ flanks barred rufous brown, not blackish. *sedentaria* larger than nominate; duller green on sides of head extends forwards under crown and eye; scapulars raised into two small peaks; bill similar to *dresseri*, but lobes narrow and untapering with rounded ends not so close to eye; feathering on bill rounded and ending close to nostrils. ♂ bill and lobes orange-yellow; ♀ paler and greyer. *v-nigrum* slightly larger than nominate; green on head extends forwards to under eye; black V under throat, apex towards chin (rarely present in other subspecies); scapulars raised into 2 small peaks; bill lobes short and narrow and feathering on bill rounded, not reaching nostrils. ♂ bill and lobes orange-red; ♀ overall paler.

MOULT: eclipsed ♂ uniform blackish brown overall with scattered whitish feathers on crown and forming supercilium, also on breast; wing coverts remain white. Eclipse plumage acquired mid June–mid July, returning to full breeding plumage Oct–Nov.

IMMATURE: dull brown as ♀ but lacking black markings. ♂ breeding plumage acquired over 3–4 years, with various and variable intermediate plumages on way, including white breast and partial white back in 2nd year giving piebald appearance. ♀ lacks defined black marks until 3rd year. Bill lobes probably not full-size until 3rd year.

DUCKLING: upperparts, centre of chin, breast and sides dark grey; broad stripe over eye and sides of chin and underparts pale grey. Bill, legs, feet and eye dark brown to olive brown; bill lobes, or horns, present. Nelson (1993) figures and describes ducklings of *v-nigrum, borealis* from Baffin Island and from Iceland, of *sedentaria* and *dresseri* which differ slightly in colour, size and shape of bill horns.

MEASUREMENTS AND WEIGHT: nominate ♂ wing (n = 20), 289–315 (304); tail (n = 17), 90–104 (96.0); bill (n = 22), 53–61 (57.2); tarsus (n = 21), 52–57 (54.2); weight in summer (n = 22), 1384–2800 (2218), in winter (n = 22), 1965–2875 (2315). ♀ wing (n = 21), 286–312 (301); tail (n = 21), 90–98 (94.7); bill (n = 23), 51–59 (54.4); tarsus (n = 23), 50–56 (52.8); weight in summer (n = 32), 1192–2895 (1915), in winter (n = 18), 1864–2595 (2142) (Cramp and Simmons 1977).

faeroeensis ♂ (n = 22) wing, 260–284 (270); bill, 48–56 (49.4). ♀ (n = 7) wing, 257–271 (264); bill, 45–50 (48.0); weight (summer) (n = 6), 1703–2223 (1847) (Cramp and Simmons 1977).

borealis ♂ wing (n = 15), 284–302 (291); bill (n = 17), 47–56 (51.1); tarsus (n = 17), 48–53 (50.2); weight (summer) (n = 12), 1560–2710 (2000). ♀ (n = 5) wing, 278–287 (282); bill, 46–52 (47.6); tarsus, 47–51 (49.1); weight in summer, East Greenland (n = 11), 1575–2165 (1810); weight in summer, Southampton Is, Canada (n = 28), 1300–2100 (1648) (Cramp and Simmons 1977; Goudie *et al.* 2000).

dresseri ♂ (n = 12) wing, 287–300 (293); bill, 56–60 (57.8); tarsus, 51–55 (52.7); weight (n = 119) 1700–2450. ♀ (n = 12) wing, 274–298 (283); bill, 49–53 (50.8); tarsus, 49–53 (50.7); weight in summer (n = 143), 850–2560 (Palmer 1976).

sedentaria ♂ (n = 4) wing, 305–315 (311); bill, 55–60 (57.8); weight in summer, 2200–2350 (2276). ♀ (n = 18) wing, 293–325 (303); bill, 47–60 (51.5); weight in summer, 1680–2500 (Goudie *et al.* 2000).

v-nigrum ♂ (n = 20) wing, 290–315 (303); bill, 48–56 (52.7); tarsus, 50–55 (52.7). ♀ (n = 13) wing, 270–295 (289); bill, 44–53 (48.9); tarsus, 49–54 (51.3) (Palmer 1976).

Field characters

Large and bulky seaduck, 500–710 mm long, ♂ appearing white above and black below, ♀ brown. Bill and head distinctly triangular in outline, forehead and bill forming continuous line. In flight, ♂ appears white in front and black behind. For distinctions of ♀ from ♀ King Eider, see that species account and Blomdahl *et al.* (2002). Immature ♂♂ have confusing range of plumages, essentially black and white, but pattern varying with age. ♂ retains white on wing in eclipse, always more than eclipsed King Eider.

Voice

♂ has coo-ing display call *ah-hOOO* or *ah-ee-OOO*, which may extend to 4 or more syllables. In group display there is noticeable rising and falling rhythm. ♀ has low-pitched, hoarse *gog-gog-gog* or *kok-kok-kok* calls. Ducklings use variety of high-pitched *peep* or *twee* notes (see Driver 1974). Sonogram of ♂ and ♀ calls in Cramp and Simmons (1977), and of duckling distress call in Kear (1968).

Range and status

Breeds on coasts of northern temperate and arctic zones of northern hemisphere, but absent from much of Siberia and more northern Canadian arctic islands.

mollissima breeds in northwest Europe, including Britain and Ireland (but not Orkney or Shetland), The Netherlands, Scandinavia and northwest Russia east to Novaya Zemlya, wintering within range and to south down Atlantic coast of France, as well as in small numbers on some central European lakes and north coast of Mediterranean. *faeroeensis* is resident in Faeroes, Shetland and Orkney. *borealis* breeds from Baffin Island and adjacent islands of northeast arctic Canada, probably south into Labrador, Greenland and Iceland to Svalbard and Franz Josef Land, wintering within range and south, including in Gulf of St Lawrence. *dresseri* breeds in eastern Canada and US, from Labrador south through Newfoundland, Nova Scotia and New Brunswick to Maine, wintering within range, from Gulf of St Lawrence southwards, and south to Massachusetts and New York. *sedentaria* is resident in Hudson and James Bays. *v-nigrum* breeds in western arctic Canada, Alaska and eastern Siberia, including Wrangel Island, as well as on islands in Bering Sea, and winters within range and short distances south.

Available population estimates mostly have wide limits (Rose and Scott 1997). *mollissima* estimated at 1.7–2.3 million, of which 1.3–1.7 million are in Baltic and southern North Sea, with 320 000–580 000 in northern Norway and Russia, and 65 000–75 000 in Britain and Ireland. *faeroeensis* 18 000–25 500, of which 6000–12 000 in Faeroes

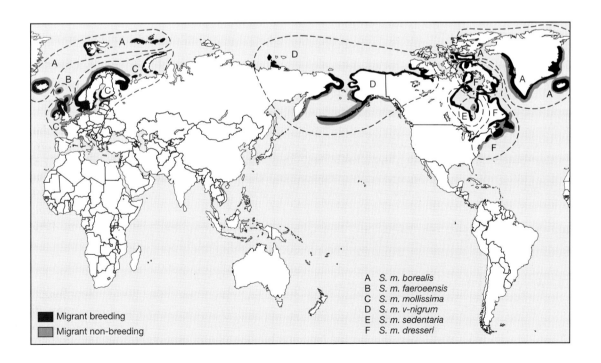

A S. m. borealis
B S. m. faeroeensis
C S. m. mollissima
D S. m. v-nigrum
E S. m. sedentaria
F S. m. dresseri

■ Migrant breeding
▨ Migrant non-breeding

and 12 000–13 500 in Shetland and Orkney. No total population figure available for *borealis*; Iceland held 600 000–900 000, Greenland 30 000–300 000 and Svalbard 40 000–80 000, with no estimate for northeast Canada. Greenland birds declining rapidly (Hansen 2002). Likewise, no figures for *dresseri*; best estimate 181 000 wintering from Maine to Massachusetts while, further north, 157 000 winter in Newfoundland and Maritime Provinces, and 155 000 in Gulf of St Lawrence, including unknown proportion of *borealis*, especially in last area. *sedentaria* has no population figure available. *v-nigrum* estimated at 150 000 with 80 000 in eastern arctic Canada, 25 000 in Alaska and 20 000 in eastern Siberia (Rose and Scott 1997); however, Miyabayashi and Mundkur (1999) raised total figure to 130 000–200 000.

Habitat and general habits

Almost exclusively coastal and marine, rarely breeding up to 5–6 km inland. Breeds on offshore islands and islets, and on coastal shores and spits, as well as on islets in brackish and freshwater lagoons close to sea. Young taken to water by ♀ on hatching, and normally on saltwater within few days. Moults in shallow marine or sheltered coastal waters. Winter quarters similar, but include offshore shallows and archipelagos. In Hudson Bay, seeks out open leads and polynias, moving as necessary when pack ice shifts.

Feeds mainly by diving to reach principally bottom-living molluscs such as Blue Mussel, and some crustaceans and echinoderms (see Guillemette 1998, 2001). In shallow water, as well as up-ending and head-dipping, excavates craters with feet before exploring with bill. Most dives reach 2–4 m, but 15–20 m depth recorded, with dive times 6–78 sec. Diet varies through year depending on availability of different species (Cramp and Simmons 1977, Goudie *et al.* 2000). Ducklings dive for amphipods in shallow water from young age, and this preference precludes their mothers from feeding in deeper water on favoured Blue Mussels, often leading to brood abandonment by mothers and crèching by young.

Displays and breeding behaviour

♂♂ perform communal courtship display, in typical groups of 5–20 with single ♀, accompanied by *ah-hOOO* calls. Main displays often preceded by lateral Head-turning with neck stretched upwards. Bill-toss consists of throwing head back, pausing with bill held vertically, and then head flicked back down again. In Neck-jerk, head thrust forwards and upwards while bill pointed down. Third main display is Reaching, starting with head held erect before being brought forward until bill just touches water, then quickly returned to vertical, puffing out breast as bird calls. ♂♂ chase ♀ who, if pressed hard, may dive, followed by more active ♂♂. ♀ incites, threatening rejected ♂ with lowered head and Bill-pointing accompanied by *gog-gog-gog* call. Pairbond seasonal and monogamous, though occasional ♂ promiscuity. Pairing commences autumn and continues through winter so pairs well formed prior to breeding.

Breeding and life cycle

Nests colonially, up to 250 nests per ha in concentrations of 10 000–15 000 (Cramp and Simmons 1977, Goudie *et al.* 2000). Nest, built by ♀, slight hollow made by turning body, lined with material within reach, grass, droppings, etc, or nothing, followed by down. Eggs green-grey, occasionally green or rarely blue, size and weight varying with race. See Table 9.32 for subspecific variation. Clutch 4–6 (1–8); nests with > 8 eggs, presumed 2 ♀♀ laying. Eggs laid one per day. Single brood. Incubation, by ♀ only, 25–28 days starting with last egg, though ♀ may sit for increasing periods towards end of laying period; ♀ may leave only infrequently and for short periods (Bolduc and Guillemette 2003). ♂ departs early in incubation. Weight of duckling at hatching of *dresseri* in Maine ♂ 77 (60–91) ($n = 74$), ♀ 76 (62–89) ($n = 101$) (Palmer 1976), *sedentaria* in northern Manitoba 72 (54–86) ($n = 123$) (Goudie *et al.* 2000), and *mollissima* in captivity 69.9 ($n = 77$). Young precocial and nidifugous, tended for 55–60 days, commonly crèching. In Finland, Kilpi *et al.* (2001) found 31% of ♀♀ abandoned their young to crèches, 23% tended alone and 46% attended crèches; lone tenders were in best body condition at hatching, abandoners in worst. See also Öst and Bäck (2003). Ducklings fledge in 65–75 days.

Data on breeding success summarized in Goudie *et al.* (2000). Age of 1st breeding 3 years, some ♀♀ breed at 2. Annual survival rate of breeding ♀♀ in Maine, based on recovery data 0.886 ± 0.076

Table 9.32 Common Eider egg statistics.

| Subspecies | Location | Egg measurements | | | |
		Size	Range	Sample	Source
mollissima	Great Britain	77 × 51	70–88 × 48–55	100	Makatsch 1974
faeroeensis		79 × 52	73–86 × 50–54	14	Palmer 1976
borealis	Devon Is	75 × 50	69–83 × 45–53	158	Goudie *et al*. 2000
dresseri	St Lawrence	78 × 53	70–87 × 50–56	72	Goudie *et al*. 2000
sedentaria	N. Manitoba	74 × 50	63–83 × 45–54	1385	Goudie *et al*. 2000
v-nigrum	Alaska	76 × 50	75–87 × 47–52	85	Goudie *et al*. 2000
		Egg weights			
mollissima	NW Russia	109	87–127	?	Cramp & Simmons 1977
mollissima	captivity	111.3	89.0–136.5	100	WWT
faeroeensis	calculated	115		14	Schönwetter 1960–66
borealis	Devon Is	103.8	±1.6	13	Goudie *et al*. 2000
dresseri	St Lawrence	125	115–134	7	Goudie *et al*. 2000
sedentaria	N. Manitoba	104	72–130	1364	Goudie *et al*. 2000
v-nigrum	captivity	105	97.5–111.5	7	WWT
		Clutch size			
mollissima	Finland	4.6	3–8	193	Cramp & Simmons 1977
faeroeensis	no data				
borealis	Svalbard	2.95	1–8	2661	Cramp & Simmons 1977
borealis	Devon Is	3.3	1–6	544	Goudie *et al*. 2000
dresseri	St Lawrence	4.3	2–8	1364	Goudie *et al*. 2000
sedentaria	N. Manitoba	4.3	3–8	323	Goudie *et al*. 2000
v-nigrum	Victoria Is	3.8	1–14	1236	Goudie *et al*. 2000

(0.641–0.971) ($n = 995$); and for breeding ♀♀ in Aberdeen, UK, 0.90 based on mark and recapture. Mean adult ♀ life span of banded *dresseri* in eastern North America 7.36 ± 0.97 years (Goudie *et al*. 2000). Potentially long-lived; longevity record of UK ringed bird 35 years 6 months (Toms and Clark 1998).

Conservation and threats

Populations in Canadian and Russian Arctic, Alaska and Greenland all thought to be declining. Populations in high Arctic subject to shooting for food, especially in spring, with impact probably increasing with greater mobility and available firepower (Hansen 2002). Considerable increase in winter sport shooting in North America, and harvest may exceed sustainable levels in some areas (Goudie *et al*. 2000). Survey of breeding ♀♀ in Newfoundland and Labrador found 39% and 54%, respectively, had lead shot in their tissues (Hansen 2002). In Europe, only legally shot in Denmark, Norway, Sweden and Finland, where annual bag *c* 115 000, *c* 85% in Denmark (Desholm *et al*. 2002). Very vulnerable to coastal pollution, including oil spills. Conflict with shellfish aquaculture in several areas (Ross and Furness 2000, Ross *et al*. 2001), but not thought to impact more than locally. Drowning in monofilament nets occurs in some areas, with few if any restrictions on fishing close to breeding colonies or favoured feeding grounds.

Malcolm Ogilvie

Harlequin Duck *Histrionicus histrionicus*
PLATE 26

Anas histrionicus Linnaeus, 1758, Syst. Nat., ed. 10, p. 127
America – Newfoundland
Histrionicus Lesson, 1828

Etymology: *histrionicus* L. for actor or theatrical, in reference to ♂'s bright colours. Vernacular name has same meaning.

Other names: Harlequin. Danish: Strømand; French: Garrot arlequin; German: Kragenente; Icelandic: Straumönd; Japanese: Shinori-gamo.

Variation: no subspecies. Pacific or Western race *H. h. pacificus* W.S. Brooks, 1915 not recognized, as differences between Atlantic and Pacific populations small.

Description

ADULT: dimorphic. ♂ generally dark grey-blue and black at distance, with pattern of white marks, mostly bordered with black, on head, base of neck, breast and scapulars. Crescentic white patch at base of bill, oval white ear patch, and another white patch down side of neck. Black median stripe through centre of crown with chestnut on either side. Narrow white collar around neck, incomplete in front and behind. Long white bar, bordered black, on side of breast (vertical in swimming bird) in front of folded wing. Small white spot in black area of side of rump at base of tail. Upperbreast bluish. Upperback and mantle medium or darker bluish. Scapulars white with narrow lead-grey margins on outer webs. Belly dark brown, often with bluish wash. Flanks chestnut. Rump and tail black. Wings dark grey-blue with sooty flight feathers. Short white wing bar. Purplish blue speculum, and white on innermost secondaries. Underwing brown. Bill lead-blue; legs pale blue with blackish webs; eyes reddish brown. ♀ head and neck dark brown with 3 white areas: behind eye, below eye and in front of eye reaching forehead. Rest of plumage blackish brown, more greyish below and becoming whitish on abdomen. Bill, legs and feet paler and duller than ♂.

MOULT: ♂ eclipse resembles ♀ but darker brown to dark grey. Innermost tertials white with black margins. ♂ flightless late July–Sept; ♀ *c* month later

(Adams *et al.* 2000, Robertson *et al.* 2000), typically at site that differs from breeding area.

IMMATURE: first autumn ♂ resembles adult ♀. Faint streak pattern begins to appear in late autumn but full adult plumage obtained in 2nd year.

DUCKLING: dark brownish grey above and white below, with white cheeks, white spot in front of eye, whitish shoulder spots, narrow buff wing patches and long rather pointed tail. Feet bluish olive-grey (Nelson 1993).

MEASUREMENTS AND WEIGHT: ♂ wing ($n = 13$), 197–214 (205), tail ($n = 12$), 87–105 (93.0); bill ($n = 13$), 24–28 (25.8); tarsus ($n = 14$), 36–40 (37.5); weight ($n = 20$), 581–750 (667.7). ♀ wing ($n = 4$), 194–201 (198); tail ($n = 4$), 74–86 (79); bill ($n = 4$), 24–26 (25.3); tarsus ($n = 4$), 34–37 (36.0); weight ($n = 9$), 485–682 (538.1) (see also Robertson and Goudie 1999, Sischer and Griffin 2000).

Field characters

Small stocky diving duck, 380–450 mm long, with small bill and slender, pointed tail. Streaks of white on blue and chestnut body of ♂ unmistakable. In flight, ♂ looks dark with white patches on head and white stripes. ♀ and ♂ in eclipse may resemble ♀ Bufflehead, but latter has single white spot on head and white speculum which Harlequin lacks.

Voice

Usually rather silent but most common sound of ♂ is high-pitched squeal, reminiscent of group of fighting mice (sonogram in Cramp and Simmons 1977). During agonistic display, becomes more vocal, uttering squeals and squeaks which become louder and more frequent as visual display intensifies (Inglis *et al.* 1989).

Range and status

Breeding range divided into 2 segments in Atlantic and Pacific. Iceland, Greenland and eastern

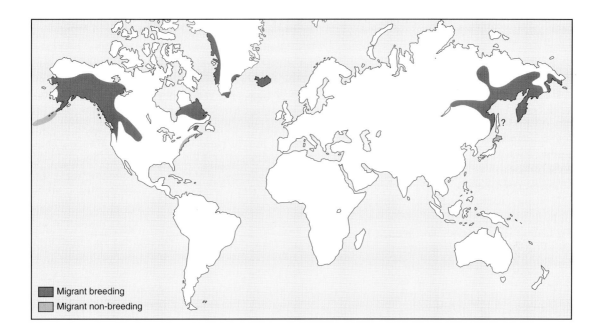

Migrant breeding
Migrant non-breeding

Canada—mainly Labrador (Rodway *et al.* 1998)—form Atlantic range; Pacific segment reaches from eastern Siberia (mountain ranges around Sea of Okhotsk, including Kamchatka) through Alaska to western Canada, extending south of US border (Voous 1960, Robertson and Goudie 1999). American part of Pacific segment estimated at 165 000 birds with rough estimate of Russian part 50 000–100 000 birds (Goudie *et al.* 1994); Icelandic population estimated from wintercounts 1998–2002 as 14 000 birds (Garðarsson and Thórarinsson 2003, Garðarsson 2004). Widely distributed in Iceland (Guðmundsson 1971) densities in 1968–71 ranging from 0.2–*c* 7 pairs per km of river (Bengtson 1972a); in America, ranged 0.15–0.91 pairs per km (summarized by Breault and Savard 1991). River Laxá, draining Lake Mývatn in Iceland, holds highest local density of breeders, where numbers in upper stretches rose from *c* 50 ♂♂ in 1965–75 to *c* 250 in 1992 (Garðarsson 1979, Garðarsson and Einarsson 1994, Einarsson *et al.* 2004). Comparable data not available from other Icelandic rivers. In eastern Siberia, seems to be declining rapidly, although situation uncertain (Miyabayashi and Mundkur 1999), and decreasing as winter visitor to Japan (mainly Hokkaido), where small population breeds (Sato and Kominato 1988, Brazil 1991). There are slight decreases in British Columbia and

retraction from former breeding range in southwestern US (Goudie *et al.* 1994). Eastern North America population winters in 2 areas; birds breeding east of Hudson Bay and Ungara Bay winter in southeast Greenland. Others (estimated at < 1000 individuals Vickery 1988) winter along Atlantic coast (Brodeur *et al.* 2002). Moulting takes place at sea. Part of eastern North American population moults off coast of south west Greenland (Brodeur *et al.* 2002).

Habitat and general habits

River specialist in summer (May–Sept), only exceptionally observed on lakes and hardly ever seen flying overland. Ducks breeding along coastal streams make feeding excursions to sea (Dzinbal 1982). When flying, keeps low over water, following bends in river and preferring to fly around islands rather than over them.

During breeding season, lives mainly on turbulent streams. Migrates upriver late Apr and begins to lay mid May. In Iceland, highest densities close to lake outlets, reflecting relatively rich food resource in form of blackfly *Simulium* larvae and pupae (Bengtson and Ulfstrand 1971, Guðmundsson 1971). Breeding pairs loaf on sand spits, rocks and riverbanks in small groups, often accompanied by unpaired ♂. Loafing sites tend to be close to rapids where most feeding occurs. Seems to show high site fidelity (Bengtson 1972a, Kuchel 1977) but does not defend loafing sites or feeding areas (Inglis *et al.* 1989). ♂♂ migrate to sea in June where moult in small groups. ♀♀ and young migrate downriver early Sept. Yearling ♂♂ rarely observed on rivers. Flocks of ♀♀ not attending young stay on some rivers throughout summer. In winter, found in small flocks scattered along exposed rocky seashores where feed mostly on intertidal and subtidal invertebrates. For details of diet see Palmer (1976), Robertson and Goudie (1999) Fischer and Griffin (2000) and Robert and Cloutier (2001).

In river habitats, main foraging method is diving for benthic insects. Food also obtained by scraping larvae off rocks just under water surface (Inglis *et al.* 1989); upending rarely employed. Bengtson (1966) noted further feeding technique that involved skimming insects off surface, behaviour that becomes common later in summer when adult blackflies emerge. Relatively little time spent feeding (7.0–7.6% during pre-nesting period), and little diurnal variation in foraging apart from drop around midnight (Inglis *et al.* 1989, but see Bengtson 1966). Mean dive duration (264 dives of 31 birds) 10.7 sec (max 26 sec) (Inglis *et al.* 1989), or 16 sec (max 35) (Bengtson 1966). ♀♀ stay longer underwater than ♂♂ (♀11.6 ± 1.1 sec; ♂ 10.3 ± 1.0) (Inglis *et al.* 1989). Feeds disproportionally more in fast than calm stretches of Laxá. Has amazing ability, even when diving in fast white water, to emerge in same position as original dive.

In winter in Aleutian Islands of Alaska (Fischer and Griffin 2000), ♂♂ spent 70% of diurnal period diving or head-dipping in intertidal and subtidal zones, and ♀♀ 76%; however, more time was spent feeding in evening, during midwinter, cold weather and during high tide. Gastropods mainly *Littorina sitkana*, crustaceans mainly gammarid amphipods, and dipteran larvae and pupae made up 83% of diet, but composition changed through winter.

For time budget at stages of life cycle, see Robertson and Goudie (1999), and for time budgets of moulting birds in Labrador, when large proportion of time spent hauled out of water resting, and only 11.6% spent foraging, see Adams *et al.* (2000).

Displays and breeding behaviour

Head-nod (Bengtson 1966) main agonistic display (Inglis *et al.* 1989) consisting of upward and forward movement of head and neck through elliptical trajectory, and performed by both sexes but most frequently by paired ♂♂. ♀ seldom initiates agonistic encounters but, after inciting by ♀, mate will usually Head-nod at or Rush intruder. Three white bands on head and flanks accentuate aggressive posture of ♂ during encounters; these and other white marks on ♂ plumage usually act as camouflage (Inglis *et al.* 1989). In Iceland, some rivers shared with Barrow's Goldeneye; Barrow's Goldeneyes often initiate agonistic encounters and chase Harlequins away (Inglis *et al.* 1989).

Extra-pair copulation by paired ♂♂ does not seem to occur, and unpaired ♂♂ accompanying pairs do not seem to copulate with paired ♀♀; forced copulation attempts rarely observed (Inglis *et al.* 1989). Copulation sequences infrequent and brief; ♂ usually initiates sequence by using Head-nod and/or Rush display. ♀ assumes prone position and ♂ most commonly pecks repeatedly at back of her outstretched neck. High-pitched squeaks heard in pre-copulation phase, apparently uttered by ♂. ♂ mounts and usually grasps back of mate's neck, by which time ♀ partially submerged. ♂ stays on ♀ for few sec and, immediately after copulation, ♀ shakes tail vigorously, rushes away and dives. ♂ Head-nods at his mate and dives after her; usually followed by preening (see Inglis *et al.* 1989 for details).

Breeders paired when fly inland in spring. Unusual among ducks in that long-term monogamy normal; pair re-unites when both members return to same moulting or wintering ground, where tend to be site-faithful (Gowans *et al.* 1997, Robertson *et al.* 1998, 2000). ♂ defends mate, but not territorial and no evidence that nest site defended.

Breeding and life cycle

In Iceland, laying mostly in last week of May, with peak laying 1st half of June, although may be delayed in late springs. Nesting primarily on small islands in river, on ground, usually not far from river (only 7 of 98 nests more than 5 m from water,

Bengtson 1972a), concealed in dense vegetation, often under low shrub, occasionally among rocks or in rock cavity. Not colonial. Eggs creamy-yellow; 58 × 41 (50–62 × 39–43) (*n* = 105); calculated weight 53. Clutch 5–7 (3–9) (Guðmundsson 1971, see Bengtson 1972a for further details). One brood. No data on re-nesting, but sightings of ducklings late in season (Aug) make it possible. Parasitic egg-laying not observed but may occur. Incubation 27–29 days, by ♀ only (Cramp and Simmons 1977). Hatch mostly 1st half of July but varies with location (summary in Breault and Savard 1991), e.g. last week of July in Labrador (Rodway *et al.* 1998). On hatching, ducklings weigh 33.8 (29.1–36.7) (*n* = 4) (Smart 1965b); attended by ♀, tend to hide in over-hanging vegetation such as *Salix* when small. Feed mostly by diving in same habitat as adults, but small young take more food from surface (Bengtson 1972a). Of 504 eggs laid in Iceland 1966–70, 81% hatched and 50–70% fledged (Bengtson 1972a). Production of young in main breeding area at upper part of Laxá at Mývatn over 28 years (1975–2002) varied 3–235, and correlated with abundance of blackflies in river (Garðarsson and Einarsson 1994, 2004). Broods usually remain separate, but amalgamation observed in densely populated areas. Fledging period varies with location, 42–>60 days (Breault and Savard 1991). In Iceland, becomes independent after post-fledging movement of ♀ to sea (Guðmundsson 1971), although some broods apparently abandoned earlier. In Pacific population of Canada and US, broods may accompany mother from breeding stream to coastal moulting and wintering area (Regehr *et al.* 2001), and then separate, although some family members maintain contact for at least 5 months.

Age at 1st breeding 2 years. ♀ adult annual survival rate 71% (Robertson *et al.* 2000), unknown for ♂, but tends to be long-lived (Goudie *et al.* 1994).

Conservation and threats

In Iceland and Greenland, protected from hunting and egg collecting. Core area, River Laxá, partly protected by law and also designated Ramsar site. Three types of threat exist in Iceland. Hydroelectric development includes diversion of river courses and silting of rivers. One colony may have vanished because of river diversion (Guðmundsson 1971) and most significant threat was hydropower scheme in River Laxá at Mývatn which was cancelled in 1973 (Jónsson 1987). Proposed release of Atlantic Salmon *Salmo salar* in upper reaches of River Laxá will probably increase competition for main food resource, blackfly larvae and pupae (Einarsson 1991). Introduction and subsequent escape of American Mink in Iceland in 1930s (*cf* Petersen and Skírnisson 1980) may have reduced potential nest sites on many rivers; rivers that hold relatively high numbers of breeding pairs need to be identified and protected (Robertson and Goudie 1999).

Potential threats to American populations listed by Breault and Savard (1991), but cannot be evaluated because of lack of data on distribution (see also Robertson and Goudie 1999).

Árni Einarsson

Labrador Duck *Camptorhynchus labradorius*

Anas labradoria Gmelin, 1789, Syst. Nat., **1**, p. 537 arctic America, Connecticut, and Labrador
Camptorhynchus 'Eyton' Bonaparte, 1838

Etymology: *kamptos* Gr. for bent or flexible, *rhunkhos* is bill; *labradorius* means of Labrador.

Other names: Pied Duck, Sand-shoal Duck (from winter habitat), Skunk Duck (from markings of ♂). Both Labrador Duck and Pied Duck have been used for other species.

Variation: no subspecies recognized.

Description

ADULT: dimorphic. ♂ (Figure 9.33) head, throat, neck, upper breast, scapulars and wing (except primaries) white; rest of plumage black and brownish black, including longitudinal stripe on crown and occiput and collar around lower neck, lower breast and sides minutely spotted with white; scapulars

9.33 A male of the extinct Labrador Duck.

and tertiaries bordered with black; patch of stiff (plush-like) feathers on cheeks, as in Spectacled and King Eiders. Bill black to brownish black, with basal part and area around nostrils possibly orange-yellow; legs probably black; iris reddish hazel to yellow. ♀ slightly smaller; uniform brownish grey, bluish on mantle, sandy on rump and upper tail coverts; tail blackish; chin and throat whitish; wings brownish grey with large white speculum formed by outer greater coverts and secondaries, soft parts probably as in ♂ (Delacour 1954–64, Humphrey and Butsch 1958). Bill of both sexes had sides of upper mandible flared and pendulous, with about 50 lamellae on sides of upper and lower jaw—numerous for size of bill (Palmer 1976) and larger than in other seaducks.

MOULT: limited data; Delacour (1954–64) wrote of ♂ eclipse that probably resembled ♀, but no skin apparently exists in this condition, and uncertain that eclipse plumage existed (Phillips 1922–26, Johnsgard 1965a). Probably 2 annual moults of body feathers, and one complete wing moult.

IMMATURE: much like ♀, but ♂♂ greyer, head basically darker with more white on head; lower breast dotted with white (Delacour 1954–64).

DUCKLING: unknown

MEASUREMENTS AND WEIGHT: (no sample sizes) ♂ wing, 210–220; tail, 75–80; culmen, 43–45; tarsus, 46; weight, 865. ♀ wing, 206–209; culmen, 40–42; tarsus, 38 (Phillips 1922–26, Delacour 1954–64, Chilton 1997).

Field characters

Small (length 510 mm) coastal, fast-flying diving duck. ♂ in breeding plumage unmistakable—black and white with wings entirely white except for primaries, and possibly orange or yellow patch at base of bill.

Voice

Unknown except for statement that whistled as they flew and fed (Pennant *in* Rowley 1877). ♂ trachea unlike that of scoters and more similar to eiders and Harlequin (Johnsgard 1965a). Wings whistled in flight (Audubon 1843).

Range and status

Last individual thought shot 12 December 1878 at Elmira, New York, before which numbers had been dwindling over many years. Breeding range never certainly known; may have nested in Labrador, or merely passed through in autumn and bred further north. In winter, seen on Atlantic coast of North America, from Labrador to Chesapeake Bay, and especially around Long Island Sound where most specimens with any data collected. One shot in St Lawrence River near Montreal in 1862.

Probably never very common. Offered in meat markets of New York, Baltimore, Philadelphia and Boston 1840–60, surprisingly, because not good table birds having 'strong unsavory flesh', dense down making them difficult to pluck (Bent 1923), and so unpopular that carcasses rotted before they could be sold. Today, 54 or 55 skins exist in North American and European museums, and sternum preserved at Zoology Museum of Cambridge University (figured *in* Rowley 1877). Most specimens obtained when monetary value of skins far outweighed need for information on date and locality of capture (Hahn 1963).

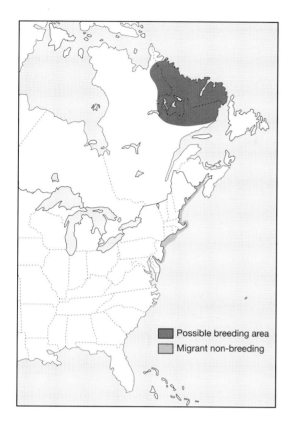

Possible breeding area
Migrant non-breeding

Habitat and general habits

Marine duck found on New England coastal bays and sandy estuaries during winter (Rowley 1877, Delacour 1954–64, Fuller 2001). Nothing known of feeding habits except that had curious soft-edged bills and may have fed on shellfish as fishermen caught them on lines baited with Blue Mussels (Palmer 1976); one specimen had broken shells in crop, suggesting mussels ingested whole and crushed in powerful gizzard, like eiders. Large liver (Wilson *in* Rowley 1877) may indicate ability to remain submerged for long periods, although mostly reported feeding in rolling surf off sand and mud-bars and, at times, walking along shore searching 'in the manner of the Spoonbill Duck' (Audubon *in* Rowley 1877). Possibly found invertebrates among Eelgrass *Zostera* (Chilton 1997), and numerous large lamellae suggest filter-feeding as one foraging technique. May have needed more specialized diet than other seaducks; suggested to

have been Atlantic's ecological equivalent of Steller's Eider, which also has soft and fleshy edges to distal half of upper mandible (*cf* Blue Duck).

Audubon (1843) described parties of 7–10, presumably in nonbreeding season; seldom reported in flocks like most seaducks—perhaps because never common, and already in decline during period of North American written history.

Displays and breeding behaviour

Nothing known of displays or pairbond. Probably, based on relative frequency of birds shot in juvenile plumage, not sexually mature for 3 or 4 years (Rowley 1877, Bent 1923).

Breeding and life cycle

Little known. Audubon's son was shown several hatched nests in Labrador, said to be of this species, at end of July 1833. They looked like eider nests, being 'very large, formed externally of fir twigs, internally of dried grass, and lined with down. It would thus seem that the Pied Duck breeds earlier than most of its tribe' (Audubon 1843). However, this account inconsistent with Audubon's other writing. If nests *were* Labrador Ducks, presence of down indicates that only ♀ incubated. Ten possible eggs in various collections, almost exactly elliptical, measure 61.0 × 42.9 (60–62 × 42–44.45) (Chilton 1997); 7 have calculated fresh weight of 60 (Schönwetter 1960–66). On one egg is written 'Labrador 8 Juin' (Glegg 1951) which does suggest early breeding season.

Reasons for extinction

Unknown. Reportedly 'unsuspicious' (Coues *in* Rowley 1877) and 'rather stupid' (Phillips 1922–26) presumably because insufficiently terrified of man; on other hand, also said to be shy and difficult to approach (Todd 1979).

Eggs possibly robbed in quantity by fishermen on nesting grounds, and down said to have had commercial value (Bellrose 1980). Plenty of coastal shooting in winter (Phillips 1922–26) and, although perhaps no more than other seaducks, long period of immaturity made it particularly vulnerable, and unlikely to survive as quarry species. No written accounts of any eggs or birds taken in breeding season. Scarce adult ♂♂ may have been targeted by collectors (Chilton 1997). Disease, and use of plumage in feather trade, suggested as contributing factors by Todd (1979). Changes in molluscan fauna of New England's coast, caused by increasing human settlement, perhaps implicated in demise (Phillips 1922–26), especially if dependent on dietary items subject to cyclical patterns of abundance and scarcity (Chilton 1997).

Janet Kear

Surf Scoter *Melanitta perspicillata*
PLATE 26

Anas perspicillata Linnaeus, 1758, Syst. Nat., ed. 10, p. 125
Canada = Hudson Bay
Melanitta Boie, 1822

Etymology: *Melanitta* Gr. *melas* black plus *netta* duck; *perspicillata* L. means spectacled. Scoter was apparently printing error for Sooter, and referred to black plumage of Common Scoter. Surf Scoter was name given in 1828 to rare vagrant to Britain.

Other names: none in English. French; Macreuse à lunettes, Macreuse à front blanc; German: Brillenente; Spanish: Pato negrón.

Variation: no subspecies.

Description

ADULT: dimorphic. ♂ black with white patches on forehead and nape of neck. Bill brightly coloured with patches of orange-yellow, scarlet, white and black, and with slight protuberence above nostril; legs and feet scarlet-orange, webs black; iris white. ♀ smaller than ♂; plumage brownish grey, darker on body, paler on side of head with two lighter patches, one between eye and bill and one behind eye. Bill dark grey; legs and feet drab yellow-orange; iris white.

MOULT: 2 plumages per annual cycle. Definitive alternate plumage acquired from moult of head and body feathers ending mid winter; basic or eclipse plumage acquired in summer moult that includes regimes (for timing of wing moult, see later). ♂ feathering in eclipse sooty black and white patch retained only on nape, bill colouring less contrasting; ♀ more uniformly brownish (Palmer 1976).

IMMATURE: both sexes similar to adult ♀ (Lesage *et al.* 1996).

DUCKLING: dark sooty brown with no contrasting markings. Cheek patch somewhat paler than body at hatch, becoming paler through half-grown stage (Nelson 1993, Lesage *et al.* 1996).

MEASUREMENTS AND WEIGHT: ♂ wing ($n = 4$), 245; culmen ($n = 7$), 35.8; tarsus (bone) ($n = 7$), 44.2; weight ($n = 7$), 990. ♀ wing ($n = 34$), 230; culmen ($n = 38$), 37.3; tarsus (bone) ($n = 38$), 41.5; weight ($n = 38$), 870.

Field characters

Medium-sized seaduck, 430–470 mm long. Distinguishable from Velvet or White-winged Scoter by smaller size and lack of white wing marking. Similar in size to Black Scoter, from which distinguishable by white patches on forehead and nape of ♂, and double pale patches on side of ♀ head. ♂ has distinctive bill pattern of red, yellow, white and black.

Voice

Generally silent but breeding ♂ produces low whistle and sharp *puk-puk*, and ♀ gutteral *krrrak krrrak* during courtship and harsh *crahh* in defence of young (Palmer 1976).

Range and status

Breeds in boreal forest wetlands, exclusively in North America, with eastern group mainly in Québec and Labrador and western group in Northwest Territories, Yukon, Alaska, and northern parts of Manitoba, Saskatchewan, Alberta and British

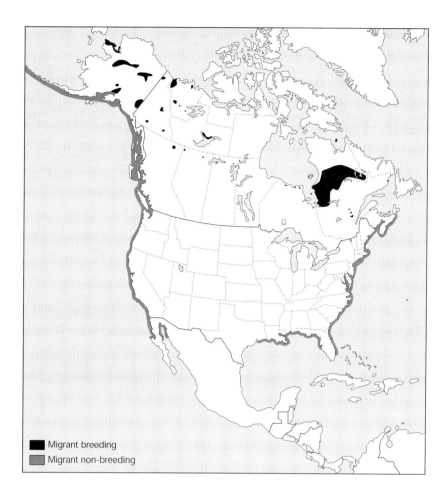

Migrant breeding
Migrant non-breeding

Columbia. Winters in large flocks on both Atlantic and Pacific coasts of North America with few present on Great Lakes. Atlantic wintering areas extend from Nova Scotia to Georgia with main concentration from New Jersey to Virginia, including Chesapeake Bay. Pacific wintering areas extend from Alaska to Mexico, concentrating in California and Baja California, Mexico.

Only crude population estimates available (see Goudie *et al.* 1994, Savard *et al.* 1998a) but breeders probably exceed 500 000, and wintering population greater than one million. Rose and Scott (1997) suggested stable population of 765 000.

Habitat and general habits

Breeds in shallow lakes of small or medium size (< 20 ha) in open boreal (spruce) forest (Décarie

et al. 1995, Savard *et al.* 1998a). During breeding season, feeds mainly on freshwater invertebrates. Winters, stages and moults in coastal waters, feeding on Blue Mussels and other bivalve molluscs (Cottam 1939, McGilvrey 1967, Vermeer 1981, Reed *et al.* 1996). Feeding flocks often show synchrony in diving and surfacing (Schenkeveld and Ydenberg 1985).

In wintering and staging areas, not restricted to protected coastal waters, but usually within 1 km of land and in water less than 10 m deep. May be seen swimming in rough seas or diving in heavy waves breaking over shoals, hence name 'surf'. Often migrates, stages and moults in impressively large flocks. Usually migrates low over sea, high over land, with frequent changes in flock formation (Palmer 1976, Savard *et al.* 1998a).

Displays and breeding behaviour

Pair formation probably begins during winter and reinforced during migration and on arrival at breeding area. Courtship occurs in small flocks with ♂♂ manoeuvring to be close to ♀, and ♀♀ threatening unwanted ♂♂ or pairs. Copulation occurs on water and typically when mated pair is several m away from other Surf Scoters. Pre-copulatory display includes False-drinking, Water-twitch, and especially Preen-behind-wing. On mounting, ♂ performs single Wing-flick and, on dismounting, Chest-lifts (Myers 1959a, Johnsgard 1965a, Savard *et al.* 1998a).

From study of breeding ecology at Lake Malbaie, Québec (Morrier *et al.* 2001), nesting pairs disperse widely over vast boreal forest range. Usually only one lake in several used, typically by single pair. Rarely, larger lake, such as Lake Malbaie (640 ha), used by several pairs (Reed *et al.* 1994). Arrive within few days of ice break-up in 2nd half of May, and ♀ feeds intensively while ♂ spends most time vigilant.

Breeding and life cycle

In last week of May (about week after arrival), egg-laying commences, with nest initiation reaching peak 1st week of June. Eggs cream-coloured; 62.4×43.9 ($n = 160$ from Québec); calculated weight of 62 (Schönwetter 1960–66). Savard *et al.* (1998a) concluded typical fresh egg weight varied 76–79. Clutch 7.6 (6–9) eggs ($n = 18$) incubated by ♀ alone. Egg-laying interval and incubation period unrecorded. ♂ departs breeding lake shortly after incubation starts. Nests typically several m inland from shore, well-hidden in dense shrub, under overhanging conifer branches or under fallen logs. Islands selected when available but many nests on mainland. Hatching synchronous in individual nests (within 24 h), with earliest nests hatching last week of June and late nests 1st week Aug with peak 2nd week July (Nero 1963, Savard and Lamothe 1991, Savard *et al.* 1998a). Precocial ducklings leave nest, accompanied by ♀, within 24 h of hatch; newly hatched young (sexes combined) weigh 43.8 ($n = 26$) and measure culmen 12.4 ($n = 26$), tarsus (bone) 22.7 ($n = 20$) (Lesage *et al.* 1996). Begin feeding by diving in shallow water almost immediately, and remain in family unit for most of pre-fledge period. ♀ parent's aggression towards other broods helps maintain unity but, where encounters occur frequently, brood amalgamation may result, with single ♀ taking charge of many ducklings (Savard *et al.* 1998b). Early in development, broods usually occupy restricted rearing area but may move from small lake to adjacent one (occasionally by overland crossing), or to distant part of same lake. Later, bond between ducklings and parent weaken such that young become increasingly independent during last 2 weeks of 55-day fledging period; grow from mean weight of 44 to *c* 820 at Day 49 ($n = 3$) (Lesage *et al.* 1996).

At Lake Malbaie, Québec, in good breeding year of 1995, 50–60 pairs nested, achieving 75% nest success and 307 ducklings, of which 45% reached flight age (Savard *et al.* 1998a). In several cases, marked ♀♀ returned to breed at same lake in following years. Age at 1st breeding and adult survival rates unrecorded.

Moult occurs in large flocks in marine waters along coasts of Labrador, St Lawrence estuary, Hudson and James Bays, Mackenzie Delta, Alaska and British Columbia. Adult ♂♂ leave breeding lakes about mid June, having spent only 3 weeks there, and move to moulting site. Failed ♀♀ leave breeding grounds in 3rd or 4th week of July. Some successful ♀♀ leave early Aug, before young capable of flight. Not known whether ♂♂ and ♀♀ of any breeding area move to same moulting site. Adult ♂♂ arrive to moult in St Lawrence estuary late June but do not become flightless until late July. ♀♀ moult flight feathers 3–4 weeks later than ♂♂ (Savard *et al.* 1998a).

Conservation and threats

Abundant in winter on both sides of North American continent but evidence of decline in recent years along both coasts (Goudie *et al.* 1994, Caithamer *et al.* 1998, Savard *et al.* 1998a), possibly as result of oil pollution and hunting; among most vulnerable waterfowl to oil pollution. Hunted by native people for food in many parts of northern Canada and in Alaska; sport-hunting also allowed in both Canada and US and, along with other North American seaducks, may be subjected to increased hunting pressure as regulations become more restrictive on other waterfowl. More and better survey data, as well as improved understanding of population dynamics, required for adequate management.

Austin Reed

Velvet Scoter *Melanitta fusca*
PLATE 26

Anas fusca Linnaeus, 1758, Syst. Nat., ed 10, p. 123 'Oceano Europaeo' (restricted to the coast of Sweden by Linnaeus)

Etymology: *fusca* is L. for dark, dusky or black. 'Velvet' in use since 1678 when Ray described feathers 'so soft and delicate'.

Other names: White-winged Scoter, Degland's Scoter, Asiatic Scoter. Danish: Fløjtsand; French: Macreuse brune, Macreuse à ailes blanches; German: Samtente; Japanese: Birōdo-kinkuro; Spanish: Pato negrón.

Variation: 3 subspecies recognized: nominate *M. f. fusca* breeding in Europe; Asiatic White-winged Scoter *M. f. stejnegeri* Ridgway, 1887 in Asia; and American White-winged Scoter *M. f. deglandi*, Bonaparte, 1850 in North America. Pacific White-winged Scoter *M. f. dixoni* W. S. Brooks, 1915 included in *deglandi*.

Description

ADULT: dimorphic. ♂ glossy black overall, white secondaries and small white spot below and behind eye. Orange bill with red tip, black basal knob; feet red-pink with blackish webs; eyes pale grey-white. *stejnegeri* ♂ differs from nominate race in larger bill knob, more extensive feathering on bill sides and more purple to orange-red bill (less yellow than *fusca*). *deglandi* ♂ has olive-brown flanks, bill characters intermediate between other races. ♀ of all subspecies dark brown, slightly paler on lower parts, white secondaries, two variable whitish to pale patches, one small in front and below eye, other larger behind and below eye. Bill dull olive-black; feet dull reddish; eyes brown.

MOULT: ♂ plumage duller outside breeding season.

IMMATURE: ♂ dull brown to black, variably heavily mottled with black on upperparts, especially from first Dec on. Immature bill may become coloured in early spring, but lacks basal swelling of adult. Assumes adult plumage from second autumn. ♀ similar to adult ♀, but paler, more mottled with white below and usually more distinct patches on side of head.

DUCKLING: as other scoters, but cheeks, sides of neck and lower throat white, underparts white except for chest band; good description and illustration in Nelson (1993).

MEASUREMENTS AND WEIGHT: *fusca* adult ♂ wing (*n* = 31), 269–286 (280), juv (1st winter) (*n* = 17), 260–282 (268); bill (*n* = 47), 41–51 (44.9); tarsus (*n* = 43), 46–53 (48.8); midwinter weight (*n* = 9), 1517–1980 (1726). Adult ♀ wing (*n* = 7), 255–271 (263), juv (*n* = 22), 232–262 (251); bill (*n* = 27), 37–44 (40.8); tarsus (*n* = 27), 43–49 (45.8); midwinter weight (*n* = 11), 1360–1895 (1658) (Cramp and Simmons 1977). *stejnegeri* measurements unrecorded; weights only from sitting ♀ reported in Dementiev and Gladkov (1952) of 957, and ♂ spring weights of 1020–1437, ♂ Nov 1300, and ♀♀ in Oct 1030. *deglandi* adult ♂ wing (*n* = 85), 282, juv (*n* = 41), 274; weight (*n* = 7), 1361–1769 (1588). Adult ♀ wing (*n* = 32), 267, juv (*n* = 39), 259; weight (*n* = 15), 953–1406 (1179) (Bellrose 1980).

Field characters

Distinguished from other scoters by white wing patch. Length 510–580 mm. Pale to whitish face patches on ♀ difficult to see at distance. Generally tamer than other scoters, being less prone to fly from ships and aircraft than Common Scoter. Flight action heavy; 'jizz' on water less eider-like than Surf Scoter, but more so than relatively long-necked Common Scoter (Pihl and Frikke *in* Komdeur *et al.* 1992). Away from main haunts, more frequently encountered in small groups.

Voice

Rather silent. Nominate race ♂♂ make *vak-vak* courtship call. ♂ *deglandi* has whistled double note *whur-er*. Winter call similar to Common Scoter, but less grating. Nominate race ♀, during morning flight display, makes *braaa-braaa-braaa* call; ♀ *deglandi* has thin whistle. Sonogram of adult calls in Cramp and Simmons (1979). No data on duckling calls.

Range and status

Found on wooded lakes of taiga zone, seemingly relying upon local invertebrate populations with predictably high abundance. Winters almost exclusively at sea.

fusca breeds in Scandinavian peninsula, except southern Norway and Sweden. Nests through Finland, especially common on offshore skerries and islands of Baltic including Estonia. Most numerous in Fennoscandia above 500 m altitude, average 3.4 pairs per 100 km² (Haapanen and Nilsson 1979). Formerly common breeder early last century in northern Finnish woodland, declined markedly throughout Scandinavia in last 80 years (Haapanen *et al.* 1966). Common and widespread in boreal areas of Russia, north to Kanin Peninsula and southern Novaya Zemlya. Breeding range drops away south from Arctic Ocean and open tundra biotopes from Vaygach, extending east to Yenisey River. Dementiev and Gladkov (1952) speculated on breeding extending east to Khatanga, but this uncorroborated. Breeding range sometimes extends south to forested areas of steppe. Important moulting concentrations in Norway, where 10 600 recorded in 1985

(Follestad *et al.* 1986) and Danish waters where numbers may have declined from estimate of *c* 45 000 in 1970s (Joensen 1973) to < 10 000 in 1989 (Laursen *et al.* 1997). Logical to assume these originate from Scandinavian breeding areas, since majority believed to moult in waters north of Russia and concentrations reported from Novaya Zemlya. Migration little studied, but in Kalmarsund, Sweden, during Mar–Nov 1962 and 1963, 17 000–20 000 birds observed with peaks in July, Aug and Nov (Rodebrand 1972). By comparison, virtually none pass Rügen on southern Baltic coast among large numbers of Common Scoters. Winters in coastal waters of northwest Europe, small numbers off Murmansk and in North Norway, along west coast of Norway, around British coasts, Ireland, Atlantic coasts of France (up to 3600 in 1990s) and Iberian peninsula. Baltic Sea most important wintering area; coordinated surveys in 1993 found 950 000 (Pihl *et al.* 1995), largest in Estonian (198 000) and Polish waters (303 000). These counts suggest 1 000 000 in northwest Europe (Pihl and Laursen 1996). Because of more eastern distribution in Baltic compared to Common Scoter, more likely to undertake extreme movements in response to formation of sea ice, as in winter of 1994 when Gulf of Riga froze in few days and > 100 000 displaced into Lithuanian waters.

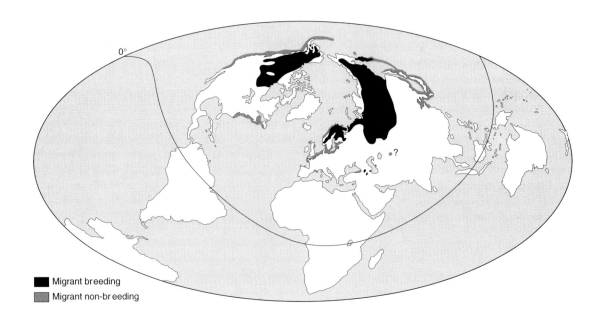

■ Migrant breeding
■ Migrant non-breeding

Spring passage dramatic in Estonia (up to 386 000 in May) (Kontkanen 1995) and Gulf of Finland (up to 60 000) (Kontiokorpi and Parviainen 1995). Since reliable population estimates only available recently, trends unknown. Data from breeding areas in central Siberia (Rogacheva 1992) and wintering areas in Denmark (Laursen *et al.* 1997) suggest little change, but contraction of breeding range in Scandinavia. Small numbers wintering in southern Black Sea thought to come from highly disjunct population breeding in Turkey, Armenia, Georgia and Turkmenistan of $< 10 000$ birds, wintering mainly in Caspian (Rose and Scott 1997).

stejnegeri breeds in Asia east from Yenisey River, with populations reported from Sakhalin Island and Kurilskiye Archipelago between Kamchatka and Japan. Most numerous in Yakutia area along Lena River, where numbers may have fallen during 1970s 8–10 fold (Degtyarev and Larianov 1982). Elsewhere, rare north and east from Anadyr and Kanchalan in northeast Asia. Breeding abundance correlates with abundance of special freshwater gammerids that survive only in deep lakes that never freeze (Kondratyev 1989). Mass assemblages of moulting ♂♂, associating with immatures occur along Okhotsk coast, with smaller numbers moulting on lakes of Kamchatka and Sakhalin peninsulas (Dementiev and Gladkov 1952). Winters in large numbers along southern and southeastern shores of Kamchatka and to lesser extent along Komandorski Islands. Winters also in Kuril Islands and extremely commonly on east and west coasts of Korea, Japan and along Chinese coast south to Fuchow. Gerasimov (1990) estimated 140 000 pass Kamchatka in spring, with up to 40 000 per h. Rose and Scott (1997), although unable to assess trends, considered population to number $< 1 000 000$ birds, while Miyabayashi and Mundkur (1999) revised this down slightly to 600 000–1 000 000.

deglandi breeds in North Dakota in US, and commonly in Manitoba, Saskatchewan and Alberta, with highest densities in open forests of Northwest Territories from Great Slave Lake north to arctic coast of Canada. Large densities occur on Old Crow Flats, Yukon Flats (where 64 000 scoters, mostly this species, summer at densities of 1.9 pairs per km²) and central Alaska (e.g. Tanana-Kuskokwim valleys with

1.1 pairs per km², Bellrose 1980). Some retraction of range noted in south Saskatchewan and Manitoba since 1940s. Population winters on Atlantic and Pacific coasts, northern ringed birds tending to migrate to eastern coast, but birds summering in northern Saskatchewan recovered on both coasts. Up to 56 000 counted along Atlantic coast (Bellrose 1980), with signs of declines amongst midwinter inventories. However, inventories not designed for seaduck census, and most recent aerial surveys carried out by US Fish & Wildlife Service did not distinguish between scoter species, so recent population estimates not available. Number shot in Atlantic Flyway states increased during 1961–75, but fell to *c*10 000 per annum with significant decline 1976–92. On west coast, along Aleutian Islands, numbers estimated at 250 000, with 39 000 along coast from Alaska to Baja California in Mexico. Total population estimated at 1 000 000 and stable (Rose and Scott 1997).

Habitat and general habits

Nests in continental northern hemisphere on boreal, northern forest and mountain lakes. May breed inland on skerries and along wooded shorelines of Baltic coast. On migration, may be common on freshwater lakes, but vast majority winter at sea (wintering numbers on Great Lakes of North America seemingly no longer regular). Often occur along exposed shorelines.

Winter diet mainly saltwater molluscs, especially Blue Mussels and cockles, also *Spisula subtruncata* which is superabundant in offshore waters down to 20 m. Off Japan, feeds mainly on crab *Pinnixa ratubuni* at depths of 30–40 m (Brazil 1991). In Baltic waters, *Mya truncata* and *Macoma baltica* taken, so probably uses whatever locally abundant amongst benthic molluscan fauna. Diet also includes variety of crustaceans, echinoderms, annelids, isopods and amphipods; in summer, eats mainly amphipods, caddis larvae and crustaceans (Cramp and Simmons 1977, Brown and Fredrickson 1986, Stempniewicz 1986, Durink *et al.* 1993).

Displays and breeding behaviour

Pair formation said to occur in late winter or spring, and birds appear to arrive at breeding site paired. Small groups of ♂♂ form around ♀♀ with active display. Courtship flights not recorded, replaced by underwater pursuits initiated by ♀ pursued by several ♂♂. ♀ in pair indulges in morning flights over land, calling persistently, circling low before returning to start point. Such display flights interrupted by swimming displays and continue into egg-laying period. Copulation follows Mock-preening and drinking by ♂, ♀ only prone as ♂ mounts.

Unusual amongst large waterfowl in not relying on endogenous reserves for egg production, clutch size not dependent on ♀ reserves (Alisauskas and Ankney 1992). Pre-nesting ♀ accumulates protein from predominantly amphipod diet (Brown and Fredrickson 1986) and slowly deposits protein into eggs (Brown 1981). Pairs may defend small territories around ultimate nest site. Pairbond thought to be seasonal, ♂ abandoning ♀ early in incubation and migrating from breeding areas to moult, often with nonbreeders, frequently in large concentrations.

Breeding and life cycle

Nest sites can be close to marine habitats (e.g. Scandinavia), but generally around large freshwater lakes in wooded areas of boreal and taiga regions, within 100 m of open water, solitary, but may nest in loose congregations, as on islands, sometimes in association with gull and tern colonies; however, nests occur up to 2–3 km from water (Dementiev and Gladkov 1952). Eggs ovate, creamy buff, 72 × 48 (64–78 × 43–52) (n = 250), weighing 92 for *fusca*, 55.4–72.5 × 35.7–49.0 for *stejnegeri* (Dementiev and Gladkov 1952), 65.3 × 46.3 (n = 100) (Bellrose 1980) and calculated to weigh 77 for *deglandi* (Schönwetter 1960–66). Clutch usually 7–9 (5–12) in *fusca* (Cramp and Simmons 1977), 6–9 in *stejnegeri* (Dementiev and Gladkov 1952) and 9.3 (5–17) eggs in *deglandi* (Bellrose 1980). Single brood, incubated for 27.5 (26–29) days (n = 23) in *fusca* (Cramp and Simmons 1977), and 28 (25–31) days (n = 22) in *deglandi* (Bellrose 1980). ♀ body weight declines up to 23% between laying and end of incubation due to absorption of ovarian tissue and use of fat and protein reserves (Brown and Fredrickson 1987a). ♀♀ show low levels of attendance during incubation (Brown and Fredrickson 1987b), covering nest

during absence. Duckling weights at hatching 54.1 (48.0–60.9) (n = 8) for *deglandi* from Alberta (Nelson 1993) and 54.7 (n = 20) for *fusca* (Koskimies and Lahti 1964).

Broods reared in amphipod-rich habitats (Brown and Fredrickson 1986). Despite large lipid-rich yolk deposits, brood survival low (Brown and Brown 1981); of 7418 eggs laid in Finland, only 3.2% produced young surviving to fledge, equivalent to 99.8%, 92% and 99% loss in 3 seasons (Hildén 1964a). Duckling growth slow, fledging in 50–55 days apparently as adaptation to long development period (Brown and Fredrickson 1983), but cold-hardy as result of high metabolic rate relative to body size (Koskimies and Lahti 1964). Susceptible to disturbance that increased swimming distance, reducing feeding time and survival of ducklings (Mikola *et al.* 1994). Same study found daily predation rates of 5%, or 70% loss of hatched ducklings, mainly as result of gull predation. Crèching frequent in *deglandi* (Kehoe 1989) and *fusca* (Koskimies 1957, Hildén 1964a). ♀ in poor condition unlikely to relinquish brood, but survival of ducklings appears to enhance ♀ survival (Kehoe 1989). Juveniles spend 1st year at sea, usually relatively close to wintering quarters or on lakes close to southern part of range (Dementiev and Gladkov 1952). Probably breeds at 2–3 years of age (Brown and Brown 1981).

Age ratios in hunters bags consistent with low recruitment, with 1.01:1 immature to adult in 1895 wings (Bellrose 1980). No data from ringing recoveries on longevity.

Conservation and threats

As with Common Scoter, little known of breeding ecology, or of conservation threats on nesting grounds. However, threatened by human exploitation of natural resources in taiga and lower tundra regions of breeding range which may not be evident from relatively poor population trend information from winter counts. Disturbance from increasingly mobile public, keen to spend leisure in remote coastal and freshwater habitats of Scandinavia and Baltic coasts, gives cause for concern in breeding areas. Basic studies of breeding biology and effective winter count networks remain high priorities for future. Moulting and wintering concentrations highly vulnerable to oil spills and other marine pollution, as well as to effects of commercial exploitation of substrate and shellfish. In Japan, takes crabs at depth where caught in fishing nets (Brazil 1991). Lack of effective conservation measures to protect inshore marine areas through range also a problem, even if adequate monitoring mechanisms could be set in place.

Stefan Pihl and Tony Fox

Common Scoter *Melanitta nigra*
PLATE 26

Anas nigra Linnaeus, 1758, Syst. Nat., ed. 10, p. 123 Lapland; England

Etymology: from *niger* L. for shining black.

Other names: American Scoter, Black Scoter. Danish: Sortand; French: Macreuse noire, Macreuse à bec jaune; German: Trauerente; Icelandic: Hrafnsönd; Japanese: Kuro-gamo; Spanish: Pato negrón negro.

Variation: 2 subspecies, nominate *M. n. nigra* of northern Europe, and American Black Scoter *M. n. americana* Swainson, 1832 of northeastern Siberia and North America.

Description

ADULT: dimorphic. ♂ black, glossy violet-blue except underparts black glossed green. Flight feathers lack sheen, inner webs paler and may be pale grey at base of primaries. Bill dull black with yellow patch on culmen from above nail extending over top and lower part of bill swelling; foot dull black, sometime dark olive-grey, webs black; eye-ring dark brown or orange, iris dark brown. ♀ head sooty black on crown to eye level, dark brown at base of bill, but remainder of head pale grey mottled buff-brown. Mantle, back, rump and flanks dark brown. Underparts dark brown, glossy. Flight feathers dark brown with paler inner webs, rest of wing grey-brown with paler tips. Bill dark olive-brown to black, sometimes with pale yellowish streak; foot olive-brown to black with dark webs; iris yellow-brown to brown. *americana* differs from nominate form in shorter bill, upper mandible yellow with black tip and edges, and completely yellow knob; bill knob also wider and longer, but less swollen. See also Bordage and Savard (1995).

MOULT: no obvious ♂ eclipse, but 2 body moults annually assumed, and mixture of old worn and new feathers gives mottled and duller appearance in summer. Large-scale moult migration prior to flightless period.

IMMATURE: ♂ in 1st winter retains brown wing coverts, flight feathers and underwing coverts, 1st primary has slight notch *c* 40 mm from tip and belly white with few black feathers. Second winter birds develop basal knob to bill, attain yellow eye-ring and have notch on 1st primary *c* 80 mm from tip; also have black wing coverts and flight feathers but, unlike older birds, retain brown underwing coverts and lack glossy sheen on rest of plumage. Bill pale yellow midway through 1st winter; legs and feet more olive than adult, but similar by 1st spring. ♀ retains juvenile wing feathers until July, otherwise much as adult. Belly pale brown in 1st year (deep brown in older birds) and dark crown contrasts pale greyish cheeks (contrast in older birds lessened because of darker cheeks, Hughes *et al.* 1997).

DUCKLING: all but sides of head, chin, lowerbreast and belly dark chocolate brown, palest on upper rump and mantle, remainder contrasting pale grey. Bill grey-brown, reddish nail, yellowish nostrils; feet dark olive (Nelson 1993).

MEASUREMENTS AND WEIGHT: *nigra* ♂ adult wing ($n = 91$), 224–247 (234), juv (1st winter) ($n = 30$), 217–241 (226); bill ($n = 47$), 43–51 (47.5); tarsus ($n = 69$), 43–48 (45.4); midwinter weight ($n = 14$), 964–1339 (1165). ♀ adult wing ($n = 31$), 216–239 (226), juv ($n = 30$), 216–239 (226); bill ($n = 32$), 41–46 (43.4); tarsus ($n = 55$), 41–46 (43.5); midwinter weight ($n = 10$), 973–1233 (1059) (Cramp and Simmons 1977). *americana* ♂ adult wing ($n = 69$) 228.6 ($n = 69$), juv ($n = 34$) 223.5; adult weight ($n = 7$), 996–1268 (1133). ♀ adult wing ($n = 30$), 221.0, juv ($n = 30$), 213.4; adult weight ($n = 2$), 861–1087 (997) (Bellrose 1980).

Field characters

Length 440–540 mm. Distinguished from Velvet Scoter by lack of white wing patches and from Surf Scoter by smaller bill and lack of head patterning. Tends to dive with forward jump with wings folded and droops head during Wing-flap behaviour, unlike other scoters. Least tame, taking flight from ships and aircraft at considerable distance. Flight action light, fast and direct. 'Jizz' on water gives rather long-necked appearance (Pihl and Frikke *in* Komdeur *et al.* 1992).

Voice

Generally silent, but ♂♂ make piping thin whistle which, under still conditions, carries far over water, and ♀ has harsh rasping note (see sonograms in Cramp and Simmons 1977). Utters repeated *gyu* during night-time migration, familiar to inhabitants of Denmark who did not know what creature they heard. No information on calls of young.

Range and status

Breeds in tundra of low Arctic south to boreal regions of New and Old World, in freshwater ponds, lakes and rivers, especially where suitable nesting cover. *nigra* nests in Iceland eastwards through northern Britain, most of Scandinavian peninsula (excepting southern Sweden and Norway). Common in Finland and east into Russia along Arctic Sea coastline as far as Yamal Peninsula where range goes inland. Breeding extends eastwards to Khatanga (where again meets sea) and as far as Olenek River in Siberia, not reaching Lena catchment. Southwards, extends into northern taiga zone. Little information on nesting densities, but twice as numerous as *M. fusca* in Fennoscandia, main centre in mountains, highest densities above 700 m altitude (Haapanen and Nilsson 1979). Atypically may occur in densities up to 6 pairs per ha in limestone lakes in Ireland where deterioration in water quality caused severe declines recently (Partridge *in* Gibbons *et al.* 1993); similar signs of decline in breeding population of UK (Underhill *et al.* 1998).

Dramatic moult migration from breeding areas from June, when nonbreeding immatures augmented by adult ♂♂, pass through White Sea, Gulfs of Finland and Riga into Baltic (Jögi 1971 and

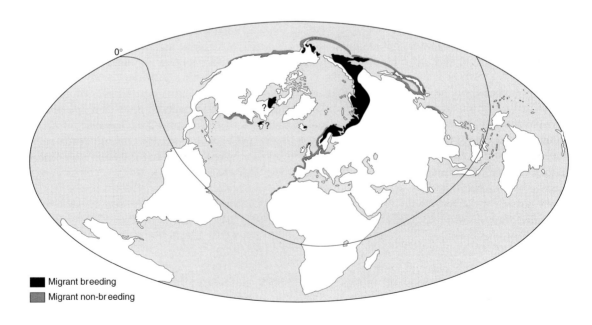

■ Migrant breeding
■ Migrant non-breeding

references in Nehls and Zöllick 1990). Up to 200 000 thought to pass island of Rügen in Germany late June–Aug (Nehls 1990), 86–98% ♂, *en route* to moulting areas in Wadden Sea, where up to 150 000 recorded (Joensen 1973, Laursen *et al.* 1997), France (2 moulting areas totalling 10 000–15 000 birds) (Girard 1992, Schricke 1993) and Britain (> 10 000 in Carmarthen Bay) (Lovegrove *et al.* 1994). Up to 50 000 moulters counted in Danish Kattegat, although extrapolation from ship-based transect counts suggest > 400 000 moult in Danish waters (Laursen *et al.* 1997). Extremely shy during moult, diving at considerable distance from survey aircraft and surface vessels, hence totals represent minima, particularly in Kattegat where dispersed over extensive area.

Migration little studied, but large numbers in Pechora Delta move westwards in late summer and several hundred thousands counted passing Estonia July–Aug, many by night (Jögi 1971). Return passage spectacular in spring with 1 500 000 recorded passing through Gulf of Finland (Bergman and Donner 1964) and recent counts of migration in May included 436 000 past Vyborg (in Russia on Gulf of Finland) (Kontiokorpi and Parviainen 1995) and 190 000 past Puhtu in Estonia (Kontkanen 1995, Rusanen 1995).

Winters along Atlantic coasts from Mauritania northwards to Norway and in western Baltic. In 1992, *c* 950 000 in Danish waters, 600 000 in single flock (Pihl *et al.* 1992). Baltic surveys of 1993 located 1 200 000 birds which, together with 400 000 more along Atlantic seaboard, gives total population of 1 600 000 in western Palearctic (Pihl 1996). Maximum numbers counted in south of range include 5500 in Morocco, 27 000 in Portugal and 45 000 in France (IWRB Seaduck Database). Hard weather, especially sea ice, may force wintering birds out of Kattegat into Norwegian waters, swelling numbers from *c* 4000 to 60 000. Hard weather movements rarely documented elsewhere.

Differences in distribution in British and Danish waters between years may be linked to local food depletion and cyclical exploitation of different areas in different years. This, plus recent improvements in coverage, make it impossible to determine long-term trends.

americana breeds in Siberia from Yana/Lena watershed eastwards into Kamchatka and northern Kurils. In North America, extends from Alaska westwards with breeding scattered across northern Canada east into Newfoundland. Rare in open tundra and closed forest. Up to 35 000 counted in July in Penzhina Valley (Gusakov 1988), 20 000 in middle Anadyr (nesting densities of 0.7 pairs per km^2) (Kondratyev 1989, 1990) and 60 000 in lower Anadyr (Kistchinski *et al.* 1983). In addition, 130 000 counted in spring eastwards from Kolyma River (including northern Kamchatka). Relatively restricted in North America, found primarily in Alaska, where 250 000 counted in late 1960s (Bellrose 1980). In Canada, widely but thinly distributed as breeder, with recent survey associated with hydroelectric schemes in Hudson Bay locating hitherto unknown concentration. Impenetrable muskegs west of James Bay and west of Hudson Bay perhaps hold huge numbers; this, plus low density of breeding pairs, make for one of least known North American waterfowl.

Large moulting congregations occur about coasts of James and Hudson Bays close to breeding boglands of interior. Migration little studied and poorly understood. Not rare along eastern coasts of Kamchatka, along Komandorski and Kuril Islands, off north and central Japan, northeastern Korea and occasionally into Chinese waters. Asian Waterfowl Census (Perennou *et al.* 1994) failed to establish numbers and distribution, mainly because of concentration on freshwater sites; however, Gerasimov and Gerasimov (1995a) recorded 62 000 off west coast of Kamchatka in May 1990. In North America, winters in Aleutian Islands, up to 250 000 (Bellrose 1980), eastern Alaskan peninsula and along Pacific coast from Vancouver south to Mexico, although Bellrose (1980) claimed only 5000 occur south of Anchorage. Large numbers winter along Atlantic coast south as far as Georgia where up to 30 000 occurred (Bellrose 1980), supposedly from breeding areas in Labrador to west coast of Hudson Bay. Numbers shot in Atlantic Flyway States increased 1961–75, but showed no significant trend 1976–92. No reliable estimates of population size of *americana* wintering in East Asia or Atlantic and Pacific coasts of North America; census remains urgent priority for future.

Habitat and general habits

Nests at high latitudes around northern hemisphere. Generally avoids steep slopes and areas enclosed by forest, using open bogland biotopes with islands and promontories. On migration may use expansive freshwater sites, but majority moult and winter at sea, generally shallow inshore waters with abundant benthic fauna < 20 m deep. Often present along exposed shorelines.

Winter diet comprises saltwater molluscs, although dietary composition varies with benthic community. Hence takes *Spisula subtruncata* in North Sea waters where superabundant down to 20 m (Durink *et al.* 1993). In Baltic, *Mya truncata* and *Macoma baltica* eaten in large numbers (Stempniewicz 1986); in Danish waters and elsewhere, *Mytilis edulis* and *Cardium* predominate, with range of other benthic invertebrates, including echinoderms, crustacea, annelid worms, isopods and amphipods (Cramp and Simmons 1977). After oil spills in Carmarthen Bay, Wales, *Pharus legumen* major dietary item (Hughes *et al.* 1997). In summer, ♀♀ take chironomid larvae and cladocerans, ducklings take seeds and adult insects from water surface, before switching to chironomid larvae and cladocerans later (Bengtson 1971a).

Displays and breeding behaviour

Courtship begins in winter and continues into May away from breeding areas; shift from large groups into small courting parties of 5–8 ♂♂ pursuing one ♀ (Bellrose 1980). Deeply emarginate outmost primaries presumably involved in production of loud noise associated with courtship flights (McKinney 1992). Full display described in Cramp and Simmons (1977). Nothing known of nutrient dynamics of reproduction, as breeding biology little studied.

Breeding and life cycle

Nests usually highly dispersed, adjacent to boreal or tundra lakes, but may be far from water in dwarf heath, often overtopped by taller vegetation, lined with vegetation and down. Late nester throughout range, broods appearing in Scotland and Alaska in July. Normally has no time to re-nest; however, of 30 2nd clutches at Mývatn, Iceland, mean was 6.1 eggs (Bengtson 1972b).

nigra eggs ovate, cream to buff, 65.7 × 44.8 (59–72 × 42–47) (*n* = 150) (Schönwetter 1960–66), weighing 60–74 (Dementiev and Gladkov 1952) or calculated at 72; *americana* 62.8 × 43.0 (55–70 × 36–46) (*n* = 70) with calculated weight of 63 (Schönwetter 1960–66). Clutch size 6–8 (5–11), 5–8 in Yukon Delta (Bellrose 1980), 8.7 (6–10) at Mývatn (*n* = 187) (Bengtson 1971c) or 6.8 (4–8) eggs in Ireland (*n* = 35) (Cramp and Simmons 1977). Clutch size declined at Lake Mývatn, Iceland, when midge production during laying period fell to 86% of normal levels in one season (Bengtson 1971c). Incubation 27–31 days; young probably fledge in 45–50 days (Cramp and Simmons 1977). Nesting success 57–89% (mean 82% Mývatn, 1961–70 Bengtson 1972b). Only 16 of 36 Irish nests hatched, largely due to corvid predation (Cramp and Simmons 1977). No data on duckling survival. In extralimital area in Scotland, ♀ rears brood on freshwater lochs on peatlands buffered by underlying base-rich rock, despite foraging and nesting near to highly acidic dubh-lochans and along rivers (Fox *et al.* 1989, Fox and Bell 1993).

Breeds at 2–3 years (Dementiev and Gladkov 1952, Cramp and Simmons 1977), juveniles spend 1st year at sea. Almost nothing known of adult survival rates (Fox *et al.* 2003b).

Conservation and threats

Nutrient enrichment of some Irish sites cited both as cause of increase and of subsequent decline in breeding. Appears that initial stages of nutrient enrichment can benefit, but continued eutrophication makes habitat unsuitable; apparent anomaly underlines lack of information relating to requirements. Completely unknown through much of range, breeding biology little understood away from Iceland but, doubtless, considerable threats exist arising from human exploitation of natural resources in taiga and lower tundra regions. Crude monitoring mechanisms are insufficiently sensitive to detect major changes in numbers and distribution in winter. Studies of breeding biology, ecology and development of effective winter count network are high priorities. During moult period, and in winter, highly aggregated nature renders scoters vulnerable to oil-spills (e.g. Hughes *et al.* 1997) and other in- and offshore pollution, as well as to effects of commercial exploitation of shellfish upon which they feed. There is current threat from offshore windfarms at scoter wintering sites throughout western Europe.

Suffers from lack of research interest, especially in North America, where not important quarry species. Conservation measures that protect inshore marine areas remain unsatisfactory in medium term.

Tony Fox and Stefan Pihl

Long-tailed Duck *Clangula hyemalis*
PLATE 26

Anas hyemalis Linnaeus, 1758, Syst. Nat., ed. 10, p. 126 arctic Europe and America
Clangula Leach, 1819

Etymology: *Clangula* from L. *clangere* to resound, in reference to ♂ voice; *hyemalis* L. for wintery, in reference to distribution in nonbreeding season. Called Long-tailed Duck in English since 1750.

Other names: Oldsquaw in North America, Sea Pintail, Cowheen. Danish: Havlit; French: Canard kakawi, Canard de Miquelon, Harelde de Miquelon; German: Eisente; Icelandic: Hávella; Japanese: Kōri-gamo; Inuktitut: Aggiajuk.

Variation: no subspecies.

Description

ADULT: dimorphic; both sexes whiter in autumn and winter during courtship, and browner in spring and summer. ♂ in winter mostly white with blackish patch on ear coverts and grey sides to face; scapulars elongated and white during courtship phase (Nov–Apr); these feathers moulted after pair formation and prior to migration and replaced with brown scapulars; has 130 mm extension to central tail feathers in all plumages except during wing moult (Peterson and Ellarson 1978, Madge and Burn 1988). Bill black with broad pinkish band just proximal to black nail; legs and feet grey; eye orange. ♀ mostly brownish black upperparts, white face in winter with black ear coverts; brown scapulars, not so long as in ♂. Bill grey-green; iris brown (for plumage details see Palmer 1976, Cramp and Simmons 1977, Robertson and Savard 2002).

MOULT: seasonally variable plumage in both sexes, and moult sequences complex (for details see

Palmer 1976, Robertson and Savard 2002). Body plumage may be in continuous moult and claim of 3 annual moults arbitrary, with no 2 adults looking exactly alike. Continuous replacement of body feathers may be adaptation to life style diving in cold water, where pristine waterproof and insulating plumage properties are priority requirement. Tail and wings moulted once annually after breeding. Bill of ♂ often black in nonbreeding season.

IMMATURE: resembles ♀. Bill blue-grey, ♂'s becoming pink from Oct. First year ♀ has grey scapulars and retains these as nonbreeder (Peterson and Ellarson 1978). Many yearlings retain juvenile tail feathers on breeding ground (Bellrose 1980).

DUCKLING: white underparts, dark unpatterned dorsal plumage, white cheek patch, whitish spots around eye and dark chest band. Feet and bill dark olive-grey or bluish grey. Bill much like scoter duckling (Nelson 1993).

MEASUREMENTS AND WEIGHT: ♂ (*n* = 12) wing, 225–237 (230); tail, 173–241 (208); bill, 25–30 (28); tarsus, 34–37 (35.2). ♀ (*n* = 12) wing, 201–220 (211); tail, 58–74 (68); bill, 26–28 (26.8); tarsus, 31–36 (34.7) (Palmer 1976). Weight in summer less than in midwinter, mean ♂ 797, ♀ 685 (Madge and Burn 1988), heaviest prior to migration and in early winter (Robertson and Savard 2002).

Field characters

Small, 360–470 mm long, diving seaduck, ♂ with Pintail-like tail, but without long neck. Flanks and belly of both sexes whitish; wings in flight dark above and below (Madge and Burn 1988). Usually unmistakable, confusion possible with Harlequin and Steller's Eider, especially young birds and females; on freshwater may be overlooked, or confused with ♀ or young Ruddy Duck. In winter, may be confused with Black Guillemot *Cephus grylle*. Flies low over water in loose flocks; flight distinctive, wings held curved and appear to move backwards on downstroke, bodies 'keeling over' (Phillips 1922–26) or 'swinging from side to side' (Madge and Burn 1988). Gregarious in winter, often in huge rafts at sea. ♂ has far-reaching, haunting cry, an unforgettable feature of arctic spring. May also be vocal on sea in winter when calls audible from land in calm weather.

Voice

♂ call, given in courtship especially late winter and spring, loud yodelling *ow-ow-owlee* or *ah-har-lik*; sonogram in Cramp and Simmons (1977) and Robertson and Savard (2002). ♀ has only weak series of quacks *urk, urk, urk, ang, ang, ang goo* (Johnsgard 1965a) uttered when Chin-lifting. May be individual variation in all calls, notably used during nocturnal migration (Alison 1975). Duckling's distress call has pitch of last syllable 'squealy' and deflected sharply downward (Nelson 1993).

Range and status

Holarctic coastal distribution in breeding season; gathers in open water at sea in autumn and winter. Perhaps most northerly breeding distribution of any duck, nests in Alaska, Canada, Greenland, Iceland, Norway, Sweden, Finland and Russia; has bred in Britain. Very cold tolerant, many winter in far north, often congregating in open water among sea ice. Large flocks also gather in Great Lakes, especially Lake Michigan; small numbers regular in Caspian Sea and on River Danube. Over 4 000 000 winter in Baltic Sea (Pihl and Laursen 1996) and possibly one million along Aleutian chain of Alaska (Bellrose 1980). Rarely moves far south in Atlantic or Pacific, e.g. while > 10 000 possibly winter off Britain, only 21 recorded in France in Jan 1994 (Anon. 1996). Large proportion of those ringed in Iceland winter in southwest Greenland (Bellrose 1980). Rare in California, Florida and Texas. In Asia, winters mainly in north; small numbers in North Korea, otherwise rare south of Hokkaido, Japan. Vagrancy uncommon but recorded in such unusual places as Midway Is, Turkey, Israel, Jordan, Nepal and India.

Rose and Scott (1997) suggested population of 150 000 in Iceland and Greenland, 4 600 000 in

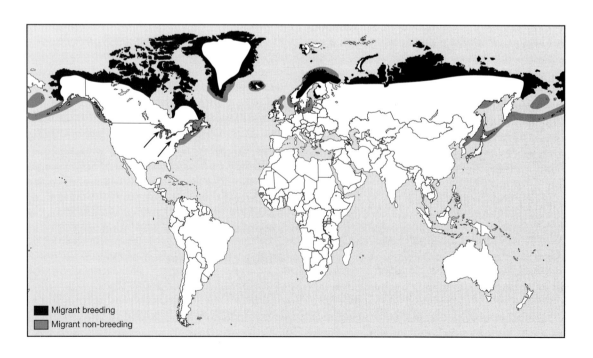

Migrant breeding
Migrant non-breeding

western Siberia and northern Europe, 100 000–
1 000 000 in eastern Asia and 2 703 000 in North
America. Miyabayashi and Mundkur (1999) revised
eastern Asian total upwards to 500 000–1 000 000,
with breeding population in Kamchatka at 500 000
(Gerasimov 1990).

Habitat and general habits

Arctic tundra breeder, and supremely adapted seaduck, feeds at greater depths than any other, opening
wings when diving and when returning to surface
(Snell 1985). Regularly dives 3–10 m, with depths to
50–60 m suggested (Schorger 1951). Dive times
longer for ♂ than ♀, possibly as result of physiology (♂
larger), but ♀ may dive more frequently (Reynolds
1987). Mostly diurnal feeder, but may forage at night.
Flocks dive synchronously, and birds in line dive in
succession. Can dive from flight.

Diet primarily molluscs, amphipods and fish
(details in Cramp and Simmons 1977). Coexists
with other seaduck in winter as feeds on smaller
items, but may compete with Harlequin (Goudie
and Ankney 1988). On Lake Michigan, typically
takes amphipods, while birds collected in Milwaukee Embayment in Jan fed almost exclusively on
Tubifex and *Limnodrilus* (Rofritz 1977). Duckling
searches for food while paddling along, head half
submerged and eyes under water looking down,
feeds on gnat larvae and small crustaceans; at
Mývatn eats almost exclusively cladocerans when
young, later dives for chironomids, cladocerans and
few molluscs (Cramp and Simmons 1977).

Migrates at night, and often overland.

Displays and breeding behaviour

♂ has several conspicuous displays, two associated
with calls (Johnsgard 1965a, Alison 1975); *ah-har-lik*
may be given with rapid Bill-tossing (Head-lifting),
while *a-oo, a-oo, a-oo-gah* associated with Rear-end
display. This display begins with head erect and neck
vertical, head then swung down over water, neck
still extended, tail erected and both feet kicked
slightly out of water. ♂♂ also Neck-stretch and
Turn-back-of-head. Rapid Chin-lifting major ♀
display, presumably functionally equivalent to Inciting (Johnsgard 1965a). Other displays described
by Alison (1975) include Lateral Head-shake, Por-
poising, Wing-flap, Body-shake, Parachute display,

Bill-dipping and Steaming. ♂ may make courtship
flights while calling. ♀ also Steams and Hunches.
Visual display may have evolved to accompany
complex calls facilitated by contortions of ♂ trachea;
immature ♂♂ reaching 2nd year can perform displays but do not call 'correctly' and do not breed
(Alison 1975).

Monogamous pairbond established in winter or
during spring migration, display peaking early Feb;
arrives paired on breeding ground. ♂♂ may be territorial around nest site. Pairbonds may be long-term.

Breeding and life cycle

Late nester, laying initiated Churchill, Manitoba, 3–23
June. Clutch usually finished before end June and
ducklings must fledge before ice forms on water. ♀♀
and eggs very hardy. ♀ selects site, close to water edge,
usually on island in freshwater pool or on tundra.
Some may nest in loose colonies, if several in same
area, nests usually clumped. Often nests in association
with Arctic Tern; however, relationship may offer no
direct benefit to either species (Alison 1975 *contra*
Evans 1970). Nest not infrequently found close to
Red-breasted Goose colony near bird of prey nest
(Quinn *et al.* 1995). Eggs oval to elongate oval, greenish to olive-buff; 53 × 37 (*n* = 139) (Bent 1923) or
54 × 38 (47–58 × 35–41) (*n* = 200) (Schönwetter
1960–66); weight 39 (38–40 no sample size) (Cramp
and Simmons 1977) and 42.7 (37–53) (*n* = 77)
(Robertson and Savard 2002). Clutch 7.27 (2–11)
(*n* = 26) (Bellrose 1980); small clutches often due to
predation of 1st eggs during laying (Alison 1975).
Incubation, by ♀, 26 (24–29) days; she leaves twice
daily to feed between 09.00 and 10.00 h, and 16.00
and 18.30 h. ♂ departs early in incubation, but sometimes re-pairs with same ♀ next season; departure of
♂ may reduce food competition for ducklings. ♂♂
gather for wing moult on water nearby or migrate to
safe site elsewhere. In Churchill, Manitoba, 19% of
eggs laid (*n* = 383) not viable, perhaps due to
extended exposure of incomplete clutch to severe
weather; weather unlikely influence during actual
incubation (Alison 1975). Nests predated by Arctic
Skua *Stercorarius parasiticus*, gulls and foxes. Overall
success also dependent on rodent population; in Sweden, twice as many ducklings produced in rodent
peak years than in years following rodent population
crashes, when predators change diet to nesting birds

(Pehrsson 1986). Newly hatched ducklings from 2 broods weighed 21.1 (20.4–22.2) ($n = 3$) and 22.4 (21.2–23.6) ($n = 2$) (Nelson 1993). Can dive from 2 days. Fledge in 35–40 days.

Does not breed until at least 2 years old (Bellrose 1980). Mean mortality of adults ringed in Iceland 28%, life expectancy 3.1 years (Cramp and Simmons 1977); longevity record of BTO ringed bird 20 years (Toms and Clark 1998).

Conservation and threats

Abundant, but tendency to gather in large concentrations in winter renders population susceptible to oil pollution, and several serious incidents have occurred in Holarctic oceans. Also hunted in some numbers, and frequently caught and drowned in fishing nets.

Glyn Young and Janet Kear

Bufflehead *Bucephala albeola*
PLATE 27

Anas Albeola Linnaeus, 1758, Syst. Nat., ed. 10, p. 124
America = Newfoundland (unlikely on present distribution; more plausibly North Carolina, where abundant in winter, as Edwards's account, used by Linnaeus, probably based on Catesby's *Natural History of Carolina, Florida, and the Bahama Islands* 1754).
Bucephala Baird, 1858

Etymology: *albeola* is diminutive of *albus* L. for white. *Bucephala* Gr. means having a head like an ox (or buffalo).

Other names: Butterball, Dipper. French: Petit garrot; Spanish: Patito crestiblanco.

Variation: no subspecies. Slight geographical variation; in fresh plumage, dark feathering of adult ♀ and fully grown immatures in southern British Columbia and northern California (west of Rockies) appears brownish, *v* blackish grey with no trace of brown in Alberta, Yukon, and interior Alaska (Erskine 1972a).

Description

ADULT: dimorphic. ♂ in breeding plumage (Sept–early July) head black in front with iridescent gloss on sides (colour rarely visible in field), white from behind eyes and broadly across nape. Back and tail black, breast, belly and flanks white. Wings black with broad white band comprising most secondaries, greater and lesser secondary coverts (but not marginal coverts). Bill bluish grey; legs and feet bright pink; eyes brown. ♀ head dark brownish black with oval whitish patch on sides behind eyes; back and tail dark brownish black; wings dark brownish grey except 4–6 secondaries white; flanks brownish grey; breast and belly dull white. Bill bluish grey; eyes brown; legs and feet dark bluish grey.

MOULT: eclipsed ♂, mid July–Aug, resembles 1st winter ♂ but wings show white secondary coverts except while those feathers moulted or growing.

IMMATURE: plumage and soft-part colours and patterns generally resemble adult ♀ in both sexes through 1st year; partial moult (variable in extent) during 1st winter produces in ♂ blacker head with larger light areas on sides, more white on flanks, and rump noticeably lighter than back and tail. Yearling ♂ Apr–June separable in field from all ♀♀ only at close range. ♂ assumes adult plumage by 15 months.

DUCKLING: 'egg-sized', mainly blackish above, whitish below, with diffuse blackish brown across breast, and white patches on cheeks, rear edge of wings, and sides of rump. Dark areas fade with age and growth, but pattern persists until feathers appear at Day 20.

MEASUREMENTS AND WEIGHT: ♂ adult ($n = 12$) wing, 169–175 (173); tail, 70–78 (75), 1st winter tail

($n = 11$), 63–69 (66); bill, 27–30 (29); tarsus, 32–35 (34). ♀ ($n = 12$) wing, 152–161 (156); tail, 59–70 (66); bill, 24–27 (25); tarsus, 30–31 (30). Great variation in weight between seasons and individuals, heavier during migrations and (♀ only) when laying; ♂ in Dec ($n = 34$), 335–600 (475); ♀ in Dec ($n = 17$), 230–470 (340), but June (incubating) ($n = 41$), 255–330 (287) (Erskine 1972a, Palmer 1976, Gauthier 1993).

Field characters

Smallest and most constantly active North American diving duck, 320–390 mm long; adult ♂ conspicuously black-and-white, other age and sex classes rather drab but usually seen with ♂♂. Much smaller than Common and Barrow's Goldeneyes, and lacks their whistling flight. Soft-part colours (eyes brown *v* yellow; tarsi and feet pink in ♂, grey in ♀, *v* yellow-orange in both) unique in genus.

Voice

Seldom heard, audible only at close range, no detailed studies. ♂ utters grating call during courtship or pairing. ♀ gives low, repeated call during pairing display, when assembling brood and during nest prospecting flights (Myres 1959b, Erskine 1972a, Eadie and Gauthier 1985, Gauthier 1993).

Range and status

Breeds across North American continent except east of 75°W (perhaps nearly extirpated further east by earlier hunting in winter range, but ecology suggests reproductive success there always poor), north as far as trees large enough to contain nest cavities,

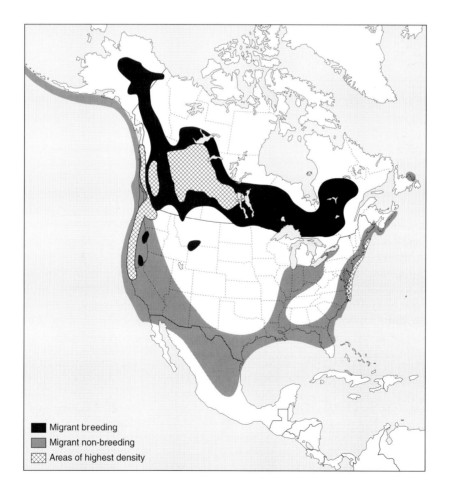

■ Migrant breeding
▨ Migrant non-breeding
▥ Areas of highest density

south to southern limit of trees in Great Basin and prairies (some late summer moulting farther south), nearly absent west of Coast and Cascade Mountains and in mountain regions. Distribution, and thus numbers, everywhere limited by habitat and perhaps by predation, thus often localized. Breeding range reduced (by 10–15% in area) in last century by clearing for agriculture of parkland habitat along northern edge of Canadian prairies.

Winter range in North America, mainly on Atlantic (Nova Scotia–North Carolina) and Pacific (Alaska–California) coasts, much fewer on Gulf coast and even fewer on inland lakes and reservoirs south of winter ice-cover. Adult ♂♂ (and ♀♀?) may winter further north, on average, than 1st winter birds on west coast; no good evidence of this on east coast (Erskine 1972a).

Migration between breeding and winter ranges (see Erskine 1964, 1972a) in Mar–Apr and Oct–Nov. Adults, including many unpaired drakes, move north earlier in spring, especially from Pacific coast; no obvious segregation of ages in autumn. Migration presumably triggered by daylength, but timing of major flights correlated with barometric pressure patterns, using favouring winds. Fat deposition may be associated with migration, especially in autumn when greatest body mass achieved. Migration divide (between movements to east, west and Gulf coasts) evident in birds banded in Alberta. Departure from breeding range usually by long overnight flight (400–1200 km), shown by band recoveries. Few birds move south (mostly to moult) outside breeding range prior to main migration period. Vagrants stray to Asia and Europe (*c* 1 report every 5 years).

Numbers increased gradually but continuously from 1920, when earliest sample counts began, to present. Total spring population *c* 500 000 by 1960 (Erskine 1972a) and 800 000 by 1980 (Canadian Wildlife Service 1981). Increases probably reflect recovery from excessive hunting of unwary species prior to 1916. Wetlands International (2002) gave figure of 1 000 000, perhaps reflecting wider surveys, and suggested stable population.

Habitat and general habits

Nests in cavities, thus restricting breeding to areas with trees (including stubs and snags) >20 cm diameter at nest height and with wood soft enough to allow excavation by flickers (medium-sized woodpeckers, genus *Colaptes*). Of *c* 150 natural cavities studied in British Columbia, only 2 (one by *Dryocopus* woodpecker, one from rot) not excavated by flickers. Poplars *Populus* most widely used trees, with conifers (spruces *Picea* east of Rockies, Douglas-Fir *Pseudotsuga menziesii* and Ponderosa Pine *Pinus ponderosa* west of Rockies) also important. Nest trees mostly near (all <30 m, few >10 m) water, especially where tree cover dense; dense ground cover may limit young in reaching shore. Nesting in burrows unconfirmed and certainly rare, but not implausible. Most breeding by small water bodies (1–100 ha) with extensive shallow areas (depth <5 m) but little emergent and submerged vegetation; water pH variable, <6–>9.5, as breed in bog ponds as well as more fertile lakes. In Alberta, brood rearing less or not successful in lakes connected by rivers or large creeks, apparently owing to predation on small ducklings by Northern Pike. Backwaters along rivers also used.

Moulting inland, mainly on larger lakes (1–5 km²), often with little adjacent tree cover but otherwise similar to breeding habitat, which also may be used for moulting. Winters in shallow, sheltered waters of bays, estuaries, and lagoons, seldom seen along exposed shores used by larger diving ducks (including goldeneyes), also on shallow freshwaters of lakes, ponds, and reservoirs. Usually encountered as singles, pairs, or small groups (5–15 birds), in larger flocks when moulting (up to >200 birds) and during migrations (up to 500). More constantly active than most other ducks, repeatedly diving for food, or engaged in social interactions; seldom loafing for extended periods. Rarely seen out of water, except ♀♀ preening during incubation pauses, and when young small; others preen while on water, often rolling over to reach all parts of plumage. Takes flight readily, even for short distances, owing to rather low wing-loading. When diving, plumage compressed, but an upward leap before submerging less general than in many diving ducks. Swimming underwater uses feet only. Rarely feeds from water surface; diving usual even in water <1 m deep.

Feeds mainly on aquatic invertebrates, especially insect larvae (Odonata, Coleoptera, Corixidae, Tendipedidae) in freshwater (all seasons), crustaceans (especially decapod shrimps *Crangon*) and small snails in marine areas (Oct–Apr). Seeds of freshwater plants, mostly *Potamogeton* and *Scirpus*, taken in autumn, but usually comprise < 20% of diet. Ducklings take fewer snails and seeds than older birds in freshwater areas. Erskine (1972a) gave seasonal tables of foods in fresh and saltwater.

Displays and breeding behaviour

♂ joining group usually triggers response by adult ♂, most often Head-forward (threat) posture, rush over water, or attack by flying or diving, sometimes with prolonged characteristic chasing on surface. Underwater approach also used to drive off other (larger) duck species. Pair-forming and pair-maintaining displays feature sequences of Flyover-and-landing, Headshake-forwards-with-wing-lifting, Head-bobbing; often several ♂♂ actively court one ♀, who remains with one of them at end of courtship session. When ♀ Follows ♂'s Leading, pair exists, at least temporarily. Other ♂♂ court paired ♀♀, whether or not mate is present, sometimes resulting in pursuit-flights around lake or lagoon. Active courtship gives impression of confused chasing, recognizable as far as birds visible, but same few actions featured in all such activity. Diving-as-pair, with 1st bird to surface waiting until other appears before diving again, another sign of pairing. Many ♂♂ start migration before pairing, early arrivals in western breeding areas may include up to 90% ♂♂. Most pairing seems to occur during migration Mar–Apr. Copulation rarely seen (Myres 1959a, 1959b) in contrast to frequency in goldeneyes, and mostly on breeding ground (Apr–June, rarely from Feb). Water-twitch and Preen-dorsally ♂ pre-copulatory displays, after which ♀ assumes prone position, mounting and copulation follows, and finally Rotations (as in goldeneyes and Hooded Merganser) indicate successful completion. (Displays described in detail, with illustrations, by Myres 1959a, 1959b, Erskine 1972a, Gauthier 1993).

Quasi-territorial, ♂ defending mated ♀ more than nest site or vicinity. Defence of ♀ or area more intense on small ponds (especially when breeding density enhanced by placement of nestboxes) than on larger lakes (> 20 ha), where areas further from shore comprise 'neutral waters' used both by sub-adults and nearby breeders. Breeding density (without nestboxes) seldom exceeds 1 pair/2 ha on small ponds, 1 pair/100 m shoreline on larger lakes.

Breeding and life cycle

Reaches nesting area from late Apr–early May, as soon as ice-free. Surviving breeders often return to same site as previous year (Erskine 1961) if still available (Erskine 1978). Nests in flicker holes (entrance diam. 6.3 cm, cavity depth 20–30 cm, cavity diam. 12–18 cm), at all heights up to bottom of tree canopy (to 6–10 m in live poplars) or to top of stubs/snags (to > 15 m in Douglas-Fir and Ponderosa Pine); nest trees close to water (usually < 10 m), stubs often standing in water.

Laying, in May, chiefly in forenoon, at intervals averaging 37 h but decreasing towards clutch completion. Eggs measure $50.5 \pm 0.12 \times 36.3 \pm 0.07$ ($n = 145$ clutches, 966 eggs); mass 37.4 ± 0.29 ($n = 69$ clutches, 307 eggs) (Gauthier 1993). Clutch size 7–11 (5–14); larger sets may include eggs laid by 2 or more ♀♀, smaller ones may involve continued laying elsewhere after original site usurped by another ♀ laying there (not appropriately termed brood parasitism; see Erskine 1990). Incubation, by ♀ only, 28–33 days, constancy *c* 80%, recesses most frequent in late afternoon. ♀♀ lose 10–15% of body mass during incubation ($340 \rightarrow 290$).

Hatching extends over 48 h, star-pipped one day, open-pipped next, young in nest 3rd day; hatchling mass 23.8 ± 2.1 (Gauthier 1993). Young dry within 12 h, leave nest 24–36 h after hatching. ♀ enters and leaves cavity several times first, reconnoitring, but (unlike goldeneyes) not known to call young, which leave in succession over several minutes, and led to water by ♀.

Young appear sedate when first on water, but exhibit 'Gyrinid-like' activity after 3–4 days, feeding from surface and diving from *c* Day 7. Growth rates summarized by Gauthier (1993), plumage stages described and illustrated by Erskine (1972a). Contour feathers start to appear at Day 20, wing feathers soon after, full-feathered Day 50, first flights from Day 55. ♀ escorts young and defends them against other waterbirds, especially goldeneyes (Barrow's Goldeneye ♀ as aggressive towards Bufflehead as to conspecifics), may brood them on shore during rain and at night for 2 weeks. Brood amalgamation (partial or complete) frequent where breeding density high, groups up to 40 half-grown young seen with one ♀, but individual broods often recognizable until ♀ departs to moult, usually when young nearing adult size. Brood territory varies with amalgamation, often becoming more restricted over 1st 4 weeks.

Loss of young begins between nest and water, mainly from nests > 10 m from shore; perhaps more important east of Rockies than in British Columbia where most detailed studies done. Most young, including complete broods, that disappear lost within 2 weeks, especially during cold, wet weather (Erskine 1972a); survival rates summarized by Gauthier (1993). Predation seldom witnessed, but Northern Pike believed to limit survival of young on larger lakes in Alberta and eastward (Erskine

1972a). No studies between fledging and fall migration of young (late Aug–late Oct).

♂ abandons incubating ♀ after 1–3 weeks, assembles on larger lakes June–July to moult, flying again by mid Aug. ♀♀ leave broods late July, often flightless into early Sept, flightless period thus *c* 3 weeks.

Both sexes can breed when nearly 2 years old (confirmed for ♀♀ by recaptures of banded birds in nests). Yearlings mostly return to breeding areas, where may prospect for nest sites. First-time breeders (including those using boxes) lay later and smaller clutches than older ♀♀, and have lower success (Gauthier 1993). Data on survivorship and lifespan summarized by Gauthier (1993).

Conservation and threats

Although vulnerable to hunting, not especially sought-after by hunters and not now considered under serious threat. Like other diving birds, affected locally by oil spills and other aquatic pollution.

Tony Erskine

Common Goldeneye *Bucephala clangula*
PLATE 27

Anas Clangula Linnaeus, 1758, Syst. Nat. ed. 10, p. 125
Europe (restricted to Sweden by Linnaeus)

Etymology: *clangula* from L. *clangere* to resound, in reference to whistling wings. John Ray first used name Goldeneye in 1678.

Other names: Goldeneye Duck, Whistler. Danish: Hvinand; French: Canard garrot, Garrot à oeil d'or, Garrot commun; German: Schellente; Icelandic: Hvinönd; Japanese: Hojiro-gamo; Spanish: Pato ojiamarillo; Swedish: Knipa (see also Phillips 1922–26).

Variation: 2 subspecies. Nominate *B. c. clangula* smaller, with thinner bill than American Goldeneye *B. c. americana* Bonaparte, 1838 (Cramp and Simmons 1977); however *B. c. americana* not recognized by Dementiev and Gladkov (1952) because of measurement overlap.

Description

ADULT: dimorphic. ♂ definitive alternate (breeding) plumage has head and upper neck black with large oval white loral spot between eye and mandible. Lower neck, uppermantle, sides of breast, and underparts white. Black lower mantle, inner scapulars, back, rump, and uppertail coverts. Outer scapulars white, edged with black outer webs (shorter feathers) or both webs edged with black (longer feathers). Black primaries and coverts. Two outermost primaries narrowly webbed. Four outermost secondaries black with white tips increasing in size proximally. Seven to 9 most proximal secondaries white. Exposed portions of secondary coverts white. Tertials black. Rectrices black to dark grey. Bill blue-black; feet and legs yellow-orange with olive-black webs; eyes bright yellow. ♀ definitive alternate has head and upper neck dark brown. White lower neck mottled grey on lower nape. Upper body brownish black. Mantle and inner scapulars with wide blue-grey edging. Outer scapulars white-tipped. Breast dark grey; flanks greyish brown feathers tipped white; pale grey rump. Thighs dark grey mixed with white. Wings and tail similar to ♂ except marginal and lesser secondary coverts grey; median secondary coverts black tipped with white; greater secondary coverts basally black with exposed portion white and tipped black (Carney 1983). Tertials grey-black. Fewer (5–8) white inner secondaries than ♂ (Eadie *et al.* 1995). Bill dark, usually greyish black; distal third, except nail, yellow-orange Feb–May, becoming duskier at onset of laying (Palmer 1976); feet and legs yellow to orange with dull black webs; eye pale yellow to white.

MOULT: ♂ definitive basic, or eclipse, plumage similar to ♀, except head and neck dark brown tinged black. ♀ basic similar to alternate, except head and upper neck dull brown (Eadie *et al.* 1995).

IMMATURE: similar to ♀ alternate (Eadie *et al.* 1995). ♂ grey-brown head and upper neck; lower neck grey; upperparts brown; chest sepia; flanks grey-brown. Greater coverts white, some black-tipped; median coverts white to grey; other upper-wing coverts grey-brown to black. Black tertials. ♀ similar to ♂. First basic similar to immature in both sexes (Cramp and Simmons 1977, Tobish 1986). First alternate ♂ with brown bases of head feathers visible; loral spot may be smaller than in older ♂; some black median upperwing coverts (Eadie *et al.* 1995). Breast feathers on sides with faint sub-terminal grey-brown barring (Cramp and Simmons 1977). First alternate ♀ similar to immature and 1st basic. First pre-basic moult variable, occurring Sept–Oct (Dementiev and Gladkov 1952); 1st pre-alternate usually begins Nov (Cramp and Simmons 1977), later in ♀ than ♂, never includes rectrices (Eadie *et al.* 1995, *contra* Cramp and Simmons 1977, US Fish & Wildlife Service 1977). Definitive pre-basic earlier in ♂ (July–late Sept) than ♀ (Aug–early Oct) (Cramp and Simmons 1977). Moult in 2nd year prolonged and variable (Eadie *et al.* 1995), later than in older birds (Dementiev and Gladkov 1952). Remiges moulted earlier by ♂

than ♀ of all ages (Dementiev and Gladkov 1952). Definitive pre-alternate soon after definitive pre-basic; ♂ completed by late Oct, ♀ by early Dec (Cramp and Simmons 1977).

DUCKLING: black-and-white pattern. Cheeks, throat, breast and belly white. Greyish sides, dorsal spots, and wing patches. Black hood, nape, winglets, and rump (good description in Nelson 1993).

MEASUREMENTS AND WEIGHT: vary among and within locations; races overlap substantially (summaries in Eadie *et al.* 1995); ♂ larger than ♀. Range of measures (both races): ♂ wing, 209–247; culmen, 30–45, tarsus 37–47. ♀ wing, 188–229; culmen, 28–37; tarsus, 33–49. Weight varies seasonally with sex, reproductive status, location, and race. Less in spring than winter; adult ♂ 888–1406 (*c* 1000 in early spring), adult ♀ 500–1133 (*c* 800 in early spring). ♀ weight loss during incubation (10–20%) varies geographically (Zicus and Riggs 1996); lowest ♀ weight occurs in unsuccessful nesters prospecting for nest sites (Zicus and Hennes 1989).

Field characters

Medium-sized diving duck, *clangula* (both sexes) 420–500 mm long, *americana* ♂ 450–510, ♀ 400–500 mm long, with compact profile, short neck and round body. Rapid wing-beat produces whistling sound especially by adult ♂, less so adult ♀, and not by immatures (Palmer 1976). Adult ♂ striking white-on-black pattern in breeding plumage, white loral spot, white sides and underparts; large solid white wing patch. Adult ♀ chocolate-brown head, slate-grey back, wings, and tail. Two white wing bars ahead of white secondary patch conspicuous in flight. Both sexes may be confused with Barrow's Goldeneye; ♂ distinguished by oval rather than crescent loral spot, more white on secondaries; ♀♀ difficult, but Barrow's ♀ has fewer white secondaries and sometimes all yellow bill (Eadie *et al.* 1995). See also Barrow's Goldeneye account.

Voice

Largely silent. ♂ vocalizes during courtship, ♀ during nest prospecting or when startled. ♂ call primarily variations (Cramp and Simmons 1977) of faint

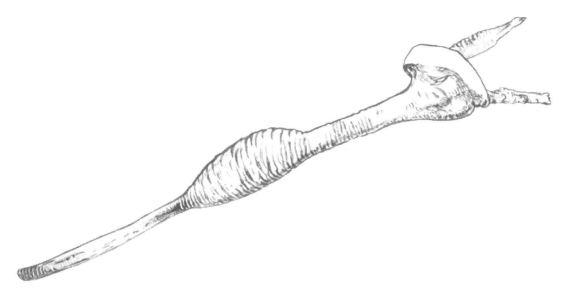

9.34 The windpipe of a male Common Goldeneye showing the structural modifications (a bony bulla and swelling of the tracheal tube) that shape the bird's calls.

peent during courtship or grunting during post-copulatory steaming; ♀ call harsh *gack* or series of *cuks* (Palmer 1976). Sonograms in Cramp and Simmons (1977). (See Figure 9.34.)

Range and status

Circumpolar breeder. In Eurasia, south of tree line Scandinavia to Kamchatka; local populations northern Europe, Scotland since 1970. Nests irregularly on southern edge of range, sporadically outside range (Cramp and Simmons 1977). In North America, south of tree line; eastern Canada south to *c* 45°N in eastern US, west through Great Lakes region; western Canada, south through parklands, British Columbia east of Coastal range; west into southern and central Alaska. Disjunct breeding populations eliminated in Eurasia and North America due to habitat loss (Phillips 1922–26, Dementiev and Gladkov 1952). Eurasian race winters coastal areas Scandinavia, northern Europe, northeastern Mediterranean, Black, and Caspian seas. Some on large ice-free inland lakes and rivers east to coasts of Kuril Islands, Kamchatka, Japan, northern China (Cramp and Simmons 1977). Winters throughout North America; most abundant along coast of northern New England to Chesapeake Bay, southeastern Alaska to British Columbia. Also occurs along St Lawrence River and upper Mississippi River drainage. Scarcer south, but occurs coastal central Florida, Gulf coast Texas and Mexico; interior Arizona, New Mexico, Mexico; coastal waters of central Baja California (Howell and Webb 1995).

Eurasian population 0.3–0.45 million (Rose and Scott 1994), with 50 000–100 000 in eastern Asia (Miyabayashi and Mundkur 1999). North American population *c* 1.5 million (US Fish & Wildlife Service 1977, Bellrose 1980, Wetlands International 2002). Both populations probably stable, but surveys incomplete or inadequate (Rose and Scott 1994, Eadie *et al.* 1995).

Habitat and general habits

Breeding habitat includes forested areas bordering lakes, streams, and wetlands. Prefers fishless oligotrophic lakes in Scandinavia and Canada (Eriksson 1978, Eadie and Keast 1982, McNicol and Wayland 1992), but fish competition perhaps less important in some habitats (Zicus and Riggs 1996). Uses larger lakes and rivers on migration. Winters primarily on shallow estuarine bays and harbours in

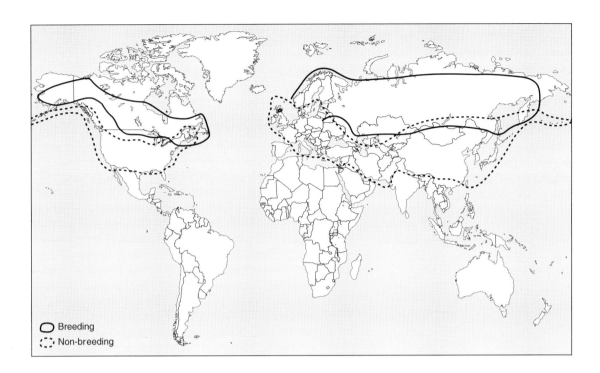

○ Breeding
⫶⁓⫶ Non-breeding

coastal areas, secondarily on larger ice-free lakes and rivers.

Diet varies seasonally and with habitat, primarily animal matter throughout year (Cottam 1939, Olney and Mills 1963, Eriksson 1976, Jepsen 1976, summaries in Eadie *et al*. 1995). Principally takes aquatic insects, molluscs and crustaceans, with occasional fish and fish spawn. Salmon flesh eaten in coastal streams (Munro 1939); plant material generally < 25%. Trichoptera and Coleoptera larvae, Odonata nymphs, and several amphipods important, also variety of molluscs, crabs, shrimp, isopods and barnacles. Studies, based on gizzard analyses, probably overestimate importance of hard foods. No indication of seasonal shift to more proteinaceous foods during breeding; however, most studies conducted during nonbreeding periods. Chiefly diurnal feeder (Palmer 1976); adults and young dive to feed, young dabble for few days after hatching.

Migratory throughout range, generally short to medium distances as small flocks. One of last ducks to leave northern breeding areas. Some migrate south only to closest open water (Bellrose 1980). Returns to breeding area as open water appears; often 1st on rivers from which visits nest sites on ice-bound lakes. Second-year birds arrive on breeding grounds shortly after 1st adults (Eadie *et al*. 1995), perhaps later in some locations (Zicus and Hennes 1989). Little known of moult migration; likely short and northerly to coastal areas (Jepsen and Joensen 1973), large lakes and rivers. Adult ♂ leaves ♀ by mid incubation, all gone by mid July. Second-year birds leave slightly later followed by adult ♀♀. Arrival in moulting areas reflects departure from nesting grounds (Jepsen 1973). Eurasian moulting concentrations noted northern Russia, western Siberia, and Kandalaksha Gulf, White Sea (Dementiev and Gladkov 1952). Also occurs in Estonia, southern Sweden, and Denmark (Cramp and Simmons 1977). North American birds reported in Ungava Bay, eastern and southern coast of Hudson Bay, and James Bay (Todd 1963, Eadie *et al*. 1995).

Displays and breeding behaviour

Small courting parties (Afton and Sayler 1982) display elaborately (Dane and van der Kloot 1964, Palmer 1976, Johnsgard 1978). ♂ repertoire includes Head-throw, slow and fast Head-throw-kicks, Bowsprit, Head-throw-bowsprit, Nodding, Masthead, Ticking, Head-flick, Head-forward, Head-up, Head-up-pumping, Head-back, and Head-back-bowsprit. Head-throw-kicks distinctive. ♀ repertoire includes Head-up, Head-forward, Dip, and Head-flick. ♀ initiates copulation on water, often preceded by ritualized Drinking, Head-lifting, and bathing. ♂ exhibits ritualized Bill-shake, Drinking, Wing-and-leg Stretch, Head-flicks, Head-rubbing, and rapid Bill-shakes. Copulation followed by Steaming (♂) and bathing (both sexes).

Fixed breeding territories defended by ♂ (*contra* Carter 1958, Gibbs 1962) against conspecifics, Barrow's Goldeneye and Bufflehead (Savard 1984). Agonistic behaviour includes threats, chases, and brief fights on water, usually terminated when intruder flies, but short pursuit flights by territorial ♂. ♀ defends brood territory aggressively; defence greatest against other ♀♀ and broods, but includes Wood Duck and Northern Mallard (Zicus and Hennes 1994). ♀ sometimes kills ducklings of goldeneye and other species (Eadie *et al.* 1995). Pair-bond, formed winter–early spring, maintained until mid incubation.

Breeding and life cycle

Typically ♀ selects tree cavity formed as bacterial or fungal heart-rot invades mature trees through frost crack injuries or incompletely callused areas around lost limbs; secondarily, woodpeckers may be important excavators in trees with heart-rot (Erskine 1972a, Eadie *et al.* 1995). Occasionally nests in rock cavities (Palmer 1976) and chimneys (Bellrose 1980); rarely, rabbit burrows (Cramp and Simmons 1977) and other ground sites (Dementiev and Gladkov 1952). Readily uses nestboxes. ♀ philopatric to nesting areas; ♂ not. First nesting by ♀ in natal vicinity; older ♀ often repeatedly use nest sites, especially if previous nest successful (Dow and Fregda 1983, 1985, Eadie *et al.* 1995, Ludwichowski *et al.* 2002). Nest prospecting during season by brood ♀, unsuccessful nesters, and 2nd-year ♀; adult ♀ prospects previously successful sites more frequently than unsuccessful or unused sites (Eadie and Gauthier 1985, Zicus and Hennes 1989).

Egg-laying begins while wetlands still frozen, early Apr in Germany, to mid May in Fenno-Scandia and western Russia (Cramp and Simmons 1977); North American nesting begins late Mar in Minnesota; early–mid Apr in British Columbia, Ontario, and New Brunswick; as late as mid May in Northwest Territories (Eadie *et al.* 1995). Eggs greenish; average size from number of locations (Cramp and Simmons 1977, Eadie *et al.* 1995) 60×43 (44.9–74.8×33.9–48.9) and mass 64 (48.0–80.5). Reported clutch size averages 8–12 eggs (Dementiev and Gladkov 1952, Rajala and Ormio 1970, Cramp and Simmons 1977, Eadie *et al.* 1995), variability due to brood parasitism; extreme sizes 1–28, but unlikely one ♀ lays > 12 in single clutch. Unusual for clutches < 4–5 to be incubated. Single brooded; re-nesting rare (Cramp and Simmons 1977, Zicus 1990b). Mixed-species clutches, including eggs of Goosander, Smew and, rarely, Northern Mallard reported in Finland and Russia (Grenquist 1963, Dementiev and Gladkov 1952). North American clutches mixed with Wood Duck, Bufflehead, Barrow's Goldeneye, Hooded Merganser, and Goosander eggs (Bouvier 1974, Zicus and Hennes 1988, Eadie 1989, Gauthier 1993). Goldeneyes reported always to abandon clutches with Goosander eggs in Finland, but not in North America.

Most information on nest success from boxes; 27–63% in Eurasia (Rajala and Ormio 1970, Eriksson 1979b, Dennis and Dow 1984, Bräger 1986), 64% in British Columbia (Eadie *et al.* 1995), and 30–70% in Minnesota. Little information from natural cavities; 7 of 16 tree-cavity nests successful in New Brunswick (Prince 1968). Predation important cause of failure in Sweden where European Pine Martens *M. martes* and Jays *Garrulus glandarius* destroyed 38% of nests; 16% were deserted (Eriksson 1979b). This contrasts with Finland, British Columbia and Minnesota where desertion primary cause of failure (Grenquist 1963, Rajala and Ormio 1970, Eadie *et al.* 1995). Desertion during egg laying and incubation accounted for 85% of failures or 30% of nests in British Columbia. Desertion most prevalent during egg laying. Black Bear *Ursus americanus*, American Pine Marten *M. americanus*, Raccoon, Northern Flicker *Colaptes auratus*, Red Squirrel *Tamiasciurus hudsonicus* and Mink are North American nest predators. Incubation, by ♀ only, 28–32 days. Average constancy (74–89%) varies with stage of incubation, location, and year; 1–7 daylight recesses recorded (Siren 1952, Mallory and Weatherhead 1994, Zicus *et al.* 1995).

Little information on ♀ success. Annual reproductive success averaged 1.3 independent young per ♀ per year in British Columbia; ♀ lifetime reproductive success averaged 2.3 young, but highly skewed (Eadie *et al.* 1995). Most ♀♀ produced no young and few produced many.

Ducklings depart nest 24–36 h after hatching, feed primarily by dabbling immediately after departure; can dive within 1–2 days. Weight of day-olds averages 36–38.9 (33.2–47.8) (Smart 1965b, Siegfried 1974b, Eadie *et al.* 1995). Brood crèching common soon after hatch; thereafter, brood cohesion strong. Complete loss of broods (18–34%) and juvenile mortality (58–77%) comparatively high (Wayland and McNicol 1994, Eadie *et al.* 1995). Up to 56% duckling mortality in 1st week (Pöysä and Virtanen 1994). ♀ broods ducklings at night or during inclement weather for 2–3 weeks; she spends 46–52% of time caring for young, and parental care varies between locations, but not with size or age of brood (Zicus and Hennes 1994). Feathers begin replacing down at 20–22 days (Bent 1923); complete by 50–55 days (Palmer 1976).

Little information for most of range on survival of adults; data lacking for ♂♂; ♀ annual survival 61–74%, estimated from small localized samples (Eadie *et al.* 1995); in northern Germany over 20 years, with no hunting, as high as 83% (Ludwichowski *et al.* 2002). Oldest BTO ringed bird still breeding at > 11 years (Clark *et al.* 2002); have lived in wild for 17 years (Johnsgard 1968a).

Conservation and threats

Tree-cavity availability of concern range-wide because of forestry practices. Nesting habitats would benefit from more extended rotation timber-harvest and better riparian area management. Welfare in eastern North America affected by habitat alteration, primarily wetland loss or degradation (US Fish & Wildlife Service 1994). Large part of breeding range susceptible to atmospheric acid deposition (McNicol *et al.* 1990). May derive short-term benefit from wetland acidification due to reduced competition with fish for invertebrate foods (Gilyazov 1993, Mallory *et al.* 1994). Wintering areas also at risk (Stewart *et al.* 1988). Organochlorines and polychlorinated biphenyls in eggs and tissues elevated in some areas (Smith *et al.* 1985, Foley and Batcheller 1988, Zicus *et al.* 1988), as are metals where wetlands acidified (Eriksson *et al.* 1989). Influence of hunting on populations unknown (Eadie *et al.* 1995); hunting kill estimates incomplete and/or highly variable, particularly in Eurasia. Annual kill estimated at 100 000–250 000 (1970s) in northwest-central Europe (Hepburn 1984). North American annual hunting kill averaged 188 208 (1971–80) (Eadie *et al.* 1995), but substantially lower (102 363) in 1992–2001 (Canadian Wildlife Service and US Fish & Wildlife Service).

Mike Zicus

Barrow's Goldeneye *Bucephala islandica*
PLATE 27

Anas islandica Gmelin, 1789, Syst. Nat., **1**, p. 541 Iceland

Etymology: *islandica* means of Iceland. Vernacular name after John Barrow (1764–1848), British Admiralty promoter of arctic exploration.

Other names: none common in English. Danish: Islandsk hvinand; French: Garrot d'Islande, Garrot de Barrow; German: Spatelente; Icelandic: Húsönd.

Variation: no subspecies, but geographical variation in bill colour.

Description

ADULT: dimorphic in colour and size. ♂ in alternate or breeding plumage has head and upper neck black, highly glossed with purple or violet and with large white crescent behind base of bill. Back, rump, tail and uppertail coverts black. Scapular black with row of 6–7 large, white, square dots over folded wing. Wing black with white speculum; white in forewing completely separated from speculum by black bar. Lower neck (all round), breast and sides white. Bill black; legs and feet orange-yellow with dusky webs; eye yellow. ♀ head brown; back, scapulars and uppertail coverts bluish grey, feathers edged pale grey; rump blackish. Uppertail coverts dark brown tipped grey. Tail greyish brown. White speculum crossed with dark bar. Upperbreast grey with white feather tips. Belly white. Sides and flanks grey, feather tips whitish. Undertail coverts white and dark grey. Bill dusky with orange band near tip, individual variation in extent of orange area, which disappears during egg-laying period and bill becomes all dark; eye pale yellow. Pacific population has more extensive orange on bill than Icelandic birds.

MOULT: ♂ in basic or eclipse plumage resembles ♀ but darker; occurs mid July–late Aug.

IMMATURE: ♂ resembles adult but row of white spots on side of body (including crescent on head) indistinct or only partly developed. ♀ resembles adult, but speculum with no dark bar, less white on forewing, orange coloration of bill fainter in winter and eyes darker. Neck ring less distinct.

DUCKLING: black and white with conspicuous cheek, wing and dorsal spots, dark bill, brown eyes and olive-coloured legs (Nelson 1993).

MEASUREMENTS AND WEIGHT: ♂ wing ($n = 21$), 236–253 (244.0); tail ($n = 8$), 86–91 (88.9); bill ($n = 41$), 21–37 (34.6); tarsus ($n = 40$), 40–48 (43.0); weight ($n = 163$), 1000–1387 (1167.1). ♀ wing ($n = 50$), 198–231 (213.7); tail ($n = 5$), 81–88 (85.0); bill ($n = 101$), 28–34 (31.2); tarsus ($n = 103$), 32–43.2 (38.3); weight ($n = 332$), 638–1056 (823.2). Weight loss of ♀ during incubation and of ♂ during moult (Einarsson 1985).

Field characters

♂ black and white duck with large head, steep forehead and hindneck outdrawn. White crescent shaped spot in front of eye and white breast. Tail usually flat on water surface except when resting. ♂ Common Goldeneye has round, not crescentic, white spot in front of eye. ♀ closely resembles Common Goldeneye but shape of head characteristic with top of head less pointed and placed more in front, and feathers of hind neck usually longer, giving head more puffy appearance. Day-olds nearly identical to Common Goldeneye, but can be distinguished on bill dimensions (Fjeldså 1977).

Voice

♂ rather silent except during courtship; most common is Burping or grunting accompanying Head-throw-kick display and weak clicking sound *tigga-tigga-tigga* . . . during Crouch display. Most common call of ♀ rapid *kad-kad-kad-kad-kad* . . . or *ga-ga-ga* . . . uttered during communal nest prospecting and also during brood season when triggers strong following response by young, e.g. when inciting ducklings to jump from nest or during interactions in brood territory of another ♀ (Einarsson 1985). ♀ utters weak hissing sound if disturbed on nest. Wings produce whistling sound in flight (sonogram of this and of ♂ call in Cramp and Simmons 1977).

Range and status

Has discontinuous distribution. Main breeding range is northwestern North America, mainly British Columbia and Alaska, where 90% of world population frequents productive, alkaline lakes and nests primarily in tree holes (Palmer 1976, Savard *et al.* 1994). Small breeding population in Québec, in forest region of Laurentian Highlands (Robert *et al.* 2000), and possibly further north in Labrador, winters mostly along St Lawrence estuary (Eadie *et al.* 2000). American population winters mainly on Pacific coast from Alaska to Puget Sound but small numbers found on interior lakes and rivers that remain open, and along Oregon and Californian coast (Savard 1987b, Goudie *et al.* 1994). Population estimates crude; *c* 45 000 reported in Alaska and 70 000–126 000 birds in British Columbia;

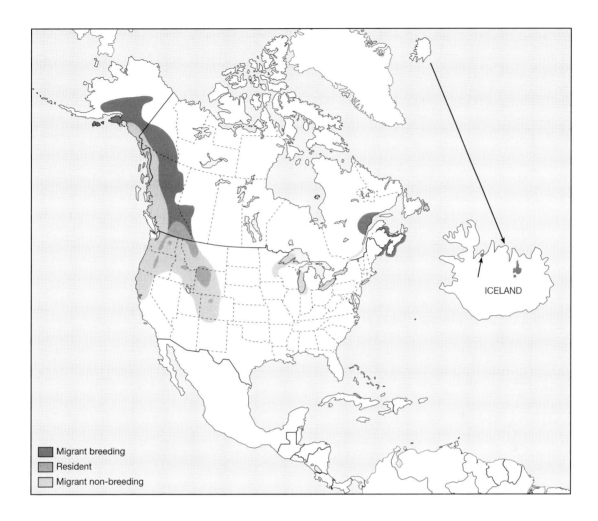

Migrant breeding
Resident
Migrant non-breeding

estimates from Washington, Oregon and California indicate less than 8000 birds (Savard 1986a). Appears to be declining in British Columbia (Goudie *et al.* 1994). Perhaps 2000–4000 winter on St Lawrence River (Robert *et al.* 2000). Single breeding record from Greenland during 19th century (Salomonsen 1950).

Well-studied resident population in Iceland numbers *c* 2000 (Garðarsson 1978), but is declining. Mostly confined to and resident in Mývatn Lake–Laxá River area of northeast Iceland which harbours 85–90% of population (Garðarsson 1978, 1979). In 1989, half population (mostly ♂♂) disappeared following marked reduction of food supply; emigration observed, coinciding with high mortality of adults (Garðarsson and Einarsson 1994).

Icelandic birds winter mainly on ice-free freshwater within breeding area but some on other partly ice-free freshwater, mostly within volcanic zone (Garðarsson 1978). No coastal wintering birds found off Iceland.

Habitat and general habits

Hole-nesting and highly territorial, preferring relatively productive lakes and rivers with little emergent vegetation. Mainly gregarious outside breeding season but, prior to and during egg-laying and early incubation, ♂♂ defend non-overlapping territories on open water along shore. Territory does not include nest site which, in Iceland, is natural hole in surrounding lava fields and, in America, is tree hole. Sympatric in distribution with Common Goldeneye in some parts of boreal forest of eastern Québec; however, may be segregation based on elevation, most breeding Barrows being associated with lakes > 500 m asl (Robert *et al.* 2000). Territories abandoned before young hatch, but many ♀♀ establish brood territories soon after hatching.

Feeds mainly on benthic invertebrates, and outlet of Lake Mývatn, which has exceptionally high density of Blackfly *Simulium vittatum* larvae, is focal point of Icelandic population (Einarsson 1988, 1990) supporting highest density of pairs in spring, and ♀♀ with young soon after hatching. Diving main feeding method but emerging midges and blackflies skimmed off surface. Mean dive duration 24.8 sec (max 38, $n = 363$) for ♂♂, and significantly shorter at 21.9 sec (max. 32, $n = 412$) for ♀♀ (Magnúsdóttir and Einarsson 1990). Associated on wintering range along Pacific coast with rocky shores that harbour Blue Mussel, preferring protected shorelines to exposed ones, and rarely found on mudflats, sandy beaches or estuaries (Savard 1987b, Eadie *et al.* 2000).

Displays and breeding behaviour

Territory boundaries maintained by threat displays between ♂♂ at 4 levels of intensity: lying flat on water between dives when feeding; lying flat but stationary on water, usually facing intruder; lying flat swimming towards intruder; attacking, usually by diving underneath intruder or flying towards him. Defended areas restricted to water surface, shore often forming one boundary, other boundaries 'invisible' lines on water, stable over 24 h but shifting over longer periods. Displays against neighbours less vigorous than towards other conspecifics. Territorial ♂♂ exclude all conspecifics except mate; also aggressive towards other duck species (Savard 1984, Savard and Smith 1987, Thompson and Ankney 2002). ♂♂ spend 20% of time in territorial defence in pre-breeding period (Einarsson 1985, Savard 1988). Main mate defence display is Crouching, with neck stretched towards intruding ♂, head low but out of water and bill open. During mating, after ♀ assumes prone position, ♂ Ceremonial-drinks and Wing-leg-stretches; before mounting, he performs vigorous Water-twitching, splashing water by series of head-shakes with bill in water; then suddenly Preens-back-between-wings on side nearest ♀ before swimming towards her with head erect. While mounted, ♂ Wing-shakes and, after dismounting, retains grip on ♀ while pair rotate on water for several sec, then steams away performing lateral Head-turns and calling.

Sex ratio in Iceland notably skewed, with large surplus of ♂♂ (Garðarsson 1978). Pair formation occurs in early winter; some territorial behaviour through winter but increasing number of pairs take up territories in late winter and spring. At Mývatn-Laxá, Iceland, territory size ranges 420–40 000 m², (Einarsson 1985), in British Columbia ranges 5000–18 500 m² (Savard 1988). Pairs spend almost all time on territories in pre-breeding period (Einarsson 1985).

Breeding and life cycle

Nest prospecting performed singly or in groups, and intense at daybreak. Several ♀♀ will circle nest sites and enter holes showing no signs of antagonism, vocalizing in flight. ♂♂ present but less active. Holes for nesting superabundant in Iceland but, at edge of breeding area, nesting encouraged by erection of nestboxes on farmhouses. After main hatch period, nest prospecting involves mostly yearlings and failed breeders (Eadie and Gauthier 1985). Maximum distance between territory and nest 2140 m but 61% ($n = 36$) of nests < 400 m from territories (Einarsson 1985). Not colonial, but 2–3 nests occasionally close together. In Iceland, egg-laying in natural holes commences late May (little earlier in nestboxes on farms) and young hatch 1st half of July. Rock crevices used for nesting usually have 2 entrances, one being emergency exit. Dump-nesting frequent, mostly intraspecific, but also interspecific with several other ducks (see Eadie 1989). Eggs ovate, bluish green; 62×45 ($57–65 \times 42–48$) ($n = 153$), and in captivity weigh 69.2 ($n = 61$). Mean clutch 10.4 ($n = 179$) (Bengtson 1972b) and incubation 32–34 days (Palmer 1976). Only ♀ attends eggs and young. Newly hatched captive ducklings weighed 42.8 ($n = 38$).

♀ defending brood territory lies flat and inconspicuous on water while swimming towards intruder who is often taken by surprise. Two brood-attending ♀♀ may fight vigorously. Brood mixing often frequent between neighbouring territorial ♀♀, or territorial and passing ♀. Whole brood or part may be transferred, with single ♀ staying with mixed brood that can contain > 100 young. ♀♀ establish well-defined non-overlapping territories while attending young, and attack adult conspecifics as well as other duck species. They also attack, and even kill, strange conspecific young, especially if different size from own. Territorial aggression towards intruding ♀♀ with broods usually directed against adult (see Einarsson 1985, Savard 1987a). Brood territories maintained for period and then moved, coinciding with changes in food conditions (Einarsson 1988). Many ♀♀ lose all young to territorial ♀♀ without establishing own territory.

Sexual dimorphism obvious in half-grown young, ♂ gaining weight faster but growing feathers more slowly than ♀. Production of young in Mývatn-Laxá breeding area of Iceland over 15 years (1975–89) varied 2–919 (Garðarsson and Einarsson 1994).

Icelandic birds moult on Mývatn and Laxá. Moulting locations of American birds still poorly known, but include Old Crow Flats in Yukon and Ungava Bay (Savard 1987b, Eadie *et al.* 2000). Wing moult delayed in brood-attending ♀♀. Maximum longevity recorded 18 years (Goudie *et al.* 2000). First breeding by ♂ and ♀ possible at 2 years; however, most individuals start later (Goudie *et al.* 2000).

Conservation and threats

Owing to dependence upon Mývatn-Laxá system, Icelandic population vulnerable to activities that reduce aquatic insects. These include plans to introduce Atlantic Salmon into upper parts of Laxá River and sediment dredging now in progress in Mývatn Lake which could reduce algal blooms. Logging identified as greatest potential threat to Pacific population (Savard 1987b) since nest sites destroyed. Is hunted in North America in autumn and winter (Goudie *et al.* 1994) but harvest rates low (Savard 1987b); protected from shooting in Iceland, and Mývatn-Laxá nature reserve is Ramsar site. Eggs collected for domestic use, but 4–5 normally left in nest according to tradition and law.

Árni Einarsson

Smew *Mergellus albellus*

Plate 28

Mergus Albellus Linnaeus, 1758, Syst. Nat., ed. 10, p. 129
Europe
Mergellus Selby, 1840

Etymology: *albellus* diminutive of *albus*, L. for white, in reference to ♂ plumage. *Mergellus* diminutive of *mergus* meaning little merganser. Common name, known since 1668, derives from Smee Duck and refers to *kur-rik* or *krr-eck* call of ♂.

Other names: none in English. French: Harle piette. German: Zwergsäger; Dutch: Nonnetje.

Variation: no subspecies nor geographical variation.

Description

ADULT: dimorphic. ♂ in breeding plumage has head white, with black frontal mask surrounding eye to base of bill and black loose feathers on sides of nape, mantle and central back. Neck and upper body mostly white, showing 2 thin black lines running from mantle down side of chest in inverted V. Rump and tail grey-black, underparts white. Primaries completely black, secondaries broadly edged white on trailing edge. Marked contrast in flight between black inner tertials and white outer ones. Greater wing coverts black with bold white tips, median wing coverts white, lesser ones black. Bill short and greyish; legs and feet greyish; iris reddish brown, pale greyish white in older ♂. ♀ crown, nape and upper hindneck rich rufous-brown, face mask blackish though less so than ♂, lower face and throat white. Upperparts and tail dull grey. Breast and flanks mottled dusky grey fading into greyish white underparts. Wings patterned as ♂ but white parts reduced.

MOULT: eclipse of ♂ resembles ♀ but black upperparts, and white patch on median wing coverts retained.

IMMATURE: superficially like adult ♀, but central white wing coverts have brownish tips and lores dark brown not black. Iris dull grey-brown.

DUCKLING: sooty black crown to below eye, nape, upper parts of body and thighs; white patch at rear edge of wing, below wing and at sides of back and rump; upper breast and sides of body, cheeks and underparts white.

MEASUREMENTS AND WEIGHT: from Cramp and Simmons (1977) who gave details of how measurements taken on museum skins; other sources, e.g. Bauer and Glutz (1968–69), in which data differ slightly, not comparable as methods unknown. ♂ adult wing ($n = 25$), 197–208 (202), juv (1st winter) ($n = 20$), 188–202 (196); adult tail ($n = 24$), 72–78 (74.8), juv ($n = 19$), 65–75 (69.3); bill ($n = 46$), 27–32 (29.6); tarsus ($n = 46$), 31–36 (34.0); toe ($n = 46$), 51–62 (55.5). ♀ adult wing ($n = 10$), 181–189 (184), juv ($n = 24$), 171–184 (177); adult tail ($n = 10$), 65–73 (69.7), juv ($n = 18$), 59–73 (65.4); bill ($n = 33$), 25–29 (26.9); tarsus ($n = 33$), 29–32 (30.6); toe ($n = 34$), 46–55 (49.6). Primary sources for weight Dementiev and Gladkov (1952) and Bauer and Glutz (1968–69) summarized, with extra data, in Cramp and Simmons (1977) and Dunning (1993). ♂ adult and juvenile significantly heavier than ♀ adult and juvenile, with heaviest weight in winter, Nov–Mar. Data from Rybinsk reservoir in Apr, ♂ adult (no sample size) 590–795 (700), in Oct 540–825 (652), in Nov 720–935 (814); juv in Oct 500–760 (630); in Nov 645–920 (882); in Jan 900. ♀ adult in Apr 510–670, in Oct 515–630 (568), in Nov 550–650 (572); juv in Oct 500–680 (556), in Nov 535–670 (588), in Jan 606.

Field characters

Compact duck, 380–440 mm long, with small bill, steep forehead, slight crest and straight neck in flight; plumage conspicuously patterned in both sexes, with seasonal variation in ♂. Distinctive plumage with compact flight silhouette, fast and agile, flying in oblique lines and V formation, more rarely in bunches over short distances. Easy take-off and manoeuvrability in limited space. Swims with notable buoyancy, diving easily, frequently and quickly; walks well with upright stance. ♂ looks mainly white on water but, in flight, darker above with conspicuous black and white wings and, in eclipse, white patches on wing larger than ♀'s; ♀ obviously smaller, greyish body with contrasting chestnut cap, brown and white wings and white lower face and throat.

Voice

Calls infrequent except during courtship and when anxious or alarmed. Courtship call of ♂ described as soft mechanical sounding rattle (Johnsgard 1965a), quite high-pitched at first but slowing and hesitating towards end. Likened to sound of fingernail being drawn along teeth of comb, and described phonetically as *kur-rik* or *krr-eck* (Bauer and Glutz 1968–69). Accompanies Pouting and Neck-stretching displays, with somewhat louder version during Head-fling (Johnsgard 1965a). Inciting call of ♀ harsh, rattling *krrrr krrrr* with louder version associated with more energetic threatening movements (Johnsgard 1965a).

Contact-trills of young given in groups of 2–4 notes. Distress calls slow and rather swooping, starting at low frequency and rapidly moving to higher (Cramp and Simmons 1977). Sonogram of *kur-rik* call in Bauer and Glutz (1968–69).

Range and status

Palearctic, with wide breeding distribution through taiga and forest-tundra zones of northern Eurasia from Norway and southern Sweden to Kamchatka, between 55°N and Arctic Circle, though eastern boundaries unclear. Wintering range normally extends south to North Sea, Black and Caspian Seas, central China and Japan and, occasionally, particularly in severe winters, large numbers move south as far as northern Africa and Iraq.

Migratory although, as few ringed, little known of origin and dispersion of main wintering groups. No discrete populations identifiable but, in western Eurasia, 3 main wintering groups recognized. Some winter in northwest and central Europe, concentrated in southern Baltic and Netherlands, with small numbers reaching eastern Britain and lakes and rivers of central Europe, in hard winters, those

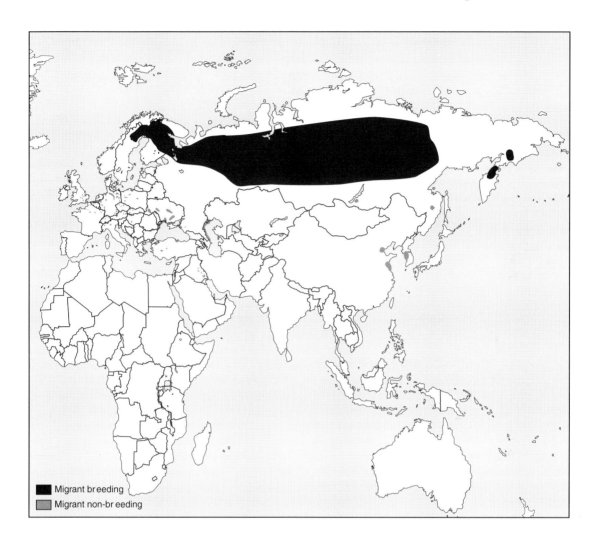

Migrant breeding
Migrant non-breeding

normally in southern Baltic may move to western Baltic and Danish waters; second group winters in Black Sea/east Mediterranean region, concentrated in Sea of Azov; third group winters in southwest Asia, especially in north Caspian and Uzbekistan with, in really hard winters, large numbers moving south as far as south Caspian in Iran (Atkinson-Willes 1976, Monval and Pirot 1989, Durinck *et al.* 1994, Perennou *et al.* 1994). Svazas *et al.* (1994) suggested that majority wintering in northwest Europe are from breeding areas in northern Russia east to Pechora, with those breeding further east wintered in Black Sea, Sea of Azov and the Caspian Sea.

In western Eurasia, wintering population estimated at 125 000–135 000 (Scott and Rose 1996); in northwest and central Europe *c* 30 000. Former estimates of 15 000 for northwest European population (Rüger *et al.* 1986, Monval and Pirot 1989) clearly too low; in 1990s 20 000 estimated in Baltic area alone in Jan 1993 (Pihl *et al.* 1995) and 30 000 in Dec 1991 on Szczecin Lagoon on Polish/German border (Svazas *et al.* 1994, Scott and Rose 1996). Higher total of *c* 35 000–45 000 suggested (Svazas *et al.* 1994), but major sites (Szczecin Lagoon and Ijsselmeer) need counting thoroughly and simultaneously. In Black Sea/east Mediterranean, *c* 35 000 (figure justified in AEWA 2000). Proposed in eastern Asia 25 000–100 000, including 20 000 in China, 1000 in South Korea and 1900 in Japan (Miyabayashi and Mundkur 1999). Krivenko (1993) estimated post-breeding population of western Siberia at 72 000 birds, which may account for those wintering in southwest Asia, and most in Black Sea region.

Habitat and general habits

Breeds around freshwater lakes, pools, rivers and muskegs of taiga zone. Winters mainly on larger lakes, ice-free rivers, coastal brackish lagoons and estuaries. Breeding sites occur in 2 main habitats containing well-grown trees with holes for nesting close to fresh water, either still or flowing, lowland oxbow lakes surrounded by forested tributaries, especially in medium-sized river valleys, and oligotrophic lakes and rivers with nearby forest in mountain or submountain regions.

Groups of moulting ♂♂ known from Siberia but not yet recorded in Europe. Leave breeding ground in early Sept, areas deserted by Oct. On passage, often rests and feeds on small bodies of water or small streams. In winter, commonly gregarious, sometimes forming flocks of over 10 000. Highly mobile and unsettled, shifting feeding and resting areas.

Food obtained mostly by diving after scanning from surface with head submerged. Depending on prey, dives nearly vertically or at long slant. Short submergence time, usually less than 30 sec but occasionally up to 45 sec, normally in depths 1–4 m. Prey usually brought to surface. Diurnal and, within flocks, often diving synchronously. In winter in Ijsselmeer, The Netherlands, 97% of densely packed group below surface for several sec (Beintema 1980); winter mass-fishing reported in flocks of *c* 750 with birds in front continuously diving and those at back making short flights to keep up with leaders (Källander *et al.* 1970).

Diet in winter and early spring mainly fish, at other times chiefly fish and benthic invertebrates, such as insects and their larvae. Freshwater fish eaten by adults include salmon and trout, Gudgeon *Gobio gobio*, Roach *Rutilus rutilus*, Bleak *Alburnus alburnus*, loach Cobitidae, stickleback Gasterosteidae, Northern Pike, Minnow *Phoxinus phoxinus*, Burbot *Lota lota*, Eel *Anguilla anguilla*, Perch *Perca fluviatilis*, and Common Carp *Cyprinus carpio*.

Marine fish include Plaice *Pleuronectes platessa*, sand-eels Ammodytidae, sandsmelt Antherinidae, Smelt *Osmerus esperlanus*, Blenny *Zoarces viviparous*, Atlantic Herring *Clupea harengus* and Common Bream *Abramis brama*. Fish mainly small, 30–60 mm long but occasionally up to 100 mm (carp) or 110 mm (perch) and exceptionally 290 mm (eel). All fish of appropriate size taken, but clear preference for pelagic rather than bottom-dwelling species. Insects mainly aquatic, both adults and larvae, especially waterbeetles Coleoptera, dragonflies Odonata and caddisflies Trichoptera. Occasionally take crustaceans, molluscs, marine polychaetes, frogs and plant material including seeds, leaves and roots (Naumann 1905, Millais 1913, Witherby *et al.* 1939, Dementiev and Gladkov 1952, Madsen 1957, Cramp and Simmons 1977, Beintema 1980, Svazas *et al.* 1994).

Displays and breeding behaviour

Outside breeding season, in small or large flocks with gregarious and nocturnal roosting. Monogamous pairbond of seasonal duration, with bonds formed mainly in late winter and on migration, ending during incubation. Aggression mostly in courting parties, although ♂ defends mate against intruding ♂♂. Courting ♂♂ frequently jab or attack other ♂♂ and sometimes ♀♀; most common form of hostility is for ♂ to rush at opponent over water with head well forward. Communal courtship in flock in late Dec with main peak late Feb–Mar. Usually 2–7 ♂♂ group around 1–2 active ♀♀; larger flocks generally divide. ♂ adopts Courtship-intent posture with neck slightly curved backwards, feathers of forehead erected and usually circles ♀ while performing display. Secondary displays include frequent Upward-shakes in which ♂ raises body to 40–60°, then shakes head backwards and forwards before resettling; lateral Head-shakes and Wing-flaps frequent. Pouting most common of major displays; bill held horizontal throughout and quiet call given. Starts from Courtship-intent posture, ♂ smoothly pumps head and neck backwards over mantle before returning to starting position. More elaborate movement, Head-fling, sometimes follows Pouting: ♂ suddenly throws head back while rising in water to *c* 45°, calling, then brings head rapidly forwards while resettling on water with bill pointing sharply down so that black V pattern on nape exhibited frontally. In Neck-stretch, ♂ suddenly extends neck fully upwards while calling, then brings it down. ♀ takes active part in courtship, swims in Courtship-intent posture with extended neck; frequently engages energetically in highly ritualized and conspicuous Inciting, typically lunging forward violently with body, bill pointing sharply down.

Pre-copulatory behaviour initiated by mutual Ceremonial-drinking, or by ♀ adopting Prone-position immediately, sometimes after directing Inciting movements at ♂. Prone-posture differs from that of *Mergus*, as ♀ floats with neck extended, head near surface, and tail elevated to *c* 30°, faces ♂ throughout, frequently Tail-quivering and sometimes Inciting. ♂ circles ♀, repeatedly approaching and retreating while displaying; displays include Ceremonial-drinking, Head-shakes, Upward-shakes and Preen-dorsally, also Water-twitch. Eventually ♂ mounts without special preliminaries, Wing-shaking 2–5 times during copulation. Afterwards ♂ may release ♀ immediately or pair may rotate; then ♂ performs single Head-fling before moving rapidly away Turning-back-of-head to ♀ who sometimes follows and Incites. Both sexes generally bathe (based on Cramp and Simmons 1997, in which Nilsson supplied most information, Hollom 1937, Lebret 1958, Johnsgard 1965a, Nilsson 1974). Klementsson (1980) observed one pair in which ♀ swam up and down and around ♂ in 10 m wide circle until copulation took place.

Breeding and life cycle

Little information, summarized in Dementiev and Gladkov (1952), Bauer and Glutz (1968–69) and Cramp and Simmons (1977). Breeds in single pairs or loose groups. Nests in tree holes, often made by Black Woodpecker, 10 m or more above ground, but takes readily to nestboxes. Nest slight depression lined with available material (often little or none) plus small feathers and down; no excavation, depression shaped by ♀. Egg-laying Apr–May in south of range and mid May–mid June in north. Eggs smooth, slightly glossy with thick shell; ovate, cream to pale buff; 52 × 38 (48–58 × 34–40) (*n* = 215) (Schönwetter 1960–66); weight of 100 captive-laid eggs 38.8 (34.5–46.0). One brood (no information on replacements), clutch size 7–9 (5–11). Incubation by ♀, 26–28 days, begins on completion of clutch, and hatching synchronous. Eggs covered with down when ♀ off nest. Shells left in nest. Ducklings precocial, nidifugous and self-feeding; 33 hatched in captivity weighed 23.1. Cared for by ♀; fledge in *c* 10 weeks. Probably breed from 2 years. No data on breeding success, adult survival or longevity.

Conservation and threats

Not globally threatened, though reliance on few major wintering sites and frequent movements between sites, particularly large scale movements associated with extremely cold weather, make calculation of trends difficult and results inconclusive (Rose 1995). In Europe, marked decline in breeding numbers during 2nd half of 19th century and most of 20th, attributed to habitat loss or degradation, especially loss of mature trees in river valleys through logging, conversion to agriculture, destruction due to river canalization, and predation by American Mink introduced in 1930s (Tucker and Heath 1994). Although range contraction continued in southern European Russia, local increases reported in Finland and Belarus (Tucker and Heath 1994). In Europe, categorized as Vulnerable (Tucker and Heath 1994). Further east, in western and central Siberia, Krivenko (1993) reported small decline in post-breeding numbers 1972–89, and Scott and Rose (1996) noted marked decline in wintering numbers in Azerbaijan during 20th century.

Peter Olney

Hooded Merganser *Lophodytes cucullatus*
PLATE 28

Mergus cucullatus Linnaeus, 1758, Syst. Nat., ed. 10, p. 129
America = Virginia and Carolina
Lophodytes Reichenbach, 1853

Etymology: *Lophodytes* Gr. *lophos* means crest plus *dutes* diver; *cucullatus* L. for hooded.

Other names: French Canadian: Bec-scie couronné, Harle couronné; Spanish: Serreta capuchona, Mergo Copeton.

Variation: no subspecies.

Description

ADULT: dimorphic. In breeding plumage ♂ has dramatic white crest bordered black. When erected, crest and yellow eye contrast sharply with black head and upper body. Breast white, separated by black and white bands from reddish brown flanks vermiculated black. Tertials may create 4 conspicuous black and white stripes along back of sitting drake depending on how tightly wings folded. Underparts mostly white. Bill black; legs and feet brown; eyes yellow. ♀ breeding plumage predominantly slate brown, sharply defined white chin; smaller than other mergansers, more uniformly dark, bill mostly dark, eyes brown, paler rufous bushy crest at back of long flat head.

MOULT: definitive basic plumage (eclipse) of ♂ resembles ♀ breeding plumage except that crest small and dusky, not brown.

IMMATURE: ♂ and ♀ prior to 2nd winter appear predominantly brown throughout. Crests, smaller than mature ♂, generally sleeked down. Juvenile ♂ and ♀ difficult to distinguish other than by cloacal examination; have whitish chins and, compared to adults, less white in wings. Year-old ♂ may show beginning of white crest.

DUCKLING: brown on back and upperbreast with buff cheeks. Throat, lowerbreast and belly white. Greyish spot on each side just anterior to tail. Darker than other mergansers and lacking marked facial stripes and dorsal spots; eyes yellowish brown (Nelson 1993).

MEASUREMENTS AND WEIGHT: ♂ (*n* = 12) wing, 191–207 (198.5); tail, 86–96 (90.8); bill, 37–41 (39.6); tarsus, 30–34 (32.4); weight (*n* = 24), max 910, mean 680. ♀ (*n* = 12) wing, 180–191 (185.2); tail, 81–93 (86.8); bill, 35–40 (38.3); tarsus, 30–32 (31.3); weight (*n* = 20), max. 680, mean 540 (Nelson and Martin 1953, Palmer 1976).

Field characters

Small, 420–500 mm long, fish-eating diving duck found exclusively in North America. Thin saw bill, high forehead and sleek appearance distinctive. Sits low in water. Flies low and fast with rapid wingbeat, wide tail apparent. Typically wary and isolated, occurring alone, in pairs or small groups rarely > 10 individuals. May be confused with Bufflehead of similar size, since ♂ has broad white patch at back of head; both found in same habitats using nesting cavities of similar size. Narrow bill, rusty flanks and less distinct patch of white on wings distinguish Hooded Merganser from Bufflehead. Juvenile and ♀ Bufflehead have short stubby bill and 'butterball' profile contrasting with slim Hooded Merganser. Eggshells in same cavity distinguishable from those of Common Goldeneye (green) and Bufflehead (ivory-yellow to olive-buff) by white colour of merganser, and from Wood Duck by shell thickness (Wood Duck 0.196–0.300 mm; Hooded Merganser 0.467–0.630 mm) (Soulliere 1987).

Voice

♂ silent except during display when produces guttural *crrroooooooo* similar to call of Pickerel Frog *Rana palustris*. Sonogram of vocalization associated with this display in Dugger *et al.* (1994). ♀ utters grunting *croo-croo-crook* call similar to that of seaducks (Palmer 1976).

Range and status

Discontinuous distribution with larger concentration in eastern North America and another in west.

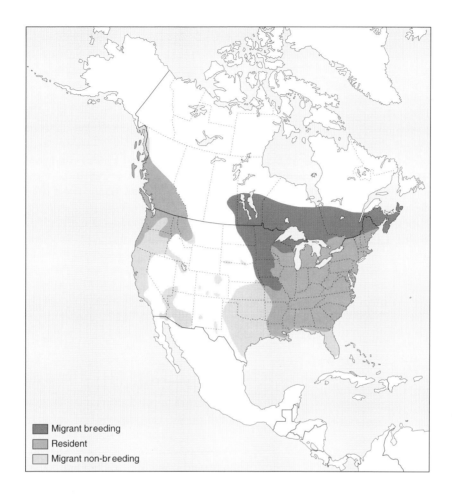

Migrant breeding
Resident
Migrant non-breeding

Primary breeding area in wooded portions of Ontario, Québec, Minnesota, Wisconsin and New York (Bellrose 1980). Western breeding concentration greatest in British Columbia, Washington and Oregon. Migratory, yet overlap between breeding and wintering areas. In east, winter inland of coast predominantly from Connecticut through Florida and in Louisiana, Tennessee and Arkansas through Texas. Along Pacific, winter inland from southern British Columbia to southern California. Winter estimates in 1970s close to 19 000 birds (Bellrose 1980). Densest breeding populations yielded 1.9 nests per km² in Minnesota (Zicus 1990a).

Habitat and general habits

Forest-dwelling, tree hole-nester found in rivers, streams, lakes, swamps and Beaver ponds. Broods in

Wisconsin observed in rivers and streams having abundant food, noticeable current, cobbled bottom and surrounded by mixed hardwoods (Kitchen and Hunt 1969). Broods feed in ponds 250–500 mm deep in Maryland (McGilvrey 1966) or along streams 350–550 mm deep in Wisconsin (Kitchen and Hunt 1969). Contents of 138 stomachs of adults (Cottam and Uhler 1937) 44% fish and 56% crustaceans and aquatic invertebrates. Various species of minnow and small fish, crayfish, frogs and dragonfly larvae consumed, as well as quantities of acorns in Mississippi during autumn and winter (Bellrose 1980).

Displays and breeding behaviour

Pair formation behaviour recorded rarely. In captive birds, Johnsgard (1961d) noted frequent raising of ♂'s ornamental crest, either independently or associated with other displays, and observed display activity throughout winter and spring. ♂ frequently shakes head laterally, erecting crest while rising slightly in water. Shaking often precedes head throwing movement including Frog call. Neck-stretching or Pumping also frequent and appears hostile. Tail-cocking, Body-shaking, Wing-flapping and Turning-head-toward ♀ with crest depressed often performed in courtship. ♀ movements include Pumping similar to that of ♂ and variation of Inciting termed Bobbing. In response to Inciting, ♂ swims ahead of ♀ and Turns-back-of-head towards her. Copulation occurs after ♀ assumes outstretched prone posture on water, often after pair has performed ritualized drinking. Elaborate crest-raised postures by ♂ precede and follow copulation (Johnsgard 1961d, 1975). Pairbond renewed annually after social display (Johnsgard 1975). ♀ returns to breeding areas used in previous years.

Breeding and life cycle

Nests occur in cavities created by rot and excavation by woodpeckers in hollow trees and snags or in artificial nestboxes. Chimneys used occasionally. In places, competes with Bufflehead, Common Goldeneye and Wood Duck for boxes (Bouvier 1974, Bellrose 1980, Doty *et al.* 1984). Lays eggs in nests of other Hooded Mergansers and in nests of other hole-nesting ducks. Incubation of dual clutches usually performed by ♀ depositing more eggs. May dominate Wood Ducks when competing for nest site (Doty *et al.* 1984). Egg laid every 2 days but interval may extend to 3 days later in clutch. Eggs 53.6 × 43.9, mass 59.2 ± 0.2 (*n* = 511, Lumsden *in* Dugger *et al.* 1994). In Oregon, experienced ♀♀ laid larger clutches earlier (mean 10.8) than birds believed breeding for first time (mean 9.4)

(Morse *et al.* 1969). In 83% of 191 nests, clutch size ranged 7–13 (Bellrose 1980). Down deposited just before last egg laid. ♂♂ leave after incubation begins. Incubation 32.6 (29–37) days (mode 33) (Morse *et al.* 1969). Nest success in natural cavities poorly known but, in nestboxes, 74% success rate relatively high (Bellrose 1980). Rates of hatching in successful nests 90–92%. Newly hatched young remain in cavity about 24 h before departing; 7 hatched in captivity weighed 31.9. First dives by ducklings shallow and of short duration, gradually increasing in depth and time (Beard 1964). McGilvrey (1966) estimated fledging at 71 days. Little known of mortality due to predation, disease and parasites. Incubating ♀♀ and clutches in nest cavities taken by Raccoons, American Mink and Black Rat Snakes *Elaphe o. obsoleta* (Dugger *et al.* 1994). Woodpeckers also destroy eggs. Not believed to breed until 3rd spring (2 years of age) from observations in captivity (Pilling *in* Morse *et al.* 1969). No data on adult survival or longevity.

Conservation and threats

Current populations appear stable. Human settlement of North America, resulting in drainage of swamps and river bottomlands, and deforestation that destroyed nesting trees, associated with earlier decline. Some recovery, along with Wood Duck, due to introduction of nestbox schemes (Heusmann *et al.* 2000) and habitat improvements. Maintaining mature forests with cavity-bearing trees appears to be key to conservation. Subject to persecution through competition with humans for fish. Hunters overharvested local populations at turn of 20th century, but not prized quarry; maximum of 26% of population may be harvested annually (Dugger *et al.* 1994).

Rodger Titman

Auckland Islands Merganser *Mergus australis*

Mergus australis Hombron and Jacquinot, 1841, Ann. Sci. Nat., Zool., Paris, sér. 2, **16**, p. 320
Auckland Islands
Mergus Linnaeus, 1758

Etymology: *australis* L. *auster* means the south.
Other names: Auckland or Southern Merganser. German: Aucklandischer Gansesäger; French: Harle australe.

Variation: no recognized subspecies. Suggestion by Kear and Scarlett (1970) that mainland mergansers were larger than those on Auckland Islands incorrect, and due to misidentification of subfossil humerus that Olson (1977) realized came from coot; however, Young *et al.* (1996) supposed bones discovered on Chatham Islands might represent locally distinct *Mergus*.

Description

ADULT: sexes rather alike (Figure 9.35). Head, crest and neck dark brown with chin and throat somewhat lighter. Mantle, scapulars, back, rump and tail dark bluish black. Breast dull grey with few lighter concentric markings; remainder of lower surface grey and white except for uniform dark grey-blue flanks. Wing coverts slate-grey like sides of breast, with lower row darker and banded white. Middle secondaries white on outer web and black on inner web and tips. Primaries and inner secondaries black. Culmen and tip of lower mandible black; cutting edge of upper mandible and rest of lower mandible yellowish orange; legs and feet orange; joints and webs dusky; iris dark brown. ♂ larger, had longer bill and crest, more rufous on crown, and 2 white wing bars instead of one (Kear and Scarlett 1970).

MOULT: Delacour (1954–64) stated no ♂ eclipse plumage. Probably two annual moults of body feathers and one complete wing moult.

IMMATURE: shorter crest or no crest at all, and no concentric markings on breast. Middle of lower

9.35 The extinct Auckland Islands Merganser.

breast and abdomen conspicuously white with few dusky markings (Salvadori 1895).

DUCKLING: dark, almost black, above with trace of pale wing, scapular and dorsal rump spots. Chin, throat and upper breast rusty chestnut, with spot of chestnut beneath eye and, unlike other downy mergansers, no white streaking on face. Remaining underparts yellowish white. Bill dark olive, brown on ridge and tip; feet olive-brown (Kear and Scarlett 1970).

MEASUREMENTS: ♂ ($n = 9$) length, 488; wing, 185.1; tail, 69.6; culmen, 59.6; tarsus, 43.4; crest, 5.6. ♀ ($n = 6$) length, 475; wing, 175; tail, 72.2; culmen, 55.0; tarsus 40.5; crest, 4.6 (Kear and Scarlett 1970, Livezey 1989b). Weight unknown.

Field characters

Only merganser in New Zealand waters. Small, with short wings that, in ♂ especially, came close to threshold of flightlessness (Livezey 1989b), short tail, and longer bill than other mergansers.

Voice

Individual (presumably ♀) said to quack 'like a domestic duck'. No information on ♂ calls; however, tracheal bulla of ♂ resembles that of Scaly-sided and Common Merganser (Humphrey 1955).

Range and status

Subfossil bones indicate inhabitants of North and South Islands of New Zealand and Stewart Island (Kear and Scarlett 1970, Horn 1983). When discovered in 1840, range restricted to Auckland Islands, 330 km south of New Zealand, where last known specimens shot in 1902. Since 1970, when Kear and Scarlett listed 26 skins, 3 skeletons, skeletal parts, plus preserved carcass in museums, another mounted ♂ adult, presented by Lord Ranfurly in Jan 1901, found in National Museum of Ireland, Dublin.

Habitat and general habits

Lived in rivers and creeks near sea and fed, by diving, mainly in fresh but also in brackish water. Food items recorded were 90 × 14 mm fish *Galaxias*

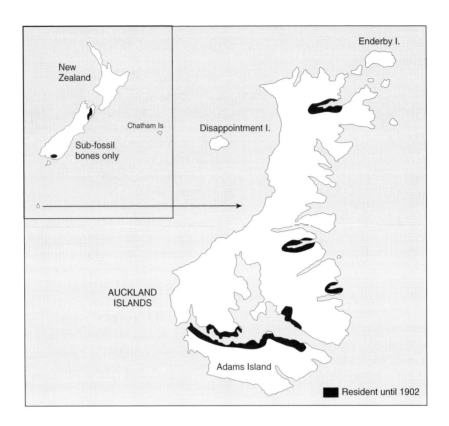

brevipinnis, errant polychaete and unidentified gastropod (Kear and Scarlett 1970).

Displays and breeding behaviour

Almost nothing known. No conspicuous ♂ plumage (indeed, both ♂ and ♀ as adults closely resembled immatures of northern mergansers); assumed pairbond relatively long-term as ♂ and ♀ shot together from Oct to, perhaps, July (Kear and Scarlett 1970).

Breeding and life cycle

Season included Nov–Dec, and nests probably made in natural cavities. Only recorded brood consisted of 4 ducklings, and both parents present when offspring captured and killed (Kear and Scarlett 1970).

Reasons for extinction

Merganser bones found in middens of New Zealand Moa-hunters (Kear and Scarlett 1970, Horn 1983) and likely extirpated from centre of range before arrival of Europeans. On Auckland Islands, pigs, dogs, cats, rabbits, sheep, goats, cattle and mice, introduced after 1806, must have altered pristine habitat drastically. Reportedly tame and easy to shoot; relatively large number of specimens collected for museums may have eliminated, ultimately, last of a rare species.

Janet Kear

Brazilian Merganser *Mergus octosetaceus*
PLATE 28

Mergus octosetaceus Vieillot, 1817, Nouv. Dict. Nat. Hist., nouv. éd., **14**, p. 222
Brazil

Etymology: *octosetaceus* from L. *octo* eight, plus *seta* bristle; said to have crest of 8 plumes.

Other names: none in English. Portuguese (Brazil): Pato-mergulhão; Spanish (Argentina): Pato serrucho.

Variation: no subspecies.

Description

ADULT: sexes rather alike. ♂ head, neck and upper parts dark brown with greenish iridescence and long occipital crest. Upperwing blackish, secondaries white with black bases, as are greater secondary coverts, forming black wing bar on white wing patch. Breast and under parts pale brown finely vermiculated grey. Bill plumbous black; legs red; iris brown. ♀ similar but slightly smaller with shorter crest (Partridge 1956, Silveira and Bartmann 2001).

MOULT: no ♂ eclipse plumage. Wing moult after breeding.

IMMATURE: breast greyish, back grey as in adult, wing bar present. No crest. Whitish cheeks and neck, white eye-ring, and dark head giving capped appearance. Upper mandible dark, lower mandible reddish; feet red (Silveira and Bartmann 2001).

DUCKLING: black above with white patches on lateral parts of wing, flanks and rump. Upperparts white with fine white line from lores to beneath eye; also small white spot in front of eye. Bill black; legs and feet drab grey with webs black; iris grey (Delacour 1954–64).

MEASUREMENTS: ♂ wing, 183–188; tail, 90–100; culmen, 49–51; tarsus, 40–42. ♀ wing, 180–184; culmen, 38–40 (Delacour 1954–64). Weight unsexed 600–700 (Silveira and Bartmann 2001).

Field characters

Length 490–510 mm. Most easily confused with distant Neotropical Cormorant *Phalacrocorax olivaceous*, since appears uniformly dark almost black; however, merganser shape characteristic, particularly head and narrow bill. Flies fast and low, along river, when white wing speculum conspicuous (cormorant has dark wings) (Narosky and Yzurieta 1987, Madge and Burn 1988, Sick 1993, Benstead *et al.* 1994).

Voice

Generally silent, but 4 calls recorded (Silveira and Bartmann 2001). Harsh *krack-krack* alarm call emitted in flight. Main call of ♂ resembles barking dog, that of ♀ raucous *rrr-rrrrr*. Contact call of adults soft *rak-rak-rak*, while that of duckling high-pitched *ik-ik-ik* (Partridge 1956, Bartmann 1988). Sonograms of ♂ and ♀ calls in Silveira and Bartmann (2001).

Range and status

Endemic to tropical and subtropical South America, historic range covered central and southern Brazil, northeast Argentina and oriental Paraguay. In Paraguay, Bertoni (1901) recorded it from what was probably Itapúa Department in 1891, while only other record from this country made in 1984 on Carapá River (Canindeyú Department) (Scott and Carbonell 1986). Once locally frequent in northern parts of Misiones Province, Argentina (Partridge 1956), but surveys in 1993 located only single individual on middle reaches of Piray Miní River. In Brazil, formerly occurred in states of Mato Grosso do Sul, São Paulo, Paraná, Santa Catarina, Goiás and Minas Gerais (see Collar *et al.* 1992). Presently persists only in latter two states, in Chapada dos Veadeiros National Park (Goiás State) (Yamashita and de Paula Valle 1990), Emas National Park (Goiás State) (Collar *et al.* 1992), and upper São Francisco River and tributaries (Minas Gerais State) (Bartmann 1994, Silveira and Bartmann 2001); however, population of at least 34 individuals discovered recently in western Bahia State, Brazil (Pineschi and Yamashita 1999). Considered extinct in Paraguay following recent surveys (Hayes and Granizo 1990, Brooks *et al.* 1993). Numbers in Argentina desperately small, and extinction seems inevitable. In

Resident

Brazil, surveys of upper São Francisco River population found 6 pairs, 2 entirely within Serra da Canastra National Park (Silveira and Bartmann 2001). Numbers within other Brazilian sites (Chapada dos Veadeiros and Emas National Parks) unknown, and surveys required. Playback of calls useful tool for locating pairs. Low population density results from territorial habit and extensive home range averaging 9 km of river (Silveira and Bartmann 2001). Entire population probably < 250 individuals.

Habitat and general habits

Shy inhabitant of clear streams and small rivers flowing through relatively undisturbed catchments in remote subtropical forest and cerrado (grasslands) with gallery forest. Most frequently recorded from upper tributaries, and current sites range 200–1400 m asl. Rivers characterized by meandering sections interspersed with rapids and small waterfalls (Johnson and Chebez 1985, Bartmann 1988, 1994, Yamashita and de Paula Valle 1990, Collar *et al.* 1992, Silveira and Bartmann 2001). Feeds during morning and evening, with day and night spent perched on stones, branches and fallen trees projecting from water. Flies swiftly, close to water surface and following river course (Partridge 1956, Bartmann 1988). May be more agile on land than other mergansers, and climbs waterfalls with ease.

Almost entirely piscivorous. Rapids and riffles favoured areas where fish with head submerged. Also feeds in deeper water, diving for 9–27 sec (Giai

1950, Partridge 1956, Bartmann 1988) or 15 sec (*n* = 17) in depths of *c* 0.5 m (Silveira and Bartmann 2001). Examination of 11 specimens taken by Partridge (1956) in Misiones, Argentina, showed that fish prey included characids, cichlids, pimelodids and hemiodontids, remains of whole fish measuring 6–19 cm. Stomach and gullet of one individual, however, contained 83.5% larvae of dobson fly *Corydalis*, 1.2% snail shells and 15.3% fish, indicating that aquatic invertebrates can be important. Bartmann (1988, 1994, Silveira and Bartmann 2001) suggested that characid fish *Astyanax fasciatus*, one of smallest fish in river, principal food item in headwaters of São Francisco River.

Displays and breeding behaviour

Limited data. Partridge (1956) observed that 'one bird (probably a female) was sometimes suddenly chased by another; without leaving the water they would move around in circles, paddling strongly with their wings . . .'; it seems likely that this was 'dashing and diving' behaviour common when ducks bath energetically (Johnsgard 1978). Partridge (1956) also saw copulation, which was preceded by ♀ becoming prone and motionless in water, both birds submerged during treading, after which ♀ uttered long cry, they bathed and perched on rocks. Silveira and Bartmann (2001) described mating in which ♂ followed ♀, lifting tail and neck and moving head up and down, ♀ making similar movements. As ♂ mounted, he held her crest and her body submerged with only neck above water; copulation lasted 15–25 sec. Alarm call accompanied by rhythmic jerking up-and-down of head and tail (Bartmann 1988).

Forms strong, long-term pairbond, and pairs remain on breeding territory year-round (Partridge 1956, Bartmann 1988, 1994, Silveira and Bartmann 2001). Home range large in comparison with other mergansers and riverine ducks. Highly territorial, and occasionally fights neighbours.

Breeding and life cycle

Limited data. Breeding season begins June, with incubation July and young emerging late July–Aug, although can be delayed by one month (Partridge 1956, Bartmann 1988, Silveira and Bartmann 2001).

Territory size perhaps correlated with number of rapids, falls, pools, and water velocity (Bartmann 1988). Single nest described located 25 m up in tree *Peltophorum dubium* cavity adjacent to Urugua-i River, Argentina; nest material fine rotten wood with no down (Partridge 1956). While ♀ incubated, ♂ remained close by on river, and joined her when she left. ♀ took one incubation break of 1–1.5 h daily, usually starting between 08.30 and 09.00 h, with most time spent feeding or preening. Fragments of hatched shell coloured light cream (Partridge 1956). Incubation period and clutch size unknown, but 3 recently hatched broods contained 4, 5 and 6 ducklings (Partridge 1956, Bartmann 1988); in Serra da Canastra National Park, brood size 2.7 (2–4) ($n = 10$) (Silveira and Bartmann 2001). Brood smaller than that of other mergansers, except extinct Auckland Islands Merganser. Bartmann (1988) found pair with ducklings occupying c 7 km of river; ♂ takes active part in brood care, and parents observed to carry young duckling on back. Ducklings feed on insects on water surface, and in rapids with heads submerged probably consuming aquatic larvae of trichopterans, plecopterans and dipterans (Partridge 1956, Bartmann 1988). Bartmann (1988) suggested fish soon replaces invertebrate diet. Research needed to determine ultimate fate of juveniles, which remain with parents until Dec–Jan. Natural predators include near-threatened Black and White Hawk Eagle *Spizastur melanoleucus*, Neotropical Otter *Lutra longicaudis* and possibly predatory fish *Saliminus maxillosus* (Giai 1951, Partridge 1956, Bartmann 1988); dark colour provides natural camouflage.

Partridge (1956) speculated that distribution limited to areas above waterfalls that prevented upstream movement of large fish such as *Salminus maxillosus* that would prey on ducklings. Little information on breeding success, and none on survival of adults.

Conservation and threats

One of most Critically Endangered birds (BirdLife International 2000). Protected in Brazil and Argentina, and 3 National Parks hold most known mergansers in Brazil; however, recently descovered population in western Bahia State (Pineschi and Yamashita 1999) unprotected, as is catchment of Piray Miní River in Argentina.

Main reason for decline probably increasing turbidity of rivers and streams through range as result of watershed degradation, mining and soil erosion. Deforestation of subtropical gallery forest, and Atlantic Forest, for timber and agriculture, widespread, while selective logging can be almost equally devastating in short term. Cultivation of cerrado intensive in northern parts; this once expansive habitat now poorly represented outside protected areas. Hydroelectric schemes destroy large areas of suitable habitat (Partridge 1956, da Fonseca 1985, Johnson and Chebez 1985, Redford 1985, Scott and Carbonell 1986, Bartmann 1988, Hayes and Granizo 1990, Yamashita and de Paula Valle 1990, Johnson 1991, Collar *et al.* 1992, Brooks *et al.* 1993). Opportunistic poaching and diamond mining also pose threats (Collar *et al.* 1992, Silveira and Bartmann 2001), while pesticides, including DDT, commonly used so that mass fish deaths frequent (Collar *et al.* 1992). Ecological tourism, especially rafting, may also pose significant threat. Productivity on headwaters of São Francisco River of Brazil worryingly low (Bartmann 1988, 1994). Competes for nest sites with other birds and mammals; nestboxes could be tried. Subject of major new conservation initiative by BirdLife International and Threatened Waterfowl Specialist Group.

Collection of specimens for museums problem in past (Partridge 1956, Giai 1976, Johnson and Chebez 1985) but not currently. Bertoni (1901) brought wild-caught adult into captivity, but bird soon died and no attempts made since to establish captive population. Silveira and Bartmann (2001) suggested that, as avicultural techniques have improved, captive breeding might now be useful.

Des Callaghan

Common Merganser (Goosander) *Mergus merganser*
PLATE 28

Mergus Merganser Linnaeus, 1758, Syst. Nat., ed. 10, p. 129
Europe

Etymology: *mergus* L. for waterbird, plus *anser* for goose. Goosander as 'Gossander' dates from 1622.

Other names: American Merganser, Sawbill, Fish Duck. Danish: Stor skallesluger; French: Grand harle, Grand bec-scie, Harle bièvre; German: Gänsesäger; Icelandic: Gulönd; Spanish: Mergo mayor, Mergo pechiblanco, Serreta grande.

Variation: 3 subspecies recognized: American Merganser *M. m. americanus* Cassin, 1852 of North America; nominate Goosander *M. m. merganser* of Palearctic occurs from Iceland east to Kamchatka and south to central Europe, northeast China and northern Japan; and Asiatic Merganser *M. m. comatus* Salvadori, 1895 (includes *M. m. orientalis* Gould, 1845 from eastern Asia) of central Asia from northeast Afghanistan east through Tibet and Himalayas to western China.

Description

ADULT: dimorphic. ♂, in alternate or breeding plumage, has head dark black-green with smooth rounded crest, appearing large; head and back contrast sharply with white breast, belly and flanks. Area around tail finely lined grey. Wing primaries black, secondaries and coverts white except for, in *americanus*, narrow black bar created by black edges to greater secondary coverts, hidden in other races. Bill red, serrated with strong hook; legs and feet reddish orange; eye brown. ♀ has reddish brown head with shaggy crest contrasting with pale greyish body. Chin and throat white, and white apparent between eye and base of bill. Shoulder and upper portion of wing blue-grey rather than sharply contrasting white of mature ♂. ♀ of all races very similar. *comatus* has shorter finer bill, longer wings and slightly paler head than *merganser* while *americanus* has deeper base to bill.

MOULT: definitive basic plumage (eclipse) of ♂ resembles ♀. Crown darker, head cinnamon, crest shorter and wings boldly marked. Basic and alternate plumages of ♀ do not differ. Pre-basic moult (to ♂ eclipse) begins early June, complete by mid Aug; pre-alternate moult occurs July–Sept.

IMMATURE: as ♀ but paler head.

DUCKLING: grey-brown upperparts, darker near rump and white underparts. White patch on either side of rump. Some have white stripe from below eye to base of bill, while stripe obscure in others. Crown tawny with rufous tinge to head (Mallory and Metz 1999).

MEASUREMENTS AND WEIGHT: *merganser* ♂ adult wing ($n = 30$), 275–295 (285 ± 5.23), juv ($n = 27$), 263–291 (275 ± 5.76); adult tail ($n = 24$), 100–111 (105 ± 2.73); bill ($n = 58$), 52–60 (55.8 ± 1.92); tarsus ($n = 58$), 49–55 (51.7 ± 1.4). ♀ adult wing ($n = 23$), 255–270 (262 ± 4.04), juv ($n = 20$), 242–260 (252 ± 4.96); adult tail ($n = 23$), 95–109 (100 ± 3.27); bill ($n = 43$), 44–52 (48.7 ± 1.83); tarsus ($n = 43$), 44–51 (47.4 ± 1.76) (Cramp and Simmons 1977).

americanus ♂ adult wing ($n = 57$), 230–259, juv ($n = 75$), 239–277; adult tail ($n = 12$), 96–102 (100.4); adult bill ($n = 59$), 49–60, juv ($n = 73$), 47–57; adult tarsus ($n = 60$), 47–60, juv ($n = 77$), 45–55; adult weight in Nov ($n = 13$), 1528–2054 (1709), juv in Oct ($n = 21$), 1348–1617 (1491). ♀ adult wing ($n = 55$), 230–259, juv ($n = 99$), 230–259; adult tail ($n = 12$), 90–98 (93.3); adult bill ($n = 56$), 45–52, juv ($n = 94$), 42–51; adult tarsus ($n = 58$), 40–48, juv ($n = 105$), 41–49; adult weight in Oct ($n = 11$), 1050–1362 (1232), juv in Oct ($n = 14$), 915–1268 (1122) (Erskine 1971, Palmer 1976).

comatus wings longer (295 *v* 278); bill shorter (51.5 *v* 55.8) than *merganser*.

Field characters

Fish-eating diver, largest of mergansers at 580–720 mm long. ♂ distinguished from Red-breasted Merganser by white of breast extending to belly and flanks, and lack of shaggy crest. At close range, central position of nostril on bill and equal feathering at base of both mandibles distinguish ♀ and immatures from Red breast having basal nostril and extended feathering on upper mandible. Brown eye differs from cherry red of Red-breasted Merganser. Found principally in freshwater systems while Red-breasted Merganser occurs along sea coasts, particularly in winter. Legs positioned posteriorly, making for efficient swimming but awkward walking. In flight, large, sleek and long-necked, underparts predominantly white, dark head, tail and primaries.

Voice

During display, ♂ utters guitar-like note as neck stretched and head feathers ruffled. Bell-like call given while stretching neck in Salute. When Inciting, ♀ produces croak followed by repeated *ack ack ack . . .*, also harsh *karr* notes. In aggressive context, both ♂ and ♀ hiss at conspecifics and potential predators. ♀'s alarm call repeated harsh guttural croaking *grrk* (Palmer 1976). Sonogram of ♀ call in Cramp and Simmons (1977).

Range and status

Found in closed boreal forest and montane forest regions of Eurasia and North America. Range not as far north as Red-breasted Merganser but extends farther south. *merganser* breeds in Iceland, Britain since 1871, Scandinavia, central Europe through Russia, Novaya Zemlya east to Mongolia and Kamchatka and winters along coasts from Norway to Spain, Mediterranean and Iran. Central Asian race *comatus* breeds in Tibet, Himalayas, Altai and Afghanistan, mostly resident but winters as far south as central India and southeastern China. *americanus* breeds in Alaska and southern Yukon below tundra, across forested central Canada to Newfoundland; absent from prairies but extends south in western North America in Rockies to Wyoming and west of mountains to northern California. Winters in coastal British Columbia and into southern Alaska, in Maritime provinces of eastern Canada and across continental US. In winter, 58% of American population found in interior US, and remainder in coastal areas (Bellrose 1980).

Populations appear stable with slight increases indicated in Canada and Europe into 1990s. In 1970s, North American summering population estimated at 640 000 birds (Bellrose 1980) and at least 110 000 winter in Eurasia (Cramp and Simmons 1977). Rose and Scott (1997) estimated 200 000 in northwest and central Europe, 900 in Iceland, 5000–8000 in UK, 3000 breeding in central Europe, 50–100 breeding in Balkans, 10 000 in northeast

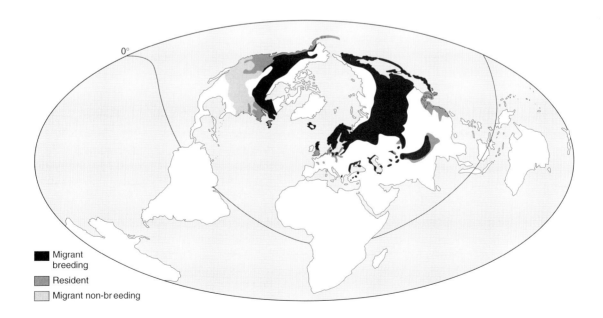

■ Migrant breeding
▨ Resident
▨ Migrant non-breeding

Europe and Black Sea region, and 20 000 in western Siberia and Caspian Sea. Estimated 50 000–100 000 *comatus* winter in eastern Asia, including 50 000 in China, 15 000 in South Korea and 5000 in Japan Miyabayashi and Mundkur (1999).

Habitat and general habits

Uses freshwater lakes, rivers and streams in forested areas, preferring upper basins of rivers and large clear inland lakes. Will use deeper waters and tolerates fast flow. Requires fairly high productivity of fish. Nesting requirements met in mature hardwood stands with natural cavities or holes excavated by large woodpeckers. No apparent territorial behaviour; occasionally ♀♀ nest in same tree or in close proximity, but typically nests isolated.

Food obtained by diving from surface, swim with head under water until prey detected and then pursued by swimming underwater, foot-propelled; will turn over rocks if necessary. In winter, groups of up to 70 birds drive or corral schools of fish. Because of propensity to consume game fish, diet much studied. Takes variety of fish, generally < 100 mm long, as well as molluscs, crustaceans, caddisfly larvae and other invertebrates. In Maritime provinces of Canada, Atlantic Salmon comprised 46–91% of fish eaten from Gaspé to Cape Breton Island and 5–36% in streams of Atlantic Nova Scotia and those entering Bay of Fundy (White 1957). Estimated that broods consumed 82 000–131 000 Coho Salmon *Oncorhynchus kisutch* fry in Big Qualicum River, British Columbia, equivalent to 24–65% of smolt production in river system (Wood 1987). Ducklings take mainly insects, changing to fish after 10–12 days.

Displays and breeding behaviour

Pair formation involves much surface chasing among ♂♂. Common ♂ display includes partly stretching neck and ruffling head feathers while vocalizing. Salute involves sudden vertical stretching of head and neck (Johnsgard 1965a, 1975). ♂♂ also suddenly kick jet of water backwards, and swim ahead of ♀, with tail cocked diagonally or flat on water, and Turn-back-of-head towards ♀, especially if Inciting. ♀'s Inciting similar to Red-breasted Merganser, and involves loud harsh call repeated once or twice accompanied by rapid forward swimming (Johnsgard 1965a). Short display flights, landing in long skid near courted ♀, also observed. Copulation preceded by preening and Bill-dipping by ♂, plus mutual drinking. ♀ lies prone on water, often for considerable time, before ♂ mounts. After treading, ♂ may immediately release ♀ or pair rotate on water as ♂ holds ♀'s nape, followed by preening and bathing. Johnsgard (1965a) observed ♂ swimming away while Turning-back-of-head and vocalizing. Pair forming displays occur from Oct through spring as birds arrive on breeding grounds. Adults generally paired upon arrival or soon after. ♀♀ show natal philopatry.

Breeding and life cycle

In central and western Europe, earliest eggs laid end Mar–mid Apr (Cramp and Simmons 1977). In Nova Scotia, laying begins mid to late Apr and broods appear beginning of June (Erskine 1972b). ♀ typically nests in hollow trees, and entry holes may be > 15 m from ground; nests also located among tree roots in undercut banks, on cliff ledges and on ground in dense shrub cover or loose boulders on islands. Also uses nestboxes. Eggs creamy white; *americanus* 66.5 × 46.5, weight 70 (Mallory and Metz 1999); nominate race somewhat larger at calculated 82 (Schönwetter 1960–66). Lays 8–12 eggs, but clutches > 13 may involve 2 or more ♀♀; clutch of nominate race 9.4 (6–12) (*n* = 35) (Hildén 1964a). Nest cavity lined with white down. Incubation by ♀, as last egg laid, 30–32 days. ♂ abandons ♀ early in incubation. Precocial young leave nest within 24 h of hatching. Newly hatched *merganser* ducklings weigh 46.2 (*n* = 9), and *americanus* 42.5 (38.4–46.1) (*n* = 11) and 38 (35.6–40.4) (*n* = 2) (Nelson 1993). Ducklings sometimes ride on ♀'s back if she moves rapidly. Brood amalgamation seen where broods of same age occur together. Young fly in 60–70 days, but continue to grow after fledging (Erskine 1971). ♀♀ may leave brood before fledging, and young typically independent early.

Yearling not known to breed; nests from 2 years. Adult annual mortality 40%, life expectancy averages 2 years (Cramp and Simmons 1977). Longevity record ♀ 13 years 10 months, ♂ 12 years 6 months (Mallory and Metz 1999).

Conservation and threats

Frequently subject of efforts to control predation on salmon or other game fish (White 1939, Elson 1962, Wood 1987). Local breeding populations along salmon rivers eliminated by shooting (Erskine 1972b). Despite this, and other threats, population not declining; indeed, in Europe, notably Britain, increasing in several areas (Kirby *et al.* 1995). Hunted, but not popular gamebird, approximately 5% of North American population harvested annually (Mallory and Metz 1999). Rates of predation appear low, and impact of predation poorly known. In Great Lakes, accumulation of toxic chemicals found in eggs and adults feeding on contaminated fish. Acid precipitation degrades favoured freshwater lakes in eastern North America. Regarded as key bio-indicator of health of river and lake environments (Mallory and Metz 1999). Nest-site availability not likely limiting factor, but nestboxes may encourage use of local areas.

Rodger Titman

Red-breasted Merganser *Mergus serrator*
PLATE 28

Mergus Serrator Linnaeus, 1758, Syst. Nat., ed. 10, p. 129
Europe

Etymology: *serrator* L. for sawyer. English name recorded in 1776.

Other names: Fish Duck, Redbreast, Sawbill. Danish: Toppet skallesluger; French: Harle huppé, Bec-scie à poitrine rousse; German: Mittelsäger; Icelandic: Toppönd; Spanish: Serreta mediana, Mergo copetón, Pato Mergo.

Variation: no subspecies recognized here; however, considerable individual variation in mass and measurements, and slight geographical variation (Vaurie 1965, Palmer 1976) led to 2 races being named, nominate *M. s. serrator* over most of range and *M. s. schiøleri* Salomonsen, 1949 in Greenland.

Description

ADULT: dimorphic. ♂ in breeding, or alternate, plumage has green head extending posteriorly into spikey double crest. White neck shades into reddish brown speckled breast. Anteriorly on flanks is wide black area with small and large white spots. Both sexes have erratic, posteriorly directed crest. Bill of ♂ red; legs and feet red; eye red. ♀ has greyish body merging into reddish brown head, and red eye.

MOULT: ♂ in definitive basic plumage (eclipse) ♀-like; crown darker and upper parts, including mantle, dark with feathers having wide grey margins. Feathers of breast, sides and flanks mostly grey with pale margins. Definitive pre-basic moult begins late May–early June, and completed by mid Aug.

IMMATURE: has dark malar stripe with light above; nape wispy, lacking adult crest. Otherwise resembles ♀.

DUCKLING: dark brownish grey upperparts and creamy white underparts. Two prominent dark stripes begin at bill and continue past eye; often continuous white line runs from under eye to base of bill, but line may be interrupted. Some ducklings have spot of white above eye. Whitish rump spots on each side (excellent description and illustration in Nelson 1993).

MEASUREMENTS AND WEIGHT: ♂ adult wing ($n = 32$), 235–255 (247 ± 5.18), juv ($n = 12$), 226–245 (236 ± 6.13) (Cramp and Simmons 1977), adult ($n = 12$) 238–257 (248.5) (Palmer 1976), adult tail ($n = 34$), 76–87 (81.2 ± 3.14), juv ($n = 10$), 67–75 (70.8 ± 2.64) (Cramp and Simmons 1977); adult ($n = 12$), 78–86 (82) (Palmer 1976); bill ($n = 46$), 56–64 (59.2 ± 2.16) (Cramp and Simmons 1977) ($n = 12$), 57–60 (59) (Palmer 1976); tarsus ($n = 45$), 44–50 (47.0 ± 1.47) (Cramp and Simmons

1977) ($n = 12$), 45–48 (46.3) (Palmer 1976); weight ($n = 11$), 947–1350 (1197 ± 118) (Cramp and Simmons 1977) ($n = 18$), max 1320, mean 1134 (Nelson and Martin 1953). ♀ adult wing ($n = 14$), 216–239 (228 ± 6.54), juv ($n = 14$), 208–221 (217 ± 4.18) (Cramp and Simmons 1977), adult ($n = 12$), 213–239 (224) (Palmer 1976); adult tail ($n = 14$), 73–81 (76.4 ± 2.82), juv ($n = 12$), 57–70 (64.0 ± 4.47) (Cramp and Simmons 1977), adult ($n = 12$), 69–78 (73.8) (Palmer 1976); bill ($n = 28$), 48–55 (52.1 ± 2.21) (Cramp and Simmons 1977) ($n = 12$), 50–58 (55) (Palmer 1976); tarsus ($n = 28$), 40–45 (42.7 ± 1.51) (Cramp and Simmons 1977) ($n = 12$), 42–49 (44) (Palmer 1976); weight ($n = 5$), 900–1100 (984 ± 84.3) (Cramp and Simmons 1977), nesting weight ($n = 30$), mean 998 (Bengtson 1972a) ($n = 17$), max 1270, mean 907 (Nelson and Martin 1953).

Field characters

Large, 520–580 mm long, sawbilled diving duck seen in northern coastal areas of northern hemisphere. Long, narrow, serrated bill with hooked tip separates from other mergansers—nostrils located on basal third of bill; feathering on side of upper mandible reaches farther forward than on lower mandible, upper mandible relatively longer and lower at base, and has smaller, narrower nail than Common Merganser or Goosander (Johnsgard 1975). Often difficult to distinguish from Common Merganser, especially at distance. Habitat helpful, since Red-breasted Merganser frequently associated with saltwater. From side, larger Common Merganser ♂ in breeding plumage has uninterrupted white breast and flanks which separate it easily. Slightly smaller breeding Red-breasted ♂ distinguished by coloured breast and shaggy crest; however, immatures, ♂♂ in basic (eclipse) plumage, and ♀♀ are challenging. Adult ♀♀ Common Mergansers in breeding (alternate) plumage have reddish brown heads and necks distinct from grey lower neck and body. Duller rusty head colour of ♀ Red-breasted Merganser fades gradually into brownish grey of body (Kaufman 1990). White on throat of Redbreast ♀ fades into brown face, whereas there is sharp line of contrast with throat of Common Merganser. ♀ Redbreast has dark line through eye not apparent in adult ♀ Common Merganser. For basic plumages, field marks given here are unreliable, but relative structure of head and bill important; Redbreast has steeper forehead and basal position of nares, in contrast to Common Merganser's central position, obvious at close range.

Voice

During display, ♂ produces catlike *yeow-yeow*, single *yeow* or loud rough purring. ♀ call similar to that of Common Merganser; during display, utters raspy or croaking *krrrr -krrrr* call. Rough croaks heard from ♀ flying to and from nest. Alarm call deep gruff *gra gro garr* or *grack*. Call to young, low husky distinctive *kha-kha-kha*. Sonograms of ♂ and ♀ calls in Cramp and Simmons (1977).

While copulating, ♂♂ flick wings vigorously, producing drumming sound that may have display function (Johnsgard 1960e).

Range and status

Extensive Holarctic distribution. Johansen (*in* Palmer 1976) suggested boreal sub-arctic distribution, expanding into Arctic in post-glacial time. Breeds to 75°N in Siberia, farther north than other mergansers, also in Scotland and northern England, Ireland, southern Greenland, Iceland, northern Germany, Scandinavia, northern Asia through Siberia to northeastern China and northern Japan. Present all year in Iceland and parts of British Isles. European birds winter in coastal areas from Baltic and North Seas south to north Mediterranean, Black, Caspian and Aral Seas. Asiatic birds winter from Kamchatka Peninsula south through Kuril Islands, Korea, Japan, east China coast and Taiwan.

In North America, breeds from Aleutian Islands in west, through Alaska, and from arctic coast of Yukon eastwards across Keewatin District, southwards to northern British Columbia, northern Alberta, central Saskatchewan and virtually all eastern provinces of Canada. Breeds on southern Baffin Island. In US, breeds locally in northern Minnesota, Wisconsin, Michigan and in Maine. Isolated breeding records farther south from western Montana and Wyoming, coastal New York, North and South Carolina and Pennsylvania. Winters along Pacific coast from southern Alaska to Baja California and

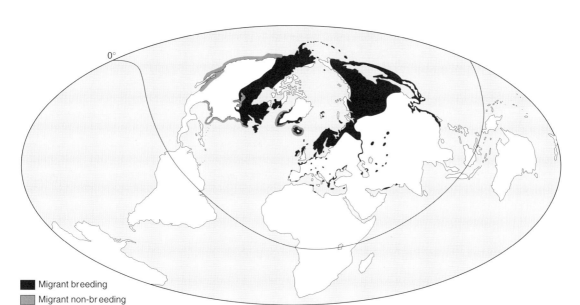

Migrant breeding
Migrant non-breeding

northern Mexico, along Atlantic coast from Nova Scotia around Florida Peninsula to southern Texas and in Great Lakes.

In North America, 237 000 estimated to winter in mid 1970s (Bellrose 1980). From 1966–89, 4.6% decline recorded in North American population (Titman 1999). In Palearctic, estimated 150 000 in 1980s, including 4300 in Britain and 1400 in Ireland. Rose and Scott (1997) estimated 125 000 in northwest and central Europe, 15 000–25 000 in east Greenland, Iceland and UK, 50 000 in northeast Europe, Black Sea and Mediterranean, < 10 000 in western Siberia, and southwest and central Asia, 25 000–100 000 wintering in eastern Asia, and 10 000–100 000 *scioleri* in west Greenland.

Habitat and general habits

Saltwater commonly favoured. Found in sheltered shallow bays or estuaries with sand substrate and in rivers or lakes. Associated with tundra as well as temperate forest zones. Rests or perches on rocks, gravel bars or sand spits. Winters predominantly on secluded bays or estuaries in marine environments.

Bulk of diet fish and crustaceans; also consume worms, insects and amphibians. In 130 stomachs

Cottam and Uhler (1937) found 34.2% minnows, sticklebacks and killifish, 42.5% other fish or fish fragments, and 23% crayfish, shrimps and miscellaneous items. Various studies show consumption of wide variety of fish. Prickly Sculpins *Cottus asper* and Pacific Herring *Clupea pallasii* and their eggs considered important prey in coastal British Columbia; flocks of 100 or more forage on herring (Munro and Clemens 1939). In Scottish salmon rivers, 113 of 148 stomachs contained Atlantic Salmon or remains thereof (Mills *in* Palmer 1976), and in Grampian, Carss and Marquiss (1992) found that 48% of spring diet was salmon, but most were young (parr) and maximum of only 9% were 2-year-old smolt. Cooperative fishing behaviour, involving several individuals herding schools of fish, enhances capture (Des Lauriers and Brattstrom 1965).

Displays and breeding behaviour

Social display occurs late Nov–June involving several ♂♂ and one ♀. Display most intense on breeding grounds during morning and evening. ♂♂ swim in characteristic 'ready' (Johnsgard 1965a) or Courtship intent (Cramp and Simmons 1977) posture, with head drawn into shoulders, crest raised and bill pointing slightly upward. Most frequent ♂ displays Head-shake and Salute-curtsy (Van der Kloot and Morse 1975). Upward-stretch, Wing-flap and Bathing also occur during display activity and appear ritualized.

Apart from aggression toward ♂, ♀ not active in courting parties. She may produce harsh *krrrr-krrrr* call while ♂♂ display around her. Inciting by ♀ indicating attachment to ♂ is Bobbing motion (Hollom 1937). During copulation, ♀ stays in prone position on water for several minutes while ♂ performs ritualized comfort movements before mounting. After treading, ♂ holds ♀'s nape as pair Rotate; ♂ steams away after release, Turning head from side to side (Johnsgard 1960e).

Gregarious during winter and migration. Social display related to pair formation begins on wintering ground (Johnsgard 1975). Typically arrive paired on breeding ground in Apr on Baltic Sea, May in New Brunswick and later farther north where arctic season short. Seasonally monogamous except that Nilsson (*in* Cramp and Simmons 1977) suggested polygyny and polyandry on rare occasions. ♀ philopatric, returning regularly to former breeding site.

Breeding and life cycle

Late nester; in New Brunswick laying starts end May–mid July. Lays egg every 1.5 days (Curth 1954) in nest on ground in dense cover, holes or depressions, often colonially on islands or small islets, usually within 25 m of water. Uses wooded shoreline along rivers and lakes, and nests found near tundra ponds in long grass, and in abandoned igloo (Brandt *in* Bellrose 1980). Eggs olive-buff; $63.4 \pm 2.5 \times 44.6 \pm 1.0$ and weigh 67.9 ± 3.3 (Titman 1999); Curth (1954) gave egg weight of 72.6. Mean clutch size 9.5 (6–14) with up to 30 occurring where several ♀♀ deposit eggs. High rates of intraspecific nest parasitism (64%) in dense nesting concentrations (Young and Titman 1988). Also parasitize other ducks nesting in close proximity.

Gregarious when breeding, ♂♂ and ♀♀ assembling on beaches or spits of land when not at nest; later ♀♀ gather during breaks in incubation. Incubation begins with laying of last egg, and lasts 30 (28–35) days. Young leave nest within 24 h of hatching. Newly hatched ducklings weighed 46 (44.0–47.6) ($n = 5$) (Nelson 1993); 12 hatched in captivity at WWT Slimbridge averaged 41.8, and one ♂ was 592 at 10 weeks. ♂♂ depart to moult at start of incubation. Crèches occur where ♀♀ tend young of several broods. Fledging takes 59–69 days. Nest abandonment rates high (23–89%), especially in dense colonies. Predation upon eggs and young hazard when nesting in association with gulls (Young and Titman 1986). Ducklings die of exposure within 7–10 days of hatching, accounting for up to 70% of losses at Lake Mývatn, Iceland; another 25% loss due to predation (Bengtson 1972b). Rates of predation, and mortality due to other factors, poorly understood for adults.

Believed to reach sexual maturity in 2 years (Dementiev and Gladkov 1952), but youngest ♀♀ exhibiting natal philopatry were 3 in New Brunswick. Oldest UK-ringed bird 12 years (Clark *et al.* 2002), and ♀ still bred at >8 years (Titman 1999).

Conservation and threats

Many breeding and winter habitats isolated from human activity, so exposed to little immediate threat. Elsewhere, persecuted where competing for fish. Almost 1200 mergansers, primarily Common Mergansers, removed from Miramichi River, New Brunswick, Canada, in 1954 (White 1957), but countless others shot illegally to 'protect' salmon and other fish stocks (Titman 1999). Accidental mortality also occurs in fishing nets. Although hunted, not sought after, and accounts for small proportion (0.13%) of ducks shot annually in US (Carney *et al.* 1983).

Rodger Titman

Scaly-sided Merganser *Mergus squamatus*
PLATE 28

Mergus squamatus Gould, 1864, Proc. Zool. Soc. London, p. 184

China

Etymology: *squamatus* L. means scaled.

Other names: Chinese Merganser. Chinese: Zhonghua qiushaya; Japanese: Kõrai-aisa; Russian: Cheshuychaty Krokhal.

Variation: no subspecies.

Description

ADULT: dimorphic. ♂ in alternate, or breeding, plumage, scapulars, neck and head black with long drooping double crest; breast and underparts white; flanks and mantle white, finely scaled black; rump and uppertail white, finely vermiculated dark grey (Buturlin 1935, Kolomiitsev 1995). Tail silvery grey. ♀ mantle and upperwings grey; throat and breast white; head and neck brown with long wispy brown crest; lores often noticeably darker brown; flanks white, characteristically scaled dark grey, retained throughout year (Hughes and Bocharnikov 1992, Kolomiitsev 1995). Tail silvery grey.

MOULT: in basic, or eclipse, plumage, ♂ resembles ♀, but retains black scapulars and more extensive white wing coverts. For timing, see later.

IMMATURE: similar to ♀, but has relatively darker head and upperparts with less extensive, paler scaling on flanks giving impression of sullied grey flanks at distance. Pale buffish white crescent below eye and line from bill to eye not present in adult ♀ (Hughes and Bocharnikov 1992). Juvenile ♂ may be separated from ♀ by paler upperwing coverts (Yelsukov 1994).

DUCKLING: has typical merganser downy plumage with reddish brown crown and upper cheeks fading into whitish cheeks (Larionov and Semashko 1955, Yelsukov 1994, Zhao *et al.* 1994b). Brown stripe below white lores, white spot above eye and white crescent under eye give cheeks striped appearance. Upperparts ash grey with brown tinge; paired white spots on shoulders and sides of rump. Underparts white.

MEASUREMENTS AND WEIGHT: data from various sources with small sample sizes (Buturlin 1935, Dementiev and Gladkov 1952, Vorobyev 1954, Dymin and Kostin 1977, Yelsukov 1994). ♂ wing, 250–265; tail, no data; culmen, 52–57; tarsus, 46–48. ♀ wing, 220–250; tail, 100–127; culmen, 'about' 45. Weight in Apr, ♂ ($n = 3$), 1125–1400 (1232); ♀ ($n = 3$), 870–1100 (956).

Field characters

Structurally intermediate between Goosander and Red-breasted Merganser (nearer latter), but both sexes separable by long droopy crest and distinctive scaly pattern on white flanks. ♂ has white breast, not red. Bill structure useful indicator, appearing long, straight and thicker than Red-breasted Merganser with paler yellowish white nail, and lacking downward protruding nail of Goosander (Hughes and Bocharnikov 1992). Nostrils located nearer centre of bill than in either Red-breasted Merganser or Goosander (Dementiev and Gladkov 1952, Vorobyev 1954). In flight, wing pattern similar to Red-breasted Merganser, but ♂ may have more white on upper lesser coverts, and ♀ has ash grey not brown-grey lesser and median coverts (Buturlin 1935). Breeds on upper stretches of rivers where Goosander, but not Red-breasted Merganser, occurs making identification more straightforward. As well as structural differences from Goosander, ♀ has less white in speculum, less russet head, darker grey mantle and wing coverts, and less well defined white throat patch (Hughes and Bocharnikov 1992). Juvenile similar to Goosander, but may be separated by paler buff-brown head, and buff-white, not whitish, crescent below eye and line from bill to eye.

Voice

Generally silent. ♀'s *kreck* alarm call is similar to Goosander, but neither so loud nor harsh. Both sexes utter quieter versions of this call when engaged in social interaction and courtship. While leading duck-lings from nest, ♀ utters muffled, murmuring, cooing *krr-krr-krr-krr-krr* call (Kolomiitsev 1992).

Range and status

World population estimated at 1200 breeding pairs (Bocharnikov 1990a) with 950–1000 in far east of Russia, remainder in northern China. Small numbers probably breed in North Korea. Russian birds located mainly south of 54°N on rivers on western slopes of Sikhote-Alin Mountains of Ussuriland, in Amur Basin between Zeya and Amgun Rivers, and in smaller numbers on eastern slopes of Sikhote-Alin (Roslyakov 1985, Mikhailov and Shibnyev 1998). Main breeding areas Bikin and Iman Rivers with estimated breeding populations of 200 and 140 pairs respectively (Bocharnikov and Shibnyev 1994, Sur-mach and Zaykin 1994). In China, breeds in Jilin province in Changbai Mountains (on Toudaibai, Sandaobai, and Gutong Rivers on northeast slopes, and on Mang River on southeast slopes) with smaller numbers in Greater and Lesser Xingan Mountains of Heilongjiang province (Zhao *et al.* 1993, 1994a).

In Russia, concentrations of moulting birds recorded in upper reaches of breeding rivers (Mikhailov and Shibnyev 1998), and along coasts of

Sea of Japan and Sea of Okhotsk (Kolomiitsev 1995). Occurs on migration at Khanka Lake on Russian–Chinese border, in China on Jingpo and Xiaobei Lakes in northeast Heilongjiang, and in North Korea on Chogchon River.

Major wintering sites largely undiscovered, but thought to be in southern and central China (Zhao *et al.* 1993, 1994a). Group of 100 found wintering in Xinjiang River, east of Poyang Lake in north-eastern Jiangxi province in 1999. Small numbers also winter in southwest South Korea, Japan and Taiwan. Vagrants recorded from Tibet, Thailand, Vietnam and Myanmar (Burma) (Dementiev 1933, Vaurie 1972, Vo Quy 1983, Brazil 1991).

Habitat and general habits

Encountered throughout year in small groups < 10, especially during breeding season when highly ter-ritorial. When breeding, both sexes actively defend territory, *c* 200–300 m around riverside nest site, against other Scaly-sided Mergansers, Goosanders and species such as Carrion Crows *Corvus corone* (Kolomiitsev 1992). Territory size varies from 500–600 m of river (Kolomiitsev 1992) to 3–4 km (Bocharnikov and Shibnyev 1994). Once ♀ incubat-ing, ♂ joins groups of 10–25 before migrating to moulting areas. Flocks of < 80 recorded during autumn migration (Surmach and Zaykin 1994).

Breeds on middle and upper reaches of rivers in mixed deciduous–coniferous forest, characterized in Russia by White-barked Elm *Ulmus propinqua*, Black Pine *Pinus koraiensis*, Lime *Tilia amurensis*, and Max-imovitch Poplar *Populus maximoviczii* (Bocharnikov and Shibnyev 1994), and in China by Daimyo Oak *Quercus dentata*, Black Pine, Lime and Linden Poplar *Populus ussuriensis* (Zhao *et al.* 1995). Region has maritime climate with cold dry winters and warm wet summers. Rivers usually frozen Oct–Mar and temperatures regularly reach −25°C. Preferred rivers typically clear and fast-flowing, with many shingle spits and islands, banks covered with dense under-growth under primary forest and with little human habitation. On Bikin River, replaced by Goosanders on upper stretches (Mikhailov *et al.* 1997).

Feeds diurnally mainly on small fish and aquatic invertebrates. Foraging technique varies according

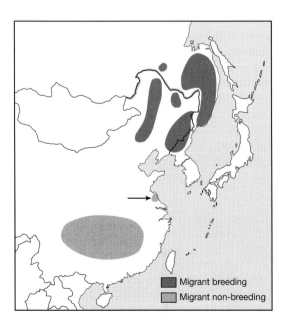

Migrant breeding
Migrant non-breeding

to water depth; in shallow water, usually only head immersed while, in deeper water, dives for food. On breeding rivers, most feeding occurs in shallow water (<1 m deep) close to river bank, probably because food more abundant there (Kolomiitsev 1992, Zhao and Pao 1998, Solovieva 2002). In China, 10 dives ranged 15–30 sec with associated inter-dive intervals of 3–5 sec (Zhao and Pao 1998). During breeding season in China, spends 14–15 h per day feeding (Zhao *et al.* 1994b, 1995), from first light at 03.00 h until dusk at 18.00–19.00 h. Foraging usually interspersed with shorter periods of sleeping, loafing, preening or bathing. Also some aggressive behaviour and social interaction. Most communal behaviour occurs at midday and evening.

Opportunist feeders, selecting most abundant food depending on habitat, time of year and seasonal distribution of prey. On Bikin River, feeds on 8 main fish species: Amur Minnow *Phoxinus lagowskii*, Grayling *Thymallus arcticus*, Lenok *Brachymystax lenok*, Gudgeon, trout, Northern Pike, Chebak and Weather Loach *Misgurnus anguillicaudatus* (Bocharnikov and Shibnyev 1994). In upper reaches of Bikin, predominant food is fry of Grayling, Lenok, Minnow, Chebak and Loach; in middle reaches, is Minnow, Gudgeon, Loach, and fry of Chebak. Other fish taken elsewhere in Primorye include Masu Salmon *Oncorhyncus masou*, Dolly Varden Char *Salvelinus malma*, Stone Loach *Nemachilus barbatulus*, Spotted Sculpin *Cottus poecilopus* and Chub *Leuciscus brandtii* (Labzyuk 1988, Semyenchenko and Yermolenko 1988, Kolomiitsev 1992). May undertake daily morning and evening feeding trips to river mouths when Smelt *Osmerus eperlanus dentex*, Pond Smelt *Hypomesus olidus* and capelin *Mallotus* spawn (Kolomiitsev 1992).

In China on Toudaibai River, feeds on stonefly *Plecoptera* larvae, caddisfly *Phryganeidae* larvae, beetles *Coleoptera*, shrimps, crayfish, Lamprey *Lampetra morii*, Loach, Lenok, Amur Sculpin *Mesocottus haitej* and Grayling (Zhao and Pao 1998). Diet changes from predominantly caddisfly larvae in June–July (90% of diet), to small fish, shrimps and crayfish after caddis emergence in Aug. In Sept, take mainly fish fry which then become more abundant. Thought to feed in winter on large rivers and lakes, although minority may remain on unfrozen sections of Chinese breeding rivers (Zhao *et al.* 1994b, 1995).

Displays and breeding behaviour

Not documented until recently (Kolomiitsev 1992, Yelsukov 1994, Zhao *et al.* 1994b). Courtship appears to be more like Goosander than Red-breasted Merganser, and involves both sexes performing variety of synchronized behaviours, such as swimming in Alert posture, Head-nodding or Head-tossing, Neck-stretching, Wing-flapping and Diving. Kolomiitsev (1992) described reciprocal diving courtship in which one partner dives as soon as other appears on water surface. Aggression frequent, with underwater attacks common, and ♀ often Incites mate by lunging or pecking at him. Also much aggressive interaction between ♂♂, often resulting in dominant ♂ winning favours of more than one ♀. During copulation, ♂ grasps crest of ♀ with bill and post-copulatory displays may be aggressive or include preening.

Yelsukov (1994) described courtship and copulation thus: 'the female and male alternately stretched their necks up and slightly forwards, swam towards each other with their tails raised then swam in ellipses of radius 1–1.5 m. The birds' movements were slow, synchronized and accompanied by head-nodding. The birds moved nearer to each other after each circular movement and immediately continued swimming. This behaviour continued for approximately 15 minutes. From time to time, the male stopped and preened his throat. Then the character of the birds' movement changed: they swam in a straight line away from each other at the same speed for approximately 1.5 m before turning and heading back towards each other. They met half-way and began to copulate. During copulation, which lasted several seconds, the male held onto the female's crest after which the male began to swim away while the female briefly pursued him, stretching her neck forward in a threatening posture. When the female's aggressive behaviour had finished the male returned. Female then stood up out of the water, flapped her wings and dipped her head into the water four times. Male shook his tail and both birds swam to the shore, male in front'. Mating system combination of monogamy and polygamy

(Kolomiitsev 1992), with trios of ♂ & 2 ♀♀ comprising up to 20% of breeding units in Far East Russia (Shokhrin and Solovieva 2003). Pair formation takes place before or just after arrival, and ♂ remains with mate until 1st week of incubation, then leaves to complete moult, either in upper reaches of breeding rivers or on coast (Yelsukov 1994, Kolomiitsev 1995, Mikhailov *et al.* 1997, Mikhailov and Shibnyev 1998).

Breeding and life cycle

Arrives on breeding grounds in both Russia and China late Mar–early Apr as rivers begin to thaw (Kolomiitsev 1992, Bocharnikov and Shibnyev 1994, Yelsukov 1994, Zhao *et al.* 1994b, 1995). Nests exclusively in holes in poplar, elm, oak, etc. (Kolomiitsev 1992, Bocharnikov and Shibnyev 1994, Yelsukov 1994, Zhao *et al.* 1994b, 1995). Nest holes usually in trees on river bank, but may be up to 120 m away. Holes typically 150–250 mm wide and 200–600 mm tall, while nest hollows 200–300 mm in diameter and 400–1200 mm deep. Nests lined with pale grey down which appears at start of egg-laying and reaches maximum density as incubation begins. When ♀ approached on nest, most leave quickly, but few puff out plumage, open bills, and hiss and snort as do Goosanders. Artificial sites, including nestboxes, used readily. ♀ may nest in close proximity to roads and human habitation, but densities lower on populated than unpopulated stretches of river (Surmach and Zaykin 1994). ♀ reported site-faithful between years in both China and Russia, especially if nesting successful (Kolomiitsev 1992, Zhao *et al.* 1994b). Young, nonbreeding ♀♀ may prospect for nest site once ♂♂ have left river, and recorded entering nest holes occupied by other mergansers and even Oriental Scops Owl *Otus sunia*.

Egg-laying begins 1st week of Apr and most eggs laid by end Apr. Eggs creamy white and indistinguishable from other large mergansers. Measurements of 89 eggs from 19 clutches on Kiyevka River 62.7 × 44.7 (56.7–67.5 × 42.8–46.8) (Kolomiitsev 1992). Clutch size 10–11 (7–14), only one clutch per year, although ♀ will re-nest if clutch lost early. Eggs laid at rate of 1 per 36 h, so 15–16 days taken to lay full clutch (Kolomiitsev 1992). Incubation, by ♀ alone, 32 days. Most ♀♀ (80%) on Kiyevka River took 2 incubation recesses, in early morning and late afternoon; ♀♀ taking single recess did so around midday. Total time spent off nest declines as incubation progresses, from *c* 95 to *c* 50 mins daily, with nest recesses declining from 50 to 20 mins. During recesses, eggs covered with nest down.

Broods hatch mainly in June; ducklings remain in nest 48–60 h while ♀ stays with them. Two newly hatched ducklings measured, wing, 34 and 34; culmen, 15.0 and 15.8; tarsus, 24.0 and 26.4; weight, 31.3 and 45.0. Hatching success on Kiyevka high (90% of 178 eggs from 17 clutches), with infertility and addling main causes of failure. Ducklings leave nest in early morning, jumping to ground after being coaxed from hole by ♀ calls. Mean brood sizes reported as 9.8 (*n* = 102) at fledging; 8.0 (*n* = 41), 7.7 (*n* = 43) and 7.1 (*n* = 15) in June; 6.2 (*n* = 65) and 4.7 (*n* = 11) in July; and 7.0 (*n* = 44) in Aug (Bocharnikov *et al.* 1991, Hughes and Bocharnikov 1992, Kolomiitsev 1992, Yelsukov 1994). Breeding densities in 1980s and 90s reported as 1.0–8.3 broods per 10 km (Iman River, Surmach and Zaykin 1994), 3.3 pairs per 10 km (Bikin River, Bocharnikov 1990), 1.3–1.7 broods per 10 km (Bikin River, Shibnyev 1985), 0.4–3.8 pairs per 10 km (Kiyevka River, Kolomiitsev 1985), and 1.1 pairs per 10 km (Avvakumovka River, Kolomiitsev 1985).

Brood amalgamation common, and ♀ often reported with up to 30 unfledged ducklings (Bocharnikov 1990). Fledging occurs Aug at *c* 8 weeks, and most birds migrate from breeding grounds mid Sept-mid Oct. ♀♀ breeding on rivers in northeastern Sikhote-Alin may move broods to sea (Yelsukov 1994). In Russia, moulting ♂♂ seen in upper Bikin River, and along coasts of Seas of Japan and Okhotsk. ♂ begins moult mid-Apr while still on breeding river. Scaly flank feathers shed first, followed by head, neck and body feathers (Kolomiitsev 1995). Nonbreeding, year-old ♂ and ♀ moult at *c* same time as adult ♂, with ♀ becoming flightless mid July while still accompanying brood.

♀ starts to breed in 3rd year. No information on adult survival.

Conservation and threats

World population recognized as Endangered by IUCN (2003), having undergone significant, yet poorly documented, declines in Russia and China. Predation by introduced North American Mink recorded as source of mortality, but other threats numerous.

On Bikin River since 1980s, numbers of breeders more than halved due to logging, hunting, human disturbance, pollution and silting up of shallow waters caused by industrial installations on upper reaches of river (Shibnyev 1985, Mikhailov and Shibnyev 1998). Logging most serious long-term threat, with commercial logging throughout much of middle reaches of Bikin catchment expected to result in major hydrological changes to river system (Mikhailov and Shibnyev 1998). Illegal hunting also common on Bikin, > 100 thought shot annually (Hughes and Bocharnikov 1992), majority being adults returning to breed in spring. Has disappeared from 2 major tributaries of Iman River (Kolumbe and Dalnyaya) which are polluted from gold mining and ore extraction, respectively, in upper reaches (Surmach and Zaykin 1994). Logging not threat on Iman, as 5 km buffer forest belt along river in which commercial logging prohibited, but timber-rafting was major source of disturbance until 1988. Disturbance from pleasure rafting increasing problem on Armu tributary. Far most serious threat on Iman is proposed construction of hydroelectric dam which would flood 25% of current breeding range.

Drowning in fishing nets causes mortality throughout Primorye. Up to 20% of young die this way on rivers on eastern slopes of Sikhote-Alin mountains (Kolomiitsev 1986, Yelsukov 1994). Disturbance from river traffic and human settlements increasing as human populations expand into breeding range. Few pairs now breed in middle reaches of Bikin River because of high level of disturbance (Bocharnikov 1990). Rivers on eastern slopes of Sikhote-Alin similarly affected.

While some authors suggest Mandarins compete for nest sites (Zhao *et al.* 1994b, 1995), competition with Goosanders represents more serious possibility. Goosanders are expanding range in far east of Russia, including on Bikin and Iman Rivers (Hughes and Bocharnikov 1992, Surmach and Zaykin 1994), and will likely compete for food and nesting holes. Competition for food with Great Cormorants *Phalacrocorax carbo* suggested, although this may not be serious as cormorants tend to take larger fish (Russell *et al.* 1996). Decline continues over much of range, despite full protection in all range states. Species protection in isolation is not working; habitat protection and reduction in hunting pressure required urgently. Reserve areas need establishment in remaining breeding strongholds on Bikin and Iman Rivers in Russia (Bocharnikov and Shibnyev 1994, Surmach and Zaykin 1994, Mikhailov and Shibnyev 1998) and on Toudaibai, Sandaobai, and Gutong Rivers in China (Zhao *et al.* 1993). Buffer zones along rivers' edges, such as on Iman, provide ideal model for protecting breeding sites. As readily takes to nestboxes (Kolomiitsev 1992), provision of artificial cavities will be appropriate in areas where cavity shortage limiting. Identification of key wintering sites and standardized monitoring of breeding populations crucial research requirements.

Baz Hughes

Glossary

accidental a stray outside its normal range

afrotropical the geographical region of sub-Saharan Africa, excluding Madagascar

air sacs thin-walled reservoirs, extensions of the bronchi in birds' lungs, that act as 'bellows' to provide tidal air flow during respiration; particularly obvious in screamers

allopatric two or more species whose ranges do not overlap

allopreening the preening of one individual by another, common in whistling-ducks and Andean Geese

alternate plumage the breeding, or nuptial, plumage of wildfowl that have more than one annual change of feathering

alula the 'bastard wing' on the first digit or thumb, to which are attached a few small quill feathers. Used by some diving ducks in swimming underwater

aquatic associated with water

arboreal tree-living

austral southern

axilla the 'arm-pit'

basic plumage the plumage worn year-round in species with a single annual body moult; in ducks, it is the name given to the nonbreeding dull plumage usually worn during wing moult

benthic living beneath the water surface and on, or in, the bottom substrate

Bergmann's rule that among polymorphic species, body size tends to be larger in cooler parts of the range and smaller in warmer parts

brood parasitism the habit of laying eggs in the nests of others in order that they may be incubated and reared by another species, as in the case of the Black-headed Duck. *See* egg-dumping

boreal northern; usually refers to the climatic region immediately south of the Arctic, including the forest zone of the northern temperate latitudes

bottleneck an impediment by constriction; as a genetic term, used when a reduction in population size reduces variability in the genetic make-up of that population. In a nutritional sense, birds face periods (such as overwinter) when food is scarce, and this may cause a nutritional bottleneck

bulla(e) a bulbous extension, particularly common in the syrinx of male ducks

caruncles small protuberances of the skin of the head or upper neck, common in the Muscovy Duck, especially in domesticated forms

Cenozoic the most recent era of geological time, divided into the Tertiary (approximately 66.4 to 1.6 million years ago) and the Quarternary Periods (1.6 million ago to today)

cere bare fleshy covering, often coloured, at the base of the bill, as in Cape Barren Geese

clade a group of organisms evolved from a common ancestor (from Greek for 'a branch')

cladistics a sytem of biological classification based on the phylogenetic relationships and evolutionary history of groups of organisms

cline a sequence of small differences that grade over the geographical range of a species, as in the bill patterns of Whooper Swans

cloaca the end of the bird's gut through which faeces are passed and eggs are laid

comb an unfeathered projection at the base of the bill and the forehead, as in comb ducks

congeneric species, or 'congeners', belonging to the same genus

conspecific races or subspecies belonging to the same species

courtship behaviour that leads to pairing (the establishment of a pairbond), copulation and reproduction. *See* display

coverts small feathers that cover the flight feathers, tail feathers or the external ear openings

crèche a gathering of young of more than one brood, especially of eiders and shelducks

Cretaceous the third and last period of the Mesozoic geological era (approximately 144 to 66.4 million years ago)

culmen the ridge along the upper bill, from the feathers of the head to the bill tip

dimorphic occurring in two forms, usually used here to mean that male and female have different plumages

display ritualized behaviour, often derived from feeding or preening, used in communication, and typically in courtship. Genetically determined and thus similar in all individuals of a species

distal furthest from, at the end of, terminal; usually used in relation to the body

diurnal active during the day

dominance hierarchy the social order within a group. One sex may dominate the other, and adults usually dominate immatures

downy young young wildfowl up to three weeks, or so, of age and covered in down

dubh-lochan small peaty pools and other surface features characteristic of oceanic blanket mire vegetation ('black pool' in Scottish Gaelic)

Eclipse a dull, juvenile-like, basic plumage assumed by many male ducks of dimorphic species at the end of the courting season. It is often of shorter duration than the alternate, courtship plumage

eclipse plumage dull inconspicuous female-like or juvenile-like, basic plumage acquired by many male ducks after courtship and breeding

ectoparasite an external parasite, such as lice or ticks, living on the skin, scales or plumage

egg dumping the laying of eggs in the nests of other members of the same or related species. *See* brood parasitism

endemic restricted to a particular locality

endoparasite an external parasite of the gut or body cavity, often a nematode worm

endogenous produced from within the body

Eocene the second epoch of the Tertiary geological period (approximately 57.8 to 36.6 million years ago)

ephemeral lasting only for a short time

eutrophic waters rich in mineral and organic nutrients that promote a proliferation of plant life, especially algae. In some systems (usually human-induced), algal growth reduces dissolved oxygen

exotic a plant or animal that is not native to an area

extralimital outside normal limits of range

extra-pair copulation copulation between male and female that do not have an established pairbond

feral domesticated species, such as cats, dogs, buffalo and Muscovies, living in the wild

fledging period time between hatching and first flight

flight feathers primary and secondary wing quills, sometimes including tail quills

flyway the entire geographical range occupied by a species throughout the year, including the major routes used on migration

fossil an impression of a long-dead plant or animal that has been preserved in stone

fulvous a brownish orange colour

genotype the group to which an individual belongs because of its genetic constitution

genus (genera) a classification that groups a number of related species, and indicated by the first word of a scientific name, e.g., *Anas*

granivorous grain and seed eating

hallux the first toe, pointing backwards and usually small, but large in screamers and Magpie Geese, and lobed in diving ducks

Holarctic the northern region that includes the Palearctic plus the Nearctic

Holocene the second and most recent epoch of the Quaternary geological period (the last 10 000 years), marked by the development of human culture

homologous similar in structure, function or form

hybrid used here to mean an individual whose parents were of different species

Hybrid swarm a hybrid population that is geographically isolated and out of genetic contact with its parent forms

immature a bird that is not yet sexually mature

imprinting attachment to an individual, usually the parent of a young duck, goose or swan, as a result of exposure to that individual during the first hours after hatching

incertae sedis a species of uncertain evolutionary relationship

intromittent organ *see* phallus

Jizz the impression that a bird gives of its specific identification in a combination of its size, colour, shape and movement

Jurassic the second period of the Mesozoic (approximately 208 to 144 million years ago), when birds first appear in the fossil record

juvenile or juvenal an individual in first plumage after the downy stage

k-**strategist** an animal that exhibits rather stable population trends (such as a swan), with a large body, small clutch size and relatively long life span

kleptoparasite an animal that steals food from others

lek communal display area where, in the breeding season, males display and compete, mating with as many females as possible, as in the Musk Duck

leucistic an absence of pigment in the plumage or skin; an individual that is white or pale in colour

Linneaus the Latinized version of the name of the Swedish botanist Carl von Linné (1707–78) who first defined and classified plants and animals, and gave them two-part names based on classic Latin or Greek. For example, the full scientific name for the Northern Mallard is *Anas platyrhynchos* Linneaus 1758, indicating that it was described first by Linneaus in a publication of the year 1758

lobe a fold of skin that, in the Musk Duck, hangs beneath the bill

loral the region between the bill and the eye

macrophyte a large (rather than microscopic) plant

mantle the upper part of the back

maxilla the maxillary area consists of the facial bones and the horny covering of the upperpart of the bill

melanistic an excess of melanin pigment producing strong black feathers, as in the primaries of Snow Geese, or an individual that is darker than normal

mitochondrial DNA genetic material, within the mitochondria of cells, that offspring (both male and female) inherit from their mother

Miocene the fourth epoch of the Tertiary geological period (approximately 23.7 to 5.3 million years ago)

molecular pertaining to molecules; usually used in relation to the analysis of DNA

muskeg Cree (native American) word for swamp, bog or marsh

monogamy breeding of one male and one female who remain together, more or less exclusively, for at least one season

monotypic a classified group that contains a single species

morphology the study of physical characters such as shape and form

moult the shedding and replacement of feathers. In wildfowl, often refers to the wing moult when all primary and secondary feathers are shed simultaneously and the bird is flightless

natal at birth

Nearctic the geographical region of North America

Neogene the geological period that includes the Miocene and Pliocene epochs of the Tertiary

Neotropics the tropical region of South and Central America

New World the region of the Americas

nidifugous leaving the nest soon after hatching

nocturnal active mainly at night

nomadic movement, or migration, that is not regular and seasonal

nominate race the first-named of a number of subspecies, with its third (or trinomial) name

being the same as its specific name, as in the Whistling Swan *Cygnus columbianus columbianus*

nuchal of the nape; the area between the crown and the hindneck

nuptial of the breeding season

occipital of the occiput; the angle at the rear of the head

ocular of the eye

Old World every geographical region except the Americas

Oligocene the third epoch of the Tertiary geological period (approximately 36.6 to 23.7 million years ago)

oligotrophic nutrient-poor; such waters are usually not much frequented by wildfowl except as roosts

omnivorous a generalist feeder, eating both animal and plant material

ossified becoming bony

Paleocene the earliest epoch of the Tertiary geological period (approximately 66.4 to 57.8 million years ago)

Paleogene the geological period that includes the Paleocene, Eocene and Oligocene epochs of the Tertiary

Palearctic the geographical region that includes Greenland, Eurasia and North Africa

phallus the male organ for the transfer of sperm to the female's cloaca. In wildfowl, the phallus is intromittent; erection is caused by engorgement with lymph, rather than blood; it is protruded by the action of a muscle and retracted by an elastic spiral ligament

philopatry fidelity to a particular area that may be a breeding, moulting or wintering site

photoperiodism the response to changes in the relative length of day and night

photorefractory a bird that is refractory (stops breeding) in response to long days

phylogeny the study of evolutionary relationships

Pipped hatching eggs showing the first cracks in the shell are said to be pipped or pipping

Pleistocene the first epoch of the Quarternary geological period (approximately 1.6 million years ago to 10 000 years ago)

Pliocene the fifth and last epoch of the Tertiary (approximately 5.3 to 1.6 million years ago)

polygamy breeding systems other than monogamy, where either sex has more than one partner

polygyny a system where a male mates with more than one female, as in the Magpie Goose

polymorphism occurring in more than one size, form or colour, as in the goslings of Ross's Geese

polynia areas of open sea in otherwise continuous sea-ice, usually the result of warm water influences or strong up-wellings (from the Russian word for a place that does not freeze)

prairie the grassy steppes of North America, approximately between 30° N and 55° N

precocial active, and usually self-feeding, soon after hatching

primaries the large flight feathers that originate from the region of the 'hand' or carpometacarpus bone at the tip of the wing

proximal nearest or closest, usually in relation to the body

proximate factor the factor that triggers an immediate response

quarry species birds that can be hunted by humans, usually legally

*r***-strategist** animals that reproduce rapidly, and have relatively small bodies, large clutch sizes and short lives

race *see* subspecies

retrices the tail quills

remiges the primary and secondary wing quills

ritualized a behaviour pattern whose original function (preening or feeding, for instance) has changed, and now evokes a response from another individual, usually during display

savanna open grassland, usually tropical or subtropical

sawbill a common name for the merganser group that refers to the serrated edge of their bills

scapulars the feathers on the shoulders

secondaries flight feathers that derive from the region of the ulna bone, the central part of the wing

secondary coverts contour feathers that cover the secondary wing feathers

semi-palmate having partially webbed feet, as in the Hawaiian Goose

sexual selection arises from the advantage that some individuals have over others of the same sex and species in competing for a mate. This may result in the development of extravagant sexual characters that are directly detrimental to survival, but beneficial to mating success (perhaps an explanation for the bright plumages of male ducks)

single-brooded making only one nesting attempt in a season

skin often used here to mean an eviscerated and preserved dead bird, used for study, that may be stuffed and mounted in a lifelike pose

sonogram calls rendered visible on paper in the form of a graph, with pitch expressed in kiloHertz on the vertical axis and time in seconds on the horizontal axis

species a population that interbreeds freely but not usually with members of other species

speculum a glossy coloured area on the secondaries of dabbling ducks and shelducks

spur conical bony projection at the 'wrist' (the carpal joint) of the wing, common in territorial wildfowl and screamers, and used in threat and fighting

stiff-tailed ducks common name for the tribe that includes the *Oxyura* ducks

subadult a bird in an immature feathering that follows the first plumage, but not yet adult

subcutaneous the area immediately beneath the skin

subfossil the ancient remains of a plant or animal that have not yet turned to stone

subspecies or race a subdivision of a species

supercilium a marking or stripe above the eye, which may also be described as supraorbital

sympatric two or more species whose ranges overlap within the same geographical area

syrinx (syringeal) the organ of voice, found at the bifurcation of the windpipe

tarsus the 'leg' of a bird. Widely but incorrectly so called, as the bone is actually the tarsometatarsus and approximately equivalent to the main bones of the human foot (birds walk on tip-toe). Often ringed for identification purposes

taxon (taxa) general term for any category used in classification

taxonomy the study of classification and evolutionary relationships

territory a defended area, often containing a nest site

tertials the innermost secondaries that arise from the region of the humerus bone, and which, in ducks, may be different in shape and colour from the other flight feathers

trachea the windpipe

tribe a taxonomic grouping of wildfowl genera

type locality the place where the type specimen was collected

type specimen or holotype the individual bird, usually preserved as a skin, from which a species received its first description and scientific name

ultimate factor factors that are remotely causative but do not lead immediately to an effect

uncinate processes projections found on several of the ribs of most birds, except screamers, giving attachment to some trunk muscles and ligaments, and presumably serving to strengthen the chest wall

up-ending feeding by tipping forward so that the head, neck and front part of body are submerged, and the rear end sticks up

vagrant rare or irregular in occurrence

vasculation with an enhanced blood supply, as in a brood patch

vent equivalent to the anus, the external opening of the cloaca

vermiculation(s) narrow lines or bars on the plumage, often wavy

wattle bare folds of skin, sometimes coloured, around the angle of the mouth or neck, as in the Spur-winged Goose

web skin between the toes, important in providing thrust for diving ducks under water. *See* semi-palmated

wing bar light coloured band or stripe across the secondary and/or primary wing feathers, especially of pochards and scaup

wing loading the area of the wing relative to the weight of the body

wing spur *see* spur

yearling an immature bird in its second year of life

zoogeography the description of, and explanation for, the distributions of extinct and living animals.

References

Aarvak, T. and Øien, I.J. 1994. Dverggås *Anser erythropus*—en truet art i Norge. *Vår Fuglefauna* 17: 70–80.

Aarvak, T. and Øien, I.J. 2003. Moult and autumn migration of non-breeding Fennoscandian Lesser White-fronted Geese *Anser erythropus* mapped by satellite telemetry. *Bird Conservation International* 13: 213–226.

Aarvak, T., Øien, I.J. and Nagy, S. 1996. *The Lesser White-fronted Goose monitoring programme, Ann. Rept. 1996*, NOF Rappportserie, No. 7. Norwegian Ornithological Society, Klaebu.

Aarvak, T., Øien, I.J., Syroechkovski Jr., E.E. and Kostadinova, I. 1997. *The Lesser White-fronted Goose Monitoring Programme. Annual Report 1997.* Klæbu, Norwegian Ornithological Society. NOF Raportserie, Report no. 5-1997.

Abbott, C.C. 1861. Notes on the birds of the Falkland Islands. *Ibis* 1: 149–67.

Abraham, K.F. 1980. Moult migration of Lesser Snow Geese. *Wildfowl* 31: 89–93.

Abraham, K.F. and Jefferies, R.L. 1997. High goose populations: causes, impacts and implications. In *Arctic ecosystems in peril: report of the Arctic Goose Habitat Working Group*, Arctic Goose Joint Venture Spec. Publ. (ed. B.D.J. Batt), pp.7–72. U.S. Fish & Wildl. Serv., Washington, and Can. Wildl. Serv., Ottawa.

Abraham, R.I. 1974. Vocalizations of the Mallard (*Anas platyrhynchos*). *Condor* 76: 401–20.

Adair, S.E., Moore, J.L. and Kiel, W.H. Jr 1996. Wintering diving duck use of coastal ponds: an analysis of alternative hypotheses. *J. Wildl. Manage.* 60: 83–93.

Adams, J. and Slavid, E.R. 1984. Cheek plumage pattern in Colombian Ruddy Duck *Oxyura jamaicensis*. *Ibis* 126: 405–07.

Adams, J.S. 1971. Black Swan at Lake Ellesmere. *Wildl. Rev.* 3: 23–25.

Adams, P.A., Robertson, G.J. and Jones, I.L. 2000. Time-activity budgets of Harlequin Ducks molting in the Gannet Islands, Labrador. *Condor* 102: 703–08.

Adrian, W.L., Spraker, T.R. and Davies, R.B. 1978. Epornitics of aspergillosis in Mallards *Anas platyrhynchos* in north central Colorado. *J. Wildl. Dis.* 14: 212–17.

AEWA 2000. Report on the conservation status of migratory waterbirds in the agreement area. *Technical Series No. 1.* Wetlands International, Wageningen, Netherlands.

Afton, A.D. 1983. Male and female strategies for reproduction in Lesser Scaup. Unpubl. Ph.D. thesis. Univ. North Dakota, Grand Forks, US.

Afton, A.D. 1984. Influence of age and time on reproductive performance of female Lesser Scaup. *Auk* 101: 255–65.

Afton, A.D. 1985. Forced copulation as a reproductive strategy of male Lesser Scaup: a field test of some predictions. *Behaviour* 92: 146–67.

Afton, A.D. 1993. Post-hatch brood amalgamation in Lesser Scaup: female behavior and return rates, and duckling survival. *Prairie Nat.* 25: 227–35.

Afton, A.D. and Ankney, C.D. 1991. Nutrient-reserve dynamics of breeding Lesser Scaup: a test of competing hypotheses. *Condor* 93: 89–97.

Afton, A.D. and Hier, R.H. 1991. Diets of Lesser Scaup breeding in Manitoba. *J. Field Ornithol.* 62: 325–34.

Afton, A.D. and Paulus, S.L. 1992. Incubation and brood care. In *The ecology and management of breeding waterfowl* (ed. B.D.J. Batt, A.D. Afton, M.G. Anderson, C.D. Ankney, D.H. Johnson, J.A. Kadlec *et al.*), pp.62–108. Univ. Minnesota Press, Minneapolis.

Afton, A.D. and Sayler, R.D. 1982. Social courtship and pair bonding of Common Goldeneyes, *Bucephala clangula*, wintering in Minnesota. *Can. Field-Nat.* 96: 295–300.

Afton, A.D., Heir, R.H. and Paulus, S.L. 1991. Lesser Scaup diets during migration and winter in the Mississippi Flyway. *Can. J. Zool.* 69: 328–33.

Albertsen, J.O. and Kanazawa, Y. 2002. Numbers and ecology of swans wintering in Japan. In *Proceedings of the Fourth International Swan Symposium, 2001* (ed. E.C. Rees, S.L. Earnst and J. Coulson), *Waterbirds* 25. Special Publication 1: 74–85.

Alder, L.P. 1963. The calls and displays of African and Indian Cotton Pygmy Geese. *Wildfowl* 14: 174–75.

Aldrich, J.W. 1946. Speciation in the white-cheeked geese. *Wilson Bull.* 58(2): 94–103.

Aldrich, J.W. and Baer, K.P. 1970. Status and speciation in the Mexican Duck (*Anas diazi*). *Wilson Bull.* 82: 63–73.

Alerstam, T. 1981. The course and timing of bird migration. In *Animal migration*, S.E.B. Seminar Ser., No. 13 (ed. D.J. Aidley), pp.9–54. Cambridge Univ. Press.

Alerstam, T. 1990. *Bird migration*. Cambridge Univ. Press.

Alerstam, T. and Hogstedt, G. 1981. Evolution of hole-nesting in birds. *Ornis Scand.* 12: 188–93.

Alerstam, T., Bauer, C-A. and Roos, G. 1974. Spring migration of Eiders *Somateria mollissima* in southern Scandinavia. *Ibis* 116: 194–210.

Alerstam, T., Gudmundsson, G.A., Junssen, P.E., Karlsson, J. and Lindstrom, A. 1991. Orientation, migration routes and flight behaviour of Knots, Turnstones and Brent Geese departing from Iceland in spring. *Arctic* 43: 201–14.

Alexander, W.C. 1980a. The behavioral ecology and sociobiology of nonbreeding diving ducks (Aythyini). Unpubl. Ph.D. thesis. Clemson Univ., S. Carolina, US.

Alexander, W.C. 1980b. Aggressive displays in non-breeding Canvasbacks. *Auk* 97: 198–201.

Alexander, W.C. 1983. Differential sex distributions of wintering diving ducks (Aythyini) in North America. *Am. Birds* 37: 26–29.

Alexander, W.C. 1987. Aggressive behavior of diving ducks (Aythyini). *Wilson Bull.* 99: 38–49.

Alferaki, S.N. 1904. *Gussi Rossyi*. Kuschnerew, Moscow.

Ali, S. 1960. The Pink-headed Duck *Rhodonessa caryophyllacea* (Latham). *Wildfowl* 11: 55–60.

Ali, S. and Ripley, S.D. 1987. *Compact handbook of the birds of India and Pakistan together with those of Bangladesh, Nepal, Bhutan and Sri Lanka* (2nd edn). OUP.

Alisauskas, R.T. 1992. *Distribution and abundance of geese in the Queen Maud Gulf Sanctuary.* Can. Wildl. Serv., Saskatoon.

Alisauskas, R.T. and Ankney, C.D. 1992. The cost of egg-laying and its relationship to nutrient reserves in waterfowl. In *The ecology and management of breeding waterfowl* (ed. B.D.J. Batt, A.D. Afton, M.G. Anderson, C.D. Ankney, D.H. Johnson, J.A. Kadlec *et al.*), pp.30–61. Univ. Minnesota Press, Minneapolis.

Alisauskas, R.T. and Ankney, C.D. 1994a. Costs and rates of egg formation in Ruddy Ducks. *Condor* 96: 11–18.

Alisauskas, R.T. and Ankney, C.D. 1994b. Nutrition of breeding female Ruddy Ducks: the role of nutrient reserves. *Condor* 96: 879–97.

Alisauskas, R.T. and Boyd, H. 1994. Previously unrecorded colonies of Ross' and Lesser Snow Geese in the Queen Maud Gulf Bird Sanctuary. *Arctic* 47: 69–73.

Alisauskas, R.T., Ankney, C.D. and Klaas, E.E. 1988. Winter diets and nutrition of midcontinental Lesser Snow Geese. *J. Wildl. Manage.* 52: 403–14.

Alison, R.M. 1975. Breeding biology and behavior of the Oldsquaw (*Clangula hyemalis* L.). *Ornithol. Monogr.* 18: 1–52.

Alison, R.M. 1976. Oldsquaw brood behavior. *Bird-Banding* 47: 210–13.

Alison, R.M. 1977. Homing of subadult Oldsquaws. *Auk* 94: 383–84.

Allen, G.M. 1905. Summer birds of the Bahamas. *Auk* 22: 113–33.

Allen, R.P. 1961. *Birds of the Caribbean*. Viking Press, New York.

Alliston, W.G. 1975. Web-tagging ducklings in pipped eggs. *J. Wildl. Manage.* 39: 625–28.

Alliston, W.G. 1979. Renesting by the Redhead Duck. *Wildfowl* 30: 40–44.

Allport, G., Poole, C.M, Park, E.M., Jo, S.R. and Eldridge, M.J. 1991. The feeding ecology, requirements and distribution of Baikal Teal (*Anas formosa*) in the Republic of Korea. *Wildfowl* 42: 98–107.

Altmann, J. 1974. Observational study of behavior: sampling methods. *Behaviour* 49: 227–67.

Alvarez, R. and Olson, S.L. 1978. A new merganser from the Miocene of Argentina. *Proc. Biological Society of Washington* 91: 522–32.

AMA 1991. Evolución de la población ibérica de Malvasía (*Oxyura leucocephala*). In *Plan rector de uso y gestión de las reservas naturales de las lagunas de Cádiz* (ed. M. Jesús Martos and J. Fernández Palacios), pp.145–51. Agencia de Medio Ambiente, Córdoba.

AMA 1995. International technical meeting on *Oxyura leucocephala* and *Oxyura jamaicensis* in the Palearctic region: conclusions and recommendations. Agencia de Medio Ambiente, Córdoba.

Amadon, D. 1949. The seventy-five percent rule for subspecies. *Condor* 51: 250–58.

Amat, J.A. 1982. The nesting biology of ducks in the Marismas of the Guadalquivir, south-western Spain. *Wildfowl* 33: 94–103.

Amat, J.A. 1984a. Actividad diurna de tres especies de patos buceadores en la Laguna de Zóñar (Córdoba, España meridional) durante el invierno. *Misc. Zool.* 8: 203–11.

Amat, J.A. 1984b. Ecological segregation between Red-crested Pochard *Netta rufina* and Pochard *Aythya ferina* in a fluctuating environment. *Ardea* 72: 229–33.

Amat, J.A. 1985. Nest parasitism of Pochard *Aythya ferina* by Red-crested Pochard *Netta rufina*. *Ibis* 127: 255–62.

Amat, J.A. 1987. Infertile eggs: a reproductive cost of female dabbling ducks inhabiting unpredictable environments. *Wildfowl* 38: 114–16.

Amat, J.A. 1990. Food usurpation by waterfowl and waders. *Wildfowl* 41: 107–16.

Amat, J.A. and Raya, C. 1989. Aves en la lista roja: la Malvasía. *La Garcilla* 75: 8–11.

Amat, J.A. and Sanchez, A. 1982. Biológia y ecología de la Malvasía *Oxyura leucocephala* en Andalucía. *Doñana Acta Vert.* 9: 251–320.

Amat, J.A. and Soriguer, R.C. 1982. Datos sobre selección de hábitat y ecología alimenticia del Porrón Pardo (*Aythya nyroca*). *Doñana Acta Vert.* 9: 388–94.

Amat, J.A. and Soriguer, R.C. 1984. Kleptoparasitism of Coots by Gadwalls. *Ornis Scand.* 15: 188–94.

Andersen-Harild, P. 1981. Weight changes in *Cygnus olor*. In 2nd IWRB Int. Swan Symp., Sapporo, 1980 (ed. G.V.T. Matthews and M. Smart), pp.120–31. IWRB, Slimbridge, UK.

Anderson, A. 1963. Patagial tags for waterfowl. *J. Wildl. Manage.* 27: 284–8.

Anderson, B.W. and Ohmart, R.D. 1988. Structure of the winter duck community on the Lower Colorado River: patterns and processes. In *Waterfowl in Winter* (ed. M.W. Weller), pp.191–236. Univ. Minnesota Press, Minneapolis.

Anderson, D.R. and Burnham, K.P. 1976. *Population ecology of the Mallard VI. The effect of exploitation on survival*, Publ., No. 128. US Fish & Wildl. Serv., Washington.

Anderson, D.R. and Sterling, R.T. 1974. Population dynamics of moulting Pintail drakes banded in south-central Saskatchewan. *J. Wildl. Manage.* 40: 233–42.

Anderson, M.G. 1985. Social behavior of breeding canvasbacks (*Anas valisineria*): male and female strategies of reproduction. Unpubl. Ph.D. thesis. Univ. Minnesota, Minneapolis, US.

Anderson, M.G. and Titman, R.D. 1992. Spacing patterns. In *The ecology and management of breeding waterfowl* (ed. B.D.J. Batt, A.D. Afton, M.G. Anderson, C.D. Ankney, D.H. Johnson, J.A. Kadlec *et al.*), pp.251–89. Univ. Minnesota Press, Minneapolis.

Anderson, M.G., Rhymer, J.M. and Rohwer, F.C. 1992. Philopatry, dispersal, and the genetic structure of waterfowl populations. In *The ecology and management of breeding waterfowl* (ed. B.D.J. Batt, A.D. Afton, M.G. Anderson, C.D. Ankney, D.H. Johnson, J.A. Kadlec *et al.*), pp.365–95. Univ. Minnesota Press, Minneapolis.

Anderson, V.R. and Alisauskas, R.T. 2001. Egg size, body size, locomotion, and feeding performance in captive King Eider ducklings. *Condor* 103: 195–99.

Anderson, V.R. and Alisauskas, R.T. 2002. Composition and growth of King Eider duckings in relation to egg size. *Auk* 119: 62–70.

Andersson, Å., Madsen, J., Mooij, J. and Reitan, O. 1999. Canada Goose *Branta canadensis*: Fennoscandia/continental Europe. In *Goose Populations of the Western Palearctic*, Publ., No. 48 (ed. J. Madsen, J. Cracknell and T. Fox), pp.236–45. Wetlands International, Wageningen, Netherlands.

Andersson, M. and Eriksson, M.O.G. 1982. Nest parasitism in Goldeneyes *Bucephala clangula*: some evolutionary aspects. *Amer. Natur.* 120: 1–16.

Ankney, C.D. 1979. Does the wing molt cause nutritional stress in Lesser Snow Geese? *Auk* 96: 68–72.

Ankney, C.D. 1980. Egg weight, survival, and growth of Lesser Snow Goose goslings. *J. Wildl. Manage.* 44: 174–82.

Ankney, C.D. 1984. Nutrient reserve dynamics of breeding and molting Brant. *Auk* 101: 361–70.

Ankney, C.D. 1996. An embarrassment of riches: too many geese. *J. Wildl. Manage.* 60: 217–23.

Ankney, C.D. and Afton, A.D. 1988. Bioenergetics of breeding Northern Shovelers: diet, nutrient reserves clutch size and incubation. *Condor* 90: 459–72.

Ankney, C.D. and Alisauskas, R.T. 1991. The use of nutrient reserves by breeding waterfowl. *Int. Orn. Congr.* 20: 2170–76.

Ankney, C.D. and Bisset, A.R. 1976. An explanation of egg weight variation in the Lesser Snow Goose. *J. Wildl. Manage.* 40: 729–34.

Ankney, C.D. and MacInnes, C.D. 1978. Nutrient reserves and reproductive performance of female Lesser Snow Geese. *Auk* 95: 459–71.

Ankney, C.D., Dennis, D.G. and Bailey, R.O. 1987. Increasing Mallards, decreasing Black Ducks: coincidence or cause and effect? *J. Wildl. Manage.* 51: 523–29.

Anon. 1972. Raising Red-breasted Geese. *Game Bird Breeders' Gazette* 21(10–11): 14–15.

Anon. 1992. Actions préliminaires pour la restauration des populations de Sarcelle d'été (*Anas querquedula*). Convention—Commission Européenne Environnement/ Office National de la Chasse, Nantes.

Anon. 1993. Agreement on the Conservation of Asian/ Australasian Waterfowl, Bonn Convention, Management Plan, Second Draft, March 1993. Bonn Convention, Bonn.

Anon. 1994. Status of the Lesser White-fronted Goose in China. *IWRB Goose Research Group Bull.* 6: 25–6.

Anon. 1996a. European News. *Brit. Birds* 89: 25–45.

Anon. 1996b. Latest news on radio-tagged Lesser White-fronted Geese. *Wetlands International Goose Specialist Group Bull.* 7: 26.

Anon. 2001. Draft Outline of the 2001–2005 Water-bird Strategy Asia–Pacific Migratory Waterbird Conservation Committee, Wetlands International—Asia Pacific 2001.

Anstey, S. 1989. *The status and conservation of the White-headed Duck Oxyura leucocephala*, Spec. Publ., No. 10. IWRB, Slimbridge, UK.

Antas, P.T.Z. and Resende, S.M.L. 1983. First record of the South American Pochard in Central Brazil. *Auk* 100: 220–21.

Antas, P.T.Z., Nascimento, J.L.X., Ataguile, B.S., Koch, M. and Scherer, S.B. 1996. Monitoring Anatidae populations in Rio Grande Do Sul State, South Brazil. *Gibier Faune Sauvage* 13: 513–30.

AOU 1957. *Checklist of North American birds* (5th edn). Lord Baltimore Press and American Ornithologists' Union, Baltimore.

AOU 1983. *Checklist of North American birds* (6th edn). Allen Press, Lawrence, Kansas.

Aramburu, R.M. 1990. Observaciones sobre posturas del Pato Barcino, Anas flavirostris, en nidos de Cotorra Comun Myiopsitta monachus. *Neotropica* 36: 101–105.

Araya, B. and Chester, S. 1993. *The birds of Chile: a field guide.* Latour, Santiago, Chile.

Araya, B. and Millie, G. 1988. *Guia de campo de las aves de Chile.* Editorial Universitaria, Chile.

Arnold, T.W. and Clark, R.G. 1996. Survival and philopatry of female dabbling ducks in southcentral Saskatchewan. *J. Wildl. Manage.* 60: 560–68.

Arnold, T.W., Rohwer, F.C. and Armstrong T. 1987. Egg viability, nest predation, and the adaptive significance of clutch size in prairie ducks. *Amer. Natur.* 130: 643–53.

Arnold, T.W., Sorenson, M.D. and Rotella, J.J. 1993. Relative success of overwater and upland Mallard nests in southwestern Manitoba. *J. Wildl. Manage.* 57: 578–81.

Arnold, T.W., Anderson, M.D., Sorenson, M.D. and Emery, R.B. 2002. Survival and philopatry of female redheads breeding in southwestern Manitoba. *J. Wildl. Manage.* 66: 162–69.

Arnold, T.W., Anderson, M.G., Emery, R.B., Sorenson, M.D. and de Sobrino, C.N. 1995. The effects of late-incubation body mass on reproductive success and survival of Canvasbacks and Redheads. *Condor* 97: 953–62.

Artiukhov, A.I. and Syroechkovski, E.E. Jr 1999. New data on the distribution of Lesser White-fronted Goose in the Abyi Lowland (Eastern Yakutia). *Casarca* 5:136–43. (In Russian with English summary.)

Ash, J.S. and Miskell, J.E. 1983. Birds of Somalia: their habitat, status and distribution. *Scopus* Spec. Suppl,. No. 1.

Ashcroft, R.E. 1976. A function of the pair bond in the Common Eider. *Wildfowl* 27: 101–05.

Astley, H.D. 1917. The Red-breasted Goose (*Bernicla ruficollis*). *Avic. Mag.* 8: 213–14.

Atkinson, I.A.E. and Millener, P.R. 1991. An ornithological glimpse into New Zealand's pre-human past. *Int. Ornith. Congr.* 20: 127–92.

Atkinson-Willes, G.L. 1963. *Wildfowl in Great Britain*. HMSO, London.

Atkinson-Willes, G.L. 1976. The numerical distribu-tion of ducks, swans and coots as a guide in assessing the importance of wetlands in mid-winter. In Int. Conf. Wetlands and Waterfowl, Heiligenhafen, Fed. Rep. Ger-many, December 1974 (ed. M. Smart), pp.199–254. IWRB, Slimbridge, UK.

Attiwill, A.R., Bourne, J.M. and Parker, S.A. 1981. Possible nest-parasitism in the Australian stiff-tailed ducks (Anatidae: Oxyurini). *Emu* 81: 41–42.

Audubon, J.J. 1843. *The birds of North America from drawings made in the United States and their territories*. Vol. 6. Published by the author, London.

Aufforth, A.D., Goetz, H. and Higgins, K.F. 1990. Duck nesting on islands at J. Clark Salyer Refuge in North Dakota, 1983–1984. *Prairie Nat.* 22: 1–12.

Austin, J.E. and Miller, M.R. 1995. Northern Pintail (*Anas acuta*). The Birds of North America, No. 163, (ed. A. Poole and F. Gill). AOU, Washington, and Academy of Natural Sciences, Philadelphia.

Austin, J.E. and Serie, J.R. 1994. Variation in body mass of wild Canvasback and Redhead ducklings. *Condor* 96: 909–15.

Austin, J.E., Serie, J.R. and Noyes, J.H. 1990. Diet of Canvasbacks during breeding. *Prairie Nat.* 22: 171–76.

Austin, J.E., Custer, C.M. and Afton, A.D. 1998. Lesser Scaup (*Aythya affinis*). The Birds of North

America, No. 338 (ed. A. Poole and F. Gill). AOU, The Birds of North America Inc., Philadelphia.

Austin, J.E., Afton, A.D., Anderson, M.G., Clark, R.G., Custer, C.M., Lawrence, J.S. *et al.* 2000. Declining scaup populations: issues, hypotheses, and research needs. *Wildl. Soc. Bull.* 28: 254–63.

Austin, O.L. and Kuroda, N. 1953. The birds of Japan: their status and distribution. *Bull. Mus. Comp. Zool. at Harvard College* 109(4): 279–637.

Bacon, P.J. 1980. Status and dynamics of a Mute Swan population near Oxford between 1976 and 1978. *Wildfowl* 31: 37–50.

Bacon, P.J. and Andersen-Harild, P. 1989. Mute Swan. In *Lifetime reproductive success in birds* (ed. I. Newton), pp.363–86. Academic Press, London.

Bacon, P.J. and Mountford, M.D. 1990. The effects of genotypic and yearly variations on the egg volumes of the Mute Swan (*Cygnus olor*). *Wildfowl* 41: 7–12.

Bailey, A.M. 1919. Notes on our Hawaiian reservation. *Natural History* 19: 382–95.

Bailey, A.M. 1942. The Portulacca flats of Laysan. *Audubon* 44: 150–61.

Bailey, A.M. 1948. *Birds of Arctic Alaska*, Pop. Ser. No. 8. Colorado Mus. Nat. Hist.

Bailey, R.O. 1981. The postbreeding ecology of the Redhead Duck (*Aythya americana*) on Long Island Bay, Lake Winnipegosis, Manitoba. Unpubl. Ph.D. thesis. McGill Univ., Montreal, Canada.

Bailey, R.O. and Titman, R.D. 1984. Habitat use and feeding ecology of postbreeding Redheads. *J. Wildl. Manage.* 48: 1144–55.

Bailey, T. and Black, J.M. 1995. Parasites of wild and captive Nene *Branta sandvicensis* in Hawaii. *Wildfowl* 46: 59–65.

Baillie, J. and Groombridge, B. 1996. 1996 IUCN red list of threatened animals. IUCN, Gland, Switzerland.

Bain, M.B. 1993. Assessing impacts of introduced aquatic species: Grass Carp in large systems. *Environmen-tal Manage.* 17: 211–24.

Baker, A.J. 1998. Identification of Canada Goose stocks using restriction analysis of mitochondrial DNA. In *Biol-ogy and management of Canada Geese*, Int. Canada Goose Symp. (ed. D.H. Rusch, M.D. Samuel, D.D. Humburg and B.D. Sullivan), pp.435–43. Milwaukee, Wisconsin.

Baker, A.J. and Marshall, H.D. 1997. Mitochondrial control region sequences as tools for understanding evolution. In *Avian molecular evolution and systematics* (ed. D.P. Mindell), pp.51–79. Academic Press, San Diego.

Baker, E.C.S. 1908. *Indian ducks and their allies*. Bombay Natural History Society, Bombay.

Baker, E.C.S. 1921. *Game-birds of India, Burma and Ceylon*, Vol 1. Bombay Natural History Society, John Bale and Danielsson Ltd, London.

Baker, E.C.S. 1922–30. *The fauna of British India—birds*. Taylor and Francis, London.

Baker, E.C.S. 1935. *The nidification of birds of the Indian Empire*, Vol 4. Taylor and Francis, London.

Baker, K. 1993. *Identification guide to European non-passerines*, Guide, No. 24. BTO, Thetford.

Baker, R.R. 1978. *The evolutionary ecology of animal migration*. Hodder and Stoughton, London.

Baldassarre, G.A. and Bolen, E.G. 1994. *Waterfowl ecology and management*. Wiley, New York.

Baldassarre, G.A., Whyte, R.J. and Bolen, E.G. 1986. Body weight and carcass composition of non-breeding Green-winged Teal on the southern High Plains of Texas. *J. Wildl. Manage.* 50: 420–26.

Baldassarre, G.A., Paulus, S.L., Tamisier, A. and Titman, R.D. 1988. Workshop summary: techniques for timing activity of wintering waterfowl. In *Waterfowl in Winter* (ed. M.W. Weller), pp.181–88. Univ. Minnesota Press, Minneapolis.

Baldassarre, G.A., Brazda, A.R. and Woodyard, E.R. 1989. The east coast of Mexico. In *Habitat management for migrating and wintering waterfowl in North America* (ed. L.M. Smith, R.L. Pederson and R.M. Kaminski), pp.407–25. Texas Tech Univ. Press, Lubbock.

Baldwin, P.H. 1945. The Hawaiian Goose, its distribution and reduction in numbers. *Condor* 47: 27–37.

Baldwin, P.H. 1947. Foods of the Hawaiian Goose. *Condor* 49: 108–20.

Ball, I.J., Gilmer, D.S., Cowardin, L.M. and Riechmann, J.H. 1975. Survival of Wood Duck and Mallard broods in north-central Minnesota. *J. Wildl. Manage.* 39: 776–80.

Ball, I.J., Frost, P.G.H., Siegfried, W.R. and McKinney, F. 1978. Territories and local movements of African Black Ducks. *Wildfowl* 29: 61–79.

Ball, S.C. 1934. Hybrid ducks, including descriptions of two crosses of *Bucephala* and *Lophodytes*. *Bull. Peabody Mus. Nat. Hist.* 3: 1–26.

Balmford, A., Mace, G.M. and Leader-Williams, N. 1996. Designing the ark: setting priorities for captive breeding. *Conservation Biology* 10: 719–27.

Balouet, J.C. and Olson, S.L. 1989. Fossil birds from the Late Quaternary deposits in New Caledonia. *Smithsonian Contributions to Zoology* 469: 1–38.

Banko, P.C. 1988. Breeding biology and conservation of the Nene, Hawaiian Goose (*Nesochen sandvicensis*). Unpubl. Ph.D. dissertation. Univ. Washington, Seattle, US.

Banko, P.C. 1992. Constraints on productivity of wild Nene or Hawaiian Geese *Branta sandvicensis*. *Wildfowl* 43: 99–106.

Banko, P.C., Black, J.M. and Banko, W.E. 1999. Hawaiian Goose (Nene) *(Branta sandvicensis)*. The Birds of North America, No. 434 (ed. A. Poole and F. Gill). AOU, The Birds of North America Inc., Philadelphia.

Banko, W.E. 1960. *The Trumpeter Swan. Its history, habits, and population in the United States*, N. American Fauna, No. 63. US Fish & Wildl. Serv., Washington.

Banko, W.E. and Elder, W.H. 1990. *History of endemic Hawaiian birds. Population histories—species accounts: scrub-grassland birds: Nene—Hawaiian Goose*, Avian History Rept., No. 13a. Cooperative National Park Resources Studies Unit, Univ. Hawaii, Honolulu.

Banks, R.C., Cicero, C., Dunn, J.L., Kratter, A.W., Rasmussen, P.C., Remsen, Jr, J.V. et al. 2003. Forty-fifth Supplement to the American Ornithologists' Union *Check-List of North American Birds*. *Auk* 121: 985–95.

Bannerman, D.A. 1921. Remarks on rare and otherwise interesting birds contained in collections made by Mr G.L. Bates in Southern Cameroon. *Ibis* 3(11): 81–121.

Bannerman, D.A. 1957–58. *The birds of the British Isles*, Vols 6 and 7. Oliver and Boyd, Edinburgh and London.

Bannister, B.H. 1870. A sketch of the classification of the American Anserinae. *Proc. Acad. Nat. Sci. Philadelphia* 22: 130–2.

Bannor, B.K. 1997. Nest sharing by captive Cape Teal *Anas capensis*. *Wildfowl* 48: 186–87.

Barker, R.D. and Vestjens, W.J.M. 1989. *The food of Australian birds*. CSIRO Div. Wildl. Ecol., Lyneham, ACT.

Barker, R.J. and Buchanan, I.M. 1993. Estimating adult survival rates of New Zealand Black Swans banded as immatures. *J. Wildl. Manage.* 57: 549–55.

Barnes, G.G. and Thomas, V.G. 1987. Digestive organ morphology, diet, and guild structure of North American Anatidae. *Can. J. Zool.* 65: 1812–17.

Barras, S.C., Kaminski, R.M. and Brennan, L.A. 1996. Acorn selection by female Wood Ducks. *J. Wildl. Manage.* 60: 592–602.

Barrett, V.A. and Vyse, E.R. 1982. Comparative genetics of three Trumpeter Swan populations. *Auk* 99: 103–08.

Barrow, J.H., Black, J.M. and Walter, W.B. 1986. Behaviour patterns and their function in the Horned Screamer. *Wildfowl* 37: 156–62.

Barry, T.W. 1962. Effect of late seasons on Atlantic Brant reproduction. *J. Wildl. Manage.* 26: 19–26.

Bart, J. and Earnst, S.L. 1991. Use of wetlands by grazing waterfowl in northern Alaska during late summer. *J. Wildl. Manage.* 55: 564–68.

Bart, J., Earnst, S. and Bacon, P.J. 1991a. Comparative demography of the swans: a review. *Wildfowl* Spec. Suppl., 1: 15–21.

Bart, J., Limpert, R., Earnst, S., Sladen, W., Hines, J. and Rothe, T. 1991b. Demography of eastern population Tundra Swans *Cygnus columbianus columbianus*. *Wildfowl* Spec. Suppl., 1: 178–84.

Bartmann, W. 1988. New observations on the Brazilian Merganser. *Wildfowl* 39: 7–14.

Bartmann, W. 1994. The Brazilian Merganser (*Mergus octoseatceus*): nearly extinct? *IUCN Conservation Breeding Specialist Group News* 5(2): 7–8.

Bartonek, J.C. and Hickey, J.J. 1969a. Food habits of Canvasbacks, Redheads, and Lesser Scaup in Manitoba. *Condor* 71: 280–90.

Bartonek, J.C. and Hickey, J.J. 1969b. Selective feeding by juvenile diving ducks in summer. *Auk* 86: 443–57.

Bartonek, J.C. and Murdy, H.W. 1970. Summer foods of Lesser Scaup in subarctic taiga. *Arctic* 23: 35–44.

Bartonek, J.C., Serie, J.R. and Converse, K.A. 1991. Mortality in Tundra Swans *Cygnus columbianus columbianus*. *Wildfowl* Spec. Suppl., 1: 356–58.

Barzen, J.A. and Serie, J.R. 1990. Nutrient reserve dynamics of breeding Canvasbacks. *Auk* 107: 75–85.

Bateson, P. 1983. Optimal outbreeding. In *Mate Choice* (ed. P. Bateson), pp.257–77. Cambridge Univ. Press.

Batt, B.D.J. (ed.) 1997. *Arctic ecosystems in peril: report of the Arctic Goose Habitat Working Group.* Arctic Goose Joint Venture Spec. Publ. US Fish & Wildl. Serv., Washington, and Can. Wildl. Serv., Ottawa.

Batt, B.D.J. and Cornwell, G.W. 1972. The effects of cold on Mallard embryos. *J. Wildl. Manage.* 36: 745–51.

Batt, B.D.J. and Prince, H.H. 1978. Some reproductive parameters of Mallards in relation to age, captivity and geographic origin. *J. Wildl. Manage.* 42: 834–42.

Batt, B.D.J. and Prince, H.H. 1979. Laying dates, clutch size and egg weight of captive Mallards. *Condor* 81: 35–41.

Batt, B.D.J., Afton, A.D., Anderson, M.G., Ankney, C.D., Johnson, D.H., Kadlec, J.A. *et al.* (ed.) 1992. *Ecology and management of breeding waterfowl.* Univ. Minnisota Press, Minneapolis.

Batzer, D.P., McGee, M. and Resh, V.H. 1993. Characteristics of invertebrates consumed by Mallards and prey response to wetland flooding schedules. *Wetlands* 13: 41–49.

Bauer, K.M. and Glutz von Blotzheim, U.N. 1968–69. *Handbuch der Vögel Mitteleuropas,* Vols 2 and 3. Akademische Verlagsgesellschaft, Frankfurt am Main.

Bauer, S. and Thielcke, G. 1982. Gefahrdete Brutvogelarten in der Bundesrepublik Deutschland und im Land Berlin: Bestandsentwicklung, Gefahrdungsursachen und Schutzmassnahmen. *Vogelwarte* 31: 183–393.

Baum, D. 1992. Phylogenetic species concepts. *Trends Ecol. Evol.* 7: 1–2.

Bayliss, P. and Yeomans, K.M. 1990. Seasonal distribution and abundance of Magpie Geese *Anseranas semipalmata* Latham, in the Northern Territory, and their relationship to habitat, 1983–1986. *Aust. Wildl. Res.* 17: 15–38.

Bazely, D.R. and Jefferies, R.L. 1985. Goose faeces: a source of nitrogen for plant growth in a grazed salt marsh. *J. Appl. Ecol.* 22: 693–703.

Bazely, D.R., Ewins, P.J. and McCleery, R.H. 1991. Possible effects of local enrichment by gulls on feeding-site selection by wintering Barnacle Geese *Branta leucopsis. Ibis* 133: 111–14.

Beard, E.B. 1953. The importance of beaver in water-fowl management at the Seney National Wildlife Refuge. *J. Wildl. Manage.* 17: 398–436.

Beard, E.B. 1964. Duck brood behavior at the Seney National Wildlife Refuge. *J. Wildl. Manage.* 28: 398–436.

Bearhop, S., Thompson, D.R., Waldron, S., Russell, I.C., Alexander, G. and Furness, R.W. 1999. Stable isotopes indicate the extent of freshwater feeding by cormorants *Phalacrocorax carbo* shot at inland fisheries in England. *J. Appl. Ecol.* 36: 75–84.

Bearhop, S., Furness, R.W., Hilton, G.M., Votier, S.C. and Waldron, S. 2003. A forensic approach to understanding diet and habitat use from stable isotope analysis of (avian) claw material. *Funct. Ecol.* 17: 270–75.

Beauchamp, G. 1998. The relationship between intra- and interspecific brood amalgamation. *Condor* 100: 153–62.

Beauchamp, G., Guillemette, M. and Ydenberg, R. 1992. Prey selection while diving by Common Eiders *Somateria mollissima. Anim. Behav.* 44: 417–26.

Beauchamp, W.D., Koford, R.R., Nudds, T.D., Clark, R.G. and Johnson, D.H. 1996a. Long-term declines in nest success of prairie ducks. *J. Wildl. Manage.* 60: 247–57.

Beauchamp, W.D., Nudds, T.D. and Clark, R.G. 1996b. Duck nest success declines with and without predator management. *J. Wildl. Manage.* 60: 258–64.

Beazley, M. 1993. *Wetlands in danger—IUCN world conservation atlas.* Reed International, London.

Bechet, A., Giroux, J.-F., Gauthier, G., Nichols, J.D. and Hines, J.E. 2003. Spring hunting changes the regional movements of migrating greater snow geese. *J. Appl. Ecol.* 40: 553–564.

Becker, J.J. 1987. The fossil birds of the late Miocene and early Pliocene of Florida. I. Geology, correlation and systematic overview. In *L'Évolution des oiseaux d'après le témoignage des fossiles*, Documents du Lab. Géol. de Lyon, No. 99 (ed. C. Mourer-Chauviré), pp.159–71. Laboratoire Géologique de Lyon.

Beckwith, S.L. and Hosford, H.J. 1956. The Florida Duck in the vicinity of Lake Okeechobee, Glades County, Florida. In *Ann. Conf. Southeastern Association Game and Fish Commissioners* 9: 188–201.

Beehler, B. 1980. Black Swan *Cygnus atratus*: a new species for the New Guinea region. *P.N.G. Bird Soc. Newsl.* 3: 173–74.

Beehler, B.M., Pratt, T.K. and Zimmerman, D.A. 1986. *Birds of New Guinea.* Princeton Univ. Press.

Beekman, J.H. 1997. Censuses of the Northwest European Bewick's Swan population, January 1990 and 1995. *Wetlands International Swan Specialist Group Newsl.* 6: 7–8.

Beekman, J.H., Dirksen, S. and Slagboom, T.H. 1985. Population size and breeding success of Bewick's Swans wintering in Europe in 1983–84. *Wildfowl* 36: 5–12.

Beekman, J.H., Rees, E.C. and Bacon, P.J. 1994. Bewick's Swans *Cygnus columbianus*. In *Birds in Europe: their conservation status* (ed. G.M. Tucker and M.F. Heath), pp.108–09. Birdlife International, Cambridge.

Beekman, J.H., Van Eerden, M.R. and Dirksen, S. 1991. Bewick's Swans *Cygnus columbianus bewickii* utilising the changing resource of *Potamogeton pectinatus* during autumn in the Netherlands. *Wildfowl* Spec. Suppl. 1: 238–48.

Beekman, J.H., Berthold, P., Nowak, E. and Querner, U. 1996a. Implementation of satellite tracking in studying migration of *Anatidae.* An overview and a case study. *Gibier Faune Sauvage* 13: 157–76.

Beekman, J.H., Van Eerden, M.R., Mineyev, Y.N., Luigujõe, L. and Den Hollander, H.J. 1996b. Landsat satellite images for detection of submerged macrophytes: in search of potential stop-over feeding sites for Bewick's Swans (*Cygnus columbianus bewickii*) along their migratory route. *Gibier Faune Sauvage* 13: 421–50.

Beekman, J.H., Nolet, B.A. and Klaassen, M. 2002. Skipping swans: fuelling rates and wind conditions determine differential use of migratory stopover sites of Bewick's Swans *Cygnus bewickii*. In The avian calendar: exploring biological hurdles in the annual cycle. Proc. 3rd Conf. European Orn. Union, Groningen, August 2001 (ed. Both C. and T. Piersma). *Ardea* 90(3) special issue: 437–60.

Beintema, A.J. 1980. The Smew *Mergus albellus. Limosa* 53: 3–10.

Bell, C.G.V. 1996a. Some observations on the African Pygmy Goose. *Honeyguide* 42: 71–74.

Bell, C.G.V. 1996b. Seasonal dimorphism, inter- and intra-specific recognition in Southern African waterfowl. *Honeyguide* 42: 137–45.

Bell, C.G.V. 1997a. Field sexing of some monomorphic Zimbabwean ducks. *Honeyguide* 43: 76–79.

Bell, C.G.V. 1997b. On the post-embryonic development of the African Pygmy Goose. *Honeyguide* 43: 103–05.

Bell, C.G.V. 1998. Pygmy Geese feeding on Paspalum grass. *Honeyguide* 44: 140.

Bell, D.V. and Owen, M. 1990. Shooting disturbance—a review. In *Managing Waterfowl Populations*. Proc. IWRB Symp., Astrakhan 1998 (ed. G.V.T. Matthews), pp.159–71. IWRB Special Publication 12, Slimbridge, UK.

Bell, J., Bruning, D. and Winnegar, A. 1970. Black-necked Screamers seen feeding chick. *Auk* 87: 805.

Bell, M. and Mitchell, C. 1996. *Survival in surface feeding ducks*. Unpubl. rept. to JNCC. WWT, Slimbridge, UK.

Bell, M.C., Fox, A.D., Owen, M., Black, J.M. and Walsh, A.J. 1993. Approaches to the estimation of survival in two arctic-nesting goose species. In *Marked individuals in the study of bird populations* (ed. J-D. Lebreton and P.M. North), pp.141–55. Birkhauser Verlag, Berlin.

Bell, M.C., Mitchell, C., Fox, A.D. and Stewart, A. 1995. Survival estimates of Pink-footed Geese *Anser brachyrhynchus*: 1987–1993. Unpubl. rept. to JNCC. WWT, Slimbridge, UK.

Bellrose, F.C. 1958a. The orientation of displaced waterfowl in migration. *Wilson Bull.* 70: 20–40.

Bellrose, F.C. 1958b. Celestial orientation in wild Mallards. *Bird Band.* 29: 75–90.

Bellrose, F.C. 1959. Lead poisoning as a factor in waterfowl populations. *Ill. Nat. Hist. Surv. Bull.* 27: 235–88.

Bellrose, F.C. 1968. *Waterfowl migration corridors east of the Rocky Mountains in the United States*, Biol. Notes, No. 61. Ill. Nat. Hist. Surv., Urbana, Ill.

Bellrose, F.C. 1980. *Ducks, geese and swans of North America* (3rd edn). Stackpole Books, Harrisburg, PA.

Bellrose, F.C. 1990. History of wood duck management in North America. In *Proc. 1988 North Am. Wood Duck Symp., St Louis* (ed. L.H. Fredrickson, G.V. Burger, S.P. Havera, D.A. Gruber, R.E. Kirby and T.S. Taylor) pp.13–20. St Louis, Missouri.

Bellrose, F.C. and Holm, D.J. 1994. *Ecology and management of the Wood Duck*. Stackpole, Mechanicsburg, Pennsylvania.

Bellrose, F.C., Scott, T.G., Hawkins, A.S. and Low, J.B. 1961. Sex ratios in North American ducks. *Ill. Nat. Hist. Surv. Bull.* 27: 391–474.

Bellrose, F.C., Paveglio, Jr, F.L. and Steffeck, D.W. 1979. Waterfowl populations and the changing environment of the Illinois River Valley. *Ill. Nat. Hist. Surv. Bull.* 32: 1–54.

Belon, P. 1555. *L'histoire de la nature des oyseaux*. Paris.

Belton, W. 1984. Birds of Rio Grande do Sul, Brazil. Part 1. Rheidae through Furnariidae. *Bull. Amer. Mus. Nat. Hist.* 178(4): 1–631.

Bengtson, S-A. 1966. Field studies on the Harlequin Duck in Iceland. *Wildfowl* 17: 79–94.

Bengtson, S-A. 1968. Inter-specific pairing in Scaup and Tufted Duck. *Wildfowl* 19: 61–63.

Bengtson, S-A. 1971a. Food and feeding of diving ducks breeding at Lake Mývatn, Iceland. *Ornis Fenn.* 48: 77–92.

Bengtson, S-A. 1971b. Habitat selection of duck broods in Lake Mývatn area, NE Iceland. *Ornis Scand.* 2: 17–26.

Bengtson, S-A. 1971c. Variations in clutch size in ducks in relation to their food supply. *Ibis* 113: 523–26.

Bengtson, S-A. 1972a. Breeding ecology of the Harlequin Duck *Histrionicus histrionicus* (L.) in Iceland. *Ornis Scand.* 3: 1–19.

Bengtson, S-A. 1972b. Reproduction and fluctuations in the size of duck populations at Lake Mývatn, Iceland. *Oikos* 23: 35–58.

Bengtson, S-A. and Ulfstrand, S. 1971. Food resources and breeding frequency of the Harlequin Duck *Histrionicus histrionicus* in Iceland. *Oikos* 22: 235–39.

Bennett, A.G. 1924. Notas sobre el pato vapor *Tachyeres patachonicus* (King) llamado 'Canvas-back' en las Falklands. *Hornero* 3: 280–82.

Bennett, J.W. and Bolen, E.G. 1978. Stress response in wintering Green-winged Teal. *J. Wildl. Manage.* 42: 81–6.

Benson, C.W. and Benson, F.M. 1977. *The birds of Malawi*. Montfort Press, Limbe, Malawi.

Benson, C.W., Brooke, R.K., Dowsett, R.J. and Irwin, M.P.S. 1971. *The Birds of Zambia*. Collins, London.

Benstead, P.J., Hearn, R.D. and Stagi Nedelcoff, A.R. 1994. A recent sighting of Brazilian Merganser *Mergus octosetaceus* in Misiones Province, Argentina. *Cotinga* 2: 35–36.

Bent, A.C. 1923. *Life histories of North American wildfowl. Order Anseres (Parts I and II)*, US Natl. Mus., Smithsonian Inst. Bull., Nos 126 and 130. Gov. Printing Office, Washington.

Benton, M.J. (ed.) 1993. *The fossil record 2*. Chapman and Hall, London.

Bergan, J.F. 1986. Aggression and habitat segregation among diving ducks wintering in South Carolina. M.S. thesis. Texas Tech Univ., Lubbock, US.

Bergan, J.F. and Smith, L.M. 1989. Differential habitat use by diving ducks wintering in South Carolina. *J. Wildl. Manage.* 53: 1117–26.

Bergan, J.F., Smith, L.M. and Mayer, J.J. 1989. Time-activity budgets of diving ducks wintering in South Carolina. *J. Wildl. Manage.* 53: 769–76.

Berger, A.J. 1970. The present status of the birds of Hawaii. *Pac. Sci.* 24: 29–42.

Berger, A.J. 1981. *Hawaiian birdlife* (2nd edn). Univ. Press Hawaii, Honolulu.

Bergman, G. and Donner, K.O. 1964. An analysis of the spring migration of the Common Scoter and Long-tailed Duck in southern Finland. *Acta Zoologica Fennica* 105: 1–59.

Bergman, R.D. 1973. Use of southern boreal lakes by postbreeding Canvasbacks and Redheads. *J. Wildl. Manage.* 37: 160–70.

Bergmann, H-H., Stock, M. and Ten Thoren, B. 1994. *Ringelganse, Arktische Gaste an unseren Kuste.* Aula-Verlag, Wiesbaden.

Berkhoudt, H. 1980. The morphology and distribution of cutaneous mechanoreceptors (Herbst and Grandry corpuscles) in bill and tongue of the Mallard (*Anas platyrhynchos* L.). *Netherlands J. Zool.* 30: 1–34.

Bernardes, A.T., Machado, A.B.M. and Rylands, A.B. 1990. *Fauna Brasileira Ameaçada de Extinção.* Fundação Biodiversitas. Belo Horizonte.

Berry, J. 1939. *The status and distribution of wild geese and wild duck in Scotland.* Cambridge Univ. Press.

Bertelsen, J. and Simonsen, N.H. 1986. *Documentation on bird hunting and the conservation of the species involved: situation in 1986.* Rept. to CEC by Min. Environment, Game and Wildlife Administration, Denmark.

Bertonatti, C., Canevari, P., Forrester, B.C., Knell, L.A. and Rumboll, M. 1991. Notes on the status of some threatened Anatidae in Argentina and Brazil. *IWRB Threatened Waterfowl Research Group Newsl.* 1: 5–6.

Bertoni, A.W. 1901. *Aves nuevas del Paraguay*, Anal. Cient. Paraguayos, Ser., No. 2, pp.1–216. Felix de Azara, Asuncion.

Beruldsen, G. 1977. The nest and eggs of the White Pygmy-Goose. *Sunbird* 8: 65–69.

Bethke, R.W. and Thomas, V.G. 1987. Differences in flight and heart muscle mass among geese, dabbling ducks, and diving ducks relative to habitat use. *Can. J. Zool.* 66: 2024–28.

Bevan, R.M. and Butler, P.J. 1992. The effects of temperature on the oxygen consumption, heart rate and deep body temperature during diving in the Tufted Duck *Aythya fuligula. J. Exp. Biol.* 163: 139–51.

Beynon, P.H. 1996. *BSAVA manual of raptors, pigeons and waterfowl.* British Small Animal Veterinary Association Ltd, Cheltenham.

Bezzel, E. 1969. *Die Tafelente.* Wittenberg, Lutherstadt.

Bickart, K.J. 1990. The birds of the late Miocene/early Pliocene Big Sandy Formation, Mohave County, Arizona. *Ornithol. Monogr.* 44: 1–72.

Billard, R.S. and Humphrey, P.S. 1972. Molts and plumages in the Greater Scaup. *J. Wildl. Manage.* 36: 765–74.

BirdLife International. 2000. *Threatened birds of the world.* Lynx Edicions, Barcelona, and BirdLife International, Cambridge, UK.

BirdLife International. 2001. *Threatened birds of Asia.* BirdLife International, Cambridge, UK.

Birkhead, M., Bacon, P.J., Walter, P. 1983. Factors affecting the breeding success of the Mute Swan *Cygnus olor. J. Anim. Ecol.* 52: 727–41.

Birkhead, M.E. and Perrins, C.M. 1986. *The Mute Swan.* Croom Helm, London.

Birkhead, T.R. and Møller, A.P. 1996. Monogamy and sperm competition in birds. In *Partnerships in birds. The study of monogamy* (ed. J.M. Black), pp.323–43. OUP.

Bishop, M.A., Song, Y. Canjue, Z. and Gu, B. 1997. Bar-headed Geese wintering in south-central Tibet. *Wildfowl* 48: 118–126.

Bisset, S.A. 1976. Foods of the Paradise Shelduck *Tadorna variegata* in the high country of North Canterbury, New Zealand. *Notornis* 23: 106–19.

Bjärvall, A. 1968. The hatching and nest exodus behaviour of Mallard. *Wildfowl* 19: 70–80.

Blaauw, F.E. 1917. The steamer duck. *Ibis* 59: 274–76.

Black, J.M. 1988. Preflight signalling in swans: a mechanism for group cohesion and flock formation. *Ethology* 70: 143–57.

Black, J.M. 1995. The Nene *Branta sandvicensis* Recovery Initiative: research against extinction. *Ibis* 137: S153–S160.

Black, J.M. 1996. *Partnerships in birds. The study of monogamy.* OUP.

Black, J.M. 1998. Flyway plan for the Svalbard population of Barnacle Geese: a summary. *Norsk Pol. Skr.* 200: 29–40.

Black, J.M. 2001. Fitness consequences of long-term pair bonds in barnacle geese: monogamy in the extreme. *Behavioral Ecology* 12: 640–45.

Black, J.M. and Banko, P.C. 1994. Is the Hawaiian Goose saved from extinction? In *Creative conservation: interactive management of wild and captive animals* (ed. P.J. Olney, G. Mace and A. Feistner), pp.394–410. Chapman and Hall, London.

Black, J.M. and Owen, M. 1987. Determinant factors of social rank in goose flocks, acquisition of social rank in young geese. *Behaviour* 102: 129–46.

Black, J.M. and Owen, M. 1988. Variations in pair bond and agonistic behaviors in Barnacle Geese on the wintering grounds. In *Waterfowl in winter* (ed. M. Weller), pp.39–57. Univ. Minnesota Press, Minneapolis.

Black, J.M. and Owen, M. 1989a. Parent–offspring relationships in wintering Barnacle Geese. *Anim. Behav.* 37: 187–98.

Black, J.M. and Owen, M. 1989b. Agonistic behaviour in Barnacle Goose flocks: assessment, investment and reproductive success. *Anim. Behav.* 37: 199–209.

Black, J.M. and Owen, M. 1995. Reproductive performance and assortative pairing in relation to age in Barnacle Geese. *J. Anim. Ecol.* 64: 234–44.

Black, J.M. and Rees, E.C. 1984. The structure and behaviour of the Whooper Swan population wintering at Caerlaverock, Dumfries and Galloway, Scotland: an introductory study. *Wildfowl* 35: 21–36.

Black, J.M., Deerenberg, C. and Owen, M. 1991a. Foraging behaviour and site selection of Barnacle Geese in a traditional and newly colonized spring staging area. *Ardea* 79: 349–58.

Black, J.M., Duvall, F., Hoshide, H., Medeiros, J., Natividad Hodges, C., Santos, H. *et al.* 1991b. The current status of the Hawaiian Goose and its recovery programme. *Wildfowl* 42: 149–54.

Black, J.M., Carbone, C., Wells, R.L. and Owen, M. 1992. Foraging dynamics in goose flocks: the cost of living on the edge. *Anim. Behav.* 44: 41–50.

Black, J.M., Prop, J. Hunter, J, Woog, F. Marshall, A.P. and Bowler, J.M. 1994. Foraging behaviour and energetics of the Hawaiian Goose *Branta sandvicensis*. *Wildfowl* 45: 65–109.

Black, J.M., Choudhury, S. and Owen, M. 1996. Do Barnacle Geese benefit from life-long monogamy? In *Partnerships in birds: the study of monogamy* (ed. J.M. Black), pp.91–117. OUP.

Black, J.M., Marshall, A.P., Gilburn, A., Santos, N., Hoshide, H., Medeiros, J. *et al.* 1997. Survival, movements and breeding of released Hawaiian geese: an assessment of the reintroduction program. *J. Wildl. Manage.* 60: 1161–73.

Black, J.M., Cooch, E.G., Loonen, M., Drent, R. and Owen, M. 1998. Body size variation in a Barnacle Goose metapopulation: evidence for saturation of local habitats. *Norsk Polar. Skr.* 200: 129–40.

Black, J.M., Prop, J. and Larsson, K. 2004. *Wild goose dilemmas. Population consequences of individual decisions.* Groningen, The Netherlands.

Blais, S., Guillemain, M., Durant, D., Fritz, H. and Guillon, N. 2001. Growth and plumage development of Pintail ducklings. *Wildfowl* 52: 69–86.

Blake, E.R. 1977. *Manual of neotropical birds*, Vol. 1. Univ. Chicago Press.

Blakers, M., Davies, S.J.J.F. and Reilly, P.N. 1984. *The atlas of Australian birds*. Melbourne Univ. Press.

Blanco, D.E. and Canevari, P. 1993. *Censo neotropical de aves acuaticas 1992*. Humedales para las Américas, Buenos Aires.

Bleiweiss, R., Kirsch, J.A.W. and Shafi, N. 1995. Confirmation of a portion of the Sibley–Ahlquist 'tapestry'. *Auk* 112: 87–97.

Blem, C.R. 1990. Avian energy storage. In *Current ornithology*, Vol. 7 (ed. D.M. Power), pp.59–113. Plenum Press, New York.

Blohm, R.J. 1979. The breeding ecology of the Gadwall in South Manitoba. Unpubl. M.Sc. thesis. Univ. Wisconsin, Madison, US.

Blokpoel, H. 1974. Migration of Lesser Snow and Blue Geese in spring across southern Manitoba. Part 1. Distribution, chronology, directions, numbers, heights and speeds. *Can. Wildl. Serv. Rept Ser.* 28.

Blokpoel, H. and Gauthier, M.C. 1975. Migration of Lesser Snow and Blue Geese in spring across southern Manitoba. Part 2. *Can. Wildl. Serv. Rept Ser.* 32.

Blomdahl, A., Breife, B and Holmström N. 2002. Flight identification of Common Eider, King Eider and Steller's Eider. *Brit. Birds* 95: 233–39.

Blomqvist, S. and Elander, M. 1988. King Eider (*Somateria spectabilis*) nesting in association with Long-tailed Skuas (*Stercorarius longicaudas*). *Arctic* 41: 138–42.

Bloomfield, C.D. and Black, M.J.S. 1963. Black Swans feeding on willow leaves. *Notornis* 10: 189.

Bluhm, C.K. 1988. Temporal patterns of pair formation and reproduction in annual cycles and associated endocrinology in waterfowl. *Current Ornithol.* 5: 123–85.

Bluhm, C.K. 1992. Environmental and endocrine control of waterfowl reproduction. In *The ecology and management of breeding waterfowl* (ed. B.D.J. Batt, A.D. Afton, M.G. Anderson, C.D. Ankney, D.H. Johnson, J.A. Kadlec *et al.*), pp.321–64. Univ. Minnesota Press, Minneapolis.

Blums, P., Mednis, A., Bauga, I., Nichols, J.D. and Hines, J.E. 1996. Age-specific survival and philopatry in three species of European ducks: a long-term study. *Condor* 98: 61–74.

Blums, P., Mednis, A. and Clark, R.G. 1997. Effect of incubation body mass on reproductive success and survival of two European diving ducks: a test of the nutrient limitation hypothesis. *Condor* 99: 916–25.

Blums, P., Clark, R.G. and Mednis, A. 2002. Patterns of reproductive effort and success in birds: path analysis of long-term data from European ducks. *J. Anim. Ecol.* 71: 280–95.

Blurton Jones, N.G. 1972. Moult migration of Emperor Geese. *Wildfowl* 23: 92–93.

Blyth, E. 1849. A supplemental note to the catalogue of the birds in the Asiatic Society's Museum. *J. Asiatic Soc. Bengal* 18: 803–21.

Blyth, E. 1870. Notes relating chiefly to the birds of India. *Ibis* 6: 157–76.

Blyth, E. 1875. Catalogue of mammals and birds of Burma. *J. Asiatic Soc. Bengal* 4: 165.

Bocharnikov, V.N. 1990a. Current status of the Chinese Merganser *Mergus squamatus* in Russia. *Bull. Inst. Ornith. Kyung Hee Univ.* III: 23–7.

Bocharnikov, V.N. 1990b. *Current status of waterfowl resources in the southern Far East of the USSR*, Spec. Publ., No. 12. IWRB, Slimbridge, UK.

Bocharnikov, V.N. and Gluschenko, Y.N. 1992. Khanka Lake wetlands and their use by geese populations. In 7th N. American Arctic Goose Conference and Workshop, January 7–12, 1992. California Maritime Academy, Vallejo, California.

Bocharnikov, V.N. and Shibnyev, Y.B. 1994. The Scaly-sided Merganser *Mergus squamatus* in the Bikin River Basin, Far-East Russia. In *The Scaly-sided Merganser Mergus squamatus in Russia and China*, IWRB Threatened Waterfowl Research Group Spec. Publ., No. 1 (ed. B. Hughes and J. Hunter), pp.3–10. WWT, Slimbridge, UK.

Bocharnikov, V.N., Surmach, S.G. and Aramilyev, A.A. 1991. Waterfowl in the basins of the large rivers of the western slopes of central Sikhote-Alin. In 10th All-Union Orn. Conf. Vityebsk, 17–20 Sept. 1991, Minsk. *Science and Technology* 1(2): 73–75.

Bock, W.J. 1969. Origin and radiation of birds. *Annals New York Acad. Sciences* 167: 147–55.

Bock, W.J. and Farrand, J., Jr 1980. The number of species and genera of recent birds: a contribution to comparative systematics. *American Museum Novitates* 2703: 1–29.

Boere, G.C. 1989. Towards an agreement and management plan for Western Palearctic waterfowl under the Bonn Convention. In: *Managing waterfowl populations* (ed. G.V.T. Matthews), pp.215–24. IWRB Spec. Publ. 12, Slimbridge, UK.

Bogoslovskaya, L.C. and Votrogov, L.M. 1981. Masses of seabirds and whales in polynya of the Bering Sea. *Biologia, Pripoda* 1981, No.1. [In Russian.]

Bolduc, F. and Guillemette, M. 2003. Incubation constancy and mass loss in the Common Eider *Somateria mollissima. Ibis* 145: 329–32.

Bolen, E.G. 1964. Weights and linear measurements of Black-bellied Tree Ducks. *Texas J. Sci.* 16: 257–60.

Bolen, E.G. 1967. Nesting boxes for Black-bellied Tree Ducks. *J. Wildl. Manage.* 31: 794–97.

Bolen, E.G. 1970. Sex ratios in the Black-bellied Tree Duck. *J. Wildl. Manage.* 34: 68–73.

Bolen, E.G. 1971. Pair-bond tenure in the Black-bellied Tree Duck. *J. Wildl. Manage.* 35: 385–88.

Bolen, E.G. 1973. Breeding Whistling Ducks *Dendrocygna* spp. in captivity. *Int. Zoo Ybk* 13: 32–38.

Bolen, E.G. and Beecham, J.J. 1970. Notes on the foods of juvenile Black-bellied Tree Ducks. *Wilson Bull.* 82: 325–26.

Bolen, E.G. and Forsyth, B.J. 1967. Foods of the Black-bellied Tree Duck in south Texas. *Wilson Bull.* 79: 43–49.

Bolen, E.G. and Rylander, M.K. 1983. *Whistling-ducks: zoogeography, ecology, and anatomy*, Spec. Publ. No. 20. Museum, Texas Tech Univ., Lubbock.

Bolen, E.G. and Smith, E.N. 1979. Notes on the incubation behavior of Black-bellied Whistling-Ducks. *Prairie Nat.* 11: 119–23.

Bonaparte, C.L. 1856. Conspectus Anserum Systematicus. *C.R. Séances Acad. Sci.* 43: 647–52.

Bond, J. 1958. *Third supplement to the checklist of the birds of the West Indies.* Acad. Nat. Sci., Philadelphia.

Bond, J. 1971. *The birds of the West Indies* (2nd edn). Houghton Mifflin, Boston.

Bookhout, T.A., Bednarik, K.E. and Kroll, R.W. 1989. The Great Lakes marshes. In *Habitat management for migrating and wintering waterfowl in North America* (ed. L.M. Smith, R.L. Pederson and R.M. Kaminski), pp.131–56. Texas Tech Univ. Press, Lubbock.

Bordage, D. and Savard, J-P.L. 1995. Black Scoter (*Melanitta nigra*). The Birds of North America, No. 177, (ed. A. Poole and F. Gill). AOU, Academy of Natural Sciences, Philadelphia.

Borodin, A.M. (ed.) 1984. *The red data book of the USSR: rare and endangered species of animals and plants*, Vol. 1 (2nd edn). Promyshlennost, Moscow.

Bortner, J.B. 1985. Bioenergetics of wintering tundra swans in the Mattamuskeet region of North Carolina. M.S. thesis. Univ. Maryland, College Park, US.

Bostwick, J.M. 1982. Habitat loss and hybridization: the dual threat to the Koloa. Unpubl. Senior Hons. thesis. Univ. Hawaii, Manoa, US.

Boswall, J. and MacIver, D. 1979. Nota sobre el pato vapor volador (*Tachyeres patachonicus*). *Hornero* 12: 75–78.

Botero, J.E. and Rusch, D.H. 1988. Recoveries of North American waterfowl in the neotropics. In *Waterfowl in winter* (ed. M. Weller), pp.469–82. Univ. Minnesota Press, Minneapolis.

Botero, J.E., Miret, H., and Velez, J.F. 1993. Andean Speckled Teal and Colombian Ruddy Duck at Lake Otun, Colombia. *IWRB Threatened Waterfowl Research Group Newsl.* 4: 8–9.

Bottjer, P.D. 1983. Systematic relationships among the Anatidae: an immunological study, with a history of Anatid classification and a system of classification. Unpubl. Ph.D. thesis. Yale Univ., New Haven, US.

Boudewijn, T. 1984. The role of digestibility in the selection of spring feeding sites by Brent Geese. *Wildfowl* 35: 97–105.

Bourne, G.R. 1979. Weights and linear measurements of Black-bellied Whistling-ducks in Guyana. In 1st Welder Wildlife Foundation Symp., Contrib. B-7, pp.186–88. Sinton, Texas.

Bourne, G.R. 1981. Food habits of Black-bellied Whistling-ducks occupying rice culture habitats. *Wilson Bull.* 93: 551–54.

Bouvier, J.M. 1974. The breeding biology of the Hooded Merganser in southwestern Québec, including interactions with Common Goldeneyes and Wood Ducks. *Can. Field-Nat.* 88: 323–30.

Bowe, M. 1997. Wasur. In *Birding Indonesia* (ed. P. Jepson and R. Ounsted), pp.176–77. Periplus, Hong Kong.

Bowler, J. 1993. The Radjah Shelduck in Seram, Maluku, Indonesia. *IWRB Threatened Waterfowl Research Group Newsl.* 3: 9–11.

Bowler, J. and Taylor, J. 1989. An annotated checklist of the birds of the Manusela National Park, Seram. Birds recorded on the Operation Raleigh Expedition. *Kukila* 4: 3–29.

Bowler, J.M. 1992. The growth and development of Whooper Swan cygnets *Cygnus cygnus. Wildfowl* 43: 27–39.

Bowler, J.M. 1994. The condition of Bewick's Swans *Cygnus columbianus bewickii* in winter as assessed by their abdominal profiles. *Ardea* 82: 241–48.

Bowler, J.M. 1996. Feeding strategies of Bewick's Swans (*Cygnus columbianus bewickii*) in winter. Unpubl. Ph.D. thesis. Univ. Bristol, UK.

Bowler, J.M., Butler, L. and Rees, E.C. 1993. Bewick's and Whooper Swans *Cygnus columbianus bewickii* and *C. cygnus*: the 1992–93 season. *Wildfowl* 44: 191–99.

Bowman, T., Stehn, R., Platte, R., Oates, R., Wege, M. and Walters, G. 1996. Population size and production of geese and eiders nesting on the Yukon-Kuskokwim Delta, Alaska in 1996, unpubl. rept. US Fish & Wildl. Serv., Anchorage.

Bowman, T.D., Stehn, R.A. and Scribner, K.T. 1997. Glaucous Gull predation of goslings on the Yukon-Kuskokwim Delta, Alaska, unpubl. rept. US Fish & Wildl. Serv., Anchorage.

Boyd, H. 1953. On encounters between White-fronted Geese in winter flocks. *Behaviour* 5: 85–129.

Boyd, H. 1957. Mortality and kill amongst British-ringed Teal *Anas crecca. Ibis* 99: 157–77.

Boyd, H. 1961. The number of Barnacle Geese in Europe in 1959–60. *Wildfowl* 12: 116–24.

Boyd, H. 1962. Population dynamics and the exploitation of ducks and geese. In *The exploitation of natural animal populations* (ed. E.D. le Cren and N.W. Holdgate), pp.85–95. Oxford, Blackwell.

Boyd, H. 1964. Wildfowl and other water birds found dead in England and Wales in January–March 1963. *Wildfowl* 15: 20–22.

Boyd, H. 1985. *The large-scale impact of agriculture on ducks in the prairie provinces, 1950–1981*, Prog. Notes, No. 119. Can. Wildl. Serv., Ottawa.

Boyd, H. 1988. Recent changes in waterfowl hunting effort and kill in Canada and the USA, Prog. Notes, No. 175. Can. Wildl. Serv., Ottawa.

Boyd, H. 1989. Waterfowl population levels in North America and their use in identifying Canadian wetlands of importance for breeding waterfowl. In *Flyways and reserve networks for waterbirds* (ed. H. Boyd and J-Y. Pirot), pp.76–84. Publ., No. 9. IWRB, Slimbridge, UK.

Boyd, H. 1990. Duck numbers in the USSR, the Western Palearctic and North America 1967–86: first comparisons. *Wildfowl* 41: 171–75.

Boyd, H. and Eltringham, S.K. 1962. The Whooper Swan in Great Britain. *Bird Study* 9: 217–41.

Boyd, H. and King, B. 1964. Effects of a severe winter on ducks breeding in north Somerset. *Wildfowl* 15: 47–50.

Boyd, H. and Madsen, J. 1997. Impacts of global change on Arctic-breeding bird populations and migration. In *Global change and Arctic terrestrial ecosystems* (ed. Oechal *et al.*), pp.201–17. New York, Springer Verlag.

Boyd, H. and Maltby, L. 1979. The Brant of the western Queen Elizabeth Islands, N.W.T. In *Management and biology of Pacific flyway geese* (ed. R.L. Jarvis and J.C. Bartonek), pp.5–21. OSU Book Store, Corvallis, Oregon.

Boyd, H., Maltby, L.S. and Reed, A. 1988. *Differences in the plumage patterns of Brant breeding in High Arctic Canada*, Prog. Notes, No. 174. Can. Wildl. Serv., Ottawa.

Bradley, P.E. 2000. *The birds of the Cayman Islands.* Checklist No. 19, BOU, Tring, UK.

Bräger, V.S. 1986. Brutbiologie und populationdynamik einer der Schellente (*Bucephala clangula*) in Norddeutschland. *Die Vogelwelt* 107: 1–18.

Braithwaite, L.W. 1976a. Breeding seasons of waterfowl in Australia. *Int. Ornith. Congr.* 16: 235–47.

Braithwaite, L.W. 1976b. Notes on the breeding of the Freckled Duck in the Lachlan River Valley. *Emu* 76: 127–32.

Braithwaite, L.W. 1977. Ecological studies of the Black Swan I. The egg, clutch and incubation. *Aust. Wildl. Res.* 4: 59–79.

Braithwaite, L.W. 1981. Ecological studies of the Black Swan. II. Behaviour and social organization. *Aust. Wildl. Res.* 8: 135–46.

Braithwaite, L.W. 1982. Ecological studies of the Black Swan. IV. The timing and success of breeding on two nearby lakes on the southern tablelands. *Aust. Wildl. Res.* 9: 261–75.

Braithwaite, L.W. and Frith, H.J. 1969. Waterfowl in an inland breeding swamp in New South Wales. *CSIRO Wildl. Res.* 14: 65–109.

Braithwaite, L.W., Maher, M.T., Briggs, S.V. and Parker, B.S. 1985a. *An aerial survey of wetland bird fauna in eastern Australia, October 1983*, Wildl. Rglds. Res. Tech. Mem., No. 21. CSIRO, Lyneham, ACT.

Braithwaite, L.W., Maher, M.T. and Parker, B.S. 1985b. *An aerial survey of wetland bird fauna in eastern Australia, October 1984*, Wildl. Rglds. Res. Tech. Mem., No. 23. CSIRO, Lyneham, ACT.

Braithwaite, L.W., Maher, M.T., Holmes, J. and Parker, B.S. 1986. *An aerial survey of wetland bird fauna in eastern Australia, October 1985*, Wildl. Rglds. Res. Tech. Mem., No. 24. CSIRO, Lyneham, ACT.

Braithwaite, L.W., Kingsford, R.T., Holmes, J. and Parker, B.S. 1987. *An aerial survey of wetland bird fauna* *in eastern Australia, October 1986*, Wildl. Rglds. Res. Tech. Mem., No. 27. CSIRO, Lyneham, ACT.

Brakhage, G.K. 1953. Migration and mortality of ducks hand-reared and wild-trapped at Delta, Manitoba. *J. Wildl. Manage.* 17: 465–77.

Brand, C.J. 1984. Avian cholera in the Mississippi Flyways during 1979–80. *J. Wildl. Manage.* 48: 399–406.

Brand, D.J. 1964. Nesting studies of the Cape Shoveller *Spatula capensis* and the Cape Teal *Anas capensis* in the Western Cape-Province 1957–1959. *Ostrich* Suppl. 6: 217–21.

Brandt, J.F. 1847. Fuligulam (Lampronettam) Fischeri. Nov. Avium Rossicarum Spec. Typis Academiae Caesareae Scientiarum, Petropoli.

Braude, M.I. 1987. Migration of *Cygnus cygnus* and *Cygnus bewickii* in the Lower Ob. In *Ecology and migration of swans in the USSR* (ed. E. Syroechkovski), pp.97–99. Nauka, Moscow.

Brazil, M.A. 1981. Geographical variation in the bill patterns of Whooper Swans. *Wildfowl* 32: 129–31.

Brazil, M.A. 1991. *The birds of Japan.* Christopher Helm and Black, London.

Brazil, M. A. 2003. *The Whooper Swan.* Poyser, London.

Breault, A.M. and Savard, J-P.L. 1991. *Status report on the distribution and ecology of Harlequin Ducks in British Columbia*, Tech. Rept. Ser., No. 110. Can. Wildl. Serv., Pacific and Yukon Region.

Brewer, G.L. 1988. Displays and breeding behavior of captive Ringed Teal *Callonetta leucophrys*. Unpubl. M.S. thesis. Univ. Minnesota, Minneapolis, US.

Brewer, G.L. 1989. Biparental care behaviour of captive Ringed Teal *Callonetta leucophrys*. *Wildfowl* 40: 7–13.

Brewer, G.L. 1990. Parental care behavior of the Chiloe Wigeon. Unpubl. Ph.D. thesis. Univ. Minnesota, Minneapolis, US.

Brewer, G.L. 1991. Courtship of ducklings by adult male Chiloe Wigeon (*Anas sibilatrix*). *Auk* 108: 969–73.

Brewer, G.L. 1997. Displays and breeding behaviour of the Chiloe Wigeon *Anas sibilatrix*. *Wildfowl* 47: 97–125.

Brewer, G.L. 2001. Displays and breeding behaviour of captive Ringed Teal *Callonetta leucophrys*. *Wildfowl* 52: 97–125.

Brewer, G.L. and Vilina, Y. 2002. Parental care behavior and double-brooding in Coscoroba Swans in Chile. In *Proceedings of the Fourth International Swan Symposium, 2001* (ed. E.C. Rees, S.L. Earnst and J. Coulson). *Waterbirds*, Special Publication 1: 278–84.

Brewer, T.M. 1854. *Wilson's American ornithology.* Charles L. Cornish, New York.

Brewster, W. 1902. An undescribed form of the Black Duck (*Anas obscura*). *Auk* 19: 183–88.

Brichetti, P.A., Canova, D.L. and Saino, N. 1984. Distribuzione e status degli Anatidae nidificanti in Italia e Corsica. *Avocetta* 8: 19–42.

Brickell, N. 1988. *Ducks, geese and swans of Africa and its outlying islands.* Fransden, Sandton.

Briggs, S.V. 1979. Daytime habitats of waterbirds at four swamps on the northern tablelands of New South Wales. *Emu* 79: 211–14.

Briggs, S.V. 1982. Food habits of the Freckled Duck and associated waterfowl in north-western New South Wales. *Wildfowl* 33: 88–93.

Briggs, S.V. 1988. Weight changes and reproduction in female Blue-billed and Musk Ducks compared with North American Ruddy Ducks. *Wildfowl* 39: 98–101.

Briggs, S.V 1989. Morphological prediction of body condition in Maned Ducks. *Aust. Wildl. Res.* 16: 605–09.

Briggs, S.V. and Lawler, W.G. 1991. Breeding adaptations of Southern Hemisphere, arid zone ducks. *Int. Ornith. Congr.* 20: 843–50.

Britton, P.L. (ed.) 1980. *Birds of East Africa.* EANHS, Nairobi, Kenya.

Brock, V.E. 1951a. Laysan Island bird census. *Elepaio* 12: 17–18.

Brock, V.E. 1951b. Some observations on the Laysan duck, *Anas wyvilliana laysanensis. Auk* 68: 371–72.

Brodeur, S., Savard, J.-P.L., Robert, M., Laporte, P., Lamothe, P., Titman, R.D. *et al.* 2002. Harlequin duck *Histrionicus histrionicus* population structure in eastern Nearctic. *J. Avian Biology* 33: 127–137.

Brodkorb, P. 1962. The systematic position of two Oligocene birds from Belgium. *Wilson Bull.* 79: 706–7.

Brodkorb, P. 1964. Catalogue of fossil birds: Part 2 (Anseriformes through Galliformes). *Bull. Florida State Mus. Biol. Sci* 8: 195–335.

Bromley, R.G. and Jarvis, R.L. 1993. The energetics of migration and reproduction of Dusky Canada Geese. *Condor* 95: 193–210.

Brooke, R.K. and Crowe, T.M. 1982. Variation in species richness among the off-shore islands of the southwestern Cape. *S. Afr. J. Zool.* 17: 49–58.

Brooks, A. 1938. Blue Duck or Mountain Duck. *Auk* 55: 272.

Brooks, A. 1945. The underwater actions of diving ducks. *Auk* 62: 517–23.

Brooks, T.M., Barnes, R., Batrina, L., Butchart, S.H.M., Clay, R.P., Esquivel, E.Z., et al. 1993. *Bird surveys and conservation in the Paraguayan Atlantic Forest: Project CANOPY '92 final report*, Internat. Study Rept., No. 57. BirdLife International, Cambridge.

Brooks, W.S. 1917. Notes on some Falkland Islands birds. *Bull. Mus. Comp. Zoo. at Harvard College.* 61: 135–60.

Brotherston, W. 1964. The numbers and behaviour of geese in the Lothians and Berwickshire. *Wildfowl* 15: 57–70.

Brouwer, G.A. and Tinbergen, L. 1939. De Verspreiding der Kleine Zwanen *Cygnus b. bewickii* Yarr. in de Zuiderzee, voor en na de verzoeting. *Limosa* 12: 1–18.

Brouwer, J. and Garnett, S. (ed.) 1990. *Threatened birds of Australia, an annotated list*, Rept., No. 68. RAOU, Moonee Pond, Victoria.

Brower, Jr, W.A., Searby, H.W., Wise, J.L., Diaz, H.F. and Prechtel, A.S. 1977. *Climatic atlas of the outer continental shelf waters and coastal regions of Alaska*, AEIDC Publ. B-77, Vol. 3. NOAA, Asheville.

Brown, A. and Gottschalk, H. 1988. Egyptian Goose (102) usurps Cape Teal (106). *Promerops, Newsletter of Cape Bird Club* 186: 12.

Brown, A.W., Brown, L.M. and Stevick, P.T. 2003. Sexing Mute Swans *Cygnus Olor* by discriminant analysis. *Ringing & Migration* 21: 174–80.

Brown, J.L. 1978. Avian communal breeding systems. *Ann. Rev. Ecol. Syst.* 9: 123–53.

Brown, J.L. 1987. *Helping and communal breeding in birds: ecology and evolution.* Princeton Univ. Press.

Brown, L.H., Urban, E.K. and Newman, K. 1982. *The birds of Africa*, Vol. 1. Academic Press, London.

Brown, M. and Dinsmore, J.J. 1986. Implications of marsh size and isolation for marsh bird management. *J. Wildl. Manage.* 50: 392–7.

Brown, M.J., Linton, E. and Rees, E.C. 1992. Causes of mortality among wild swans in Britain. *Wildfowl* 43: 70–79.

Brown, P.W. 1981. Reproductive ecology and productivity of white-winged scoter. Unpubl. Ph.D. thesis. Univ. Missouri, Columbia, US.

Brown, P.W. 1987. Influence of an unidentified epornitic on waterfowl nesting at Jessie Lake, Alberta. *Can. Field-Nat.* 101: 454–56.

Brown, P.W. and Brown, M.A. 1981. Nesting biology of the White-winged Scoter. *J. Wildl. Manage.* 45: 38–45.

Brown, P.W. and Fredrickson, L.H. 1983. Growth and moult progression of White-winged Scoter ducklings. *Wildfowl* 34: 115–19.

Brown, P.W. and Fredrickson, L.H. 1986. Food habits of breeding White-winged Scoters. *Can. J. Zool.* 64: 1652–54.

Brown, P.W. and Fredrickson, L.H. 1987a. Body and organ weights, and carcass composition of breeding female White-winged Scoters. *Wildfowl* 38: 103–7.

Brown, P.W. and Fredrickson, L.H. 1987b. Time budget and incubation behavior of breeding White-winged Scoters. *Wilson Bull.* 99: 50–55.

Brown, R., Ferguson, J., Lawrence, M. and Lees, D. 1987. *Tracks and signs of the birds of Britain and Europe. An identification guide.* Christopher Helm, London.

Brown, R.J. and Brown, M.N. 1997. Observations of breeding Musk Ducks. *Australian Bird Watcher* 17: 98–100.

Brown, R.J. and Brown, M.N. 1981. *Reports of the Middlesex Field Study Centre I–IV, 1976–1981.* RAOU, Perth.

Browne, R.A., Griffin, C.R., Chang, P.R., Hubley, M. and Martin, A.E. 1993. Genetic divergence among populations of the Hawaiian duck, Laysan duck, and Mallard. *Auk* 110: 49–56.

Brua, R.B. 1999. Ruddy Duck nesting success: do nest characteristics deter nest predation? *Condor* 101: 867–70.

Brugger, C. and Taborsky, M. 1993. Male incubation and its effect on reproductive success in the Black Swan *Cygnus atratus. Ethology* 96: 138–46.

Brush, A.H. 1976. Waterfowl feather proteins: analysis of use in taxonomic studies. *J. Zool., Lond.* 179: 467–98.

Bruzual, J.V. and Bruzual, I.B. 1983. Feeding habits of whistling ducks in the Clabozo ricefields, Venezuela, during the non-reproductive period. *Wildfowl* 34: 20–26.

Bryan, E.H., Jr 1942. *American Polynesia and the Hawaiian Chain.* Tongg Publishing Company, Honolulu.

Bryant, D.M. and Leng, J. 1975. Feeding distribution and behaviour of Shelduck in relation to food supply. *Wildfowl* 26: 26–30.

Buchsbaum, R., Wilson, J. and Valiela, I. 1986. Digestibility of plant constituents by Canada Geese and Atlantic Brant. *Ecology* 67: 386–93.

Budeau, D.A, Ratti, J.T. and Ely, C.R. 1991. Energy dynamics, foraging ecology and behavior of pre-nesting Greater White-fronted Geese. *J. Wildl. Manage.* 55: 556–63.

Buden, D.W. 1987. *The birds of the Caribbean.* Viking Press, New York.

Buffard, E. 1995. Anti-predator behaviour of flightless Kerguelen Pintail *Anas eatoni* in a cave on the Kerguelen Archipelago. *Wildfowl* 46: 66–68.

Buitron, D. and Nuechterlein, G.L. 1989. Male parental care of Patagonian Crested Ducks *Anas (Lophonetta) specularioides. Wildfowl* 40: 14–21.

Buller, W.L. 1888. *A history of the birds of New Zealand* (2nd edn). The Author, London.

Burger, J. 1974. Breeding adaptations of Franklin's Gull (*Larus pipixcan*) to a marsh habitat. *Anim. Behav.* 22: 521–67.

Burger, J. 1984. Grebes nesting in gull colonies: protective associations and early warning. *Amer. Natur.* 123: 327–37.

Burgers, J., Smit, J.J. and van der Voet, H. 1991. Origins and systematics of the Bean Goose *Anser fabilis* (Latham 1787) wintering in the Netherlands. *Ardea* 79: 307–16.

Burla, H. and Ribi, G. 1998. Density variation of the zebra mussel *Dreissena polymorpha* in Lake Zurich from 1976 to 1988. *Aquatic Sciences* 60: 145–56.

Burn, J. and Brickle, N. 1992. Status and notes on the ecology of *Cairina scutulata* (White-winged Wood

Duck) and *Ciconia stormi* (Storm's Stork) in the Sumatran provinces of Riau and Jambi, Indonesia. Spirit of Sumatra 1992: prelim. rept. WWT, Slimbridge, UK.

Burton, J.F. 1995. *Birds and climate change.* Helm, A. & C. Black, London.

Bustnes, J.O. 1996. Is parental care a constraint on the habitat use of Common Eider females? *Condor* 98: 22–26.

Bustnes, J.O. and Erikstad, K.E. 1988. The diets of sympatric wintering populations of Common Eiders *Somateria mollissima* and King Eider *S. spectabilis* in northern Norway. *Ornis Fenn.* 5: 163–68.

Bustnes, J.O. and Erikstad, K.E. 1990a. Effects of patagial tags on laying dates and egg size of Common Eiders. *J. Wildl. Manage.* 54: 216–18.

Bustnes, J.O. and Erikstad, K.E. 1990b. Size selection of common mussels, *Mytilus edulis*, by Common Eiders, *Somateria mollissima*: energy maximization or shell weight minimization? *Can. J. Zool.* 68: 2280–83.

Bustnes, J.O. and Lonne, O.J. 1997. Habitat partitioning among sympatric wintering Common Eiders *Somateria mollissima* and King Eider *Somateria spectabilis* in northern Norway. *Ibis* 139: 549–54.

Bustnes, J.O., Asheim, M., Bjorn, T.H., Gabrielsen, H. and Systad, G.H. 2000. The diet of Steller's Eiders wintering in Varangerfjord, northern Norway. *Wilson Bull.* 112: 8–13.

Butchart, D. (ed.) 2000. Interesting bird observations at Londolozi. *CCA Ecological Journal* 2: 172.

Butler, G.D., Jr 1961. Insects and other arthropods from Laysan Island. *Proc. Hawaiian Entomological Society* 17: 379–87.

Butler, P.J. 1991. Physiology of diving in ducks and other aquatic birds (excluding penguins). *Int. Ornith. Congr.* 20: 1875–86.

Butler, P.J. and Woakes, A.J. 1979. Changes in heart rate and respiratory frequency during natural behaviour of ducks, with particular reference to diving. *J. Exp. Biol.* 79: 283–300.

Butler, P.J. and Woakes, A.J. 1998. Behaviour and energetics of Svalbard Barnacle Geese during their autumn migration. *Norsk Pol. Skr.* 200: 165–74.

Butler, W.I. and Eldridge, W.D. 1998. Development of an aerial survey for Dusky Canada Geese on the Copper River Delta (abstract). In *Biology and management of*

Canada Geese, Int. Canada Goose Symp. (ed. D.H. Rusch, M.D. Samuel, D.D. Humburg and B.D. Sullivan), p.39. Milwaukee, Wisconsin.

Butler, W.I., Stehn, R.A. and Eldridge, W.D. 1998. Aerial surveys of Cackling Canada Geese nesting on the Yukon-Kuskokwim Delta, Alaska (abstract). In *Biology and management of Canada Geese*, Int. Canada Goose Symp. (ed. D.H. Rusch, M.D. Samuel, D.D. Humburg and B.D. Sullivan), p.40. Milwaukee, Wisconsin.

Buturlin, S.A. 1910. The true home of the Spectacled Eider. *Condor* 12: 46.

Buturlin, S.A. 1935. *Complete key to the birds of the USSR*, Vol. 2. Moscow.

Byrd, G.V. 1998. Current breeding status of the Aleutian Canada Goose, a recovering endangered species. In *Biology and management of Canada Geese*, Int. Canada Goose Symp. (ed. D.H. Rusch, M.D. Samuel, D.D. Humburg and B.D. Sullivan), pp.21–28. Milwaukee, Wisconsin.

Byrd, G.V., Williams, J.C. and Durand, A. 1992. Observations of Emperor Geese in the Aleutian Islands during the winter of 1991–1992, unpubl. rept. US Fish & Wildl. Serv., Adak, Alaska.

Byrd, G.V., Trapp, J.L. and Zeillemaker, C.F. 1994. Removal of introduced foxes: a case study in restoration of native birds. *Trans. N. Amer. Wildl. Nat. Res. Conf.* 59: 317–21.

Cadman, M.D., Eagles, P.F.J. and Heilleiner, F.M. 1987. *Atlas of the breeding birds of Ontario*. University of Waterloo Press. 617 pp.

Cain, B.W. 1970. Growth and plumage development of the Black-bellied Tree Duck, *Dendrocygnus autumnalis* (Linneaus). TAIUS, A&I Univ. Studies III, No. 1.

Cain, B.W. 1973. Effect of temperature on energy requirements and northward distribution of the Black-bellied Tree Duck. *Wilson Bull.* 85: 308–17.

Caithamer, D.F., Otto, M., Padding, P.I., Sauer, J.R. and Haas, G.H. 2000. Sea ducks in the Atlantic flyway: population status and a review of special hunting seasons. US Fish & Wildl. Serv., Office of Migratory Bird Management, Laurel, MD.

Calder, W.A. and King, J.R. 1974. Thermal and caloric relations of birds. In *Avian Biology*, Vol. 4 (ed. D.S. Farner, J.R. King and K.C. Parkes), pp.259–413. Acad. Press, New York.

Caldwell, P.J. and Cornwell, G.W. 1975. Incubation behavior and temperatures of the Mallard duck. *Auk* 92: 706–31.

Callaghan, D.A. 1997. Conservation status of the Torrent Ducks *Merganetta*. *Wildfowl* 48: 166–79.

Callaghan, D.A. (comp.) 2001. European Union Species Action Plan for the Ferruginous Duck *(Aythya nyroca)*. In N. Schäffer and U. Gallo-Orsi (eds), *European Union action plans for eight priority bird species*. European Commission.

Callaghan, D.A. and Green, A.J. 1993. Wildfowl at risk. *Wildfowl* 44: 149–69.

Callaghan, D.A. and Kirby, J.S. 1996. Releases of *Anatidae* for hunting and the effects on wetland biodiversity: a review and evaluation. *Gibier Faune Sauvage* 13: 1049–68.

Callaghan, D.A., Kirby, J.S. and Hughes, B. 1998. The effects of waterfowl hunting on biodiversity: implications for sustainability. In *Harvesting wild species: implications for biodiversity* (ed. C. Freese), pp.507–74. Johns Hopkins Univ. Press.

Calvo, B. and Furness, R.W. 1992. A review of the use and the effects of marks and devices on birds. *Ringing & Migration* 13: 129–51.

Campbell, A.J. 1899. On the trachea of the Freckled Duck of Australia. *Ibis* ser. 7, 5: 362.

Campbell, A.J. 1901. *Nests and eggs of Australian birds*. Pawson and Brailsford, Sheffield, Australia.

Campbell, B. 1985. Breeding age of Tule White-fronted Geese. *J. Field Ornithol.* 56: 286.

Campbell, C.R.G. and Ogilvie, M.A. 1982. Failure of Whooper Swan to moult wing feathers. *Brit. Birds* 75: 578.

Campbell, H. 1989. Stray feathers. *Albratross, Newsletter of Natal Bird Club* 299: 7.

Campbell, J.W. 1947. The food of some British waterfowl. *Ibis* 89: 429–32.

Campbell, L.H. 1984. The impact of changes in sewage treatment on seaducks wintering in the Firth of Forth. *Biol. Cons.* 28: 173–80.

Campbell, R.W., Dawe, N.K., McTaggart-Cowan, I., Cooper, J.M., Kaiser, G.W. and McNall, M.C.E. 1990. *The birds of British Columbia*, Vol. 1. Royal British Columbia Museum, Victoria.

Camphuysen, C.J., Berrevoets, C.M., Cremers, H.J.W.M., Dekinga, A., Dekker, R, Ens, B.J. *et al.* 2002. Mass mortality of common eiders (*Somateria mollisima*) in the Dutch Wadden Sea, winter 1999/2000: starvation in a commercially exploited wetland of international importance. *Biol. Cons.* 106: 303–17.

Campredon, P. 1981. Hivernage du canard siffleur *Anas penelope* L. en Carmargue (France): Stationnements et activités. *Alauda* 49: 161–93.

Canevari, M., Canevari, P., Carrizo, G.R., Harris, G., Rodríguez Mata, J. and Straneck, R.J. 1991. *Nueva guía de las aves Argentinas*. Fundación Acindar, Buenos Aires.

Carbone, C. and Houston, A.I. 1994. Patterns in the diving behaviour of the Pochard, *Aythya ferina*: a test of an optimality model. *Anim. Behav.* 48: 457–65.

Carbone, C. and Owen, M. 1995. Differential migration of the sexes of Pochard *Aythya ferina*: results from a European survey. *Wildfowl* 46: 99–108.

Carbonell, M. 1983. Comparative studies of stiff-tailed ducks (Tribe Oxyurini, Anatidae). Unpubl. Ph.D. thesis. Univ. Cardiff, UK.

Cargill, S.M. and Jefferies, R.L. 1984. The effects of grazing by Lesser Snow Geese on the vegetation of a sub-arctic salt marsh. *J. Appl. Ecol.* 21: 669–86.

Carney, S.M. 1983. Species, age, and sex identification of nearctic goldeneyes from wings. *J. Wildl. Manage.* 47: 754–61.

Carney, S.M. 1992. *Species, age and sex identification of ducks using wing plumage.* US Fish & Wildl. Serv., Washington.

Carney, S.M., Sorenson, M.F. and Martin, E.M. 1983. *Distribution of waterfowl species harvested in the states and counties during 1971–80 hunting seasons,* Spec. Sci. Rep.- Wildl. No. 254. US Fish & Wildl. Serv., Washington.

Caroll, J.J. 1932. A change in the distribution of the Fulvous Whistling Duck (*Dendrocygna bicolor helva*) in Texas. *Auk* 49: 343–44.

Carp, E. 1991. *Censo neotropical de aves acuaticas 1990.* IWRB, Slimbridge, UK.

Carss, D.N. and Marquiss, M. 1992. Avian predation of farmed and natural fisheries. In *Interactions between fisheries and the environment* (eds M.C. Lucas, I. Diack and L. Laird), pp.179–96. Proc. Inst. Fisheries Management.

Carter, B.C. 1958. *The American Goldeneye in central New Brunswick,* Wildl. Manage. Bull., Ser. 2, No. 9. Can. Wildl. Serv., Ottawa.

Carter, T. 1904. Birds occurring in the region of the north-west Cape. *Emu* 3: 207–13.

Casal, P.S. 1950. La Avutarda de Mar *Chloëphaga hibrida hibrida* (Molina). *Hornero* 9: 167–74.

Casares, J. 1934. Palmípedos Argentinos. Las avutardas. *Hornero* 5: 289–306.

Caspers, G-J., Uit de Weerd, D., Wattel, J. and de Jong, W.W. 1997. a-Crystallin sequences support a galliform/anseriform clade. *Mol. Phylogen. Evol.* 7: 185–88.

Caspers, H. 1967. Biology of a hypersaline lagoon in a tropical atoll island (Laysan). *Symp. Recent Advances in Tropical Ecology:* 326–33.

Caspers, H. 1981. On the ecology of hypersaline lagoons on Laysan Atoll and Kauai Island, Hawaii, with special reference to the Laysan duck, *Anas laysanensis,* Rothschild. *Hydrobiologia* 82: 261–70.

Cassels, R. 1984. The role of prehistoric man in the faunal extinctions of New Zealand and other Pacific islands. In *Quaternary extinctions* (ed. P.S. Martin and R.G. Klein), pp.741–67. Univ. Arizona Press, Tucson.

Castellanos, A. 1935. Observaciones de algunas aves de Tierra del Fuego y Isla de los Estados (part 1). *Hornero* 6: 22–37.

Castelli, P.M. and Applegate, J.E. 1989. Economic loss caused by Tundra Swans feeding in cranberry bogs. *Trans. N.E. Sect. Wildl. Soc.* 46: 17–23.

Castro, H., Nevado, J.C. , Paracuellos, M. and López, J.M. 1994. La Malvasía (*Oxyura leucocephala*) en la provincia de Almería. Evolución poblacional, nidificación y selección de hábitat. *Oxyura* 7: 119–33.

Chabreck, R.H., Joanen, R. and Paulus, S.L. 1989. Southern coastal marshes and lakes. In *Habitat management for migrating and wintering waterfowl in North America* (ed. L.M. Smith, R.L. Pederson and R.M. Kaminski), pp.249–77. Texas Tech Univ. Press, Lubbock.

Chalmers, M.L. 1986. *Annotated checklist of the birds of Hong Kong.* Hong Kong Birdwatching Society, Hong Kong.

Chamberlain, E.B. 1960. *Florida waterfowl populations, habitats and management,* Tech. Bull., No. 7. Florida Game and Fresh Water Fish Comm. Tallahassee.

Chambers, A. 1990. The White-winged Wood Duck, *Cairina scutulata*, in Way Kambas National Park. Unpubl. expedition rept. Southampton Univ.

Chandler, R.M. 1990. Fossil birds of the San Diego Formation, late Pliocene, Blancan, San Diego County, California. *Ornithol. Monogr.* 44: 76–161.

Chapin, J.P. 1932. Birds of the Belgian Congo, I. *Bull. Am. Mus. Nat. Hist.* 65: 503–7.

Chapman, F.M. 1943. *Birds and man*, Guide Leaflet Ser., No. 115. Am. Mus. Nat. Hist., New York.

Charman, K. 1979. Feeding ecology and energetics of the Dark-bellied Brent Goose (*Branta bernicla bernicla*) in Essex and Kent. In *Ecological processes in coastal environments* (ed. R.L. Jefferies and A.J. Davy), pp.451–65. Blackwell Scientific Publications, Oxford.

Charnov, E.L. and Krebs, J.R. 1974. On clutch-size and fitness. *Ibis* 116: 217–19.

Chaudhry, A.A., Gill, A.H. and Ali, Z. 1997. Conservation of the White-headed Duck in the Salt Range Lakes (Ucchali complex), Punjab-Pakistan. Unpubl. rept. Punjab Wildlife Research Institute, Faisalabad, Pakistan.

Chavez-Ramirez, F. 1995. Sex-biased kleptoparasitism of Hooded Mergansers by Ring-billed Gulls. *Wilson Bull.* 107: 379–82.

Cheke, A.S. 1987. An ecological history of the Mascarene Islands, with particular reference to extinctions and introductions of land vertebrates. In *Studies of Mascarene Island birds* (ed. A.W. Diamond), pp.5–89. Cambridge Univ. Press.

Cheneval, J. 1984. Les oiseaux aquatiques du grisement Aquitanien de Saint-Gerandle Puy (France): revision systematique. *Palaeovertebrata* 14: 33–115.

Cheneval, J. 1987. Les Anatidae (Aves, Anseriformes) du Miocene de France: révision systématique et évolution. In *L'evolution des oiseaux d'après le témoignage des fossiles* (ed. C. Mourer-Chauviré), pp.137–57. Documents du Lab. Géol. de Lyon, No. 99. Laboratoire Géologique de Lyon.

Cheng, K.M., Burns, J.T. and McKinney, F. 1982. Forced copulation in captive Mallards (*Anas platyrhynchos*). II. Temporal factors. *Anim. Behav.* 30: 695–99.

Cheng, T.H. 1941. A winter census of birds along the Shaowu River in North Fukian. *Peking Nat. Hist. Soc. Bull.* 16: 85–90.

Cheng, T.H. (ed.) 1964. *China's Economic Fauna: Birds* (trans. US Dept of Commerce, Washington.). Science Publishing Society, Peking.

Cheng, T.H. (ed.) 1979. *Fauna Sinica Aves*, Vol. 2. Science Press, Academia Sinica, Peking.

Chi, Y.L. 1961. Bird Island. *Orn. Mitt.* 13: 222–24.

Chilton, G. 1997. Labrador Duck (*Camptorhynchus labradorius*). The Birds of North America, No. 307 (ed. A. Poole and F. Gill). AOU, Washington, and Academy of Natural Sciences, Philadelphia.

Ching, H.L. 1989. *Profilicollis botulus* (Van Cleave, 1916) from diving ducks and shore crabs of British Columbia. *J. Parasitol.* 75: 33–37.

Chisholm, A. and Leigh-Hunt, S. 1996. Age and sex determination in captive Marbled Teal. Unpubl. undergrad. thesis. Univ. Bristol, UK.

Choudhury, A.U. 1990 *Checklist of the birds of Assam*. Sofia Press, Guwahati. (AC-LWD)

Choudhury, A.U. 1991. Bird observations from Sibsagar District, Assam, India. *Forktail* 6: 35–42.

Choudhury, S. 1995. Divorce in birds: a review of the hypotheses. *Anim. Behav.* 50: 413–29.

Choudhury, S. and Black, J.M. 1992. Testing the behavioural dominance and dispersal hypothesis in a wintering flock of pochard. *Ornis Scand.* 22: 155–59.

Choudhury, S. and Black, J.M. 1993. Mate choice strategies in geese: evidence for a 'partner-hold' strategy. *Anim. Behav.* 46: 747–57.

Choudhury, S. and Black, J.M. 1994. Barnacle Geese preferentially pair with familiar associates from early life. *Anim. Behav.* 48: 81–88.

Choudhury, S., Jones, C., Black, J.M. and Prop, J. 1993. Adaption of young and intraspecific nest parasitism in Barnacle Geese. *Condor* 95: 860–68.

Choudhury, S., Black, J.M. and Owen, M. 1996. Body size, fitness and compatibility in Barnacle Geese. *Ibis* 138: 175–84.

Christensen, N.H. 1967. Moult migration of Pink-footed Goose (*Anser fabilis brachyrhynchus* Baillon) from Iceland to Greenland. *Dansk Ornith. Foren. Tidsskr.* 61: 55–66.

Christidis, L. and Boles, W.E. 1994. *The taxonomy and species of birds of Australia and its territories.* Monogr., No. 2. RAOU, Melbourne.

Christmas, J.Y. 1960. Greater and Lesser Scaup feeding on dead Gulf Menhaden. *Auk* 77: 346–47.

Christopher, M.W., Hill, E.P. and Steffen, D.E. 1988. Use of catfish ponds by waterfowl wintering in Mississippi. In *Waterfowl in winter* (ed. M. Weller), pp.413–18. Univ. Minnesota Press, Minneapolis.

Chronister, C.D. 1985. Egg-laying and incubation behavior of Black-bellied Whistling Ducks. Unpubl. M.S. thesis. Univ. Minnesota, Minneapolis, US.

Chu, D.S., Nichols, J.D., Hestbeck, J.B. and Hines, J.E. 1995. Banding reference areas and survival rates of Green-winged Teal, 1950–89. *J. Wildl. Manage.* 59: 487–98.

Clancey, P.A. 1967. *Gamebirds of southern Africa*. Purnell, Cape Town.

Clancey, P.A. 1996. *The birds of Southern Mozambique*. African Bird Book Publishing, Westville, KwaZulu-Natal.

Clapp, R.B. and Wirtz, W.O. 1975. *Natural history of Lisianski Island, northwestern Hawaiian Islands*, Atoll Research Bull. 186.

Clapp, R.B., Klimkiewicz, K. and Kennard, J.H. 1982. Longevity records of North American birds: Gaviidae through Alcidae. *J. Field Ornithol.* 53: 81–124.

Clark, A. 1964. The Maccoa Duck (*Oxyura maccoa* (Eyton)). *Ostrich* 35: 264–76.

Clark, A. 1965. Identification of sexes of the Hottentot Teal *Anas punctata* Burchell in the field. *Ostrich* 36: 95.

Clark, A. 1966. The social behaviour patterns of the Southern Pochard *Netta erythrophthalma brunnea*. *Ostrich* 37: 45–46.

Clark, A. 1969. The behaviour of the White-backed Duck. *Wildfowl* 20: 71–74.

Clark, A. 1971. The behaviour of the Hottentot Teal. *Ostrich* 42: 131–36.

Clark, A. 1978. Some aspects of the behaviour of whistling ducks in South Africa. *Ostrich* 49: 31–39.

Clark, A. 1979a. The breeding of the White-backed Duck on the Witwatersrand. *Ostrich* 50: 59–60.

Clark, A. 1979b. Variations in the external features of the Spur-winged Goose. *Bull. BOC* 99: 83–85.

Clark, A. 1980. Notes on the breeding biology of the Spur-winged Goose. *Ostrich* 51: 179–82.

Clark, G.M., O'Meara, D. and Van Weelden, J.W. 1958. An epizootic among eider ducks involving an acanthocephalid worm. *J. Wildl. Manage.* 22: 204–5.

Clark, J.A., Wernham, C.V., Balmer, D.E, Adams, S.Y., Blackburn, J.R., Griffin B.M. *et al.* 2000. Bird ringing in Britain and Ireland in 1998. *Ringing & Migration* 20: 39–93.

Clark, J.A., Wernham, C.V., Balmer, D.E, Adams, S.Y., Griffin B.M., Blackburn, J.R. *et al.* 2001. Bird ringing in Britain and Ireland in 1999. *Ringing & Migration* 20: 239–88.

Clark, J.A., Balmer, D.E, Blackburn, J.R., Milne, L.J., Robinson, R.A., Wernham, C.V. *et al.* 2002. Bird ringing in Britain and Ireland in 2000. *Ringing & Migration* 21: 25–61.

Clark, J.A., Balmer, D.E., Adams, S.Y., Grantham, M.J., Blackburn, J.R., Robinson, R.A. *et al.* 2002. Bird ringing in Britain and Ireland in 2001. *Ringing & Migration* 21: 80–143.

Clark, R.G. and Gentle, G.C. 1990. Estimates of grain passage time in captive Mallards. *Can. J. Zool.* 68: 2275–79.

Clarke, T., Lorenzo Gutiérrez, J.A. and King, J. 1995. The Lesser Scaup on the Canary Islands: the first female for the western Palearctic. *Birding World* 8(2): 52–55.

Clausen, P. and Bustnes, J.O. 1998. Flyways of North Atlantic Light-bellied Brent Geese *Branta bernicla hrota* reassessed by satellite telemetry. *Norsk Pol. Skr.* 200: 235–51.

Clawson, R.L., Hartman, G.W. and Fredrickson, L.H. 1979. Dump nesting in a Missouri Wood Duck population. *J. Wildl. Manage.* 43: 347–55.

Cleland, J.B. 1911. Examination of contents of stomachs and crops of Australian birds. *Emu* 11: 79–95.

Clutton-Brock, T.H. (ed.) 1988. *Reproductive success*. Chicago Univ. Press.

Coates, B.J. 1985. *Birds of Papua New Guinea*, Vol. 1. Dove Public., Alderley, Queensland, Australia.

Cody, M.L. 1966. A general theory on clutch size. *Evol.* 20: 174–84.

Cohen, J.B., Barclay, J.S., Major, A.R. and Fisher, J.P. 2000. Wintering Greater Scaup as biomonitors of metal contamination in federal wildlife refuges in the Long Island region. *Arch. Environ. Contam. Toxicol.* 38: 83–92.

Coimbra-Filho, A.F. 1964. Notas sobre a marreca-ananai *Amazonetta brasiliensis* (Gmelin, 1782), sua reproducao em cativeiro e ensaios de repovoamento. *Rev. Brasil. Biol.* 24: 383–91.

Coimbra-Filho, A.F. 1965. Apontamentos sobre 'Cairina moschata' (L., 1758) e seu hibridismo com 'Anas p. platyrhynchos' L., 1758 (Anatidae, Aves). *Rev. Brasil. Biol.* 25: 387–94. [Notes on *Cairina moschata* and its hybrid with *Anas platyrhynchos*.]

Coker, C.R., McKinney, F., Hays, H., Briggs, S.V. and Cheng, K.M. 2002. Intromittent organ morphology and testis size in relation to mating system in waterfowl. *Auk* 119: 403–13.

Colahan, B.D. 1984. The ecology and conservation of waterfowl in Natal. Unpublished MSc dissertation, University of Natal, Pietermaritzburg.

Coleman, A.E. and Minton, C.D.T. 1979. Pairing and breeding of Mute Swans in relation to natal area. *Wildfowl* 30: 27–30.

Coleman, A.E. and Minton, C.D.T. 1980. Mortality of Mute Swan progeny in an area of south Staffordshire. *Wildfowl* 31: 22–28.

Coles, B. and Coles, J. 1989. *People of the wetlands*. Thames and Hudson, London.

Coles, J. 1984. *The archeology of wetlands*. Edinburgh Univ. Press.

Collar, N.J. 1996. Species concepts and conservation: a response to Hazevoet. *Bird Conserv. Int.* 6: 197–200.

Collar, N.J., Gonzaga, L.P., Krabbe, N., Madrono-Nieto, A., Narango, L.G., Parker, T.A., III. 1992. *Threatened birds of the Americas: the ICBP/IUCN red data book*. ICBP, Cambridge, UK.

Collar, N.J., Crosby, M.J. and Stattersfield, A.J. 1994. *Birds to watch 2. The world list of threatened birds*, Cons. Ser., No. 4. BirdLife International, Cambridge, UK.

Collias, N.E. 1962. The behaviour of ducks. In *The behaviour of domestic animals* (ed. E.A.E. Hafez), pp.565–85. London.

Collier, K.J., Moralee, S.J. and Wakelin, M.D. 1993. Factors affecting distribution of Blue Duck *Hymenolaimus malacorhynchos* on New Zealand rivers. *Biol. Cons.* 63: 119–26.

Conant, B., Hodges, J.I. and King, J.G. 1991a. Continuity and advancement of Trumpeter Swan *Cygnus buccinator* and Tundra Swan *Cygnus columbianus* population monitoring in Alaska. *Wildfowl* Spec. Suppl. 1: 125–36.

Conant, B., Hodges, J.I., Groves, D.J. and King, J.G. 1991b. *Alaska Trumpeter Swan status report*. US Fish & Wildl. Serv., Juneau, Alaska.

Conant, B., Hodges, J.I., Groves, D.J. and King, J.G. 2002. Census of Trumpter Swans on Alaskan nesting habitats, 1968–2000 In *Proceedings of the Fourth International Swan Symposium, 2001* (ed. E.C. Rees, S.L. Earnst and J. Coulson). *Waterbirds*, Special Publication 1: 3–7.

Conant, S., Christensen, C.C., Conant, P., Gagne, W.C. and Goff, M.L. 1983. The unique terrestrial biota of the northwestern Hawaiian Islands. In 2nd Symp. Resource Investigations in the Northwestern Hawaiian Islands, Vol. 1 (ed. R.W. Grigg and K.Y. Tanoue).

Conover, B. 1943. A study of the Torrent Ducks. *Field Mus. Nat. Hist. (Zool. Ser.)* 24: 345–56.

Conover, H.B., Boardman H. and Hellmayr, C.E. 1948. *Catalogue of birds of the Americas and adjacent islands*, Field Mus. Nat. Hist., Zool. Ser. 13, Publ., No. 615, Part 1, No. 2. Quoted in Ecology of the migrating and wintering flocks of the small white-cheeked geese within the south central United States (R.E. Marquardt 1962). Unpubl. Ph.D. thesis, Oklahoma State Univ., Oklahoma, US.

Conover, M.R. and Kaina, G.S. 1999. Reproductive success of exotic Mute Swans in Connecticut. *Auk* 116: 1127–31.

Conover, M.R, Reese, J.G. and Brown, A.D. 2000. Costs and benefits of subadult plumage in Mute Swans: testing hypotheses for the evolution of delayed plumage maturation. *Amer. Natur.* 156: 193–200.

Conroy, M.J. and Eberhardt, R.T. 1983. Variation in survival and recovery rates of Ring-necked Ducks. *J. Wildl. Manage.* 47: 127–37.

Cooch, E.G. and Cooke, F. 1991. Demograpic changes in a Snow Goose population: biological and management implication. In *Bird population studies. Relevance to conservation and management.* (ed. C.M. Perrins, J-D. Lebreton and G.M. Hirons), pp.168–89. OUP.

Cooch, E.G., Lank, D.B., Dzubin, A., Rockwell, R.F. and Cooke, F. 1991. Body size variation in Lesser Snow Geese: environmental plasticity in gosling growth rate. *Ecology* 72: 503–12.

Cooch, F.G. 1961. Ecological aspects of the Blue-Snow Goose complex. *Auk* 78: 72–89.

Cooke, F. and Ryder, P.J. 1971. The genetics of polymorphism in the Ross's Goose (*Anser rossii*). *Evolution* 25: 483–90.

Cooke, F., MacInnes, C.D. and Prevett, J.P. 1975. Gene flow between breeding populations of the Lesser Snow Goose. *Auk* 92: 493–510.

Cooke, F., Bousfield, M.A. and Sadura, A. 1981. Mate change and reproductive success in the Lesser Snow Goose. *Condor* 83: 322–27.

Cooke, F., Findlay, C.S. and Rockwell, R.F. 1984. Recruitment and the timing of reproduction in Lesser Snow Geese (*Chen caerulescens caerulescens*). *Auk* 101: 451–58.

Cooke, F., Rockwell, R.F. and Lank, D.B. 1995. *The Snow Geese of La Pérouse Bay: natural selection in the wild*. OUP.

Cooper, A., Rhymer, J., James, H.F., Olson, S.L., McIntosh, C.E., Sorenson, M.D. et al. 1996. Ancient DNA and island endemics. *Nature* 381: 484.

Cooper, J.A. 1978. The history and breeding biology of the Canada Geese of Marshy Point, Manitoba. *Wildl. Monogr.* 61: 1–87.

Cooper, J.A. 1979. Trumpeter Swan nesting behaviour. *Wildfowl* 30: 55–71.

Cooper, J.A. and Hickin, J.R. 1972. Chronology of hatching by laying sequence in Canada Geese. *Wilson Bull.* 84: 90–92.

Corbin, K.W., Livezey, B.C. and Humphrey, P.S. 1988. Genetic differentiation among the steamer-ducks (Anatidae: *Tachyeres*): an electrophoretic analysis. *Condor* 90: 773–81.

Cornelius, S.E. 1977. Food and resource utilization of wintering Redheads on lower Laguna Madre. *J. Wildl. Manage.* 41: 374–85.

Corrick, A.H. 1981. Wetlands of Victoria II. Wetlands and waterbirds of south Gippsland. *Proc. R. Soc. Vict.* 92: 187–200.

Corrick, A.H. 1982. Wetlands of Victoria III. Wetlands and waterbirds between Port Phillip Bay and Mount Emu Creek. *Proc. R. Soc. Vict.* 94: 69–87.

Corrick, A.H. and Norman, F.I. 1980. Wetlands and waterbirds of the Snowy River and Gippsland Lakes catchment. *Proc. R. Soc. Vict.* 91: 1–15.

Coscrove, P. 2003. Mandarin Ducks in northern Scotland and the potential consequences for breeding Goldeneye. *Scottish Birds* 24: 1–10.

Cottam, C. 1939. *Food habits of North American diving ducks*, Tech. Bull., No. 643. US Dept Agric., Washington.

Cottam, C. and Glazener, W.C. 1959. Late nesting of water birds in South Texas. *Trans. N. Amer. Wildl. Nat. Res. Conf.* 24: 382–94.

Cottam, C. and Uhler, F.M. 1937. *Birds in relation to fishes*, Wildlife Research and Management Leaflet BS-83. Bur. Biol. Survey, Washington.

Cottam, C., Lynch, J.J. and Nelson, A.L. 1944. Food habits and management of American sea brant. *J. Wildl. Manage.* 8: 36–56.

Cotter, W.B., Jr 1957. A seriological analysis of some Anatid classifications. *Wilson Bull.* 69: 291–300.

Coues, E. 1884. *Key to North American birds* (2nd edn). Estes and Lauriat, Boston.

Coulson, J.C. 1984. The population dynamics of the Eider Duck *Somateria mollissima* and evidence of extensive non-breeding by adult ducks. *Ibis* 126: 525–43.

Coulson, J.C. and Thomas, C.S. 1983. Mate choice in the Kittiwake Gull. In *Mate choice* (ed. P.P.G. Bateson), pp.361–76. Cambridge Univ. Press.

Couto de Magalhaes, A. 1939. *Ensaio sobre a fauna brasileira*. Tipografica Brasil, Rothschild, Sao Paulo.

Cowan, P.J. 1974. Individual differences in alarm calls of Canada Geese leading broods. *Auk* 91: 189–91.

Cowardin, L.M. and Blohm, R.J. 1992. Breeding population inventories and measures of recruitment. In *The ecology and management of breeding waterfowl* (ed. B.D.J. Batt, A.D. Afton, M.G. Anderson, C.D. Ankney, D.H. Johnson, J.A. Kadlec *et al.*), pp.423–45. Univ. Minnesota Press, Minneapolis.

Cowardin, L.M., Gilmer, D.S. and Shaiffer, C.W. 1985. Mallard recruitment in the agricultural environment of North Dakota. *Wildl. Monogr.* 92: 1–37.

Cowardin, L.M., Shaffer, T.L. and Kraft, K.M. 1995. How much habitat management is needed to meet Mallard production objectives. *Wildl. Soc. Bull.* 23: 48–55.

Cowles, G.S. 1987. The fossil record. In *Studies of Mascarene Island birds* (ed. A.W. Diamond), pp.90–100. Cambridge Univ. Press.

Cowles, G.S. 1994. A new genus, three new species and two new records of extinct Holocene birds from Reúnion Island, Indian Ocean. *Geobios* 27: 87–93.

Cowling, S.J. and Davies, S.J.J.F. 1983. *Status of Australian birds with special reference to captive breeding*, Tech. Rept. Ser., No. 1: 1–21. Field Management Branch, Dept Conservation, Forests and Lands, Fisheries and Wildlife Service, Victoria.

Cox, C.B. and Moore, P.D. 1973. *Biogeography: an ecological and evolutionary approach.* Blackwell, Oxford.

Cox, J.A. 1975. *The endangered ones.* Crown, New York.

Crabtree, R.L. and Wolfe, M.L. 1988. Effects of alternate prey on skunk predation of waterfowl nests. *Wildl. Soc. Bull.* 16: 163–69.

Cracraft, J. 1980. Avian phylogeny and intercontinental biogeographic patterns. *Int. Ornith. Congr.* 18(2): 1302–8.

Cracraft, J. 1981. Toward a phylogenetic classification of the recent birds of the world (Class Aves). *Auk* 98: 681–714.

Cracraft, J. 1983. Species concepts and speciation analysis. *Current Ornithol.* 1: 159–87.

Cracraft, J. 1986. The origin and early diversification of birds. *Paleobiology* 12: 383–99.

Cracraft, J. 1987. DNA hybridization and avian phylogenies. *Evol. Biol.* 21: 47–96.

Cracraft, J. and Clarke, J. 2001. The basal clades of modern birds. In *New perspectives on the origin and early evolution of birds: proceedings of the international symposium in honor of John H. Ostrom* (ed. J. Gauthier and L.F. Gall), pp.143–56. Yale Univ. Press, New Haven, US.

Cracraft, J. and Mindell, D.P. 1989. The early history of modern birds: a comparison of molecular and morphological evidence. In *The hierarchy of life* (ed. B. Fernholm, K. Bremer and H. Jörnvall), pp.389–403. Elsevier, Amsterdam.

Cracraft, J., Barker, F.K., Braun, M.J., Harshman, J., Dyke, G., Feinstein, J. et al. 2004. Phylogenetic relationships among modern birds (Neornithes): Toward an avian tree of life. In *Assembling the tree of life* (eds. J. Cracraft and M.J. Donoghue), pp 468–69. Oxford University Press, New York.

Craib, C.L. 1975. The repetitive use of a nest site, and predator response in the Egyptian Goose. *Witwatersrand Bird Club News* 91: 5.

Cramp, S. and Simmons, K.E.L. (ed.) 1977. *The birds of the Western Palearctic. Handbook of the birds of Europe, the Middle East and North Africa*, Vol. 1. OUP.

Cranswick, P.A., Bowler, J.M., Delany, S.N., Einarsson, Ó., Garðarsson, A., McElwaine, J.G. et al. 1996. Numbers of Whooper Swans *Cygnus cygnus* in Iceland, Ireland and Britain in January 1995: results of the international Whooper Swan census. *Wildfowl* 47: 17–30.

Cranswick, P.A., Paynter, D.B., Sultanov, E.H., Abuladze, A., Hearn, R.D. and Quinn, J.L. 1998. Ornithological Surveys of the Western Route Export Pipeline in Azerbaijan and Georgia: September/October 1997 and February/March 1998. WWT Wetlands Advisory Service rept to Environment and Resource Technology Ltd and Azerbaijan International Operating Company.

Cranswick, P.C., Colhoun, K., Einarsson, Ó., McElwaine, G., Garðarsson, A., Pollitt, M. and Rees, E.C. 2002. The status and distribution of the Icelandic Whooper Swan population: results of the international Whooper Swan census 2000. In Proceedings of the Fourth International Swan Symposium, 2001 (ed. E.C. Rees, S.L. Earnst and J. Coulson), *Waterbirds* 25, Special Publication 1: 37–48.

Crawshay, R. 1907. *The birds of Tierra del Fuego.* Quaritch, London.

Cresswell, W., Yerekov, S., Berezovikov, N., Mellanby, R., Bright, S., Catry, P. et al. 1999. Important wetlands in northern and eastern Kazakhstan. *Wildfowl* 50: 181–94.

Crissey, W.F. 1969. *Prairie potholes from a continental viewpoint*, Rept Ser., No. 6, pp.161–71. Can. Wildl. Serv., Ottawa.

Crome, F.H.J. 1985a. Australian waterfowl do not necessarily breed on a rising water level. *Aust. Wildl. Res.* 13: 461–80.

Crome, F.H.J. 1985b. An experimental investigation of filter-feeding on zooplankton by some specialized waterfowl. *Aust. J. Zool.* 33: 849–62.

Crompton, D. 1985. Recherche Island Geese *Cereopsis novaehollandiae griseus. Avic. Mag.* 91(3): 157–59.

Cruz, M.A. 1991. La situacion actual del pato real (*Cairina moschata*) en Mexico. III Symp. Internacional del Fauna Silvestre, Universidad Autonoma De Tamaulipas, Victoria, Tamps.

Cullen, E. 1957. Adaptations in the Kittiwake to cliff-nesting. *Ibis* 99: 275–302.

Cunningham, E. 2003. Female mate preferences and subsequent resistance to copulation in the mallard. *Behavioral Ecology* 14: 326–33.

Cunningham, R.O. 1871. On some points in the anatomy of the Steamer Duck (*Micropterus cinereus*). *Trans. Zool. Soc. London* 7: 493–501.

Curio, E. 1983. Why do young birds reproduce less well? *Ibis* 125: 400–3.

Curth, P. 1954. *Der Mittelsäger: Soziologie und Brutbiologie*, Neue BrehmBucherei, Heft Nu. 126. Ziemsen, Leipzig.

Custer, C.M. and Custer, T.W. 1996. Food habits of diving ducks in the Great Lakes after the zebra mussel invasion. *J. Field Ornithol.* 67: 86–99.

Custer, C.M., Custer, T.W. and Zwank, P.J. 1997. Migration chronology and distribution of Redheads on the Lower Laguna Madre, Texas. *Southwest Naturalist* 42: 40–51.

CWS 1981. *Waterfowl Management Plan for Canada*. Can. Wildl. Serv., Ottawa.

CWS/USFWS. 1986. *North American waterfowl management plan*. Can. Wildl. Serv., Ottawa, and US Fish & Wildl. Serv., Washington.

da Fonseca, G.A.B. 1985. The vanishing Brazilian Atlantic Forest. *Biol. Cons.* 34: 17–34.

Daan, S., Dijkstra, C. and Tinbergen, J.M. 1990. Family planning in the kestrel (*Falco tinnunculus*): the ultimate control of covariation in laying date and clutch size. *Behaviour* 114: 83–116.

Daciuk, J. 1976. Notas faunísticas y bioecológicas de Península Valdes y Patagonia. XVIII. Comportamiento del pato vapor volador observado durante el ciclo reproductivo en costas e islas de Chubut (Rep. Argentina)—(Anserif., Anatidae). *Neotropica* 22: 27–29.

Dahl, T.E. 1990. *Wetland losses in the United States 1780's to 1980's*. US Fish & Wildl. Serv., Washington.

Dalhaug, L., Tombre, I.M. and Erikstad, K.E. 1996. Seasonal decline in clutch size of the Barnacle Goose in Svalbard. *Condor* 98: 42–47.

Dane, B. and Van der Kloot, W.G. 1964. An analysis of the display of the Goldeneye duck *Bucephala clangula* (L.). *Behaviour* 22: 282–328.

Dane, C.W. and Johnson, D.H. 1975. Age determination of female Redhead Ducks. *J. Wildl. Manage.* 39: 256–63.

Danell, K. and Sjöberg, K. 1977. Seasonal emergence of chironomids in relation to egg-laying and hatching of ducks on a restored lake (northern Sweden). *Wildfowl* 28: 129–35.

Danell, K. and Sjöberg, K. 1982. Seasonal and diet changes in the feeding behaviour of some dabbling duck species on a breeding lake in northern Sweden. *Ornis Scand.* 13: 129–34.

Danforth, S.T. 1929. Notes on the birds of Hispaniola. *Auk* 46: 358–75.

Darrieu, C.A., Martinez, M.M. and Soave, G.E. 1989. Estudio de la avifauna de la Reserva Provincial Llancanelo, Mendoza. III. Nuevos registros de nidificacion de aves acuaticas (Podicipedidae, Threskiornithidae, Anatidae, Rallidae, Laridae). *Rev. Asoc. Cienc. Nat. Litoral* 20: 81–90.

Darwin, C. 1871. *The descent of man and selection in relation to sex*. Random House, New York.

Dau, C.P. 1974. Nesting biology of the Spectacled Eider, *Somateria fischeri* (Brandt), on the Yukon-Kuskokwim delta, Alaska. Unpubl. M.S. thesis. Univ. Alaska, Fairbanks, US.

Dau, C.P. 1975. Occurrence and possible significance of an abnormal plumage in a Spectacled Eider. *Murrelet* 56(3): 17.

Dau, C.P. 1976. Clutch sizes of the Spectacled Eider on the Yukon-Kuskokwim Delta, Alaska. *Wildfowl* 27: 111–13.

Dau, C.P. 1978. Observations on helminth parasites of the Spectacled Eider, *Somateria fischeri* (Brandt), in Alaska. *Can. J. Zool.* 56: 1882–85.

Dau, C.P. 1981. Population structure and productivity of *Cygnus columbianus columbianus* on the Yukon Delta, Alaska. In 2nd IWRB Int. Swan Symp., Sapporo, 1980 (ed. G.V.T. Matthews and M. Smart), pp.161–9. IWRB, Slimbridge, UK.

Dau, C.P. and Kistchinski, A.A. 1977. Seasonal movements and distribution of the Spectacled Eider. *Wildfowl* 28: 65–75.

Dau, C.P. and Mickelson, P.G. 1979. Relation of weather to spring migration and nesting of Cackling Geese on the Yukon-Kuskokwim Delta, Alaska. In *Management and Biology of Pacific Flyway Geese* (ed. R.L. Jarvis and J.C. Bartonek), pp.94–104. OSU Bookstore, Corvallis.

Dau, C.P. and Stehn, R.A. 1991. Population size and distribution of Spectacled Eider on the Yukon-Kuskokwim Delta, Alaska. In *Shared Avian Resources of Beringia*, Alaska Bird Conf. and Workshop, 19–22 Nov. 1991, Anchorage, Alaska. US Fish & Wildl. Serv., Anchorage. [Abstract only.]

Daugherty, C.H., Williams, M. and Hay, J.M. 1999. Genetic differentiation, taxonomy and conservation of Australasian teals *Anas* spp. *Bird Conserv. Int.* 9: 29–42.

Davies, J.C. and Cooke, F. 1983a. Annual nesting production in Snow Geese: prairie droughts and Arctic springs. *J. Wildl. Manage.* 47: 291–96.

Davies, J.C. and Cooke, F. 1983b. Intraclutch hatch synchronization in the Lesser Snow Goose. *Can. J. Zool.* 61: 1398–401.

Davies, S.J.J.F. 1957. The gosling of the Magpie Goose. *Emu* 57: 354–55.

Davies, S.J.J.F. 1961. The orientation of pecking in very young Magpie Geese *Anseranas semipalmata. Ibis* 103: 277–83.

Davies, S.J.J.F. 1962. The nest-building behaviour of the Magpie Goose *Anseranas semipalmata. Ibis* 104: 147–57.

Davies, S.J.J.F. 1963. Aspects of the behaviour of the Magpie Goose *Anseranas semipalmata. Ibis* 105: 76–98.

Davies, S.J.J.F. and Frith, H.J. 1964. Some comments on the taxonomic position of the Magpie Goose *Anseranas semipalmata* (Latham). *Emu* 63: 265–72.

Davis, A. 1988. The distribution and status of the Mandarin in Britain. *Bird Study* 35: 203–8.

Dawkins, R. 1976. *The selfish gene.* OUP.

Day, D.H. 1977. A morphological study of Yellowbilled duck and Redbilled teal. *Ostrich* Suppl. 12: 86–96.

de Azara, F. 1805. *Apuntamientos para la historia natural de los paxaros del Paraguay y Rio de la Plata,* Vol. 3. Madrid.

de la Peña, M.R. 1987. *Nidos y huevos de aves Argentinas.* Taller Grafico de Impresas, Argentina.

De Leeuw, J.J. 1999. Food intake rates and habitat segregation of Tufted Duck *Aythya fuligula* and Scaup *Aythya marila* exploiting Zebra Mussels *Dreissena polymorpha. Ardea* 87: 15–31.

De Leeuw, J.J. and van Eerden, M.R. 1992. Size selection in diving Tufted Ducks *Aythya fuligula* explained by differential handling of small and large mussels *Dreissena polymorpha. Ardea* 80: 353–62.

de Schauensee, R.M. 1971. *A guide to the birds of South America.* Oliver and Boyd, Edinburgh.

de Schauensee, R.M. and Phelps, W.H., Jr 1978. *A guide to the birds of Venezuela.* Princeton Univ. Press.

de Vos, A. 1964. Observations on the behaviour of captive Trumpeter Swans during the breeding season. *Ardea* 52: 166–89.

Des Lauriers, J.R. and Brattstrom, B.H. 1965. Cooperative feeding behavior in Red-breasted Mergansers. *Auk* 62: 639.

Dean, W.R.J. 1970. *Anas hottentota* and *Oxyura maccoa* eggs in one nest. *Ostrich* 41: 216.

Dean, W.R.J. 1978. Moult seasons of some Anatidae in the western Transvaal. *Ostrich* 49: 76–84.

Dean, W.R.J. and Macdonald, I.A.W. 1981. A review of African birds feeding in association with mammals. *Ostrich* 52: 135–55.

Dean, W.R.J. and Skead, D.M. 1978. A note on the sex ratio in the South African Shelduck. *Ostrich* 49: 203–4.

Dean, W.R.J. and Skead, D.M. 1979. The weights of some southern African Anatidae. *Wildfowl* 30: 114–17.

Décarie, R., Morneau, F., Lambert, D., Carrière, S. and Savard, J-P.L. 1995. Habitat use by brood-rearing waterfowl in subarctic Québec. *Arctic* 48: 383–90.

Degtyarev, A.G. 1995. Localization and status of geese mass moult sites in north Yakutia. *Goose Study Group Bull. of Eastern Europe and Northern Asia* 1: 167–69.

Degtyarev, A.G. and Larionov, G.P. 1982. Distribution and numbers of Lamellirostres in central Yakutia. In *Migration and ecology of birds in Siberia, Novosibirsk,* pp.87–103.

Deiroy, L.B., Robinson, A.L. and Waterman, M.H. 1989. Monitoring of Cape Barren Goose populations in South Australia. 2. The 1987 breeding season and further banding recoveries. *South Aust. Ornithol.* 30: 184–89.

del Hoyo, J., Elliott, A. and Sargatal, J. (ed.) 1992. *Handbook of the birds of the world,* Vol. 1. Lynx Edicions, Barcelona.

Delacour, J. 1950. Variability in *Chloephaga picta,* Am. Mus. Novit., No. 1478, pp.1–4. American Museum Natural History, New York.

Delacour, J. 1951. Taxonomic notes on the Bean Geese *Anser fabalis* Latham. *Ardea* 39: 135–42.

Delacour, J. 1954–64. *The waterfowl of the world.* Country Life, London.

Delacour, J. and Mayr, E. 1945. The family Anatidae. *Wilson Bull.* 57: 3–55.

Delacour, J. and Mayr, E. 1946. Supplementary notes on the family Anatidae. *Wilson Bull.* 58: 104–10.

Delacour, J. and Ripley, S.D. 1975. *Description of a new sub-species of the White-fronted Goose, Anser albifrons,* Am. Mus. Novit., No. 2565. American Museum Natural History, New York.

Delacour, J. and Zimmer, J.T. 1952. The identity of *Anser nigricans* Lawrence 1846. *Auk* 69: 82–84.

Delany, S. 1993. Introduced and escaped geese in Britain in summer 1991. *Brit. Birds* 86: 591–99.

Delany, S.N. and Greenwood, J.J.D. 1993. The 1990 national Mute Swan survey: provisional results. In *Britain's birds in 1990–91: the conservation and monitoring review* (ed. J. Andrews), pp.130–4. BTO/JNCC, Thetford, UK.

Delany, S.N., Pettifor, R.A. and Kirby, J.S. 1994. *Summer numbers and breeding success of Shelducks on the Severn Estuary 1988–1993.* Unpubl. rept to JNCC. WWT, Slimbridge, UK.

Delany, S.N., Reyes, C., Hubert, E., Pihl, S., Rees, E., Haanstra, L. *et al*. 1999. *Results from the international waterbird census in the Western Palearctic and Southwest Asia 1995 and 1996,* Publ., No. 54. Wetlands International, Wageningen, Netherlands.

DeLeeuw, J.J. 1999. Food intake rates and habitat segregation of Tufted Duck *Aythya fuligula* and Scaup *Aythya marila* exploiting Zebra Mussels *Dreissena polymorpha. Ardea* 87: 15–31.

DeLeeuw, J.J. and van Eerden, M.R. 1992. Size selection in diving Tufted Ducks *Aythya fuligula* explained by differential handling of small and large mussels *Dreissena polymorpha. Ardea* 80: 353–62.

DeLeeuw, J.J., van Eerden, M.R. and Visser, G.H. 1999. Wintering Tufted Ducks *Aythya fuligula* diving for Zebra Mussels *Dreissena polymorpha* balance feeding costs with narrow margins of their energy budget. *J. Avian Biol.* 30: 182–92.

Delnicki, D.E. and Bolen, E.G. 1975. Natural nest site availability for Black-bellied Whistling-ducks in south Texas. *Southwestern Nat.* 20: 371–78.

Delnicki, D.E. and Bolen, E.G. 1976. Renesting by the Black-bellied Whistling-duck. *Auk* 93: 535–42.

Delnicki, D.E., Bolen, E.G. and Cottam, C. 1976. An unusual clutch size for the Black-bellied Whistling-duck. *Wilson Bull.* 88: 347–48.

Delroy, L.B., Robinson, A.L. and Waterman, M.H. 1989. Monitoring of Cape Barren Goose populations in South Australia. 2. The 1987 breeding season and further banding recoveries. *South Aust. Ornithol.* 30(7): 184–89.

DeMay, L.S. 1940. A study of the pterylosis and pneumacity of the screamer. *Condor* 42: 112–18.

Dementiev, G. 1933. Notes sur le Harle de Gould *Mergus squamatus* Gould. *Alauda* 1933(3): 395–96.

Dementiev, G.P. and Gladkov, N.A. (ed.). 1952. *Birds of the Soviet Union* (trans. 1967. Israel Prog. for Scientific Translations, Jerusalem). US Dept Interior and National Science Foundation, Washington.

Demey, R. 2001. Recent Reports. *Bull. African Bird Club* 8: 145–55.

Demey, R. and Kirwan, G.M. 2001. Africa Round-up. *Bull. African Bird Club* 8: 5–9.

Dennis, D.G., North, N.R. and Lumsden, H.G. 2000. Range expansion and population growth of Giant Canada Geese in southern Ontario: benefits, drawbacks, and management techniques. In *Towards conservation of the diversity of Canada Geese* (Branta canadensis), pp.159–165. K.M. Dickson (ed.). *Can. Wildl. Serv. Occas. Paper* No. 103.

Dennis, R.H. and Dow, H. 1984. The establishment of a population of Goldeneyes *Bucephala clangula* breeding in Scotland. *Bird Study* 31: 217–22.

Denny, M.J.H., Clausen, P., Percival, S.M., Anderson, G.Q.A., Koffijberg, K. and Robinson J.A. 2004. Light-bellied Brent Goose *Branta bernicla hrota* (East Atlantic population) in Svalbard, Greenland, Franz Josef Land, Norway, Denmark, The Netherlands and Britain 1960/61–2000/01. *Waterbird Review Series,* WWT/JNCC, Slimbridge.

Derksen, D.V. and King, J.G. 1986. Alaska goose populations: past, present and future. *51st N.A. Wildl. Nat. Res. Conf.*, pp.464–79. Wildl. Manage. Inst., Washington.

Derksen, D.V., Rothe, T.C. and Eldridge, W.D. 1981. *Use of wetland habitats in the National Petroleum Reserve-Alaska,* Resource Publ., No. 141. US Fish & Wildl. Serv., Washington.

Derrickson, S.R. 1977. Aspects of breeding behavior in the Pintail (*Anas acuta*). Unpubl. Ph.D. thesis. Univ. Minnesota, Minneapolis, US.

Desgranges, J.L. and Darveau, M. 1985. Effect of lake acidity and morphometry on the distribution of aquatic birds in southern Quebec. *Holarct. Ecol.* 8: 181–90.

Desholm, M., Christensen, T.K., Scheiffarth, G., Hario, M., Andersson, Å., Ens, B. *et al.* 2002. Status of the Baltic/Wadden Sea population of the Common Eider *Somateria m. mollissima. Wildfowl* 53: 167–203.

Dewar, J.M. 1924. *The bird as a diver.* Witherby, London.

Dewar, J.M. 1942. The Mute Swan and the 20–10 seconds rule. *Brit. Birds* 35: 224–26.

Dick, G. 1987. The significance of the Lake Neusiedl area of Austria for migrating geese. *Wildfowl* 38: 9–27.

Dick, G. 1993. Greylag Goose *Anser anser* migration patterns between Europe and Maghreb. *Annales Musée Royal de l'Afrique Centrale (Zoologie)* 268: 587–90.

Dickinson, E.C., Kennedy, R.S. and Parkes, K.C. 1991. *The Birds of the Philippines. An annotated check-list.* Check-list No. 12. BOU, Tring.

Dickson, K.M. 2000. Towards conservation of the diversity of Canada Geese (*Branta canadensis*). CWS Occ. Paper, No. 103. Environment Canada, Ottawa.

Diefenbach, D.R., Nichols, J.D. and Hines, J.E. 1988. A comparison of the distribution patterns of American Black Duck and Mallard winter band-recoveries. *J. Wildl. Manage.* 52: 704–10.

Dimitrov, M., Profirov, L., Nyagolov, K. and Michev, T. 2000. Record counts of White-headed Duck in Bulgaria. *Threatened Waterfowl Specialist Group News* 12: 18–20.

Direktoratet for naturforvaltning 1996. *Handlingsplan for forvaltning af gjess,* DN-rapport 1996–2. Adresseavisen Offset, Trondheim.

Dirksen, S. and Beekman, J.H. 1991. Population size, breeding success and distribution of Bewick's Swans *Cygnus columbianus bewickii* wintering in Europe in 1986–87. *Wildfowl Spec. Suppl.* 1: 120–24.

Dirschl, H.J. 1969. Foods of Lesser Scaup and Blue-winged Teal in the Saskatchewan River Delta. *J. Wildl. Manage.* 33: 77–87.

Dobrush, G.R. 1986. The accumulation of nutrient reserves and their contribution to reproductive success in the White-winged Scoter. Unpubl. M.Sc. thesis. Univ. Guelph, Canada.

Dodman, T. and Taylor, V. 1995. *African waterfowl census 1995—Les dénombrements internationaux d'oiseaux d'eau en Afrique, 1995.* IWRB, Slimbridge, UK.

Donkin, R.A. 1989. *The Muscovy Duck.* Balkema, Rotterdam.

Donne-Gousse, C., Laudet, V. and Hanni, C. 2002. A molecular phylogeny of Anseriformes based on mitochondrial DNA analysis. *Mol. Phylogen. Evol.* 23: 339–56.

Dorward, D.F. 1967. The status of the Cape Barren Goose *Cereopsis novae-hollandiae. Bull. ICBP.* 10: 56–71.

Doty, H.A., Lee, F.B., Kruse, A.D., Matthews, J.W., Foster, J.R. and Arnold, P.M. 1984. Wood Duck and Hooded Merganser nesting on Arrowwood NWR, North Dakota. *J. Wildl. Manage.* 48: 577–80.

Doughty, R.W. 1979. Eider husbandry in the North Atlantic: trends and prospects. *Polar Record* 19: 447–59.

Douse, A.F.G. 1987. The impact of sheldgoose grazing on reseeded pasture in the Falkland Islands. Unpubl. rept to the Overseas Development Administration, London.

Douthwaite, R.J. 1976. Weight changes and wing moult in the Red-billed Teal. *Wildfowl* 27: 123–27.

Douthwaite, R.J. 1978. Geese and Red-knobbed Coot on the Kafue Flats in Zambia, 1970–74. *E. Afr. Wildl. J.* 16: 29–47.

Douthwaite, R.J. 1980. Seasonal changes in the food supply, numbers and male plumages of Pygmy Geese on the Thamalakane River in northern Botswana. *Wildfowl* 31: 94–98.

Dow, H. and Fredga, S. 1983. Breeding and natal dispersal of the Goldeneye, *Bucephala clangula. J. Anim. Ecol.* 52: 681–95.

Dow, H. and Fredga, S. 1984. Factors affecting reproductive output of the Goldeneye duck *Bucephala clangula. J. Anim. Ecol.* 53: 679–92.

Dow, H. and Fredga, S. 1985. Selection of nest sites by a hole nesting duck, the Goldeneye, *Bucephala clangula. Ibis* 127: 16–30.

Downer, A. and Sutton, R. 1990. *Birds of Jamaica: a photographic field guide.* Cambridge Univ. Press.

Dowsett, R. 1993. Afrotropical avifaunas: annotated country checklists. *Tauraco Research Report* 5: 1–322.

Dowsett, R.J. and Forbes-Watson, A.D. 1993. *Checklist of birds of the Afrotropical and Malagasy Regions,* Vol. 1. Tauraco Press, Liege.

Draffen, R.D.W., Garnett, S.T. and Malone, G.J. 1983. Birds of the Torres Strait: an annotated list and biogeographical analysis. *Emu* 83: 207–34.

Draulans, D. 1982. Foraging and size selection of mussels by the Tufted Duck, *Aythya fuligula. J. Anim. Ecol.* 51: 943–56.

Drent, R.H. and Swierstra, P. 1977. Goose flocks and food finding: field experiments with Barnacle Geese in winter. *Wildfowl* 28: 15–20.

Drent, R.H., Weijand, B. and Ebbinge, B. 1980. Balancing the energy budgets of arctic breeding geese throughout the annual cycle: a progress report. *Verh. Orn. Ges. Bayern.* 23: 239–64.

Drewien, R.C. and Bouffard, S.H. 1994. Winter body mass and measurements of Trumpeter Swans *Cygnus buccinator. Wildfowl* 45: 22–32.

Drewien, R.C., Herbert, J.T., Aldrich, T.W. and Bouffard, S.H. 1999. Detecting Trumpeter Swans harvested in Tundra Swan hunts. *Wildl. Soc. Bull.* 27: 95–102.

Drilling, N., Titman, R. and McKinney, F. 2002. Mallard (*Anas platyrhynchos*). The birds of North America, No. 658 (ed. A. Poole and F. Gill). AOU, The Birds of North America Inc., Philadelphia.

Driver, P.M. 1974. *In search of the Eider.* Saturn Press, London.

Drobney, R.D. and Fredrickson, L.H. 1979. Food selection by Wood Ducks in relation to breeding status. *J. Wildl. Manage.* 43: 109–20.

Drobovtsev, V.I. and Zaborskaya, V.N. 1987. Migrations, numbers and distribution of *Cygnus cygnus* and *Cygnus olor* in the forest-steppe of Northern Kazakhstan. In *Ecology and migration of swans in the USSR* (ed. E.E. Syroechkovksi), pp.104–6. Nauka, Moscow.

du Toit, R. 2001. Perilous panhandle. *Africa—Birds & Birding* 5: 32–34.

Dubbeldam, W and Zijlstra, M. 1996. *Ganzen in Oostelijk- en Zuidelijk Flevoland 1972/73–1991/92,* Flevobericht, No. 385. Rijkswaterstaat Directie Ijsselmeergebied, Lelystad.

Dubovsky, J.A., Caithamer, D.F., Moore, C.T., Smith, G.W., Keywood, P.D. and Bladen, J.P. 1994. *Trends in duck breeding populations, 1955–94,* Admin. rept. US Fish & Wildl. Serv., Washington.

Dubovsky, J.A., Moore, C.T., Bladen, J.P., Smith, G.W. and Keywood, P.D. 1997. *Trends in duck breeding populations, 1955–97,* Admin. rept. US Fish & Wildl. Serv., Washington.

DuBowy, P.J. 1988. Waterfowl communities and seasonal environments: temporal variability in interspecific competition. *Ecology* 69: 1439–53.

Dubs, B. 1992. *Birds of southwestern Brazil: catalogue and guide to the birds of the Pantanal of Mato Grosso and its border areas.* Betrona-Verlag, Switzerland.

Duckworth, K. 1986. A comparison between the population dynamics of colonising and established Paradise Shelduck populations. Unpubl. B.Sc. thesis. Victoria Univ., Wellington, New Zealand.

Duebbert, H.F. 1966. Island nesting of the Gadwall in North Dakota. *Wilson Bull.* 78: 12–25.

Dugger, B.D., Dugger, K.M. and Fredrickson, L.H. 1994. Hooded Merganser (*Lophodytes cucullatus*), The Birds of North America, No. 98 (ed. A. Poole and F. Gill) AOU, Washington, and Academy of Natural Sciences, Philadelphia.

Dumbell, G.S. 1986. The New Zealand Brown Teal. *Wildfowl* 37: 71–87.

Dumbell, G.S. 1987. The ecology, behaviour and management of New Zealand Brown Teal or Pateke (*Anas aucklandica chlorotis*). Unpubl. Ph.D. thesis. Univ. Auckland, New Zealand.

Duncan, D.C. 1986a. Does food limit clutch size in prairie ducks? *Auk* 103: 637–38.

Duncan, D.C. 1986b. Survival of dabbling duck broods on prairie impoundments in southeastern Alberta. *Can. Field-Nat.* 100: 110–13.

Duncan, D.C. 1987a. Nesting of northern pintails in Alberta: laying date, clutch size and renesting. *Can. J. Zool.* 65: 234–46.

Duncan, D.C. 1987b. Nest-site distribution and overland brood movements of Northern Pintails in Alberta. *J. Wildl. Manage.* 51: 716–23.

Duncan, R. 1990. Female natal philopatry in a Scottish Wigeon population. *Scottish Birds* 16(3): 222.

Dunning, J.B. (ed.) 1993. *CRC handbook of avian body masses.* CRC Press, Boca Raton, Florida.

Durant, D. 2003. The digestion of fibre in herbivorous Anatidae – a review. *Wildfowl* 54: 7–24.

Durink, J., Christensen, K.D., Skov, H. and Danielsen, F. 1993. Diet of the Common Scoter *Melanitta nigra* and Velvet Scoter *Melanitta fusca* wintering in the North Sea. *Ornis Fenn.* 70: 215–18.

Durinck, J., Skov, H., Jensen, F.P. and Pihl, S. 1994. Important marine areas for wintering birds in the Baltic Sea, winter 1992. *Ornis Svecica* 3: 11–26.

Dvorak, M., Nemeth, E., Tebbich, S., Rössler, S. and Busse, K. 1996. *Bestand, okologie und habitatwahl schifblenohnender vogel arten in der naturzone des Nationalparks Neusiedlersee-Seewinkel.* Unpubl. rept BirdLife Austria, Wien, Austria.

Dwernychuk, L.W. and Boag, D.A. 1972. How vegetative cover protects duck nests from egg-eating birds. *J. Wildl. Manage.* 36: 955–58.

Dwyer, T.J. 1974. Social behaviour of breeding Gadwalls in North Dakota. *Auk* 91: 375–86.

Dybbro, T. 1976. *De danske ynglefugles udbredlese.* Danish Ornithological Society, Copenhagen.

Dybbro, T. 1985. *Status for danske fuglelokaliteter.* Danish Ornithological Society, Copenhagen.

Dymin, V.A. and Kostin, B.G. 1977. *M. squamatus* Gould—a breeding species of the upper Amur region. In VII All Union Orn. Conf., Cherkassy, 27–30 Sept., 1977 (ed. M.A. Voinstvenskiy), p.221. Naukova Dumka, Kiev.

Dzerzhinsky, F.Y. 1995. Evidence for a common ancestry of the Galliformes and Anseriformes. *Courier Forschungsinstitut Senckenberg* 181: 325–36.

Dzinbal, K.A. 1982. Ecology of Harlequin Ducks in Prince William Sound, Alaska during summer. Unpubl. M.S. thesis. Oregon State Univ., Corvallis, US.

Dzinbal, K.A. and Jarvis, R.L. 1984. Coastal feeding ecology of Harlequin Ducks in Prince William Sound, Alaska, during summer. In *Marine Birds: their feeding ecology and commercial fisheries relationships* (ed. D.N. Nettleship, G.A. Sanger and P.F. Springer), pp.6–10. Proc. Pacific Seabird Gp. Symp., Seattle, Wash.. 6–8 Jan. 1982.

Dzubin, A. 1959. Growth and plumage development of wild-trapped juvenile Canvasback (*Aythya valisineria*). *J. Wildl. Manage.* 23: 279–90.

Dzubin, A. and Cooch, E. 1992. *Measurements of geese: general field methods.* California Waterfowl Association, Sacramento.

Eadie, J.McA. 1989. Alternative reproductive tactics in a precocial bird: the ecology and evolution of brood parasitism in goldeneyes. Unpubl. Ph.D. thesis. Univ. British Columbia, Canada.

Eadie, J.McA. and Gauthier, G. 1985. Prospecting for nest sites by cavity-nesting ducks of the genus *Bucephala. Condor* 87: 528–34.

Eadie, J.McA. and Keast, A. 1982. Do Goldeneyes and Perch compete for food? *Oecologia* 55: 225–30.

Eadie, J.McA. and Lumsden, H.G. 1985. Is nest parasitism always deleterious to Goldeneyes? *Amer. Natur.* 126: 859–66.

Eadie, J. McA. and Lyon, B.E. 1998. Cooperation, conflict and creching behavior in goldeneye ducks. *Amer. Natur.* 151: 397–408.

Eadie, J.McA., Kehoe, F.P. and Nudds, T.D. 1988. Pre-hatch and post-hatch brood amalgamation in North American Anatidae: a review of hypotheses. *Can. J. Zool.* 66: 1709–21.

Eadie, J.McA., Mallory, M.L. and Lumsden, H.G. 1995. Common Goldeneye (*Bucephala clangula*), The Birds of North America, No. 170 (ed. A. Poole and F. Gill). AOU, Washington, and Academy of Natural Sciences, Philadelphia.

Eadie, J.McA., Savard, J-P.L. and Mallory, M.L. 2000. Barrow's Goldeneye (*Bucephala islandica*), The Birds of North America, No. 548, (ed. A. Poole and F. Gill). AOU, The Birds of North America Inc., Philadelphia.

Earnst, S.L. 1992a. Behaviour and ecology of Tundra Swans during summer, autumn and winter. Unpubl. Ph.D. thesis. Ohio State Univ., Columbus, US.

Earnst, S.L. 1992b. The timing of wing molt in Tundra Swans: energetic and non-energetic constraints. *Condor* 94: 847–56.

Earnst, S.L. 1994. Tundra Swan habitat preferences during migration in North Dakota. *J. Wildl. Manage.* 58: 546–51.

Earnst, S.L. 2002. Parental care in Tundra Swans during the pre-fledging period. In *Proceedings of the Fourth International Swan Symposium, 2001* (ed. E.C. Rees, S.L. Earnst and J. Coulson). *Waterbirds*, Special Publication 1: 268–77.

Earnst, S.L. and Bart, J. 1991. Costs and benefits of extended parental care in Tundra Swans *Cygnus columbianus columbianus. Wildfowl* Spec. Suppl., 1: 260–67.

Eastham, C., Quinn, J.L. and Fox, N. 2000. Saker (*Falco cherrug*) and Peregrine Falcons (*Falco peregrinus*) in Asia: determining migration routes and trapping pressure. In Vth World Conference on Birds of Prey and Owls, Johannesburg, 4–11 August 1998 (ed. B.U. Meyburg and R.D. Chancellor), pp.247–58. Hancock House, Blaine, Washington.

Ebbinge, B.S. 1989. A multifactorial explanation for variation in breeding performance of Brent Geese. *Ibis* 131: 196–204.

Ebbinge, B.S. 1991. Wild goose populations in northern Asia. *IWRB Goose Research Group Bull.* 1: 26.

Ebbinge, B.S 1992. Regulation of numbers of Dark-bellied Brent Geese on spring staging areas. *Ardea* 80: 203–28.

Ebbinge, B.S. and Ebbinge-Dallmeijer, D. 1977. Barnacle Geese (*Branta leucopsis*) in the Arctic summer—a reconnaissance trip to Svalbard. *Norsk Pol. Årbok* 1975: 119–38.

Ebbinge, B.S. and Spaans, B. 1995. The importance of body reserves accumulated in spring staging areas in the temperate zone for breeding in Dark-bellied Brent Geese *Branta b. bernicla* in the high Arctic. *J. Avian Biol.* 26: 105–13.

Ebbinge, B.S., Canters, K. and Drent, R. 1975. Foraging routines and estimated daily food intake in Barnacle Geese wintering in the northern Netherlands. *Wildfowl* 26: 5–19.

Ebbinge, B.S, St Joseph, A., Prokosch, P. and Spaans, B. 1982. The importance of spring staging areas for arctic-breeding geese wintering in western Europe. *Aquila* 89: 249–58.

Ebbinge, B.S., van der Meulen, H.T. and Smit, J.J. 1984. Changes in winter distribution and population size of Pink-footed Geese breeding in Svalbard. *Norsk Pol. Skr.* 181: 11–17.

Ebbinge, B.S., van Biezen, J.B. and van der Voet, H. 1991. Estimation of annual adult survival rates of Barnacle Geese *Branta leucopsis* using multiple resightings of marked individuals. *Ardea* 79: 73–112.

Ebbinge, B.S., Berrevoets, C., Clausen, P., Ganter, B., Gunther, K., Koffijberg, K. *et al.* 1999. Dark-bellied Brent Goose *Branta bernicla bernicla*. In *Goose populations of the Western Palearctic. A review of status and distribution*, Publ., No. 48 (ed. J. Madsen, G. Cracknell and T. Fox), pp.284–98. Wetlands International, Wageningen, Netherlands, and National Environmental Research Institute, Rønde, Denmark.

Eberhard, I.H. and Pearse, R.J. 1981. Conservation of Cape Barren Geese *Cereopsis novaehollandiae* in Tasmania. *Aust. Wildl. Res.* 8: 147–62.

Eberhardt, R.T. and Riggs, M. 1995. Effects of sex and reproductive status on diets of breeding Ring-necked Ducks (*Aythya collaris*) in north-central Minnesota. *Can. J. Zool.* 73: 392–99.

Edelsten, G. 1932. Notes on the nest of the South African Shelduck. *Ostrich* 3: 61.

Edroma, E.L. and Jumbe, J. 1983. The number and daily activity of the Egyptian Goose in Queen Elizabeth National Park Uganda. *Wildfowl* 34: 99–104.

Einarsson, Á. 1985. Use of space in relation to food in Icelandic Barrow's Goldeneye. Unpubl. Ph.D. thesis. Univ. Aberdeen, UK.

Einarsson, Á. 1988. Distribution and movements of Barrow's Goldeneye *Bucephala islandica* young in relation to food. *Ibis* 130: 153–63.

Einarsson, Á. 1990. Settlement into breeding habitats by Barrow's Goldeneyes *Bucephala islandica*: evidence for temporary oversaturation of preferred habitat. *Ornis Scand.* 21: 7–16.

Einarsson, Á. 1991. *Lax í efri Laxá. Greinargerð um líkleg áhrif laxaflutninga á lífríki árinnar ofan Brúa*. Nature Conservation Council, Reykjavík. [*Salmon in the upper part of the River Laxá. Probable effects of salmon planting on the biota.* In Icelandic.]

Einarsson, Á., Garðarsson, A., Gíslason, G.M. and Guðbergsson, G. 2005. Populations of ducks and trout of the River Laxá, Iceland, in relation to variation in food resources. *Hydrobiologia* (in press).

Einarsson, Ó. 1996. Breeding biology of the Whooper Swan and factors affecting its breeding success, with notes on its social dynamics and life cycle in the wintering range. Unpubl. Ph.D. thesis. Univ. Bristol, UK.

Einarsson, Ó. and Rees, E.C. 2002. Occupancy and turnover of Whooper Swans on territories in northern Iceland: results of a long-term study. In *Proceedings of the Fourth International Swan Symposium, 2001* (ed. E.C. Rees, S.L. Earnst and J. Coulson), *Waterbirds* 25, Special Publication 1: 202–10.

Eisenhauer, D.I. and Kirkpatrick, C.M. 1977. Ecology and behavior of the Emperor Goose in Alaska. *Wildl. Monogr.* 57: 1–62.

Eitinear, J.C. 1988. Return of the Muscovy Duck. *Watchbird* April/May. Center for Study of Tropical Birds, San Antonio.

Eitniear, J.C. 1999. Masked Duck (*Nomonyx dominica*). The Birds of North America, No. 393 (ed. A. Poole and F. Gill). AOU, The Birds of North America Inc., Philadelphia.

Ekman, S. 1922. *Djurvärldens utbredningshistoria på den skandinaviska halvön*. Stockholm. [The history and distribution of the fauna of Scandinavia.]

Eldridge, J.L. 1979. Display inventory of the Torrent Duck. *Wildfowl* 30: 5–15.

Eldridge, J.L. 1985. Display inventory of Blue Duck. *Wildfowl* 36: 109–21.

Eldridge, J.L. 1986a. Observations on a pair of Torrent Ducks. *Wildfowl* 37: 113–22.

Eldridge, J.L. 1986b. Territoriality in a river specialist: the Blue Duck. *Wildfowl* 37: 123–35.

Elgood, J.H. 1994. *Birds of Nigeria: an annotated checklist.* Check-list No. 4 (2nd edn). BOU, London.

Elkins, N. 1979. High altitude flight by swans. *Brit. Birds* 72: 238–39.

Elkins, N. 1983. *Weather and bird behaviour.* Poyser, Calton.

Ellig, L.J. 1955. *Waterfowl relationships to Greenfields Lake, Teton County, Montana,* Tech. Bull., No. 1. Montana Fish Game Dept., Helena, Montana.

Ellis-Joseph, S., Hewston, N. and Green, A. (comps) 1992. *Global waterfowl conservation assessment and management plan.* IUCN Captive Breeding Specialist Group, Minnesota, and WWT, Slimbridge, UK.

Elmberg, J., Nummi, P., Pöysä, H. and Sjöberg, K. 1993. Factors affecting species number and density of dabbling duck guilds in north Europe. *Ecography* 16: 251–60.

Elmberg, J., Nummi, P., Pöysä, H. and Sjöberg, K. 1994. Relationships between species number, lake size and resource diversity in assemblages of breeding waterfowl. *J. Biogeog.* 21: 75–84.

Elson, P.F. 1962. *Predator–prey relationships between fish-eating birds and Atlantic Salmon,* Bull., No. 133, pp.1–87. Fish. Res. Board Can, Ministry of Fisheries, Ottawa.

Eltringham, S.K. 1974. The survival of broods of the Egyptian Goose in Uganda. *Wildfowl* 25: 41–48.

Ely, C.A. and Clapp, R.B. 1973. The natural history of Laysan Island, northwestern Hawaiian Islands. *Atoll Res. Bull.* 171: 1–361.

Ely, C.R. 1989. Extra-pair copulation in the Greater White-fronted Goose. *Condor* 91: 990–91.

Ely, C.R. 1993. Family stability in Greater White-fronted Geese. *Auk* 110: 425–35.

Ely, C.R. and Dzubin, A.X. 1994. Greater White-fronted Goose (*Anser albifrons*). The Birds of North America, No. 131, (ed. A. Poole and F. Gill). AOU, Academy of Natural Sciences, Philadelphia.

Ely, C.R. and Raveling, D.G. 1984. Breeding biology of Pacific White-fronted Geese. *J. Wildl. Manage.* 48: 823–37.

Ely, C.R. and Raveling, D.G. 1989. Body composition and weight dynamics of wintering Greater White-fronted Geese. *J. Wildl. Manage.* 53: 80–87.

Ely, C.R. and Scribner, K.T. 1994. Genetic diversity in Arctic nesting geese: implications for management and conservation. *Trans. N. Amer. Wildl. Nat. Res. Conf.* 59: 91–110.

Ely, C.R., Dau, C.P. and Babcock, C.A. 1994. Decline in a population of Spectacled Eiders nesting on the Yukon-Kuskokwim Delta, Alaska. *Northwestern Naturalist* 75: 81–87.

Emlen, S.T. and Vehrencamp, S.L. 1985. Cooperative breeding strategies among birds. *Exptl. Behav. Ecol.* 31: 359–74.

Engilis, A., Jr and Pratt, T.K. 1993. Status and population trends of Hawaii native waterbirds, 1977–1987. *Wilson Bull.* 105: 142–58.

Engilis, A., Jr., Uyehara, K.J. and Giffin, J.G. 2002. Hawaiian Duck (*Anas wyvilliana*). The Birds of North America, No. 694 (ed. A. Poole and F. Gill). AOU, The Birds of North America Inc., Philadelphia.

Ens, B.J., Safriel, U.N. and Harris, M.P. 1993. Divorce in the long-lived and monogamous Oystercatcher *Haematopus ostralegus*: incompatability or choosing the better option? *Anim. Behav.* 45: 1199–217.

Erftemeijer, P., Allen, G., Zuwendra and Kosamah, S. 1991. Birds of the Bintuni Bay region, Irian Jaya. *Kukila* 5: 85–98.

Ericson, P.G.P. 1996. The skeletal evidence for a sister-group relationship of anseriform and galliform birds: a critical evaluation. *J. Avian Biol.* 27: 195–202.

Ericson, P.G.P. 1997. Systematic relationships of the palaeogene family Presbyornithidae (Aves: Anseriformes). *Zool. J. Linn. Soc.* 121: 429–83.

Ericson, P.G.P., Parsons, T. and Johansson, U.S. 2001. Morphological and molecular support for non-monophyly of the Galloanserae. In *New perspectives on the origin and early evolution of birds: proceedings of the international symposium in honor of John H. Ostrom* (ed. J. Gaultier and L.F. Gall), pp.157–68. Yale Univ. Press, New Haven, US.

Eriksson, M.O.G. 1976. Food and feeding habits of downy Goldeneye *Bucephala clangula* (L.) ducklings. *Ornis Scand.* 7: 159–69.

Eriksson, M.O.G. 1978. Lake selection by Goldeneye ducklings in relation to the abundance of food. *Wildfowl* 29: 81–85.

Eriksson, M.O.G. 1979a. Competition between freshwater fish and Goldeneyes *Bucephala clangula* (L.) for common prey. *Oecologia* (Berl.) 41: 99–107.

Eriksson, M.O.G. 1979b. Aspects of the breeding biology of the goldeneye *Bucephala clangula. Holarct. Ecol.* 2: 186–94.

Eriksson, M.O.G. 1983. The role of fish in the selection of lakes by nonpiscivorous ducks: Mallard, Teal and Goldeneye. *Wildfowl* 34: 27–32.

Eriksson, M.O.G., Henrikson, L. and Oscarson, H.G. 1989. Metal contents in liver tissues of non-fledged Goldeneye, *Bucephala clangula,* ducklings: a comparison between samples from acidic, circumneutral, and limed lakes in south Sweden. *Arch. Environ. Contam. Toxicol.* 18: 255–60.

Erikstad, K.E., Bustnes, J.O. and Moum, T. 1993. Clutch-size determination in precocial birds: a study of the Common Eider. *Auk* 110: 623–28.

Erskine, A.J. 1961. Nest-site tenacity and homing in the Bufflehead. *Auk* 78: 389–96.

Erskine, A.J. 1964. Bird migration during April in southern British Columbia. *Murrelet* 45: 15–22.

Erskine, A.J. 1971. Growth and annual cycles in weights, plumages and reproductive organs of Goosanders in eastern Canada. *Ibis* 113: 42–58.

Erskine, A.J. 1972a. *Buffleheads*, Monogr. Ser., No. 4. Can. Wildl. Serv., Ottawa.

Erskine, A.J. 1972b. *Populations, movements and seasonal distribution of mergansers in northern Cape Breton Island,* Rept. Ser., No. 17, pp.1–36. Can. Wildl. Serv., Ottawa.

Erskine, A.J. 1978. Durability of tree holes used by Buffleheads. *Can. Field-Nat.* 92: 94–95.

Erskine, A.J. 1988. The changing patterns of Brant migration in eastern North America. *J. Field Ornithol.* 59: 110–19.

Erskine, A.J. 1990. Joint laying in *Bucephala* ducks— 'parasitism' or nest-site competition? *Ornis Scand.* 21: 52–56.

Esler, D. and Grand, J.B. 1994. The role of nutrient reserves for clutch formation by Northern Pintails in Alaska. *Condor* 96: 422–32.

Essen von, L. 1996. Reintroduction of Lesser White-fronted Geese (*Anser erythropus*) in Swedish Lapland (1981–1991). *Gibier Faune Sauvage, Game Wildl.* 13: 1169–80.

Estes, J.A., Bacon, C.E., Jarman, W.M., Norstrom, R.J., Anthony, R.G. and Mile, A.K. 1997. Organochlorines in Sea Otters and Bald Eagles from the Aleutian archipelago. *Mar. Poll. Bull.* 34: 486–90.

Euliss, N.H., Jr and Harris, S.W. 1987. Feeding ecology of Northern Pintails and Green-winged Teal wintering in California. *J. Wildl. Manage.* 51: 724–32.

Euliss, N.H., Jr, Jarvis, R.L. and Gilmer, D.S. 1997. Relationship between waterfowl nutrition and condition on agricultural drainwater ponds in the Tulare Basin, California: waterfowl body composition. *Wetlands* 17: 106–15.

Evans, M.E. 1975. Breeding behaviour of captive Bewick's Swans. *Wildfowl* 26: 117–30.

Evans, M.E. 1979a. Aspects of the life cycle of the Bewick's Swan, based on recognition of individuals at a wintering site. *Bird Study* 26: 149–62.

Evans, M.E. 1979b. The effects of weather on the wintering Bewick's Swans *Cygnus columbianus bewickii* at Slimbridge, England. *Ornis Scand.* 10: 124–32.

Evans, M.E. 1980. The effects of experience and breeding status on the use of a wintering site by Bewick's Swans *Cygnus columbianus bewickii. Ibis* 122: 287–97.

Evans, M.E. 1982. Movements of Bewick's Swans *Cygnus columbianus bewickii*, marked at Slimbridge, England, from 1960–1979. *Ardea* 70: 59–75.

Evans, M.E. and Kear, J. 1978. Weights and measurements of Bewick's Swans during winter. *Wildfowl* 29: 118–22.

Evans, M.E. and Lebret, T. 1973. Leucistic Bewick's Swans. *Wildfowl* 24: 61–62.

Evans, M.E. and Sladen, W.J.L. 1980. A comparative analysis of the bill markings of Whistling and Bewick's Swans and out-of-range occurrences of the two taxa. *Auk* 97: 697–703.

Evans, R.M. 1970. Oldsquaws nesting in association with Arctic Terns at Churchill, Manitoba. *Wilson Bull.* 82: 383–90.

Evans, T.D., Robichaud, W.G. and Tizard, R.J. 1996. The White-winged Duck *Cairina scutulata* in Laos. *Wildfowl* 47: 81–96.

Evarts, S. and Williams, C.J. 1987. Multiple paternity in a wild population of Mallards. *Auk* 104: 597–602.

Everett, W.T., Ward, M. L. and Brueggeman, J.J. 1989. Birds observed in the central Bering Sea pack ice in February and March 1983. *Gerfaut* 79: 159–66.

Ewans, M. 1989. *Bharatpur—bird paradise.* Witherby, London.

Eyton, T.C. 1838. *A monograph on the Anatidae, or duck tribe.* Longman, Orme, Brown Green and Longman, London.

Fabricius, E. 1983. *Kanadagasen i Sverige.* Statens naturvardsverk PM 1678. Solna, Sweden.

Fabricius, E. and Radesater, T. 1972. [title not given.] *Zool. Rev.* 33: 60–69.

Faith, D.P. 1989. Homoplasy as pattern: multivariate analysis of morphological convergence in Anseriformes. *Cladistics* 5: 235–58.

Falla, R.A. 1937. *Birds,* B.A.N.Z. Antarctica Research Expedition, 1929–31, rpt B(2), pp.1–288. BANZAR Expedition Committee, Adelaide.

Farago, S., Kovacs, G. and Sterbetz, I. 1991. Goose populations staging and wintering in Hungary 1984–1988. *Ardea* 79: 161–64.

Fay, F.H. 1961. The distribution of waterfowl to St. Lawrence Island, Alaska. *Wildfowl* 12: 70–80.

Fay, F.H., Kelly, B.P. and Sease, J.L. 1989. Managing the exploitation of Pacific walruses: a tragedy of delayed response and poor communication. *Mar. Mammal Sci.* 5: 1–16.

Feduccia, A. 1978. *Presbyornis* and the evolution of ducks and flamingos. *Amer. Sci.* 66: 298–304.

Feduccia, A. 1996. *The origin and evolution of birds.* Yale Univ. Press, New Haven and London.

Feduccia, A. and McGrew, P.O. 1974. A flamingo-like wader from the Eocene of Wyoming. *Contributions to Geology* 13: 49–61.

Feekes, F. 1991. The Black-bellied Whistling Duck in Mexico—from traditional use to sustainable management. *Biol. Cons.* 56: 123–31.

Feret, M., Gauthier, G., Bechet, A., Giroux, J.-F. and Hobson, K.A. 2003. Effect of spring hunt on nutrient storage by greater snow geese in southern Quebec. *J. Wildl. Manage.* 67: 796–807.

Fernholm, B., Bremer, K. and Jörnvall, H. (ed.) 1989. *The hierarchy of life.* Elsevier, Amsterdam.

ffrench, R. 1973 (rev. 1980). *A guide to the birds of Trinidid and Tobago.* Harrowood Books, Newton Square, Pennsylvania.

Fiala, V. 1988. Populationsgrösse und Bruterfolg bei *Aythya ferina* und *Aythya fuligula. Folia Zool.* 37: 41–57.

Figuerola, J., Green, A.J. and Santamaria, L. 2002. Comparative dispersal effectiveness of wigeongrass seeds by waterfowl wintering in south-west Spain: quantitative and qualitative aspects. *J. of Ecol.* 90: 989–1001.

Filchagov, A.V., Bianki, V.V. and Mikhailov, K.T. 1985. Bean Geese (*Anser fabalis*) on the Kola Peninsula. *Ornithologica* 20: 26–32. [In Russian with English summary.]

Findlay, C.S. and Cooke, F. 1982a. Breeding synchrony in the Lesser Snow Goose (*Anser caerulescens caerulescens*). I. Genetic and environmental components of hatch date variability and their effects on hatch synchrony. *Evolution* 36: 342–51.

Findlay, C.S. and Cooke, F. 1982b. Breeding synchrony in the Lesser Snow Goose (*Anser caerulescens caerulescens*) II. The adaptive value of reproductive synchrony. *Evolution* 36: 786–99.

Finlayson, C. 1992. *Birds of the Strait of Gibraltar.* Poyser, London.

Finlayson, M. and Moser, M. (ed.) 1991. *Wetlands.* Toucan Books, London.

Finn, F. 1909. *The waterfowl of India and Asia.* Thacker, Spink and Co., Calcutta.

Fischer, D.H., Sanchez, J., McCoy, M. and Bolen, E.G. 1982. Aggressive displays of male Muscovy Ducks. *Brenesia* 19/20: 541–44.

Fischer, H. 1965. Das Triumphgeschrei der Graugans. *Z. Tierpsychol.* 22: 247–304.

Fischer, J.B. and Griffin, C.R. 2000. Feeding behavior and food habits of wintering Harlequin Ducks at Shemya Island, Alaska. *Wilson Bull.* 112: 318–25.

Fisher, C. and Kear, J. 2002. The taxonomic importance of two early paintings of the Pink-headed Duck *Rhodonessa caryophyllacea* (Latham 1790). *Bull. BOC* 122: 244–48.

Fisher, J., Simon, N. and Vincent, J. 1969. *The red book: wildlife in danger.* Collins, London.

Fisher, W.K. 1903. Birds of Laysan and the leeward islands, Hawaiian group. *Bull. U.S. Fish Comm.* 23: 767–807.

Fitzgerald, J.C. 1906. Frolicsome Musk Ducks. *Emu* 5: 204–5.

Fjeldså, J. 1972. Endringer i sangsvanens, *Cygnus cygnus*, utbredelse pa den skandinaviske halvoy i nyere tid. *Sterna* 11: 145–63.

Fjeldså, J. 1977. *Guide to the young of European precocial birds.* Skarv Nature Publications, Strandgarden, Denmark.

Fjeldså, J. 1985. Classification of waterbird communities in south-eastern Australia. *Emu* 85: 141–49.

Fjeldså, J. 1986. Color variation in the Ruddy Duck (*Oxyura jamaicensis andina*). *Wilson Bull.* 98: 592–94.

Fjeldså, J. and Krabbe, N. 1986. Some range extensions and other unusual records of Andean birds. *Bull. BOC* 106: 115–24.

Fjeldså, J. and Krabbe, N. 1990. *Birds of the High Andes.* Zoological Museum, Univ. Copenhagen, and Apollo Books, Svendborg, Denmark.

Flegg, J. and Longmore, N. 1994. *Photographic field guide to the birds of Australia.* New Holland, London.

Fleming, J. 1822. *The philosophy of zoology.* Edinburgh.

Fleming, J.H. 1935. *A new genus and species of flightless duck from Campbell Island,* Occ. Papers, No. 1. Royal Ontario Museum of Zoology.

Flint, P.L. and Grand, J.B. 1997. Survival of Spectacled Eider adult females and ducklings during brood rearing. *J. Wildl. Manage.* 61: 217–21.

Flint, P.L. and Grand, J.B. 1999. Patterns of variation in size and composition of Greater Scaup eggs: are they related? *Wilson Bull.* 111: 465–71.

Flint, P.L. and Sedinger, J.S. 1992. Reproductive implications of egg-size variations in the Black Brant. *Auk* 109: 896–903.

Flint, P.L., Lindberg, M.S., Maccluskie, M.C. and Sedinger, J. 1994. The adaptive significance of hatching synchrony of waterfowl eggs. *Wildfowl* 45: 248–54.

Flint, P.L., Petersen, M.R. and Grand, J.B. 1997. Exposure of Spectacled Eiders and other diving ducks to lead in western Alaska. *Can. J. Zool.* 75: 439–43.

Flint, V.E., Boehme, R.L., Kostin, Y.V. and Kuznetsov, A.A. 1984. *A field guide to birds of the USSR.* Princeton Univ. Press.

Fokin, S., Kuzyakin, V., Kalchreuter, H. and Kirby, J.S. 2000. *The Garganey in the former USSR. A compilation of life-history information.* Wetlands International Publication, Global Series 7. 50pp.

Foley, R.E. and Batcheller, G.R. 1988. Organochlorine contaminants in Common Goldeneye wintering on the Niagara River. *J. Wildl. Manage.* 52: 441–45.

Folk, C. 1971. A study of diurnal activity rhythm and feeding habits of *A. fuligula* L. *Acta Sc. Nat. Brna* 5: 1–39.

Folk, C., Hudec, K. and Toufar, J. 1966. The weight of the Mallard *Anas platyrhynchos* and its changes in the course of the year. *Zool. Listy* 15: 249–60.

Follestad, A., Larsen, B.H. and Nygård, T. 1986. *Sjøfuglundersøkelser langs kysten av Sør- og Nord-Trøndelag og sørlige deler av Nordland 1983–1986,* Viltrapport No. 41. Direktoratet for Naturforvaltning, Trondheim.

Follestad, A., Nygård, T., Røv, N. and Larsen, B.H. 1988. Distribution and numbers of moulting non-breeding Greylag Geese in Norway. *Wildfowl* 39: 82–87.

Fooks, H.A. 1947. Duck in India. *Avic. Mag.* 53: 209–11.

Forbes, P. 2001. Baboons killing Egyptian Geese goslings at Mana Pools. *Honeyguide* 47: 92.

Forbes, W.A. 1882a. On the convoluted trachea of two species of manucode (*Manucodia atra* and *Phonygama gouldi*); with remarks on similar structures in other birds. *Proc. Zool. Soc. Lond.,* 1882: 347–53.

Forbes, W.A. 1882b. Notes on some points in the anatomy of an Australian duck (*Biziura lobata*). *Proc. Zool. Soc. Lond.,* 1882: 455–8.

Forrester, B.C. 1993. *Birding Brazil: a check-list and site guide.* Publ. privately by the author, Rankinston, Ayrshire, Scotland.

Forslund, P. and Larsson, K. 1995. Intraspecific nest parasitism in the Barnacle Goose: behavioural tactics of parasites and hosts. *Anim. Behav.* 50: 509–17.

Fox, A.D. 1988. Breeding status of the Gadwall in Britain. *Brit. Birds* 81: 51–66.

Fox, A.D. 1993. Pre-nesting feeding selectivity of Pink-footed Geese *Anser brachyrhynchus* in artificial grasslands. *Ibis* 135: 417–23.

Fox, A.D. 1996. *Zostera* exploitation by Brent Geese and Wigeon on the Exe Estuary, southern England. *Bird Study* 43: 257–68.

Fox, A.D. 2003a. The Greenland White-fronted Goose *Anser albifrons flavirostris*. The annual cycle of a migratory herbivore on the European continental fringe. Doctor's dissertation (DSc). National Environment Research Institute, Denmark.

Fox, A.D. 2003b. Diet and habitat use of scoters *Melanitta* in the Western Palearctic–a brief overview. *Wildfowl* 54: 163–82.

Fox, A.D. and Bell, M.C. 1993. Breeding bird communities and environmental variable correlates of Scottish peatland sites. *Hydrobiologia* 279/280: 297–307.

Fox, A.D. and Kahlert, J. 1999. Adjustments to nitrogen metabolism during wing moult in Greylag Geese. *Functional Ecol.* 13: 661–69.

Fox, A.D. and Madsen, J. 1981. The pre-nesting behaviour of the Greenland White-fronted Goose *Anser albifrons flavirostris*. *Wildfowl* 32: 48–52.

Fox, A.D. and Mitchell, C. 1988. Migration and seasonal distribution of Gadwall from Britain and Ireland: a preliminary assessment. *Wildfowl* 39: 145–52.

Fox, A.D. and Mitchell C. 1996. Rafting behaviour and anti-predator response of Steller's Eiders (*Polysticta stelleri*) in Varangerfjord, northern Norway. *J. Orn.* 138: 103–09.

Fox, A.D. and Mitchell C. 1997. Spring habitat use and feeding behaviour of Steller's Eider *Polysticta stelleri* in Varangerfjord, northern Norway. *Ibis* 139: 542–48.

Fox, A.D. and Salmon, D.G. 1988. Changes in the non-breeding distribution and abundance of Pochard *Aythya ferina* in Britain. *Biol. Cons.* 46: 303–16.

Fox, A.D. and Salmon, D.G. 1989. The winter status and distribution of Gadwall in Britain and Ireland. *Bird Study* 36: 37–44.

Fox, A.D. and Stroud, D.A. 1988. The breeding biology of the Greenland White-fronted Goose. *Meddelelser om Grønland, Bioscience* 27: 1–16.

Fox, A.D. and Stroud, D.A. 2002. Greenland White-fronted Goose *Anser albifrons flavirostris*. *BWP Update* 4(2): 65–88. Oxford University Press, UK.

Fox, A.D. and Vinogradov, V.G. 1994. Gadwall. In *Birds in Europe: their conservation status* (ed. G.M. Tucker and M.F. Heath), pp.120–1. BirdLife International, Cambridge.

Fox, A.D., Glahder, C.M. and Walsh, A.J. 2003a. Spring migration routes and timing of Greenland white-fronted geese—results from satellite telemetry. *Oikos* 103: 415–25.

Fox, A.D., Jarrett, N., Gitay, H. and Paynter, D. 1989. Late summer habitat selection by breeding waterfowl in northern Scotland. *Wildfowl* 40: 106–14.

Fox, A.D., Jones, T.A., Singleton, R. and Agnew, A.D.Q. 1993. Food supply and the effects of recreational disturbance on the abundance and distribution of wintering Pochard on a gravel pit in southern Britain. *Hydrobiologia* 279/280: 253–61.

Fox, A.D., Green, A.J., Hughes, B. and Hilton, G. 1994a. Rafting as an antipredator response in wintering White-headed Ducks *Oxyura leucocephala*. *Wildfowl* 45: 232–41.

Fox, A.D., Mitchell, C., Stewart, A., Fletcher, J.D., Turner, J.V.N., Boyd, H. *et al.* 1994b. winter movements and site fidelity of Pink-footed Geese *Anser brachyrhynchus* ringed in Britain, with particular emphasis on those marked in Lancashire. *Bird Study* 41: 221–34.

Fox, A.D., Norriss, D.W., Stroud, D.A. and Wilson, H.J. 1994c. *Greenland White-fronted Geese in Ireland and Britain, 1982/83–1993/94.* Irish National Parks and Wildlife Service and Greenland White-fronted Goose Study, Dublin/Aberystwyth.

Fox, A.D., Boyd, H. and Bromley, R.G. 1995a. Mutual benefits of associations between breeding and non-breeding White-fronted Geese *Anser albifrons*. *Ibis* 137: 151–56.

Fox, A.D., Kahlert, J., Ettrup, H., Nilsson, L. and Hounisen, J.P. 1995b. Moulting Greylag Geese *Anser anser* on the Danish island of Saltholm; numbers, phenology, status and origins. *Wildfowl* 46: 16–30.

Fox, A.D., Mitchell, C., Henriksen, G., Lund, E. and Frantzen, B. 1997. The conservation of Steller's Eider *Polysticta stelleri* in Varangerfjord, Finnmark, Norway. *Wildfowl* 48: 156–65.

Fox, A.D., Glahder, C., Mitchell, C.R., Stroud, D.A., Boyd, H. and Fikke, J. 1996. North American Canada geese (*Branta canadensis*) in West Greenland. *Auk* 113: 231-33.

Fox, A.D., Kahlert, J., Walsh, A.J., Stroud, D.A., Mitchell, C., Kristiansen, J.N. *et al*. 1998a. Patterns of body mass change during moult in three different goose populations. *Wildfowl* 49: 45–56.

Fox, A.D., Norriss, D.W., Stroud, D.A., Wilson, H.J. and Merne, O.J. 1998b. The Greenland White-fronted Goose in Ireland and Britain 1982/83–1994/95: Population change under conservation legislation. *Wildlife Biol.* 4: 1–12.

Fox, A.D., Kahlert, J. and Ettrup, H. 1998c. Diet and habitat use of moulting Greylag Geese *Anser anser* on the Danish island of Saltholm. *Ibis* 140: 676–83.

Fox. A.D., Norriss, D.W., Wilson, H.J., Merne, O.J., Stroud, D.A., Sigfusson, A. and Glahder, C. 1999. Greenland White-fronted Goose *Anser albifrons flavirostris*. In *Goose populations of the Western Palearctic. A review of status and distribution*, Publ., No. 48 (ed. J. Madsen, G. Cracknell and T. Fox), pp.130–42. Wetlands International Wageningen, Netherlands, and National Environmental Research Institute, Rønde, Denmark.

Fox, A.D., Einarsson, Ó., Hilmarsson, J-Ó., Boyd, H. and Mitchell, C. 2000. Viðdvöl heiðagæsa á Suðurlandi að vori. *Bliki* 20: 11–20.

Fox, A.D., Hilmarsson, J. Ó., Einarsson, Ó., Walsh, A.J., Boyd, H. and Kristiansen, J.N. 2002. Staging site fidelity of Greenland White-fronted Geese *Anser albifrons flavirostris* in Iceland. *Bird Study* 49: 42–49.

Fox, A.D., Petersen, Æ. and Fredericksen, M. 2003b. Annual survival and site-fidelity of breeding female Common Scoter *Melanitta nigra* at Mývatn, Iceland, 1925–58. *Ibis* 145: 346.

Francis, C.M., Richards, M.H., Cooke, F. and Rockwell, R.F. 1992. Long term changes in survival rates of Lesser Snow Geese. *Ecology* 73: 1346–62.

Franson, J.C., Hoffman, D.J. and Schmutz, J.A. 2002. Blood selenium concentrations and enzyme activities related to glutathione metabolism in wild Emperor Geese. *Environmental Toxicology and Chemistry* 21: 2179–84.

Franson, J.C., Petersen, M.R., Meteyer, C.U. and Smith, M.R. 1995. Lead poisoning of Spectacled Eider (*Somateria fischeri*) and of a Common Eider (*Somateria mollissima*) in Alaska. *J. Wildl. Dis.* 31: 268–71.

Franson, J.C., Schmutz, J.A., Creekmore, L.H. and Fowler, A.C. 1999. Concentrations of selenium, mercury, and lead in blood of Emperor Geese in western Alaska. *Environmental Toxicology and Chemistry* 18: 965–69.

Franzmann, N.E. 1983. The migration and survival of an Eider *Somateria m. mollissima* population in the southern Baltic. *Ornis Fennica* Suppl. 3: 73–74.

Fraser, M. and McMahon, L. 1991. Marine Egyptian Geese. *Promerops* 198: 7–8.

Frayer, W.E. and Hefner, J.M. 1991. *Florida wetlands: status and trends, 1970s to 1980s.* US Fish & Wildl. Serv., Atlanta.

Fredrickson, L.H. and Hansen, J.L. 1983. Second broods in wood ducks. *J. Wildl. Manage.* 47: 320–26.

Fredrickson, L.H., Burger, G.V., Havera, S.P., Gruber, D.A., Kirby, R. E. and Taylor, T.S. (ed.) 1990. *Proceedings of the 1988 North American Wood Duck Symposium, St Louis, Missouri.*

Fredericksen, M. 2002. Indirect estimation of the number of migratory Greylag and Pink-footed Geese shot in Britain. *Wildfowl* 53: 27–34.

Frederiksen, M., Fox, A.D., Madsen, J. and Colhoun, K. 2001. Estimating the total number of birds using a staging site. *J. Wildl. Manage.* 65: 282–89.

Friedmann, H. 1947. Geographic variations of the Black-bellied, Fulvous, and White-faced Tree Ducks. *Condor* 49: 189–95.

Friedmann, H. and Smith, F.D. 1950. A contribution to the ornithology of northeastern Venezuela. *Proc. U.S. Nat. Mus.* 100: 411–538.

Friend, M., McLean, R.G. and Dein, F.J. 2001. Disease emergence in birds: challenges for the twenty-first century. *Auk* 118: 290–303.

Friend, M.L. and Pearson, G.L. 1973. Duck plague: the present situation. *Western Proc. Ann. Conf. State Game and Fish Commissioners* 53: 315–25.

Frimer, O. 1994. Autumn arrival and moult in King Eiders, *Somateria spectabilis*, at Disko, West Greenland. *Arctic* 47: 137–41.

Frith, H.J. 1955. The downy ducklings of the Pink-eared and White-eyed Ducks. *Emu* 55: 310–12.

Frith, H.J. 1959. The ecology of wild ducks in inland New South Wales. *CSIRO Wildl. Res.* 3: 97–107.

Frith, H.J. 1962. Movements of the Grey Teal, *Anas gibberifrons* Muller (Anatidae). *CSIRO Wildl. Res.* 7: 50–70.

Frith, H.J. 1964a. Taxonomic relationship of *Stictonetta naevosa* (Gould). *Nature* 202: 1352–53.

Frith, H.J. 1964b. The downy young of the Freckled Duck *Stictonetta naevosa. Emu* 64: 42–47.

Frith, H.J. 1965. Ecology of the Freckled Duck *Stictonetta naevosa* (Gould). *CSIRO Wildl. Res.* 10: 125–39.

Frith, H.J. 1977. Band recoveries of the Magpie Goose, *Anseranas semipalmata. Aust. Wildl. Res.* 4: 81–84.

Frith, H.J. 1982. *Waterfowl in Australia* (revised edn). Angus and Robertson, Sydney.

Frith, H.J. and Davies, S.J.J.F. 1961a. Breeding seasons of birds in subcoastal Northern Territory. *Emu* 61: 97–111.

Frith, H.J. and Davies, S.J.J.F. 1961b. Ecology of the Magpie Goose *Anseranas semipalmata* Latham (Anatidae). *CSIRO Wildl. Res.* 6: 91–141.

Frith, H.J., Braithwaite, L.W. and McKean, J.L. 1969. Waterfowl in an inland swamp in New South Wales. *CSIRO Wildl. Res.* 14: 17–64.

Frost, P.G.H., Ball, I.J., Siegfried, W.R. and McKinney F. 1979. Sex ratios, morphology and growth of the African Black Duck. *Ostrich* 50: 220–33.

Fry, C.H. 1977. The evolutionary significance of co-operative breeding in birds. In *Evolutionary ecology* (ed. C.M. Perrins and B. Stonehouse), pp.127–35. Macmilllan, London.

Fullagar, P.J. 1992. The taxonomic and conservation status of the Indonesian Teal *Anas gibberifrons. IWRB Threatened Waterfowl Research Group Newsl.* 2: 7–8.

Fullagar, P.J. and Carbonell, M. 1986. The display postures of the Musk Duck. *Wildfowl* 37: 142–50.

Fullagar, P.J., Davey, C.C. and Rushton, D.K. 1990. Social behaviour of the Freckled Duck *Stictonetta naevosa* with particular reference to the axle-grind. *Wildfowl* 41: 53–61.

Fuller, E. 2001. *Extinct birds* (2nd edn). OUP.

Fyodorov, Y.G. and Khodkov, G.I. 1987. *Cygnus cygnus* on water bodies of central Baraba (western Siberia). In *Ecology and migration of swans of the USSR* (ed. E. Syroechkovski), pp.100–1. Nauka, Moscow.

Gadallah, F.L. and Jefferies, R.L. 1995. Forage quality in brood rearing areas of the Lesser Snow Goose and the growth of captive goslings. *J. Appl. Ecol.* 32: 276–87.

Gale, R.S., Garton, E.O. and Ball, I.J. 1987. *The history, ecology, and management of the Rocky Mountain population of Trumpeter Swans.* US Fish & Wildl. Service, Montana Cooperative Wildl. Research Unit, Missoula.

Galhoff, H. 1987. Untersuchungen zum Energiebedarf und zur Nahrungsnutzung auf einem Stansee Überwinternder Tafelenten (*Aythya ferina* L.). *Ökol. Vögel* 9: 71–84.

Gallo-Orsi, U., Lambertini, M. and Tallone, G. 1994. In situ and ex situ conservation of the White-headed Duck *Oxyura leucocephala* in Italy. *Oxyura* 7: 147–54.

Gamble, K.E. 1966. Breeding biology and food habits of the Musk Duck, *Biziura lobata.* Unpubl. M.S. thesis. Univ. Wisconsin, US.

Gamble, L.R. and Woodin, M.C. 1993. Contaminants in Redhead Ducks wintering in Baffin Bay and Redfish Bay, Texas. Unpubl. rept to US Fish & Wildl. Serv., Corpus Christi, Texas.

Gammonley, J.H. 1995a. Spring feeding ecology of Cinnamon Teal in Arizona. *Wilson Bull.* 107: 62–70.

Gammonley, J.H. 1995b. Nutrient reserve and organ dynamics of breeding Cinnamon Teal. *Condor* 97: 985–92.

Gammonley, J.H. 1996. Cinnamon Teal (*Anas cyanoptera*). The Birds of North America, No. 209 (ed. A. Poole and F. Gill). AOU, Washington, and Academy of Natural Sciences, Philadelphia.

Gammonley, J.H. and Heitmeyer, M.E. 1990. Behavior, body condition, and foods of Buffleheads and Lesser Scaups during spring migration through the Klamath Basin, California. *Wilson Bull.* 102: 672–83.

Ganter, B. and Cooke, F. 1996. Pre-incubation feeding activities and energy budgets of Snow Geese: can food on the breeding grounds influence fecundity? *Oecologia* 106: 153–65.

Ganter, B. and Cooke, F. 1998. Colonial nesters in a deteriorating habitat: site fidelity and colony dynamics of Lesser Snow Geese. *Auk* 115: 642–52.

Ganter, B. and Madsen, J. 2001. An examination of methods to estimate population size in wintering geese. *Bird Study* 48: 90–101.

Ganter, B., Larsson, K., Syroechkovsky, E.V., Litvin, K.E., Leito, A. and Madsen, J. 1999. Barnacle Goose *Branta leucopsis*: Russia/Baltic. In *Goose populations of the Western Palearctic. A review of status and distribution*, Publ. No. 48 (ed. J. Madsen, G. Cracknell and A.D. Fox), pp.270–283. Wetlands International, Wageningen, Netherlands, and National Environmental Research Institute, Rønde, Denmark.

Ganter, B., Cooke, F. and Mineau, P. 1996. Long-term vegetation changes in a Snow Goose nesting habitat. *Can. J. Zool.* 74: 965–69.

Gantlett, S. 1993. The status and separation of White-headed Duck and Ruddy Duck. *Birding World* 6: 273–81.

Garcia, P.A. 2001. Competition with carp may limit White-headed Duck populations in Spain. TWSG News 13: 31–32.

García-Moreno, J. and Mindell, D.P. 2000. Rooting a phylogeny with homologous genes on opposite sex chromosomes (gametologs): a case study using avian CHD. *Mol. Biol. Evol.* 17: 1826–32.

Garðarsson, A. 1975. Íslenskir votlendisfuglar. In *Rit Landverndar*, No. 4, pp.100–34. Landvernd, Reykjavik. [The birds of Icelandic wetlands. In Icelandic with a summary in English.]

Garðarsson, A. 1976. Þjorsarver. Framleidsla Grodurs og Heiðargaesar. Univ. Iceland, Reykjavik.

Garðarsson, A. 1978. Íslenski húsandarstofninn. *Náttúrufrædingurinn* 48: 162–91. [Distribution and numbers of the Barrow's Goldeneye (*Bucephala islandica*) in Iceland. In Icelandic with a summary in English.]

Garðarsson, A. 1979. Waterfowl populations of Lake Mývatn and recent changes in numbers and food habits. *Oikos* 32: 250–70.

Garðarsson, A. 1982. Andfuglar og adrir vatnafuglar. In *Rit Landverndar*, No. 8 (ed. A. Garðarsson), pp.77–116. Landvernd, Reykjavik.

Garðarsson, A. 1991a. Fuglalif við Mývatn og Laxá. In *Náttúra Mývatns* (ed. A. Garðarsson and Á. Einarsson), pp.278–319. Icelandic Natural History Society, Reykjavik. [The bird-life of Mývatn and Laxa, in *The wildlife of Mývatn*. In Icelandic.]

Garðarsson, A. 1991b. Movements of Whooper Swans *Cygnus cygnus* neckbanded in Iceland. *Wildfowl* Spec. Suppl., 1: 189–94.

Garðarsson, A. 1997. Fjoldi heiðagaeser i Þjorsarvenn 1996. *Liffroedistofaun Haskolass Fjolvit* 40: 1–20.

Garðarsson, A. 2005. Status of Harlequin Ducks in Iceland. In Robertson, G.J. and Thomas, P.W. (eds.), *Harlequin Ducks in the Northwest Atlantic.* Can. Wildl. Occ. Pap. (in press).

Garðarsson, A. and Einarsson, Á. 1994. Responses of breeding duck populations to changes in food supply. *Hydrobiologia* 279/280: 15–27.

Garðarsson, A. and Einarsson, Á. 1997. Numbers and production of Eurasian Wigeon in relation to conditions in a breeding area, Lake Mývatn, Iceland. *J. Anim. Ecol.* 66: 439–51.

Garðarsson, A. and Einarsson, Á. 2005. Relationships among food, reproductive success and density of Harlequin Ducks on the River Laxá at Mývatn, Iceland (1975–2002). In Robertson, G.J. and Thomas, P.W. (eds.), *Harlequin Ducks in the Northwest Atlantic.* Can. Wildl. Occ. Pap. (in press).

Garðarsson, A. and Skarphéðinsson, K.H. 1984. A census of the Icelandic Whooper Swan population. *Wildfowl* 35: 37–47.

Garðarsson, A. and Thórarinsson, Th.L. 2003. Útbreidsla og fjöldi straumandar á Íslandi ad vetrarlagi. (Summary: Distribution and numbers of Harlequin Ducks wintering in Iceland). *Bliki* 23: 5–20.

Garden, E.A., Rayski, C. and Thom, V.M. 1964. A parasitic disease in eider ducks. *Bird Study* 11: 280–87.

Garnett, S. (ed.) 1992. *Threatened and extinct birds of Australia*, Rept, No. 82. RAOU, Melbourne, Victoria, Australia.

Gaston, G.R. 1992. Green-winged Teal ingest epibenthic meiofauna. *Estuaries* 15: 227–29.

Gates, J.M. 1962. Breeding biology of the Gadwall in northern Utah. *Wilson Bull.* 74: 43–67.

Gates, R.J., Caithamer, D.F., Tacha, T.C. and Paine, C.R. 1993. The annual molt cycle of *Branta canadensis interior* in relation to nutrient reserve dynamics. *Condor* 95: 680–93.

Gauthier, G. 1986. Experimentally-induced polygyny in Buffleheads: evidence for a mixed reproductive strategy? *Anim. Behav.* 34: 300–2.

Gauthier, G. 1987a. Further evidence of long-term pair bonds in ducks of the genus *Bucephala*. *Auk* 104: 521–22.

Gauthier, G. 1987b. The adaptive significance of territorial behaviour in breeding Buffleheads: a test of three hypotheses. *Anim. Behav.* 35: 348–60.

Gauthier, G. 1988. Territorial behaviour, forced copulations and mixed reproductive strategy in ducks. *Wildfowl* 39: 102–14.

Gauthier, G. 1993. Bufflehead (*Bucephala albeola*). The Birds of North America, No. 67 (ed. A. Poole and F. Gill). AOU, Washington, and Academy of Natural Sciences, Philadelphia.

Gauthier, G. and Tardif, J. 1991. Female feeding and male vigilance during nesting in Greater Snow Geese. *Condor* 93: 701–11.

Gauthier, G., Bedard, Y. and Bedard, J. 1988. Habitat use and activity budgets of Greater Snow Geese in spring. *J. Wildl. Manage.* 52: 191–201.

Gauthier, J., Bedard, J. and Reed, A. 1976. Overland migration by Common Eiders of the St. Lawrence estuary. *Wilson Bull.* 88: 333–44.

Gauthier, G., Bety, J. and Hobson, K.A. 2003. Are greater snow geese capital breeders? New evidence from a stable-isotope model. *Ecology* 84: 3250–64.

Gauthier, G., Pradel, R., Menu, S. and Lebreton, J.D. 2001. Seasonal survival of Greater Snow Geese and effect of hunting under dependence in sighting probability. *Ecology* 82: 3105–19.

Gauthier, J., Bedard, J. and Reed, A. 1976. Overland migration by Common Eiders of the St. Lawrence estuary. *Wilson Bull.* 88: 333–44.

Gauthreaux, S.A. 1978. The ecological significance of behavioural dominance. In *Perspectives in ethology* (ed. P.P.G. Bateson and P.H. Klopfer), pp.17–54. Plenum Press, New York.

Geffen, E. and Yom-Tov, Y. 2001. Factors affecting the rates of intraspecific nest parasitism among Anseriformes and Galliformes. *Anim. Behav.* 62: 1027–38.

Gehrman, K.H. 1951. An ecological study of the Lesser Scaup Duck (*Aythya affinis* Eyton) at West Medical Lake, Spokane County Washington. Unpubl. M.S. thesis. State Coll. Washington, Pullman, US.

Geis, A.D. and Crissey, W.F. 1969. Effect of restrictive hunting regulations on Canvasback and Redhead harvest rates and survival. *J. Wildl. Manage.* 33: 860–66.

Geldenhuys, J.N. 1975. Waterfowl (Anatidae) on irrigation lakes in the Orange Free State. *Ostrich* 46: 219–35.

Geldenhuys, J.N. 1976a. Relative abundance of waterfowl in the Orange Free State. *Ostrich* 47: 27–54.

Geldenhuys, J.N. 1976b. Breeding status of waterfowl at large lakes in the Orange Free State. *Ostrich* 47: 137–39.

Geldenhuys, J.N. 1976c. Physiognomic characteristics of wetland vegetation in South African Shelduck habitat. *S. Afr. J. Wildl. Res.* 6: 75–78.

Geldenhuys, J.N. 1977. Feeding habits of South African Shelduck. *S. Afr. J. Wildl. Res.* 7: 5–9.

Geldenhuys, J.N. 1980a. Breeding seasons of Egyptian Geese and South African Shelducks in central South Africa. *Pan-Afr. Ornith. Congr.* 4: 267–75.

Geldenhuys, J.N. 1980b. Breeding ecology of the South African Shelduck in the southern Orange Free State. *S. Afr. J. Wildl. Res.* 10: 94–111.

Geldenhuys, J.N. 1981a. Moults and moult localities of the South African Shelduck. *Ostrich* 52: 129–34.

Geldenhuys, J.N. 1981b. Effect of temperature and rainfall on the distribution of the South African Shelduck *Tadorna cana*. *S. Afr. J. Zool.* 16: 167–71.

Geldenhuys, J.N. 1983. Morphological variation in wing-moulting South African Shelducks. *Ostrich* 54: 19–25.

Gentilli, J. and Bekle, H. 1983. Modelling a climatically pulsating population: Grey Teal in south-western Australia. *J. Biogeog.* 10: 75–96.

George, J.C. and Berger, A.J. 1966. *Avian myology*. Academic Press, New York.

George, R.R. and Bolen, E.G. 1975. Endoparasites of Black-bellied Whistling-ducks in southern Texas. *J. Wildl. Dis.* 11: 17–22.

Gerasimov, N.N. 1990. Spring migration and number of Anseriformes in Kamchatka. In *Managing Waterfowl Populations*, IWRB Symp., Astrakhan 1989, Publ., No. 12 (ed. G.V.T. Matthews), pp.46–7. IWRB, Slimbridge, UK.

Gerasimov, N.N. and Gerasimov, Y.N. 1995a. Investigation of waterfowl migration in Kamchatka. *Goose Study* 9: 1–7.

Gerasimov, N.N. and Gerasimov, Y.N. 1995b. Present status and perspectives for protection of geese in Kamchatka. *Goose Study* 9: 10–14.

Gerasimov, N.N. and Gerasimov, Y.N. 1997a. Spring migration of geese on Khaarchinskoe Lake. *Casarca* 3: 384–87. (In Russian with English summary.)

Giai, A.G. 1950. Notas de viajes. II. Por el norte de Misiones. *Hornero* 9: 139–64.

Giai, A.G. 1951. Notas sobre la avifauna de Salta y Misiones. *Hornero* 9: 247–76.

Giai, A.G. 1976. *Vida de un naturalista en Misiones*. Editorial Albatros, Buenos Aires.

Gibbons, D.W., Reid, J.B. and Chapman, R.A. 1993. *The new atlas of breeding birds in Britain and Ireland*. Poyser, London.

Gibbs, R.M. 1962. Juvenile mortality in the Common Goldeneye, *Bucephala clangula*, in Maine. *Maine Field Nat.* 18: 67–68.

Gibson, E. 1920. Further ornithological notes from the neighbourhood of Cape San Antonio, Buenos Aires. *Ibis* 11: 1–97.

Gibson, D.D. 2002. Correct type locality of the Emperor Goose (*Chen canagica*). *Proceedings of the Biological Society of Washington* 115: 706–07.

Giles, N. 1994. Tufted Duck (*Aythya fuligula*) habitat use and brood mortality increases after fish removal from gravel pit lakes. *Hydrobiologia* 280: 387–92.

Gill, F.B., Stokes, F.J. and Stokes, C.C. 1974. Observations on the Horned Screamer. *Wilson Bull.* 86: 43–50.

Gill, J.A. 1996. Habitat choice in Pink-footed Geese: quantifying the constraints determining winter site use. *J. Appl. Ecol.* 33: 884–92.

Gill, J.A., Watkinson, A.R. and Sutherland, W.J. 1997. Causes of the redistribution of Pink-footed Geese *Anser brachyrhynchus* in Britain. *Ibis* 139: 497–503.

Gill, R.E., Jr and Kincheloe, K.L. 1993. Are Bald Eagles important predators of Emperor Geese. *J. Raptor Res.* 27: 34–36.

Gillham, E., Harrison, J.M. and Harrison, J.G. 1966. A study of certain *Aythya* hybrids. *Wildfowl* 17: 49–65.

Gillham, E.H. 1987. *Tufted Ducks in a royal park*. Hythe Printers, Hythe, Kent, England.

Gilyazov, A.S. 1993. Air pollution impact on the bird communities of the Lapland Biosphere Reserve. In *Aerial pollution in Kola Peninsula*, Int. Workshop, April 14–16, 1992 (ed. M.V. Kozlov, E. Haokioja and V.T. Yarmishko), pp.383–90. Apatity, St. Petersburg.

Ginn, H.B. and Melville, D.S. 1983. *Moult in birds*, Guide, No. 19. BTO, Tring.

Girard, O. 1992. Report on seaducks in France. *IWRB Seaduck Research Group Bull.* 1: 34–5.

Girard, O. 1994. Sarcelle d'été. In *Nouvel atlas des oiseaux nicheurs de France* (ed. D. Yeatman-Berthelot and G. Jarry), pp.140–41. S.O.F, Paris.

Girard, O. 1996. Analyse des ailes de Sarcelle d'été (*Anas querquedula*). *Bull. mens. ONC* 212: 3–9.

Giroux, J-F. 1981a. Ducks nesting on artificial islands during drought. *J. Wildl. Manage.* 45: 783–86.

Giroux, J-F. 1981b. Interspecific nest parasitism by Redheads on islands in southeastern Alberta. *Can. J. Zool.* 59: 2053–57.

Giroux, J-F. 1991. Roost fidelity of Pink-footed Geese *Anser brachyrhynchus* in north-east Scotland. *Bird Study* 38: 112–17.

Gizenko, A.I. 1955. *Birds of Sakhalin region*. Izd-vo AS USSR, Moscow.

Gizenko, A.I. and Mishin, I.P. 1952. New data on the geographic distribution and biology of *Anser cygnoides* on Sakhalin Island. *Zoologischeskii Zhurnal* (*J. Zoology*) 31: 312–14.

Gjershaug, J.O., Thingstad, P.G., Eldoy, S. and Byrkjeland, S. (ed.) 1994. *Norsk Fugleatlas—Hekkefuglenes utbredelse og bestandsstatus i Norge*. Norwegian Ornithological Society, Oslo. [Norwegian bird atlas—the status and distribution of breeding birds in Norway.]

Glade, A.A. (Ed.). 1993. *Libro Rojo de los Vetebrados Terrestres de Chile*. Corporación Nacional Forestal (CONAF). Santiago.

Gladstone, P. and Martell, C. 1968. Some field notes on the breeding of the Greater Kelp Goose. *Wildfowl* 19: 25–31.

Glegg, W.E. 1951. On seven eggs attributed to the Labrador Duck *Camptorhynchus labradorius*. *Ibis* 93: 305–6.

Gloutney, M.L., Alisauskas, R.T. and Afton, A.D. 1999. Use of supplemental food by breeding Ross's Geese and Lesser Snow Geese: evidence for variable anorexia. *Auk* 116: 97–108.

Goeldi, E.A. 1894. *Las Aves do Brazil*. Rio de Janeiro.

Golding, F.D. 1934. Notes on some birds of the Lake Chad area, NE Bornu. *Ibis* 76: 738–57.

Goldsmith, A.R. 1982. The Australian Black Swan *Cygnus atratus*: prolactin and gonadotrophin secretion during breeding including incubation. *Gender. Comp. Endocrinol.* 46: 458–62.

Gole, P. 1982. Status of *Anser indicus* in Asia with special reference to India. *Aquila* 89: 141–49.

Gole, P. 1990. *Anser indicus*: a relegated goose species. *IWRB Newsl.* 3: 20–22.

Gole, P. 1997. The elusive Bar-headed Goose. *J. Ecol. Soc.* 10: 3–5.

Gollop, J.B. and Marshall, W.H. 1954. *A guide for aging duck broods in the field*, Tech. Sec. Rept. Miss. Flyway Council.

Gomez, F. 1979. Algunos aspectos sobre la ecología del pato güirirí pico negro (*Dendrocygna viduata* L.) en el llano inundable alto Apure de Venezuela. Unpubl. thesis. Univ. Central Venezuela, Caracas, Venezuela.

Gómez-Dallmeier, F. and Cringan, A.T. 1990. *Biology, conservation and management of waterfowl in Venezuela.* Editorial Ex Libris, Caracas, Venezuela.

Gomez Ventura, J.A. 1985. Reproduccion de *Dendrocygna autumnalis* (Anseriformes: Anatidae) en cajas de anidacion. Laguna el Jocotal, San Miguel, El Salvador. In *The Wildl. Soc. de Mexico, Asoc. Civil and Secret*, pp.916–37. Desarrollo Urbano y Ecol., Mexico, DF.

Gonzales, P.C. 1983. *Birds of Catanduanes*, Zool. Papers, No. 2, Nat. Mus., Manila.

Gonzales, P.C. and Rees, C.P. 1988. *Birds of the Philippines*. Haribon Foundation, Manila.

Goodall, J.D., Johnson, A.W. and Philippi, R.A. 1951. *Las aves de Chile*, Vols 1 and 2. Platt, Establecimientos Gráficos, S.A., Buenos Aires.

Goodburn, B.F. 1984. Mate guarding in the Mallard *Anas platyrhynchos*. *Ornis Scand.* 15: 261–65.

Goode, D. 1981. *Report of the Nature Conservancy Council's Working Group on Lead Poisoning in Swans.* Nature Conservancy Council, London.

Goodfellow, D.L. 2001. *Birds of Australia's top end.* Scrubfowl Press, Parap, Northern Territory.

Goodman, D.C. and Fisher, H.I. 1962. Functional anatomy of the feeding apparatus in waterfowl (Aves: Anatidae). S. Illinois Univ. Press, Carbondale.

Goodman, S.M. and Meininger, P.L. (ed.) 1989. *The birds of Egypt*. OUP.

Goodman, S.M. and Rakotozafy, L.M.A. 1997. Subfossil birds from coastal sites in western and southwestern Madagascar: a paleo-environmental reconstruction. In *Natural change and human impact in Madagascar* (ed. S.M. Goodman and B.D. Patterson), pp.257–79. Smithsonian Institution Press, Washington.

Gordienko, N.S., Drobovtsev, V.I. and Koshelyev, A.I. 1986. Biology of *Oxyura leucocephala* in northern Kazakhstan and in the south of western Siberia.

In *Rare, disappearing and little known birds of the USSR*, pp.8–15. Central Board for Nature Conservation of the RSFSR, Central Science Research Laboratory, Moscow.

Gore, M.E.J. 1990. *Birds of the Gambia: an annotated check-list*. Check-list No. 3 (2nd edn). BOU, Tring.

Gorman, G. 1996. *The birds of Hungary*. Christopher Helm, London.

Gorman, M.L. and Milne, H. 1972. Creche behavior in the Common Eider *Somateria m. mollissima* L. *Ornis Scand.* 3: 21–25.

Gosper, D.G. 1981. Survey of birds on flood-plain estuarine wetlands on the Hunter and Richmond Rivers in northern New South Wales. *Corella* 5: 1–18.

Gottschaldt, K-M. 1974. The physiological basis of tactile sensibility in the beak of geese. *J. Comp. Physiol.* 95: 29–47.

Goudie, R.I. and Ankney, C.D. 1986. Body size, activity budgets, and diets of sea ducks wintering in Newfoundland. *Ecology* 67: 1475–82.

Goudie, R.I. and Ankney, C.D. 1988. Patterns of habitat use by sea ducks wintering in southeastern Newfoundland. *Ornis Scand.* 19: 249–56.

Goudie, R.I., Brault, S., Conant, B., Kondratyev, A.V., Petersen, M.R. and Vermeer, K. 1994. The status of sea ducks in the North Pacific rim towards their conservation and management. In *Trans. 59th North American Wildlife and Natural Resources Conf.*, pp.27–49. Wildl. Manage. Inst., Washington.

Goudie, R.I., Robertson, G.J., and Reed, A. 2000. Common Eider (*Somateria mollissima*). The Birds of North America, No. 546 (ed. A. Poole and F. Gill). AOU, The Birds of North America Inc., Philadelphia.

Goudswaard, R. 1991. The search for the Campbell Island Flightless Teal *Anas aucklandica nesiotis*. *Wildfowl* 42: 145–48.

Gowans, B., Robertson, G.J. and Cooke, F. 1997. Behaviour and chronology of pair formation by Harlequin Ducks *Histrionicus histrionicus*. *Wildfowl* 48: 135–46.

Grand, J.B. and Flint, P.L. 1997. Productivity of nesting Spectacled Eiders on the lower Kashunuk River, Alaska. *Condor* 99: 926–32.

Grand, J.B., Flint, P.L., Petersen, M.R. and Moran, C.L. 1998. Effect of lead poisoning on Spectacled Eider survival rates. *J. Wildl. Manage.* 62: 1103–9.

Grant, T.A. 1991. Foraging ecology of Trumpeter Swans breeding in the Copper River Delta, Alaska. Unpubl. M.Sc. thesis. Univ. Minnesota, Minneapolis, US.

Gray, A.P. 1958. *Bird hybrids: a checklist with bibliography.* Commonweath Agriculture Bureaux, Farnham Royal, England.

Gray, B.J. 1980. Reproduction, energetics and social structure of the Ruddy Duck. Unpubl. Ph.D. thesis. Univ. California (Davis), US.

Gray, G.R. 1871. *Hand-list of genera and species of birds: distinguishing those contained in the British Museum. Part III. Struthiones, Grallæ, and Anseres, with indices of generic and specific names.* Brit. Mus. (Nat. Hist.), London.

Gray, P.N. 1993. *Biology of the southern Mallard, Florida's Mottled Duck.* Unpubl. Ph.D. thesis. Univ. Florida, US.

Grebmeier, J.M. and Cooper, L.W. 1995. Influence of the St Lawrence Island polynya on the Bering Sea benthos. *J. Geophysical Res.* 100: 4439–60.

Green, A.J. 1992a. *The status and conservation of the White-winged Wood Duck* Cairina scutulata, Spec. Publ., No. 17. IWRB, Slimbridge, UK.

Green, A.J. 1992b. Wildfowl at risk 1992. *Wildfowl* 43: 160–84.

Green, A.J. 1993a. *The status and conservation of the Marbled Teal* Marmaronetta angustirostris. Spec. Publ., No. 23. IWRB, Slimbridge, UK.

Green, A.J. 1993b. The biology of the White-winged Duck *Cairina scutulata. Forktail* 8: 65–82.

Green, A.J. 1993c. The status and habitat of the White-winged Duck *Cairina scutulata. Bird Conserv. Int.* 3: 119–43.

Green, A.J. 1996. *The summer ecology of the Marbled Teal* (Marmaronetta angustirostris), *Ferruginous Duck* (Aythya nyroca) *and other ducks in the Göksu Delta, Turkey in 1995.* Unpubl. Rept. Doñana Biological Station, Seville, Spain.

Green, A.J. 1997. Brood attendance and brood care in the Marbled Teal, *Marmaronetta angustirostris. J. für Orn.* 138: 443–49.

Green, A.J. 1998a. Comparative feeding behaviour and niche organization in a Mediterranean duck community. *Can. J. Zool.* 76: 500–7.

Green, A.J. 1998b. Habitat selection by the Marbled Teal *Marmaronetta angustirostris*, Ferruginous Duck *Aythya nyroca* and other ducks in the Göksu Delta, Turkey in late summer. *Rev. Ecol. Terre et Vie* 53: 225–43.

Green, A.J. 1998c. Clutch size, brood size and brood emergence in the Marbled Teal *Marmaronetta angustirostris* in the Marismas del Guadalquivir, southwest Spain. *Ibis* 140: 670–75.

Green, A.J. 2000a. *Threatened wetlands and waterbirds in Morocco: a final report.* Doñana Biological Station, Sevilla.

Green, A.J. 2000b. Sexual dimorphism in morphometry and allometry in the Marbled Teal *Marmaronetta angustirostris. J. Avian Biol.* 31: 345–50.

Green, A.J. 2000c. The habitat requirements of the Marbled Teal (*Marmaronetta angustirostris*), Ménétr., a review. In *Limnology and aquatic birds: monitoring, modelling and management*, 2nd SIL Int. Cong. Universidad Autónoma del Yucatán, Mérida (ed. F.A. Comín, J.A. Herrera and J. Ramírez), pp.131–40. Univ. Autónoma del Yucatán, Mérida, Mexico.

Green, A.J. (comp.) 1996. International action plan for the Marbled Teal *Marmaronetta angustirostris*. In *Globally threatened birds in Europe* (ed. B. Heredia, L. Rose and M. Painter), pp.99–117. Council of Europe Publishing, Strasbourg.

Green, A.J. and Anstey, S. 1992. The status of the White-headed Duck *Oxyura leucocephala. Bird Conserv. Int.* 2: 185–200.

Green, A.J. and El Hamzaoui, M. 2000. Diurnal behaviour, habitat use and interspecific associations of non-breeding Marbled Teal *Marmaronetta angustirostris. Can. J. Zool.* 78: 2112–18.

Green, A.J., El Hamzaoui, M., El Agbani, M.A. and Franchimont, J. 2002. The conservation status of Moroccan wetlands with particular reference to waterbirds and to changes since 1978. *Biol. Cons.* 104: 71–82.

Green, A.J. and Hughes, B. 1996. Action plan for the White-headed Duck *Oxyura leucocephala*. In *Globally threatened birds in Europe* (ed. B. Heredia, L. Rose and M. Painter), pp.119–46. Council of Europe Publishing, Strasbourg.

Green, A.J. and Hunter, J. 1996. The declining White-headed Duck: a call for information. *Wetlands International–IUCN Threatened Waterfowl Specialist Group News* 9: 19–21.

Green, A.J. and Navarro, J.D. 1997. National censuses of the Marbled Teal, *Marmaronetta angustirostris*, in Spain. *Bird Study* 44: 80–87.

Green, A.J. and Selva, N. 2000. The diet of post-breeding Marbled Teal *Marmaronetta angustirostris* and

Mallard *Anas platyrhynchos* in the Göksu Delta, Turkey. *Rev. Ecol. Terre et Vie* 55: 161–9.

Green, A.J. and Sánchez, M.I. 2003. Spatial and temporal variation in the diet of Marbled Teal *Marmaronetta angustirostris* in the western Mediterranean. *Bird Study* 50: 153–60.

Green, A.J. and Yarar, M. 1996. Rapid decline of White-headed Ducks at Burdur Lake, Turkey. *Wetlands International–IUCN Threatened Waterfowl Specialist Group News* 9: 16–18.

Green, A.J., Webber, L.C. and Etheridge, A. 1992. Studies of the White-winged Wood Duck *Cairina scutulata* in captivity. *Wildfowl* 43: 200–10.

Green, A.J., El Hamzaoui, M., El Agbani, M.A. and Franchimont, J. 2002. The conservation status of Moroccan wetlands with particular reference to waterbirds and to changes since 1978. *Biol. Cons.* 104: 71–82.

Green, A.J., Hilton, G.M., Hughes, B., Fox, A.D. and Yarar, M. 1993. The ecology and behaviour of the White-headed Duck *Oxyura leucocephala* at Burdur Gölü, Turkey, February–March 1993. Internal rept. WWT, Slimbridge, UK.

Green, A.J., Young, H.G., Rabarisoa, R.G.M., Ravonjiarisoa, P. and Andrianarimisa, A. 1994. The dry season diurnal behaviour of the Madagascar Teal *Anas bernieri* at Lake Bemamba. *Wildfowl* 45: 124–33.

Green, A.J., Fox, A.D., Hilton, G, Hughes, B., Yarar, M. and Salathe, T. 1996. Threats to Burdur Lake ecosystem, Turkey and its waterbirds, particularly the White-headed Duck *Oxyura leucocephala*. *Biol. Cons.* 76: 241–52.

Green, A.J., Fox, A.D., Hughes, B. and Hilton, G.M. 1999a. Time-activity budgets and site selection of White-headed Ducks *Oxyura leucocephala* at Burdur Lake, Turkey in late winter. *Bird Study* 46: 62–73.

Green, A.J., Navarro, J.D., Dolz, J.C. and Aragoneses, J. 1999b. Brood emergence patterns in a Mediterranean duck community. *Bird Study* 46: 116–18.

Green, R.H. 1977. *Birds of Tasmania*. Launceston, Tasmania.

Greenway, J.C., Jr 1967. *Extinct and vanishing birds of the world* (2nd revised edn). Dover, New York.

Greenwood, P.J. 1980. Mating systems, philopatry and dispersal in birds and mammals. *Anim. Behav.* 28: 1140–62.

Greenwood, R.J., Sargeant, A.B., Johnson, D.H., Cowardin, L.M. and Shaffer, T.L. 1995. Factors associated with duck nest success in the prairie pothole region of Canada. *Wildl. Monogr.* 128: 1–57.

Grenquist, P. 1963. Hatching losses of Common Goldeneyes in the Finnish archipelago. *Int. Ornith. Congr.* 13: 685–89.

Griffin, C.R. and Brown, R.A. 1990. Genetic variation and hybridization in Hawaiian Duck and Mallards in Hawaii. Unpubl. rept. US Fish & Wildl. Serv., Hawaiian and Pacific Islands National Wildlife Refuge Complex.

Grimes, L.G. 1987. *The birds of Ghana: an annotated check-list*. Check-list No. 9. BOU, London.

Grinchenko, A.B. 2001. Migration and wintering of Lesser White-fronted Geese in Crimea. *Casarca* 7: 130–36.

Grinchenko, A.B., Popenko, V., Aarvak, T., Nordenswan, G. and Pynnönen, J. 2003. Survey of wintering gesse on Lake sivash and the Crimea. *Casarca* 9: 313–16.

Griswold, J.A. 1968. First breeding of the Magellanic Steamer Duck in captivity. *Wildfowl* 19: 32.

Griswold, J.A. 1973. The Coscoroba. *Int. Zoo Ybk* 13: 38–40.

Groth, J.G. and Barrowclough, G.F. 1999. Basal divergences in birds and the phylogenetic utility of the nuclear RAG-1 gene. *Mol. Phylogen. Evol.* 12: 115–123.

Guan, G.X., Zhang, Y.S. and Jin, J.H. 1963. A preliminary survey on the wintering ducks in Southern China. *Chinese J. Zool.* 5(2): 70–72. [In Chinese.]

Gudmunðsson, F. 1971. Straumendur (*Histrionicus histrionicus*) á Íslandi. *Náttúrufræðingurinn* 41: 1–28; 64–98. [The Harlequin Duck (*Histrionicus histrionicus*) in Iceland. In Icelandic with a summary in English].

Guiler, E.R. 1966. The breeding of the Black Swan *Cygnis atrata* Latham in Tasmania with special reference to some management problems. *Proc. Royal Soc. of Tasmania.* 100: 31–52.

Guiler, E.R. 1967. The Cape Barren Goose, its environment, numbers and breeding. *Emu* 66: 211–35.

Guiler, E.R. 1970. The use of breeding sites by Black Swans in Tasmania. *Emu* 70: 3–8.

Guiler, E.R. 1974. The conservation of the Cape Barren Goose. *Biol. Cons.* 6: 252–57.

Guillemette, M. 1998. The effect of time and digestion constraints in Common Eiders while feeding and diving over blue mussel beds. *Funct. Ecol.* 12: 123–31.

Guillemette, M. 2001. Foraging before spring migration and before breeding in Common Eiders: does hyperphagia occur? *Condor* 103: 633–38.

Guillemette, M., Himmelman, J.H., Barette, C. and Reed, A. 1993. Habitat selection by Common Eiders in winter and its interaction with flock size. *Can. J. Zool.* 71: 1259–66.

Gullestad, N., Owen, M. and Nugent, M.J. 1984. Numbers and distribution of Barnacle Geese on Norwegian staging islands and the importance of the staging area to the Svalbard population. *Norsk Pol. Skr.* 181: 57–65.

Gummer, H. 2000. A progress report on the Campbell Island Teal in New Zealand. *TWSG News* 12: 54–56.

Gummer, H. and Williams, M. 1999. Campbell Island Teal: conservation update. *Wildfowl* 50: 133–38.

Gurtovaya, E., Tolvanen, P., Eskelin, T., Øien, I.J., Bragina, T., Aarvak, T. *et al.* 1999. Preliminary results of the Lesser White-fronted Goose monitoring in Kazakhstan in October 1999. *Casarca* 5: 145–54.

Gusakov, Y.S. 1987. Numbers and populations of Whooper Swans in the Penzhina-Parapol valley. In *Ecology and migration of swans in the USSR* (ed. E. Syroechkovski), pp.126–30. Nauka, Moscow.

Gusakov, Y.S. 1988. Landscape and waterfowl population dynamics of Penzhina-Parapol Dale. In *Chronological changes of game animal numbers in Russia*, pp.22–43. Moscow. [In Russian.]

Gustin, M., Rizzi, V. and Gallo-Orsi, U. 2000. White-headed Duck reintroduction in Apulia, Southern Italy: 1999 update. *Wetlands International–IUCN Threatened Waterfowl Specialist Group News* 12: 15.

Gysels, H. 1969. *On the intermediary position of the screamers (Anseriformes: Anhimidae) between the Anseriformes and the Galliformes: lens protein evidence.* Laboratorium voor Dierkunde-Systematiek, Rijksuniversteit Gent, Belgium.

Haapanen, A. 1991. Whooper Swan population dynamics in Finland. *Wildfowl* Spec. Suppl., No. 1: 137–41.

Haapanen, A. and Nilsson, L. 1979. Breeding waterfowl populations in northern Fennoscandia. *Ornis Scand.* 10: 145–219.

Haapanen, A., Ulmanen, I. and Valste, J. 1966. Observations on the bird fauna in Koitilaiskaira (Finnish Lapland). *Ornis Fenn.* 43: 45–54.

Haapanen, A., Helminen, M. and Soumalainen, H.K. 1973a. The spring arrival and breeding phenology of the Whooper Swan *Cygnus c. cygnus* in Finland. *Finnish Game Research* 33: 31–38.

Haapanen, A., Helminen, M. and Soumalainen, H.K. 1973b. Population growth and breeding biology of the Whooper Swan *Cygnus c. cygnus* in Finland in 1950–1970. *Finnish Game Research* 33: 39–60.

Haapenen, A., Helminen, M. and Soumalainen, H.K. 1977. The summer behaviour and habitat use of the Whooper Swan. *Finn. Game Res.* 36: 49–81.

Hachisuka, M. 1932. Notes sur les oiseaux des Philippines. *L'Oiseaux* 2: 226.

Haedo Rossi, J.A. 1953. Contribucion al conocimiento de la biologia del cisne de cuello negro. *Hornero* 10: 1–17.

Haffer, J. 1968. Notes on the wing and tail moult of the screamers, the Sunbittern, and immature guans. *Auk* 85: 633–38.

Haffer, J. 1975. *Avifauna of northwestern Colombia, South America*, Bonner Zool. Monogr., No. 7. Zoologisches Forschunginstitut und Museum Alexander Koenig, Bonn.

Haffer, J. 1992. The history of species concepts and species limits in ornithology. *Bull. BOC* 112A: 107–58.

Hagan, A.A. and Heath, J.E. 1980. Regulation of heat loss in the duck by vasomotion in the bill. *J. Therm. Biol.* 5: 95–101.

Hagey, L.R., Schteingart, C.D., Ton-Nu, H-T., Rossi, S.S., Odell, D. and Hofmann, A.F. 1990. β-Phocacholic acid in bile: biochemical evidence that the flamingo is related to an ancient goose. *Condor* 92: 593–97.

Hahn, P. 1963. *Where is that vanished bird? An index to the known specimens of the extinct and near extinct North American species.* Univ. Toronto Press.

Hale, W.G. 1980. *Waders.* Collins, London.

Hallam, A. 1988. The contribution of palaeontology to systematics and evolution. In *Prospects in systematics* (ed. D.L. Hawksworth), pp.128–47. Systematics Association Spec. Vol. 36. Clarendon Press, Oxford.

Halleux, D. 1998. Un nouveau site pour la Sarcelle de Bernier *Anas bernieri*. *Working Group on Birds in the Madagascar Region, Newsl.* 8: 8.

Halliday, T. 1978. *Vanishing birds: their natural history and conservation.* Sidgwick and Jackson, London.

Halse, S.A. 1983. Weight and particle size of grit in gizzards of Spur-winged Geese. *Ostrich* 54: 180–82.

Halse, S.A. 1984a. Food intake, digestive efficiency and retention time in Spur-winged Geese *Plectropterus gambensis. S. Afr. J. Wildl. Res.* 14: 106–10.

Halse, S.A. 1984b. Diet, body condition and gut size of Egyptian Geese. *J. Wildl. Manage.* 48: 569–73.

Halse, S.A. 1985a. Activity budgets of Spur-winged and Egyptian Geese at Barberspan during winter. *Ostrich* 56: 104–10.

Halse, S.A. 1985b. Diet and size of the digestive organs of Spur-winged Geese. *Wildfowl* 36: 129–34.

Halse, S.A. and Dobbs, J.C. 1985. Carcass composition of Spur-winged Geese with comments on reproduction and moulting. *Afr. J. Ecol.* 23: 171–78.

Halse, S.A. and Jaensch, R.P. 1989. Breeding seasons of waterbirds in South-western Australia—the importance of rainfall. *Emu* 89(4): 232–49.

Halse, S.A. and Skead, D.M. 1983. Wing moult, body measurements and condition indices of Spur-winged Geese. *Wildfowl* 34: 108–14.

Halse, S.A., Williams, M.R., Jaensch, R.P. and Lane, J.A.K. 1993. Wetland characteristics and waterbird use of wetlands in south-western Australia. *Wildl. Res.* 20: 103–26.

Halse, S.A., Burbridge, A.A., Lane, J.A.K., Haberley, B., Pearson, G.B. and Clarke, A. 1995. Size of the Cape Barren Goose population in Western Australia. *Emu* 95: 77–83.

Hamilton, D.J. and Ankney, C.D. 1994. Consumption of Zebra Mussels *Dreissena polymorpha* by diving ducks in Lakes Erie and St. Clair. *Wildfowl* 45: 159–66.

Hamilton, D.J., Neate, J. and Nudds, T.D. 1999. Size-selective predation of Blue Mussels (*Mytilus edulis*) by Common Eiders (*Somateria mollissima*) under controlled field conditions. *Auk* 116: 403–16.

Hammell, G.S. 1973. The ecology of the Lesser Scaup (*Aythya affinis* Eyton) in southwestern Manitoba. Unpubl. M.S. thesis. Univ. Guelph, Canada.

Hammond, M.C. and Mann, G.E. 1956. Waterfowl nesting islands. *J. Wildl. Manage.* 20: 345–52.

Handel, C.M. and Gill, R.E., Jr 1983. Yellow birds stand out in a crowd. *North American Bird Bander* 8: 6–9.

Handley, C.O., Jr 1950. The brant of Prince Patrick Island, Northwest Territories. *Wilson Bull.* 42: 128–32.

Handley, L.R. 1995. Seagrass distribution in the northern Gulf of Mexico. In *Our living resources: a report to the nation on the distribution, abundance, and health of U.S. plants, animals, and ecosystems* (ed. E.T. LaRoe, G.S. Farris, C.E. Puckett, P.D. Doran and M.J. Mac), pp.273–75. US Dept Interior, National Biological Service, Washington.

Handrinos, G. and Acriotis, T. 1997. *The birds of Greece.* Helm, London.

Hansen, H.A., Shepard, P.E.K., King, J.G. and Troyer, W.A. 1971. The Trumpeter Swan in Alaska. *Wildl. Monogr.* 26: 1–83.

Hansen, K. 2002. *A farewell to Greenland's wildlife.* Bære Dygtighed & Gads Forlag, Copenhagen, Denmark.

Hanski, I. 1994. A practical model of metapopulation dynamics. *J. Anim. Ecol.* 63: 151–62.

Hanski, I. and Gilpin, M. 1991. Metapopulation dynamics: brief history and conceptual domain. *Biol. J. Linn. Soc.* 42: 3–16.

Hanson, H.A. 1961. Loss of waterfowl production to tide floods. *J. Wildl. Manage.* 25: 242–48.

Hanson, H.C. 1962. *The dynamics of condition factors in Canada Geese and their relation to seasonal stresses.* Tech. Paper, No. 12. Arctic Inst. N. Am., Univ. Calgary.

Hanson, H.C. 1997. *The Giant Canada Goose* (revised edn). Ill. Nat. Hist. Surv., Southern Illinois Univ. Press, Urbana.

Hanson, M.A. and Butler, M.G. 1994. Responses to food web manipulation in a shallow water lake. *Hydrobiologia* 279/280: 457–66.

Haramis, G.M. 1982. Records of Redhead x Canvasback hybrids. *Wilson Bull.* 94: 599–602.

Haramis, G.M. 1991a. Redhead *Aythya americana.* In *Habitat requirements for Chesapeake Bay living resources* (2nd edn) (ed.. S.L. Funderburk, S.J. Jordan, J.A. Mihursky, and D. Riley), pp.8–10. Rept. No. 18. Chesapeake Research Consortium, Inc., Solomons, Maryland.

Haramis, G.M. 1991b. Canvasback *Aythya valisineria.* In *Habitat requirements for Chesapeake Bay living resources* (2nd edn) (ed. S.L. Funderburk, J.A. Mihursky, S.J. Jordan and D. Riley), pp.17.1–17.10. Living Resources Subcommittee, Chesapeake Bay Program, Annapolis.

Haramis, G.M. and Nice, A.D. 1980. An improved web tagging technique for waterfowl. *J. Wildl. Manage.* 44: 898–99.

Haramis, G.M., Nichols, J.D., Pollock, K.H. and Hines, J.E. 1986. The relationship between body mass and survival of wintering Canvasbacks. *Auk* 103: 506–14.

Haramis, G.M., Jorde, D.G. and Bunck, C.M. 1993. Survival of hatching-year female Canvasbacks wintering on Chesapeake Bay. *J. Wildl. Manage.* 57: 763–70.

Haramis, G.M., Derlath, E.L. and Link, W.A. 1994. Flock sizes and sex ratios of Canvasbacks in Chesapeake Bay and North Carolina. *J. Wildl. Manage.* 58: 123–31.

Harding, M. 1990. Observations of fruit eating by Blue Duck. *Notornis* 37: 150–52.

Harland, W.B. 1989. *A geological time scale.* Cambridge Univ. Press.

Harmon, B.G. 1962. Mollusks as food of Lesser Scaup along the Louisiana coast. *Trans. N. Amer. Wildl. Nat. Res. Conf.* 27: 132–38.

Harper, D.G.C. 1982. Competitive foraging in Mallards: 'ideal free' ducks. *Anim. Behav.* 30: 575–84.

Harper, M. 1996. Baikal Teal *Anas formosa* in Hovsgol, northern Mongolia. *Wetlands International–IUCN Threatened Waterfowl Specialist Group News* 9: 27–29.

Harper, M.J. and Hindmarsh, M. 1990. Lead poisoning in Magpie Geese *Anseranas semipalmata* from ingested lead pellet at Bool Lagoon Game Reserve (South Australia) *Aust. Wildl. Res.* 17: 141–45.

Harradine, J. 1977. General Ecology. Unpubl. rept to Min. Overseas Development, London.

Harradine, J. 1982. Some mortality patterns of Greater Magellan Geese on the Falkland Islands. *Wildfowl* 33: 7–11.

Harradine, J. 1985. Duck shooting in the United Kingdom. *Wildfowl* 36: 81–94.

Harris, A., Tucker, L. and Vinicombe, K. 1993. *The Macmillan Field Guide to Bird Identification.* Macmillan, London.

Harris, H.J., Jr 1970. Evidence of stress response in breeding Blue-winged Teal. *J. Wildl. Manage.* 34: 747–55.

Harris, M. 1974. *A field guide to the birds of the Galapagos.* Collins, London.

Harrison, C. 1975. *A field guide to the nests, eggs and nestlings of British and European birds.* Collins, London.

Harrison, C.J.O. and Walker, C.A. 1979. Birds of the British Lower Oligocene. *Tertiary Research* 5: 29–43.

Harrison, J.A., Allan, D.G., Underhill, L.G., Herremans, M., Tree, A.J., Parker, V. *et al.* (ed.) 1997. *The atlas of southern African birds*, Vol. 1. BirdLife South Africa, Johannnesburg.

Harrop, A.H.J. 2002. The Ruddy Shelduck in Britain: a review. *Brit. Birds* 95: 123–28.

Harshman, J. 1994. Reweaving the tapestry: what can we learn from Sibley and Ahlquist (1990)? *Auk* 111: 377–88.

Harshman, J. 1996. Phylogeny, evolutionary rates, and ducks. Unpubl. Ph.D. thesis, Univ. Chicago, US.

Harvey, N.G. 1999. A hierarchical genetic analysis of swan relationships. Unpubl. Ph.D. thesis. Univ. Nottingham, UK.

Harwood, J. 1977. Summer feeding ecology of Lesser Snow Goose. *J. Wildl. Manage.* 41: 48–55.

Hasbrouk, S.M. 1944. Fulvous Whistling Ducks in the Louisiana rice fields. *Auk* 61: 305–6.

Hausberger, M. and Black, J.M. 1990. Do females turn males on and off in Barnacle Goose social display? *Ethology* 84: 232–38.

Hausberger, M., Black, J.M. and Pichard, J.P. 1991. Bill opening and sound spectrum in Barnacle Goose loud calls, individuals with 'wide mouths' have higher pitched voices. *Anim. Behav.* 42: 319–22.

Hausberger, M., Richard, J.P., Black, J.M. and Quirs, R. 1994. Quantitative analysis of individuality in Barnacle Goose loud calls. *Bioacoustics* 5: 247–60.

Havera, S.P., Boens, L.R., Georgi, M.M. and Shealy, R.T. 1992a. Human disturbance of waterfowl on Keokuk Pool, Mississippi River. *Wildl. Soc. Bull.* 20: 290–98.

Havera, S.P., Whitton, R.M. and Shealy, R.T. 1992b. Blood lead and ingested shot in diving ducks during spring. *J. Wildl. Manage.* 56: 539–45.

Haverschmidt, F. 1968. *Birds of Surinam.* Oliver and Boyd, Edinburgh.

Havlín, J. 1966a. Breeding season and clutch size in the European Pochard (*Aythya ferina*) and the Tufted Duck (*A. fuligula*) in Czechoslovakia. *Zool. Listy* 15: 333–44.

Havlín, J. 1966b. Breeding season and success of Pochard and Tufted Duck in Czechoslovakia. *Bird Study* 13: 306–10.

Hawkes, B. 1970. The Marbled Teal. *Wildfowl* 21: 87.

Hawkings, J.S., Breault, A., Boyd, S., Norton, M., Beyersbergen, G. and Latour, P. 2002. Trumpeter Swan numbers and distribution in Western Canada. In *Proceedings of the Fourth International Swan Symposium, 2001* (ed. E.C. Rees, S.L. Earnst and J. Coulson). *Waterbirds*, Special Publication 1: 8–21.

Hawkins, A.S., Hanson, R.C., Nelson, H.K. and Reeves, H.M. (ed.) 1984. *Flyways: pioneering waterfowl management in North America.* US Fish & Wildl. Serv., Washington.

Hawkins, L.L. 1986a. Tundra Swan *Cygnus columbianus columbianus* breeding behavior. Unpubl. M.S. thesis. Univ. Minnesota, Minneapolis, US.

Hawkins, L.L. 1986b. Nesting behaviour of male and female Whistling Swans and implications of male incubation. *Wildfowl* 37: 5–27.

Hayes, F. and Granizo, T. 1990. A tippy canoe and waterfalls too. In search of the endangered Brazilian Merganser. *La Kuatia Ñe'é*, March–April 1990: 25–28.

Hayes, F.E. 1995. Status, distribution and biogeography of the birds of Paraguay. *American Birding Association Monographs in Field Ornithology* 1: 1–230.

Hearn, R. 2004a. Bean Goose *Anser fabalis* in Britain an Ireland 1960/61–1999/2000. *Waterbird Review Series*, WWT/JNCC, Slimbridge.

Hearn, R. 2004b. Greater White-fronted Goose *Anser albifrons albifrons* (Baltic/North Sea population) in Britain 1960/61–1999/2000. *Waterbird Review Series*, WWT/JNCC, Slimbridge.

Hearn, R. and Mitchell, C. 1995. Goose distribution and feeding around Loch Leven NNF. Unpubl. rept to Scottish Natural Heritage, Loch Leven Laboratory, Kinross. WWT, Slimbridge, UK.

Hearn, R. and Mitchell C. 2004. Greylag Goose *Anser anser* (Iceland population) in Britain and Ireland 1960/61–1999/2000. *Waterbird Review Series*, WWT/JNCC, Slimbridge.

Heather, B.D. and Robertson, H.A. 1996. *The field guide to the birds of New Zealand.* Viking, Auckland.

Heaton, A. 2001. *Duck decoys.* Shire Publications, Princes Risborough, UK.

Hecker, N. 1994. Ferruginous Duck *Aythya nyroca*. In *Actions to prevent avoidable mortality for threatened waterbirds in the European Union* (ed. J. Van Vessem). Unpubl. rept. IWRB, Slimbridge, UK. pp.67–106.

Hedenstrom, A. and Alerstam, T. 1992. Climbing performance of migrating birds as a basis for estimating limits for fuel-carrying capacity and muscle work. *J. Exp. Biol.* 164: 19–38.

Heim De Balsac, H. and Mayaud, N. 1962. *Les oiseaux du Nord-Ouest de l'Afrique.* Lechevalier, Paris.

Heinz, G.H., Pendleton, G.W., Krynitsky, A.J. and Gold, L.G. 1990. Selenium accumulation and elimination in Mallards. *Arch. Environ. Contam. Toxicol.* 19: 374–79.

Heitmeyer, M.E. 1987. The pre-basic moult and basic plumage of female Mallards (*Anas platyrhynchos*). *Can. J. Zool.* 65: 2248–61.

Heitmeyer, M.E. 1988. Protein costs of the prebasic molt of female Mallards. *Condor* 90: 263–66.

Hellebrekers, W.P.J. and Voous, K.H. 1964. Nestparasitisme van de Kroonend. *Limosa* 37: 5–11. [Nest parasitism by Red Crested Pochard.]

Hellmayr, C.E. 1932. *The birds of Chile.* Field Mus. Nat. Hist., Chicago.

Hennig, W. 1966. *Phylogenetic systematics.* Univ. Illinois Press, Urbana.

Henny, C.J. 1973. Drought displacement of North American Pintails into Siberia. *J. Wildl. Manage.* 37: 23–29.

Henny, C.J. and Holgerson, N.E. 1974. Range expansion and population increase of the Gadwall in eastern North America. *Wildfowl* 25: 95–101.

Henriksen, G. and Lund, E. 1994. Migration times, local movements, biometric parameters and the size and composition of Steller's Eider *Polysticta stelleri* in Varangerfjord in Finnmark, Northern Norway. *Cinclus* 17: 95–106.

Henshaw, H.W. 1902. *Birds of the Hawaiian Islands, being a complete list of the birds of the Hawaiian possessions, with notes on their habits.* Thrum, Honolulu.

Henson, P. and Cooper, J.A. 1992. Division of labour in breeding Trumpeter Swans *Cygnus buccinator*. *Wildfowl* 43: 40–48.

Hepburn, I.R. 1984. *Migratory bird hunting in European Community countries. A compendium of population and hunting data.* Federation of Hunting Associations of the EEC, Brussels.

Hepp, G.R. and Bellrose, F.C. 1995. Wood Duck (*Aix sponsa*). The Birds of North America, No. 169 (ed. A. Poole and F. Gill). AOU, Washington, and Academy of Natural Sciences, Philadelphia.

Hepp, G.R.R., Hoppe, R.T. and Kennamer, R.A. 1987. Population parameters and philopatry of breeding female Wood Ducks. *J. Wildl. Manage.* 51: 401–4.

Herman, C.M., Barrow, J.H. and Tarshis, I.B. 1975. Leucocytozoonosis in Canada Geese at the Seney National Wildlife Refuge. *J. Wildl. Dis.* 11: 404–11.

Hestbeck, J. 1993a. Overwinter distribution of northern pintail populations in North America. *J. Wildl. Manage.* 57: 582–89.

Hestbeck, J. 1993b. Survival of northern pintails banded during winter in North America, 1950–1988. *J. Wildl. Manage.* 57: 590–97.

Heusmann, H.W. 1974. Mallard–Black Duck relationships in the Northeast. *Wildl. Soc. Bull.* 2: 171–77.

Heusmann, H.W. 1984. The effects of weather on local Wood Duck production. *J. Wildl. Manage.* 48: 573–77.

Heusmann, H.W., Early, T.J. and Nikula, B.J. 2000. Evidence of an increasing Hooded Merganser population in Massachusetts. *Wilson Bull.* 112: 413–15.

Hewish, M. 1988. *Waterfowl count in Victoria, February 1988*, Rep., No. 52. RAOU, Melbourne.

Hickey, J.J. 1952. *Survival studies of banded birds*, Spec. Sci. Rept. Wildlife, No. 15. US Fish & Wildl. Serv., Washington.

Hiebl, J., Schneegans, D. and Braunitzer, G. 1986. The primary structures of the α D chains of the Bar-headed Goose (*Anser indicus*), the Greylag Goose (*Anser anser*) and the Canada Goose (*Branta canadensis*). *Biol. Chem. Hope-Seyler* 367: 591–99.

Higgins, K.F. 1977. Duck nesting in intensively farmed areas of North Dakota. *J. Wildl. Manage.* 41: 232–41.

Hik, D.S. and Jefferies, R.L. 1990. Increases in the net above-ground primary production of a salt-marsh forage grass: a test of the predictions of the herbivore-optimization model. *J. Ecol.* 78: 180–95.

Hildén, O. 1964a. Ecology of duck populations in the island group of Valassaaret, Gulf of Bothnia. *Ann. Zool. Fenn.* 1: 153–279.

Hildén, O. 1964b. Habitat selection in birds—a review. *Ann. Zool. Fenn.* 2: 53–75.

Hill, D.A. 1982. The comparative population ecology of Mallard and Tufted Duck. Unpubl. D.Phil. thesis. Univ. Oxford, UK.

Hill, D.A. 1984. Clutch predation in relation to nest density in Mallard and Tufted Duck. *Wildfowl* 35: 151–56.

Hill, D.A. and Ellis, N. 1984. Survival and age related changes in the foraging behaviour and time budget of Tufted Ducklings *Aythya fuligula*. *Ibis* 126: 544–50.

Hill, K. 1994. It's the law. *Florida Wildlife* 48: 41.

Hillgarth, N. and Kear, J. 1979a. Diseases of seaducks in captivity. *Wildfowl* 30: 135–41.

Hillgarth, N. and Kear, J. 1979b. Diseases of sheldgeese and shelducks in captivity. *Wildfowl* 30: 142–46.

Hillgarth, N. and Kear, J. 1981. Diseases of perching ducks in captivity. *Wildfowl* 32: 156–63.

Hillgarth, N, and Kear, J. 1982a. Causes of mortality among whistling ducks in captivity. *Wildfowl* 33: 133–9.

Hillgarth, N. and Kear, J. 1982b. Diseases of stiff-tailed ducks in captivity. *Wildfowl* 33: 140–44.

Hillgarth, N., Kear, J. and Horky K. 1983. Mortality of northern geese in captivity. *Wildfowl* 34: 153–62.

Hilty, S.L. and Brown, W.L. 1986. *A guide to the birds of Colombia*. Princeton Univ. Press.

Hinde, R.A. 1956. The biological significance of the territories of birds. *Ibis* 98: 340–69.

Hindwood, K.A. 1971. Sizes and weights of Musk Duck eggs. *Aust. Bird Watcher* 4: 59.

Hines, J.E. 1977. Nesting and brood ecology of Lesser Scaup at Waterhen Marsh, Saskatchewan. *Can. Field-Nat.* 91: 248–55.

Hines, J.E. and Mitchell, G.J. 1983. Breeding ecology of the Gadwall at Waterhen Marsh, Saskatchewan. *Can. J. Zool.* 61: 1532–39.

Hinshaw, V.S., Nettles, V.F., Schorr, L.F., Wood, J.M. and Webster, R.G. 1986. Influenza virus surveillance in waterfowl in Pennsylvania after the H5N2 outbreak. *Avian Diseases* 30: 207–12.

Hipes, D.L. and Hepp, G.R. 1995. Nutrient-reserve dynamics of breeding male Wood Ducks. *Condor* 97: 451–60.

Hobson, K.A., Brua, R.B., Hohman, W.L. and Wassenaar, L.I. 2000. Low frequency of 'double molt' of remiges in Ruddy Ducks revealed by stable isotopes: implications for tracking migratory waterfowl. *Auk* 117: 129–35.

Hochbaum, G.S. and Bossenmaier, E.F. 1972. Response of Pintails to improved breeding habitat in southern Manitoba. *Can. Field-Nat.* 86: 79–81.

Hochbaum, H.A. 1944. *The Canvasback on a prairie marsh.* American Wildlife Institute, Washington.

Hochbaum, H.A. 1946. Status of the Redhead in southern Manitoba. *Wilson Bull.* 58: 62–65.

Hochbaum, H.A. 1955. *Travels and traditions of waterfowl.* Univ. Minnesota Press, Minneapolis.

Hockey, P.A.R., Underhill, L.G., Neatherway, M. and Ryan, P.R. 1989. *Birds of the southwestern Cape.* Cape Bird Club, Cape Town.

Hodges, J.I. and Eldridge, W.D. 1995. Aerial waterfowl surveys on the arctic coast of eastern Russia, 1994. Unpubl. rept to US Fish & Wildl. Serv.

Hodges, J.I. and Eldridge, W.D. 1996. Aerial waterfowl surveys near the arctic coast of eastern Russia, 1995. Unpubl. rept to US Fish & Wildl. Serv.

Hodges, J.I. and Eldridge, W.D. 2001. Aerial surveys of eiders and other waterbirds on the eastern Arctic coast of Russia. *Wildfowl* 52: 127–42.

Högström, S. 1977. Alförrädarens *Polysticta stelleri* Beteende under vintern. *Vår Fågelvärld* 36: 250–59.

Hohman, W.L. 1984a. Diurnal time-activity budgets for Ring-necked Ducks wintering in central Florida. *Southeast. Assoc. Fish & Wildl. Agencies* 38: 158–64.

Hohman, W.L. 1984b. Aspects of the breeding biology of Ring-necked Ducks (*Aythya collaris*). Unpubl. Ph.D. thesis. Univ. Minnesota, Minneapolis, US.

Hohman, W.L. 1985. Feeding ecology of breeding Ring-necked Ducks in northwestern Minnesota. *J. Wildl. Manage.* 49: 546–57.

Hohman, W.L. 1986a. Incubation rhythms of Ring-necked Ducks. *Condor* 88: 290–96.

Hohman, W.L. 1986b. Changes in body weight and composition of breeding Ring-necked Ducks (*Aythya collaris*). *Auk* 103: 181–88.

Hohman, W.L. 1993. Body composition of wintering Canvasbacks in Louisiana: dominance and survival implications. *Condor* 95: 377–87.

Hohman, W.L. and Ankney, C.D. 1994. Body size and condition, age, plumage quality, and foods of prenesting male Cinnamon Teal in relation to pair status. *Can. J. Zool.* 72: 2172–76.

Hohman, W.L. and Crawford, R.D. 1995. Molt in the annual cycle of Ring-necked Ducks. *Condor* 97: 473–83.

Hohman, W.L. and Cypher, B.L. 1986. Age-class determination of Ring-necked Ducks. *J. Wildl. Manage.* 50: 442–45.

Hohman, W.L. and Eberhardt, R.T. 1998. Ring-necked Duck (*Aythya collaris*). The Birds of North America, No. 329 (ed. A. Poole and F. Gill). AOU, The Birds of North America Inc., Philadelphia.

Hohman, W.L. and Lee, S.A. 2001. Fulvous Whistling-Duck (*Dendrocygna bicolor*). The Birds of North America, No. 562 (ed. A. Poole and F. Gill). AOU, The Birds of North America Inc., Philadelphia.

Hohman, W.L. and Rave, D.P. 1990. Diurnal time-activity budgets of wintering Canvasbacks in Louisiana. *Wilson Bull.* 102: 645–54.

Hohman, W.L. and Weller, M.W. 1994. Body mass and composition of Ring-necked Ducks wintering in southern Florida. *Wilson Bull.* 106: 494–507.

Hohman, W.L., Taylor, T.S. and Weller, M.W. 1988. Annual body weight change in Ring-necked Ducks (*Aythya collaris*). In *Waterfowl in winter* (ed. M. Weller), pp.257–69. Univ. Minnesota Press, Minneapolis.

Hohman, W.L., Woolington, D.W. and Devries, J.H. 1990a. Food habits of wintering Canvasbacks in Louisiana. *Can. J. Zool.* 68: 2605–9.

Hohman, W.L., Pritchert, R.D., Pace, R.M., Woolington, D.W. and Helm, R. 1990b. Influence of ingested lead on body mass of wintering canvasbacks. *J. Wildl. Manage.* 54: 211–15.

Hohman, W.L., Ankney, C.D. and Gordon, D.H. 1992. The ecology and management of postbreeding waterfowl. In *The ecology and management of breeding waterfowl* (ed. B.D.J. Batt, A.D. Afton, M.G. Anderson, C.D. Ankney, D.H. Johnson, J.A. Kadlec *et al.*), pp.128–89. Univ. Minnesota Press, Minneapolis.

Hohman, W.L., Pritchert, R.D., Moore, J.L. and Schaeffer, D.O. 1993. Survival of female Canvasbacks wintering in coastal Louisiana. *J. Wildl. Manage.* 57: 758–62.

Hohman, W.L., Moore, J.L. and Franson, F.C. 1995a. Winter survival of immature Canvasbacks in inland Louisiana. *J. Wildl. Manage.* 59: 384–92.

Hohman, W.L., Haramis, G.M., Jorde, D.G., Korschgen, C.E. and Takekawa, J.Y. 1995b.

Population status and trends of Canvasbacks. In *Our living resources 1994: a report to the nation on the distribution, abundance, and health of U.S. plants, animals, and ecosystems* (ed. E.T. LaRoe, G.S. Farris, C.E. Puckett, P.D. Doran and M.J. Mac), pp.40–43. National Biological Service, Washington.

Hohman, W.L., Stark, T.M. and Moore, J.L. 1996. Food availability and feeding preferences of breeding Fulvous Whistling-ducks in Louisiana ricefields. *Wilson Bull.* 108: 137–50.

Hokhlova, T.Y. and Artemjev, A.V. 2002. Reassessment of the southern limit for Whooper Swans breeding in Northwest Russia. In *Proceedings of the Fourth International Swan Symposium, 2001* (ed. E.C. Rees, S.L. Earnst and J. Coulson). *Waterbirds*, Special Publication 1: 67–73.

Holdaway, R.N. 1989. New Zealand's pre-human avifauna and its vulnerability. *N.Z. J. Ecol.* 12: 11–25.

Holian, J.J. and Forley, J.E. 1992. Lesser Scaup: new to the western Palearctic. *Brit. Birds* 85: 370–76.

Hollom, P.A.D. 1937. Observations on the courtship and mating of Smew. *Brit. Birds* 31: 106–11.

Holloway, S. 1996. *The historical atlas of breeding birds in Britian and Ireland 1875–1900*. Poyser, London.

Holm, J.W. 1984. Nest success and cover relationships of upland-nesting ducks in northcentral Montana. Unpubl. M.S. thesis. Univ. Montana, US.

Holmes, D.A. 1977. A report on the White-winged Wood Duck in southern Sumatra. *Wildfowl* 28: 61–64.

Holmes, J. 1994. *1992 duck season in Victoria*, Tech. Rept. Ser., No. 132. Arthur Rylah Institute for Environmental Research, Melbourne.

Holmes, J.S. and Clement, P. (ed.) 1996. *Fish-eating birds: proceedings of a seminar to review status, interactions with fisheries and licensing issues*, UK Nature Conservation No. 15. J.N.C.C., Peterborough.

Holyoak, D.T. 1980. *Guide to Cook Island birds*. Publ. privately.

Holzinger, J. 1987. *Die Vögel Baden Wurttembergs. Gefardung und Schutz*. Ulmer, Karlsruhe.

Hood, D.W. and Calder, J.A. (ed.) 1981. *The Eastern Bering Sea Shelf: Oceanography and Resources*, Vol. 2. Univ. Washington Press, Seattle.

Hood, D.W. and Kelly, E.J. (ed.) 1974. *Oceanography of the Bering Sea, with emphasis on renewable resources*, Occ. Pap., No. 2. Inst. Marine Sci., Univ. Alaska., Fairbanks.

Hoogerwerf, A. 1950. De Witvlengeleend, *Cairina scutulata*, van de Grote Soenda eilanden. *Ardea* 38: 64–69.

Hoppe, R.T., Smith, L.M. and Wester, D.B. 1986. Foods of wintering diving ducks in South Carolina. *J. Field. Ornithol.* 57: 126–34.

Hori, J. 1964. The breeding biology of the Shelduck *Tadorna tadorna*. *Ibis* 106: 333–60.

Hori, J. 1966. Observations on Pochard and Tufted Duck breeding biology with particular reference to colonisation of a home range. *Bird Study* 13: 297–305.

Hori, J. 1987. Distribution, dispersion and regulation in a population of the Common Shelduck. *Wildfowl* 38: 127–42.

Horn, P.L. 1983. Subfossil avian deposits from Poukawa, Hawkes Bay, and the first record of *Oxyura australis* (Blue-billed Duck) from New Zealand. *J. Roy. Soc. New Zealand* 13: 67–78.

Horn, P.L., Rafalski, J.A. and Whitehead, P.J. 1996. Molecular genetic (RAPD) analysis of breeding Magpie Geese. *Auk* 113: 552–57.

Horsbrugh, B. 1912. *The game-birds and water-fowl of South Africa*. Witherby, London.

Hoshide, H.M., Price, A.J. and Katahira, L. 1990. A progress report on Nene *Branta sandvicensis* in Hawaii Volcanoes National Park from 1974–89. *Wildfowl* 41: 152–55.

Houde, P. 1987. Critical analysis of DNA hybridization studies in avian systematics. *Auk* 104: 17–32.

Housse, P.R. 1945. *Las Aves de Chile*. Ediciones de la Universidad de Chile, Santiago.

Howard, H. 1950. Fossil evidence of avian evolution. *Ibis* 92: 1–21.

Howard, H. 1955. New records and a new species of *Chendytes*, an extinct genus of diving geese. *Condor* 57: 135–43.

Howard, H. 1964a. Fossil Anseriformes. In *The waterfowl of the world*, Vol. 4 (ed. J. Delacour), pp.233–326. Country Life, London.

Howard, H. 1964b. *A new species of the 'pygmy goose', Anabernicula, from the Oregon Pleistocene, with a discussion of the genus*, Am. Mus. Novit., No. 2200, pp.1–14. American Museum Natural History, New York.

Howell, S.N.G. and Webb, S. 1995. *A guide to the birds of Mexico and northern Central America*. OUP.

Howells, W.W. 1982. African Fish Eagle preys on Egyptian Goose gosling. *Honeyguide* 111/112: 66.

Howerter, D.W. 1990. Movements and bioenergetics of Canvasbacks wintering in the upper Chesapeake Bay. Unpubl. M.S. thesis. Virginia Polytechnic Instit. State Univ., Blacksburg, US.

Howey, P., Board, R.G., Davis, D.H. and Kear, J. 1984. The microclimate of the nests of waterfowl. *Ibis* 126: 16–32.

Hu, H. and Cui, Y. 1990. The effect of habitat destruction on the waterfowl of lakes in the Yangtze and the Han river basins. In *Managing Waterfowl Populations*, IWRB Symp., Astrakhan 1989, Publ., No. 12 (ed. G.V.T. Matthews), pp.189–93. IWRB, Slimbridge, UK.

Hubbard, J.P. 1977. The biological and taxonomic status of the Mexican Duck. *New Mexico Dept Fish and Game Bull.* 16: 1–56.

Hudson, W.H. 1920. *Birds of La Plata*, Vol. 2. Dutton, New York.

Huey, W.S. 1961. Comparison of female Mallard with female New Mexican Duck. *Auk* 78: 428–31.

Hughes, B. 1991. The Wildfowl & Wetlands Trust expedition to the Soviet Far East (20 June to 19 August 1991). Unpubl. rept. WWT, Slimbridge, UK.

Hughes, B. 1992. The ecology and behaviour of the North American Ruddy Duck *Oxyura jamaicensis jamaicensis* (Gmelin) in Great Britain. Unpubl. Ph.D. thesis. Univ. Bristol, UK.

Hughes, B. 1996a. The Ruddy Duck (*Oxyura jamaicensis*) in Europe and the threat to the White-headed Duck (*Oxyura leucocephala*). *Oxyura* 8: 51–64.

Hughes, B. 1996b. The feasibility of control measures for North American Ruddy Ducks *Oxyura jamaicensis* in the United Kingdom. Unpubl. WWT rept. to UK Dept Environment.

Hughes, B. and Bocharnikov, V.N. 1992. Status of the Scaly-sided Merganser *Mergus squamatus* in the Far East of Russia. *Wildfowl* 43: 193–99.

Hughes, B., Stewart, B., Brown, M.J and Hearn, R.D. 1997. Studies of Common Scoter *Melanitta nigra nigra* killed during the Sea Empress oil spill. Sea Empress Environmental Evaluation Committee rpt. Countryside Council for Wales, Bangor, Wales.

Hughes, B., Criado, J., Delany, S., Gallo-Orsi, U., Green, A.J., Grussu, M., *et al.* 1999. *The status of the North American Ruddy Duck Oxyura jamaicensis in the*

Western Palearctic: towards an action plan for eradication, Publ. T-PVS/Birds (99), No. 9. Council of Europe, Strasbourg.

Hughes, M.R. 1970. Relative kidney size in non-passerine birds with functional salt glands. *Condor* 72: 164–68.

Hughes, R.J., Reed, A. and Gauthier, G. 1994. Space and habitat use by Greater Snow Goose broods on Bylot Island, Northwest Territories. *J. Wildl. Manage.* 58: 536–45.

Hume, A.O. and Marshall, C.H.T. 1879–81. *Game Birds of India, Burmah and Ceylon*, Vol. 3. Publ. privately, Calcutta.

Humphrey, P. 1955. The relationships of the sea ducks (Tribe Mergini). Unpubl. Ph.D. thesis. Univ. Michigan, Ann Arbor, US.

Humphrey, P.S. 1958a. Classification and systematic position of the eiders. *Condor* 60: 129–35.

Humphrey, P.S. 1958b. Diving of a captive Common Eider. *Condor* 60: 408–10.

Humphrey, P.S. and Butsch, R.S. 1958. The anatomy of the Labrador Duck, *Camptorhynchus labradorius* (Gmelin). *Smithsonian Misc. Coll.* 135(7): 1–23.

Humphrey, P.S. and Clark, G.A., Jr 1964. The anatomy of waterfowl. In *The waterfowl of the world* (ed. J. Delacour), pp.167–72. Country Life, London.

Humphrey, P.S. and Livezey, B.C. 1982a. Flightlessness in flying steamer-ducks. *Auk* 99: 368–72.

Humphrey, P.S. and Livezey, B.C. 1982b. Molts and plumages of flying steamer-ducks (*Tachyeres patachonicus*). *Univ. Kansas Mus. Natur. Hist. Occas. Pap.* 103: 1–30.

Humphrey, P.S. and Livezey, B.C. 1985. Nest, eggs, and downy young of the White-headed Flightless Steamer-Duck. *Ornithol. Monogr.* 36: 944–53.

Humphrey, P.S. and Parkes, K.C. 1959. An approach to study of molts and plumages. *Auk* 76: 1–31.

Humphrey, P.S. and Ripley, S.D. 1962. The affinities of the Pink-headed Duck *Rhodonessa caryophyllacea*. *Postilla* 61: 1–21.

Humphrey, P.S. and Thompson, M.C. 1981. A new species of steamer-duck (Tachyeres) from Argentina. *University of Kansas Museum of Natural History Occasional Papers* 95: 1–12.

Humphrey, P.S., Bridge, D., Reynolds, P.W. and Peterson, R.T. 1970. *Birds of Isla Grande (Tierra del Fuego)*. Univ. Kansas Mus. Nat. Hist. and Smithsonian Institution Press, Washington.

Humphrey, P.S., Livezey, B.C. and Siegel-Causey, D. 1987. Tameness of birds of the Falkland Islands: an index and preliminary results. *Bird Behav.* 7: 67–72.

Hunter, J.M. and Black, J.M. 1996. International action plan for the Red-breasted Goose (*Branta ruficollis*). In *Globally threatened birds in Europe: action plans* (ed. B. Heredia, L. Rose and M. Painter), pp.79–98. Council of Europe, Strasbourg.

Hustings, F., van Winden, E. and Voslamber, B. 1998. Looking for a needle in a haystack: the Red-breasted Goose in the Netherlands; a rare species, but regular visitor. *Casarca* 4: 133–37.

Hutchinson, C.D. 1989. *Birds in Ireland.* Poyser, Calton.

Huyskens, P.R.G. 1986. The Bean Goose problem in Europe. *Oriolus* 52: 105–256.

ICONA 1993. The spread of the Ruddy Duck in Spain and its impact on the White-headed Duck. *IWRB Threatened Waterfowl Specialist Group News* 3: 3–4.

Imber, M.J. 1968. Sex ratios in Canada Goose populations. *J. Wildl. Manage.* 32: 905–20.

Impekoven, M. 1964 Zugwege und Verbreitung der Knakente, *Anas querquedula*; eine Analyse der europaischen Beringsresultate. *Orn. Beob.* 61: 7–34.

Inglis, I.R. 1977. The breeding behaviour of the Pink-footed Goose: behavioural correlates of nesting success. *Anim. Behav.* 25: 747–64.

Inglis, I.R. and Isaacson, A.J. 1978. The responses of Dark-bellied Brent Geese to models of geese in various postures. *Anim. Behav.* 26: 953–68.

Inglis, I.R., Lazarus, J. and Torrance, R. 1989. The pre-nesting behaviour and time budget of the Harlequin Duck *Histrionicus histrionicus*. *Wildfowl* 40: 55–73.

Inskipp, C. and Inskipp, T. 1991. *A guide to the birds of Nepal* (2nd edn). Helm, London.

International Commission on Zoological Nomenclature 1991. Opinion 1648. *Micropterus patachonicus* King, 1831 and *Anas pteneres* Forster, 1844 (both currently in *Tachyeres* Owen, 1875; Aves, Anseriformes): specific names conserved. *Bull. Zool. Nomen.* 48: 187–8.

Irwin, M.P.S. 1981. *The birds of Zimbabwe.* Quest, Salisbury, Zimbabwe.

IUCN 1994. *IUCN Red List Categories.* IUCN, Gland, Switzerland.

IUCN 1998. *IUCN guidelines for re-introductions.* IUCN, Gland, Switzerland.

IUCN 2003. 2003 IUCN Red List of Threatened Species. www.redlist.org.

Isakov, Y.A. 1970. Status and distribution of waterfowl resources in the western part of the USSR. In *International regional meeting on conservation of wildfowl resources (Europe, western Asia, northern and tropical Africa)* (ed. Y.A. Isakov). [publisher not stated] Moscow, Russia. pp.24–45.

Iwabuchi, S. 1997. Distribution and status of lesser white-fronted geese (*Anser erythropus*). *Bull. Sendai Science Museum* 7: 96–102.

Iwabuchi, S., Ikeuchi, T., Lei, G., Jiang, Y. and Sun, P.Y. 1997. The short report on survey of lesser white-fronted geese at Dongting Lakes in China. *Bull. Sendai Science Museum* 7: 103–05.

Izask, P. 1978. *Red data book of the Kazakh SSR.*

Jacob, J. and Glaser, A. 1975. Chemotaxonomy of the Anseriformes. *Biochem. Syst. Ecol.* 2: 215–20.

Jacobsen, O.W. 1991. Feeding behaviour of breeding Wigeon *Anas penelope* in relation to seasonal emergence and swarming behaviour of chironomids. *Ardea* 79: 409–18.

Jacobsen, O.W. 1992. Factors affecting selection of nitrogen-fertilized grassland areas by breeding Wigeon *Anas penelope*. *Ornis Scand.* 23: 121–31.

Jacobsen, O.W. and Ugelvik, M. 1994. Effects of presence of waders on grazing and vigilance behaviour in breeding Wigeon, *Anas penelope*. *Anim. Behav.* 47: 488–90.

Jacobsen, O.W. and Ugelvik, M. 1995. A case of polygyny in the Eurasian Wigeon *Anas penelope*. *Wildfowl* 46: 72–75.

Jaensch, R.P. and Vervest, R.M. 1988a. *Ducks, Swans and Coots in South-Western Australia: the 1986 and 1987 counts*, Rept. No. 31. RAOU, Moonee Ponds, Victoria.

Jaensch, R.P. and Vervest, R.M. 1988b. *Ducks, Swans and Coots in South-Western Australia: the 1988 count and recommendations*, Rept. No. 46. RAOU, Moonee Ponds, Victoria.

Jaensch, R.P., Vervest, R.M. and Hewish, M.J. 1988. *Waterbirds in Nature Reserves of South-Western Australia 1981–1985: Reserve Accounts*, Rept. No. 30. RAOU, Moonee Ponds, Victoria.

James, J.D. and Thompson, J.E. 2001. Black-bellied Whistling-Duck (*Dendrocygna autumnalis*). The Birds of North America, No. 578 (ed. A. Poole and F. Gill). AOU, The Birds of North America Inc., Philadelphia.

Jarvis, R.L. and Bromley, R.G. 2000. Incubation behaviour of Richardson's Canada Geese on Victoria Island, Nunavut, Canada. *Towards conservation of the diversity of Canada Geese* (Branta canadensis), pp.59–66. K.M. Dickson (ed.). *Can. Wildl. Serv. Occas. Paper* No. 103.

Jarvis, R.L. and Noyes, J.H. 1986. Foods of Canvasbacks and Redheads in Nevada: paired males and ducklings. *J. Wildl. Manage.* 50: 199–203.

Jefferies, R.L. 1998. Herbivores, nutrients and trophic cascades in terrestrial ecosystems. In *Herbivores: between plants and predators*, 30th Symp. Brit. Ecol. Soc., (ed. H. Olff, V.K. Brown and R.H. Drent), pp.301–32. Blackwell Scientific Publications, Oxford.

Jenni, D. 1969. Diving times of the Least Grebe and Masked Duck. *Auk* 86: 355–56.

Jepsen, P.U. 1973. Studies of the moult migration and wing-feather moult of the Goldeneye (*Bucephala clangula*) in Denmark. *Dan. Rev. Game Biol.* 8(6): 1–23.

Jepsen, P.U. 1976. Feeding ecology of Goldeneye (*Bucephala clangula*) during the wing-feather moult in Denmark. *Dan. Rev. Game Biol.* 10(4): 1–23.

Jepsen, P.U. and Joensen, A.H. 1973. The distribution and numbers of Goldeneye (*Bucephala clangula*) moulting in Denmark. *Dan. Rev. Game Biol.* 8(5): 1–8.

Jepson, P. 1993. Recent ornithological observations from Buru. *Kukila* 6: 85–109.

Jepson, P. 1997. *Birding Indonesia: a bird-watcher's guide to the world's largest archipelago*. Peripatus Editions, Singapore.

Jeske, C.W. 1985. Time and energy budgets of wintering Ring-necked Ducks Aythya collaris (L.) in north-central Florida. Unpubl. M.S. thesis. Univ. Florida, US.

Jeske, C.W. and Percival, H.F. 1995. Time and energy budgets of wintering Ring-necked Ducks Aythya collaris in Florida, USA. *Wildfowl* 46: 109–18.

Jobling, J.A. 1991. *A dictionary of scientific bird names*. OUP.

Joensen, A.H. 1973. Moult migration and wing-feather moult of seaducks in Denmark. *Dan. Rev. Game Biol.* 8(4): 1–42.

Joensen, A.H. 1974. Waterfowl populations in Denmark 1965–1973. *Dan. Rev. Game Biol.* 9(1): 1–206.

Jögi, A. 1971. Zum Mauserzug der Schellente (*Bucephala clangula*) und Trauerente (*Melanitta nigra*) in der Estonischen SSR. *Orn. Mitteil.* 23: 65–67.

Johansen, H. 1956. *Revision und Entstehung der Arktische Vogelfauna. Fasc. VIII.* Munksgaard, Kobenhavn.

Johnsgard, P.A. 1960a. Hybridization in the Anatidae and its taxonomic implications. *Condor* 62: 25–33.

Johnsgard, P.A. 1960b. Comparative behaviour of the Anatidae and its evolutionary implications. *Wildfowl* 11: 31–45.

Johnsgard, P.A. 1960c. A quantitative study of sexual behavior of Mallards and Black Ducks. *Wilson Bull.* 72: 133–55.

Johnsgard, P.A. 1960d. The systematic position of the Ringed Teal. *Bull. BOC* 80: 165–67.

Johnsgard, P.A. 1960e. Classification and evolutionary relationships of the sea ducks. *Condor* 62: 426–33.

Johnsgard, P.A. 1961a. The taxonomy of the Anatidae—a behavioural analysis. *Ibis* 103: 71–85.

Johnsgard, P.A. 1961b. Breeding biology of the Magpie Goose. *Wildfowl* 12: 92–103.

Johnsgard, P.A. 1961c. The tracheal anatomy of the Anatidae and its taxonomic significance. *Wildfowl* 12: 58–69.

Johnsgard, P.A. 1961d. The sexual behavior and systematic position of the Hooded Merganser. *Wilson Bull.* 73: 226–36.

Johnsgard, P.A. 1961e. The systematic position of the Marbled Teal. *Bull. BOC* 81: 37–41.

Johnsgard, P.A. 1961f. Evolutionary relationships among the North American Mallards. *Auk* 78: 3–43.

Johnsgard, P.A. 1962. Evolutionary trends in the behaviour and morphology of the Anatidae. *Wildfowl* 13: 130–48.

Johnsgard, P.A. 1963. Behavioural isolating mechanisms in the family Anatidae. *Int. Ornith. Congr.* 13: 531–43.

Johnsgard, P.A. 1964a. Comparative behavior and relationships of the eiders. *Condor* 66: 113–29.

Johnsgard, P.A. 1964b. Observations on the biology of the Spectacled Eider. *Wildfowl* 15: 104–7.

Johnsgard, P.A. 1965a. *Handbook of waterfowl behavior.* Cornell University Press, Ithaca, and Constable, London.

Johnsgard, P.A. 1965b. Observations on some aberrant Australian Anatidae. *Wildfowl* 16: 73–83.

Johnsgard, P.A. 1966a. Behavior of the Australian Musk Duck and Blue-billed Duck. *Auk* 83: 98–110.

Johnsgard, P.A. 1966b. The biology and relationships of the Torrent Ducks. *Wildfowl* 17: 66–74.

Johnsgard, P.A. 1967. Observations on the behaviour and relationships of the White-backed Duck and the stiff-tailed ducks. *Wildfowl* 18: 98–107.

Johnsgard, P.A. 1968a. *Waterfowl. Their biology and natural history.* Univ. Nesbraska Press, Lincoln.

Johnsgard, P.A. 1968b. Some observations on Maccoa Duck behaviour. *Ostrich* 39: 219–22.

Johnsgard, P.A. 1973. Proximate and ultimate determinants of clutch size in Anatidae. *Wildfowl* 24: 144–49.

Johnsgard, P.A. 1974. The taxonomy and relationships of the northern swans. *Wildfowl* 25: 155–61.

Johnsgard, P.A. 1975. *Waterfowl of North America.* Indiana Univ. Press, Bloomington.

Johnsgard, P.A. 1978. *Ducks, geese and swans of the world.* Univ. Nebraska Press, Lincoln.

Johnsgard, P.A. 1995. *Ducks in the wild, conserving waterfowl and their habitats.* Swan Hill Press, UK.

Johnsgard, P.A. and Carbonell, M. 1996. *Ruddy Ducks and other stifftails, their biology and behavior.* Univ. Oklahoma Press, Norman and London.

Johnsgard, P.A. and Hagemeyer, D. 1969. The Masked Duck in the United States. *Auk* 84: 691–95.

Johnsgard, P.A. and Kear, J. 1968. A review of parental carrying of young by waterfowl. *Living Bird* 7: 89–102.

Johnsgard, P.A. and Nordeen, C. 1981. Display behaviour and relationships of the Argentine Blue-billed Duck. *Wildfowl* 32: 5–9.

Johnson, A. and Chebez, J.C. 1985. Sobre la situacion de *Mergus octocetaceus* Vieillot (Anseriformes: Anatidae) en la Argentina. *Historia Natural* Supl. 1: 1–16.

Johnson, A.E. 1992. The conservation of the evergreen humid subtropical forest within the province of Misiones, Argentina. *Selbyana* 13: 156.

Johnson, A.W. 1963. Notes on the distribution, reproduction and display of the Andean Torrent Duck (*Merganetta armata*). *Ibis* 105: 114–16.

Johnson, A.W. 1965. *The birds of Chile and adjacent regions of Argentine, Bolivia and Peru,* Vol. 1. Platt Establecimientos Gráficos, Buenos Aires.

Johnson, D.H. 1979. Estimating nest success: the Mayfield method and an alternative. *Auk* 96: 651–61.

Johnson, D.H. and Grier, J.W. 1988. Determinants of breeding distributions of ducks, *Wildl. Monogr.* 100: 1–37. (See also http://www.npwrc.usgs.gov/resource/distr/birds/DISTDUCK/mallard.htm#tab04)

Johnson, D.H. and Sargeant, A.B. 1977. *Impact of red fox predation on the sex ratio of prairie mallards,* Wildl. Resource Rept., No. 6. US Fish & Wildl. Serv., Washington.

Johnson, D.H., Sargeant, D.B. and Greenwood, R.J. 1989. Importance of individual species of predators on nesting success of ducks in the Canadian Prairie Pothole Region. *Can. J. Zool.* 67: 291–97.

Johnson, D.H., Nichols, J.D. and Schwartz, M.D. 1992. Population dynamics of breeding waterfowl. In *The ecology and management of breeding waterfowl* (ed. B.D.J. Batt, A.D. Afton, M.G. Anderson, C.D. Ankney, D.H. Johnson, J.A. Kadlec *et al.*), pp.446–85. Univ. Minnesota Press, Minneapolis.

Johnson, F.A. and Montalbano, F., III. 1984. Selection of plant communities by wintering waterfowl on Lake Okeechobee, Florida. *J. Wildl. Manage.* 48: 174–78.

Johnson, F.A. and Montalbano, F., III. 1989. Southern reservoirs and lakes. In *Habitat management for migrating and wintering waterfowl in North America* (ed. L.M. Smith, R.L. Pederson and R.M. Kaminski), pp.93–116. Texas Tech. Univ. Press, Lubbock.

Johnson, F.A., Montalbano, F., III., Truitt, J.D. and Eggeman, D.R. 1991. Distribution, abundance and habitat use by Mottled Ducks in Florida. *J. Wildl. Manage.* 55: 476–82.

Johnson, K. 1995. Green-winged Teal (*Anas crecca*). The Birds of North America, No. 193 (ed. A. Poole and F. Gill). AOU, Washington, and Academy of Natural Sciences, Philadelphia.

Johnson, K.P. 1997. The evolution of behavior in the dabbling ducks (Anatini): a phylogenetic approach. Unpubl. Ph.D. thesis. Univ. Minnesota, Minneapolis, US.

Johnson, K.P. and Sorenson, M.D. 1998. Comparing molecular evolution in two mitochondrial protein coding genes (cytochrome *b* and ND2) in the dabbling ducks (Tribe: Anatini). *Mol. Phylogenet. Evol.* 10: 82–94.

Johnson, K.P. and Sorenson, M.D. 1999. Phylogeny and biogeography of the dabbling ducks (genus *Anas*): a comparison of molecular and morphological evidence. *Auk* 116: 792–805.

Johnson, K.P., McKinney, F., Wilson, R. and Sorenson, M.D. 2000. The evolution of postcopulatory displays in dabbling ducks (Anatini): a phylogenetic perspective. *Anim. Behav.* 59: 953–63.

Johnson, L.L. 1971. The migration, harvest, and importance of waterfowl at Barrow, Alaska. Unpubl. M.Sc. thesis. Univ. Alaska, US.

Johnson, T.W. 1973. The wing molt of the Florida Duck. *Wilson Bull.* 85: 77–78.

Johnson, W., Holbrook, R. and Rohwer, F. 2002. Nesting chronology, clutch size and egg size of the Mottled Duck. *Wildfowl* 53: 155–66.

Johnstone, S. 1957. On breeding whistling-ducks. *Avicult. Mag.* 63: 23–25.

Johnstone, S.T. 1960. Notes from the New Grounds. *Avic. Mag.* 66: 67–71.

Johnstone, S.T. 1965. 1964 breeding results at the Wildfowl Trust. *Avic. Mag.* 71: 20–23.

Johnstone, S.T. 1970. Waterfowl eggs. *Avic. Mag.* 76: 52–55.

Jones, G. 1987. Time and energy constraints during incubation in free-living Swallows (*Hirundo rustica*): an experimental study using precision electronic balances. *J. Anim. Ecol.* 56: 229–45.

Jones, J.J. and Drobney, R.D. 1986. Winter feeding ecology of scaup and Common Goldeneye in Michigan. *J. Wildl. Manage.* 50: 446–52.

Jones, N.G.B. 1972. Moult migration of Emperor Geese. *Wildfowl* 23: 92–93.

Jones, P.D. 2000. The Mersey estuary—back from the dead? Solving a 150-year old problem. *J. CIWEM* 14: 124–30.

Jones, T. 1946. The 1946 waterfowl breeding season at Leckford. *Avic. Mag.* 52: 193–96.

Jones, T. 1948. The Andean Crested Duck (*Anas cristata alticola*). *Avic. Mag.* 54: 196–99.

Jones, T. 1953. 1952 breeding results at Leckford. *Avic. Mag.* 59: 8–12.

Jones, T. 1972. 1971 breeding season at Leckford. *Avic. Mag.* 78: 22–24.

Jónsson, B., Karlsson, J. and Svensson, S. 1985. Incidence of lead shot in tissues of the Bean Goose (*Anser fabalis*) wintering in South Sweden. *Swedish Wildlife Research* 13: 257–71.

Jónsson, G. 1987. *Saga Laxárvirkjunar*. Landsvirkjun, Akureyri. [History of the Laxá Hydropower Station. In Icelandic.]

Jouventin, P., Stahl, J-C. and Weimerskirch, H. 1988. *Livre rouge des oiseaux menacés des regions Françaises d'Outre-Mer,* Monographie, No. 5, pp.225–51. ICPB, St. Cloud, France.

Joyner, D.E. 1975. Nest parasitism and brood-related behavior of the Ruddy Duck (*Oxyura jamaicensis rubida*). Unpubl. Ph.D. thesis. Univ. Nebraska, US.

Joyner, D.E. 1976. Effects of interspecific nest parasitism by Redheads and Ruddy Ducks. *J. Wildl. Manage.* 40: 33–38.

Joyner, D.E. 1977. Behavior of Ruddy Duck broods in Utah. *Auk* 94: 343–49.

Joyner, D.E. 1983. Parasitic egg laying in Redheads and Ruddy Ducks in Utah: incidence and success. *Auk* 100: 717–25.

Junor, F.J.R. 1983. The relationship between Egyptian Geese and Dabchicks at Lake Kyle, Zimbabwe. *Honeyguide* 114/115: 10–14.

Kadlec, J.A. and Smith, L.M. 1992. Habitat management for breeding areas. In *The ecology and management of breeding waterfowl* (ed. B.D.J. Batt, A.D. Afton, M.G. Anderson, C.D. Ankney, D.H. Johnson, J.A. Kadlec *et al.*), pp.590–610. Univ. Minnesota Press, Minneapolis.

Kahlert, J. Fox, A.D. and Ettrup, H. 1996. Nocturnal feeding in moulting Greylag Geese *Anser anser*—An anti-predator response? *Ardea* 84: 15–22.

Kakizawa, R. and Sugawara, H. 1989. Twenty Japanese sketches of extinct Crested Shelduck *Tadorna cristata* (Kuroda) from the Edo Period (1603–1867). *J. Yamashina Inst. Ornithol.* 21: 326–39.

Källender, H., Mawdsley, T., Nilsson, L. and Waden, K. 1970. Mass-feeding by Smews. *Brit. Birds* 63: 32–33.

Kalmbach, E.R. 1937. *Crow-waterfowl relationships: based on preliminary studies on Canadian breeding grounds*, Circ., No. 433. US Dept Agric., Washington.

Kältenhäuser, D. 1971. Über Evolutionsvorgänge in der Schwimmentenbalz. *Z. Tierpsychol.* 29: 481–540.

Kalyakin, V.N. 1995. Notes on the distribution of goose species in coastal regions of the Barent Sea and in the north of western Siberia. *Goose Study Group Bull. of Eastern Europe and Northern Asia* 1: 150–57.

Kalyakin, V.N. and Vinogradov, V.G. 1987. Swans in southern Yamal. In *Ecology and migration of swans in the USSR* (ed. E. Syroechkovski), pp.95–96. Nauka, Moscow.

Kaminski, R.M. and Weller, M.W. 1992. Breeding habitats of Nearctic waterfowl. In *The ecology and management of breeding waterfowl* (ed. B.D.J. Batt, A.D. Afton, M.G. Anderson, C.D. Ankney, D.H. Johnson, J.A. Kadlec *et al.*), pp.568–89. Univ. Minnesota Press, Minneapolis.

Kanai, Y., Sato, F., Ueta, M., Minton, J., Higuchi, H., Soma, M., *et al.* 1997. The migration routes and important rest-sites of Whooper Swans satellite-tracked from northern Japan. *Strix* 15: 1–13.

Kantrud, H.A. and Stewart, R.E. 1977. Use of natural basin wetlands by breeding waterfowl in North Dakota. *J. Wildl. Manage.* 41: 243–53.

Kaplan, N.O. 1964. Lactate dehydrogenase—structure and function. *Brookhaven Symposia in Biology* 17: 131–53.

Karelse, D. 1994. Duck decoys in The Netherlands. *Wildfowl* 45: 260–66.

Kaufman, K. 1990. The practiced eye: Common Merganser and Red-breasted Merganser. *Amer. Birds* 44: 1203–5.

Kear, J. 1963. The history of potato-eating by wildfowl in Britain. *Wildfowl* 14: 54–65.

Kear, J. 1964. Colour preference in young Anatidae. *Ibis* 106: 361–69.

Kear, J. 1967a. Notes on the eggs and downy young of *Thalassornis leuconotus*. *Ostrich* 38: 19–21.

Kear, J. 1967b. Experiments with young nidifugous birds on a visual cliff. *Wildfowl* 18: 122–24.

Kear, J. 1968. The calls of very young Anatidae. *Beihefte der Vogelwelt* 1: 93–113.

Kear, J. 1970a. Studies on the development of young Tufted Duck. *Wildfowl* 21: 123–32.

Kear, J. 1970b. The adaptive radiation of parental care in waterfowl. In *Social behavior in birds and mammals* (ed. J.H. Crook), pp.357–92. Academic Press, New York.

Kear, J. 1972. Reproduction and family life. In *The swans* (ed. P. Scott and The Wildfowl Trust), pp.80–124. Michael Joseph, London.

Kear, J. 1973a. Effect of age on breeding in the Nene. *Ibis* 115: 473.

Kear, J. 1973b. The Magpie Goose *Anseranas semipalmata* in captivity. *Int. Zoo Ybk* 13: 28–32.

Kear, J. 1975. Salvadori's Duck of New Guinea. *Wildfowl* 26: 104–11.

Kear, J. 1977. The problems of breeding endangered species in captivity. *Int. Zoo Ybk* 17: 5–14.

Kear, J. 1979. Wildfowl at risk, 1979. *Wildfowl* 30: 159–61.

Kear, J. 1985. *Eric Hosking's wildfowl*. Croom Helm, London.

Kear, J. 1990. *Man and wildfowl*. Poyser, London.

Kear, J. 1991. *Ducks of the world*. Letts, London.

Kear, J. 1993. Duck decoys, with particular reference to the history of bird ringing. *Arch. Nat. Hist.* 20: 229–40.

Kear, J. 2001. Three early medieval accounts of agricultural damage by wild geese. *Arch. Nat. Hist.* 28: 245–55.

Kear, J. 2003. Cavity-nesting ducks: why woodpeckers matter. *British Birds* 96(5): 217–33.

Kear, J. and Berger, A.J. 1980. *The Hawaiian Goose: an experiment in conservation*. Poyser, Calton.

Kear, J. and Burton, P.J.K. 1971. The food and feeding apparatus of the Blue Duck *Hymenolaimus*. *Ibis* 113: 483–93.

Kear, J. and Johnsgard, P.A. 1968. Foraging dives by surface-feeding ducks. *Wilson Bull.* 80: 231.

Kear, J. and Murton, R.K. 1973. The systematic status of the Cape Barren Goose as judged by its photoresponses. *Wildfowl* 24: 141–43.

Kear, J. and Scarlett, R.J. 1970. The Auckland Islands Merganser. *Wildfowl* 21: 78–86.

Kear, J. and Williams, G. 1978. Waterfowl at risk. *Wildfowl* 29: 5–21.

Kehoe, F.P. 1989. The adaptive significance of creching behavior in the White-winged Scoter. *Can. J. Zool.* 67: 406–11.

Kehoe, F.P. and Ankney, C.D. 1985. Variation in digestive organ size among five species of diving ducks (*Aythya* spp.). *Can. J. Zool.* 63: 2339–42.

Kehoe, F.P. and Thomas, V.G. 1987. A comparison of interspecific differences in the morphology of external and internal feeding apparatus among North American Anatidae. *Can. J. Zool.* 65: 1818–22.

Keith, L.B. 1961. A study of waterfowl ecology on small impoundments in southeastern Alberta, *Wildl. Monogr.* 6: 1–88.

Keller, V. 2000. Winter distribution and population change of Red-crested Pochard *Netta rufina* in southwestern and central Europe. *Bird Study* 47: 176–85.

Keller, V. and Burkhardt, M. 2004. Monitoring Überwinternde Wasservögel: Ergebnisse der Wasservogelzählungen 2002/03 in der Schweiz. Schweizerische Vogelwarte, Sempach, Switzerland.

Kellett, D.K. and Alisauskas, R.T. 2000. Body-mass dynamics of King Eiders during incubation. *Auk* 117: 812–17.

Kelly, J.F., Atudorei, V., Sharp, Z.D. and Finch, D.M. 2002. Insights into Wilson's warbler migration from analyses of hydrogen isotope ratios. *Oecologia* 130: 216–21.

Kennard, J.H. 1975. Longevity records of North American birds. *Bird Banding* 46: 55–59.

Kennedy, M. and Spencer, H.G. 2000. Phylogeny, biogeography, and taxonomy of Australasian teals. *Auk* 117: 154–63.

Kenow, K.P. and Rusch, D.H. 1996. Food habits of Redheads at the Horicon Marsh, Wisconsin. *J. Field Ornithol.* 67: 649–59.

Kershaw, M. and Cranswick, P.A. 2002. Numbers of wildfowl and selected waterbirds wintering in Great Britain. *Biol. Cons.* 73: 189–98

Kertell, K. 1991. Disappearance of the Steller's Eider from the Yukon-Kuskokwim Delta, Alaska. *Arctic* 44: 177–84.

Kessel, B. 1989. *Birds of the Seward Peninsula, Alaska*. Univ. Alaska Press, Fairbanks.

Kessel, B., Rocque, D.A. and Barclay, J.S. 2002. Greater Scaup (*Aythya marila*). The Birds of North America, No. 650 (ed. A. Poole, and F. Gill). AOU, The Birds of North America Inc., Philadelphia.

Kessler, L.G. and Avise, J.C. 1984. Systematic relationships among waterfowl (Anatidae) inferred from restriction endonuclease analysis of mitochondrial DNA. *Syst. Zool.* 33: 370–80.

Kestenholz, M. 1994. Body mass dynamics of wintering Tufted Duck *Aythya fuligula* and Pochard *A. ferina* in Switzerland. *Wildfowl* 45: 147–58.

Kiel, W.H., Jr 1953. Waterfowl breeding population and production in the Newdale-Erickson district of Manitoba—1953. In *Waterfowl populations and breeding conditions, summer 1953*, Spec. Sci. Rep. Wildl., No. 25., pp.81–85. US Fish & Wildl. Serv., Washington.

Kilpi, M., Öst, M., Lindström, K. and Rita, H. 2001. Female characteristics and parental care mode in the crèching system of Eiders, *Somateria mollissima*. *Anim. Behav.* 62: 527–34.

King, B., Woodcock, M. and Dickinson, E.C. 1975. *A field guide to the birds of South-East Asia*. Collins, London.

King, J.G. 1973. A cosmopolitan duck moulting resort: Takslesluk Lake Alaska. *Wildfowl* 24: 103–9.

King, J.G. 1992. Where 15,630 wild Trumpeter Swans were counted in summer 1990. *Trumpetings* 2: 3.

King, J.G. and Dau. C.P. 1981. Waterfowl and their habitats in the eastern Bering Sea. In *The eastern Bering Sea shelf: oceanography and resources*, Vol. 2 (ed. D.W. Hood and J.A. Calder), pp.739–53. Univ. Washington Press, Seattle.

King, J.G. and Derksen, D.V. 1986. Alaska goose populations: past, present and future. *Trans. N. Amer. Wildlife and Nat. Res. Conf.* 51: 464–79.

King, J.G. and Hodges, J.I. 1981. A correlation between *Cygnus columbianus columbianus* territories and water bodies in western Alaska. In 2nd IWRB Int. Swan Symp., Sapporo, 1980 (ed. G.V.T. Matthews and M. Smart), pp.26–33. IWRB, Slimbridge, UK.

King, J.R. 1980. Energetics of avian moult. *Int. Ornith. Congr.* 17: 312–17.

King, W.B. 1977. Endangered birds of the world: the ICBP bird red data book. Smithsonian Institution Press, Washington, and IUCN, Morges, Switzerland.

Kingsford, R.T. 1989. Food of the Maned Duck *Chenonetta jubata* during the breeding season. *Emu* 89: 119–24.

Kingsford, R.T. 1990. Biparental care in the Australian Wood Duck *Chenonetta jubata*. *Wildfowl* 41: 83–91.

Kingsford, R.T. 1992. Maned Ducks and farm dams: a success story. *Emu* 92: 163–69.

Kingsford, R.T. 1996. Wildfowl (Anatidae) movements in arid Australia. *Gibier Faune Sauvage* 13: 141–55.

Kingsford, R.T. and Porter, J.L. 1994. Waterbirds on an adjacent freshwater lake and salt lake in arid Australia. *Biol. Cons.* 69: 219–28.

Kingsford, R.T., Braithwaite, L.W., Dexter, N. and Lawler, W. 1988. *An aerial survey of wetland bird fauna in eastern Australia—October 1987*, Wildl. Rglds. Res. Tech. Mem., No. 30. CSIRO, Lyneham, ACT.

Kingsford, R.T., Smith, J.D.B. and Lawler, W. 1989. *An aerial survey of wetland birds in eastern Australia—October 1988*, Occ. Pap., No. 8. NSW National Parks and Wildlife Service.

Kingsford, R.T., Wong, P.S., Braithwaite L.W. and Maher, M.T. 1999. Waterbird abundance in eastern Australia, 1983–92. *Wildl. Res.* 26: 351–66.

Kingsford, R.T., Webb, G. and Fullagar, P. 2000. *Scientific panel review of open seasons for waterfowl in New South Wales.* New South Wales Nat. Parks and Wildl. Serv.

Kirby, J.S. 1999. Canada Goose *Branta canadensis* Introduced: United Kingdom. In *Goose Populations of the Western Palearctic*, Publ., No. 48 (ed. J. Madsen, G. Cracknell and T. Fox), pp.228–34. Wetlands International, Wageningen, Netherlands.

Kirby, J.S. and Mitchell, C. 1993. Distribution and status of wintering Shoveler in Great Britain. *Bird Study* 40: 170–80.

Kirby, J.S., Rees, E.C., Merne, O.J. and Garðarsson, A. 1992. International census of Whooper Swans in Britain, Ireland and Iceland. *Wildfowl* 43: 20–26.

Kirby, J.S., Evans, R.J. and Fox, A.D. 1993. Wintering seaducks in Britain and Ireland: populations, threats, conservation and research priorities. *Aquatic Conservation: Marine and Freshwater Ecosystems* 3: 105–37.

Kirby, J.S., Salmon, D.G., Atkinson-Willes, G.L. and Cranswick, P.A. 1995. Index numbers for waterfowl populations. III. Long-term trends in the abundance of wintering wildfowl in Great Britain 1966/67 to 1991/92. *J. Appl. Ecol.* 32: 536–51.

Kiss, J.B., Rékási, J. and Sterbetz, J. 1984. A study of the foods of the Mallard (*Anas platyrhynchos*) and of the Ferruginous Duck (*Aythya nyroca*) in the Danube Delta (Romania). *Puszta* 2: 39–51.

Kistchinski, A.A. 1973. Waterfowl in north-east Asia. *Wildfowl* 24: 88–102.

Kistchinski, A.A. 1988. *The avifauna of NE Asia, history and modern status.* Nauka, Moscow. [In Russian.]

Kistchinski, A.A. and Flint, V.E. 1974. On the biology of the Spectacled Eider. *Wildfowl* 25: 5–15.

Kitchen, D.W. and Hunt, G.S. 1969. Brood habitat of the Hooded Merganser. *J. Wildl. Manage.* 33: 605–9.

Kitson, A. 1978. Notes on the waterfowl of Mongolia. *Wildfowl* 29: 23–30.

Klein, D.R. 1966. Waterfowl in the economy of the Eskimos on the Yukon-Kuskokwim Delta, Alaska. *Arctic* 19: 319–36.

Klementsson, A. 1980. Copulatory behaviour of the Smew *Mergus albellus*. *Vår Fågelvärld* 39(3): 161–62.

Klett, A.T., Shaffer, T.L. Johnson, D.H. 1988. Duck nest success in the Prairie Pothole Region. *J. Wildl. Manage.* 52: 431–40.

Klimkiewicz, M.K. and Futcher, A.G. 1989. Longevity records of North American Birds. Suppl. 1. *J. Field Ornithol.* 60: 469–94.

Klomp, H. 1970. The determination of clutch-size in birds: a review. *Ardea* 58: 1–124.

Knights, C. 1984. Gadwalls and Black-headed Gulls feeding with Coots. *Brit. Birds* 77: 21–22.

Knudsen, H.L., Laubek, B. and Ohtonen, A. 2002. Growth and survival of Whooper Swan cygnets reared in different habitats in Finland. In *Proceedings of the Fourth International Swan Symposium, 2001* (ed. E.C. Rees, S.L. Earnst and J. Coulson), *Waterbirds* 25, Special Publication 1: 211–20.

Koepcke, H-W. and Koepcke, M. 1963. *Las aves silvestres de importancia económica del Perú.* Min. Agr., Dir. Gen. Forestal, Caza y Tierras, Lima.

Koepcke, H-W. and Koepcke, M. 1965. *Huallata* (Chloephaga melanoptera), Las aves silvestres de importancia económica del Perú, No. 8. Ministerio de Agricultura, Servicio Forestal y de Caza, Lima.

Koepcke, M. 1964. *The birds of the Department of Lima, Peru.* Harrowood Books, Newtown Square, Pennsylvania.

Kohl, I. 1958. The Red-necked Goose (*Branta ruficollis*) in Rumania. *Larus* 9–10: 184–87.

Köhler, P., Köhler, U., Pykal. J., von Krosigk, E. and Firsching, U. 1995. Sustained pair-bonds during moult migration? Pair-formation during break up of family groups in Gadwall. *J. Orn.* 136: 167–75.

Kojima, I. 1978. Breeding behavior of Coscoroba Swan in Kyoto Municipal Zoo. *Proc. 1st Int. Symp. Birds in Captivity, Seattle, Washington* (ed. A.C. Risser, L.F. Baptista, S.R. Wylie and N.B. Gale), pp.278–89.

Kokorev, Y. and Quinn, J.L. 1999. Geese in the Pura basin, Taymyr: their status, trends and the effects of the lemming cycle on breeding parameters. *Casarca* 5: 272–96.

Kolbe, H. 1972. *Die Entenvögel der Welt.* Newmann Verlag, Leipzig.

Kolomiitsev, N.P. 1985. The Scaly-sided Merganser *Mergus squamatus* and the Mandarin Duck *Aix galericulata* in the Lazo State Reserve. In *Rare and endangered birds of the Far East*, pp.85–88. Far East Science Centre, USSR Academy of Science, Vladivostok.

Kolomiitsev, N.P. 1986. Factors limiting the number of Scaly-sided Mergansers and recommendations for the conservation of the species. In *A study of the birds of the USSR, their conservation and management,* Proc. 1st Meeting All-Union Ornithol. Soc. and IX All-Union Ornithol. Conf. 16–20.12.1986, Part 1, pp.306–7. Leningrad.

Kolomiitsev, N.P. 1992. *Mergus squamatus* biology in the Kiyevka Basin (S. Primorye). In *Ornithological research in state reserves* (ed. Ye Sokolov), pp.68–73. Nauka, Moscow.

Kolomiitsev, N.P. 1995. New data for moult in the Chinese Merganser *Mergus squamatus*. *Russ. J. Orn.* 4: 19–23.

Kolosov, A.M. 1983. *Red data book of the RSFSR: animals.* Rossel 'khozizdat, Moscow.

Komdeur, J., Bertelsen, J., and Cracknell, G. (ed.) 1992. *Manual for aeroplane and ship surveys of waterfowl and seabirds,* Spec. Publ., No. 19. IWRB, Slimbridge, UK.

Kondratyev, A.V. 1989. A comparative ecology of *Melanitta americana, M. deglandi* and *Clangula hyemalis* in the Anadyr river middle stream basin. *Zool. J.* 68(8): 93–103. [In Russian.]

Kondratyev, A.V. 1990. Waterfowl resources of the Magadanskaya region. In *Managing waterfowl populations,* IWRB Symp., Astrakhan 1989, Publ., No. 12 (ed. G.V.T. Matthews), pp.44–45. IWRB, Slimbridge, UK.

Kondratyev, A.V. 1991. The distribution and status of Bewick's Swan *Cygnus bewickii,* Tundra Swan *C. columbianus* and Whooper Swan *C. cygnus* in the Extreme Northeast of the USSR. *Wildfowl* Spec. Suppl., 1: 56–61.

Kondratyev, A.V. 1993. Breeding biology, habitat selection, and population number of four goose species

along the south-west coast of Anadyr Bay. *Russ. J. Orn.* 2: 287–302. [In Russian.]

Kondratyev, A.V. 1995. Status of goose populations in northeast Asia (Chukotka) and their conservation. *Goose Study* 9: 15–18.

Kondratyev, A.V. and Zadorina, L.V. 1992. Comparative ecology of the King Eider *Somateria spectabilis* and Spectacled Eider *Somateria fischeri* on the Chaun tundra. *Zool. Zhur.* 71(1): 99–108.

Kontiokorpi, J. and Parviainen, A. 1995. The spring migration of arctic waterfowl in Vyborg and Repino (Russia) in spring 1993. *IWRB Seaduck Research Group Bull.* 5: 25–29.

Kontkanen, H. 1995. The visual observation of the spring migration of arctic waterfowl on the western coast of Estonia. *IWRB Seaduck Research Group Bull.* 5: 19–24.

Konyukov, N.B. 1998. Waterfowl of the Chukotka Peninsula coast. *Casarca* 4: 319–30.

Kooloos, J.G.M., Kraaijeveld, A.R., Langenbach, G.E.J. and Zweers, G.A. 1989. Comparative mechanics of filter feeding in *Anas platyrhynchos, Anas clypeata* and *Aythya fuligula* (Aves, Anseriformes). *Zoomorphology* 108: 269–90.

Koons, D.N. and Rotella, J.J. 2003. Comparative nesting success of sympatric Lesser Scaup and Ring-necked Ducks. *J. Field Ornithol.* 74: 222–29.

Korschgen, C.E. 1989. Riverine and deepwater habitats for diving ducks. In *Habitat management for migrating and wintering waterfowl in North America* (ed. L.M. Smith, R.L. Pederson and R.M. Kaminski), pp.157–89. Texas Tech Univ. Press, Lubbock.

Korschgen, C.E., Gibbs, H.C. and Mendall, H.L. 1978. Avian cholera in eider ducks in Maine. *J. Wildl. Dis.* 14: 254–58.

Korschgen, C.E., George, L.S. and Green, W.L. 1985. Disturbance of diving ducks by boaters on a migrational staging area. *Wildl. Soc. Bull.* 13: 290–96.

Korschgen, C.E., George, L.S. and Green, W.L. 1988. Feeding ecology of Canvasbacks staging on Pool 7 of the upper Mississippi River. In *Waterfowl in winter* (ed. M. Weller), pp.237–49. Univ. Minnesota Press, Minneapolis.

Kortlandt, A. 1942. Levensloop, samenstelling en structuur der Nederlandse aalscholverbevolking. *Ardea* 31: 175–280.

Kortright, F.H. 1942. *The ducks, geese and swans of North America*. Stackpole, Harrisburg, and Wildl. Manage. Inst., Washington.

Koskimies, J. 1957. Verhalten und Ökologie der jungen und der jungenfuhrenden Weibchen der Samtente. *Ann. Zool. Fenn.* 18: 1–69.

Koskimies, J. and Lahti, L. 1964. Cold-hardiness of the newly hatched young in relation to ecology and distribution in ten species of European ducks. *Auk* 81: 281–307.

Koskimies, P. 1989. Distribution and numbers of Finnish birds. Appendix to Suomen Lintuatlas. SLY: n Lintutielo Oy. Helsinki.

Koslowa-Puschkarewa, E.W. 1933. *Die Vögel und das Wild der Ostchentei*. Trudy MK 10, Leningrad.

Kostin, I.O. 1985. Biology of *Rubifrenta ruficollis* and problems of its conservation. Unpubl. Ph.D. thesis. Univ. Moscow, Russia.

Kostin, I.O. and Mooij, J.H. 1995. Influence of weather conditions and other factors on the reproductive cycle of Red-breasted Geese (*Branta ruficollis*) at the Taymyr Peninsula. *Wildfowl* 46: 45–54.

Kostow, K.E. 1981. The role of duckling vocalizations in maintaining the spatial distribution of a foraging brood. Unpubl. M.S. thesis. Univ. Minnesota, St. Paul, US.

Kotanen, P.M. and Jefferies, R.L. 1997. Long-term destruction of sub-arctic wetland vegetation by Lesser Snow Geese. *Ecoscience* 4: 179–82.

Kozlik, F.M. 1972. *California Pacific flyway report, second and third quarters, 1972*, Pacific Flyway Waterfowl Rep., No. 68. State of California, Dept of Fish & Game, Sacramento.

Kraft, R.H. 1991. Status report on the Lacreek Trumpeter Swan flock. In 12th Trumpeter Swan Soc. Conf., (ed. J. Voight-Englund), pp.88–90. Trumpeter Swan Society, Maple Plain.

Krapu, G.L. 1974a. Feeding ecology of Pintail hens during reproduction. *Auk* 91: 278–90.

Krapu, G.L. 1974b. Foods of breeding Pintail in North Dakota. *J. Wildl. Manage.* 38: 408–17.

Krapu, G.L. 1979. Nutrition of female dabbling ducks during reproduction. In *Waterfowl and wetlands—an integrated review*, Proc. Symp. 39th Midwest Fish & Wildl. Conf., Madison, Wisconsin (ed. T.A. Bookhout), pp.59–70. Wildlife Society, Madison.

Krapu, G.L. 1981. The role of nutrient reserves in Mallard reproduction. *Auk* 98: 29–38.

Krapu, G.L. and Reinecke, K.J. 1992. Foraging ecology and nutrition. In *The ecology and management of breeding waterfowl* (ed. B.D.J. Batt, A.D. Afton, M.G. Anderson, C.D. Ankney, D.H. Johnson, J.A. Kadlec et al.), pp.1–29. Univ. Minnesota Press, Minneapolis.

Krapu, G.L., Talent, L.G. and Dwyer, T.J. 1979. Marsh nesting by Mallards. *Wildl. Soc. Bull.* 7: 104–10.

Krapu, G.L., Sargeant, G.A. and Perkins, E.H. 2002. Does increasing daylength control seasonal changes in clutch sizes of Northern Pintails (*Anas acuta*)? *Auk* 119: 498–506.

Krebs, C.J. 1972. *Ecology*. Harper and Row, New York.

Krebs, J.R. and Davies, N.B. 1987. *An introduction to behavioural ecology* (2nd edn). Blackwell Scientific Publications, Oxford.

Krechmar, A.V. 1965. Zur Brutbiologie der Rothalsgans *Branta ruficollis* (Pallas) in West-Taimyr. *J. Orn.* 106: 440–5.

Krechmar, A.V. and Kondratyev, A.V. 1982. Ecology of nesting of *Philacte canagicus* on the north part of Chukotka Peninsula. *Zoologischeskii Zhurnal* (*J. Zoology*) 61: 254–64. [In Russian.]

Krechmar, A.V. and Leonovich, V.V. 1967. Distribution and biology of the Red-breasted Goose in the breeding season. *Problemy Severa* 11: 229–34. [In Russian.]

Krechmar, A.V., Andreev, A.V. and Kondratyev, A.V. 1978. *Ekologiya I rasprostranenie ptits na severo-vostoke SSSR*. Moscow.

Krechmar, A.V., Andreev, A.V. and Kondratyev, A.V. 1991. *Birds of the northern plains*. Nauka, Leningrad. [In Russian.]

Krementz, D.G., Conroy, M.J., Hines, J.E. and Percival, H.F. 1987. Sources of variation in survival and recovery rates of American Black Ducks. *J. Wildl. Manage.* 51: 689–700.

Kreuzberg-Mukhina, E. and Lanovenko, E. 2000. White-headed Ducks at the Sudochie Wetlands, Uzbekistan. *Wetlands International–IUCN Threatened Waterfowl Specialist Group News* 12: 15–16.

Kriese, K.D. 2004. Breeding ecology of the Orinoco Goose (*Neochen jubata*) in the Venezuelan llanos: the paradox of a tropical grazer. Unpubl. Ph.D. thesis. Univ. California, Davis, USA.

Kristiansen, J.N. 1997. Estimating the population size of breeding Greylag Geese *Anser anser* based on vertical aerial photographs. *Wildfowl* 48: 65–71.

Kristiansen, J.N. 1998. Egg predation in reedbed nesting Greylag Geese *Anser anser* in Vejlerne, Denmark. *Ardea* 86: 137–45.

Kristiansen, J.N. and Jarrett, N.S. 2002. Interspecific competition between Greenland White-fronted Geese *Anser albifrons flavirostris* and Canada Geese *Branta canadensis interior* moulting in West Greenland: mechanisms and consequences. *Ardea* 90(1): 1–13.

Kristiansen, J.N., Fox, A.D., Stroud, D.A. and Boyd, H. 1998. Dietary and microtopographical selectivity of Greenland White-fronted Geese feeding on Icelandic hayfields. *Ecography* 21: 480–3.

Kristiansen, J.N., Fox, A.D. and Nachman, G. 2000. Does size matter? Maximising nutrient and biomass intake by shoot size selection amongst herbivorous geese. *Ardea* 88: 119–25.

Krivenko, V.G. 1984. Present numbers of waterfowl in the central region of the USSR. In *Present status of waterfowl stocks*, All-Union Seminar, Moscow 1984 (ed. V.G. Krivenko), pp.8–11.

Krivenko, V.G. 1993. The current status of waterfowl resources and their habitats in the Middle Region of the Former USSR. In *Wetlands and Waterfowl Conservation in South and West Asia*, Int. Symp., Karachi, Pakistan, 14–20 December 1991 (ed. M. Moser and J. van Vessem), pp.72–77. IWRB Spec. Publ., No. 25 and AWB Publ. 85. IWRB, Slimbridge, and Asian Wetland Bureau, Kuala Lumpur.

Krivonosov, G.A. 1991. The status and distribution of the Mute Swan *Cygnus olor* in the USSR. *Wildfowl* Spec. Suppl., 1: 33–38.

Krivonosov, G.A. and Rusanov, G.M. 1990. Wintering waterfowl in the northern Caspian. In *Managing Waterfowl Populations*, IWRB Symp., Astrakhan 1989, Publ., No. 12 (ed. G.V.T. Matthews), pp.27–31. IWRB, Slimbridge, UK.

Krogman, B.D. 1979. A systematic study of *Anser albifrons* in California. In *Management and biology of Pacific Flyway geese* (ed. R.L. Jarvis and J.C. Bartonek), pp.22–43. Oregon State Univ., Cornwallis.

Krull, J.N. 1970. Aquatic plant-macroinvertebrate associations and waterfowl. *J. Wildl. Manage.* 34: 707–18.

Kuchel, C.R. 1977. Some aspects of the behavior and ecology of Harlequin Ducks breeding in Glacier National Park, Montana. Unpubl. M.S. thesis. Univ. Montana, US.

Kurechi, M. 1983. The Bean Goose subspecies *Anser fabalis middendorffii* predominates in Japan. *Anima* 129: 18–22.

Kurechi, M. 1991. Report on East Asian races of the Bean Goose in Japan and Kamchatka. *IWRB Threatened Waterfowl Research Group Newsl.* 1: 11–12.

Kurechi, M., Gerasimov, N.N., Gerasimov, Y.N., Andreev, A.V., Kondratyev, A.V., Takekawa, J.Y. *et al.* 1995. Migration of *Anser fabalis* and *A. albifrons* in northeast Asia with special reference to the population wintering in Japan. *Goose Study* 9: 8–9.

Kuroda, N. 1924. On a third specimen of rare *Pseudotadorna cristata* Kuroda. *Tori* 4: 17–20.

Küsters, E. 2000. Influence of eutrophication of gravel pit lakes on birds numbers. In *Limnology and aquatic birds. monitoring, modelling and management*, Proc. 2nd Int. Symp. on Limnology and Aquatic Birds (ed. F.A. Comín, J.A. Herrera and J. Ramírez), pp.221–30. Universidad Autónoma de Yucatán, Mérida.

Kux, Z. 1963. Beitrag zur Kenntnis der Verbreitung und Bionomie der Entvögel (Anatidae) im Inundationsgebiet des Unterlaufs der Thaya und den anliegenden Teichen. *Acta Mus. Moraviae* 48: 167–208.

Kydyraliew, A.K. 1967. Die Streifengans im Tienschan-Gebirge. *Ornitologija* 8: 245–53. [In Russian.]

La Touche, J.D.D. 1925–1934. *A handbook of the birds of Eastern China.* Taylor and Francis, London.

Labutin, Y.V. and Perfilyev, V.I. 1991. Composition and distribution by habitat of the Ozhogina valley bird fauna. In *Fauna and ecological studies of animals in Yakutia*, pp.78–97. Yakutsk. [In Russian.]

Labzyuk, V.I. 1972. *Tadorna cristata* in Southern Primorye. *Ornitologia* 10: 356–57.

Labzyuk, V.I. 1988. *Mergus squamatus* Gould in the Avvakumovka (Primorye). In *Rare birds of the Far East and their conservation*, pp.43–45. Far East Science Centre, USSR Academy of Sciences, Vladivostok.

Labzyuk, V.I. and Nazarov, Y.N. 1967. Rare and new birds of Southern Primorye. *Ornitologia* 8: 363–64.

Lack, D. 1967. The significance of clutch-size in waterfowl. *Wildfowl* 18: 125–28.

Lack, D. 1968a. *Ecological adaptations for breeding in birds.* Methuen, London.

Lack, D. 1968b. The proportion of yolk in the eggs of waterfowl. *Wildfowl* 19: 67–69.

Lack, D. 1970. The endemic ducks of remote islands. *Wildfowl* 21: 5–10.

Lack, D. 1974. *Evolution illustrated by waterfowl.* Blackwell, Oxford.

Lagerquist, B.A. and Ankney, C.D. 1989. Interspecific differences in bill and tongue morphology among diving ducks (*Aythya* spp., *Oxyura jamaicensis*). *Can. J. Zool.* 67: 2694–99.

LaHart, D.E. and Cornwell, G.W. 1971. Habitat preference and survival of Florida Duck broods. *Proc. Ann. Conf. Southeastern Assoc. Game and Fish Commissioners* 24: 117–21.

Lahti, K and Markkola, J. 1994. Ringing recovery of a Finnish Lesser White-fronted Goose from the Russian wintering areas. *IWRB Goose Research Group Bull.* 6: 27–28.

Laing, K.K. 1991. Habitat and food selection, behavior and body composition of nesting Emperor Geese. Unpubl. M.S. thesis. Univ. Calif., Davis, US.

Laing, K.K. and Raveling, D.G. 1993. Habitat and food selection by Emperor Goose goslings. *Condor* 95: 879–88.

Lambert, F.R. 1994. Notes on the avifauna of Bacan, Kasiruta and Obi, North Moluccas. *Kukila* 7: 1–9.

Lambrecht, K. 1933. *Handbuch der Palaeornithologie.* Gebruder Borntraeger, Berlin.

Lamoureux, C.H. 1963. The flora and vegetation of Laysan Island. *Atoll Res. Bull.* 97: 1–14.

Lampila, P. 2000. Adult mortality as a key factor determining population growth in Lesser White-fronted Goose. Annual report 2000. *WWF Finland Report* 9: 45–47.

Lamprecht, J. 1986. Social dominance and reproductive success in a goose flock *Anser indicus*. *Behaviour* 97: 50–65.

Lamprecht, J. 1987. Female reproductive strategies in Bar-headed Geese (*Anser indicus*): why are geese monogamous? *Behav. Ecol. Sociobiol.* 21: 297–305.

Lamprecht, J. 1989. Mate guarding in geese: awaiting female receptivity, protection of paternity or support of female feeding? In *The sociobiology of sexual and reproductive strategies* (ed. A.E. Rasa, C. Vogel and E. Voland), pp.48–66. Chapman and Hall, London.

Lamprecht, J. and Burhow, H. 1987. Harem polygyny in Bar-headed Geese (*Anser indicus*). *Ardea* 75: 285–92.

Landers, J.L. and Johnson, A.S. 1976. Foods of Fulvous Whistling Ducks in coastal South Carolina. *Wilson Bull.* 88: 659–60.

Langrand, O. 1985. *Les oiseaux de Madagascar: inventaire et étude de la collection d'oiseaux de Madagascar conservée au Muséum d'Histoire de Grenoble.* Série inventaire des collections Muséum d'Histoire Naturelle, Ville de Grenoble, France.

Langrand, O. 1990. *Guide to the birds of Madagascar.* Yale Univ. Press.

Langrand, O. and Goodman, S. 1995. Monitoring Madagascar's ecosystem: a look at the past, present and future of its wetlands. In *Ecosystem monitoring and protected areas.* 2nd Int. Conf. on Sci. and Management of Protected Areas, Halifax, Canada, Univ. Dalhousie, 16–20 May 1994 (ed. T.B. Herman), pp.204–14. Science and Management of Protected Areas Association, Wolfville, Nova Scotia.

Lank, D.B., Cooch, E.G., Rockwell, R.F. and Cooke, F. 1989a. Environmental and demographic correlates of intraspecific nest parasitism in Lesser Snow geese (*Chen caerulescens caerulescens*). *J. Anim. Ecol.* 58: 29–45.

Lank, D.B., Mineau, P., Rockwell, R.F. and Cooke, F. 1989b. Intraspecific nest parasitism and extra-pair copulation in Lesser Snow Geese. *Anim. Behav.* 37: 74–89.

Lank, D.B., Rockwell, R.F., and Cooke, F. 1990a. Fitness consequences and frequency-dependent success of alternative reproductive tactics of female Lesser Snow Geese. *Evolution* 44: 1436–53.

Lank, D.B., Bousfield, M.A., Cooke, F. and Rockwell, R.F. 1990b. Why do geese adopt eggs? *Behav. Ecol.* 2: 181–87.

Lanovenko, E., Filatov, A. and Zagrebin, S. 2000. White-headed Ducks at Dengizkul Lake, Uzbekistan. *Wetlands International–IUCN Threatened Waterfowl Specialist Group News* 12: 16.

Lanyon, W.E. 1982. The subspecies concept: then, now and always. *Auk* 99: 603–4.

Larionov, V.F. and Semashko, L.L. 1955. *Mergus squamatus* in the Soviet Union. *Proc. Acad. Sci. USSR* 101(6): 1141–43.

Larned, W.W. 2001. Steller's Eider spring migration surveys, 2000. U.S. Fish and Wildlife Service. Unpubl. Rept. 15pp.

Larned, W.W., Butler, W.I. and Balogh, G.R. 1994. Steller's Eider migration surveys 1992–1993. Prog. Rept., US Fish & Wildl. Serv., Office of Migratory Bird Management, Anchorage.

Larned, W.W., Tiplady, T., Platte R. and Stehn, R. 1999. Eider breeding population survey, Arctic Coastal Plain, Alaska, 1997–98. Unpubl. rept US Fish & Wildl. Serv., Washington.

Larsson, K., Forslund, P. Gustafsson, L. and Ebbinge, B.S. 1988. From the high Arctic to the Baltic: the successful establishment of a Barnacle Goose *Branta leucopsis* population on Gotland, Sweden. *Ornis Scand.* 19: 182–89.

Larsson, K., Tegelstom, H. and Forslund, P. 1995. Intraspecific nest parasitism and adoption of young in the Barnacle Goose: effects on survival and reproductive performance. *Anim. Behav.* 50: 1349–60.

Latham, J. 1798. An essay on the trachea or windpipes of various kinds of birds. *Trans. Linn. Soc., Lond.* 4: 90–128.

Latham, J. 1824. *A general history of birds*, Vol. 10. Winchester, Jacob and Johnson.

Latta, W.C. and Sharkey, R.F. 1966. Feeding behavior of the American Merganser in captivity. *J. Wildl. Manage.* 30: 17–23.

Laubek, B. 1995a. Distribution and phenology of staging and wintering Whooper Swan *Cygnus cygnus* and Bewick's Swans *Cygnus columbianus bewickii* in Denmark, 1991–1993. *Dansk Orn. Foren. Tidsskr.* 89: 67–82.

Laubek, B. 1995b. Habitat use by Whooper Swans *Cygnus cygnus* and Bewick's Swans *Cygnus columbianus bewickii* wintering in Denmark: increasing agricultural conflicts. *Wildfowl* 46: 8–13.

Laubek, B. 1998. The Northwest European Whooper Swan (*Cygnus cygnus*) population: ecological and management aspects of an expanding waterfowl population. Unpubl. Ph.D. thesis. Univ. Aarhus, Denmark.

Laubek, B., Nilsson, L., Wieloch, M., Koffijberg, K., Sudfelt, C. and Follestad, A. 1999. Distribution, number and habitat choice of the Northwest European Whooper Swan (*Cygnus cygnus*) population: results of an international Whooper Swan census January 1995. *Vogelwelt* 120: 141–54.

Laurie-Ahlberg, C.C. and McKinney, F. 1979. The nod-swim display of male Green-winged Teal (*Anas crecca*). *Anim. Behav.* 27: 165–72.

Laursen, K., Pihl, S., Durinck, J., Hansen, M. Skov, H., Frikke, J. and Danielsen, F. 1997. Numbers and distribution of waterbirds in Denmark. *Dan. Rev. Game Biol.* 15(1): 1–181.

Lavery, H.J. 1966. Pygmy-geese in Australia *Qld Agri. J.* 92: 294–99.

Lavery, H.J. 1967a. The Magpie Goose in Queensland. *Qld Agric. J.* 93: 46–50.

Lavery, H.J. 1967b. The Black Swan in Queensland. *Qld Agric. J.* 93: 146–50.

Lavery, H.J. 1967c. *Whistling-ducks in Queensland*, Advisory leaflet, No. 917. Dept. Primary Industries, Brisbane, Queensland.

Lavery, H.J. 1970a. Studies of waterfowl (Anatidae) in North Queensland. 4. Movements. *Qld J. Agric. Anim. Sci.* 27: 411–24.

Lavery, H.J. 1970b. Studies of waterfowl (Anatidae) in North Queensland. 5. Breeding. *Qld J. Agric. Anim. Sci.* 27: 425–36.

Lavery, H.J. 1970c. The comparative ecology of waterfowl in north Queensland. *Wildfowl* 21: 69–77.

Lavery, H.J. 1971a. Studies of waterfowl (Anatidae) in north Queensland. 6. Feeding methods and foods. *Qld J. Agric. Anim. Sci.* 28: 255–73.

Lavery, H.J. 1971b *Wild ducks and other waterfowl in Queensland*. Department of Primary Industries, Queensland.

Lavery, H.J. 1972. Studies of waterfowl (Anatidae) in north Queensland. 8. Moults of the Grey Teal (*Anas gibberifrons*). *Qld J. Agric. Anim. Sci.* 29: 209–22.

Laycock, G. 1970. The Hawaiian islands of birds. *Audubon* 72: 44–61.

Lazarus, J. 1978. Vigilance, flock size and the domain of danger in the White-fronted Goose. *Wildfowl* 29: 135–45.

Lazarus, J. and Inglis, I.R. 1978. The breeding behaviour of the Pink-footed Goose: parental care and vigilant behaviour during the fledging period. *Behaviour* 65: 62–88.

Lazarus, J. and Inglis, I.R. 1986. Shared and unshared parental investment, parent–offspring conflict and brood size. *Anim. Behav.* 34: 1791–804.

Leach, J.H. 1993. Impacts of the Zebra Mussel (*Dreissena polymorpha*) on water quality and fish spawning reefs in the western Lake Erie. In *Zebra Mussels: biology, impacts, and control* (ed. T.F. Nalepa and D.W. Schloesser), pp.381–97. Lewis, Boca Raton, Florida.

Leafloor, J.O. and Rusch, D.H. 1997. Clinal size variation in Canada Geese affects morphometric discrimination techniques. *J. Wildl. Manage.* 61: 183–90.

Leafloor, J.O., Ankney, C.D. and Rusch, D.H. 1998. Environmental effects on body size of Canada geese. *Auk* 115: 26–33.

Lebret, T. 1958. Baltsbewegingen van het Nonnetje. *Ardea* 46: 75–79.

Ledger, J. 1985. Courage. *African Wildlife* 39: 174–75.

Lee, F.B., Jessen, R.L., Ordal, N.J., Benson, R.I., Lindmeier, J.P. and Johnson, L.L. 1964. *Waterfowl in Minnesota*, Tech. Bull., No. 7 (ed. J.B. Moyle). Minn. Dep. Conserv., St. Paul.

Lees, P.R. and Street, M. 1974. The feeding ecology of young Mallard and Tufted Duck in wet gravel quarries. *Congr. Int. Union Game Biologists* 11: 249–53.

Lees-May, N. 1974. Egg of Maccoa Duck in Red-knobbed Coot nest. *Ostrich* 45: 39–40.

Lefebvre, E.A. and Raveling, D.G. 1967. Distribution of Canada Geese in winter as related to heat loss at varying environmental temperature. *J. Wildl. Manage.* 31: 538–46.

Leibak, E., Lilleheht, V. and Veromann, H. 1994. *Birds of Estonia. Status, distribution and numbers.* Estonian Academy Publishers, Tallinn.

Leitch, W.G. 1952. Ecology of nesting waterfowl in the Missouri Coteau of southern Saskatchewan. Unpubl. M.S. thesis. Univ. Manitoba, Winnipeg, Canada.

Lekagul, B. and Round, P.D. 1991 *A guide to the birds of Thailand*. Saha Karn Bhaet, Bangkok.

Lensink, C.J. 1973. Population structure and productivity of Whistling Swans on the Yukon Delta, Alaska. *Wildfowl* 24: 21–25.

Lensink, R. 1999. Aspects of the biology of Egyptian Goose *Alopochen aegyptiacus* colonizing The Netherlands. *Bird Study* 46: 195–204.

Leonard, J.P., Anderson, M.G., Prince, H.H. and Emery, R.B. 1996. Survival and movements of Canvasback ducklings—effects of brood density and parasitic Redheads. *J. Wildl. Manage.* 60: 863–74.

Leopold, A.S. 1959. *Wildlife of Mexico: the game birds and mammals.* Univ. California Press, Berkeley.

Ler, P.A., Kostenko, V.A., Nechaev, V.A. and Shibaev, Y.V. (ed.) 1989. *Rare vertebrates of the Soviet Far East and their protection.* Nauka, Leningrad.

Lernould, J-M. 1983. The breeding of Hartlaub's Duck. In *Breeding Birds in Captivity*, 1983 Jean Delacour/IFCB Symp., (ed. A.C. Risser, Jr, L.F. Baptista, S.R. Wylie and N.B. Gale), pp.495–501. Int. Foundation for Conservation of Birds, Hollywood, California.

Lesage, L., Reed, A. and Savard, J-P.S. 1996. Plumage development and growth in wild Surf Scoter *Melanitta perspicillata* ducklings. *Wildfowl* 47: 205–10.

LeSchack, C.R. and Hepp, G.R. 1995. Kleptoparisitism of American Coots by Gadwalls and its relationship to social dominance and food abundance. *Auk* 112: 429–35.

Lessells, C.M. 1985. Natal and breeding dispersal of Canada Geese *Branta canadensis. Ibis* 127: 31–41.

Lessells, C.M. 1986. Brood size in Canada Geese: a manipulation experiment. *J. Anim. Ecol.* 55: 669–89.

Lessells, C.M. 1987. Parental investment, brood size and time budgets: behaviour of Lesser Snow Goose families. *Ardea* 75: 189–203.

Lessells, C.M., Cooke, F., and Rockwell, R.F. 1989. Is there a trade-off between egg weight and clutch size in Lesser Snow Geese (*Anser caerulescens caerulescens*)? *J. Evol. Biol.* 2: 457–72.

Lever, C. 1977. *The naturalized animals of the British Isles.* Hutchinson, London.

Lever, C. 1987. *Naturalized birds of the world.* Longman, Harlow.

Lever, C. 1989. *The Mandarin Duck.* Shire Publications, Princes Risborough, UK.

Levy, B. and Sivak, J.G. 1980. Mechanisms of accommodation in the bird eye. *J. Comp. Physiol.* 137: 267–72.

Lewington, I., Alström, P. and Colston. P. 1991. *A field guide to the rare birds of Britain and Europe.* Harper-Collins, London.

Lewis, A. and Pomeroy, D. 1989. *A bird atlas of Kenya.* Balkema, Rotterdam.

Lewis, H.F. 1937. Migrations of the American Brant (*Branta bernicla hrota*). *Auk* 54: 73–95.

Li, X. 1996. The status and conservation of wildfowl (Anatidae) in the Heilongjiang Province, China. *Gibier Faune Sauvage* 13: 1111–18.

Li, X. and Yiqing, M. 1996. Numerical distribution and conservation of Whooper Swans (*Cygnus cygnus*) in China. *Gibier Faune Sauvage* 13: 477–86.

Lightbody, J.P. 1985. Growth rates and development of Redhead ducklings. *Wilson Bull.* 97: 554–59.

Lightbody, J.P. and Ankney, C.D. 1984. Seasonal influence on the strategies of growth and development of Canvasback and Lesser Scaup ducklings. *Auk* 101: 121–33.

Limpert, R.J. 1974. Feeding preferences and behaviour of Whistling Swans on the Upper Mississippi River. Unpubl. thesis. St. Mary's College, Winona, Minnesota, US.

Limpert, R.J. and Earnst, S.L. 1994. Tundra Swan (*Cygnus columbianus*). The Birds of North America, No. 89 (ed. A. Poole and F. Gill). AOU, Washington, and Academy of Natural Sciences, Philadelphia.

Limpert, R.J., Allen, H.A., Jr and Sladen, W.J.L. 1987. Weights and measurements of wintering Tundra Swans. *Wildfowl* 38: 108–13.

Limpert, R.J., Sladen, W.J.L. and Allen, H.A., Jr 1991. Winter distribution of Tundra Swans *Cygnus columbianus columbianus* breeding in Alaska and Western Canadian Arctic. *Wildfowl* Spec. Suppl. 1: 78–83.

Lindholm, A., Gauthier, G. and Desrochers, A. 1994. Effects of hatch date and food supply on gosling growth in arctic-nesting Greater Snow Geese. *Condor* 96: 898–908.

Lindroth, A. and Bergstöm, E. 1959. Notes on the feeding technique of the Goosander in streams. *Rep. Inst. Freshw. Res. Drottningholm* 40: 165–67.

Lindsey, A.A. 1946. The nesting of the New Mexican Duck. *Auk* 63: 483–92.

Linduska, J.P. (ed.) 1964. *Waterfowl tomorrow.* US Fish & Wildl. Serv., Washington.

Linsley, M.D. 1995. Some bird records from Obi, Maluku. *Kukila* 7: 142–51.

Lint, K.C. 1956. Breeding of the Horned Screamer. *Avic. Mag.* 62: 127–28.

Litvin, K.E., Pulyaev, A.I. and Syroechkovski, E.V. 1985. Colonies of the Snow Goose *Anser caerulescens*, Brent Goose *Branta bernicla* and Eider *Somateria mollissima* near the Snowy Owl *Nyctea scandiaca* nests on Wrangel Island. *Zoologischeskii Zhurnal* (*J. Zoology*) 64: 1012–23. [English summary.]

Livezey, B.C. 1981. Locations and success of duck nests evaluated through discriminant analysis. *Wildfowl* 32: 23–27.

Livezey, B.C. 1986a. A phylogenetic analysis of Recent anseriform genera using morphological characters. *Auk* (103): 737–54.

Livezey, B.C. 1986b. Phylogeny and historical biogeography of steamer-ducks (Anatidae: *Tachyeres*). *Syst. Zool.* 35: 458–69.

Livezey, B.C. 1986c. Geographic variation in skeletons of Flying Steamer-ducks (*Tachyeres patachonicus*). *J. Biogeogr.* 13: 511–25.

Livezey, B.C. 1987. Personal perspectives and lack of data underlie different interpretations of interspecific aggression. *Condor* 89: 444–45.

Livezey, B.C. 1988. Feeding morphology, foraging behavior, and foods of steamer-ducks (Anatidae: *Tachyeres*). Occas. Pap., No. 126, pp.1–41. Mus. Natur. Hist., Univ. Kansas.

Livezey, B.C. 1989a. Phylogenetic relationships of several subfossil Anseriformes of New Zealand. Occas. Pap., No. 128, pp.1–25. Mus. Natur. Hist., Univ. Kansas.

Livezey, B.C. 1989b. Phylogenetic relationships and incipient flightlessness of the extinct Auckland Islands Merganser. *Wilson Bull.* 101: 410–35.

Livezey, B.C. 1989c. *Micropterus patachonicus* King, 1831 and *Anas pteneres* Forster, 1844 (both currently in *Tachyeres* Owen, 1875; Aves, Anseriformes): proposed conservation of the specific names. *Bull. Zool. Nomen.* 46: 181–84.

Livezey, B.C. 1990. Evolutionary morphology of flightlessness in the Auckland Islands Teal. *Condor* 92: 639–73.

Livezey, B.C. 1991. A phylogenetic analysis and classification of Recent dabbling ducks (Tribe Anatini) based on comparative morphology. *Auk* 108: 471–507.

Livezey, B.C. 1993a. Comparative morphometrics of *Anas* ducks, with particular reference to the Hawaiian Duck *Anas wyvilliana*, Laysan Duck *A. laysanensis*, and Eaton's Pintail *A. eatoni*. *Wildfowl* 44: 75–100.

Livezey, B.C. 1993b. Morphology of flightlessness in *Chendytes*, fossil seaducks (Anatidae: Mergini) of coastal California. *J. Vertebr. Paleontol.* 13: 185–99.

Livezey, B.C. 1995a. A phylogenetic analysis of the whistling and White-backed ducks (Anatidae: Dendrocygninae) using morphological characters. *Ann. Carnegie Mus.* 64: 65–97.

Livezey, B.C. 1995b. Phylogeny and comparative ecology of stiff-tailed ducks (Anatidae: Oxyurini). *Wilson Bull.* 107: 214–34.

Livezey, B.C. 1995c. Phylogeny and evolutionary ecology of modern seaducks (Anatidae: Mergini). *Condor* 97: 233–55.

Livezey, B.C. 1996a. A phylogenetic analysis of modern pochards (Anatidae: Aythyini). *Auk* 113: 74–93.

Livezey, B.C. 1996b. A phylogenetic analysis of geese and swans (Anseriformes: Anserinae), including selected fossil species. *Syst. Biol.* 45: 415–50.

Livezey, B.C. 1996c. A phylogenetic reassessment of the tadornine–anatine divergence (Aves: Anseriformes: Anatidae). *Ann. Carnegie Museum* 65: 27–88.

Livezey, B.C. 1997a. A phylogenetic analysis of basal Anseriformes, the fossil *Presbyornis*, and the interordinal relationships of waterfowl. *Zool. J. Linn. Soc.* 121: 361–428.

Livezey, B.C. 1997b. A phylogenetic classification of modern waterfowl (Anseriformes), including selected fossil species. *Ann. Carnegie Mus.* 66: 455–94.

Livezey, B.C. 1997c. A phylogenetic analysis of modern sheldgeese and shelducks (Anatidae: Tadornini). *Ibis* 139: 51–66.

Livezey, B.C. 1998. Erratum. *Zool. J. Linnean Soc.* 124: 397–98.

Livezey, B.C. and Humphrey, P.S. 1982. Escape behaviour of steamer ducks. *Wildfowl* 33: 12–16.

Livezey, B.C. and Humphrey, P.S. 1983. Mechanics of steaming in steamer-ducks. *Auk* 100: 485–88.

Livezey, B.C. and Humphrey, P.S. 1984a. Sexual dimorphism in continental steamer-ducks. *Condor* 86: 368–77.

Livezey, B.C. and Humphrey, P.S. 1984b. Diving behaviour of steamer ducks *Tachyeres* spp. *Ibis* 126: 257–60.

Livezey, B.C. and Humphrey, P.S. 1985a. Territoriality and interspecific aggression in steamer-ducks. *Condor* 87: 154–57.

Livezey, B.C. and Humphrey, P.S. 1985b. Commentary. *Condor* 87: 567–68.

Livezey, B.C. and Humphrey, P.S. 1986. Flightlessness in steamer-ducks (Anatidae: *Tachyeres*): its morphological bases and probable evolution. *Evolution* 40: 540–58.

Livezey, B.C. and Humphrey, P.S. 1992. Taxonomy and identification of steamer-ducks (Anatidae: *Tachyeres*). *Univ. Kansas Mus. Natur. Hist. Monogr.* 8: 1–125.

Livezey, B.C., Humphrey, P.S. and Thompson, M.C. 1985. Notes on coastal birds of Puerto Melo, Chubut, Argentina. *Bull. BOC* 105: 17–21.

Livezey, B.C., Jacob, J. and Humphrey, P.S. 1986. Biochemical composition of secretions from uropygial glands of steamer-ducks. *Biochem. Syst. Ecol.* 14: 445–50.

Livezey, B.C. and Martin, L.D. 1988. The systematic position of the Miocene Anatid *Anas (?) blanchardi* Milne-Edwards. *J. Vertebr. Paleontol.* 8: 196–211.

Locke, L.N. and Friend, M. 1987. Avian botulism. In *Field guide to wildlife diseases*, Vol. 1, Resource Publ,. No. 167 (ed. M. Friend and C.J. Laitman), pp.83–94. US Fish & Wildl. Serv., Washington.

Lockman, D.C., Wood, R., Burgess, H., Burgess, R. and Smith, H. 1987. *Rocky Mountain Trumpeter Swan population. Wyoming flock. 1982–1986.* Wyoming Game and Fish Dept., Cheyenne.

Lockwood, M.W. 1997. A closer look: Masked Duck. *Birding* 5: 386–90.

Lockwood, W.B. 1984. *The Oxford book of British bird names.* OUP.

Loesch, C.R., Kaminski, R.M. and Richardson, D.M. 1992. Endogenous loss of body mass by Mallards in winter. *J. Wildl. Manage.* 56: 735–39.

Lofts, B. and Murton, R.K. 1968. Photoperiodic and physiological adaptations regulating avian breeding cycles and their ecological significance. *J. Zool., Lond.* 155: 327–94.

Lokemoen, J.T. 1966. Breeding ecology of the Redhead Duck in western Montana. *J. Wildl. Manage.* 30: 668–81.

Lokemoen, J.T. 1991. Brood parasitism among waterfowl nesting on islands and peninsulas in North Dakota. *Condor* 93: 340–45.

Lokemoen, J.T., Duebbert, H.F. and Sharp, D.E. 1984. Nest spacing, habitat selection and behavior of waterfowl on Miller Lake Island, North Dakota. *J. Wildl. Manage.* 48: 309–21.

Lokemoen, J.T., Duebbert, H.F. and Sharp, D.E. 1990. Homing and reproductive habits of Mallards, Gadwalls, and Blue-winged Teal. *Wildl. Monogr.* 106: 1–26.

Long, J.L. 1981. *Introduced birds of the world*. David and Charles, Newton Abbot.

Long, R.J. 1970. A study of nest-site selection by island nesting anatids in central Alberta. Unpubl. M.S. thesis. Univ. Alberta, Edmonton, Canada.

Longcore, J.R. and Cornwell, G.W. 1964. The consumption of natural foods by captive Canvasbacks and Lesser Scaups. *J. Wildl. Manage.* 28: 527–31.

Longcore, J.R., McAuley D.G., Hepp, G.R. and Rhymer J.M. 2000. American Black Duck (*Anas rubripes*). The Birds of North America, No. 481 (ed. A. Poole and F. Gill). AOU, National Academy of Sciences, Philadelphia.

Loonen, M.J.J.E., Zijlstra, M. and van Eerden, M.R. 1991. Timing of wing moult in Greylag Geese *Anser anser* in relation to the availability of their food plants. *Ardea* 79: 253–60.

Lorentsen, S-H. and Spjøtvoll, Ø. 1990. A note on the food choice of breeding Lesser White-fronted Geese *Anser erythropus*. *Fauna Norv. Ser. C., Cinclus* 13: 87–88.

Lorentsen, S-H., Øien, I.J. and Aarvak, T. 1998. Migration of Fennoscandian lesser white-fronted geese *Anser erythropus* mapped by satellite telemetry. *Biol. Cons.* 84: 47–52.

Lorenz, K. 1951–53. Comparative studies on the behaviour of the Anatinae. *Avic. Mag.* 57: 157–82; 58: 8–17, 61–72, 86–94, 172–84; 59: 24–34, 80–91. Reprinted as: Lorenz, K. 1971. *Studies in animal and human behaviour*, Vol. 2. Methuen, London.

Lorenz, K. 1979. *The year of the Greylag Goose*. Eyre Methuen, London.

Lorenz, K. 1991. *Here I am—where are you?* (trans. R. Martin). HarperCollins, London.

Lorenz, K. and Von de Wall, W. 1960. Die Ausdrucksbewegung der Sichelente, *Anas falcata* L. *J. Orn.* 101: 50–60.

Lovegrove, R., Williams, G. and Williams, I. 1994. *Birds in Wales.* Poyser, London.

Løvenskiold, H.L. 1964. Avifauna Svalbardensis. *Norsk Pol. Skr.* 129: 1–460.

Lovvorn, J.R. 1987. Behavior, energetics, and habitat relations of Canvasback ducks during winter and early spring migration. Unpubl. Ph.D. thesis. Univ. Wisconsin, Madison, US.

Lovvorn, J.R. 1989a. Distributional responses of Canvasbacks to weather and habitat change. *J. Appl. Ecol.* 26: 113–30.

Lovvorn, J.R. 1989b. Food defendability and antipredator tactics: implications for dominance and pairing in Canvasbacks. *Condor* 91: 826–36.

Lovvorn, J.R. 1990. Courtship and aggression in Canvasbacks: influence of sex and pair-bonding. *Condor* 92: 369–78.

Lovvorn, J.R. and Barzen, J.A. 1988. Molt in the annual cycle of Canvasbacks. *Auk* 105: 543–52.

Lovvorn, J.R. and Gillingham, M.P. 1996. Food dispersion and foraging energetics: a mechanistic synthesis for field studies of avian benthivores. *Ecology* 77: 435–51.

Lovvorn, J.R., Jones, D.R. and Blake, R.W. 1991. Mechanics of underwater locomotion in diving ducks: buoyancy and acceleration in size gradient of species. *J. Exp. Biol.* 159: 89–108.

Low, J.B. 1941. Nesting of Ruddy Duck in Iowa. *Auk* 58: 506–17.

Low, J.B. 1945. Ecology and management of the Redhead, *Nyroca americana*, in Iowa. *Ecol. Monogr.* 15: 35–69.

Lowe, P.R. 1934. On the evidence for the existence of two species of steamer duck (*Tachyeres*), and primary and secondary flightlessness in birds. *Ibis* 76: 467–95.

Lowe, V.T. 1966. Notes on the Musk-duck, *Biziura lobata*. *Emu* 65: 279–90.

Lu, J. 1990. *The wetlands of China*. General Univ. Eastern China Press.

Lu, J. 1993. The utilization of migratory waterfowl in China. *Waterfowl and wetlands conservation in the 1990s: a global perspective*, Spec. Publ., No. 26 (ed. M. Moser and C. Prentice), pp.90–92. IWRB, Slimbridge, UK.

Lu, J. 1996. Current distribution and bioenergetics of wintering Swan Geese (*Anser cygnoides*). *Gibier Faune Sauvage* 13: 327–36.

Lu, J. 1997. Distribution of Bar-headed Goose in China. *J. Ecol. Soc.* 10: 8–9.

Lubbock, M. 1980. The rearing of Pink-eared Ducks (*Malacorhynchus membranaceous*), Musk Ducks (*Biziura* *lobata*), and Blue-billed Ducks (*Oxyura australis*). *Avic. Mag.* 86: 81–84.

Ludwichowski, I., Barker, R. and Bräger, S. 2002. Nesting area fidelity and survival of female Common Goldeneyes *Bucephala clangula*: are they density-dependent? *Ibis* 144: 452–60.

Luigujõe, L., Kuresoo, A., Keskpaik, J., Ader, A. and Leito, A. 1996. Migration and staging of the Bewick's Swan (*Cygnus columbianus bewickii*) in Estonia. *Gibier Faune Sauvage* 13: 451–61.

Luigujõe, L., Kuresoo, A. and Leivits, A. 2002. Numbers and distribution of Whooper Swans breeding, wintering and on migration in Estonia. In *Proceedings of the Fourth International Swan Symposium, 2001* (ed. E.C. Rees, S.L. Earnst and J. Coulson), *Waterbirds* 25, Special Publication 1: 61–66.

Lumsden, H.G. 1984. The pre-settlement breeding distribution of Trumpeter *Cygnus buccinator* and Tundra Swans *Cygnus columbianus* in eastern Canada. *Can. Field-Nat.* 98: 415–24.

Lumsden, H.G. 1988. Productivity of Trumpeter Swans in relation to condition. In 10th Trumpeter Swan Soc. Conf., (ed. D. Compton), pp.150–54. Trumpeter Swan Society, Maple Plain, MN.

Lüttschwager, J. 1955. Lamellenzahl an Entenschnäbeln. *Bonn. Zool. Beitr.* 6: 90–94.

Lynch, J. 1984. Escape from mediocrity: a new approach to American waterfowl hunting regulations. *Wildfowl* 35: 5–13.

Lysenko, V.I. 1990. Current status of waterfowl in Ukraine. In *Managing Waterfowl Populations*, IWRB Symp., Astrakhan 1989, Publ., No. 12 (ed. G.V.T. Matthews), p.43. IWRB, Slimbridge, UK.

Lyster, S. 1985. *International wildlife law: an analysis of international treaties concerned with the conservation of wildlife.* Grotius Publ., Cambridge, UK.

Ma, M. and Cai, D. 1999. Breeding ecology of Bar-headed Goose in Tianshan, Xinjiang. *Casarca* 5: 177–81.

Ma, M. and Cai, D. 2000. *Swans in China.* Trumpeter Swan Society, Maple Plain, Minnesota, USA.

Ma, M. and Cai, D. 2002. Threats to Whooper Swans in Xinjiang, China. In *Proceedings of the Fourth International Swan Symposium, 2001* (ed. E.C. Rees, S.L. Earnst and J. Coulson), *Waterbirds* 25, Special Publication 1: 331–33.

Mabbott, D.C. 1920. *Food habits of seven species of American shoal-water ducks,* Bull. No. 862. US Dept Agric., Washington.

Macdonald, J.W., Lea, D. and Hamilton, G.A. 1978. Parasitic worms causing deaths of Mute Swans. *Brit. Birds* 71: 358–59.

MacDonald, S.D. 1954. Report on biological investigations at Mould Bay, Prince Patrick Island, N.W.T., in 1952. *Ann. Rept. Nat. Mus. Canada, 1952–53* 132: 214–38.

Mace, G.M. and Collar, N.J. 1995. Extinction risk assessment for birds through quantitative criteria. *Ibis* 137: S240–S246.

Mack, G.D. and Flake, L.D. 1980. Habitat relationships of waterfowl broods on South Dakota stock ponds. *J. Wildl. Manage.* 44: 695–700.

Mackenzie, M.J.S. 1986. The captive breeding of the White-winged Wood Duck. Assam Valley Wildlife Society, *Preserve* 1: 6–8.

Mackenzie, M.J.S. 1990. White-winged Wood Duck—*Cairina scutalata* (*sic*)—the question of Indonesian albinism. *Wildfowl* 41: 163–66.

Mackenzie, M.J.S. and Kear, J. 1976. The White-winged Wood Duck. *Wildfowl* 27: 5–17.

Mackworth-Praed, C.W. and Grant, C.H.B. 1970. *Birds of West Central and West Africa,* Vol. 1. Longman, London.

Mackworth-Praed, C.W. and Grant, C.H.B. 1980. *Birds of Eastern and North Eastern Africa,* Vol. 1. Longman, London.

Maclean, G.L. 1986. *Ducks of Sub-Saharan Africa.* Acorn, Randburg.

Maclean, G.L. 1988. Egyptian Goose. *Pelea* 7: 30–39.

Maclean, G.L. 1993. *Roberts' birds of Southern Africa,* (6th edn). John Voelcker Book Fund, Cape Town.

Maclean, G.L. 1997a. Egyptian Goose. In *The atlas of Southern African birds,* Vol. 1 (ed. J.A. Harrison, D.G. Allan, L.G. Underhill, M. Herremans, A.J. Tree, V. Parker *et al.*), pp.122–3. BirdLife South Africa, Johannesburg.

Maclean, G.L. 1997b. Cape Shelduck. In *The atlas of Southern African birds,* Vol. 1 (ed. J.A. Harrison, D.G. Allan, L.G. Underhill, M. Herremans, A.J. Tree, V. Parker *et al.*), pp.124–5. BirdLife South Africa, Johannesburg.

Maclean, G.L. 1997c. Yellowbilled Duck *Anas undulata*. In *The atlas of Southern African birds,* Vol. 1 (ed. J.A. Harrison, D.G. Allan, L.G. Underhill, M. Herremans, A.J. Tree, V. Parker *et al.*), pp.126–7. BirdLife South Africa, Johannesburg.

Maclean, G.L. 1997d. Hottentot Teal *Anas hottentota*. In *The atlas of Southern African birds,* Vol. 1 (ed. J.A. Harrison, D.G. Allan, L.G. Underhill, M. Herremans, A.J. Tree, V. Parker *et al.*), pp.132–3. BirdLife South Africa, Johannesburg.

Maclean, G.L. 1997e. Redbilled Teal *Anas erythrorhyncha*. In *The atlas of Southern African birds,* Vol. 1 (ed. J.A. Harrison, D.G. Allan, L.G. Underhill, M. Herremans, A.J. Tree, V. Parker *et al.*), pp.134–5. BirdLife South Africa, Johannesburg.

Maclean, G.L. 1997f. Cape Shoveller *Anas smithii*. In *The atlas of Southern African birds,* Vol. 1 (ed. J.A. Harrison, D.G. Allan, L.G. Underhill, M. Herremans, A.J. Tree, V. Parker *et al.*), pp.136–7. BirdLife South Africa, Johannesburg.

Maclean, G.L. 1997g. Pygmy Goose *Nettapus auritus*. In *The atlas of Southern African birds,* Vol. 1 (ed. J.A. Harrison, D.G. Allan, L.G. Underhill, M. Herremans, A.J. Tree, V. Parker *et al.*), pp.144–5. BirdLife South Africa, Johannesburg.

Madge, S. and Burn, H. 1988. *Wildfowl: an identification guide to ducks, geese and swans of the world.* Christopher Helm, London.

Madriz, M. 1979. Notas sobre la historia natural y energetica del pato Farra-farro (*Amazonetta brasiliensis*) en el alto Apure. Unpubl. thesis. Univ. Central Venezuela, Caracas, Venezuela.

Madriz, M. 1983. Food habits of the Brazilian Duck in Apure state, Venezuela. *J. Wildl. Manage.* 47(2): 531–33.

Madsen, C.S., McHugh, K.P. and de Kloet, S.R. 1988. A partial classification of waterfowl (Anatidae) based on single-copy DNA. *Auk* 105: 452–59.

Madsen, F.J. 1954. On the food habits of diving ducks in Denmark. *Dan. Rev. Game Biol.* 2(3): 157–266.

Madsen, F.J. 1957. On the food habits of some fish-eating birds in Denmark. *Dan. Rev. Game Biol.* 3(2): 19–83.

Madsen, J. 1986. *Danske rastepladser for gæs.* Miljøministeriet, Fredningsstyrelsen.

Madsen, J. 1987. Status and management of goose populations in Europe, with special reference to populations resting and breeding in Denmark. *Dan. Rev. Game Biol.* 12(4): 1–76.

Madsen, J. 1988. Autumn feeding of herbivorous waterfowl in the Danish Wadden Sea, and impact of food supply and hunting on movements. *Dan. Rev. Game Biol.* 13(4): 1–32.

Madsen, J. 1989. Spring feeding ecology of Brent Geese *Branta bernicla*: annual variation in salt marsh food supplies and effects of grazing on growth of vegetation. *Dan. Rev. Game Biol.* 13(7): 1–16.

Madsen, J. 1995. Impacts of disturbance on migratory waterfowl. *Ibis* 137: S67–S74.

Madsen, J. 1996. (comp.) International Action Plan for the Lesser White-fronted Goose (*Anser erythropus*). In *Globally threatened birds in Europe—action plans* (ed. H. Heredia, L. Rose and M. Painter), pp.67–78. Council of Europe, Strasbourg.

Madsen, J. and Fox, A.D. 1995. Impacts of hunting disturbance on waterbirds—a review. *Wildl. Biol.* 1: 193–207.

Madsen, J. and Mortensen, C.E. 1987. Habitat exploitation and interspecific competition of moulting geese in east Greenland. *Ibis* 129: 25–44.

Madsen, J. and Noer, H. 1996. Decreased survival of Pink-footed Geese *Anser brachyrhynchus* carrying shotgun pellets. *Wildlife Biol.* 2: 75–82.

Madsen, J., Brenballe, T. and Mehlum, F. 1989. Study of the breeding ecology and behaviour of the Svalbard population of Light-bellied Brent Goose *Brant bernicla hrota*. *Polar Research* 7: 1–21.

Madsen, J., Reed, A. and Andreev, A. 1996a. Status and trends of geese (*Anser* sp., *Branta* sp.) in the world: a review, updating and evaluation. *Gibier Faune Sauvage* 13: 337–53.

Madsen, J., Asferg, T., Clausager, I. and Noer, H. 1996b. Status og jagttider for dansk vildtarter. TEMA-rapport fra Danmarks Miljøundersøgelser 1996/6. National Environmental Research Institute, Rønde, Denmark.

Madsen, J., Pihl, S. and Clausen, P. 1998. Establishing a reserve network for waterfowl in Denmark. A biological evaluation of needs and consequences. *Biol. Cons.* 85(3): 241–55.

Madsen, J., Cracknell, G. and Fox, A.D. (ed.) 1999a. *Goose populations of the Western Palearctic. A review of status and distribution.* Publ., No. 48. Wetlands International, Wageningen, Netherlands, and National Environmental Research Institute, Rønde, Denmark.

Madsen, J., Kuijken, E., Meire, P., Cottaar, F., Haitjema, T., Nicolaisen, P.I. et al. 1999b. Pink-footed Goose *Anser brachyrhynchus* Svalbard. In *Goose populations of the Western Palearctic. A review of status and distribution,* Publ., No. 48 (ed. J. Madsen, G. Cracknell and A.D. Fox), pp.82–93. Wetlands International, Wageningen, Netherlands, and National Environmental Research Institute, Rønde, Denmark.

Madsen, J., Frederiksen, M. and Ganter, B. 2002. Trends in annual and seasonal survival of Pink-footed Geese *Anser brachyrhynchus. Ibis* 144: 218–26.

Madsen, J., Matus, R., Blank, O., Benegas, L., Mateazzi G. and Blanco, D.E. 2003. Population status of the Ruddy-headed Goose (*Chloephaga rubidiceps*) in Tierra del Fuego and mainland Patagonia (Chile and Argentina). *Ornit. Neotrop.* 14: 15–28.

Maes, P. and Voet, H. 1988. Sarcelle d'été, *Anas querquedula.* In *Atlas des oiseaux nicheurs de Belgique* (ed. P. Devillers, W. Roggeman, J. Tricot, P. del Marmol, C. Kerwijn, J.P. Jacob and A. Anselin), pp.58–9. Inst. Royal Sc. Nat. Belgique, Brussels.

Magnúsdóttir, M.L. and Einarsson, Á. 1990. *Köfunartími anda á Mývatni,* Rept., No. 23, pp.69–79. Nature Conservation Council, Reykjavik. [Diving times of ducks at Lake Mývatn. In Icelandic.]

Mainguy, J., Bety, J., Gauthier, G. and Giroux, J.-F. 2003. Are body condition and reproductive effort affected by the spring hunt? *Condor* 104: 156–61.

Makatsch, W. 1974. *Die Eier der Vögel Europas,* Vol. 1. Neumann Verlag, Radebeul.

Malcom, J.M. 1971. Two female Trumpeter Swans share a nest. *Murrelet* 52: 24–25.

Malecki, R.A. and Trost, R.E. 1998. Status of breeding Canada Geese in North America. In *Biology and management of Canada Geese,* Int. Canada Goose Symp. (ed. D.H. Rusch, M.D. Samuel, D.D. Humburg and B.D. Sullivan), pp.3–8. Milwaukee, Wisconsin.

Malecki, R.A., Fox, A.D. and Batt, B.J.D. 2000. An aerial survey of White-fronted and Canada Geese in west Greenland. *Wildfowl* 51: 49–58.

Mallory, M. 2000. The Black-headed Duck lays ordinary eggs. *Wildfowl* 51: 109–15.

Mallory, M. L. 2003. Partial clutch loss in Wood Ducks *Aix sponsa* nesting near Ottawa, Canada. *Wildfowl* 54: 63–70.

Mallory, M. and Metz, K. 1999. Common Merganser (*Mergus merganser*). The Birds of North America,

No. 442 (ed. A. Poole and F. Gill). AOU, The Birds of North America Inc., Philadelphia.

Mallory, M.L. 2003. Partial clutch loss in Wood Ducks *Aix sponsa* nesting near Ottawa, Canada. *Wildfowl* 54: 63–70.

Mallory, M.L. and Weatherhead, P.J. 1990. Effects of nest parasitism and nest location on eggshell strength in waterfowl. *Condor* 92: 1031–39.

Mallory, M.L. and Weatherhead, P.J. 1994. Incubation rhythms and mass loss of Common Goldeneyes. *Condor* 95: 849–59.

Mallory, M.L., McNicol, D.K. and Weatherhead, P.J. 1994. Habitat quality and reproductive effort of Common Goldeneyes nesting near Sudbury, Canada. *J. Wildl. Manage.* 58: 552–60.

Mangnall, M.J. and Crowe, T.M. 2001. Managing Egyptian Geese on the croplands of the Agulhas Plain, Western Cape, South Africa. *S. Afr. J. Wildl. Res.* 31: 25–34.

Manlove, C.A. and Hepp, G.R. 1998. Effects of mate removal on incubation behavior and reproductive success of female Wood Ducks. *Condor* 100: 688–93.

Manlove, C.A. and Hepp, G.R. 2000. Patterns of nest attendance in female Wood Ducks. *Condor* 102: 286–91.

Mann, F.E. and Sedinger, J.S. 1993. Nutrient-reserve dynamics and control of clutch size in Northern Pintails breeding in Alaska. *Auk* 110: 264–78.

Manning, T.H., Hohn, E.O. and Macpherson, A.H. 1956. The birds of Banks Island. *Nat. Mus. Canada Bull.* 143: 1–144.

Manuel, C.G. 1953. Philippine wildlife problems. In 7th. Pacific Sci. Cong., Auckland and Christchurch, New Zealand, pp.683–91. Whitcombe and Toombs, Auckland.

Marchant, S. 1958. The birds of the Santa Elena Peninsula, S.W. Ecuador. *Ibis* 100: 349–87.

Marchant, S. 1960. The breeding of some S.W. Ecuadorian birds. *Ibis* 102: 349–82.

Marchant, S. and Higgins, P.J. 1990. *Handbook of Australian, New Zealand and Antarctic Birds,* Vol. 1B. OUP, Melbourne.

Markham, D.E. and Baldassarre, G.A. 1989. Ground nesting by Black-bellied Whistling Ducks on islands in Mexico. *J. Wildl. Manage.* 53: 707–13.

Marler, P. 1961. The logical analysis of animal communication. *J. Theor. Biol.* 1: 295–317.

Marler, P. and Hamilton, W., III. 1972. *Tierisches Verhalten*. BLV, Munich.

Marquiss, M. and Duncan, K. 1994. Diurnal activity patterns of Goosanders *Mergus merganser* on a Scottish river system. *Wildfowl* 45: 209–21.

Marquiss, M., Carss, D.N., Armstrong, J.D. and Gardiner, R. 1998. *Fish-eating birds and salmonids in Scotland: report on fish-eating birds research (1990–97), to the Scottish Office Agriculture, Environment and Fisheries Dept.* ITE, Banchory, and Freshwater Fisheries Laboratory, Pitlochry.

Marra, P. P., Hobson, K.A. and Holmes, R. T. 1998. Linking winter and summer events in a migratory bird by using stable carbon isotopes. *Science* 282: 1884–86.

Marriott, R.W. 1970. The food and the water requirements of Cape Barren Geese *Cereopsis novaehollandiae* Latham. Unpubl. Ph.D. thesis. Univ. Monash, Australia.

Marriott, R.W. and Forbes, D.K. 1970. The digestion of lucerne chaff by Cape Barren Geese. *Aust. J. Zool.* 18: 257–63.

Marsden, S.J. and Bellamy, G.S. 2000. Microhabitat characteristics of feeding sites used by diving duck *Aythya* wintering on the grossly polluted Manchester Ship Canal, UK. *Env. Conserv.* 27: 278–83.

Marshall, A.P. 1989. The behavior of Laysan ducks (*Anas laysanensis*) in captivity and on Laysan Island. Unpubl. Ph.D. thesis. Ohio State Univ., Columbus, US.

Marshall, A.P. 1992. Activity budgets of captive Laysan ducklings (*Anas laysanensis*). *Zool. Biol.* 11: 353–62.

Marshall, A.P. and Black, J.M. 1992. The effect of rearing experience on subsequent behavioural traits in Hawaiian geese *Branta sandvicensis*: implications for the recovery programme. *Bird Conserv. Int.* 2: 131–47.

Martin, A.R. 2002. The South Georgia Pintail *Anas g. georgica* in captivity: history, management and implications for conservation. *Wildfowl* 53: 215–23.

Martin, B.P. 1993. *Wildfowl of the British Isles and North-West Europe*. David and Charles, Newton Abbott.

Martin, F.W., Pospahala, R.S. and Nichols, J.D. 1979. Assessment and population management of North American migratory birds. In *Environmental biomonitoring, assessment, prediction, and management—certain case studies and related quantitative issues* (ed. J. Cairns, Jr, G.P. Patil and W.E. Waters), pp.187–239. International Cooperative Publishing House, Fairland, Maryland.

Martin, K., Cooch, E.G., Rockwell, R.F. and Cooke, F. 1985. Reproductive performance in Lesser Snow Geese: are two parents essential? *Behav. Ecol. Sociobiol.* 17: 257–63.

Martin, S.I. 1984. La Avutarda Magallánica (*Chloephaga picta*) en la Patagonia: su ecología, alimentación, densidad y control. *Idia* 429–32: 6–24.

Martin, S.I., Pelliza-Sbriller, A., Bellati, J. and Bonino, N. 1979. Determinación de la dieta de la Avutarda (*Chloëphaga picta*) en mallines del N.O. de la Patagonia. Unpubl. INTA rept, Bariloche.

Martin, S.I., Bellati, J. and Bonino, N. 1982. Determinación del impacto de la avutarda (*Chloëphaga* spp.) en Tierra del Fuego: datos preliminares. Unpubl. INTA rept, Bariloche.

Martin, S.I., Tracanna, N. and Summers, R.W. 1986. Distribution and habitat use by sheldgeese populations wintering in Buenos Aires province, Argentina. *Wildfowl* 37: 55–62.

Martindale, J. 1984. *Counts of the Freckled Duck Stictonetta naevosa in eastern Australia during January–February 1983*, Rept No. 13. RAOU, Moonee Ponds, Victoria.

Martindale, J. 1986. The Freckled Duck—an RAOU conservation statement. RAOU Rept No. 22, Moonee Pond, Victoria.

Martindale, J. 1988. *Waterfowl count in Victoria, January 1987*, Rept, No. 37. RAOU, Moonee Ponds, Victoria.

Matamala, J.J., Aguilar, F.J., Ayala, J.M. and López, J.M. 1994. La Malvasía (*Oxyura leucocephala*). Algunas referencias históricas, situación, problemática y distribución en España. Importancia de los humedales almerienses para la recuperación de una especie amenazada. In *Especies Singulares Almerienses, La Malvasía Comun.*, pp.35–84. Agencia de Medio Ambiente, Almería, Spain.

Mateo, R, Guitart, R. and Green, A.J. 2000. Determinants of lead shot, rice and grit ingestion in ducks and coots. *J. Wildl. Manage.* 64: 939–47.

Mateo, R., Green, A.J, Jeske, C.W., Urios, V. and Gerique, C. 2001. Lead poisoning in the globally threatened Marbled Teal and White-headed Duck in Spain. *Environmental Toxicology and Chemistry* 20: 2860–68.

Mathews, G.L. 1937. Notes on New Zealand birds. *Emu* 37: 31–32.

Mathews, G.M. 1910–1927. *The birds of Australia*. Witherby, London.

Mathews, G.M. 1914. Additions and corrections to my list of the birds of Australia. *Austral. Avian Record* 2: 90.

Mathiasson, S. 1973a. A moulting population of non-breeding Mute Swans with special reference to flight-feather moult, feeding ecology and habitat selection. *Wildfowl* 24: 43–53.

Mathiasson, S. 1973b. Moulting grounds of Mute Swans (*Cygnus olor*) in Sweden, their origin and relation to the population dynamics of Mute Swans in the Baltic area. *Viltrevy* 8: 399–452.

Mathiasson, S. 1991. Eurasian Whooper Swan *Cygnus cygnus* migration, with particular reference to birds wintering in southern Sweden. *Wildfowl* Spec. Suppl., 1: 201–8.

Mathiasson, S. 1992. Hybrider mellan Knölsvan och Sångsvan. *Gotebords Naturhisoriska Museums arstryck 1992*: 43–59.

Matthews, G.V.T. 1961. 'Nonsense' orientation in Mallard, *Anas platyrhynchos*, and its relation to experiments on bird navigation. *Ibis* 103a: 211–30.

Matthews, G.V.T. 1968. *Bird navigation* (2nd edn). Cambridge Univ. Press.

Matthews, G.V.T. 1973. Some problems facing captive breeding and restoration programmes for waterfowl. *Int. Zoo Ybk* 13: 8–11.

Matthews, G.V.T. 1984. 'Nonsense' orientation in Mallard; a resumé and an investigation of the mechanism of a sun-compass. *Wildfowl* 34: 81–92.

Matthews, G.V.T. 1993. *The Ramsar Convention on Wetlands: its history and development*. Ramsar Convention Bureau, Gland, Switzerland. (Editions in German and Japanese.)

Matthews, G.V.T. and Campbell, C.R.G. 1969. Weights and measurements of Greylag Geese in Scotland. *Wildfowl* 20: 86–93.

Matthews, G.V.T. and Evans, M.E. 1974. On the behaviour of the White-headed Duck with especial reference to breeding. *Wildfowl* 25: 56–66.

Mattocks, J.G. 1971. Goose feeding and cellulose digestion. *Wildfowl* 22: 107–13.

Mattson, M.E. and Evans, R.M. 1974. Visual imprinting and auditory-discrimination learning in young of the Canvasback and semiparasitic Redhead (Anatidae). *Can. J. Zool.* 52: 421–27.

Matus, R., Blank, O., Blanco, D.E., Madsen, J., Benegas, L. and Mateazzi, G. 2000. El Canquén Colorado (*Chloephaga rubidiceps*): Antecedentes sobre sítios de reproducción y concentración en la XII región de Magallanes, Chile. *Boletín Chileno de Ornitología* 7: 13–18.

Maxson, S.J. and Pace, R.M., III. 1992. Diurnal time-activity budgets and habitat use of Ring-necked Ducks ducklings in northcentral Minnesota. *Wilson Bull.* 104: 472–84.

Mayhew, P.W. 1987. Vigilance levels in European Wigeon in winter—sexual differences. *Wildfowl* 38: 77–81.

Mayhew, P.W. 1988. The daily energy intake of European Wigeon in winter. *Ornis Scand.* 19: 217–23.

Mayr, E. 1931. Zur Anatomie und systematischen Stellung der Salvadori-Ente (*Salvadorina waiguensis* Rothsch. and Hartert). *Ornithol. Monatsber.* 39: 69–70.

Mayr, E. 1942. *Systematics and the origin of species*. Columbia Univ. Press, New York.

Mayr, E. 1982a. *The growth of biological thought*. Belknap Press, Cambridge, Massachusetts.

Mayr, E. 1982b. Of what use are subspecies? *Auk* 99: 593–95.

Mayr, E. 1992. A local flora and the biological species concept. *American J. Botany* 79: 222–38.

Mayr, E. and Bock, W.J. 1994. Provisional classifications *v* standard avian sequences: heuristics and communication in ornithology. *Ibis* 136: 12–18.

Mayr, G. and Clarke, J. 2003. The deep divergences of neornithine birds: A phylogenetic analysis of morphological characters. *Cladistics* 19: 527–53.

Mazourek, J.C. and Gray, P.N. 1994. The Florida Duck or the Mallard? We can't have both. *Florida Wildlife* 48: 29–31.

McAllum, H.J.F. 1965. The adaptation and increase in the Paradise Shelduck *Tadorna variegata* within a man-modified environment. *Trans. Roy. Soc. NZ., Zool.* 6: 115–25.

McArthur, P.D. and Gorman, M.L. 1978. The salt gland of the incubating Eider Duck *Somateria mollissima*: the effects of natural salt deprivation. *J. Zool., Lond.* 184: 83–90.

McAuley, D.G. and Longcore, J.R. 1988. Survival of juvenile Ring-necked Ducks on wetlands of different pH. *J. Wildl. Manage.* 52: 169–76.

McAuley, D.G. and Longcore, J.R. 1989. Nesting phenology and success of Ring-necked Ducks in east-central Maine. *J. Field Ornithol.* 60: 112–19.

McCamant, R.E. and Bolen, E.G. 1977. Response of incubating Black-bellied Whistling-ducks to loss of mates. *Wilson Bull.* 89: 621.

McCamant, R.E. and Bolen, E.G. 1979. A 12-year study of nest box utilization by Black-bellied Whistling Ducks. *J. Wildl. Manage.* 43: 936–43.

McCartney, R.B. 1963. *The Fulvous Whistling Duck in Louisiana.* Louisiana Wildlife and Fisheries Comm., New Orleans.

McClelland, P. 1993. *Sub-antarctic teal recovery plan,* Threatened Species Recovery Plan, No. 7. Department of Conservation, Wellington.

McClure, H.E. 1974. *Migration and survival of the birds of Asia.* US Army Medical Component, South-East Asia Treaty Organisation (SEATO) Medical Project, Bangkok.

McCoy, J.J. 1963. The fossil avifauna of Itchtucknee River, Florida. *Auk* 80: 335–51.

McCoy, C.P., Stoker, S.W., Hall, G.E. and Muktoyuk, E. 1971. Winter observations of mammals and birds, St Matthew Island. *Arctic* 24: 63–64.

McCracken, K.G. 1999. Systematics, ecology, and social biology of the Musk Duck (*Biziura lobata*) of Australia. Unpubl. Ph.D. thesis. Louisiana State Univ., Baton Rouge, US.

McCracken, K.G. 2000. The 20 cm spiny penis of the Argentine Lake Duck (*Oxyura vittata*). *Auk* 117: 820–25.

McCracken, K.G. and Sorenson, M.D. 2004. Is homoplasy or lineage sorting the source of incongruent mtDNA and nuclear gene trees in the staff-tailed ducks (Nomonyx–Oxyura)? *Systematic Biology* (in press).

McCracken, K.G., Afton, A.D. and Paton, D.C. 2000a. Nest and eggs of Musk Ducks *Biziura lobata* at Murray Lagoon, Cape Gantheaume Conservation Park, Kangaroo Island, South Australia. *South Aust. Ornithol.* 33: 65–70.

McCracken, K.G., Paton, D.C. and Afton, A.D. 2000c. Sexual size dimorphism of the Musk Duck. *Wilson Bull.* 112: 457–66.

McCracken, K.G., Johnson W.P. and Sheldon F.H. 2001a. Molecular population genetics, phytogeography and conservation biology of the Mottled Duck (*Anas fulvigula*). *Conservation Genetics* 2: 87–102.

McCracken, K.G., Wilson P.J. and Johnson K.P. 2001b. Are ducks impressed by drakes' display? *Nature* 413: 128.

McCracken, K.G., Harshman, J., McClellan, D.A. and Afton, A.D. 1999. Data set incongruence and correlated character evolution: an example of functional convergence in the hind-limbs of stifftail diving ducks. *Syst. Biol.* 48: 683–714.

McCracken, K.G., Harshman, J., Sorenson, M.D. and Johnson, K.P. 2000b. Are Ruddy Ducks and White-headed Ducks the same species? *Brit. Birds.* 93: 396–98.

McCracken, K.G., Fullagar, P.J., Slater, E.C., Paton, D.C. and Afton, A.D. 2002. Advertising displays of male Musk Ducks indicate population subdivision across the Nullarbor Plain of Australia. *Wildfowl* 53: 137–54.

McDaniel, B., Tuff, D. and Bolen, E.G. 1966. External parasites of the Black-bellied Tree Duck and other dendrocygnids. *Wilson Bull.* 78: 462–68.

McElwaine, J.G., Wells, J.H. and Bowler, J.M. 1995. Winter movements of Whooper Swans visiting Ireland: preliminary results. *Irish Birds* 5: 265–78.

McFadden, I. 1983. Nesting of Grey Teal in nest boxes. *Flight* 38: 3–6.

McGilvrey, F.B. 1966. Nesting of Hooded Mergansers on the Patuxent Wildlife Research Center, Laurel, Maryland. *Auk* 83: 477–79.

McGilvrey, F.B. 1967. Food habits of sea ducks from the northeastern United States. *Wildfowl* 18: 142–45.

McGregor, R.C. 1909 *A manual of Philippine Birds,* Pt. 1. Bureau of Science, Manila.

McKay, H.V., Bishop, J.D., Feare, C.J. and Stevens M.C. 1993. Feeding by Brent Geese can reduce yield of oilseed rape. *Crop. Prot.* 12: 101–5.

McKinney, F. 1954. An observation of Redhead parasitism. *Wilson Bull.* 66: 146–48.

McKinney, F. 1965a. The displays of the American Green-winged Teal. *Wilson Bull.* 77: 112–21.

McKinney, F. 1965b. The comfort movements of Anatidae. *Behaviour* 25: 120–220.

McKinney, F. 1965c. Spacing and chasing in breeding ducks. *Wildfowl* 16: 92–106.

McKinney, F. 1965d. The spring behavior of wild Steller's Eiders. *Condor* 67: 273–90.

McKinney, F. 1970. Displays of four species of blue-winged ducks. *Living Bird* 9: 29–64.

McKinney, F. 1973. Ecoethological aspects of reproduction. In *Breeding biology of birds* (ed. D.S. Farner), pp. 6–21. National Academy of Sciences, Washington.

McKinney, F. 1975. The evolution of duck displays. In *Function and evolution of behaviour* (ed. G. Baerands, C. Beer and A. Manning), pp.331–57. Clarendon Press, Oxford.

McKinney, F. 1985. Primary and secondary reproductive strategies of dabbling ducks. *Ornithol. Monogr.* 37: 68–82.

McKinney, F. 1986. Ecological factors influencing the social systems of migratory dabbling ducks. In *Ecological aspects of social evolution,* (ed. D.I. Rubenstein and R.W. Wrangham), pp.153–71. Princeton Univ. Press.

McKinney, F. 1992. Courtship, pair formation, and signal systems. In *The ecology and management of breeding waterfowl,* (ed. B.D.J. Batt, A.D. Afton, M.G. Anderson, C.D. Ankney, D.H. Johnson, J.A. Kadlec *et al.*), pp. 214–50. Univ. Minnesota Press, Minneapolis.

McKinney, F. and Brewer, G. 1989. Parental attendance and brood care in four Argentine dabbling ducks. *Condor* 91: 131–38.

McKinney, F. and Bruggers, D.J. 1983. Status and breeding behavior of the Bahama Pintail and the New Zealand Blue Duck. In *Breeding Birds in Captivity*, 1983 Jean Delacour/IFCB Symp. (ed. A.C. Risser, Jr, L.F. Baptista, S.R. Wylie and N.B. Gale), pp.211–21. Int. Foundation for Conservation of Birds, Hollywood, CA.

McKinney, F. and Evarts, S. 1997. Sexual coercion in waterfowl and other birds. *Ornithol. Monogr.* 49: 163–95.

McKinney, F. and Stolen, P. 1982. Extra-pair bond courtship and forced copulation amongst captive Green-winged Teal *Anas crecca carolinensis. Anim. Behav.* 30: 461–74.

McKinney, F., Derrickson, S.R. and Mineau, P. 1983. Forced copulation in waterfowl. *Behaviour* 86: 250–94.

McKinney, F., Siegfried, W.R., Ball, I.J. and Frost, P.G.H. 1978. Behavioral specializations for river life in the African Black Duck (*Anas sparsa* Eyton). *Z. Tierpsychol.* 48: 349–400.

McKinney, F., Cheng, K.M. and Bruggers, D. 1984. Sperm competition in apparently monogamous birds. In *Sperm competition and the evolution of animal mating systems* (ed. R.L. Smith), pp.523–45. Academic Press, New York.

McKinney, F., Buitron, D. and Derrickson, S.R. 1990a. Persistent quacking in dabbling ducks: a predator-luring signal? *Wildfowl* 41: 92–98.

McKinney, F., Sorenson, L.G. and Hart, M. 1990b. Multiple functions of courtship displays in dabbling ducks (Anatini). *Auk* 107: 188–91.

McKinnon, S.L. and Mitchell, S.F. 1994. Eutrophication and Black Swan (*Cygnus atratus* Latham) populations: tests of two simple relationships. *Hydrobiologia* 279/280: 163–70.

McKitrick, M.C. and Zink, R.M. 1988. Species concepts in ornithology. *Condor* 90: 1–14.

McKnight, D.E. 1974. Dry-land nesting by Redheads and Ruddy Ducks. *J. Wildl. Manage.* 38: 112–19.

McMahan, C.A. 1970. Food habits of ducks wintering on Laguna Madre, Texas. *J. Wildl. Manage.* 34: 946–49.

McNeil, R., Drapeau, P. and Goss-Custard, J.D. 1992. The occurrence and adaptive significance of nocturnal habits of waterfowl. *Biol. Rev.* 67: 381–419.

McNicol, D.K. and Wayland, M. 1992. Distribution of waterfowl broods in Sudbury area lakes in relation to fish, macroinvertebrates, and water chemistry. *Can. J. Fish. Aquat. Sci.* 49 (suppl. 1): 122–33.

McNicol, D.K., Ross, R.K. and Blancher, P.J. 1990. Waterfowl as indicators of acidification in Ontario, Canada. *Trans. Int. Union Game Biol. Congr.* 19: 251–58.

McRoy, C.P., Stoker, S.W., Hall, G.E. and Muktoyuk, E. 1971. Winter observations of mammals and birds, St. Matthew Island. *Arctic* 24: 63–64.

McWilliams, S.R. and Raveling, D.G. 1998. Habitat use and foraging behaviour of Cackling Canada and Ross's Geese during spring: implications for the analysis of ecological determinants of goose social behavior. In *Biology and management of Canada Geese*, Int. Canada Goose Symp. (ed. D.H. Rusch, M.D. Samuel, D.D. Humburg and B.D. Sullivan), pp.167–78. Milwaukee, Wisconsin.

Meanley, B. and Meanley, A.G. 1958. Post-copulatory display of Fulvous and Black-bellied Tree Ducks. *Auk* 75: 96.

Meanley, B. and Meanley, A.G. 1959. Observations on the Fulvous Whistling Duck in Louisiana. *Wilson Bull.* 71: 33–45.

Meier, A.J., Noble, R.E., McKenzie, P.M. and Zwank, P.J. 1989. Observations on the nesting ecology of the White-cheeked Pintail. *Carib. J. Science* 25: 92–93.

Meile, P. 1991. Die Bedeutung der Gemeinschaftlichen Wasserjagd für überwinternde Wasservögel am Ermertinger Becken. *Orn. Beob.* 88: 27–55.

Meinhertzhagen, R. 1912. On the birds of Mauritius. *Ibis* (9)6: 82–108.

Mellquist, H. and van Bothmer, R. 1984. The effects of haymaking on Bean Goose *Anser fabalis* breeding habitats in Sweden. *Swedish Wildlife Research* 13: 49–58.

Meltofte, H. 1978. A breeding association between eiders and tethered huskies in north-east Greenland. *Wildfowl* 29: 45–54.

Mendall, H.L. 1958. *Ring-necked Duck in the northeast.* Univ. Maine Stud., No. 73. Univ. Maine, Orono.

Mendenhall, V.M. and Milne, H. 1985. Factors affecting duckling survival of Eiders *Somateria mollissima* in northeast Ireland. *Ibis* 127: 148–58.

Menegheti, J.O., Rilla, F. and Burger, M.I. 1990. Waterfowl in South America: their status, trends and distribution. In *Managing Waterfowl Populations*, IWRB Symp., Astrakhan 1989, Publ., No. 12 (ed. G.V.T. Matthews), pp.97–103. IWRB, Slimbridge, UK.

Merne, O.J., Boertmann, D., Boyd, H., Mitchell, C., Briain, M.Ó., Reed, A. and Sigfusson, A. 1999. Light-bellied Brent Goose *Branta bernicla hrota*: Canada. In *Goose populations of the Western Palearctic. A review of status and distribution*, Publ., No. 48 (ed. J. Madsen, G. Cracknell and A.D. Fox), pp.298–311. Wetlands International, Wageningen, Netherlands, and National Environmental Research Institute, Rønde, Denmark.

Meriggi, A. 1983. Territorialismo, preferenze ambientali e produttivita di una popolazione di fagiano. *Avocetta* 7: 1–12.

Merritt, A. 1994. Wetlands, Industry & Wildlife: a manual of principles and practices. WWT, Slimbridge, UK.

Michot, T.C. 1997. Carrying capacity of seagrass beds predicted for Redheads wintering in Chandeleur Sound, Louisiana, USA. In *Effect of habitat loss and change on waterbirds*, Publ., No. 42 (ed. J. Goss-Custard, R. Rufino and A. Luis), pp.93–102. Wetlands International, Wageningen, Netherlands.

Michot, T.C. 2000. Comparison of wintering Redhead populations in four Gulf of Mexico seagrass beds. In *Limnology and aquatic birds: monitoring, modelling, and management*, 2nd Int. Symp. Limnology and Aquatic Birds (ed. F.A. Comin, J.A. Herrera-Silveira and J. Ramirez-Ramirez), pp.243–60. Universidad Autonoma de Yucatan, Merida, Mexico.

Michot, T.C. and Chadwick, P.C. 1994. Winter biomass and nutrient values of three seagrass species as potential foods for Redheads (*Aythya americana* Eyton) in Chandeleur Sound, Louisiana. *Wetlands* 14: 276–83.

Michot, T.C. and Nault, A.J. 1993. Diet differences in Redheads from nearshore and offshore zones in Louisiana. *J. Wildl. Manage.* 57: 238–44.

Michot, T.C. and Reynolds, L.A. 2000. Food habits of four diving duck species wintering in seagrass beds, Apalachee Bay, Florida. *Sylvia* 36: 25–26.

Michot, T.C., Low, J.B. and Anderson, D.R. 1979. Decline of Redhead Duck nesting in Knudson Marsh, Utah. *J. Wildl. Manage.* 43: 224–29.

Michot, T.C., Moser, E.B. and Norling, W. 1994a. Effect of weather and tides on feeding and flock positions of Redheads wintering in the Chandeleur Sound, Louisiana. *Hydrobiologia* 279/280: 263–78.

Michot, T.C., Custer, T.W., Nault, A.J. and Mitchell, C.M. 1994b. Environmental contaminants in Redheads wintering in coastal Louisiana and Texas. *Arch. Environ. Contam. Toxicol.* 26: 425–34.

Michot, T.C., Garvin, M.C. and Weidner, E.H. 1995. Survey for blood parasites in Redheads (*Aythya americana*) wintering at the Chandeleur Islands, Louisiana. *J. Wildl. Dis.* 31: 90–92.

Michot, T.C., Woodin, M.C., Adair, S.E. and Moser, E.B. 1997. Diurnal time activity budgets of Redheads wintering in Louisiana and Texas. Unpubl. manuscript.

Michot, T.C. and Woodin, M.C. 1997. Redheads wintering in Louisiana and Texas have similar diets. *Duck Specialist Group Bull.* 1: 13–14. Wetlands International, Wageningen, Netherlands.

Mickelson, P.G. 1975. Breeding biology of Cackling Geese and associated species on the Yukon-Kuskokwim Delta, Alaska. *Wildl. Monogr.* 45: 1–35.

Middlemiss, E. 1958. The Southern Pochard *Netta erythrophthalma brunnea*. *Ostrich* Suppl. 2: 1–34.

Middleton, B. and Van der Valk, A.G. 1987. The food habits of Greylag and Bar-headed Geese in the Keoladeo National Park, India. *Wildfowl* 38: 93–102.

Miers, K.H. and Williams, M.J. 1969. Nesting of the Black Swan at Lake Ellesmere, New Zealand. *Wildfowl* 20: 23–32.

Mikhailov, K.E. and Shibnyev, Y.B. 1998. The threatened and near-threatened birds of northern Ussuriland, south-east Russia, and the role of the Bikin River basin in their conservation. *Bird Conserv. Int.* 8: 141–71.

Mikhailov, K.Y., Koblik, Y.A. and Shibnyev, Y.B. 1997. Rare and locally-distributed birds of Russia in the Upper Bikin River basin (north Primorski Territory). *Russ. J. Orn.* 7: 3–7.

Mikhel, N.M. 1935. Notes on the birds of the Indigirka territory. *Trudy Arktichesk. Inst.* 31: 1–104. [In Russian.]

Mikola, J., Miettinen, M., Lehikoinen, E. and Lehtila, K. 1994. The effects of disturbance caused by boating on survival and behaviour of Velvet Scoter *Melanitta fusca* ducklings. *Biol. Cons.* 67: 119–24.

Miles, A.K. and Ohlendorf, H.M. 1993. Environmental contaminants in Canvasbacks wintering on San Francisco Bay, California. *Calif. Fish Game* 79: 28–38.

Millais, J.G. 1902. *British dabbling ducks.* Longmans, London.

Millais, J.G. 1913. *The natural history of British diving ducks.* Longmans, Green and Co., London.

Miller, A.H. 1937. Structural modifications in the Hawaiian goose (*Nesochen sandvicensis*)—a study in adaptive evolution. *Univ. Calif. Publ. Zoology* XLII: 1–79.

Miller, A.W. and Collins, B.D. 1954. A nesting study of ducks and coots on Tule Lake and Lower Klamath National Wildlife Refuges. *Calif. Fish Game* 40: 17–37.

Miller, K.J. 1976. Activity patterns, vocalizations, and site selection in nesting Blue-winged Teal. *Wildfowl* 27: 33–43.

Miller, L.H. 1925. Avifauna of the McKittrick pleistocene. *Univ. California Publ. in Geol. Sci.* 15: 314.

Miller, M.R. 1983. Foraging dives by post-breeding Northern Pintails. *Wilson Bull.* 95: 294–96.

Miller, M.R. 1986. Northern Pintail body condition during wet and dry winters in the Sacramento Valley, California. *J. Wildl. Manage.* 50: 189–98.

Miller, M.R. 1987. Fall and winter foods of Northern Pintails in the Sacramento Valley, California. *J. Wildl. Manage.* 51: 405–14.

Miller, M.R., McLandress, R.M. and Gray, B.J. 1977. The display flight of the North American Ruddy Duck. *Auk* 94: 140–42.

Mills, H.B., Starrett, W.C. and Bellrose, F.C. 1966. *Man's effect on the fish and wildlife of the Illinois River.* Biol. Notes, No. 57. Ill. Nat. Hist. Surv., Urbana.

Mills, J.A. 1976. Status, mortality and movements of Grey Teal (*Anas gibberifrons*) in New Zealand. *N.Z.J. Zool.* 3: 261–67.

Milne, H. 1976. Body weights and carcass composition of the Common Eider. *Wildfowl* 27: 115–22.

Milne, H. and Campbell, L.H. 1973. Wintering seaducks off the East Coast of Scotland. *Bird Study* 20: 153–72.

Milon, P., Petter, J-J. and Randrianasolo, G. 1973. *Faune de Madagascar,* Vol. 35. ORSTOM and CNRS, Tananarive and Paris.

Milstein, P. le S. 1975. The biology of Barberspan, with special reference to the avifauna. *Ostrich* Suppl. 10: 1–74.

Milstein, P le S. 1993. A study of the Egyptian Goose *Alopochen aegyptiacus.* Unpubl. Ph.D. thesis. Univ. Pretoria, South Africa.

Mindell, D.P. and Honeycutt, R.L. 1989. Variability in transcribed regions of ribosomal DNA and early divergences in birds. *Auk* 106: 539–48.

Mineau, P. and Cooke, F. 1979a. Rape in the Lesser Snow Goose. *Behaviour* 70: 280–91.

Mineau, P. and Cooke, F. 1979b. Territoriality in the Snow Geese or the protection of parenthood—Ryder's and Inglis's hypotheses reassessed. *Wildfowl* 30: 16–19.

Mineyev, Y.N. 1987. Ecology, numbers and conservation of swans in the northeastern European part of the USSR. In *Ecology and migration of swans in the USSR* (ed. E. Syroechkovski), pp.17–19. Nauka, Moscow.

Mineyev, Y.N. 1990. Seasonal concentrations of *Anser fabalis* in the European northeast of the USSR. In *Managing Waterfowl Populations,* IWRB Symp., Astrakhan 1989, Publ., No. 12 (ed. G.V.T. Matthews), pp.50–51. IWRB, Slimbridge, UK.

Mineyev, Y.N. 1991. Distribution and numbers of Bewick's Swans *Cygnus bewickii* in the European northeast of the USSR. *Wildfowl* Spec. Suppl. 1: 62–67.

Minton, C.D.T. 1971. Mute Swan flocks. *Wildfowl* 22: 71–80.

Mitchell, C. 1990. Movements of British-ringed Shoveler. Unpubl. rept to JNCC. WWT, Slimbridge, UK.

Mitchell, C. 1993. Shoveler. In *The new atlas of breeding birds in Britain and Ireland 1988–1991,* (ed. D.W. Gibbons, J.B. Reid and R.A. Chapman), pp.78–9. BTO/SOC/IWC, Calton.

Mitchell, C. 1995. Midwinter and spring counts of Pink-footed and Greylag Geese in Britain, 1995. Unpubl. rept to SNH. WWT, Slimbridge, UK.

Mitchell, C. 1997. Re-mating in migratory Eurasian Wigeon. *Ardea* 85: 275–77.

Mitchell, C., Owen, M. and Etheridge, B. 1995. Within-winter movements, winter site fidelity and age ratios of Wigeon in Britain and Ireland. Unpubl. rept to JNCC. WWT, Slimbridge, UK.

Mitchell, C., Stewart, B., Heriksen, G. and Fox, A.D. 1996. Oesophagael and gizzard contents of wintering Steller's Eider (*Polysticta stelleri*) from Varangerfjord Norway. *Wetlands International Seaduck Specialist Group Bull.* 6: 13–20.

Mitchell, C., Fox, A.D., Boyd, H., Sigfusson, A. and Boertmann, D. 1999. Pink-footed Goose *Anser brachyrhynchus* Iceland/Greenland. In *Goose populations of the Western Palearctic. A review of status and distribution,* Publ., No. 48 (ed. J. Madsen, G. Cracknell and A.D. Fox), pp.68–81. Wetlands International, Wageningen, Netherlands, and National Environmental Research Institute, Rønde, Denmark.

Mitchell, C., Patterson, D., Boyer, P., Cunningham, P., McDonald, R., Meek, E. *et al.* 2000. The summer status and distribution of Greylag Geese in north and west Scotland. *Scottish Birds* 21: 69–77.

Mitchell, C.A. 1992. Water depth predicts Redhead distribution in the lower Laguna Madre, Texas. *Wildl. Soc. Bull.* 20: 420–24.

Mitchell, C.A., Custer, T.W. and Zwank, P.J. 1992. Redhead Duck behavior on Lower Laguna Madre and adjacent ponds of southern Texas. *Southwest Naturalist* 37: 65–72.

Mitchell, C.A., Custer, T.W. and Zwank, P.J. 1994. Herbivory on shoalgrass by wintering Redheads in Texas. *J. Wildl. Manage.* 58: 131–41.

Mitchell, C.D. 1994. Trumpeter Swan (*Cygnus buccinator*). The Birds of North America, No. 105 (ed. A. Poole

and F. Gill). AOU, Washington, and Academy of Natural Sciences, Philadelphia.

Mitchell, C.D. 1998. Whooper Swans (*Cygnus cygnus*) in North America. *Wetlands International Swan Specialist Group Newsl.* 7: 7–8.

Mitchell, C.D. and Rotella, J.J. 1997. Brood amalgamation in Trumpeter Swans. *Wildfowl* 48: 1–5.

Mitchell, C.D., Shea, R., Lockman, D.C. and Balcomb, J.R. 1991. Demographic analysis of a Trumpeter Swan *Cygnus cygnus buccinator* population in western U.S.A. *Wildfowl* Spec. Suppl., 1: 142.

Mitchell, C.R. and Hearn, R.D. 2004. Pink-footed Goose *Anser brachyrhynchus* (Greenland/Icelandic population) in Britain and Ireland 1960/61–1999/2000. *Waterbird Review Series,* WWT/JNCC, Slimbridge.

Mitchell, P.C. 1911. On longevity and relative viability in mammals and birds; with a note on the theory of longevity. *Proc. Zool. Soc. London* 1911: 425–49.

Mitchell, S.F. and Wass, R.T. 1995. Food consumption and faecal deposition of plant nutrients by Black Swans (*Cygnus atratus* Latham) in a shallow New Zealand Lake. *Hydrobiologia* 306(3): 189–97.

Mitchell, S.F., Hamilton, D.P., MacGibbon, W.S., Bhashkarn Nayar, P.K. and Reynolds, R.N. 1988. Interrelations between phytoplankton, submerged macrophytes, Black Swans (*Cygnus atratus*) and zooplankton in a shallow New Zealand Lake. *Int. Revue ges. Hydrobiol.* 73: 145–70.

Mitsch, W.J. and Gosselink, J.G. 1993. *Wetlands* (2nd edn). Van Nostrand Reinhold, New York.

Miyabayashi, Y. 1994. *Inventory of goose habitat in Japan.* Japanese Association for Wild Geese Protection, Wakayanagi, Japan.

Miyabayashi, Y. and Mundkur, T. 1999. *Atlas of key sites for Anatidae in the East Asian Flyway.* Wetlands International—Japan, Tokyo, and Wetlands International—Asia Pacific, Kuala Lumpur.

Mlikovsky, J. 1989 Note on the osteology and taxonomic position of Salvadori's Duck *Salvadorina waigiuensis* (Aves: Anseridae (Anatidae)). *Bull. BOC* 109: 22–25.

Moffett, G.M., Jr 1970. A study of nesting Torrent Ducks in the Andes. *Living Bird* 9: 5–27.

Møller, A.P. and Birkhead, T.R. 1993. Cuckoldry and sociality: a comparative study of birds. *Amer. Natur.* 142: 118–40.

Monda, M.J. 1991. Reproductive ecology of Tundra Swans on the Arctic National Wildlife Refuge, Alaska. Unpubl. Ph.D. thesis. Univ. Idaho, Moscow, US.

Monda, M.J., Ratti, J.T. and McCabe, T.R. 1994. Reproductive ecology of Tundra Swans on the Arctic National Wildlife Refuge, Alaska. *J. Wildl. Manage.* 58: 757–73.

Mondain-Monval, J-Y. and Girard, O. 2000. Le canard colvert, la sarcelle d'hiver et autres canards de surface in enquête nationale sur les tableaux de chasse à tir. Saison 1998/1999. *Faune Sauvage* 251: 124–39.

Montalbano, F., III., Johnson, F.A. and Conroy, M.J. 1985. Status of wintering Ring-necked Ducks in the southern Atlantic Flyway. *J. Wildl. Manage.* 49: 543–46.

Monval, J-Y. and Pirot, J-Y. 1989. *Results of the IWRB International Waterbird Census 1967–1986*, Spec. Publ., No. 8. IWRB, Slimbridge, UK.

Moore, J.L. 1991. Habitat-related activities and body mass of wintering Redhead Ducks on coastal ponds in south Texas. Unpubl. M.S. thesis. Texas A & M Univ., College Station, US.

Moores, N. 1996. Baikal Teal in South Korea. *Hong Kong Bird Rept* 1995: 231–35.

Moores, N. and Kyoung-Won, K. 2000. Baikal Teal in South Korea. *Wetlands International, Threatened Waterfowl Research Group News* 12: 14.

Moorman, A.M., Moorman, T.E., Baldassarre, G.A. and Richard, D.R. 1991. Effects of saline water on growth and survival of Mottled Duck ducklings in Louisiana. *J. Wildl. Manage.* 55: 471–76.

Moorman, T.E. and Gray, P.N. 1994. *Mottled Duck (Anas fulvigula)*. The Birds of North America, No. 81 (ed. A. Poole and F. Gill). AOU, Washington, and Academy of Natural Sciences, Philadelphia.

Moorman, T.E., Baldassarre, G.A. and Hess, T.J. 1993. Carcass mass and nutrient dynamics of Mottled Ducks during remigial molt. *J. Wildl. Manage.* 57: 224–28.

Morejohn, G.V. 1976. Evidence of survival to recent times of the extinct flightless duck *Chendytes lawi* Miller. *Smithsonian Contributions to Paleobiology* 27: 207–11.

Morony, J.J., Bock, W.J. and Farrand, J. 1975. *Reference list of the birds of the world*. American Museum of Natural History, New York.

Morowitz, H.J. 1978. *Foundations of bioenergetics*. Academic Press, New York.

Morozov, V.V. 1995. Status, distribution and trends of the Lesser White-fronted Goose (*Anser erythropus*) population in Russia. *Goose Study Group Bull. of Eastern Europe and Northern Asia* 1: 131–44.

Morozov, V.V. 1999. The last news on Lesser White-fronted Goose in the east of Bolshezemelskaya tundra and the western macro-slope of the Polar Urals. *Casarca* 5: 127–35. (In Russian with English summary.)

Morris, A.K., McGill, A.R. and Holmes, G. 1981. *Handlist of birds in New South Wales*. NSW Field Ornith. Club, Sydney.

Morris, F.O. 1855. *A history of British birds*. Groombridge, London.

Morse, T.E., Jakabosky, J.L. and McCrow, V.P. 1969. Some aspects of the breeding biology of the Hooded Merganser. *J. Wildl. Manage.* 33: 596–604.

Mortensen, H.C.C. 1950. *Studies in bird migration*. Danish Ornithological Society, Munksgaard, Copenhagen.

Morton, S.R., Brennan, K.G. and Armstrong, M.D. 1990a. Distribution and abundance of Magpie Geese, *Anseranas semipalmata*, in the Alligator Rivers Region, Northern Territory. *Aust. J. Ecol.* 15: 307–20.

Morton, S.R., Brennan, K.G. and Armstrong, M.D. 1990b. Distribution and abundance of ducks in the Alligator rivers region, Northern Territory. *Aust. Wildl. Res.* 17: 573–90.

Moulton, D.W. and Marshall, A.P. 1996. Laysan Duck (*Anas laysanensis*). The Birds of North America, No. 242 (ed. A. Poole and F. Gill). AOU, Washington, and Academy of Natural Sciences, Philadelphia.

Moulton, D.W. and Weller, M.W. 1984. Biology and conservation of the Laysan Duck (*Anas laysanensis*). *Condor* 86: 105–17.

Moulton, D.W., Frentress, C.D., Stutzenbaker, C.D., Lobpries, D.S. and Brownlee, W.C. 1988. Ingestion of shotshell pellets by waterfowl wintering in Texas. In *Waterfowl in winter* (ed. M. Weller), pp.597–607. Univ. Minnesota Press, Minneapolis.

Mourer-Chauviré, C., Bour, R., Ribes, S. and Moutou, F. 2000. The avifauna of Réunion Island (Mascarene Islands) at the time of the arrival of the first Europeans. *Smithsonian Contributions to Paleobiology* 89: 1–38.

Mowbray, T. 1999. American Wigeon (*Anas americana*). The Birds of North America, No. 401 (ed. A. Poole and F. Gill). AOU, The Birds of North America Inc., Philadelphia.

Mowbray, T. 2002. Canvasback (*Aythya valisineria*). The Birds of North America, No. 659 (ed. A. Poole, and F. Gill). AOU, The Birds of North America Inc., Philadelphia.

Mowbray, T.D., Cooke, F., and Ganter, B. 2000. Snow Goose (*Chen caerulescens*). The Birds of North America, No. 514 (ed. A. Poole and F. Gill). AOU, National Academy of Sciences, Philadelphia.

Mowbray, T.B., Ely, C.R., Sedinger, J.S. and Trost, R.E. 2002. Canada Goose (*Branta canadensis*). The Birds of North America, No. 682 (ed. A. Poole and F. Gill). The Birds of North America Inc., Philadelphia, USA.

Moynihan, M. 1958. Notes on the behavior of the Flying Steamer Duck. *Auk* 75: 183–202.

Müller, S. 1842. In *Verhandelingen over de Natuurlijke Geschiedenis der Nederlandsche Overzeesche Bezittingen. Land- en Volkenkunde* (Temminck), p.159, 1: footnote (Java).

Mumford, R.E. and Keller, C.E. 1984. *The birds of Indiana*. Indiana Univ. Press, Bloomington.

Mundkur, T. and Sridhar, S. 1993. Preliminary observations on factors governing the selection of wintering sites by Bar-headed Goose (*Anser indicus*) in Karnataka. In *Bird conservation strategies for the nineties and beyond,* (ed. A. Verghese, S. Sridhar and A.K. Chakravarthy), pp. 251–54. Ornithological Society of India.

Munro, G.C. 1960. *Birds of Hawaii*. Bridgeway, Rutland.

Munro, J. and Bedard, J. 1977a. Gull predation and crèching behaviour in the Common Eider. *J. Anim. Ecol.* 46: 799–810.

Munro, J. and Bedard, J. 1977b. Crèche formation in the Common Eider. *Auk* 94: 759–71.

Munro, J.A. 1930. Waterfowl and sculpins. *Condor* 32: 261.

Munro, J.A. 1939. Studies of waterfowl in British Columbia, Barrow's Golden-eye, American Golden-eye. *Trans. R. Can. Inst.* 24: 259–318.

Munro, J.A. and Clemens, W.A. 1939. The food and feeding habits of the Red-breasted Merganser in British Columbia. *J. Wildl. Manage.* 3: 46–53.

Munro, R.E. 1981a. Traditional return of *Cygnus columbianus columbianus* to wintering areas in Maryland's Chesapeake Bay. In 2nd IWRB Int. Swan Symp., Sapporo, 1980 (ed. G.V.T. Matthews and M. Smart), pp. 81–98. IWRB, Slimbridge, UK.

Munro, R.E. 1981b. Field feeding by *Cygnus columbianus columbianus* in Maryland. In 2nd IWRB Swan Symp., Sapporo, 1980 (ed. G.V.T. Matthews and M. Smart), pp. 261–72. IWRB, Slimbridge, UK.

Muntaner, J., Ferrer, X. and Martinez-Vivalta, A. 1983. *Atlas dels ocells nidificants de Catalunya i Andorra*. Ketres, Barcelona.

Munteanu, D. 2000. White-headed Ducks in Romania. *Wetlands International–IUCN Threatened Waterfowl Specialist Group News* 12: 17.

Murase, M. 1993. The first record of Trumpeter Swan *Cygnus buccinator* for Japan. *Japanese J. Orn.* 41(2): 51–55.

Murden, B., Woodin, M.C., Michot, T.C., Weller, M.W., Moore, J.L., Adair, S.E. et al. 1997. Feather mineral content of Redheads (*Aythya americana*) wintering along the Gulf of Mexico. In *Limnology and waterfowl: monitoring, modelling and management*, Publ., No. 43 (ed. S. Farago and J.J. Kerekes), pp 65–80. Wetlands International, Wageningen, Netherlands.

Murdy, H.W. 1964. *Population dynamics and breeding biology of waterfowl on the Yellowknife study area, Northwest Territories,* Unpubl. Progress Rept for 1964. US Fish & Wildl. Serv., Northern Prairie Wildlife Research Center, Jamestown.

Murphy, M.E. and King, J.R. 1991. Nutritional aspects of avian molt. *Int. Ornith. Congr.* 20: 2186–94.

Murphy, R.C. 1916. Anatidae of South Georgia. *Auk* 33: 270–77.

Murphy, R.C. 1936. *Oceanic birds of South America*. Macmillan, New York, and American Museum of Natural History, New York.

Murphy, S.M., Kessel, B. and Vining, L.J. 1984. Waterfowl populations and limnologic characteristics of taiga ponds. *J. Wildl. Manage.* 48: 1156–63.

Murton, R.K. and Kear, J. 1973. The nature and evolution of the photoperiodic control of reproduction in wildfowl of the family Anatidae. *J. Reprod. Fert.* Suppl. 19: 67–84.

Murton, R.K. and Kear, J. 1975. The role of daylength in regulating the breeding seasons and distributions of wildfowl. In *Light as an ecological factor: II* (ed.

G.C. Evans, R. Bainbridge and O. Rackham), pp. 337–57. Blackwell, Oxford.

Murton, R.K. and Kear, J. 1978. Photoperiodism in waterfowl: phasing of breeding cycles and zoogeography. *J. Zool., Lond.* 186: 243–83.

Murton, R.K. and Westwood, N.J. 1977. *Avian breeding cycles.* OUP.

Musgrove, A., Pollitt, M., Hall., H., Hearn, R., Holloway, S., Marshall, P., et al. 2001. *The wetland bird survey 1999–2000.* BTO/WWT/RSPB/JNCC, UK.

Myneni, R.B., Keeling, C.D., Tucker, C.J., Asrar, G. and Nemani, R.R. 1997. Increased plant growth in the northern high latitudes from 1981 to 1991. *Nature* 386: 698–702.

Myong Sok, O. 1984. Wiederentdeckung der Schopfkasarka, *Tadorna cristata,* in der Koreanischen Demokratischen Volksrepublik. *J. Orn.* 125: 102–3.

Myres, M.T. 1959a. Display behaviour of Bufflehead, scoters, and goldeneyes at copulation. *Wilson Bull.* 71: 159–68.

Myres, M.T. 1959b. The behaviour of the sea ducks, and its value in the systematics of the tribes Mergini and Somateriini, of the family Anatidae. Unpubl. Ph.D. thesis. Univ. British Columbia, Vancouver, Canada.

Nankinov, D. 1992. Lesser White-fronted Goose *Anser erythropus* migration routes, wintering sites and conservation in Western Eurasia. *Gibier Faune Sauvage* 9: 257–68.

Naranjo, L.G. 1986. Aspects of the biology of the Horned Screamer in southwestern Colombia. *Wilson Bull.* 98: 243–56.

Narosky, T. and Yzurieta, D. 1987. *Birds of Argentina and Uruguay: a field guide.* Asociacion Ornitologica del Plata, Buenos Aires, Argentina.

Nascimento, J. and Antas, P. 1990. Analise dos dados de anilhamento de *Amazonetta brasiliensis* no Brasil. *Ararajuba* 1: 85–90.

Nascimento, J.L.X., Flores, J.M., Ataguile, B.S., Koch, M., Scherer, S.B. and Santos, P.J.P. 2001. Biological aspects of the Black-necked Swan (*Cygnus melancoryphus*) and Coscoroba Swan (*Coscoroba coscoroba*) in Rio Grande do Sul state, Brazil. *Melopsittacus* 4:31–38.

National Research Council 1977. *Nutrient requirements of poultry.* Natl Acad. Sci., Natl Res. Counc., Washington.

Naumann, J.A. 1905. *Naturgeschichte der Vögel Mitteleuropas,* Vol. 10. Köhler, Gera-Untermhaus.

Naumov, S.P. 1931. *Mammals and birds of the Gyda Peninsula (North-eastern Siberia).* Trudy Polyrn. Komm. Akad. Nauk SSSR 4. [In Russian.]

Navarro, J.D. and Robledano, F. (ed.) 1995. *La Cerceta Pardilla Marmaronetta angustirostris en España.* ICONA–MAPA, Madrid.

Navas, J.R. 1977. *Aves Anseriformes. Fauna de Agua Dulce de la Republica Argentina,* Vol. 42. Fundación para la Educación, la Ciencia, y la Cultura, Buenos Aires.

Nechaev, V.A. 1992. Status of the Swan Goose and the Mandarin Duck on Sakhalin Island, Russian Far East. *IWRB Threatened Waterfowl Research Group Newsl.* 2: 12–14.

Nechaev, V.A. and Gluschenko, Y.N. 1993. Baer's Pochard in the Far East of Russia. *IWRB Threatened Waterfowl Research Group Newsl.* 3: 5–7.

Nehls, G. 1996. Low costs of salt turnover in Common Eiders *Somateria mollissima. Ardea* 84: 23–30.

Nehls, N.W. 1990. The moult migration of the Common Scoter *Melanitta nigra* in the south-western Baltic Sea. *IWRB Western Palearctic Seaduck Database Newsl.* December 1990: 28–9.

Nehls, N.W. and Zöllick, H. 1990. The moult migration of the Common Scoter *Melanitta nigra* off the coast of the GDR. *Baltic Birds* 5(2): 36–46.

Neithammer, G. 1952. Zür Anatomie und systematischen Stellung der Sturzbach-Ente (*Merganetta armata*). *J. Orn.* 93: 357–60.

Nelson, A.D. and Martin, A.C. 1953. Gamebird weights. *J. Wildl. Manage.* 17: 36–42.

Nelson, C.H. 1964. Observations on the day-old young of the Spectacled Eider *Somateria fischeri. Auk* 81: 219–21.

Nelson, C.H. 1976a. The color phases of downy Mute Swans. *Wilson Bull.* 88: 1–3.

Nelson, C.H. 1976b. A key to downy cygnets with analysis of plumage characters. *Wilson Bull.* 88: 4–15.

Nelson, C.H. 1993. *The downy waterfowl of North America.* Delta Station Press, Delta Waterfowl and Wetlands Research Station, Portage La Praire, Manitoba.

Nelson, C.H. 1996. Identification of Greater Scaup, *Aythya marila,* and Lesser Scaup, *A. affinis,* ducklings. *Can. Field-Nat.* 110: 288–93.

Nelson, E.W. 1887. *Report upon natural history collections made in Alaska between the years 1877 and 1881*, Arctic Ser. Publ. No. 3. US Signal Service, Washington.

Nelson, J.W. and Connolly, M.B. 1996. Techniques for improving the quality of the breeding areas for Anatidae in North America. *Gibier Faune Sauvage* 13: 903–17.

Nero, R.W. 1963. *Birds of the Lake Athabaska region, Saskatchewan*, Spec. Publ., No.5. Saskatchewan Natural History Society, Regina.

Newman, K. 1989. *Birds of Botswana*. Southern Book Publishers.

Newton, I. 1966. The moult of the Bullfinch. *Ibis* 108: 41–67.

Newton, I. 1998. *Population limitation in birds*. Academic Press, London.

Newton, I. and Campbell, C.R.G. 1975. Breeding ducks at Loch Leven, Kinross. *Wildfowl* 26: 83–103.

Newton, I. and Kerbes, R.H. 1974. Breeding of Greylag Geese *Anser anser* on the Outer Hebrides, Scotland. *J. Anim. Ecol.* 43: 771–83.

Nichols, J.D. 1991. Extensive monitoring programme viewed as long-term population studies—the case for North American waterfowl. *Ibis* 133: S89–S98.

Nichols, J.D. and Haramis, G.M. 1980a. Sex-specific differences in winter distribution patterns of Canvasbacks. *Condor* 82: 406–16.

Nichols, J.D. and Haramis, G.M. 1980b. Inferences regarding survival and recovery rates of winter-banded Canvasbacks. *J. Wildl. Manage.* 44: 164–73.

Nichols, J.D., Conroy, M.J., Anderson, D.R. and Burnham, K.P. 1984. Compensatory mortality in waterfowl populations: a review of evidence and implications for research and management. *Trans. N. Amer. Wildl. Nat. Res. Conf.* 49: 535–54.

Nichols, J.D., Bart, J., Limpert, R.J., Sladen, W.J.L. and Hines J.E. 1992. Annual survival rates of adult and immature eastern population Tundra Swans. *J. Wildl. Manage.* 56: 485–94.

Nicolai, B. 1993. Atlas der Brutvögel Ostdeutschlands. Gustav Fischer, Jena.

Nieman, D.J., Didiuk, A.B. and Smith, J.R. 2000. Status of Canada Geese of the Canadian prairies. In *Towards conservation of the diversity of Canada Geese* (Branta canadensis), pp.139–150. K.M. Dickson (ed.). *Can. Wildl. Serv. Occas. Paper* No. 103.

Niethammer, G. (ed.) 1968. *Handbuch der Vögel Mitteleuropas*, Vol. 2. Akad. Verlag, Frankfurt am Main.

Nilsson, L. 1969. Food consumption of diving ducks wintering at the coast of south Sweden in relation to food resources. *Oikos* 20: 128–35.

Nilsson, L. 1970. Food-seeking activity of south Swedish diving ducks in the non-breeding season. *Oikos* 21: 145–54.

Nilsson, L. 1972. Habitat selection, food choice, and feeding habits of diving ducks in coastal waters of South Sweden during the non-breeding season. *Ornis Scand.* 3: 55–78.

Nilsson, L. 1974. The behaviour of wintering Smew in southern Sweden. *Wildfowl* 25: 84–88.

Nilsson, L. 1979. Variation in the production of young swans wintering in Sweden. *Wildfowl* 30: 129–34.

Nilsson, L. 1984. Migrations of Fennoscandian Bean Geese *Anser fabalis*. *Swedish Wildlife Research* 13: 83–106.

Nilsson, L. 2002. Numbers of Mute Swans and Whooper Swans in Sweden, 1967–2000. In *Proceedings of the Fourth International Swan Symposium, 2001* (ed. E.C. Rees, S.L. Earnst and J. Coulson). *Waterbirds*, Special Publication 1: 53–60.

Nilsson, L. and Persson, H. 1984. Non-breeding distribution, numbers and ecology of Bean Goose *Anser fabalis* in Sweden. *Swedish Wildlife Research* 13: 107–70.

Nilsson, L. and Persson, H. 1989. Site tenacity and turn-over rate of staging and wintering Bean Geese *Anser fabalis* in southern Sweden. In *Food selection, movements and energy budgets of staging and wintering geese in south Sweden farmland*, (H. Persson), pp.143–57. Publ. Ph.D. thesis. Univ. Lund, Sweden.

Nilsson, L. and Persson, H. 1992. Feeding areas and local movement patterns of post-breeding Greylag Geese *Anser anser* in south Sweden. *Ornis Svecica* 2: 77–90.

Nilsson, L. and Persson H. 1993. Variation in survival in an increasing population of the Greylag Goose *Anser anser* in Scania, southern Sweden. *Ornis Svecica* 3: 137–46.

Nilsson, L. and Persson, H. 1994. Factors affecting the breeding performance of a marked Greylag Goose *Anser anser* population in south Sweden. *Wildfowl* 45: 33–48.

Nilsson, L. and Pirkola, M.K. 1986. The migration pattern of Bean Geese *Anser fabalis* in the Baltic area. *Vår Fågelvärld* 11: 147–53.

Nilsson, L., Andersson, O., Gustafsson, R. and Svensson, M. 1998. Increase and changes in distribution of breeding Whooper Swans *Cygnus cygnus* in northern Sweden from 1972–75 to 1997. *Wildfowl* 49: 6–17.

Noble, G.K. 1939. The role of dominance in the social life of birds. *Auk* 56: 263–73.

Noer, H. and Madsen, J. 1996. Shotgun pellet loads and infliction rates in Pink-footed Geese *Anser brachyrhynchus*. *Wildlife Biol.* 2: 65–73.

Nogge, G. 1973. Ornithologische Beobachtungen im afghanischen Pamir. *Bonn. Zool. Beitr.* 24: 254–69.

Nolet, B.A., Andreev, V.A., Clausen, P., Poot, M.J.M. and Wessel, E.G.J. 2001. Significance of the White Sea as a stopover for Bewick's Swans *Cygnus columbianus bewickii* in spring. *Ibis* 143: 63–71.

Norderhaug, A. and Norderhaug, M. 1984. Status of the Lesser White-fronted Goose *Anser erythropus* in Fennoscandia. *Swedish Wildlife Research, Viltrevy* 13: 171–85.

Norderhaug, M. 1970. The present status of the Barnacle Goose *Branta leucopsis* in Svalbard. *Norsk Pol. Årbok* 1968: 8–23.

Nores, M. and Yzurieta, D. 1980. *Aves de ambientes acuáticos de Córdoba y Centro de Argentina.* Secr. de Estado de Agricult. y Ganad, Córdoba.

Norman, F.I. 1982. Eggs, egg-laying and incubation in the Chestnut Teal. *Emu* 82: 195–98.

Norman, F.I. and Brown, R.S. 1988. Aspects of the distribution and abundance of Chestnut Teal in south-eastern Australia. *Emu* 88: 70–80.

Norman, F.I. and Horton, P. 1993. Notes on Freckled Duck *Stictonetta naevosa* shot at Bool Lagoon, South Australia 1980. *Rec. S. Aust. Mus.* 26: 149–52.

Norman, F.I. and Norris, K.C. 1982. Some notes on Freckled Duck shot in Victoria, Australia, 1981. *Wildfowl* 33: 81–87.

Norman, F.I., Kingsford, R.T. and Briggs, S.V. 1994. The Freckled Duck *Stictonetta naevosa* as a threatened taxon. *IWRB Threatened Waterfowl Research Group Newsl.* 5: 11–13.

Norment, C.J., Hall, A. and Hendricks, P. 1999. Important bird and mammal records in the Thelon River valley, Northwest Territories: range expansions and possible causes. *Can. Field-Nat.* 113(3): 375–85.

North, A.J. 1901–14. *Nests and eggs of birds found breeding in Australia and Tasmania,* Spec. Cat., No. 1. Australian Museum, Sydney.

Norton, R.L., Yntema, J.A. and Sladen, F.W. 1986. Abundance, distribution and habitat use by Anatids in the Virgin Islands. *Carib. J. Science* 22: 99–106.

Nováková, J.M., Veselovský, Z. and Kuzera, K. 1987. Contributions to phylogeny of the order Anseriformes. *Gazella* 14: 105–8.

Nowak, E. 1970. The waterfowl of Mongolia. *Wildfowl* 21: 61–68.

Nowak, E. 1983. Die Schopfkasarka, *Tadorna cristata* (Kuroda, 1917): eine vom Aussterben bedrohte Tierart (Wissensstand und Vorschläge zum Schutz). *Bonn. Zool. Beitr.* 34: 235–71.

Nowak, E. 1984. Über das vermutliche Brut- und Überwinterungsgebiet der Schopfkasarka, *Tadorna cristata. J. Orn.* 125: 103–5.

Noyes, J.H. and Jarvis, R.L. 1985. Diet and nutrition of breeding female Redhead and Canvasback Ducks in Nevada. *J. Wildl. Manage.* 49: 203–11.

Nudds, T.D. 1992. Patterns in breeding waterfowl communities. In *The ecology and management of breeding waterfowl,* (ed. B.D.J. Batt, A.D. Afton, M.G. Anderson, C.D. Ankney, D.H. Johnson, J.A. Kadlec *et al.*), pp.540–67. Univ. Minnesota Press, Minneapolis.

Nudds, T.D. and Bowlby, J.N. 1984. Predator–prey size relationships in North American dabbling ducks. *Can. J. Zool.* 62: 2002–8.

Nudds, T.D. and Cole, R.W. 1991. Changes in populations and breeding success of boreal forest ducks. *J. Wildl. Manage.* 55: 569–73.

Nudds, T.D., Sjöberg, K. and Lundberg, P. 1994. Ecomorphological relationships among palearctic dabbling ducks on Baltic coastal wetlands and a comparison with the nearctic. *Oikos* 69: 295–303.

Nudds, T.D., Elmberg, J., Sjöberg, K., Pöysä, H. and Nummi, P. 2000. Ecomorphology in breeding Holarctic dabbling ducks: the importance of lamellar density and body length varies with habitat type. *Oikos* 91: 583–88.

Nuechterlein, G.L. and Storer, R.W. 1985. Aggressive behavior and interspecific killing by Flying Steamer-ducks in Argentina. *Condor* 87: 87–91.

Nummi, P. 1993. Food-niche relationships of sympatric Mallards and Green-winged Teals. *Can. J. Zool.* 71: 49–55.

Nummi, P. and Pöysä, H. 1993. Habitat associations of ducks during different phases of the breeding season. *Ecography* 16: 319–28.

Nummi, P. and Pöysä, H. 1995. Habitat use by different-aged duck broods and juvenile ducks. *Wildl. Biol.* 1: 181–87.

Nummi, P. and Väänänen, V-M. 2001. High overlap in diets of sympatric dabbling ducks—an effect of food abundance. *Ann. Zool. Fennici* 38: 123–30.

Nummi, P., Pöysä, H., Elmberg, J. and Sjöberg, K. 1994. Habitat distribution of the Mallard in relation to vegetation structure, food, and population density. *Hydrobiologia* 279/280: 247–52.

Nummi, P., Elmberg, J., Pöysä, H. and Sjöberg, K. 1995. Occurrence and density of Mallard and Green-winged Teal in relation to prey size distribution and food abundance. *Ann. Zool. Fennici* 32: 385–90.

Nygård, T., Frantzen, B. and Svaza, S. 1995. Steller's Eider *Polysticta stelleri* wintering in Europe: numbers, distribution and origin. *Wildfowl* 46: 140–56.

Nyström, K.G.K. and Pehrsson, O. 1988. Salinity as a constraint affecting food and habitat choice of mussel-feeding diving ducks. *Ibis* 130: 94–110.

Oatley, T.B. and Prŷs-Jones, R.P. 1986. A comparative analysis of movements of southern African waterfowl (Anatidae), based on ringing recoveries. *S. Afr. J. Wildl. Res.* 16: 1–6.

Oberthür, W., Braunitzer, G. and Würdinger, J. 1982. Das Hämoglobin der Streifengans *Anser indicus*. Primärstruktur und Physiologie der Atmung, Systematik und Evolution. *Hoppe-Seyler's. Z. Physiol. Chem.* 363: 581–90.

O'Brien, F. 1995. Ecology of the West Indian Whistling-Duck on Grand Cayman: a study of a wild population of *Dendrocygna arborea* under human influence. Unpubl. M.Sc. thesis, Queen's Univ., Belfast, UK.

Ogilvie, M.A. 1964. A nesting study of Mallard in Berkeley New Decoy, Slimbridge, UK. *Wildfowl* 15: 84–88.

Ogilvie, M.A. 1967. Population changes and mortality of the Mute Swan in Britain. *Wildfowl* 18: 64–73.

Ogilvie, M.A. 1969. Bewick's Swans in Britain and Ireland during 1956–69. *Brit. Birds* 62: 505–22.

Ogilvie, M.A. 1972. Large numbered leg bands for individual identification of swans. *J. Wildl. Manage.* 36: 1261–65.

Ogilvie, M.A. 1975a. *Ducks of Britain and Europe.* Poyser, Berkhamsted.

Ogilvie, M.A. 1975b. The Musk Duck. *Wildfowl* 26: 113.

Ogilvie, M.A. 1978. *Wild geese.* Buteo Books, Vermillion, SD.

Ogilvie, M.A. and Rare Breeding Birds Panel 1996. Rare breeding birds in the United Kingdom in 1994. *Brit. Birds* 89: 387–417.

Ogilvie, M.A. and Rare Breeding Birds Panel 2000. Non-native birds breeding in the United Kingdom in 1998. *Brit. Birds* 93: 428–33.

Ogilvie, M.A. and Rare Breeding Birds Panel. 2002. Rare breeding birds in the United Kingdom in 2000. *Brit. Birds* 95: 542–582.

Ogilvie, M.A., Boertmann, D., Cabot, D., Merne, O., Percival, S.M. and Sigfusson, A. 1999. Barnacle Goose *Branta leucopsis*: Greenland. In *Goose populations of the Western Palearctic. A review of status and distribution*, Publ. No. 48 (ed. J. Madsen, G. Cracknell and A.D. Fox), pp. 246–57. Wetlands International, Wageningen, Netherlands, and National Environmental Research Institute, Rønde, Denmark.

Ohmori, T. 1981. Artificial feeding of swans in Japan. In 2nd IWRB Swan Symp., Sapporo, 1980 (ed. G.V.T. Matthews and M. Smart), pp.244–6. IWRB, Slimbridge, UK.

Ohtonen, A. 1988. Bill patterns of the Whooper Swan in Finland during autumn migration. *Wildfowl* 39: 153–54.

Ohtonen, A. and Huhtala, K. 1991. Whooper Swan *Cygnus cygnus* egg production in different nesting habitats in Finland. *Wildfowl Spec. Suppl.*, 1: 256–59.

Oka, N., Yamamuro, M., Hiratsuka, J. and Satoh, H. 1999. Habitat selection by wintering Tufted Ducks with special reference to their digestive organ and to possible segregation between neighbouring populations. *Ecol. Res.* 14: 303–15.

Olavarría, C., Coria, N., Schlatter, R., Hucke-Gaete, R., Vallejos, V., Godoy, C. *et al.*

1999. Cisne de cuello Negro, *Cygnus melanocorhypha* (Molina, 1782) en el área de las isles Shetland del Sury Península Antárctica. Serie Centífica. INACH 49: 79–87.

Oliver, W.R.B. 1945. Avian evolution in New Zealand and Australia. *Emu* 45: 119–52.

Olney, P.J.S. 1963. The food and feeding habits of Tufted Duck *Aythya fuligula. Ibis* 105: 55–62.

Olney, P.J.S. 1965. The food and feeding habits of the Shelduck *Tadorna tadorna. Ibis* 107: 527–32.

Olney, P.J.S. 1968. The food and feeding habits of the Pochard. *Biol. Cons.* 1: 71–76.

Olney, P.J.S. and Beer, J.V. 1961. Eating of metal by ducks. *Wildfowl* 12: 169.

Olney, P.J.S. and Mills, D.H. 1963. The food and feeding habits of Goldeneye *Bucephala clangula* in Great Britain. *Ibis* 105: 293–300.

Olrog, C.C. 1948. Observaciones sobre la avifauna de Tierra del Fuego y Chile. *Acta Zool. Lilloana* (Tucuman) 5: 437–531.

Olrog, C.C. 1963. *Lista y distribución de las aves Argentinas.* Univ. Nac. Tucuman Inst. Miguel Lillo, Tucuman, Argentina.

Olrog, C.C. 1984. *Las aves Sudamericanas: Una guía de campo,* Vol. 1. Univ. Nac. Tucuman, Fund. Inst. Miguel Lillo, Tucuman, Argentina.

Olson, S.L. 1977. Notes on subfossil Anatidae from New Zealand, including a new species of Pink-eared Duck *Malacorhynchus. Emu* 77: 132–35.

Olson, S.L. 1985. The fossil record of birds. In *Avian biology,* Vol. 8 (ed. D.S. Farner, J.R. King and K.C. Parkes), pp.79–238. Academic Press, New York.

Olson, S.L. and Feduccia, A. 1980a. *Presbyornis* and the origin of the Anseriformes (Aves: Charadriomorphae). *Smithsonian Contributions to Zoology* 323: 1–24.

Olson, S.L. and Feduccia, A. 1980b. Relationships and evolution of the flamingos. *Smithsonian Contributions to Zoology* 316: 1–73.

Olson, S.L. and James, H.F. 1982. *Prodromus* of the fossil avifauna of the Hawaiian Islands. *Smithsonian Contributions to Zoology* 365: 1–59.

Olson, S.L. and James, H.F. 1991. Descriptions of 32 new species of birds from the Hawaiian Islands: Part 1, non-Passeriformes. *Ornithol. Monogr.* 45: 1–88.

Olson, S.L. and Jouventin, P. 1996. A new species of small flightless duck from Amsterdam Island, southern Indian Ocean (Anatidae: *Anas). Condor* 98: 1–9.

Olson, S.L. and Wetmore, A. 1976. Preliminary diagnoses of two extraordinary new genera of birds from Pleistocene deposits in the Hawaiian Islands. *Proc. Biol. Soc. of Washington* 89: 247–58.

Olson, S.L. and Ziegler, A.C. 1995. Remains of land birds from Lisianski Island, with observations on the terrestrial avifauna of the Northwestern Hawaiian Islands. *Pac. Sci.* 49: 111–25.

Omland, K.E. 1994. Character congruence between a molecular and a morphological phylogeny for dabbling ducks (*Anas). Syst. Biol.* 43: 369–86.

Onuf, C.P. 1995. Seagrass meadows of the Laguna Madre of Texas. In *Our living resources: a report to the nation on the distribution, abundance, and health of U.S. plants, animals, and ecosystems,* (ed. E.T. LaRoe, G.S. Farris, C.E. Puckett, P.D. Doran and M.J. Mac), pp.275–77. US Department of the Interior, National Biological Service, Washington.

Onuf, C.P. 1996. Biomass patterns in seagrass meadows of the Laguna Madre, Texas. *Bull. Marine Sci.* 58: 404–20.

Oring, L. 1964. Behavior and ecology of certain ducks during the postbreeding season. *J. Wildl. Manage.* 28: 223–33.

Oring, L. 1968. Growth, molts and plumages of the Gadwall. *Auk* 85: 355–80.

Oring, L. 1969. Summer biology of the Gadwall at Delta, Manitoba. *Wilson Bull.* 81: 44–54.

Oring, L. and Sayler, R.D. 1992. The mating systems of waterfowl. In *The ecology and management of breeding waterfowl* (ed. B.D.J. Batt, A.D. Afton, M.G. Anderson, C.D. Ankney, D.H. Johnson, J.A. Kadlec *et al.*) pp. 190–213. Univ. Minnesota Press, Minneapolis.

Orthmeyer, D., Takekawa, J.Y. and Ely, C.R. 1992. Morphological differences in Greater White-fronted Goose populations from the Pacific flyway. *Proc. N. Amer. Arctic Goose Conference and Workshop 7, California Maritime Academy, Vallejo, California 7–12 Jan 1992.*

Orthmeyer, D., Takekawa, J.Y., Ely, C.R., Wege, M.L. and Newton, W.E. 1995. Morphological variation in Greater White-fronted Geese in the Pacific Flyway. *Condor* 97: 123–32.

Ortiz Crespo, F. 1988. A new locality for the Comb Duck *Sarkidiornis melanotus* from western Ecuador and notes on the distribution of the Horned Screamer. *Bull. BOC* 108: 141–44.

Osborne, P.E and Tigar, B.J. 1990. The status and distribution of birds in Lesotho. Unpubl. rept. Dept Zool., Univ. Oxford.

Osborne, S. 1955. *Duck shooting in Australia*. Hudson, Sydney.

Osgood, W.H. and Conover, B. 1922. Game birds from northwestern Venezuela. *Field Mus. Nat. Hist. Zool.* 12: 19–41.

Öst, M. and Bäck, A. 2003. Spatial structure and parental aggression in eider broods. *Anim. Behav.* 66: 1069–75.

Ostapenko, V.A. 1991. Migrations of Bewick's Swans *Cygnus bewickii* and Whooper Swans *C. cygnus* wintering in Japan through Sakhalin Island and adjacent territories, USSR. *Wildfowl* Spec Suppl., 1: 224–26.

Ounsted, M., Soemarna, K., Ramono, W., Seal, U., Green, A., Rudyanto et al. 1994. White-winged Wood Duck in Sumatra: population and habitat viability analysis. Unpubl. rept. Captive Breeding Specialist Group, Species Survival Commission, IUCN.

Oustalet, E. 1891. *Mission scientifique du Cap Horn, 1882–1883*, Vol. VI. Gauthier-Villars, Paris.

Owen, M. 1971. The selection of feeding site by White-fronted Geese in winter. *J. Appl. Ecol.* 8: 905–17.

Owen, M. 1972. Some factors affecting food intake and selection in White-fronted Geese. *J. Anim. Ecol.* 41: 79–92.

Owen, M. 1973. The management of grassland areas for wintering geese. *Wildfowl* 24: 123–30.

Owen, M. 1976a. The selection of winter food by White-fronted Geese. *J. Appl. Ecol.*, 13: 715–29.

Owen, M. 1976b. Factors affecting the distribution of geese in the British Isles. *Wildfowl* 27: 143–47.

Owen, M. 1977. *Wildfowl of Europe*. Macmillan, London.

Owen, M. 1980. *Wild geese of the world*. Batsford, London.

Owen, M. 1981a. Food selection in geese. *Verh. Orn. Ges. Bayern* 23: 105–24.

Owen, M. 1981b. Abdominal profile—a condition index for wild geese in the field. *J. Wildl. Manage.* 45: 227–30.

Owen, M. 1991. Nocturnal feeding in waterfowl. *Int. Orn. Congr.* 20: 1105–12.

Owen, M. 1996. Review of the migration strategies of the Anatidae: challenges for conservation. *Gibier Faune Sauvage* 13: 123–39.

Owen, M. and Black, J.M. 1989a. Factors affecting the survival of Barnacle Geese on migration from the breeding grounds. *J. Anim. Ecol.* 58: 603–18.

Owen, M. and Black, J.M. 1989b. Barnacle Goose. In *Lifetime reproductive success in birds* (ed. I. Newton), pp. 349–62. Academic Press, London.

Owen, M. and Black, J.M. 1990. *Waterfowl ecology*. Blackie, Glasgow.

Owen, M. and Black, J.M. 1991. The importance of migration mortality in non-passerine birds. In *Bird population studies, relevance to conservation and management* (ed. C.M. Perrins, J-D. Lebreton and G.J.M. Hirons), pp. 360–72. OUP.

Owen, M. and Black, J.M. 1999. Barnacle Goose *Branta leucopsis*: Svalbard. In *Goose populations of the Western Palearctic. A review of status and distribution*, Publ. No. 48 (ed. J. Madsen, G. Cracknell and A.D. Fox), pp.258–68. Wetlands International, Wageningen, Netherlands, and National Environmental Research Institute, Rønde, Denmark.

Owen, M. and Cadbury, C.J. 1975. The ecology and mortality of swans at the Ouse Washes, England. *Wildfowl* 26: 31–42.

Owen, M. and Cook, W.A. 1977. Variation in body weight, wing length and condition of Mallard *Anas platyrhynchos platyrhynchos* and their relationship to environmental change. *J. Zool., Lond.* 183: 377–95.

Owen, M. and Dix, M. 1986. Sex ratios in some common British wintering ducks. *Wildfowl* 37: 104–12.

Owen, M. and Gullestad, N. 1984. Migration routes of Svalbard Barnacle Geese *Branta leucopsis* with a preliminary report on the importance of the Bjørnoya staging area. *Norsk Pol. Skr.* 181: 37–47.

Owen, M. and Kear, J. 1972. Food and feeding habits. In *The Swans* (ed. P. Scott and The Wildfowl Trust), pp. 58–77. Michael Joseph, London.

Owen, M. and Kerbes, R.H. 1971. On the autumn food of Barnacle Geese at Caerlaverock National Nature Reserve. *Wildfowl* 22: 114–19.

Owen, M. and King, J.G. 1981. The duration of the flightless moult in free-living Mallard. *Bird Study* 27: 267–69.

Owen, M. and Mitchell, C. 1988. The movements and migrations of Wigeon *Anas penelope* wintering in Britain and Ireland. *Bird Study* 35: 47–59.

Owen, M. and Montgomery, S. 1978. Body measurements of Mallard caught in Britain. *Wildfowl* 29: 123–34.

Owen, M. and Norderhaug, M. 1977. Population dynamics of Barnacle Geese *Branta leucopsis* breeding in Svalbard, 1948–1976. *Ornis Scand.* 8: 161–74.

Owen, M. and Ogilvie, M.A. 1979. Wing molt and weights of Barnacle Geese in Spitzbergen. *Condor* 81: 42–52.

Owen, M. and Shimmings, P. 1992. The occurrence and performance of leucistic Barnacle Geese *Branta leucopsis*. *Ibis* 134: 22–26.

Owen, M. and Wells, R. 1979. Territorial behaviour in breeding geese—a re-examination of Ryder's hypothesis. *Wildfowl* 30: 20–26.

Owen, M. and Williams, G. 1976. Winter distribution and habitat requirements of Wigeon in Britain. *Wildfowl* 27: 83–90.

Owen, M., Atkinson-Willes, G.L. and Salmon, D.G. 1986. *Wildfowl in Great Britain* (2nd edn). Cambridge Univ. Press.

Owen, M., Black, J.M., Agger, M.C. and Campbell, C.R.G. 1987. The use of the Solway Firth by an increasing population of Barnacle Geese in relation to changes in refuge management. *Biol. Cons.* 39: 63–81.

Owen, M., Black, J.M. and Liber, H. 1988. Pair bond duration and timing of its formation in Barnacle Geese (*Branta leucopsis*). In *Waterfowl in Winter* (ed. M.W. Weller), pp.257–69. Univ. Minnesota Press, Minneapolis.

Owen, M., Delany, S., Merne, O.J., Mitchell, C., Mudge, G.P. and Ogilvie, M.A. 1995. Conservation of the population of Greenland-breeding Barnacle Geese in relation to changes in legislation and farming practice. Unpubl. rept to SNH. WWT, Slimbridge, UK.

Owen, R. 1875. On *Dinornis* (Part X): containing a restoration of the skeleton of *Cnemiornis calcitrans*, Ow., with remarks on its affinities in the lamellirostral group. *Trans. Zool. Soc. Lond.* 9: 253–92.

Owre, O.T. 1973. A consideration of the exotic avifauna of southeastern Florida. *Wilson Bull.* 85: 491–500.

Pacific Flyway Council 1994. *Pacific Flyway management plan for Emperor Geese*. Emperor Goose Subcomm., Pacific Flyway Comm. US Fish & Wildl. Serv., Portland, Oregon.

Pak, U-I. 1995. On the distribution and ecology of Anatidae in D.P.R. Korea. Unpubl. rept for Workshop on Action Plan for Anatidae, during 1995 Northeast Asia and North Pacific Environment Forum, Kushiro, Japan, 25–29 September 1995.

Pakenham, R.H.W. 1979. *The birds of Zanzibar and Pemba.* Check-list No. 2. BOU, Tring.

Palmer, R.S. (ed.) 1976. *Handbook of North American birds.* Vols 2, 3. Waterfowl. Yale University Press, New Haven.

Pamplin, W.L., Jr 1986. Cooperative efforts to halt population declines of geese nesting on Alaska's Yukon-Kuskokwim Delta. *Trans. N. Amer. Wildl. Nat. Res. Conf.* 51: 487–506.

Panayotopoulou, M. and Green, A. 2000. White-headed Ducks in Greece. *Wetlands International–IUCN Threatened Waterfowl Specialist Group News* 12: 16–17.

Panek, M. and Majewski, P. 1990. Remex growth and body mass of Mallards during wing molt. *Auk* 107: 255–59.

Paquette, G.A. and Ankney, C.D. 1996. Wetland selection by American Green-winged Teal breeding in British Columbia. *Condor* 98: 27–33.

Park, J-Y. and Won, P-Y. 1993. Wintering ecology of Bean Geese *Anser fabalis* and White-fronted Geese *A. albifrons* in Juram Reservoirs, Korea. *Bull. Inst. Ornithol., Kyung Hee Univ. IV*: 1–24.

Parker, G.R., Petrie, M.J. and Sears, D.T. 1992. Waterfowl distribution relative to wetland acidity. *J. Wildl. Manage.* 56: 268–74.

Parker, L.E., Bolen, E.G. and Baker, R.J. 1981. Genetic variation in a winter population of Mallard ducks. *Southwest Nat.* 26: 425–28.

Parker, T.A., III., Parker, S.A. and Plenge, M.A. 1982. *An annotated checklist of Peruvian birds.* Buteo Books, South Dakota.

Parker, S.A., Eckert, H.J. and Ragless, G.B. 1985. *An annotated checklist of the birds of South Australia,* No. 2A. South Aust. Ornithol. Assoc., Adelaide.

Parker, V. 1994. *Swaziland bird atlas.* Websters, Mbabane.

Parker, V. 1999. *The bird atlas of southern Mozambique.* Avian Demography Unit, Cape Town, and Endangered Wildlife Trust, Johannesburg.

Parrott, D. and McKay, H.V. 2001. Mute swan grazing on winter crops: estimation of yield loss in oilseed rape and wheat. *Crop Protection* 20: 913–19.

Parry, D.E. 1989. Black Swans at Merauke. *Kukila* 4: 64.

Parslow-Otsu, M. 1991. Bean Geese in the Yare Valley, Norfolk. *Brit. Birds* 84: 161–69.

Partridge, W.H. 1956. Notes on the Brazilian Merganser in Argentina. *Auk* 73: 473–88.

Paspaleva, M., Kiss, B.J. and Tipeanu, M. 1984. Sur la dynamique de quelques espèces d'oiseaux dominants dans le Delta du Danube. *Travaux du Muséum d'Histoire Naturelle Grigore Antipa* 25: 313–29.

Paterson, A. 1972. *Birds of the Bahamas.* Durell Publications, Kennebunkport, Maine.

Patrikeev, M. 1996. The status of the Ferruginous Duck in Azerbaijan. *Threatened Waterfowl Specialist Group News* 9: 30–32. WWT, Slimbridge, UK.

Patterson, I.J. 1982. *The Shelduck, a study in behavioural ecology.* Cambridge Univ. Press.

Patterson, I.J. and Giroux, J-F. 1990. Breeding success of Icelandic Pink-footed Geese *Anser brachyrhynchus* and Greylag Geese *A. anser* in different areas of Iceland in 1987 and 1988. *Wildfowl* 41: 13–17.

Patterson, I.J. and Makepeace, M. 1979. Mutual interference during nest-prospecting in the Shelduck, *Tadorna tadorna. Anim. Behav.* 27: 522–35.

Patterson, I.J., Young, C.M. and Tompa, F.S. 1974. The Shelduck population of the Ythan Estuary, Aberdeenshire. *Wildfowl* 25: 16–28.

Patterson, I.J., Abdul Jahil, S. and East, M.L. 1989. Damage to winter cereals by Greylag and Pink-footed Geese in north-east Scotland. *J. Appl. Ecol.* 26: 879–95.

Patterson, J.H. 1989. The North American Waterfowl Management Plan. In *Managing waterfowl populations,* (ed. G.V.T. Matthews), pp.225–28. IWRB Spec. Publ. 12, Slimbridge, UK.

Patton, J.C. and Avise, J.C. 1986. Evolutionary genetics of birds IV: rates of protein divergence in waterfowl (Anatidae). *Genetica* 68: 129–43.

Paulus, S.L. 1983. Dominance relations, resource use and pairing chronology of Gadwalls in winter. *Auk* 100: 947–52.

Paulus, S.L. 1984a. Activity budget of non-breeding Gadwalls in Louisiana. *J. Wildl. Manage.* 48: 371–80.

Paulus, S.L. 1984b. Behavioral ecology of Mottled Ducks in Louisiana. Unpubl. Ph.D. thesis. Univ. Auburn, Alabama, US.

Paulus, S.L. 1988a. Social behavior and pairing chronology of Mottled Ducks during autumn and winter in Louisiana. In *Waterfowl in winter* (ed. M.W. Weller), pp.59–70. Univ. Minnesota Press, Minneapolis.

Paulus, S.L. 1988b. Time-activity budgets of non-breeding Anatidae: a review. In *Waterfowl in Winter* (ed. M.W. Weller), pp.135–52. Univ. Minnesota Press, Minneapolis.

Paulus, S.L. 1988c. Time activity budgets of Mottled Ducks in Louisiana in winter. *J. Wildl. Manage.* 52: 711–18.

Paxinos, E., James, H.F., Olson, S.L., Sorenson, M.D., Jackson, J. and Fleischer, R.C. 2002a. MtDNA from fossils reveals a radiation of Hawaiian geese recently derived from the Canada goose (*Branta canadensis*). *Proc. Natl. Acad. Sci.* 99: 1399–1404.

Paxinos, E., James, H.F., Olson, S.L., Sorenson, M.D., Jackson, J. and Fleischer, R.C. 2002b. Prehistoric decline of genetic diversity in the Nene. *Science* 296: 1827.

Payne, R.B. 1972. Mechanisms and control of molt. In *Avian Biology,* Vol. 2 (ed. D.S. Farner and J.R. King), pp.103–55. Academic Press, New York.

Paynter, D. 1996. Counts of Lesser White-fronted Geese in Azerbejzhan, January/February 1996. *Wetlands International Goose Specialist Group Bull.* 8: 7–8.

Peaker, M. and Linzell, J.L. 1975. Salt glands in birds and reptiles. Cambridge Univ. Press.

Pearce, A. 1999. Behavioral evidence of the systematic relationships of the Garganey and Silver Teals. Unpubl. M.S. thesis, Minnesota Univ., Minneapolis, US.

Pearce, A. 2000. Displays of the Garganey *Anas querquedula*: evidence of multiple functions. *Wildfowl* 51: 83–101.

Pearce, J.M., Pierson, B.J., Talbot, S.L., Derksen, D.V., Kraege, D. and Scribner, K.T. 2000. A genetic evaluation of morphology used to identify harvested Canada Geese. *J. Wildl. Manage.* 64: 863–74.

Pedroli, J-C. 1982. Activity and time budget of Tufted Ducks on Swiss lakes during winter. *Wildfowl* 33: 105–12.

Pehrsson, O. 1986. Duckling production of the Old-squaw in relation to spring weather and small-rodent fluctuations. *Can. J. Zool.* 64: 1835–41.

Pehrsson, O. 1987. Effects of body condition on molting in Mallards. *Condor* 89: 329–39.

Pelayo, J.T. and Clark, R.G. 2002. Variation in size, composition, and quality of Ruddy Duck eggs and ducklings. *Condor* 104: 457–62.

Pelayo, J.T. and Clark, R.G. 2003. Consequences of egg size for offspring survival: a cross-fostering experiment in Ruddy Ducks. *Auk* 120: 384–93.

Pellis, S.M. 1982. An analysis of courtship and mating in the Cape Barren Goose *Cereopsis novaehollandiae* Latham based on the Eshkol-Wachman movement notation. *Bird Behaviour* 4: 30–41.

Pennycuick, C.J., Einarsson, Ó., Bradbury, T.A.M. and Owen, M. 1996. Migrating Whooper Swans *Cygnus cygnus*: satellite tracks and flight performance calculations. *J. Avian Biology* 27: 118–34.

Pennycuick, C.J., Bradbury, T.A.M., Einarsson, Ó. and Owen, M. 1999. Response to weather and light conditions of migratory Whooper Swans *Cygnus cygnus* and flying height profiles, observed with Argos satellite system. *Ibis* 141: 434–43.

Perennou, C. 1991. *Les recensements internationaux d'oiseaux d'eau en Afrique Tropicale.* Spec. Publ., No. 15. IWRB, Slimbridge, UK.

Perennou, C. 1992. *African waterfowl census 1992—Les dénombrements internationaux d'oiseaux d'eau en Afrique 1992.* IWRB, Slimbridge, UK.

Perennou, C. and Cantera, J-P. 1993. Etude de faisabilité sur las réintroduction de l'Érismature à tête blanche sur l'étang de Biguglia, Haute Corse. Unpubl. rept. AGENC, Bastia and Station Biologique de la Tour du Valat, Arles.

Perennou, C. and Mundkhur, T. 1992. *Asian and Australasian Waterfowl Census 1992.* IWRB, Slimbridge, UK.

Perennou, C., Mundkur, T., Scott, D.A., Follestad, A. and Kvenild, L. 1994. *The Asian waterfowl census 1987–91. Distribution and status of Asian waterfowl,* AWB Publ., No. 86; IWRB Publ., No. 24. Asian Wetland Bureau, Kuala Lumpur, and IWRB, Slimbridge, UK.

Perez-Arteaga, A., Gaston, K.J. and Kershaw, M. 2002. Population trends and priority conservation sites for Mexican Duck *Anas diazi. Bird Conserv. Int.* 12: 35–52.

Pergolani de Costa, M.J.I. 1955. Las 'avutardas'. Especies que dañan a los cereales y las pasturas. *IDIA* 88: 1–9.

Perkins, C.R. and Barclay, J.S. 1997. Accumulation and mobilization of organochlorine contaminants in wintering Greater Scaup. *J. Wildl. Manage.* 61: 444–49.

Perkins, R.C.L. 1903. *Fauna Hawaiiensis,* Vol. 1. Clay, London.

Perrins, C.M. 1970. The timing of birds' breeding seasons. *Ibis* 112: 242–55.

Perrins, C.M. 1980. Survival of young Great Tits, *Parus major. Int. Ornith. Congr.* 17: 159–74.

Perrins, C.M. and Birkhead, T.R. 1983. *Avian ecology.* Blackie, Glasgow.

Perrins, C.M. and McCleery, R.H. 1995. The disadvantages of late moulting by Mute Swans *Cygnus olor. Wildfowl* 46: 1–7.

Perrins, C.M. and Moss, D. 1975. Reproductive rates in the Great Tit. *J. Anim. Ecol.* 44: 695–706.

Perrins, C.M. and Ogilvie, M.A. 1981. A study of the Abbotsbury Mute Swans. *Wildfowl* 32: 35–47.

Perrins, C.M. and Reynolds, C.M. 1967. A preliminary study of the Mute Swan. *Wildfowl* 18: 74–84.

Perrins, C.M. and Sears, J. 1991. Collisions with overhead wires as a cause of mortality in Mute Swans *Cygnus olor. Wildfowl* 42: 5–11.

Perry, M.C. and Deller, A.S. 1995. Waterfowl population trends in the Chesapeake Bay area, In *Toward a sustainable coastal watershed: the Chesapeake experiment,* Publ., No. 149. (ed. P. Hill and S. Nelson), pp.490–504. Chesapeake Research Consortium, Inc., Edgewater, MD.

Perry, M.C. and Deller, A.S. 1996. Review of factors affecting the distribution and abundance of waterfowl in shallow-water habitats of Chesapeake Bay. *Estuaries* 19: 272–78.

Perry, M.C. and Uhler, F.M. 1982. Food habits of diving ducks in the Carolinas. *Proc. Ann. Conf. Southeast. Assoc. Fish Wildl. Agencies* 36: 492–504.

Perry, M.C. and Uhler, F.M. 1988. Food habits and distribution of wintering Canvasbacks, *Aythya valisineria,* on Chesapeake Bay. *Estuaries* 11: 57–67.

Perry, M.C., Kuenzel, W.J, Williams, B.K and Serafin, J.A. 1986. Influence of nutrients on feed intake and condition of captive Canvasbacks in winter. *J. Wildl. Manage.* 50: 427–34.

Persson, H. and Urdiales, C. 1995. The disappearance of the Tundra Bean Goose *Anser fabalis* from the Iberian Peninsula. *IWRB Goose Research Bull.* 6: 17–19.

Persson, L., Borg, K. and Falt, H. 1974. On the occurrence of endoparasites in Eider Ducks in Sweden. *Viltrevy* 9: 1–24.

Peter, J. 1989. *Waterfowl count in Victoria, February 1989,* Rept, No. 57. RAOU, Melbourne.

Peters, J.L. 1931. *Checklist of the birds of the world*, Vol. 1. Harvard Univ. Press, Cambridge, Massachusetts.

Peters, J.L., Brewer, G.L. and Bowe, L.M. 2003. Extra-pair paternity and breeding synchrony in gadwalls (*Anas strepera*) in North Dakota. *Auk* 120: 883–88.

Petersen, Æ. and Skírnisson, K. 1980. Minkur. *Rit Landverndar* 7: 80–94. Landvernd, Reykjavik. [The mink in Iceland. In Icelandic with a summary in English].

Petersen, M.R. 1980. Observations of wing-feather moult and feeding ecology of Steller's Eiders at Nelson Lagoon, Alaska. *Wildfowl* 31: 99–106.

Petersen, M.R. 1990. Nest-site selection by Emperor Geese and Cackling Canada Geese. *Wilson Bull.* 102: 413–26.

Petersen, M.R. 1991. Reproductive ecology of Emperor Geese. Unpubl. Ph.D. thesis. Univ. California, Davis, US.

Petersen, M.R. 1992a. Reproductive ecology of Emperor Geese: Annual and individual variation in nesting. *Condor* 94: 383–97.

Petersen, M.R. 1992b. Intraspecific variation in egg shape among individual Emperor Geese. *J. Field Ornithol.* 63: 344–54.

Petersen, M.R. 1992c. Reproductive ecology of Emperor Geese: survival of adult females. *Condor* 94: 398–406.

Petersen, M.R. and Douglas, D.C. 2004. Winter ecology of Spectacled Eiders: environmental characteristics and population change. *Condor* 106: 79–94.

Petersen, M.R. and Gill, R.E., Jr 1982. Population status of Emperor Geese along the north side of the Alaska Peninsula. *Wildfowl* 33: 31–38.

Petersen, M.R., Schmutz, J.A. and Rockwell, R.F. 1994. Emperor Goose (*Chen canagica*), The Birds of North America, No. 97, (ed. A. Poole and F. Gill). AOU, Washington, and Academy of Natural Sciences, Philadelphia.

Petersen, M.R., Douglas, D.C. and Mulcahy, D.M. 1995. Use of implanted satellite transmitters to locate Spectacled Eiders at sea. *Condor* 97: 276–78.

Petersen, M.R., Piatt, J.F. and Trust, K.A. 1998. Foods of Spectacled Eiders *Somateria fischeri* in the Bering Sea, Alaska. *Wildfowl* 49: 124–28.

Petersen, M.R., Larned, W.W. and Douglas, D.C. 1999. At-sea distribution of Spectacled Eiders: a 120-year-old mystery resolved. *Auk* 116: 1009–20.

Petersen, M.R., Grand, J.B. and Dau, C.P. 2000. Spectacled Eider (*Somateria fischeri*). The Birds of North America, No. 547, (ed. A. Poole and F. Gill). AOU, The Birds of North America Inc., Philadelphia.

Peterson, S.R. 1976. Variation in Oldsquaw rectrix numbers. *Auk* 93: 190–92.

Peterson, S.R. and Ellarson, R.S. 1978. Bursae, reproductive structures, and scapular color in wintering female Oldsquaws. *Auk* 95: 115–21.

Petraitus, A. 1991. Steller's Eider *Polysticta stelleri* at the Lithuanian Baltic Coast in 1969 to 1991. *Acta Ornithologica Lituanica* 4: 96–106.

Petrides, G.A. and Bryant, C.R. 1951. An analysis of the 1949–50 fowl cholera epizootic in Texas Panhandle waterfowl. *Trans. N. Amer. Wildl. Nat. Res. Conf.* 16: 193–216.

Petrie, M.J., Drobney, R.D. and Graber, D.A. 1997. Evaluation of true metabolizable energy for waterfowl. *J. Wildl. Manage.* 61: 420–25.

Petrie, S.A. 1996. Red-billed Teal foods in semiarid South Africa: a north-temperate contrast. *J. Wildl. Manage.* 60: 874–81.

Petrie, S.A. 1998. Molt patterns of nonbreeding White-faced Whistling-ducks in South Africa. *Auk* 115: 774–80.

Petrie, S.A. and Francis, C.M. 2003. Rapid increase in the lower Great Lakes population of feral mute swans: a review and recommendation. *Wildl. Soc. Bull.* 31(2): 407–16.

Petrie, S.A. and Petrie, V. 1998. Activity budget of White-faced Whistling Ducks during winter and spring in northern Kwa Zulu-Natal, South Africa. *J. Wildl. Manage.* 62: 1119–26.

Petrie, S.A. and Rogers, K.H. 1997a. Satellite tracking of White-faced Whistling Ducks in a semiarid region of South Africa. *J. Wildl. Manage.* 61: 1208–13.

Petrie, S.A. and Rogers, K.H. 1997b. Foods consumed by breeding White-faced Whistling Ducks (*Dendrocygna viduata*) on the Nyl River floodplain, South Africa. *Gibier Faune Sauvage* 13: 755–71.

Petrie, S.A. and Rogers, K.H. 1997c. Activity budget of breeding white-faced whistling ducks *Dendrocygna viduata* on stock-ponds in semi-arid South Africa, and a comparison with north-temperate waterfowl. *S. Afr. J. Wildl. Res.* 27: 79–85.

Pettifor, R.A., Perrins, C.M. and McCleery, R.H. 1988. Individual optimization of clutch size in great tits. *Nature* 336: 160–62.

Pettingill, O.S., Jr 1965. Kelp Geese and Flightless Steamer Ducks in the Falkland Islands. *Living Bird* 4: 65–78.

Phelps, W.H., Snr and Phelps, W.H., Jr 1958. *Lista de las aves de Venezuela con su distribucion*. Seperata del Boletin de la Sociedad Venezolana de Ciencias Naturales, Vol. 19, no. 90. pp.427.

Philippi, B.R.A., Johnson, A.W., Goodall, J.D. and Behn, F. 1954. Notas sobre aves de Magallanes Tierra del Fuego. *Boletin del Museo Nacional de Historia Natural de Chile* 26(3): 1–65.

Philippona, J. 1966. Geese in cold winter weather. *Wildfowl* 17: 95–97.

Phillips, J.C. 1916. A new form of *Chloëphaga hybrida*. *Auk* 33: 423–24.

Phillips, J.C. 1917. The Steamer Duck. *Ibis* 59: 116–19.

Phillips, J.C. 1922–26. *A natural history of the ducks*, Vols 1–4. Houghton Mifflin, Boston. (Facsimile edn republ. 1986 by Dover Publications, New York.)

Phillips, R.A., Cope, D.R., Rees, E.C. and O'Connell, M.J. 2003. Site fidelity and range size of wintering Barnacle Geese *Branta leucopsis*. *Bird Study* 50: 161–69.

Phillips, S. 1953. An incident concerning the Peruvian Torrent Duck. *Avic. Mag.* 59: 134.

Phillips, V. 1991. Pochard *Aythya ferina* use of chironomid-rich feeding habitat in winter. *Bird Study* 38: 118–22.

Phillips, V.E. 1992. Variation in the winter wildfowl numbers on gravel pits at Great Linford, Buckinghamshire, 1974–79 and 1984–91, with particular reference to the effects of fish removal. *Bird Study* 39: 177–85.

Piechocki, R. 1968. Beiträge zur Avifauna der Mongolei, Teil 1. Ergebnisse der Mongolisch-Deutschen Expedition seit 1962. *Mitt. Zool. Mus., Berlin* 44: 149–292.

Pienkowski, M.W. and Evans, P.R. 1982. Clutch parasitism and nesting interference between shelducks at Aberlady Bay. *Wildfowl* 33: 159–63.

Pihl, S. 1996. Western Palearctic wintering seaduck numbers. *Gibier Faune Sauvage* 13: 191–206.

Pihl, S. 1997. Action Plan for the Steller's Eider *Polysticta stelleri*. Rept comm. by Wetlands International Seaduck Specialist Group for European Commission. Danish National Environmental Research Institute, Kalø.

Pihl, S. and Laursen, K. 1996. A reestimation of Western Palearctic wintering seaduck numbers from the Baltic Sea 1993 survey. *Gibier Faune Sauvage* 13: 191–99.

Pihl, S., Laursen, K., Hounisen, J-P. and Frikke, J. 1992. *Landsdækkende optælling af vandfugle fra flyvemaskine, januar/februar 1991 og januar/marts 1992*, National Environmental Research Institute, Tech. Rept, No. 44. NERI, Rønde, Denmark.

Pihl, S., Durink, J. and Skov, H. 1995. Waterbird numbers in the Baltic Sea, winter 1993. Tech. Rpt No. 145. Danish National Environmental Research Institute, Kalø.

Pineschi, R.B. and Yamashita, C. 1999. Occurrence, census and conservation of the Brazilian Merganser (*Mergus octosetaceus*) in Brazil with notes about feeding behaviour and habitat preferences. *Proc. Neotropical Waterfowl Symposium, VI Neotropical Ornithology Congress, 7 October 1999*. Monterrey, Mexico.

Pirkola, M. and Kalinainen, P. 1984. The status, habitats and productivity of breeding Bean Goose *Anser fabalis fabalis* in Finland. *Swedish Wildlife Research* 13: 9–48.

Pitman, C.R.S. 1965. The nesting and some other habits of *Alopochen, Nettapus, Plectropterus* and *Sarkidiornis*. *Wildfowl* 16: 115–21.

Pizzey, G. 1986. *A field guide to the birds of Australia*. Collins, Sydney.

Ploeger, P.L. 1968. Geographic differentiation in arctic Anatidae as a result of isolation during the last glacial. *Ardea* 56: 1–159.

Plotnick, R. 1961a. La Avutarda de Pecho Rayado. Zoogeografía, sistemática y control. *IDIA* 157: 9–22.

Plotnick, R. 1961b. Migración de las avutardas. *IDIA* 167: 3–13.

Polivanova, N.N. 1971. *The birds of the Khanka Lake.* Far East Sci. Centre, Acad. Sci. USSR, Vladivostok.

Ponyi, J.E. 1984. Abundance and feeding of wintering and migrating aquatic birds in two sampling areas of Lake Balaton in 1983–1985. *Hydrobiologia* 279/280: 63–69.

Poorter, E.P.R. 1991. *Bewick's Swans Cygnus columbianus bewickii, an analysis of breeding success and changing resources.* Ministrie van Verker en Waterstaat, Rijkwaterstaat, Directie Flevoland, Netherlands.

Popham, H.L. 1897. Notes of birds observed on the Yenisei River, Siberia, in 1895. *Ibis* 7(3): 89–108.

Port, J. 1998a. Reproductive strategies of an arboreal dabbling duck: the Speckled Teal *Anas flavirostris* in eastern Argentina. Unpubl. Ph.D. thesis. Univ. Minnesota, Minneapolis, US.

Port, J. 1998b. Long-term pair bonds and male parental care in Speckled Teal *Anas flavirostris* in eastern Argentina. *Wildfowl* 49: 139–49.

Port, J. 2000. Alloparental care of ducklings by unrelated male speckled teal *Anas flavirostris* in eastern Argentina. *Wildfowl* 51: 103–8.

Port, J. and Brewer, G.L. 2004. Use of Monk Parakeet (*Myiopsitta monachus*) nests by Speckled Teal (*Anas flavirostris*) in eastern Argentina. *Ornit. Neotrop.* 15: 209–18.

Port, J. and F. McKinney. 2001. Behavioral adaptations for breeding in arboreal-nesting speckled teal. *Wilson Bull.* 113: 177–88.

Portenko, L.A. 1952. Age and seasonal changes in eider plumages. *Trudy Zool. Inst. AN., USSR.* 9(4): 1100–32. (trans. Can. Wildl. Serv.)

Portenko, L.A. 1972. *Ptitsy Chukotskogo Plouostrova i Ostrova Vrangelya,* Vol. 1. Nauka, Leningrad. [The birds of the Chukotsk Peninsula and Wrangel Island.]

Porter, S. 1940. The ducks of New Zealand. *Avic. Mag.* 5: 142–51.

Post, W. and Enders, F. 1970. The occurrence of Mallophaga on two bird species occupying the same habitat. *Ibis* 112: 539–40.

Poston, H.J. 1969. Home range and breeding biology of the Shoveler. Unpubl. M.S. thesis. Utah State Univ., Logan, US.

Poyarkov, N.D. 1984. Status of the *Anser cygnoides* population in the Amur Region. In *Present status of waterfowl resources,* All-Union Seminar, 20–23 October 1984. Moscow.

Poyarkov, N.D. 1992. On the recent state of the Swan Goose population in Russia. In 7th N. American Arctic Goose Conference and Workshop, January 7–12th 1992. California Maritime Academy, Vallejo, California.

Pöysä, H. 1983. Resource utilisation pattern and guild structure in a waterfowl community. *Oikos* 40: 295–307.

Pöysä, H. 1985. Circumstantial evidence of foraging interference between two species of dabbling ducks. *Wilson Bull.* 97: 541–43.

Pöysä, H. 1987a. Numerical and escape responses of foraging teals *Anas crecca* to predation risk. *Bird Behaviour* 71: 87–92.

Pöysä, H. 1987b. Costs and benefits of group foraging in the Teal. *Behaviour* 103: 123–40.

Pöysä, H. 1991. Effects of predation risk and patch quality on the formation and attractiveness of foraging groups of Teal, *Anas crecca. Anim. Behav.* 41: 285–94.

Pöysä, H. and Virtanen, J. 1994. Habitat selection and survival of Common Goldeneye (*Bucephala clangula*) broods—preliminary results. *Hydrobiologia* 279/280: 289–96.

Pöysä, H., Runko, P. and Ruusila, V. 1997. Natal philopatry and the local resource competition hypothesis: data from the Common Goldeneye. *J. Avian Biol.* 28: 63–67.

Pozdnayakov, V.I. and Sofronov, Y.N. 1995. Status of Bean Goose *Anser fabalis* populations in the Lena delta 1994. *Goose Study Group Bull. of Eastern Europe and Northern Asia* 1: 147–49.

Pradel, R., Rioux, N., Tamisier, A. and Lebreton, J-D. 1997. Individual turnover amongst wintering Teal in the Camargue: a mark–recapture study. *J. Wildl. Manage.* 61: 816–21.

Praeger, E.M. and Wilson, A.C. 1976. Congruency of phylogenies derived from different proteins. *J. Molecular Evolution* 9: 45–47.

Prager, E.M. and Wilson, A.C. 1978. Phylogenetic relationships and rates of evolution in birds. *Int. Ornith. Congr.* 17: 1209–14.

Pratt, H.D., Bruner, P.L. and Berrett, D.G. 1987. *A field guide to the birds of Hawaii and the tropical Pacific.* Princeton Univ. Press.

Prawiradilaga, D.M. 1985. A comparative study of the courtship behaviour of the Grey Teal (*Anas gibberifrons*) and the Chestnut Teal (*Anas castanea*). Unpubl. M. Rural Sci. thesis. Univ. New England, Armidale, US.

Prestrud, P., Black, J.M. and Owen, M. 1989. The relationship between an increasing population of Barnacle Geese and the number and size of their colonies in Svalbard. *Wildfowl* 40: 32–38.

Prevett, J.P. and MacInnes, C.D. 1980. Family and other social groups in Snow Geese. *Wildl. Monogr.* 71: 6–44.

Prince, H.H. 1968. Nest sites used by Wood Ducks and Common Goldeneyes in New Brunswick. *J. Wildl. Manage.* 32: 489–500.

Prince, H.H., Siegel, P.B. and Cornwell, G.W. 1969. Hatchability, clutch position, and hatching sequence in Mallards. *Auk* 86: 762–63.

Prince, P.A. and Croxall, J.P. 1996. The birds of South Georgia. *Bull. BOC* 116: 81–104.

Prince, P.A. and Poncet, S. 1996. South Georgia distribution of the South Georgia Pintail (*Anas g. georgica*). In *South Georgia: an Ecological Atlas* (ed. P.N. Trathan, F.H.J. Daunt and E.J. Murphy), map 2–28. British Antarctic Survey, Cambridge.

Pringle, J.D. 1985. *The waterbirds of Australia*. Angus Robertson, Sydney.

Prins, H.H.T., Ydenberg, R.C. and Drent, R.H. 1980. The interaction of Brent Geese *Branta bernicla* and Sea Plantain *Plantago maritima* during spring staging: field observations and experiments. *Acta Botanica Nederlands* 29: 585–96.

Projet ZICOMA 1999. Les zones d'importance pour la conservation des oiseaux à Madagascar. Projet ZICOMA, Antananarivo.

Prop, J. and de Vries, J. 1993. Impact of snow and food conditions on the reproductive performance of Barnacle Geese *Branta leucopsis*. *Ornis Scand.* 24: 110–21.

Prop, J. and Vulink, T. 1992. Digestion by Barnacle Geese in the annual cycle: the interplay between retention time and food quality. *Functional Ecology* 6: 180–89.

Prop, J., van Eerden, M.R., Daan, S., Drent, R.H., Tinbergen, J.M. and St Joseph, A.M. 1981. Ecology of the Barnacle Goose during the breeding season: preliminary results from expeditions to Svalbard 1977 and 1978. In Norwegian–Netherlands Symp. on Svalbard (ed. A.G.F. van Holk, H.K. St. Jacob, E.H. Liefferink), pp. 5–112. Arctic Center, Groningen.

Prop, J., van Eerden, M.R. and Drent, R.H. 1984. Reproductive success of the Barnacle Goose *Branta leucopsis* in relation to food exploitation on the breeding grounds, western Svalbard. *Norsk Pol. Skr.* 181: 87–117.

Prop, J., Black, J.M. and Shimmings, P. 2003. Travel schedules to the high arctic: barnacle geese trade-off the timing of migration with accumulation of fat reserves. *Oikos* 103: 403–14.

Prozesky, O.P.M. 1959. Preliminary observations on clutch laying, incubation, and fledging period of Spur-winged Goose. *Bull. S. Afr. Mus. Assoc.* 7: 52–54.

Przewalski [Przevalskiy], N. 1877–78. The birds of Mongolia, the Tangut Country, and the solitudes of Northern Tibet. In *Orn. misc.* 3, Parts XI and XII, pp. 47–53 and 87–100. Trübner, London.

Pulido, V. 1991. *El libro rojo de la fauna silvestre del Peru*. Biblioteca Nacional del Peru, Lima, Peru.

Pulliam, H.R. 1973. On the advantages of flocking. *J. Theor. Biol.* 38: 419–22.

Pyong-Oh Won 1981. Present status of the swans wintering in Korea and their conservation. In 2nd IWRB Swan Symp., Sapporo, 1980 (ed. G.V.T. Matthews and M. Smart), pp.15–19. IWRB, Slimbridge, UK.

Pziclonskij, S. (ed.). 1976. *Rare, threatened and inadequately known birds of the USSR*. Moscow.

Quakenbush, L.T., Suydam, R.S., Fluetsch, K.T. and Donaldson, C.L. 1995. Breeding biology of Steller's Eider nesting near Barrow, Alaska, 1991–1994. Tech. Rept., NAES-TR-93-01, US Fish & Wildl. Serv., Ecological Services, Fairbanks, Alaska.

Quammen, M.L. and Onuf, C.P. 1993. Laguna Madre: seagrass changes continue decades after salinity reductions. *Estuaries* 16: 302–10.

Quicke, D.L.J. 1993. *Principles and techniques of contemporary taxonomy*. Blackie, London.

Quinlan, E.E. and Baldassarre, G.A. 1984. Activity budgets of nonbreeding Green-winged Teal on Playa Lakes in Texas. *J. Wildl. Manage.* 48: 838–45.

Quinn, J.L. and Kokorev, Y. 2000. Direct and indirect estimates of a Peregrine Falcon population size in northern Eurasia. *Auk* 117: 455–64.

Quinn, J.L., Prop, J. and Kokorev, Y. 1995. The ecology of Red-breasted Geese in summer: report on a preliminary expedition to the Taymyr peninsula in 1995. Unpubl. rept. WWT, Slimbridge, UK.

Quinn, J.L., Prop, J., Kokorev, Y. and Black, J.M. 2003. Predator protection or similar habitat selection in red-breasted goose nesting associations: extremes along a continuum. *Animal Behaviour* 65: 297–307.

Quinn, J.L., Prop, J., Kokorev, Y, Hunter, J. and Rosenfield, S. 1996a. The ecology of Red-breasted Geese on the Taymyr peninsula in 1996. Unpubl. rept. WWT, Slimbridge, UK.

Quinn, J.L., Still, L., Kirby, J.S., Carrier, M.C. and Lambdon, P. 1996b. Scaup *Aythya marila* numbers and the Cockle *Cardium edule* fishery on the Solway Firth: are they related? *Wildfowl* 47: 187–94.

Quinn, J.L., Kokorev, Y., Prop, J., Fox, N. and Black, J.M. 2000. Are Peregrine Falcons in Northern Siberia still affected by organochlorines? In Vth World Conference on Birds of Prey and Owls, Johannesburg, 4–11 August 1998 (ed. B.U. Meyburg and R.D. Chancellor), pp.279–94. Hancock House, Blaine, Washington.

Quinn, T.W., Shields, G.F. and Wilson, A.C. 1991. Affinities of the Hawaiian Goose based on two types of mitochondrial DNA data. *Auk* 108: 585–93.

Rabor, D.S. 1977. *Philippine birds and mammals*. U.P. Science Education Center, Univ. Philippines.

Radester, T. 1974. On the ontogeny of orientating movements in the Triumph ceremony in two species of geese (*Anser anser* L. and *Branta canadensis* L.). *Behaviour* 50: 1–15.

Radović, D. Kralj, J. and Tutiš, V. 1998. Ferruginous Ducks at Draganić Fish-ponds, NW Croatia, and a population estimate for Croatia. *Threatened Waterfowl Specialist Group News* 11: 23–25. WWT, Slimbridge, UK.

Raffaele, H., Wiley, J., Garrido, O., Keith, A. and Raffaele, J. 1998. *Birds of the West Indies*. Helm, London.

Rahn, H. and Ar, A. 1974. The avian egg: incubation time and water loss. *Condor* 76: 147–52.

Raikow, R.J. 1970. Evolution of diving adaptations in the stifftail ducks. *Univ. Calif. Publ. Zool.* 94: 1–52.

Raikow, R.J. 1971. The osteology and taxonomic position of the White-backed Duck *Thalassornis leuconotus*. *Wilson Bull.* 83: 270–77.

Raikow, R.J. 1973. Locomotor mechanisms in North American ducks. *Wilson Bull.* 85: 295–307.

Raj, M. 1991. Field observations on Lesser Whistling Teal. *Newsletter for Birdwatchers* 31(5 and 6): 4–6.

Rajala, P. and Ormio, T. 1970. On the nesting of the Goldeneye, *Bucephala clangula* (L.) in the Meltaus game research area in northern Finland, 1959–1966. *Finn. Game Res.* 31: 3–9.

Rakowski, P.W. and Chabot, B.P. 1983. Changes in land use in the Minnedosa district of southwestern Manitoba: an update on the Kiel-Hawkins transects. Unpubl. rept. Can. Wildl. Serv. Rep., Winnipeg.

Rand, A.L. 1936. The distribution and habits of Madagascar birds; summary of field notes on the Mission Zoologique Franco-Anglo-Americaine à Madagascar. *Bull. Am. Mus. Nat. Hist.* 72: 143–499.

Rand, A.L. 1951. Birds of Negros Island. *Fieldiana, Zoology* 31(48): 571–96.

Rand, A.L. and Rabor, D.S. 1960. Birds of the Philippine Islands: Siquijor, Mount Malindang, Bohol and Samar. *Fieldiana, Zoology* 35(7): 221–441.

Rank, M. 1991. 'Extinct' shelduck rediscovered in China? *Bull. OBC* 14: 14–15.

Rank, M. 1992. Crested Shelduck update. *Bull. OBC* 15: 10.

Ratcliffe, D. 1993. *The Peregrine Falcon* (2nd edn). Poyser, London.

Ratcliffe, L., Rockwell, R.F. and Cooke, F. 1988. Recruitment and maternal age in Lesser Snow Geese *Chen caerulescens caerulescens*. *J. Anim. Ecol.* 57: 553–63.

Raud, H. and Faure, J.M. 1988. Descriptive study of sexual behavior of male Muscovy Ducks. *Bio. of Behav.* 13: 175.

Rave, D.P. and Baldassarre, G.A. 1989. Activity budget of Green-winged Teal wintering in coastal wetlands of Louisiana. *J. Wildl. Manage.* 53: 753–59.

Rave, D.P. and Baldassarre, G.A. 1991. Carcass mass and composition of Green-winged Teal wintering in Louisiana and Texas. *J. Wildl. Manage.* 55: 457–61.

Rave, L., Fleischer, R.C., Duvall, F. and Black, J.M. 1995. Genetic analysis through DNA fingerprinting of captive populations of Hawaiian geese. *Cons. Biol.* 8: 744–51.

Rave, L., Fleischer, R.C., Duvall, F. and Black, J.M. 1998. Effects of inbreeding on reproductive success in captive populations of Hawaiian Geese. *Wildfowl* 49: 36–44.

Raveling, D.G. 1969. Social classes of Canada Geese in winter. *J. Wildl. Manage.* 33: 304–18.

Raveling, D.G. 1970. Dominance relationships and agonistic behaviour of Canada Geese in winter. *Behaviour* 37: 291–319.

Raveling, D.G. 1978a. Dynamics of distribution of Canada Geese in winter. *N. Am. Wildl. Natur. Resour. Conf. Trans.* 43: 206–25.

Raveling, D.G. 1978b. The timing of egg-laying by northern geese. *Auk* 95: 294–303.

Raveling, D.G. 1979. The annual cycle of body composition of Canada Geese with special reference to control of reproduction. *Auk* 96: 234–52.

Raveling, D.G. 1981. Survival, experience, and age in relation to breeding success of Canada Geese. *J. Wildl. Manage.* 45: 817–29.

Raveling, D.G. 1984. Geese and hunters of Alaska's Yukon Delta: management problems and political dilemmas. In 49th N.A. Wildl. Nat. Res. Conf., pp.555–75. Wildl. Manage. Inst., Washington.

Raveling, D.G. 1989. Nest predation rates in relation to colony size of Black Brant. *J. Wildl. Manage.* 53: 87–90.

Raveling, D.G. and Lumsden, H.G. 1977. *Nesting ecology of Canada Geese in the Hudson Bay lowlands of Ontario: evolution and population regulation.* Fish & Wildlife Res. Rep., No. 98. Ministry of Natural Resources, Ontario.

Raveling, D.G., Crews, W.E. and Klimstra, W.D. 1972. Activity patterns of Canada Geese during winter. *Wilson Bull.* 84: 278–95.

Raya Rey, A. and Schiavini, A. 2002. Distribution and density of Kelp Geese and Flightless Steamer Ducks along the Beagle Channel, Tierra del Fuego, Argentina. *Waterbirds* 25: 225–29.

Rayner, J.M.V. 1985. Flight, speeds of. In *A dictionary of birds* (ed. B. Campbell and E. Lack), pp.224–26. Poyser, Calton.

Razafindrahanta, H.V. 1999. Investigation of the diet of wild Madagascar Teal *Anas bernieri. Dodo* 35: 87–92.

Redfern, C.P.F. 1989. Rates of primary-feather growth in nestling birds. *Ornis Scand.* 20: 59–64.

Redford, K.H. 1985. Emas National Park and the plight of the Brazilian cerrados. *Oryx* 19(4): 210–14.

Reed, A. 1968. Habitat and breeding ecology. Eastern Canada. In *The Black Duck: evaluation, management and research* (ed. P. Barske), pp.57–89. Atlantic Waterfowl Council, Boston, Massachusetts.

Reed, A. 1975 Migration, homing and mortality of breeding female eiders *Somateria mollissima dresseri* of the St. Lawrence estuary, Quebec. *Ornis Scand.* 6: 41–47.

Reed, A. 1975. Reproductive output of Black Ducks in the St. Lawrence estuary. *J. Wildl. Manage.* 39: 243–55.

Reed, A. (ed.) 1986. Eider ducks in Canada. *Can. Wildl. Serv. Rep. Ser. no. 46.*

Reed, A. and Bourget, A. 1977. Distribution and abundance of waterfowl wintering in southern Quebec. *Can. Field-Nat.* 91: 1–7.

Reed, A. and Cousineau, J-G. 1967. Epidemics involving Common Eiders *Somateria mollissima* at Ile Blanche, Quebec. *Le Naturaliste canadien* 94: 327–34.

Reed, A. and Plante, N. 1997. Decline in body mass, size and condition of Greater Snow Geese, 1975–94. *J. Wildl. Manage.* 61: 413–19.

Reed, A., Aubry, Y. and Reed, E. 1994. Surf Scoter, *Melanitta perspicillata*, nesting in southern Québec. *Can. Field-Nat.* 108: 364–65.

Reed, A., Hughes, R.J. and Gauthier, G. 1995. Incubation behavior and body mass of female Greater Snow Geese. *Condor* 97: 993–1001.

Reed, A., Benoît, R., Lalumière, R. and Julien, M. 1996. *Duck use of the coastal habitats of northeastern James Bay*, Occ. Pap., No. 90. Can. Wildl. Serv., Ottawa.

Reed, E.T., Cooch, E.G., Goudie, R.I. and Cooke, F. 1998. Site fidelity of Black Brant wintering and spring staging in the Strait of Georgia, British Columbia. *Condor* 100: 426–37.

Rees, E.C. 1982. The effect of photoperiod on the timing of spring migration in the Bewick's Swan. *Wildfowl* 33: 119–32.

Rees, E.C. 1987. Conflict of choice within pairs of Bewick's Swans regarding their migratory movement to and from the wintering grounds. *Anim. Behav.* 35: 1685–93.

Rees, E.C. 1989. Consistency in the timing of migration of individual Bewick's Swans. *Anim. Behav.* 38: 384–93.

Rees, E.C. 1990. Bewick's Swans: their feeding ecology and coexistence with other grazing Anatidae. *J. Appl. Ecol.* 27: 939–51.

Rees, E.C. 1991. Distribution within the USSR of Bewick's Swans *Cygnus columbianus bewickii* marked in Britain. *Wildfowl* Spec. Suppl., 1: 209–13.

Rees, E.C. 1997. *Cygnus columbianus* Bewick's Swan. In *European ornithological atlas* (ed. M. Blair and W. Hagemeijer), p.63. Poyser, London.

Rees, E.C. and Bacon, P.J. 1996. Migratory tradition in Bewick's Swans (*Cygnus columbianus bewickii*). *Gibier Faune Sauvage* 13: 407–20.

Rees, E.C. and Bowler, J.M. 1991. Feeding activities of Bewick's Swans *Cygnus columbianus bewickii* at a migratory site in the Estonian SSR. *Wildfowl* Spec. Suppl. 1: 249–55.

Rees, E.C. and Bowler, J. 1996. Fifty years of swan research and conservation by the Wildfowl & Wetlands Trust. *Wildfowl* 47: 248–63.

Rees, E., and Bowler, J. 2002. Tundra Swan (Bewick's Swan) *Cygnus columbianus*. In *The migration atlas: movements of the birds of Britain and Ireland* (ed. C.V. Wernham, M.P. Toms, J.H. Marchant, J.A. Clark, G.M. Siriwardena and S.R. Baillie), pp.149–53. Poyser, London.

Rees, E.C. and Hillgarth, N. 1984. The breeding biology of captive Black-headed Ducks and the behavior of their young. *Condor* 86: 242–50.

Rees, E.C., Bowler, J.M. and Butler, L. 1990. Bewick's and Whooper Swans: the 1989–90 season. *Wildfowl* 41: 176–81.

Rees, E.C., Black, J.M., Spray, C.J. and Thorisson, S. 1991a. Comparative study of the breeding success of Whooper Swans *Cygnus cygnus* nesting in upland and lowland regions of Iceland. *Ibis* 133: 365–73.

Rees, E.C., Bowler, J.M. and Butler, L. 1991b. Bewick's and Whooper Swans *Cygnus columbianus bewickii* and *C. cygnus*: the 1990–91 season. *Wildfowl* 42: 169–75.

Rees, E.C., Lievesley, P., Pettifor, R.A. and Perrins, C. 1996. Mate fidelity in swans: an interspecific comparison. In *Partnerships in birds: the study of monogamy* (ed. J.M. Black), pp.118–37. OUP.

Rees, E.C., Einarsson, Ó. and Laubek, B. 1997a. *Cygnus cygnus* Whooper Swan. *BWP Update*, Vol. 1, No. 1: 27–35.

Rees, E.C., Kirby, J.S. and Gilburn, A. 1997b. Site selection by swans wintering in Britain and Ireland; the importance of geographic location and habitat. *Ibis* 139: 337–52.

Rees, E.C., Bowler, J.M. and Beekman. J.H. 1997c. *Cygnus columbianus* Bewick's Swan and Whistling Swan. *BWP Update* 1: 63–74.

Rees, E.C., Colhoun, K., Einarsson, Ó., McElwaine, G., Petersen, Æ. and Thorstensen, S. 2002. Whooper Swan *Cygnus cygnus*. In *The migration atlas: movements of the birds of Britain and Ireland* (ed. C.V. Wernham, M.P. Toms, J.H. Marchant, J.A. Clark, G.M. Siriwardena and S.R. Baillie), pp.154–57. Poyser, London.

Reeves, H.M. 1976. *Canvasback and Redhead background information—a review,* Admin. Rept. US Fish & Wildl. Serv., Washington.

Regehr, H.M., Smith, C.M., Arquilla, B. and Cooke, F. 2001. Post-fledging broods of migratory Harlequin Ducks accompany females to wintering areas. *Condor* 103: 408–12.

Rehfisch, M.M., Austin, G.E., Holloway, S.J., Allan J.R. and O'Connell M. 2002. An approach to the assessment of change in the numbers of Canada Geese *Branta canadensis* and Greylag Geese *Anser anser* in southern Britain. *Bird Study* 49: 50–59.

Reichel, J.D. and Glass, P.O. 1991. Checklist of the birds of the Mariana Islands. *'Elepaio* 51: 3–11.

Reichel, J.D. and Lemke, T.O. 1994. Ecology and extinction of the Mariana Mallard. *J. Wildl. Manage.* 58: 199–205.

Reichholf, J. 1983. Ausbrüche von Enten-Botulismus im Sommer 1982 in Bayern. *Anz. Orn. Ges. Bayern* 22: 37–56.

Reid, B.R and Roderick, C. 1973. New Zealand Scaup *Aythya novaeseelandiae* and Brown Teal *Anas aucklandica chlorotis* in captivity. *Int. Zoo Ybk* 13: 12–15.

Reimnitz, E. and Maurer, D.K. 1979. Effects of storm surges on the Beaufort Sea coast, northern Alaska. *Arctic* 32(4): 329–44.

Reinecke. K.J. and Owen, R.B., Jnr 1980. Food use and nutrition of Black Ducks nesting in Maine. *J. Wildl. Manage.* 44: 549–58.

Reinecke, K.J., Stone, T.L. and Owen, R.B., Jr 1982. Seasonal carcass composition and energy balance of female Black Ducks in Maine. *Condor* 84: 420–26.

Reinecker, W.C. 1987. Survival and band recovery rate estimates of Northern Pintail banded in California, 1948–1979. *Calif. Fish Game* 73: 230–37.

Remsen, J.V. and Taylor, M.A., Jnr 1989. *An annotated list of the birds of Bolivia.* Buteo, Vermillion, South Dakota.

Renssen, T.A. 1974. New breeding records from Surinam. *Ardea* 62: 123–27.

Reynolds, C.M. 1972. Mute Swan weights in relation to breeding performance. *Wildfowl* 23: 111–18.

Reynolds, M.H. 2002. The foraging ecology, habitat use, and population dynamics of the Laysan Duck (*Anas laysanensis*). Ph.D. dissertation. Virginia Polytechnic, Blacksburg, VA, USA.

Reynolds, P. 1987. Observations on the time budget and diving ecology of Long-tailed Ducks in Eqalung-miut Nunaat, West Greenland. *Wildfowl* 38: 55–61.

Reynolds, R. 1995. Waterfowl breeding pair distributions. Jamestown, ND: Northern Prairie Wildlife Research Center Home Page. http://www.npwrc. usgs.gov/resource/distr/birds/thunder/thunder.htm (Version 16 October 1998).

Rheinwald, G. 1982. *Brutvogelatlas der Bundesrepublik Deutschland, Kartierung 1980*, Vol. 6. Dachverbandes Deutscher Avifaunisten, Bonn.

Rhymer, J.M. 1988. The effect of egg size variability on thermoregulation of Mallard (*Anas platyrhynchos*) offspring and its implications for survival. *Oecologia* 75: 20–24.

Rhymer, J.M. 2001. Evolutionary relationships and conservation of the Hawaiian anatids. *Studies in Avian Biology* 22: 61–67.

Rhymer, J.M. and Simberloff, D. 1996. Extinction by hybridization and introgression. *Ann. Rev. Ecol. Syst.* 27: 83–109.

Rhymer, J.M., Williams, M.J. and Braun, M.J. 1994. Mitochondrial analysis of gene flow between New Zealand Mallards (*Anas platyrhynchos*) and Grey Ducks (*A. superciliosa*). *Auk* 111: 970–78.

Rhymer, J.M., Williams, M.J. and Kingsford, R.T. 2004. Implications of phylogeography and population genetics for subspecies taxonomy of Grey (Pacific Black) Duck *Anas superciliosa* and its conservation in New Zealand. *Pacific Cons. Biol.* 10: 57–66.

Rice, D.W. and Wolman, A.A. 1971. *Life history and ecology of the gray whale Eschrichtius robustus*, Spec. Publ., No. 3. Am. Soc. Mammalogists, Lawrences, KS.

Ricklefs, R.F. 1979. Adaptation, constraint and compromise in avian post-natal development. *Biol. Rev.* 54: 269–90.

Ridgely, R.S. and Gwynne, J.A., Jr 1989. *A guide to the birds of Panama, with Costa Rica, Nicaragua and Honduras*. Princeton Univ. Press.

Ridgeway, R. 1880. Revision of nomenclature of North American birds. *Proc. U.S. Nat. Mus.* 3: 15–16.

Ridgill, S.C. and Fox, A.D. 1990. *Cold weather movements of waterfowl in Western Europe*, IWRB Spec. Publ., No. 13. IWRB, Slimbridge, UK.

Ridgill, S.C., McKay, C.R. and Rees, E.C. 1994. *Greenland White-fronted Geese wintering on Islay*. WWT report to Scottish Natural Heritage. WWT, Slimbridge.

Rienecker, W.C. 1968. A summary of band recoveries from Redheads (*Aythya americana*) banded in northeastern California. *Calif. Fish and Game* 54: 17–26.

Rigdon, R.H. 1959. The respiratory system in the normal White Pekin Duck. *Poultry Science* 38: 196–210.

Riggert, T.L. 1966. *Study of the wetlands of the Swan Coastal Plain*. Dept Fish Fauna, Perth.

Riggert, T.L. 1977. The biology of the mountain duck on Rottnest Island, Western Australia, *Wildl. Monogr.* 52: 1–67.

Ringelman, J.K. and Longcore, J.R. 1982a. Movements and wetland selection by brood-rearing Black Ducks. *J. Wildl. Manage.* 46: 615–21.

Ringelman, J.K. and Longcore, J.R. 1982b. Survival of juvenile Black Duck during brood rearing. *J. Wildl. Manage.* 46: 622–28.

Ringelman, J.K., Longcore, J.R. and Owen, R.B., Jr 1982. Nest and brood attentiveness in female Black Ducks. *Condor* 84: 110–16.

Ripley, L. 1984. *Alberta/B.C. cooperative Trumpeter Swan restoration programme—1983*. Alberta Dept Forestry, Lands and Wildlife, Brooks, Alberta.

Ripley, S.D. 1942. A review of the species *Anas castanea*. *Auk* 59: 90–99.

Ripley, S.D. 1950. A small collection of birds from Argentine Tierra del Fuego. *Postilla* 3: 1–11.

Ripley, S.D. 1951. Remarks on the Philippine Mallard. *Wilson Bull.* 63(3): 189–91.

Ripley, S.D. 1959. Laysan Teal at Litchfield. *Avic. Mag.* 65: 172–74.

Ripley, S.D. 1960. Laysan Teal in captivity. *Wilson Bull.* 72: 244–47.

Ripley, S.D. 1964. A systematic and ecological study of the birds of New Guinea. *Bull. Peabody Mus. Nat. Hist.* 19.

Ripley, S.D. 1985. The Laysan Teal—recent history and future? *Avic. Mag.* 91: 76–78.

Ripley, S.D. and Rabor, D.S. 1958. Notes on a collection of birds from Mindoro Island. *Bull. Peabody Mus. Nat. Hist.* 13: 1–83.

Robb, J.R. and Bookhout, T.A. 1995. Factors influencing Wood Duck use of natural cavities. *J. Wildl. Manage.* 89: 372–83.

Robbins, C.T. 1993. *Wildlife feeding and nutrition* (2nd edn). Academic Press, San Diego.

Robert, M. and Cloutier, L. 2001. Summer food habits of harlequin ducks in eastern North America. *Wilson Bull.* 113: 78–84.

Robert, M., Bordage, D., Savard, J-P.L., Fitzgerald, G. and Morneau, F. 2000. The breeding range of the Barrow's Goldeneye in eastern North America. *Wilson Bull.* 112: 1–7.

Roberts, T.S. 1932. *The birds of Minnesota*, Vol. 1. Mus. Nat. Hist. and Univ. Minnesota Press, Minneapolis.

Robertson, C.J.R. 1976. *The Campbell Island Teal*, Wildlife—a review, No. 7. NZ Wildlife Service, Wellington.

Robertson, G.J. and Cooke, F. 1999. Winter philopatry in migratory waterfowl. *Auk* 116: 20–34.

Robertson, G.J. and Goudie, R.I. 1999. Harlequin Duck (*Histrionicus histrionicus*), The Birds of North America, No. 466, (ed. A. Poole and F. Gill). AOU, The Birds of North America Inc., Philadelphia.

Robertson, G.J. and Savard, J-P.L. 2002. Long-tailed Duck (*Clangula hyemalis*). The Birds of North America, No. 651 (ed. A. Poole and F. Gill). AOU, The Birds of North America Inc., Philadelphia.

Robertson, G.J., Watson, M.D. and Cooke, F. 1992. Frequency, timing and costs of intraspecific nest parasitism in the Common Eider. *Condor* 94: 871–79.

Robertson, G.J., Cooke, F., Goudie, R.I. and Boyd, W.S. 1998. The timing of pair formation in Harlequin Ducks. *Condor* 100: 551–55.

Robertson, G.J., Cooke, F., Goudie, R.L. and Boyd, W.S. 2000. Spacing patterns, mating systems, and winter philopatry in Harlequin Ducks. *Auk* 117: 299–307.

Robertson, I. 1992. New information on birds in Cameroon. *Bull. BOC* 112: 36–42.

Robinson, A.L. and Delroy, L.B. 1986. Monitoring of Cape Barren Goose populations in South Australia. *South Aust. Ornithol.* 30(2): 45–51.

Robinson, F.N. and Robinson, A.H. 1970. Regional variation in the visual and acoustic signals of the male Musk Duck, *Biziura lobata*. *CSIRO Wildl. Res. Rep.* 15: 73–78.

Robinson, J.A., Colhoun, J.G., McElwaine, J.G. and Rees, E.C. 2004a. Whooper Swan *Cygnus cygnus* (Iceland population) in Britain and Ireland 1960/61–1999/2000. *Waterbird Review Series*, WWT/JNCC, Slimbridge.

Robinson, J.A., Colhoun, J.G., McElwaine, J.G. and Rees, E.C. 2004b. Bewick's Swan *Cygnus columbianus bewickii* (Northwest Europe population) in Britain and Ireland 1960/61–1999/2000. *Waterbird Review Series*, WWT/JNCC, Slimbridge.

Robson, C. 2000. From the field. *Bull. OBC* 32: 66–76.

Roche, P. 1988. Annales du Centre Ornithologique Auvergne. *Le Grand Duc* 32: 53–69.

Rockwell, R.F., Findlay, C.S. and Cooke, F. 1983. Life history studies of the Lesser Snow Goose (*Anser caerulescens caerulescens*) I. The influence of age and time on fecundity. *Oecologia* 56: 318–22.

Rockwell, R.F., Cooch, E.G., Thompson, C.B. and Cooke, F. 1993. Age and reproductive success in female Lesser Snow Geese: experience, senescence, and the cost of philopatry. *J. Anim. Ecol.* 62: 323–33.

Rockwell, R.F., Petersen, M.R. and Schmutz, J.A. 1996. *The Emperor Goose: an annotated bibliography*, Biol. Papers Univ. Alas., No. 25. Univ. Alaska, Fairbanks.

Rodebrand, S. 1972. Fågelstracket genom Kalmarsund 1962 och 1963. *Vår Fågelvärld* 31: 247–51.

Rodrigues, D., Figueiredo, M. and Fabião, A. 2001. Mallard *Anas platyrhychos* lead poisoning risk in central Portugal. *Wildfowl* 52: 169–74.

Rodway, M.S., Gosse, J.W., Jr, Fong, I. and Montevecchi, W.A. 1998. Discovery of a Harlequin Duck nest in eastern North America. *Wilson Bull.* 110: 282–85.

Rofritz, D.J. 1977. Oligochaeta as a winter food source for the old squaw. *J. Wildl. Manage.* 41: 590–91.

Rogacheva, H. 1992. *The birds of Central Siberia.* Husum: Husum Druck-u. Verlagsges.

Rogers, J.P. 1959. Low water and Lesser Scaup reproduction near Erickson, Manitoba. *Trans. N. Am. Wildl. Conf.* 24: 216–24.

Rogers, J.P. 1964. Effects of drought on reproduction of the Lesser Scaup. *J. Wildl. Manage.* 28: 213–22.

Rohwer, F.C. 1984. Patterns of egg laying in prairie ducks. *Auk* 101: 603–5.

Rohwer, F.C. 1985. The adaptive significance of clutch size in prairie ducks. *Auk* 102: 354–61.

Rohwer, F.C. 1986. Composition of Blue-winged Teal eggs in relation to egg size, clutch size, and the timing of laying. *Condor* 88: 513–19.

Rohwer, F.C. 1988. Inter- and intraspecific relationships between egg size and clutch size in waterfowl. *Auk* 105: 161–76.

Rohwer, F.C. 1992. Evolution of reproductive patterns. In *Ecology and management of breeding waterfowl* (ed. B.D. Batt, A.D. Afton, M.G. Anderson, C.D. Ankney, D.H. Johnson, J.A. Kadlec *et al.*), pp.486–539. Univ. Minnesota Press, Minneapolis.

Rohwer, F.C. and Anderson, M.G. 1988. Female-biased philopatry, monogamy, and the timing of pair formation in migratory waterfowl. *Current Ornithol.* 5: 187–221.

Rohwer, F.C. and Eisenhauer, D.I. 1989. Egg mass and clutch size relationships in geese, eiders, and swans. *Ornis Scand.* 20: 43–48.

Rohwer, F.C., Johnson, W.P and Loos, E.R. 2002. Blue-winged Teal (*Anas discors*). The Birds of North America, No. 625 (ed. A. Poole and F. Gill). AOU, The Birds of North America Inc., Philadelphia.

Rojas, R.M. 1954. Los patos silvestres en Mexico (su identificacion distribucion y notas relativas a su biologia). *Revista de la Sociedad Mexicana de Historia Natural* 15: 95–107.

Romanov, A.A. 2003. New breeding areas of Lesser White-fronted Geese in the Putorana Plateau. *Casarca* 9: 139–53.

Rose, P.M. 1995. *Western Palearctic and South-west Asia waterfowl census 1994*, Publ., No. 35. IWRB, Slimbridge, UK.

Rose, P.M. 1996. Status and trends of Western Palearctic duck (Anatinae), swans (*Cygnus* sp.) and Coot (*Fulica atra*) populations. *Gibier Faune Sauvage* 13: 531–45.

Rose, P.M. and Scott, D.A. 1994. *Waterfowl population estimates*. Publ., No. 29. IWRB, Slimbridge, UK.

Rose, P.M. and Scott, D.A. 1997. *Waterfowl population estimates*, (2nd edn), Publ., No. 44. Wetlands International, Wageningen, Netherlands.

Roselaar, C.S. 1977. De geografische variatie van de rietgans. *Watervogels* 2: 61–88.

Roselaar, C.S. 1979. Fluctuaties in aantallen Krombek strandlopers *Calidris ferruginea*. *Watervogels* 4: 202–10.

Rosen, D.E. 1979. Fishes from the uplands and intermontane basins of Guatemala: revisionary studies and comparative geography. *Bull. Am. Mus. Nat. Hist.* 162: 267–376.

Rosen, M.N. 1971. Avian Cholera. In *Infectious and parasitic diseases of wild birds* (ed. J.W. Davis, R.C. Anderson, L. Karsted and D.O. Trainer), pp.59–74. Iowa Univ. Press, Ames.

Roslyakov, G.Y. 1985. Information on the numbers of *Aix galericulata* and *Mergus squamatus* over Khabarovsk Territory. In *Rare and endangered birds of the Far East*, pp. 101–2. Far East Science Centre, USSR Academy of Sciences, Vladivostok.

Roslyakov, G.Y. 1987. Swans of the Lower Amur region and Shantar Islands. In *Ecology and migration of swans in the USSR* (ed. E. Syroechkovski), pp.136–37. Nauka, Moscow.

Ross, B.P. and Furness, R.W. 2000. *Minimising the impact of eiders on mussel farms.* University of Glasgow, UK.

Ross, B.P., Lein, J., and Furness, R.W. 2001. Use of underwater playback to reduce the impact of eiders on mussel farms. *ICES J. Marine Science* 58: 517–24.

Rossi, J.A.H. 1959. Algunos datos sobre huevos, postura e incubación de la Avutarda de Cabeza Colorada. *Physis* 21: 240–44.

Rotella, J.J. and Ratti, J.T. 1992. Mallard brood movements and wetland selection in southwestern Manitoba. *J. Wildl. Manage.* 56: 508–15.

Rotella, J.J., Clark, R.G. and Afton, A.D. 2003. Survival of female lesser scaup: effects of body size, age, and reproductive effort. *Condor* 105: 336–347.

Roth, P.G. and Scott, D.A. 1987. The avifauna of the Baixada Maranhense. *Economic Development and Environmental Impact in Humid Tropical Forest Areas of Brazil,* Int. sem., Belem, October 1986. Companhia Vale do Rio Doce, Rio de Janeiro. [In Portuguese with English abstracts.]

Roth, R.R. 1976. Effects of a severe thunderstorm on airborne ducks. *Wilson Bull.* 88: 654–56.

Rothschild, W. 1893–1900. *The avifauna of Laysan.* Porter, London.

Rottmann, J. and López-Calleja, M.V. 1992. *Estrategia nacional de conservación de aves*, Publicacion de Servicio Agricola y Ganadero, División de Protección de Recursos Naturales Renovables, Serie Técnica, Año 1, No. 1. Unión de Ornitologos de Chile y CIPA, Santiago.

Roux, F. and Jarry, G. 1984. Numbers, composition and distribution of populations of Anatidae wintering in West Africa. *Wildfowl* 35: 48–60.

Roux, F., Maheo, R. and Tamisier, A. 1978. L'exploitation de la basse vallée du Sénégal (quartier d'hiver tropical) par trois espèces de canards paléactiques et éthiopiens. *La Terre et la Vie* 32: 387–416.

Rowan, M.K. 1963. The Yellowbill Duck *Anus* (sic) *undulata* Dubois in Southern Africa. *Ostrich* Suppl. 5: 1–56.

Rowcliffe, J.M., Watkinson, A.R., Sutherland, W.J. and Vickery, J.A. 1995. Cyclic winter grazing patterns in Brent Geese and the regrowth of salt-marsh grass. *Funct. Ecol.* 9: 931–41.

Rowley G.D. 1877. *Somateria labradoria* (J.F. Gmelin) (The Pied Duck). *Ornithological Miscellany*, Vol. 2. Trübner, London.

Rufino, R. 1989. Atlas das aves que nidificam em Portugal Continental. CEMPA/SNPRCN, Lisbon.

Rüger, A., Prentice, C. and Owen, M. 1986. *Results of the IWRB international census 1967–1983,* Spec. Publ., No. 6. IWRB, Slimbridge, UK.

Rumboll, M.A.E. 1975. El Cauquén de Cabeza Colorada (*Chloëphaga rubidiceps*). Una nota de alarma. *Hornero* 11: 315–16.

Ruokonen, M. 2001. *Phylogeography and conservation genetics of the Lesser White-fronted Goose (Anser erythropus).* Oulu University Press, Oulu, Finland.

Rusanen, P. 1995. Observations of arctic waterfowl migration in Puhtu, western Estonia in May 1992. *IWRB Seaduck Research Group Bull.* 5: 15–18.

Rusch, D.H., Ankney, C.D., Boyd, H., Longcore, J.R., Montalbano, F., III, Ringelman, J.K. et al. 1989. Population ecology and harvest of the American Black Duck: a review. *Wildl. Soc. Bull.* 17: 379–406.

Rusch, D.H., Samuel, M.D., Humburg, D.D. and Sullivan, B.D. (ed.) 1998. *Biology and management of Canada Geese,* Int. Canada Goose Symp., 1991, Milwaukee, Wisconsin.

Rusev, I. and Korzukov, A. 2001. Red-breasted Goose in Ukraine. *Goose 2001,* pp.56–57. Wetlands International Goose Specialist Group.

Russell, I.C., Dare, P.J., Eaton, D.R. and Armstrong, J.D. 1996. *Assessment of the problem of fish-eating birds in inland fisheries in England and Wales.* Directorate of Fisheries Research, Lowestoft, UK.

Rutschke, E. 1987. *Die Wildgänse Europas.* VEB Deutscher Landwirtschaftsverlag, Berlin. [The wild geese of Europe, in German.]

Rutschke, E. 1990. *Die Wildenten Europas.* VEB Deutscher Landwirtschaftsverlag, Berlin. [The wild ducks of Europe, in German.]

Ruttledge, R.F. 1929. The birds of Loughs Mask and Carra and surrounding district. *Irish Naturalists' Journal* 11: 223.

Ryan, P.G., Bosman, A.L. and Hockey, P.A.R. 1988. Notes on the foraging behaviour of Magellanic Flightless Steamer Ducks and Flying Steamer Ducks. *Wildfowl* 39: 29–33.

Ryder, J.P. 1970. A possible factor in the evolution of clutch size in Ross' Goose. *Wilson Bull.* 82: 5–13.

Ryder, J.P. 1972. Biology of nesting Ross's Geese. *Ardea* 60: 185–215.

Ryder, J.P. and Alisauskas, R.T. 1995. Ross' Goose (*Chen rossii*). The Birds of North America, No. 162 (ed. A. Poole and F. Gill). AOU, Washington, and Academy of Natural Sciences, Philadelphia.

Ryder, J.P. and Cooke, F. 1973. Ross' Geese nesting in Manitoba. *Auk* 90: 691–92.

Rydzewski , W. 1974. Longevity records. *The Ring* 80: 169–70.

Rylander, M.K., Bolen, E.G. and McCamant, R.E. 1980. Evidence of incubation patches in whistling-ducks. *Southwestern Nat.* 25: 123–28.

Ryley, K. and Bowler, J.M. 1994. A change of moulting site for Mute Swans *Cygnus olor* in Gloucestershire. *Wildfowl* 45: 15–21.

Safford, R. 1993. The Madagascar Teal *Anas bernieri*: a preliminary survey from Antsalova to Morondava. *Dodo* 29: 95–102.

Safford, R. 1995. Meller's Duck in Mauritius. *IWRB Threatened Waterfowl Research Group Newsl.* 7: 17.

Safran, R.J., Isola, C.R., Colwell, M.A. and Williams, O.E. 1997. Benthic invertebrates at foraging locations of nine waterbird species in managed wetlands of the northern San Joaquin Valley, California. *Wetlands* 17: 407–15.

Salasse, J-P. 1979. Annales du C.O.A. période du 15.7.77 au 14.7.78. *Le Grand Duc* 14: 63–101.

Salmon, D.G. 1988. The numbers and distribution of scaup *Aythya marila* in Britain and Ireland. *Biol. Cons.* 43: 267–78.

Salmon, D.G. and Black, J.M. 1986. The January 1986 Whooper Swan census in Britain, Ireland and Iceland. *Wildfowl* 37: 172–74.

Salomonsen, F. 1950. *Grönlands Fugle*. Ejnar Munksgaard, Köbenhavn. [The Birds of Greenland.]

Salomonsen, F. 1968. The moult migration. *Wildfowl* 19: 5–24.

Salvadori, T. 1895. *Catalogue of birds in the British Museum*, Vol. 27. British Museum, London.

Salvan, J. 1970. Remarques sur l'évolution de l'avifaune Malgache depuis 1945. *Alauda* 38: 191–203.

Salyer, J.C., II and Lagler, K.F. 1940. The food and habits of the American Merganser during winter in Michigan, considered in relation to fish management. *J. Wildl. Manage.* 4: 186–219.

Sánchez, M.I., Green, A.J. and Dolz, C. 2000. The diets of the White-headed Duck *Oxyura leucocephala*, Ruddy Duck *O. jamaicensis* and their hybrids from Spain. *Bird Study* 47: 275–84.

Sanderson, G.C. and Bellrose, F.C. 1986. *A review of the problem of lead poisoning in waterfowl*, Spec. Publ., No. 4. Ill. Nat. Hist. Surv., Urbana, Ill.

Sangster, G. 2000. Taxonomic status of *bernicla* and *nigricans* Brent Geese. *Brit. Birds* 93: 94–96.

Sangster, G., Hazevoet, C.J., van den Berg, A.B. and Roselaar, C.S. 1997. Dutch avifaunal list: taxonomic changes in 1977–97. *Dutch Birding* 19: 21–28.

Sangster, G., Collinson, M., Helbig, A.J., Knox, A.G., Parkin, D.T. and Prater, T. 2001. The taxonomic status of Green-winged Teal *Anas carolinensis*. *Brit. Birds* 94: 218–26.

Sankhala, K. 1990. *Gardens of God—the waterbird sanctuary at Bharatpur*. Vikas, New Delhi.

Sankowski, T.P. and Joynt, B.L. 1992. Completed project evaluation in the Peace River Region of northwestern Alberta, 1989–1991. Unpubl. rept. Inst. Wetland and Waterfowl Res., Ducks Unlimited-Canada, Winnipeg.

Sargeant, A.B. 1972. Red Fox spatial characteristics in relation to waterfowl predation. *J. Wildl. Manage.* 36: 225–36.

Sargeant, A.B. and Raveling, D.G. 1992. Mortality during the breeding season. In *Ecology and management of breeding waterfowl* (ed. B.D. Batt, A.D. Afton, M.G. Anderson, C.D. Ankney, D.H. Johnson, J.A. Kadlec *et al.*), pp.396–422. Univ. Minnesota Press, Minneapolis.

Sargeant, A.B., Allen, S.A. and Eberhardt, R.T. 1984. Red fox predation on breeding ducks in midcontinental America. *Wildl. Monog.* 89.

Sarvis, J.E. 1972. The breeding biology and ecology of Ring-necked Ducks in northern Michigan. Unpubl. M.S. thesis. Utah State Univ., Logan, US.

Satchel, C. and Satchel, R. 2000. Unusual aggression in Egyptian Geese. *Promerops, Newsletter of Cape Bird Club* 244: 14.

Sato, H. and Kominato, I. 1988. The breeding records and breeding ecology of the Harlequin Duck (*Histrionicus histrionicus*) along the Ichihazama River of Mt. Kurikoma, northern Honshu. *Strix* 7: 159–76.

Saunders, D.A. and de Rebeira, C.P. 1985. *The birdlife of Rottnest Island*. Guildford, Western Australia.

Saunders, D.S. 1976. *Insect clocks*. Pergamon, Oxford.

Saunders, G.B. and Saunders, D.C. 1981. *Waterfowl and their wintering grounds in Mexico, 1937–64*, Resour. Publ., No. 138. US Fish & Wildl. Serv., Washington.

Savage, C. 1963. Wildfowling in Northern Iran. *Wildfowl* 14: 30–46.

Savard, J-P. and Lamothe, P. 1991. Distribution, abundance and aspects of breeding ecology of Black Scoters, *Melanitta nigra*, and Surf Scoters, *M. perspicillata*, in northern Quebec. *Can. Field-Nat.* 105: 488–96.

Savard, J-P.L. 1984. Territorial behaviour of Common Goldeneye, Barrow's Goldeneye and Bufflehead in areas of sympatry. *Ornis Scand.* 15: 211–16.

Savard, J-P.L. 1985. Evidence of long-term pair bonds in Barrow's Goldeneye *Bucephala islandica*. *Auk* 102: 389–91.

Savard, J-P.L. 1986a. Territorial behaviour, nesting success and brood survival in Barrow's Goldeneye and its congeners. Unpubl. Ph.D. thesis. Univ. British Columbia, Vancouver, Canada.

Savard, J-P.L. 1986b. Polygyny in Barrow's Goldeneye. *Condor* 88: 250–52.

Savard, J-P.L. 1987a. Causes and functions of brood amalgamation in Barrow's Goldeneye and Bufflehead. *Can. J. Zool.* 65: 1548–53.

Savard, J-P.L. 1987b. *Status report on Barrow's Golden Eye,* Tech. Rept. Ser., No. 23. Can. Wildl. Serv., Pacific and Yukon Region.

Savard, J-P.L. 1988. Winter, spring and summer territoriality in Barrow's Goldeneye: characteristics and benefits. *Ornis Scand.* 19: 119–28.

Savard, J-P.L. and Smith, J.N.M. 1987. Interspecific aggression by Barrow's Goldeneye: a descriptive and functional analysis. *Behaviour* 102: 168–84.

Savard, J-P.L., Boyd, W.S. and Smith, G.E.J. 1994. Waterfowl–wetland relationship in the Aspen Parkland of British Columbia: comparison of analytical methods. *Hydrobiologia* 279/280: 309–25.

Savard, J-P.L., Bordage, D. and Reed, A. 1998a. Surf Scoter (*Melanitta persicillata*), The Birds of North America, No. 363 (ed. A. Poole and F. Gill). The Birds of North America Inc., Philadelphia.

Savard, J-P.L., Reed, A. and Lesage, L. 1998b. Brood amalgamation in Surf Scoters (*Melanitta persicillata*) and other Mergini. *Wildfowl* 49: 129–38.

Saw Han 1996. White-winged Duck in Thamanthi Wildlife Sanctuary, Myanmar. *Wetlands International–IUCN Threatened Waterfowl Specialist Group News* 9: 22–3.

Sayler, R.D. 1992. Ecology and evolution of brood parasitism in waterfowl. In *The ecology and management of breeding waterfowl* (ed. B.D.J. Batt, A.D. Afton, M.G. Anderson, C.D. Ankney, D.H. Johnson, J.A. Kadlec *et al.*), pp.290–322. Univ. Minnesota Press, Minneapolis.

Sayler, R.D. 1995. Multivariate age assessments of Redheads in spring. *J. Wildl. Manage.* 59: 506–15.

Sayles, M.A., Aagaard, K. and Coachman, L.K. 1979. *Oceanographic atlas of the Bering Sea basin.* Univ. Washington. Press, Seattle.

Schäfer, E. 1938. Ornithologische Ergebnisse zweier Forschungsreisen nach Tibet. *J. Orn.* 86, spec. publ.

Schekkerman, H., Meininger, P.L. and Meire, P.M. 1994. Changes in the waterbird populations of the Oosterschelde (SW Netherlands) as a result of large-scale coastal engineering works. *Hydrobiologia* 282/283: 509–24.

Schenkeveld, L.E. and Ydenberg, R.C. 1985. Synchronous diving by Surf Scoter flocks. *Can. J. Zool.* 63: 2516–19.

Scherer, S. and Hilsberg, T. 1982. Hybridisierung und Verwandtscheftsgrade innerhalb der Anatidae: eine systematische und evolutionstheoretische Betrachtung. *J. Orn.* 123: 357–80.

Schifferli, A., Géroudet, P., Winkler, R., Jacquat, B., Praz, J-C., Schifferli, L. 1980. *Atlas des oiseaux nicheurs de Suisse.* Station ornithologique suisse de Sempach, Sempach, Switzerland.

Schiller, E.L. 1954. Studies on the helminth fauna of Alaska XVIII. Cestode parasites of young anseriformes on the Yukon Delta nesting grounds. *Trans. Am. Microsc. Soc.* 73: 194–201.

Schiller, E.L. 1955. Studies on the helminth fauna of Alaska XXIII. Some cestode parasites of eider ducks. *J. Parasitol.* 41: 79–88.

Schindler, M. and Lamprecht, J. 1987. Increase of parental effort with brood size in a nidifugous bird. *Auk* 104: 688–93.

Schiøler, E.L. 1925. *Danmarks fugle,* Vol. 1. Gyldendalske Boghandel, Copenhagen.

Schlatter, R.P. 1997. South American swan studies. *Wetlands International Swan Specialist Group Newsl.* 6: 19–20.

Schlatter, R.P. 1998. El cisne de cuello negro (*Cygnus melanocoryphus*) en Chile. In *La Conservacion de la Fauna nativa de Chile, logros y perspectivas.* (ed. V. Valverde), pp. 121–31. Corporacion Nacional Forestal, Min. de Agricultura, Santiago.

Schlatter, R.P., Aldridge, D.K., Romero, M.M. and Hofmann, M.E. 1983. Ecological studies of Chilean ducks. First Western Hemisphere Waterfowl and Waterbird Symp. (ed. H. Boyd), pp.133–7. IWRB, Slimbridge, UK, and Can. Wildl. Serv., Ottawa.

Schlatter, R.P., Salazar, J., Villa, A. and Meza, J. 1991a. Demography of Black-necked Swans *Cygnus melancoryphus* in three Chilean wetland areas. *Wildfowl* Spec. Suppl. 1: 88–94.

Schlatter, R.P., Salazar, J., Villa, A. and Meza, J. 1991b. Reproductive biology of Black-necked Swans *Cygnus melancoryphus* at three Chilean wetland areas and feeding ecology at Rio Cruces. *Wildfowl* Spec. Suppl. 1: 268–71.

Schlatter, R.P. Navarro, R.A. and Corti, P. 2002. Effects of El Niño Southern Oscillation on Numbers of

Black-necked Swans at Río Cruces Sanctuary, Chile. In *Proceedings of the Fourth International Swan Symposium. 2001* (ed. E.C. Rees, S.L. Earnst and J. Coulson). *Waterbirds* Special Publication 1: 114–22.

Schlatter, R.P., Vergara, P. and Briones, M. 2002. Ashy-headed Goose (*Chloephaga poliocephala:* Anatidae) in Tierra del Fuego woodlands: distribution and predators. *Anales Instituto Patagonia*, Serie Cs. Nat. (Chile) 30: 61–66.

Schmutz, J.A. 1993. Survival and pre-fledging body mass in juvenile Emperor Geese. *Condor* 95: 222–25.

Schmutz, J.A. 1994. Age, habitat, and tide effects on feeding activity of Emperor Geese during autumn migration. *Condor* 96: 46–51.

Schmutz, J.A. 2000. Age-specific breeding in Emperor Geese. *Wilson Bull.* 112: 261–63.

Schmutz, J.A. 2001. Selection of habitats by Emperor Geese during brood rearing. *Waterbirds* 24: 394–401.

Schmutz, J.A. and Hobson, K.A. 1998. Geographic, temporal, and age-specific variation in diets of Glaucous Gulls in western Alaska. *Condor* 100: 119–30.

Schmutz, J.A. and Kondratyev, A.V. 1995. Evidence of Emperor Geese breeding in Russia and staging in Alaska. *Auk* 112: 1037–38.

Schmutz, J.A. and Laing, K.K. 2002. Variation in foraging behavior and body mass in broods of Emperor Geese (*Chen canagica*): evidence for interspecific density dependence. *Auk* 119: 996–1009.

Schmutz, J.A. and Morse, J.A. 2000. Effects of neck-collars and radio-transmitters on survival and reproduction of Emperor Geese. *J. Wildl. Manage.* 64: 231–37.

Schmutz, J.A., Cantor, S.E. and Petersen, M.R. 1994. Seasonal and annual survival of Emperor Geese. *J. Wildl. Manage.* 58: 525–35.

Schmutz, J.A., Manly, B.F.J. and Dau, C.P. 2001. Effects of glaucous gulls and weather on survival of Emperor Goose goslings. *J. Wildl. Manage.* 65: 248–257.

Schmutz, J.A., Rockwell, R.F. and Petersen, M.R. 1997. Relative effects of survival and reproduction on the population dynamics of Emperor Geese. *J. Wildl. Manage.* 61: 191–201.

Schneider, J.P., Tacha, T.C. and Lobpries, D. 1993. Breeding distribution of Black-bellied Whistling Ducks in Texas. *Southwestern Nat.* 38: 383–85.

Schneider, K.B. 1965. Growth and plumage development of ducklings in interior Alaska. Unpubl. M.S. thesis. Univ. Alaska, Fairbanks, US.

Schneider-Jacoby, M. and Vasic, F. 1989. The Red-crested Pochard breeding and wintering in Yugoslavia. *Wildfowl* 40: 39–44.

Schoener, T.W. 1968. Sizes of feeding territories among birds. *Ecology* 49: 123–41.

Schönwetter, M. 1960–66. *Handbuch der Oologie*, (ed. W. Meise). Akademie-Verlag, Berlin.

Schorger, A.W. 1947. The deep diving of the Loon and Old-squaw and its mechanism. *Wilson Bull.* 59: 151–59.

Schorger, A.W. 1951. Deep diving of the Old-squaw. *Auk* 63: 112.

Schricke, V. 1993. La Baie du Mont Saint-Michel premiere zone de mue en France pour la Macreuse Noir *Melanitta nigra. Alauda* 61: 35–38.

Schubert, C.A. and Cooke, F. 1993. Egg-laying interval in the Lesser Snow Goose. *Wilson Bull.* 105: 414–26.

Schulten, G.G.M. 1974. The food of some duck species occurring at Lake Chilwa, Malawi. *Ostrich* 45: 224–26.

Schwartz, C.W. and Schwartz, E.R. 1953. Notes on the Hawaiian duck. *Wilson Bull.* 65: 18–25.

Sclater, P.L. 1880. List of the certainly known species of Anatidae, with notes on such as have been introduced into the zoological gardens of Europe, and remarks on their distribution. *Proc. Zool. Soc. London* 1880: 496–536.

Sclater, P.L. 1890. Exhibition of, and remarks upon, a hybrid duck. *Proc. Zool. Soc. Lond.*: 1–2.

Sclater, P.L. and Salvin, O. 1876 A revision of the neotropical Anatidae. *Proc. Zool. Soc. Lond.*: 358–414.

Scott, D. and Lubbock, J. 1974. Preliminary observations on waterfowl in western Madagascar. *Wildfowl* 25: 117–20.

Scott, D.A. 1982. Problems with the management of waterfowl. In Proc. 2nd Tech. Mtng. Western Palearctic Migratory Bird Management, Paris 1979 (ed. D.A. Scott and M. Smart), pp.89–106. IWRB, Slimbridge, UK.

Scott, D.A. (ed.) 1989. *A directory of Asian wetlands.* IUCN, Gland, Switzerland, and Cambridge, UK.

Scott, D.A. and Carbonell, M. 1986. *A directory of neotropical wetlands.* IUCN, Cambridge, and IWRB, Slimbridge, UK.

Scott, D.A. and Rose, P.M. (ed.) 1996. *Atlas of Anatidae populations in Africa and Western Eurasia*, Publ., No. 41. Wetlands International, Wageningen, Netherlands.

Scott, D.A., van der Ven, J. and Rose, P.M. 1990. The Asian Waterfowl Census. In *Managing Waterfowl Populations*, IWRB Symp., Astrakhan 1989, Publ., No. 12 (ed. G.V.T. Matthews), pp.70–77. IWRB, Slimbridge, UK.

Scott, D.K. 1980a. Functional aspects of prolonged parental care in Bewick's Swans. *Anim. Behav.* 28: 938–52.

Scott, D.K. 1980b. Functional aspects of the pair bond in wintering Bewick's Swans (*Cygnus columbianus bewickii*). *Behav. Ecol. Sociobiol.* 7: 323–27.

Scott, D.K. 1981. Geographical variation in the bill patterns of Bewick's Swans. *Wildfowl* 32: 123–28.

Scott, D.K. 1984. Winter territoriality of Mute Swans *Cygnus olor*. *Ibis* 126: 168–76.

Scott, D.K. 1988. Breeding success of Bewick's Swans. In *Reproductive success* (ed. T.H. Clutton-Brock), pp. 220–36. Chicago Univ. Press.

Scott, D.K. and Birkhead, M.E. 1983. Resources and reproductive performance in Mute Swans *Cygnus olor. J. Zool., Lond.* 200: 539–47.

Scott, D.K. and Clutton-Brock, T.H. 1989. Mating systems, parasites and plumage dimorphism in waterfowl. *Behav. Ecol. Sociobiol.* 26: 261–73.

Scott, N.J. and Reynolds, R.P. 1984. Phenotypic variation of the Mexican Duck (*Anas platyrhynchos diazi*) in Mexico. *Condor* 86: 266–74.

Scott, P. 1952. The Pink-footed Geese of the Þjórsárver við Hofsjökul. *Wildfowl* 5: 84–101.

Scott, P. 1954. South America—1953. *Wildfowl* 6: 54–69.

Scott, P. 1958a. *A coloured key to the wildfowl of the world*. Wildfowl Trust, Slimbridge, UK.

Scott, P. 1958b. Notes on Anatidae seen on world tour. *Wildfowl* 9: 86–112.

Scott, P. 1966. The Bewick's Swans at Slimbridge. *Wildfowl* 17: 20–26.

Scott, P. and The Wildfowl Trust 1972. *The swans*. Michael Joseph, London.

Scott, Ph. 1972. Photograph of *Cereopsis* oiling young. *Wildfowl* 23: plate 6.

Scribner, K.T., Malecki, R.A., Batt, B.D.J., Inman, R.L., Libants, S. and Prince, H.H. 2003. Identification of source population for Greenland Canada Geese: Genetic assessment of a recent colonization. *Condor* 105: 771–82.

Scribner, K.T., Talbot, S.L., Pearce, J.M., Pierson, B.J., Bollinger, K.S. and Derksen, D.V. 2003. Phylogeography of Canada geese (*Branta canadensis*) in western North America. *Auk* 120(3): 889–907.

Sedinger, J.S. 1986. Growth and development of Canada Goose goslings. *Condor* 88: 169–80.

Sedinger, J.S. 1992. Ecology of prefledging waterfowl. In *Ecology and management of breeding waterfowl* (ed. B.D. Batt, A.D. Afton, M.G. Anderson, C.D. Ankney, D.H. Johnson, J.A. Kadlec *et al.*), pp.109–27. Univ. Minnesota Press, Minneapolis.

Sedinger, J.S. 1997. Adaptations to and consequences of an herbivorous diet in grouse and waterfowl. *Condor* 99: 314–26.

Sedinger, J.S. and Bollinger, K.S. 1987. Autumn staging of Cackling Canada Geese on the Alaska Peninsula. *Wildfowl* 38: 13–18.

Sedinger, J.S. and Raveling, D.G. 1984. Dietary selectivity in relation to availability and quality of food for goslings of Cackling Geese. *Auk* 101: 295–306.

Sedinger, J.S. and Raveling, D.G. 1986. Timing of nesting of Canada Geese in relation to the quality and availability of their food plants. *J. Anim. Ecol.* 55: 1083–102.

Sedinger, J.S., White, R.G., Mann, F.E., Burris, F.A. and Kedrowski, R.A. 1989. Apparent metabolizability of alfalfa components by yearling Pacific Black Brant. *J. Wildl. Manage.* 53: 726–34.

Sedinger, J.S., White, R.G. and Hupp, J. 1995. Metabolizability and partitioning of energy and protein in green plants by yearling Lesser Snow Geese. *Condor* 97: 116–22.

Sedinger, J.S., Chelgren, N.D., Lindberg, M.S., Obritchkewitch, T., Kirk, M.T., Martin, P. *et al.* 2002. Life-history implications of large-scale spatial variation in adult survival of Black Brant (*Branta bernicla nigricans*). *Auk* 119: 510–14.

Seijas, M.S. 1997. Age differentiation in the Black-necked Swan *Cygnus melancoryphus*. *Wetlands International Swan Specialist Group Newsl.* 6: 20–26.

Seijas, M.S. 1999. National census of swans in Argentina. *Wetlands International Swan Specialist Group Newsl.* 8: 14.

Sell, D.L. 1979. Fall foods of teal on the Texas High Plains. *Southwest. Nat.* 24: 373–75.

Semel, B. and Sherman, P.W. 2001. Intraspecific parasitism and nest-site competition in wood ducks. *Animal Behaviour* 61: 787–803.

Semel, B., Sherman, P.W. and Byers, S.M. 1988. Effects of brood parasitism and nest-box placement on wood duck breeding ecology. *Condor* 90: 920–30.

Semyenchenko, A.Y. and Yermolenko, A.V. 1988. Notes on the numbers and distribution of *Mergus squamatus* in the Yedinka Basin (Northern Primorye). In *Rare birds of the Far East and their conservation*, pp.46–47. Far East Science Centre, USSR Acad. Sci., Vladivostok.

Serie, J.R. and Bartonek, J.B. 1991a. Population status and productivity of Tundra Swans *Cygnus columbianus columbianus* in North America. *Wildfowl* Spec. Suppl. 1: 172–77.

Serie, J.R. and Bartonek, J.B. 1991b. Harvest management of Tundra Swans *Cygnus columbianus columbianus* in North America. *Wildfowl* Spec. Suppl. 1: 359–67.

Serie, J.R. and Sharp, D.E. 1989. Body weight and composition dynamics of fall migrating Canvasbacks. *J. Wildl. Manage.* 53: 431–41.

Serie, J.R. and Swanson, G.A. 1976. Feeding ecology of breeding Gadwalls on saline wetlands. *J. Wildl. Manage.* 40: 69–81.

Serie, J.R., Trauger, D.L. and Sharp, D.E. 1983a. Migration and winter distributions of Canvasbacks staging on the upper Mississippi River. *J. Wildl. Manage.* 47: 741–53.

Serie, J.R., Trauger, D.L., Doty, H.A. and Sharp, D.E. 1983b. Age-class determination of Canvasbacks. *J. Wildl. Manage.* 47: 894–904.

Serie, J.R., Trauger, D.L. and Austin, J.E. 1992. Influence of age and selected environmental factors on reproductive performance of Canvasbacks. *J. Wildl. Manage.* 56: 546–56.

Serie, J.R., Luszcz, D. and Raftovich, R.V. 2002. Population trends, productivity and harvest of eastern population Tundra Swans. In *Proceedings of the Fourth International Swan Symposium, 2001* (ed. E.C. Rees, S.L. Earnst and J. Coulson) *Waterbirds*, Special Publication 1: 32–36.

Serle, W. and Morel, G.L. 1977. *Birds of West Africa*. Collins, London.

Serventy, D.L. and Whittell, H.M. 1976. *Birds of Western Australia*. Paterson Brokensha, Perth.

Serventy, V.N. (ed.) 1985. *The waterbirds of Australia*. Angus and Robertson, Sydney.

Sharland, M. 1981. *A guide to the birds of Tasmania*. Drinkwater, Hobart.

Sharrock, J.T.R. 1976. *The atlas of breeding birds in Britain and Ireland*. Poyser, Calton.

Shaughnessy, P.D. and Haberley, B. 1994. Surveys of Cape Barren Geese *Cereopsis novaehollandiae* in Western Australia 1987–1992. *Corella* 18: 8–13.

Shaw, J.R. 1993. Territorial Egyptian Geese and reaction to crocodiles. *Honeyguide* 39: 144–45.

Shaw, T.H. 1936. *The birds of Hopei Province*. Peking.

Shchadilov, Y.M., Belousova, A.V., Rees, E.C. and Bowler, J.M. 1998. Long-term study of the nesting success in the Bewick's Swans in the coastal tundra in the Nentskiy Autonomous Okrug. *Casarca* 4: 217–28.

Shea, R.E., Lockman, D.C. and Mitchell, C.D. 1991. Trumpeter Swan *Cygnus buccinator* range expansion programmes in northern Rocky Mountains, USA. *Wildfowl* Spec. Suppl. 1: 348–51.

Shea, R.E., Nelson, H.K., Gillette, L.N., King, J.G. and Weaver, D.K. 2002. Restoration of Trumpeter Swans in North America: a century of progress and challenges. In *Proceedings of the Fourth International Swan Symposium, 2001* (ed. E.C. Rees, S.L. Earnst and J. Coulson). *Waterbirds*, Special Publication 1: 296–300.

Sheppard, P. and Sheppard, S. 1991. Egyptian Geese at sea. *Promerops* 197: 96.

Sherwood, G.A. 1960. The Whistling Swan of the west with particular reference to Great Salt Lake Valley, Utah. *Condor* 62: 370–77.

Sherwood, G.A. 1967. Behavior of family groups of Canada Geese. In 32nd North American Wildlife Conference, pp.340–55. American Wildlife Institute, Washington.

Shewell, E.L. 1959. The waterfowl of Barberspan. *Ostrich* Suppl. 3: 160–79.

Shibaev, Y.V., Litvinenko, N.M. and Nazarov, A.A. 1992. Status of Baikal Teal *Anas formosa* in the southern Far East of Russia. *IWRB Threatened Waterfowl Research Group Newsl.* 2: 14–16.

Shibnyev, Y.B. 1985. Present status of *Aix galericulata* and *Mergus squamatus* on the River Bikin. In *Rare and endangered birds of the Far East*, pp.95–99. Far East Sci. Centre, USSR Acad. Sci, Vladivostok.

Shields, G.F. 1990. Analysis of mitochondrial DNA of Pacific Black Brant *Branta bernicla nigricans. Auk* 107: 620–23.

Shields, G.F. and Cotter, J.P. 1998. Phylogenies of North American geese: the mitochondrial DNA record. In *Biology and management of Canada Geese*, Int. Canada Goose Symp. (ed. D.H. Rusch, M.D. Samuel, D.D. Humburg and B.D. Sullivan), pp.405–11. Milwaukee, Wisconsin.

Shoffner, R.N. Wang, F. Lee, R. King and Otis, J.S. 1979. Chromosome homology between the Ross Goose and the Emperor Goose. *J. Her.* 70: 395–400.

Shokhrin, V. and Solovieva, D. 2003. Scaly-sided Merganser Breeding Population Increase in Far East Russia. *TWSG News* 14: 43–51. WWT, Slimbridge, UK.

Short, L.L. 1969. Taxonomic aspects of avian hybridisation. *Auk* 86: 84–105.

Short, L.L. 1970. Mid-Pleistocene birds from western Nebraska, including a new species of sheldgoose. *Condor* 72: 147–52.

Shufeldt, R.W. 1913. Review of the fossil fauna of the desert region of Oregon, with a description of additional material collected there. *Bull. Am. Mus. Nat. Hist.* 32: 123–78.

Shulpin, L.M. 1936. *Gamebirds and raptors of Primor'ye.* Far East Branch, Acad. Sci. USSR, Vladivostok. [In Russian.]

Shurtleff, L.L. and Savage, C. 1996. *The Wood Duck and the Mandarin: the northern wood ducks.* Univ. California Press, Berkeley.

Sibley, C.G. 1957. The evolutionary and taxonomic significance of sexual dimorphism and hybridization in birds. *Condor* 58: 166–91.

Sibley, C.G. and Ahlquist, J.E. 1972. A comparative study of egg-white proteins of non-passerine birds. *Bull. Peabody Mus. Nat. Hist.* 32: 1–131.

Sibley, C.G. and Ahlquist, J.E. 1990. *Phylogeny and classification of birds: a study in molecular evolution.* Yale Univ. Press, New Haven and London.

Sibley, C.G. and Monroe, B.L., Jr 1990. *Distribution and taxonomy of the birds of the world.* Yale Univ. Press, New Haven and London.

Sibley, C.G., Corbin, K.W. and Haavie, J.H. 1969. The relationship of the flamingos as indicated by egg-white proteins and hemoglobins. *Condor* 71: 155–79.

Sibley, C.L. 1967. The wild Muscovy Duck. *Modern Game Breeding* 3(4): 12.

Sick, H. 1993. *Birds in Brazil: a natural history.* Princeton Univ. Press.

Siegfried, W.R. 1964a. The numbers of feathers in the nests of South African Anatidae. *Ostrich* 35: 61.

Siegfried, W.R. 1964b. Parasitic egg laying in South African Anatidae. *Ostrich* 35: 61–62.

Siegfried, W.R. 1965a. Migrational homing in the Egyptian Goose. *Bokmakierie* 17(3): 57–58.

Siegfried, W.R. 1965b. Branchiopoda (Phyllopoda) in the diet of the African Shelduck. *Ostrich* 36: 140.

Siegfried, W.R. 1965c. The Cape Shoveler *Anas smithii* in southern Africa. *Ostrich* 36: 155–98.

Siegfried, W.R. 1966. On the post-embryonic development of the South African Shelduck, *Tadorna cana* (Gmel.). *Ostrich* 37: 149–51.

Siegfried, W.R. 1967. Trapping and ringing of Egyptian Geese and African Shelduck at Vogelvlei, Cape. *Ostrich* 38: 173–78.

Siegfried, W.R. 1968a. The Black Duck in the south-western Cape. *Ostrich* 39: 61–75.

Siegfried, W.R. 1968b. Non-breeding plumage in the adult Maccoa Duck. *Ostrich* 39: 91–93.

Siegfried, W.R. 1969. The proportion of yolk in the egg of the Maccoa Duck. *Wildfowl* 20: 78.

Siegfried, W.R. 1970. Double wing moult in the Maccoa Duck. *Wildfowl* 21: 122.

Siegfried, W.R. 1973a. Platform building by male and female Ruddy Ducks. *Wildfowl* 24: 150–53.

Siegfried, W.R. 1973b. Post-embryonic development of the ruddy duck *Oxyura jamaicensis* and some other diving ducks. *Int. Zoo Ybk* 13: 77–87.

Siegfried, W.R. 1973c. Wing moult of Ruddy Ducks in Manitoba. *Bull. BOC* 93: 98–99.

Siegfried, W.R. 1973d. Morphology and ecology of the southern African whistling ducks (Dendrocygna). *Auk* 90: 198–201.

Siegfried, W.R. 1974a. Brood care, pair bonds and plumage in southern African Anatini. *Wildfowl* 25: 33–40.

Siegfried, W.R. 1974b. Climbing ability of ducklings of some cavity-nesting waterfowl. *Wildfowl* 25: 74–80.

Siegfried, W.R. 1974c. Time budget of behavior among Lesser Scaup on Delta Marsh. *J. Wildl. Manage.* 38: 708–13.

Siegfried, W.R. 1976a. Sex ratio in the Cape Shelduck. *Ostrich* 47: 113–16.

Siegfried, W.R. 1976b. Segregation in feeding behavior of four diving ducks in southern Manitoba. *Can. J. Zool.* 54: 730–36.

Siegfried, W.R. 1976c. Social organisation in Ruddy and Maccoa Ducks. *Auk* 93: 560–70.

Siegfried, W.R. 1977. Notes on the behaviour of Ruddy Ducks during the brood period. *Wildfowl* 28: 126–28.

Siegfried, W.R. 1979. Social behaviour of the African Comb Duck. *Living Bird* 17: 85–104.

Siegfried, W.R. 1985. Socially induced suppression of breeding plumage in the Maccoa Duck. *Wildfowl* 36: 135–37.

Siegfried, W.R. and van der Merwe, F.J. 1975. A description and inventory of the displays of the Maccoa Duck *Oxyura maccoa. Z. Tierpsychol.* 37: 1–23.

Siegfried, W.R., Burger, A.E and van der Merwe, F.J. 1976a. Activity budgets of male Maccoa Ducks. *Zool. Africana* 11: 111–25.

Siegfried, W.R., Burger, A.E. and Frost, P. 1976b. Energy requirements for breeding in the Maccoa Duck. *Ardea* 64: 171–91.

Siegfried, W.R., Hockey, P.A.R., Ryan, P.G. and Bosman, A.L. 1988. Sex and plumage-type ratios of the Lesser Magellan Goose in southern Chile. *Wildfowl* 39: 15–21.

Silva, C. and Vilina, Y.A. 1999. Effect of El Nino on abundance and reproduction of the Black-necked Swan (*Cygnus melancorhyphus*) in central Chile. In Neotropical Waterfowl Symp., October 7 1999 (ed. M. Carbonell, T.E. Crane, K. McKnight and S.M. Stai), pp.13–14. Ducks Unlimited, Inc, Memphis.

Silva-García, C.M. 2003. Breeding behavior, spacing patterns, and sex roles in the Coscoroba Swan (*Coscoroba coscoroba*) in central Chile. M.S. thesis. Frostburg State University, Frostburg, Maryland USA. 78 pp.

Silveira, L.F. and Bartmann, W. 2001. Natural history and conservation of Brazilian Merganser *Mergus octosetaceus* at Serra da Canastra National Park, Minas Gerais, Brazil. *Bird Conserv. Int.* 11: 287–300.

Simpson, K. and Day, N. 1993. *Field guide to the birds of Australia* (4th edn). Penguin Books, Australia.

Sinclair, I., Hockey, P. and Tarboton, W. 1993. *Illustrated guide to the birds of Southern Africa.* New Holland, London.

Sincock, J.L. 1962. Estimating consumption of food by wintering waterfowl populations. *Proc. Ann. Conf. SE Assoc. Game Fish Comm.* 16: 217–21.

Sincock, J.L. and Kridler, E. 1977. The extinct and endangered endemic birds of the Northwest Hawaiian Islands. (Unpubl. ms.)

Singleton, J.R. 1953. *Texas coastal waterfowl survey,* F.A. Rep. Ser., No. 11. Texas Game and Fish Comm.

Singleton, J.R. 1968. Texas' mistaken Mallards. *Texas Parks and Wildlife* 26: 8–11.

Siren, M. 1952. Undersökningar över knipans, *Bucephala clangula,* fortplantningbiologi, Riistatiet. *Julkaisuja* 8: 101–11.

Siriwardena, G.M. and Black, J.M. 1999. Parent and gosling strategies in wintering Barnacle Geese *Branta leucopsis. Wildfowl* 49: 18–26.

Sjöberg, K. 1988a. Food selection, food-seeking patterns and hunting success of captive Goosanders *Mergus merganser* and Red-breasted Mergansers *Mergus serrator* in relation to the behaviour of their prey. *Ibis* 130: 79–93.

Sjöberg, K. 1988b. The flightless period of free-living male Teal *Anas crecca* in northern Sweden. *Ibis* 130: 164–71.

Skakuj, M. 1990. Identification of the eiders *Somateria mollissima, spectablis, fischeri* and *polysticta. Limicola* 4(6): 285–306. [In German. English summary.]

Skarphéðinsson, K.H. and Gudmunðsson, G.A. 1990. Fuglalíf í Skógum, Skagafirði, og nágrenni, 1987. *Bliki* 9: 49–66.

Skead, D.M. and Dean, W.R.J. 1977. Seasonal abundance of Anatidae at Barberspan. *Ostrich* Suppl. 12: 49–64.

Skead, D.M. and Mitchell, R.J.H. 1983. Grit ingested by waterfowl in relation to diet. *S.-Afr. Tydskr. Natuurnav.* 13: 32–34.

Skerrett, A. 1999. Ferruginous Duck *Aythya nyroca*: the first record for Seychelles. *Bull. ABC* 6(2): 148.

Skoruppa, M.K. and Woodin, M.C. 2000. Impact of wintering Redhead Ducks on pond water quality in Southern Texas. In *Limnology and aquatic birds: monitoring, modelling, and management,* 2nd Int. Symp. Limnology and Aquatic Birds (ed. F.A. Comin, J.A. Herrera-Silveira and J. Ramirez-Ramirez), pp.31–41. Universidad Autonoma de Yucatan, Merida, Mexico.

Sladen, W.J.L. 1952. Kelp Geese and Flightless Steamer Duck from the Falkland Islands for The Severn Wildfowl Trust. *Avic. Mag.* 58: 220–25.

Sladen, W.J.L. 1973. A continental study of Whistling Swans using neck collars. *Wildfowl* 24: 8–14.

Sladen, W.J.L. 1991. Swans should not be hunted. *Wildfowl* Spec. Suppl., 1: 68–75.

Sladen, W.J.L. and Cochran, W. 1969. Studies of the Whistling Swan, 1967–68. *Trans. N. Amer. Wildl. Nat. Res. Conf.* 34: 42–50.

Sladen, W.J.L., Gunn, W.W.H. and Cochran, W.W. 1969. Studies on the migrations of the Whistling Swan, 1969. In *World conference on bird hazards to aircraft*, pp.231–44. Queens Univ., Kingston, Ontario.

Slattery, S.M. and Alisaukas, R.T. 1995. Egg characteristics and body reserves of neonate Ross's and Lesser Snow Geese. *Condor* 97: 970–84.

Smart, G. 1965a. Development and maturation of primary feathers of Redhead ducklings. *J. Wildl. Manage.* 29: 533–36.

Smart, M.G. 1965b. Body weights of newly hatched Anatidae. *Auk* 82: 645–48.

Smith, A.G. 1953. Waterfowl breeding ground surveys in special study areas in Alberta—1953. In *Waterfowl populations and breeding conditions, summer 1953*, Spec. Sci. Rep. Wildl., No. 25, pp.30–42. US Fish & Wildl. Serv., Washington.

Smith, A.G. 1955. Waterfowl breeding ground surveys of special study areas in Alberta—1955. In *Waterfowl populations and breeding conditions, summer 1955*, Spec. Sci. Rep. Wildl., No. 30, pp.33–44. US Fish & Wildl. Serv., Washington.

Smith, A.G. 1971. *Ecological factors affecting waterfowl production in the Alberta Parklands*, Resource Publ., No. 98. US Fish & Wildl. Serv., Washington.

Smith, D.W. 2000. Management of Canada Geese in the Lower Fraser Valley, southwestern British Columbia. In *Towards conservation of the diversity of Canada Geese* (Branta canadensis), pp.151–58. K.M. Dickson (ed.). *Can. Wildl. Serv. Occas. Paper* No. 103.

Smith, G.W. 1995. *A critical review of the aerial and ground surveys of breeding waterfowl in North America*, Rep., No. 5. Natl. Biol. Serv., Washington.

Smith, J.D. 1952. The Hawaiian Goose (Nene) restoration program. *J. Wildl. Manage.* 16: 1–9.

Smith, L.M. and Sheeley, D.G. 1993a. Factors affecting condition of northern pintails wintering in the Southern High Plains. *J. Wildl. Manage.* 57: 62–71.

Smith, L.M. and Sheeley, D.G. 1993b. Molt patterns of wintering northern pintails in the Southern High Plains. *J. Wildl. Manage.* 57: 229–38.

Smith, R.H., Dufresne, F. and Hansen, H.A. 1964. Northern watersheds and deltas. In *Waterfowl tomorrow* (ed. J.P. Linduska), pp.51–66. US Govt Printing Office, Washington.

Smith, R.I. 1963. Lesser Scaup and Ring-necked Duck shooting pressure and mortality rates, Admin. Rep., No. 20. US Bur. Sport Fish. Wildl., Washington.

Smith, R.I. 1968. The social aspects of reproductive behaviour in the Pintail. *Auk* 85: 381–96.

Smith, R.I. 1970. Response of Pintail breeding populations to drought. *J. Wildl. Manage.* 34: 943–46.

Smith, V.E., Spurr, J.M., Filkins, J.C. and Jones, J.J. 1985. Organochlorine contaminants of wintering ducks foraging on Detroit River sediments. *J. Great Lakes Res.* 11: 231–46.

Smythies, B.E. 1940. *Birds of Burma*. American Baptist Mission Press, Rangoon (reprinted 1984 by International Book Distributors, Dehra Dun).

Smythies, B.E. 1986. *The birds of Burma* (3rd edn). Nimrod Press, England, and Silvio Mattacchione and Co, Canada.

Sneath, P.H.A. and Sokal, R.R. 1973. *Numerical taxonomy*. Freeman, San Francisco.

Snell, R.R. 1985. Underwater flight of Long-tailed Duck (Oldsquaw) *Clangula hyemalis*. *Ibis* 127: 267.

Snow, D.W. 1978. *An atlas of speciation in African non-passerine birds*. Trustees of British Museum (Natural History), London.

Snyder, D.E. 1966. *The birds of Guyana*. Peabody Museum, Salem.

Snyder, L.L. and Lumsden, H.G. 1951. *Variation in Anas cyanoptera*, Occas. Pap., No. 10, pp.1–18. R. Ont. Mus. Zool.

Snyder, N.F.R., Derrickson, S.R., Beissinger, S.R., Wiley, J.W., Smith, T.B, Toone, W.D. *et al.* 1996. Limitations of captive breeding in endangered species recovery. *Conservation Biology* 10: 338–48.

Soikkeli, M. 1973. Decrease in numbers of migrating Lesser White-fronted Geese *Anser erythropus* in Finland. *Finnish Game Research* 33: 28–30.

Solovieva, D.V. 2002. Foraging behaviour and daily time budget of Scaly-sided Merganser *Mergus squamatus* breeding on Iman River, Russia. *Wildfowl* 53: 205–13.

Solovieva, D.V., Pihl, S., Fox, A.D. and Bustnes, J-O. 1998. Steller's Eider. *BWP Update* 2 (3): 143–58.

Sonobe, K. and Usui, S. (ed.) 1993. *A field guide to the birds of Asia.* Wild Bird Society of Japan, Tokyo.

Soothill, E. and Whitehead, P. 1978. *Wildfowl of the world.* Blandford, Poole.

Soper, M.F. 1984. *Birds of New Zealand and outlying islands.* Whitcouls, Christchurch, NZ.

Sorenson, L.G. 1990. Breeding behavior and ecology of a sedentary tropical duck: the White-cheeked Pintail (*Anas bahamensis bahamensis*). Unpubl. Ph.D. thesis. Univ. Minnesota, Minneapolis, US.

Sorenson, L.G. 1991. Mating systems of tropical and southern hemisphere dabbling ducks. *Int. Ornith. Congr.* 20: 851–59.

Sorenson, L.G. 1992. Variable mating system of a sedentary tropical duck: the White-cheeked Pintail (*Anas bahamensis bahamensis*). *Auk* 109: 277–92.

Sorenson, L.G. 1994a. Forced extra-pair copulation and mate guarding in the White-cheeked Pintail: timing and trade-offs in an asynchronously breeding duck. *Anim. Behav.* 48: 519–33.

Sorenson, L.G. 1994b. Forced extra-pair copulation in the White-cheeked Pintail: male tactics and female responses. *Condor* 96: 400–10.

Sorenson, L.G., Woodworth, B.L., Ruttan, L.M. and McKinney, F. 1992. Serial monogamy and double brooding in the White-cheeked (Bahama) Pintail *Anas bahamensis. Wildfowl* 43: 156–59.

Sorenson, M.D. 1991. The functional significance of parasitic egg-laying and typical nesting in Redhead Ducks: an analysis of individual behaviour. *Anim. Behav.* 42: 771–96.

Sorenson, M.D. 1993. Parasitic egg laying in Canvas-backs: frequency, success, and individual behavior. *Auk* 110: 57–69.

Sorenson, M.D., Cooper, A., Paxinos, E.E., Quinn, T.W., James, H.F., Olson, S.L. and

Fleischer, R.C. 1999. Relationships of the extinct moa-nalos, flightless Hawaiian waterfowl, based on ancient DNA. *Proc. R. Soc. Lond. B.* 266: 2187–93.

Soulliere, G.J. 1987. Distinguishing Hooded Merganser and Wood Duck nests by eggshell thickness. *J. Wildl. Manage.* 51: 534.

Southern Duck Hunter. 1999. Breeding test area map and 40 year breeding charts of overall duck population and 10 specific species. http://duckcentral.com/40year.htm (Version 19 March 1999).

Southwick, C. 1953. A system of age classification for field studies of waterfowl broods. *J. Wildl. Manage.* 17: 1–8.

SOVON 1987. *Atlas van de Nederlandse Vogels.* Samenwerkende Organisaties Vogelanderzock Nederland, Arnhem.

Sowls, L.K. 1955. *Prairie ducks: a study of their behaviour, ecology and management.* Stackpole, Harrisburg, and Wildl. Manage. Inst., Washington.

Spaans, A.L., Holthuijzen, A.M.A. and Dejong, B.H.J. 1978. Spatial distribution and food of ducks in the coastal area of Surinam. *Ardea* 66: 24–31.

Spence, T. 1959. The Horned Screamer. *Avic. Mag.* 65: 97–99.

Spencer, H.E., Jr 1979. *Black Duck management plan for North America.* Black Duck Comm Atl. Flyway Counc., Augusta, Maine.

Spencer, K.G. 1953. *The Lapwing in Britain.* Brown and Sons, London.

Spindler, M.A. and Hall, K.F. 1991. Local movements and habitat use of Tundra or Whistling Swans *Cygnus columbianus* in the Kobuk-Selawik lowlands of northwest Alaska. *Wildfowl* 42: 17–32.

Spray, C.J. 1981. An isolated population of *Cygnus olor* in Scotland. In 2nd IWRB Swan Symp., Sapporo, 1980 (ed. G.V.T. Matthews and M. Smart), pp.191–208. IWRB, Slimbridge, UK.

Spurr, E.B. and Milne, H. 1976. Adaptive significance of autumn pair formation in the Common Eider *Somateria mollissima* (L.). *Ornis Scand.* 7: 85–89.

Squires, J.R. 1991. Trumpeter Swan food habits, forage processing, activities and habitat use. Unpubl. Ph.D. thesis. Univ. Wyoming, Laramie, US.

Sraml, M., Christides, L., Easteal, S., Horn, P. and Collet, C. 1996. Molecular relationships within Australian waterfowl (Anseriformes). *Aust. J. Zool.* 44: 47–58.

Sridhar, S. 1992. *Important wintering areas for Bar-headed Geese* (Anser indicus) *in Karnataka, South India.* Asian and Australian Waterfowl Census, IWRB, Slimbridge, UK.

St Joseph, A.K.M. 1979. The seasonal distribution and movements of *Branta bernicla* in western Europe. In Proc. 1st Tech. Mtng. on Western Palearctic Migratory Bird Management, Paris, 1977 (ed. M. Smart), pp.45–56. IWRB, Slimbridge, UK.

Stacey, P.B. and Ligon, J.D. 1991. The benefits-of-philopatry hypothesis for the evolution of cooperative breeding: variation in territory quality and group size effects. *Amer. Natur.* 137: 831–46.

Stahl, J-C., Mougin, J-L., Jouventin, P. and Weimerskirch, H. 1984. Le Canard d'Eaton, *Anas eatoni drygalskii,* des Iles Crozet: systematique, comportement alimentaire et biologie de reproduction. *Gerfaut* 74: 305–26.

Staicer, C.A., Freedman, B., Srivastava, D., Dowd, N., Kilgar, J., Hayden, J. *et al.* 1994. Use of lakes by Black Duck broods in relation to biological, chemical, and physical features. *Hydrobiologia* 279/280: 185–99.

Standen, P.J. 1976. The social behaviour of the Chilean Teal. Unpubl. Ph.D. thesis. Univ. Leicester, UK.

Standen, P.J. 1980. The social display of the Chilean Teal *Anas flavirostris flavirostris. J. Zool., Lond.* 191: 293–313.

Staus, N.L. 1998a. Habitat use and home range of West Indian Whistling-ducks. *J. Wildl. Manage.* 62: 171–78.

Staus, N.L. 1998b. Behaviour and natural history of the West Indian Whistling Duck on Long Island, Bahamas. *Wildfowl* 49: 194–206.

Stawarczyk, T. 1995. Reproductive strategies of ducks breeding at high densities in Milicz Fishponds. *Prace Zoologiczne Uniw. Wroclawskiego* 31: 3–110. (In Polish with English summary.)

Steadman, D.W. 1992. Extinct and extirpated birds from Rota, Mariana Islands. *Micronesia* 25: 71–84.

Stehn, R.A., Dau, C.P., Conant, B. and Butler, W.I., Jr 1993. Decline of Spectacled Eiders nesting in western Alaska. *Arctic* 46(3): 264–77.

Steinbacher, G. 1960. Zur Balz der Tauchenten. *Vogelwelt* 81: 1–16.

Stempniewicz, L. 1986. The food intake of two Scoters *Melanitta fusca* and *M. nigra* wintering in the Gulf of Gdansk, Polish Baltic Coast. *Vår Fågelvärld* Suppl. 11: 211–14.

Stephenson, R. 1997. Effects of oil and other surface-active organic pollutants on aquatic birds. *Environ. Conserv.* 24: 121–29.

Stephenson, R., Lovvorn, J.R., Heieis, M.R.A., Jones, D.R. and Blake, R.W. 1989. A hydromechanical estimate of the power requirements of diving and surface swimming in Lesser Scaup (*Aythya affinis*). *J. Exp. Biol.* 147: 507–19.

Sterbetz, I. 1968. Der Zug der Zwerggans auf der Ungarischen Pustza. *Ardea* 56: 259–66.

Sterbetz, I. 1969. Feeding ecology of the Ferruginous Duck in Hungary. Unpubl. rept. Hungarian Ornithological Institute, Budapest, Hungary.

Sterbetz, I. 1982. Migration of *Anser erythropus* and *Branta ruficollis* in Hungary 1971–1980. *Aquila* 89: 107–14.

Sterbetz, I. 1986. Percentage of juvenile Lesser White-fronted Geese (*Anser erythropus*) in Hungary. *Aquila* 92: 81–88.

Sterbetz, I. 1990. Variations in the habitat of the Lesser White-fronted Goose (*Anser erythropus*) in Hungary. *Aquila* 96–97: 17.

Sterling, T. and Dzubin, A. 1967. Canada Goose molt migrations to the North west Territories. *Trans. N. Amer. Wildl. Nat. Res. Conf.* 31: 355–73.

Stewart, A.G. 1978. Swans flying at 8,000 metres. *Brit. Birds* 71: 459–60.

Stewart, R.E. 1962. *Waterfowl populations in the Upper Chesapeake region,* Spec. Sci. Rept.—Wildlife, No. 65. US Fish & Wildl. Serv., Washington.

Stewart, R.E. 1975. *Breeding birds of North Dakota.* Tri-College Center for Environmental Studies, Fargo.

Stewart, R.E. and Aldrich, J.W. 1956. Distinction of maritime and prairie populations of Blue-winged Teal. *Proc. Biol. Soc. Wash.* 69: 29–34.

Stewart, R.E. and Kantrud, H.A. 1973. Ecological distribution of waterfowl populations in North Dakota. *J. Wildl. Manage.* 37: 39–50.

Stewart, R.E. and Kantrud, H.A. 1974. Breeding waterfowl populations in the Prairie Pothole Region of North Dakota. *Condor* 76: 70–90.

Stewart, R.E. and Manning, J.H. 1958. Distribution and ecology of Whistling Swans in the Chesapeake Bay region. *Auk* 75: 203–11.

Stewart, R.E., Jr, Krapu, G.L., Conant, B., Percival, H.F. and Hall, D.L. 1988. Workshop summary: habitat loss and its effect on waterfowl. In *Waterfowl in winter* (ed. M. Weller), pp.613–17. Univ. Minneapolis Press, Minneapolis.

Stieglitz, W.O. 1966. Utilization of available foods by diving ducks on Apalachee Bay, Florida. *Proc. Ann. Conf. Southeastern Assoc. Game and Fish Commissioners* 20: 42–50.

Stieglitz, W.O. 1972. Food habits of the Florida Duck. *J. Wildl. Manage.* 32: 921–34.

Stieglitz, W.O. and Wilson, C.T. 1968. Breeding biology of the Florida Duck. *J. Wildl. Manage.* 32: 921–34.

Stokes, S. 1991. Aspects of the breeding biology of New Zealand Scaup *Aythya novaeseelandiae*. Unpubl. M.Sc. thesis. Univ. Canterbury, New Zealand.

Stolen, P. and McKinney, F. 1983. Bigamous behaviour of Cape Teal. *Wildfowl* 34: 10–13.

Stone, C.P., Hoshide, H.M. and Banko, P.C. 1983. Productivity, mortality, and movements of Nene in the Kau Desert, Hawaii Volcanoes National Park, 1981–1982. *Pac. Sci.* 38: 301–11.

Stonor, C.R. 1939. Notes on the breeding habits of the Common Screamer. *Ibis* 14: 45–49.

Storkersen, O.R. 1994. Knekkand *Anas querquedula*. In *Norsk fugleatlas* (ed. J.O. Gjershaug, P.G. Thingstad, S. Eldoy and S. Byrkjeland), p.82. Norsk Ornitologisk Forening, Klaebu.

Storr, G.M. 1980a. The western subspecies of the Cape Barren Goose *Cereopsis novaehollandiae orisea* (Vieillot). *Western Australian Naturalist* 14: 202–3.

Storr, G.M. 1980b. Birds of the Kimberley Division, Western Australia. *W. Aust. Mus.* Spec. Publ., 11: 1–117.

Storr, G.M. and Johnstone, R.E. 1988. Birds of the Swan Coastal Plain and adjacent sea islands. *Rec. West Aust. Mus.* Suppl. 28: 1–26.

Stotts, V.D. and Davis, D.E. 1960. The Black Duck in the Chesapeake Bay of Maryland: breeding behaviour and biology. *Chesapeake Sci.* 1: 127–54.

Stoudt, I.J. and Cornwell, G.W. 1976. Nonhunting mortality of North American waterfowl. *J. Wildl. Manage.* 40: 681–93.

Stoudt, J.H. 1971. *Ecological factors affecting waterfowl production in the Saskatchewan parklands*, Resour. Publ., No. 99. US Fish & Wildl. Serv., Washington.

Stoudt, J.H. 1982. *Habitat use and productivity of Canvasbacks in southwestern Manitoba, 1961–72*, Spec. Sci. Rep. Wildl., No. 248. US Fish & Wildl. Serv., Washington.

Straml, M., Christidis, L., Easteal, S., Horn, P. and Collet, C. 1996. Molecular relationships within Australian waterfowl (Anseriformes). *Aust. J. Zool.* 44: 47–58.

Straneck, R., Livezey, B.C. and Humphrey, P.S. 1983. Predation on steamer-ducks by killer whale. *Condor* 85: 255–56.

Strang, C.A. 1976. Feeding behavior and ecology of Glaucous Gulls in western Alaska. Unpubl. Ph.D. thesis. Purdue Univ., Indiana, US.

Street, M. 1977. The food of Mallard ducklings in a wet gravel quarry, and its relation to duckling survival. *Wildfowl* 28: 113–25.

Street, M. 1978. The role of insects in the diet of Mallard ducklings—an experimental approach. *Wildfowl* 29: 93–100.

Streseman, E. 1927–34. *Handbuch der Zoologie*, Vol. 7(2). Kukenthal–Krumbach.

Stroud, D.A. 1981a. Breeding behaviour of the Greenland White-fronted Goose. In *Report of the 1979 Greenland White-fronted Goose Study Expedition to Eqalungmiut Nunat* (ed. D.A. Fox and D.A. Stroud), pp.82–102. Greenland White-fronted Goose Study, Aberystwyth.

Stroud, D.A. 1981b. Plumage variation in the Greenland White-fronted Goose. In *Report of the 1979 Greenland White-fronted Goose Study Expedition to Eqalungmiut Nunat* (ed. D.A. Fox and D.A. Stroud), pp.139–42. Greenland White-fronted Goose Study, Aberystwyth.

Stutzenbaker, C.D. 1988. *The Mottled Duck: its life history, ecology and management*. Texas Parks Wildlife Dept., Austin.

Sugden, L.G. 1973. *Feeding ecology of Pintail, Gadwall, American Widgeon and Lesser Scaup ducklings in southern Alberta*, Rep. Ser., No. 24. Can. Wildl. Serv., Ottawa.

Sugden, L.G. 1978. *Canvasback habitat use and productivity in Saskatchewan parklands*, Occas. Pap., No. 34. Can. Wildl. Serv., Ottawa.

Sugden, L.G. 1980. Parasitism of Canvasback nests by Redheads. *J. Field Ornithol.* 51: 361–64.

Summers, R.W. 1982. The absence of flightless moult in the Ruddy-headed Goose in Argentina and Chile. *Wildfowl* 33: 5–6.

Summers, R.W. 1983a. Moult-skipping by Upland Geese *Chloëphaga picta* in the Falkland Islands. *Ibis* 125: 262–66.

Summers, R.W. 1983b. The life cycle of the Upland Goose *Chloëphaga picta* in the Falkland Islands. *Ibis* 125: 524–44.

Summers, R.W. 1985a. The size and composition of sheld-geese populations and their food consumption on different vegetation types in the Falkland Islands. *J. Appl. Ecol.* 22: 1–17.

Summers, R.W. 1985b. Demographic variations in the movements of Upland Geese *Chloëphaga picta* and Ruddy-headed Geese *Chloëphaga rubidiceps* in the Falkland Islands. *J. Zool., Lond.* 206: 1–15.

Summers, R.W. 1990a. The effect on winter wheat of grazing by Brent Geese *Branta bernicla. J. Appl. Ecol.* 27: 821–33.

Summers, R.W. 1990b. The exploitation of beds of green algae by Brent Geese. *Estuarine, Coastal and Shelf Science* 31: 107–12.

Summers, R.W. and Castro, G. 1988. Population size and feeding behaviour of Andean Geese at Lake Junin, Perú. *Wildfowl* 39: 22–28.

Summers, R.W. and Critchley, C.N.R. 1990. Use of grassland and field selection by Brent Geese *Branta bernicla. J. Appl. Ecol.* 27: 834–46.

Summers, R.W. and Dunnet, G.M. 1984. Sheld-geese and man in the Falkland Islands. *Biol. Cons.* 30: 319–40.

Summers, R.W. and Grieve, A. 1982. Diet, feeding behaviour and food intake of the Upland Goose (*Chloëphaga picta*) and Ruddy-headed Goose (*C. rubidiceps*) in the Falkland Islands. *J. Appl. Ecol.* 19: 783–804.

Summers, R.W. and Martin, S.I. 1985. Moult-skipping by the Lesser Magellan Goose in Argentina. *Wildfowl* 36: 42–44.

Summers, R.W. and McAdam, J.H. 1993. *The Upland Goose.* Bluntisham Books, Bluntisham, UK.

Summers, R.W. and Underhill, L.G. 1987. Factors related to breeding production of Brent Geese *Branta b. bernicla* and waders (Charadrii) on the Taimyr Peninsula. *Bird Study* 34: 161–71.

Summers, R.W., Underhill, L.G., Middleton, D. and Buckland, S.T. 1985. Turnover in the population of Ruddy-headed Geese (*Chloëphaga rubidiceps*) at Goose Green, Falkland Islands. *J. Appl. Ecol.* 22: 635–43.

Summers, R.W., Stansfield, J., Perry, S., Atkins, C. and Bishop, J. 1993. Utilization, diet and diet selection by Brent Geese *Branta bernicla bernicla* on saltmarshes in Norfolk. *J. Zool., Lond.:* 231: 249–73.

Summers, R.W., Underhill, L.G., Syroechkovski, E.E., Jr, Lappo, H.G., Prŷs-Jones, R.P. and Karpov, V. 1994. The breeding biology of Dark-bellied Brent Geese *Branta b. bernicla* and King Eiders *Somateria spectabilis* on the northeastern Taimyr Peninsula, especially in relation to Snowy Owl *Nyctea scandiaca* nests. *Wildfowl* 45: 110–18.

Surmach, S.G. and Zaykin, D.V. 1994. The Scaly-sided Merganser *Mergus squamatus* (Gould) in the Iman Basin, Far-East Russia. In *The Scaly-sided Merganser Mergus squamatus in Russia and China*, IWRB Threatened Waterfowl Research Group Spec. Publ., No. 1 (ed. B. Hughes and J. Hunter), pp.11–17. WWT, Slimbridge, UK.

Suter, W. and Schifferli, L. 1988. Überwinternde Wasservögel in der Schweiz und ihren Grenzgebieten: Bestandsentwicklungen 1967–1987 im internationalen Vergleich. *Orn. Beob.* 85: 261–98.

Suter, W. and van Eerden, M.R. 1992. Simultaneous mass starvation of wintering diving ducks in Switzerland and the Netherlands: a wrong decision in the right strategy? *Ardea* 80: 229–42.

Sutherland, W.J. and Allport, G.A. 1991. The distribution and ecology of naturalized Egyptian Geese *Alopochen aegyptiacus* in Britain. *Bird Study* 38: 128–34.

Sutherland, W.J. and Allport, G.A. 1994. A spatial depletion model of the interaction between Bean Geese and Wigeon with the consequences for habitat management. *J. Anim. Ecol.* 63: 51–59.

Sutherland, W.J. and Crockford, N.J. 1993. Factors affecting the feeding distribution of Red-breasted Geese *Branta ruficollis* wintering in Romania. *Biol. Cons.* 63: 61–65.

Sutherland, W.J. and Parker, G.A. 1985. Distribution of unequal competitors. In *Behavioural ecology* (ed. R.M. Sibly and R.H. Smith), pp.255–74. Blackwell Scientific Publications, Oxford.

Suydam, R.S. 2000. King Eider (*Somateria spectabilis*). The Birds of North America, No. 491 (ed. A. Poole and F. Gill). AOU, The Birds of North America Inc., Philadelphia.

Svazas, S. Meissner, W. and Nehls, H.W. 1994. Wintering populations of Goosander (*Mergus merganser*) and Smew (*Mergus albellus*) at the south eastern Baltic coast. *Acta Ornithologica Lituanica* 9–10: 56–69.

Sveriges Ornitologiska Forening 1990. *Sveriges faglar.* SOF, Stockholm.

Swan, L.W. 1970. Goose of the Himalayas. *Nat. History* 79: 68–75.

Swanson, G.A. and Meyer, M.I. 1977. Impact of fluctuating water levels on feeding ecology of breeding Blue-winged Teal. *J. Wildl. Manage.* 41: 426–33.

Swanson, G.A., Meyer, M.I. and Serie, J.R. 1974. Feeding ecology of breeding Blue-winged Teals. *J. Wildl. Manage.* 38: 396–407.

Swanson, G.A., Krapu, G.L. and Serie, J.R. 1979. Foods of laying female dabbling ducks on the breeding grounds. In *Waterfowl and wetlands—an integrated review*, Symp. North Central Section of Wildlife Society (ed. T.A. Bookhout), pp.47–57. La Crosse Printing Co., La Crosse, Wisconsin.

Swanson, G.A., Adomatis, V.A., Lee, F.B., Serie, J.R. and Shoesmith, J.A. 1989. Limnological conditions influencing duckling use of saline lakes in south-central North Dakota. *J. Wildl. Manage.* 48: 340–49.

Swedberg, G.E. 1967. *The Koloa. Preliminary report on the life history and status of the Hawaiian Duck (Anas wyvilliana)*. Federal Aid to Wildlife Restoration Act (W-5-R), Dept. Land and Nat. Res., Honolulu, Hawaii.

Swennen, C. 1983. Reproductive output of Eiders *Somateria m. mollissima* on the southern border of its breeding range. *Ardea* 71: 245–54.

Swennen, C. 1991. Ecology and population dynamics of the Common Eider in the Dutch Wadden Sea. Unpubl. Doctoral thesis. Rijksuniversiteit, Groningen, The Netherlands.

Syroechkovski, E.E., Jr 1995. On the taxonomic status of Pacific Black Brant *Branta bernicla nigricans. Bull. Goose Study Group of Eastern Europe and North Asia* 1: 68–72. [In Russian.])

Syroechkovski, E.E., Jr 1996. Present status of the Lesser White-fronted Goose (*Anser erythropus*) populations in Taimyr and some peculiarities of the system of species migrations in the Western Palearctic. *Casarca* 2: 71–112.

Syroechkovski, E.E. 2000. The hypothesis about the origin of the Emperor Goose. *Casarca* 6: 45–57. [In Russian with English summary.]

Syroechkovski, E.E. and Rogecheva, E.V. 1994. The Great Arctic Reserve and problems of nature conservation in the Arctic. In *Arctic tundras of Taimyr and Kara Sea Islands: nature, fauna and conservation problems*, Vol. 1, pp. 14–40. Inst. Ecol. and Evol., Russian Acad. Sci., Moscow.

Syroechkovski, E.E., Jr 2002. Distribution and population estimates for swans in the Siberian arctic in the 1990s. In *Proceedings of the Fourth International Swan Symposium, 2001* (ed. E.C. Rees, S.L. Earnst and J. Coulson). *Waterbirds*, Special Publication 1: 100–13.

Syroechkovski, E.E., Jr and Zochler, Z. 1997. Threatened waterfowl in the Lower Yana River, Yakutia, Russia. *Wetlands International Threatened Waterfowl Research Group News* 10: 26–29.

Syroechkovski, E.E., Zockler, C. and Lappo, E. 1998. Status of Brent Goose in northwest Yakutia, East Siberia. *Brit. Birds* 91: 565–72.

Syroechkovsky, E.V., Litvin, K.E. and Gurtovaya, E.N. 2002. Nesting ecology of Bewick's Swans on Vaygach Island, Russia. In *Proceedings of the Fourth International Swan Symposium, 2001* (ed. E.C. Rees, S.L. Earnst and J. Coulson). *Waterbirds*, Special Publication 1: 221–26.

Sytsma, K.J. 1990. DNA and morphology: inference of plant phylogeny. *Trends Ecol. Evol.* 5: 104–10.

Szijj, J. 1983. Okologische Wertanalyse des Achelos-Delta, Westgriechenland. Unpubl. thesis. Univ. Essen, Germany.

Szymczak, M.R. and Rexstad, E.A. 1991. Harvest distribution and survival of a Gadwall population. *J. Wildl. Manage.* 55: 592–600.

Takekawa, J.Y. 1987. Energetics of Canvasbacks staging on the Upper Mississippi River pool during fall migration. Unpubl. Ph.D. thesis. Iowa State Univ., Ames, US.

Takekawa, J.Y., Orthmeyer, D.L., Kurechi, M., Sabano, Y., Syroechkovsky, E.V. Litkin, K.E. et al. 1994 Restoration of lesser snow geese to east Asia: a North Pacific conservation project. *Trans. N. Amer. Wildl. Nat. Res. Conf.* 59: 132–45.

Talent, L.G., Krapu, G.L. and Jarvis, R.L. 1982. Habitat use by Mallard broods in south-central North Dakota. *J. Wildl. Manage.* 46: 629–35.

Talent, L.G., Jarvis, R.L. and Krapu, G.L. 1983. Survival of Mallard broods in south-central North Dakota. *Condor* 85: 74–78.

Tamisier, A. 1974. Etho-ecological studies of Teal wintering in the Carmargue (Rhone delta, France). *Wildfowl* 25: 107–17.

Tamisier, A. and Dehorter, O. 1999. *Camargue, canards et foulques.* Centre Ornithologique du Gard, Nîmes.

Tarboton, W. 2001. *Nests and eggs of Southern African birds.* Struik Publishers, Cape Town.

Tarboton, W.R., Kemp, M.I. and Kemp, A.C. 1987. *Birds of the Transvaal*. Transvaal Museum, Pretoria.

Taylor, J. 1953. A possible moult-migration of Pink-footed Geese. *Ibis* 95: 638–42.

Taylor, J.S. 1944. Notes on the South African Shelduck. *Ostrich* 15: 188–93.

Taylor, J.S. 1957. Notes on the birds of inland waters in the eastern Cape Province with special reference to the Karoo. *Ostrich* 28: 1–80.

Taylor, J.S. and Vincent, J. 1949. Breeding dates of game birds. *Ostrich* 20: 38–39.

Taylor, P.B., Navarro, R.A., Wren-Sargent, M., Harrison, J.A. and Kieswetter, S.L. 1999. Total CWAC Report. Co-ordinated Waterbird Counts in South Africa, 1992–1997. Avian Demography Unit, Cape Town.

Teixeira, R.M. (ed.) 1979. *Atlas van de Nederlandse broedvogels*. Natuurmonumenten, 's-Graveland.

Temme, M. 1976. Beitrage zur Kenntis der Philippinenente (*Anas luzonica* Frazer (*sic*)). *Orn. Mitt.* 28: 184–89.

TERA 1995. Distribution and abundance of Spectacled Eiders in the vicinity of Prudhoe Bay, Alaska: 1991–1993. Unpubl. rept. Troy Ecological Research Associates, Anchorage, to BP Exploration (Alaska), Inc.

Teunissen, W., Spaans, B and Drent, R. 1985. Breeding success in Brent Geese in relation to individual feeding opportunities during spring in the Wadden Sea. *Ardea* 73: 109–19.

Therkildsen, O.R. and Madsen, J. 2000. Energetics of feeding on winter wheat versus pasture grasses: a window of opportunity for winter range expansion in the Pink-footed Goose *Anser brachyrhynchus*. *Wild. Biol.* 6: 65–74.

Theron, G. 1992. A feeding frenzy around a rise of termite alates. *Witwatersrand Bird Club News* 157: 20.

Thomas, B.T. 1979. The birds of a ranch in the Venezuelan llanos. In *Vertebrate ecology of the northern neotropics* (ed. J.F. Eisenberg), pp.213–32. Smithsonian Institution Press, Washington.

Thomas, D. 1979. *Tasmanian bird atlas, fauna of Tasmania handbook*, No. 2. Univ. Tasmania, Hobart.

Thomas, D.D. and Condy, J.B. 1965. Breeding of Hottentot Teal *Anas punctata* Burchell in Southern Rhodesia. *Ostrich* 36: 88–89.

Thomas, G.J. 1980. Breeding waterfowl at the Ouse Washes. *Wildfowl* 31: 73–88.

Thomas, G.J. 1982. Autumn and winter feeding ecology of waterfowl at the Ouse Washes, England. *J. Zool., Lond.* 197: 131–72.

Thomas, G.J., Owen, M. and Richards, P. 1977. Grit in waterfowl at the Ouse Washes, England. *Wildfowl* 28: 136–38.

Thompson, A.B. 1985. Transmission dynamics of *Profilicollis botulus* (Acanthocephala) from crabs (*Carcinus maenas*) to Eider Ducks (*Somateria mollissima*) on the Ythan estuary, N.E. Scotland. *J. Anim. Ecol.* 54: 605–16.

Thompson, B.C., Tabor, J.E. and Turner, C.L. 1988. Diurnal behavior patterns of waterfowl wintering on the Columbia River, Oregon and Washington. In *Waterfowl in winter* (ed. M. Weller), pp.153–67. Univ. Minneapolis Press, Minneapolis.

Thompson, D. 1973. Feeding ecology of diving ducks on Keokuk Pool, Mississippi River. *J. Wildl. Manage.* 37: 367–81.

Thompson, D.Q. and Person, R.A. 1963. The eider pass at Point Barrow, Alaska. *J. Wildl. Manage.* 27: 348–56.

Thompson, J.E. 1992. The nutritional ecology of molting male Canvasbacks (*Aythya valisineria*) in central Alberta. Unpubl. M.S. thesis. Univ. Missouri, Columbia, US.

Thompson, J.E. and Davison Ankney, C. 2002. Role of food in territoriality and egg production of Buffleheads (*Bucephala albeola*) and Barrow's Goldeneye (*Bucephala islandica*). *Auk* 119(4): 1075–90.

Thompson, J.E. and Drobney, R.D. 1995. Intensity and chronology of postreproductive molts in male Canvasbacks. *Wilson Bull.* 107: 338–58.

Thompson, P.M., Harvey, W.G., Johnson, D.L., Millin, D.J., Rashid, S.M.A., Scott, D.A., et al. 1993. Recent notable bird records from Bangladesh. *Forktail* 9: 13–44.

Thompson, S.C. and Raveling, D.G. 1987. Incubation behavior of Emperor Geese compared with other geese: interactions of predation, body size, and energetics. *Auk* 104: 707–16.

Thompson, S.C. and Raveling, D.G. 1988. Nest insulation and incubation constancy of arctic geese. *Wildfowl* 39: 124–32.

Thorn, T.D. and Zwank, P.J. 1993. Foods of migrating Cinnamon Teal in central New Mexico. *J. Field Ornithol.* 64: 452–63.

Thornberg, D.G. 1973. Diving duck movements on Keokuk Pool, Mississippi River. *J. Wildl. Manage.* 37: 382–9.

Thorstrom, R. and Rabarisoa, R.G.M. 1996. An observation of Madagascar Teal *Anas bernieri* in north-western Madagascar. *Wildfowl* 47: 212–15.

Threatened Waterfowl Specialist Group. 2001. Threatened waterfowl species and subspecies. In *TWSG News* 13: 2–4. WWT, Slimbridge, UK.

Threatened Waterfowl Specialist Group. 2003. Threatened waterfowl species and subspecies. *TWSG News* 14: 2–4. WWT, Slimbridge, UK.

Threatened Waterfowl Specialist Group. (In prep.) Global Action Plan for the Conservation of Anseriformes (Ducks, Geese, Swans and Screamers). IUCN, Gland, Switzerland, and WWT, Slimbridge, UK.

Ticehurst, N.F. 1957. *The Mute Swan in England.* Cleaver-Hume Press, London.

Tichotsky, J. 1991. *Use and allocation of natural resources in the Chukotka Autonomous District.* I.S.E.R., Univ. Alaska, Anchorage.

Tietje, W.D. and Teer, J.G. 1988. Winter body condition of Northern Shovelers on freshwater and saline habitats. In *Waterfowl in winter* (ed. M.W. Weller), pp.353–76. Univ. Minnesota Press, Minneapolis.

Tietje, W.D. and Teer, J.G. 1996. Winter feeding ecology of Northern Shovelers on freshwater and saline wetlands in south Texas. *J. Wildl. Manage.* 60: 843–55.

Timm, D.E. and Dau, C.P. 1979. Productivity, mortality, distribution and population status of Pacific Flyway White-fronted Geese. In *Management and biology of Pacific geese,* (ed. R.L. Jarvis and J.C. Bartonek), pp.280–98. Oregon State Univ. Press, Corvallis.

Timmermann, G. 1963. Fragen der Anatidensystematik in parasitologischer Sicht. *Int. Ornith. Congr.* 13: 189–97.

Tingay, A. 1974. Aggression in the Black Swan. *Emu* 74: 35–38.

Tingay, A., Tingay, S. and Goodsell, J. 1977. Report on a management programme for Black Swans in south-western Australia. *Emu* 77: 185–87.

Titman, R.D. 1983. Spacing and three-bird flights of Mallards breeding in pothole habitat. *Can. J. Zool.* 61: 839–47.

Titman, R.D. 1999. Red-breasted Merganser *(Mergus serrator).* The Birds of North America, No. 443 (ed.

A. Poole and F. Gill). AOU, The Birds of North America Inc., Philadelphia.

Titman, R.D. and Lowther, J.K. 1975. The breeding behavior of a crowded population of Mallards. *Can. J. Zool.* 53: 1270–83.

Titman, R.D. and Seymour, N.R. 1976. Unusual fighting in Ring-necked Ducks. *Wilson Bull.* 88: 507–8.

Titman, R.D. and Seymour, N.R. 1981. A comparison of pursuit flights by six North American ducks of the genus *Anas. Wildfowl* 32: 11–18.

Tkachenko, E.E. 1995. The Swan Goose in south-east Transbaikalia. *IWRB Threatened Waterfowl Research Group Newsl.* 8: 10–11.

Tobish, T. 1986. Separation of Barrow's and Common Goldeneyes in all plumages. *Birding* 18: 17–30.

Todd, F.S. 1979. *Waterfowl: ducks, geese and swans of the world.* Harcourt-Brace Jovanovich, New York, and Sea World Press, San Diego.

Todd, F.S. 1996. *Natural history of the waterfowl.* Ibis Publishing Company, California, and San Diego Natural History Museum, California.

Todd, W.E.C. 1916. The birds of the Isle of Pines. *Ann. Carnegie Mus.* 10: 146–296.

Todd, W.E.C. 1963. *Birds of the Labrador peninsula and adjacent areas.* Carnegie Mus. Pittsburgh, and Univ. Toronto Press, Toronto.

Toft, C.A., Trauger, D.L., and Murdy, H.W. 1982. Tests for species interactions: breeding phenology and habitat use in subarctic ducks. *Am. Nat.* 120: 586–613.

Tolvanen, P., Aarvak, T. and Bragina, T. 2000. Conservation work for the wetlands and monitoring the autumn staging of Lesser White-fronted Goose in the Kustanay region, north-west Kazakstan, in 2000. Annual report 2000. *WWF Finland Report* 9: 30–33.

Tolvanen, P., Ruokolainen, K., Markkola, J. and Karvonen, R. (eds.). 1998. Finnish Lesser White-fronted Goose conservation project. Annual report 1997. *WWF Finland Report* 9: 30–32.

Tombre, I.M., Erikstad, K.E., Gabrielsen, G.W., Strann, K-B. and Black, J.M. 1996. Body condition and spring migration in high arctic Barnacle Geese. *Wildlife Biol.* 2: 247–51.

Tombre, I.M., Black, J.M. and Loonen, M.J.J.E. 1998. Critical components of the dynamics of a Barnacle Goose colony: a sensitivity analysis. *Norsk Pol. Skr.* 200: 81–89.

Tome, M.W. 1981. Reproductive bioenergetics of female Ruddy Ducks in Manitoba. Unpubl. M.S. thesis. Univ. Maine, Orono, US.

Tome, M.W. 1984. Changes in nutrient reserves and organ size of female Ruddy Ducks breeding in Manitoba. *Auk* 101: 830–37.

Tome, M.W. 1987. An observation of renesting by a Ruddy Duck, *Oxyura jamaicensis. Can. Field-Nat.* 101: 153–54.

Tome, M.W. 1989. Search-path characteristics of foraging Ruddy Ducks. *Auk* 106: 42–48.

Tome, M.W. 1991. Diurnal activity budget of female Ruddy Ducks breeding in Manitoba. *Wilson Bull.* 103: 183–89.

Tome, M.W. and Wrubleski, D.A. 1988. Underwater foraging behaviour of Canvasbacks, Lesser Scaups and Ruddy Ducks. *Condor* 90: 168–72.

Tomkovich, P.S., Soloviev, M.Y. and Syroechkovski, E.E., Jr 1994. Birds of the Arctic tundra of northern Taimyr (Knipovich Bay area). In *Arctic tundras of Taimyr and Kara Sea Islands: nature, fauna and conservation problems*, Vol. 1, pp.41–107. Inst. Ecol. and Evol., Russian Acad. Sci., Moscow.

Toms, M.P. and Clark, J.A. 1998. Bird Ringing in Britain and Ireland in 1996. *Ringing & Migration* 19: 95–168.

Torres, J.A. 1984. Caractères distinctifs de deux femelles d'*Oxyura leucocephala* d'Espagne. *Alauda* 52: 232–35.

Torres, J.A. and Alcalá-Zamora, A. 1997. Seguimiento de la población española de Malvasía Cabeciblanca (*Oxyura leucocephala*) durante los años 1996 y 1997. *Oxyura* 9: 85–99.

Torres, J.A. and Arenas, R. 1985. Nuevos datos relativos a la alimentación de *Oxyura leucocephala. Ardeola* 32: 127–31.

Torres, J.A. and Ayala, J.M. 1986. Variation de dessin céphalique des mâles de l'erismature á tête blanche (*Oxyura leucocephala*). *Alauda* 54: 197–206.

Torres, J.A. and Moreno-Arroyo, B. 2000. La recuperación de la malvasía cabeciblanca (*Oxyura leucocephala*) en España durante el último decenio del siglo XX. *Oxyura* 10: 5–51.

Torres, J.A., Raya, C., Arenas, R.M. and Moreno, J.M. 1985. Estudio del comportamiento reproductór de la Malvasía (*Oxyura leucocephala*). *Oxyura* 2: 5–22.

Torres, J.A., Arenas, R., Ayala, J.M., Muñoz, T., Castelló, V. and Mulero, A. 1989. *Plan Rector de Uso y Gestión de las Reservas Integrales de las Zonas Húmedas del Sur de Córdoba.* Agencia de Medio Ambiente, Junta de Andalucía, Córdoba.

Torres, J.A., Alcalá-Zamora, A. and Moreno, B. 1996. Resultados de los censos coordinados de Malvasía Cabeciblanca (*Oxyura leucocephala*) durante el año 1994 y 1995. *Oxyura* 8: 5–14.

Tostain, O., Dujardin, J.L., Érard, C. and Thiollay, J.M. 1992. *Oiseaux de Guyane.* Société d'Études Ornithologique, Brunoy, France.

Townsend, G.H. 1966. A study of waterfowl nesting on the Saskatchewan River Delta. *Can. Field-Nat.* 80: 74–88.

Trauger, D.L. 1971. Population ecology of Lesser Scaup (*Aythya affinis*) in subarctic taiga. Unpubl. Ph.D. thesis. Iowa State Univ., Ames, US.

Trauger, D.L. 1974. Eye color of female Lesser Scaup in relation to age. *Auk* 91: 243–54.

Treca, B. 1979. Note sur la reproduction du canard armé *Plectropterus gambensis* au Senegal. *Malimbus* 1: 29–31.

Treca, B. 1980. Nouvelles données sur la reproduction du canard armé *Plectropterus gambensis* au Senegal. *Malimbus* 2: 25–28.

Tremblay, S. and Couture, R. 1986. Interspecific variations of bucco-lingual characteristics in a guild of dabbling ducks. *Can. J. Zool.* 64: 2176–80.

Triggs, S.J., Williams, M., Marshall, S.J. and Chambers, G.K. 1991. Genetic relationships in a population of Blue Ducks. *Wildfowl* 42: 87–93.

Triggs, S.J., Williams, M., Marshall, S.J. and Chambers, G.K. 1992. Genetic structure of Blue Duck *Hymenolaimus malacorhynchos* populations revealed by DNA fingerprinting. *Auk* 109: 80–89.

Trivers, R.L. 1972. Parental investment and sexual selection. In *Sexual selection and the descent of man* (ed. B. Campbell), pp.136–79. Aldine, Chicago.

Trolliet, B. 1986. Le prélèvement cynégétique de canards en France. Saison 1983–1984. *Bull. mens. ONC* 108: 64–70.

Trolliet, B., Girard, O. and Fouquet, M. 2003. Evaluation des populations d'oiseaux d'eau en Afrique de l'Ouest. *ONCFS Rapport scientifique* 2002: 51–55.

Trost, R.E. and Drut, M.S. 2001. *Waterfowl harvest and status, hunter participation and success, and certain hunt-*

ing regulations in the Pacific flyway and United States. US Fish & Wildl. Serv., Portland, Oregon.

Tucker, G.M. and Heath, M.F. 1994. *Birds in Europe: their conservation status*, Conservation Ser., No. 3. BirdLife International, Cambridge, UK.

Tullock, D.G. and McKean, J. L. 1983. Magpie Goose populations on the coastal plains of the Northern Territory (1958–1980). *Corella* 7: 32–36.

Tuohy, J.M., McHugh, K.P. and de Kloet, S.R. 1992. Systematic relationships among some Anatini as derived from restriction-endonuclease analysis of a repeated DNA component. *Auk* 109: 465–73.

Turbott, G.A. 1990. *Checklist of the birds of New Zealand* (3rd edn). Random Century, Auckland.

Turnbull, R.E., Brakhage, D.H. and Johnson, F.A. 1986. Lesser Scaup mortality from commercial trotlines on Lake Okeechobee, Florida. *Proc. Ann. Conf. Southeast. Assoc. Fish Wildl. Agencies* 40: 465–69.

Turner, B.C., Hochbaum, G.S., Caswell, F.D. and Nieman, D.J. 1987. Agricultural impacts on wetland habitats on the Canadian prairies, 1981–85. *Trans. N. Amer. Wildl. Nat. Res. Conf.* 52: 206–15.

Tveit, G. 1984. Autumn migration, wintering areas and survival of Bean Goose *Anser fabalis* marked on the moulting grounds in Finmark, North Norway. *Swedish Wildlife Research* 13: 73–82.

Tyler, C. 1964. A study of egg shells of the Anatidae. *Proc. Zool. Soc. London* 142: 547–83.

Udvardy, M.D.F. 1963. Data on the body temperature of tropical sea and water birds. *Auk* 80: 191–94.

Underhill, L.G. 1989. Egyptian Geese *Alopochen aegyptiacus* with young in surf at Dassen Island, South Africa. *Cormorant* 17: 77.

Underhill, L.G., Tree, A.J., Oschadleus, H.D. and Parker, V. 1999. *Review of ring recoveries of waterbirds in southern Africa*. Avian Demography Unit, Univ. Cape Town.

Underhill, M.C., Gittings, T., Callaghan, D.A., Hughes, B., Kirby, J.S. and Delany, S.N. 1998. Status and distribution of breeding Common Scoters *Melanitta nigra nigra* in Britain and Ireland in 1995. *Bird Study* 45: 146–56.

Urban, E.K. 1991. Palaearctic and Afrotropical ducks and geese at Gaferssa Reservoir, Ethiopia, 1964–1970. *Scopus* 14: 92–96.

Urban, E.K. 1993. Status of wildfowl in northeast and east Africa. *Wildfowl* 44: 133–48.

Urban, E.K. and Brown, L.H. 1971. *A checklist of the birds of Ethiopia*. Haile Sellassie I Univ. Press, Addis Ababa.

Urdiales, C. and Pereira, P. 1993. Identification key of *O. jamaicensis*, *O. leucocephala* and their hybrids. ICONA, Madrid.

Urfi, A.J. 1997. The status of the Barheaded Goose in Delhi and the adjoining areas of Haryana and Western Uttar Pradesh. *J. Ecol. Soc.* 10: 10–12.

USFWS 1967. Native fish and wildlife: endangered species. *Federal Register* 32(48): 4001.

USFWS 1977. *North American bird banding techniques*. US Fish & Wildl. Serv., Washington.

USFWS 1980. *Selected vertebrate endangered species of the seacoast of the United States: Laysan Duck*. US Fish & Wildl. Serv., Washington.

USFWS 1982. *The Laysan Duck recovery plan*. US Fish & Wildl. Serv., Portland.

USFWS 1983. Recovery plans for Laysan Duck, Sonoran pronghorn approved. *Endangered Species Tech. Bull.* 8: 6.

USFWS 1992. *January 1992 midwinter waterfowl census, United States summary*. Office of Migratory Bird Management, Washington.

USFWS 1994. *Update to the North American waterfowl management plan*. US Fish & Wildl. Serv., Washington.

USFWS 1996. *Spectacled Eider Recovery Plan*. US Fish & Wildl. Serv., Anchorage.

USFWS 1999. *Draft revised recovery plan for Hawaiian waterbirds* (2nd revised edn). US Fish & Wildl. Serv., Portland.

USFWS/CWS 1986. *North American Waterfowl Management Plan*. US Fish & Wildl. Serv., Washington, and Can. Wildl. Serv., Ottawa.

USFWS/CWS 1992. *The 1992 Status of Waterfowl and Flight Forecast*. US Fish & Wildl. Serv. Migratory Bird Management Office, Patuxent.

Uspenski, S.M. 1960. The Brent Goose (*Branta bernicla* L.) in the Soviet Union. *Wildfowl* 11: 80–93.

Uspenski, S.M. 1965. *Die Wildgänse Nordeurasiens*. Neue Brehm-Bucherei, Wittenberg, Lutherstadt.

Uspenski, S.M. 1966. Verbreitung und Ökologie der Rothalsgans. *Falke* 13: 83–85.

Väänänen, V-M. 2000. Predation risk associated with nesting in gull colonies by two *Aythya* species: observations and an experimental test. *J. Avian Biol.* 31: 31–35.

Valinkangas, I. 1933. Finnische Zugvogel aus englisher Vogeleiern. *Vogelzug* 4: 159–66.

Valverde, J. 1964. Datos sobre Cerceta Pardilla en las Marismas. *Ardeola* 9: 121–32.

Van den Bergh, L. 1999. Tundra Bean Goose *Anser fabalis rossicus*. In *Goose populations of the Western Palearctic. A review of status and distribution*, Publ. No. 48 (ed. J. Madsen, G. Cracknell and A.D. Fox). pp.38–66. Wetlands International, Wageningen, Netherlands, and National Environmental Research Institute, Rønde, Denmark.

Van der Kloot, W. and Morse, M.J. 1975. A stochastic analysis of the display behavior of the Red-breasted Merganser (*Mergus serrator*). *Behaviour* 54: 181–216.

van der Ven, J. 1997. Barheads on their breeding grounds. *J. Ecol. Soc.* 10: 5–7.

Van Dijk, K. and Van Eerden, R. 1991. Biometrics and timing of primary moult of non-breeding Mute Swans *Cygnus olor* at Lake Ijsselmeer, the Netherlands. *Wildfowl* Spec. Suppl. 1: 296–303.

Van Ee, C.A. 1971. Variation in the head pattern of the female South African Shelduck. *Ostrich* 42: 149–50.

van Eerden, M.R. 1984. Waterfowl movements in relation to food stocks. In *Coastal waders and wildfowl in winter* (ed. P.R. Evans, J.D. Goss-Custard and W.G. Hale), pp.84–100. Cambridge Univ. Press.

van Eerden, M.R., Loonen, M.J.J.E. and Zijlstra, M. 1997. Moulting Greylag Geese *Anser anser* defoliating a reed marsh *Phragmites australis*: seasonal constraints versus long-term commensalism between plants and herbivores. In *Patchwork: patch use, habitat exploitation and carrying capacity for waterbirds in Dutch freshwater wetlands*, pp.239–64. Publ. doctoral thesis. Directoraat-Generaal Rijkswaterstaat, Lelystad, The Netherlands.

van Horn, K. 1991. Habitat use and activity patterns of interior Alaskan waterbirds. Unpubl. M.S. thesis. Univ. Missouri, Columbia, US.

van Impe, J. 1973. Bepaling in het veld van leeftijdsklassen bij de rietgans *Anser fabalis. Limosa* 46: 192–98.

van Tuinen, M., Sibley, C.G. and Hedges, S.B. 2000. The early history of modern birds inferred from DNA sequences of nuclear and mitochondrial ribosomal genes. *Mol. Biol. Evol.* 17: 451–57.

van Tuinen, M., Butvill, D.B., Kirsch, J.A.W. and Hedges, S.B. 2001. Convergence and divergence in the evolution of aquatic birds. *Proc. R. Soc. Lond.* 268: 1345–50.

Vancouver, G. 1799. *Voyage de decouvertes à l'Océan Pacifique du Nord et autour du monde*. De l'Imprimerie de la Republique, Paris.

Vanhoof, M. 1996. Growth and development in captive Marbled Teal. Unpubl. undergrad. thesis. Katholieke Hogeschool Kempen, Belgium.

Vaught, R.W. 1964. Results of transplanting flightless young Blue-winged Teal. *J. Wildlife Manage.* 28: 208–12.

Vaught, R.W. and Kirsch, L.M. 1966. *Canada Geese of the eastern prairie population, with special reference to the Swan Lake flock*, Tech. Bull., No. 3. Missouri Dept Conservation.

Vaught, R.W., McDougle, H.C. and Burgess, H.H. 1967. Fowl cholera in waterfowl at Squaw Creek National Wildlife Refuge, Missouri. *J. Wildl. Manage.* 31: 248–53.

Vaurie, C. 1965. *Birds of the Palearctic Fauna: Non-passeriformes*. Witherby, London.

Vaurie, C. 1972. *Tibet and its birds*. Witherby, London.

Vaz-Ferreira, R. and Rilla, F. 1991. Black-necked Swan *Cygnus melancoryphus* and Coscoroba Swan *Coscoroba coscoroba* in a wetland in Uruguay. *Wildfowl* Spec. Suppl., 1: 272–77.

Veltman, C. and Williams, M. 1990. Diurnal use of time and space by breeding Blue Duck *Hymenolaimus malacorhynchos. Wildfowl* 41: 62–74.

Veltman, C., Triggs, S., Williams, M., Collier, K.C., McNab, B.K., Newton, L., et al. 1991. The Blue Duck mating system—are river specialists any different? *Int. Ornith. Congr.* 20: 860–67.

Veltman, C.J., Collier, K.J., Henderson, I.M. and Newton, L. 1995. Foraging ecology of Blue Ducks *Hymenolaimus malacorhynchos* on a New Zealand River: implications for conservation. *Biol. Cons.* 74: 187–94.

Venegas, C. and Jory, J. 1979. *Guia de campo para las aves de Magallanes*. Instituto de la Patagonia, Punta Arenas.

Verheyen, R. 1953. Contribution à l'ostéologie et à la systématique des Anseriformes. *Gerfaut* 43: 373–497.

Verheyen, R. 1955. La systematique des Anseriformes basée sur l'osteologie comparée. *Bull. Inst. Royal Sci.*

Nat. Belgique 31(35): 1–18; 31(36): 1–16; 31(37): 1–22; 31(38): 1–16.

Verheyen, R. 1961. A new classification of the birds of the world. *Bull. Inst. R. Sci. Nat. Belg.* 37: 1–36.

Vermeer, K. 1968. Ecological aspects of ducks nesting in high densities among larids. *Wilson Bull.* 80: 78–83.

Vermeer, K. 1972. Variation in density of breeding ducks across the aspen parklands and grasslands of Canada. *Blue Jay* 30: 154–58.

Vermeer, K. 1981. Food and populations of Surf Scoters in British Columbia. *Wildfowl* 32: 107–16.

Vermeer, K. and Bourne, N. 1984. The White-winged Scoter diet in British Columbia waters: resource partitioning with other scoters. In *Marine birds: their feeding ecology and commercial fisheries relationships*, Proc. Pacific seabird group symp. (ed. D.N. Nettleship, G.A. Sanger and P.F. Springer), pp.30–38. Can. Wildl. Serv., Ottawa.

Vermeer, K. and Levings, C.D. 1977. Populations, biomass and food habits of ducks on the Fraser Delta intertidal area, British Columbia. *Wildfowl* 28: 49–60.

Veselovský, Z. 1970. Zur Ethologie der Hühnengans (*Cereopsis novaehollandiae* Lath.). *Z. Tierpsychol.* 27: 915–45.

Veselovský, Z. 1973. The breeding biology of the Cape Barren Goose *Cereopsis novaehollandiae. Int. Zoo Ybk* 13: 48–55.

Veselovský, Z. 1976. Biological notes on the Australian Radjah Shelduck (*Tadorna radjah rufitergum* (Hartert, 1905)) (Anseriformes). *Vest. Cs. spol. zool.* 40: 64–74.

Vestjens, W.J.M. 1977. *Status, habitats, and food of vertebrates at Lake Cowal*, CSIRO Wildl. Res. Tech. Mem., No. 12. CSIRO, Lyneham, ACT.

Vicens, P. 2000. Reintroducción de la malvasía cabeciblanca (*Oxyura leucocephala*) en S'Albufera de Mallorca. *Oxyura* 10: 229–30.

Vickery, P.D. 1988. Distribution and population status of Harlequin Duck (*Histrionicus histrionicus*) wintering in Eastern North America. *Wilson Bull.* 100: 119–26.

Vielliard, J. 1970. La distribution du casarca roux *Tadorna ferruginea. Alauda* 38: 87–125.

Vijayan, L. 1996. Status and conservation of the Andaman Teal *Anas gibberifrons albogularis. Gibier Faune Sauvage* 13: 831–42.

Vilina, Y.A. 1994. Apuntes para la conservación del Humedal 'Estero El Yali'. *Boletín Chileno de Ornitología* 1: 15–20.

Vilina, Y.A., Cofré, H.L., Silva-García, C., García, M.D. and Pérez-Friedenthal, C. 2002. Effects of El Niño on abundance and breeding of Black-necked Swans on El Yali wetland in Chile. In *Proceedings of the Fourth International Swan Symposium, 2001* (ed. E.C. Rees, S.L. Earnst and J. Coulson). *Waterbirds*, Special Publication 1: 123–27.

Vince, M.A. 1968. The effect of rate of stimulation on hatching time in the Japanese Quail. *Brit. Poult. Sci.* 9: 87–91.

Vinicombe, K.E. 2000. Identification of Ferruginous Duck and its status in Britain and Ireland. *Brit. Birds* 93: 4–21.

Vinicombe, K.E. and Harrop, A.H.J. 1999. Ruddy Shelducks in Britain and Ireland, 1986–94. *Brit. Birds* 92: 225–55.

Vinogradov, V. 1990. *Anser erythropus* in the USSR. In *Managing Waterfowl Populations*, IWRB Symp., Astrakhan 1989, Publ., No. 12 (ed. G.V.T. Matthews), pp.199–203. IWRB, Slimbridge, UK.

Vleck, C.M., Vleck, D. and Hoyt, D.F. 1980. Patterns of metabolism and growth in avian embryos. *Amer. Zool.* 20: 405–16.

Vo Quy 1983. A catalogue of Vietnam Birds. In *Fauna and ecology of Vietnam animals* (ed. L.N. Medvedev), pp. 12–43. Nauka, Moscow.

Vogrin, M. 1996. Wintering geese of the River Drava, Slovenia. *Wetlands International Goose Specialist Group Bull.* 7: 13.

von Boetticher, H. 1929. *Gänse- und Entenvögel aus aller Welt.* Geest und Portig K-G., Leipzig.

von Boetticher, H. 1942. Über die Einteilung der Familie der Entenvögel (Anatidae) in Unterfamilien und Sektionen. *Zool. Anz.* 140: 37–48.

von Boetticher, H. 1943. Die phylogenetisch-systematische Stellung von *Anseranas. Zool. Anz.* 142: 55–58.

Von de Wall, W. 1963. Bewegungsstudien an Anatinen. *J. Orn.* 104: 1–15.

von Der Steinen, K. 1890. Allgemeines über die zoologische Thätigkeit und Beobachtungen über das Leben der Robben und Vögel auf Sud-Georgien. In *Die internationale Polarforschung 1882–1883. Die Deutschen Expeditionen und ihre Ergebnisse*, Vol. 2 (ed. G. Neumayer), pp. 194–279. Asher, Berlin.

Von Essen, L. 1991. A note on the Lesser White-fronted Goose *Anser erythropus* in Sweden and the results of the re-introduction scheme. *Ardea* 79: 305–6.

von Kittlitz, F.H. 1834. Nachricht von den Brüteplätzen einiger tropischen Seevögel im stillen Ocean. *Mus. Senckenbergianum* 1: 115–26.

von Taube, O. 1957. *Tibetanisches Vogelbuch*. Ars Tibetana, Zürich.

von Treuenfels, C-A. 1996. *Unter Pandas und Pinguinen—Reportagen aus der bedrohten Natur*, (2nd edn). Rasch und Röhring, Hamburg.

Voous, K.H. 1960. *Atlas of European birds*. Nelson.

Voous, K.H. 1992. Reflections on the genus in ornithology. *Bull. BOC* 112A: 261–66.

Vorderman, A.G. 1892. Over eene collectie vogels afkomstig van de Lampongs (Zuid Sumatra). *Natuurk Tijdschr. Ned. Indie, Batavia* 51: 201–49.

Vorobyev, K.A. 1954. *Birds of the Ussuri Krai*. USSR Academy of Sciences, Moscow.

Vorobyev, K.A. 1963. *Ptitsy Yakutii*. Moscow.

Vuilleumier, F. 1997. A large autumn concentration of swans (*Cygnus melancoryphus* and *Coscoroba coscoroba*) and other waterbirds at Puerto Natales, Magallanes, Chilean Patagonia, and its significance for swan and waterfowl conservation. *Ornitología Neotropical* 8: 1–5.

Wainwright, C.B. 1967. Results of wildfowl ringing at Abberton Reservoir, Essex, 1949–1966. *Wildfowl* 18: 28–35.

Wakeley, J.S. and Mendall, H.L. 1976. Migrational homing and survival of adult female Eiders in Maine. *J. Wildl. Manage.* 40: 15–21.

Wakelin, M.D. 1993. Contents of Blue Duck faeces from the Tongariro River. *Notornis* 40: 205–12.

Walasz, K. and Mielczarek, P. 1992. *The atlas of breeding birds in Malopolska 1985–1991 (south-eastern Poland)*. Biologica Silesiae, Warsaw.

Wallraff, H.G. 1972. An approach toward an analysis of the pattern recognition involved in the stellar orientation of birds. In *Animal Orientation and Navigation* (ed. S.R. Galler, K. Scmidt-Koenig, G.J. Jacobs and R.E. Belleville), pp.211–22. NASA, Washington.

Walls, G.L. 1942. The vertebrate eye and its adaptive radiation. *Cranbrook Inst. Sci. Bull.* 19: 1–785.

Walmsley, J.G. and Moser, M.E. 1981. The winter food and feeding habits of Shelduck in the Camargue, France. *Wildfowl* 32: 99–106.

Walter, P.J., Bacon, P.J. and Sears, J. 1991. An analysis of Mute Swan *Cygnus olor* breeding data. *Wildfowl* Spec. Suppl. 1: 151–56.

Walters, M. 1998. The eggs of the Pink-headed Duck. *Bull. BOC* 118: 187–91.

Ward, R.M. 2004. Dark-bellied Brent Goose *Branta bernicla bernicla* in Britain 1960/61–1999/2000. *Waterbird Review Series*, WWT/JNCC, Slimbridge.

Warner, R.E. 1963. Recent history and ecology of the Laysan Duck. *Condor* 65: 2–23.

Warnock, N.D. and Troy, D.M. 1992. Distribution and abundance of Spectacled Eiders at Prudhoe Bay, Alaska, 1991. Unpubl. Report, TERA, Anchorage, US.

Warren, S.M., Fox, A.D., Walsh, A. and O'Sullivan, P. 1992a. Age of first pairing and breeding amongst Greenland White-fronted Geese. *Condor* 94: 791–93.

Warren, S.M., Fox, A.D., Walsh, A., Merne, O.J. and Wilson, H.J. 1992b. Wintering site interchange amongst Greenland White-fronted Geese *Anser albifrons flavirostris* captured at Wexford Slobs, Ireland. *Bird Study* 39: 186–94.

Warren, S.M., Fox, A.D. and Walsh, A. 1993. Extended parent–offspring relationships amongst the Greenland White-fronted Goose. *Auk* 110: 145–48.

Watson, M.D., Robertson, G.J., and Cooke, F. 1993. Egg-laying time and laying interval in the Common Eider. *Condor* 95: 869–78.

Wayland, M. and McNicol, D.K. 1994. Movements and survival of Common Goldeneye broods near Sudbury, Ontario, Canada. *Can. J. Zool.* 72: 1252–59.

Weathers, W.W., Buttemer, W.A., Hayworth, A.M. and Nagy, K.A. 1984. An evaluation of time-budget estimates of daily energy expenditure in birds. *Auk* 101: 459–72.

Webb, C.S. 1936. Collecting waterfowl in Madagascar. *Avic. Mag.* 5: 36–39.

Webb, D. 1973. Letters to the editor. *Honeyguide* 76: 42.

Weeks, J.L. 1969. Breeding behaviour of Mottled Ducks in Louisiana. Unpubl. M.S. thesis. Louisiana State Univ., Baton Rouge, US.

Weigmann, C. and Lamprecht, J. 1991. Intraspecific nest parasitism in Bar-headed Geese, *Anser indicus. Anim. Behav.* 41: 677–88.

Weller, M.W. 1957. Growth, weights, and plumages of the Redhead, *Aythya americana. Wilson Bull.* 69: 5–38.

Weller, M.W. 1959. Parasitic egg laying in the Redhead (*Aythya americana*) and other North American Anatidae. *Ecol. Monogr.* 29: 333–65.

Weller, M.W. 1964a. General habits. In *The waterfowl of the world*, Vol. IV (ed. J. Delacour), pp.15–34. Country Life, London.

Weller, M.W. 1964b. The reproductive cycle. In *The waterfowl of the world*, Vol. IV (ed. J. Delacour), pp.35–79. Country Life, London.

Weller, M.W. 1964c. Distribution and species relationships. In *The waterfowl of the world*, Vol. IV (ed. J. Delacour), pp.108–20. Country Life, London.

Weller, M.W. 1964d. Distribution and migration of the Redhead. *J. Wildl. Manage.* 28: 64–103.

Weller, M.W. 1965. Chronology of pair formation in some Nearctic *Aythya* (Anatidae). *Auk* 82: 227–35.

Weller, M.W. 1967a. Distribution and habitat selection of the Black-headed Duck. *Hornero* 10: 299–306.

Weller, M.W. 1967b. Notes on some marsh birds of Cape San Antonio, Argentina. *Ibis* 109: 391–441.

Weller, M.W. 1967c. Notes on the plumages and weights of the Black-headed Duck *Heteronetta atricapilla. Condor* 69: 133–45.

Weller, M.W. 1967d. Courtship of the Redhead (*Aythya americana*). *Auk* 84: 544–59.

Weller, M.W. 1968a. The breeding biology of the parasitic Black-headed Duck. *Living Bird* 7: 169–207.

Weller, M.W. 1968b. Notes on some Argentine Anatids. *Wilson Bull.* 80: 189–212.

Weller, M.W. 1968c. Plumages and wing spurs of the Torrent Ducks *Merganetta armata. Wildfowl* 19: 33–40.

Weller, M.W. 1970. Additional notes on the plumages of the Redhead (*Aythya americana*). *Wilson Bull.* 82: 320–23.

Weller, M.W. 1972. Ecological studies of Falkland Islands' waterfowl. *Wildfowl* 23: 25–44.

Weller, M.W. 1974. Habitat selection and feeding patterns of Brown Teal *Anas castanea chlorotis* on Great Barrier Island. *Notornis* 21: 25–35.

Weller, M.W. 1975a. Ecological studies of the Auckland Islands flightless teal. *Auk* 92: 280–97.

Weller, M.W. 1975b. Ecology and behaviour of the South Georgia Pintail *Anas g. georgica. Ibis* 117: 217–31.

Weller, M.W. 1975c. Habitat selection by waterfowl of Argentine Isla Grande. *Wilson Bull.* 87: 83–90.

Weller, M.W. 1976. Ecology and behaviour of steamer ducks. *Wildfowl* 27: 45–53.

Weller, M.W. 1980. *The island waterfowl.* Iowa State Univ. Press, Ames.

Weller, M.W. and Ward, P. 1959. Migration and mortality of hand-reared Redheads (*Aythya americana*). *J. Wildl. Manage.* 23: 427–33.

Welsh, D. and Sedinger, J.S. 1990. Extra-pair copulations in Black Brant. *Condor* 92: 242–44.

Wentworth, C. and Seim, S.G. 1996. Subsistence waterfowl harvest survey—Yukon-Kuskokwim Delta: Comprehensive rept 1985–1995. Unpubl. rept, US Fish & Wildl. Serv., Anchorage.

Wernham, C.V., Toms, M.P., Marchant, J.H., Clark, J.A., Siriwardena, G.M. and Baillie, S.R. 2002. *The migration atlas: movements of the birds of Britain and Ireland.* T. & A.D. Poyser, London.

Wetlands International. 2002. *Waterbird Population Estimates—Third Edition.* Wetlands International Global Series No.12, Wageningen, The Netherlands.

Wetmore, A. 1916. Birds of Porto Rico. *US Dept Agriculture Bull.* 80: 189–212.

Wetmore, A. 1917. On certain secondary sexual characters in the male Ruddy Duck, *Erismatura jamaicensis* (Gmelin). *USA National Museum* 52: 479–82.

Wetmore, A. 1918. A note on the tracheal air sac of the Ruddy Duck. *Condor* 20: 19–20.

Wetmore, A. 1920. Birds of Lake Burford, New Mexico. *Auk* 37: 221–47.

Wetmore, A. 1925. Bird life among lava rock and coral sand. *Natl. Geogr. Mag.* 48: 76–108.

Wetmore, A. 1926a. Fossil birds from the Green River Deposits of eastern Utah. *Ann. Carnegie Mus.* 16: 391–402.

Wetmore, A. 1926b. *Report on a collection of birds made by J.R. Pemberton in Patagonia.* Univ. California Publications.

Wetmore, A. 1965. The birds of the Republic of Panama, Part I. *Smithsonian Misc. Coll.* 150: 1–483.

White, C.M.N. and Bruce, M.D. 1986. *The birds of Wallacea (Sulawesi, The Moluccas and Lesser Sunda Islands, Indonesia).* Check-list No. 7. BOU, London.

White, G. 1985. *Birds and other vertebrates of south west Tasmania.* White, Sydney.

White, H.C. 1939. *Bird control to increase the Margaree River Salmon,* Bull., No. 58, pp.1–30. Fish. Res. Board. Can, Ministry of Fisheries, Ottawa.

White, H.C. 1957. *Food and natural history of mergansers on salmon waters in the maritime provinces of Canada,* Bull., No. 116, pp.1–63. Fish. Res. Board Can., Min. Fisheries, Ottawa.

White, J.M. 1987. The New England lagoons as drought refuges for waterbirds. *Emu* 87: 253–55.

White, J.R., Hofmann, P.S., Hammond, D. and Baumgartner, S. 1988. *Selenium verification study, 1986–87.* Rept to California State Water Resources Control Board. California Dept Fish and Game, Sacramento.

White, R. and Henry, A. 2001. Rare and Vagrant birds in the Falkland Islands 1996–2000. *Wildlife Conservation in the Falkland Islands.* Issue1. Falklands Conservation.

Whitehead, P.J. 1998. Boofheads with deep voices: sexual dimorphism in the Magpie Goose. *Wildfowl* 49: 72–91.

Whitehead, P.J. 1999. Aspects of the nesting biology of the Magpie Goose *Anseranas semipalmata*: incubation period, hatching synchrony and patterns of nest attendance and defense. *Emu* 99: 121–34.

Whitehead, P.J. and Tschirner, K. 1990a. Magpie Goose *Anseranas semipalmata* nesting on the Mary River floodplain, Northern Territory, Australia: extent and frequency of flooding losses. *Aust. Wildl. Res.* 17: 147–57.

Whitehead, P.J. and Tschirner, K. 1990b. Eggs and hatchlings of the Magpie Goose *Anseranas semipalmata. Emu* 90: 154–60.

Whitehead, P.J. and Tschirner, K. 1991. Patterns of egg laying and variation in egg size in the Magpie Goose *Anseranas semipalmata*: Evidence for intra-specific egg parasitism. *Emu* 91: 26–31.

Whitehead, P.J. and Tschirner, K. 1992. Sex and age related variation in foraging strategies of Magpie Geese *Anseranas semipalmata. Emu* 92: 28–32.

Whitehead, P.J., Bayliss, P.G. and Fox, R.E. 1988. Recreational waterfowl hunting activity and harvests in the Top End of the Northern Territory. *Aust. Wildl. Res.* 15: 625–31.

Whitehead, P.J., Freeland, W.J. and Tschirner, K. 1990a. Early growth of Magpie Geese, *Anseranas semipalmata*: sex differences and influence of egg size. *Aust. J. Zool.* 38: 249–62.

Whitehead, P.J., Wilson, B.A. and Bowman, D.M.J.S. 1990b. Conservation of coastal wetlands of the Northern Territory of Australia: the Mary River Floodplain. *Biol. Cons.* 52: 85–111.

Whitford, P.C. 1998. Vocal and visual communication of Giant Canada Geese. In D.H. Rusch, M.D. Samuel, D.D. Humburg and B.D. Sullivan (eds.) *Biology and management of Canada Geese,* pp. 375–86. *Proc. Intl Canada Goose Symposium,* Milwaukee, WI.

Whitley, G.R. 1973. The Muscovy Duck in Mexico. *Anthropological J. of Canada* 11: 2–8.

Wick, W.Q. and Rogers, H.E. 1957. An unusual merganser fatality. *Condor* 59: 342–43.

Wicker, A.M. and Endres, K.M. 1995. Relationship between waterfowl and American Coot abundance with submersed macrophytic vegetation in Currituck Sound, North Carolina. *Estuaries* 18: 428–31.

Wielicki, D.J. 1986. Aspects of Mallard nutrition during the molt. Unpubl. M.S. thesis. Univ. Manitoba, Winnipeg, Canada.

Wieloch, M. 1991. Population Trends of the Mute Swan *Cygnus olor* in the Palearctic. *Wildfowl* Spec. Suppl., 1: 22–32.

Wieloch, M. and Czapulak, A. 1991. *Cygnus olor immutabilis* in Poland. *Wildfowl* Spec. Suppl., 1: 304–9.

Wilder, G.P. 1930. Report of a trip to Laysan in the summer of 1930. USDA—Bur. Biol. Surv. US National Archives, Records group 22.

Wilk, R.J. 1988. Distribution, abundance, population structure and productivity of Tundra Swans in Bristol Bay, Alaska. *Arctic* 41: 288–92.

Wilkins, K.A., Otto, M.C. and Smith, G.W. 2000. Trends in duck breeding populations, 1955–2000. U.S. Fish & Wildlife Service, Admin. Rept, Washington, D.C., US.

Williams, C.C. 1967. *Honker: a discussion of the habits and needs of the largest of our Canada geese.* Van Nostrand, Princeton, NJ.

Williams, C.S. and Nelson, M.C. 1943. Management of the Redhead Duck in Utah. Unpubl. rept. US Fish & Wildl. Serv., Washington.

Williams, G.C. 1966. Natural selection, the cost of reproduction and a refinement of Lack's principle. *Amer. Natur.* 100: 687–90.

Williams, M. 1971. The distribution and abundance of the Paradise Shelduck (*Tadorna variegata*, Gmelin) in New Zealand from pre-European times to the present day. *Notornis* 18: 71–86.

Williams, M. 1972. Mortality and exploitation of Paradise Shelduck. *Wildfowl* 23: 94–102.

Williams, M. 1973. Mortality of the Black Swan in New Zealand—a progress report. *Wildfowl* 24: 94–102.

Williams, M. 1974. Creching behaviour of the Shelduck *Tadorna tadorna* L. *Ornis Scand.* 5: 131–43.

Williams, M. 1977. Locations of recoveries of Black Swans *Cygnus atratus* Latham, banded at Lake Whangape and Lake Ellesmere, New Zealand. *Aust. Wildl. Res.* 4: 289–99.

Williams, M. 1979a. The social structure, breeding and population dynamics of Paradise Shelduck in the Gisborne-East Coast District. *Notornis* 26: 213–72.

Williams, M. 1979b. The moult gatherings of Paradise Shelduck in the Gisborne-East Coast district. *Notornis* 26: 369–90.

Williams, M. 1986. The numbers of Auckland Island Teal. *Wildfowl* 37: 63–70.

Williams, M. 1991. Social and demographic characteristics of Blue Duck *Hymenolaimus malacorhynchos*. *Wildfowl* 42: 65–86.

Williams, M. 1995. Social structure, dispersion and breeding of the Auckland Island Teal. *Notornis* 42: 219–62.

Williams, M. and McKinney, F. 1996. Long-term monogamy in a river specialist—the Blue Duck. In *Partnerships in birds. The study of monogamy* (ed. J.M. Black), pp.73–90. OUP.

Williams, M. and Robertson, C.J.R. 1996. The Campbell Island Teal *Anas nesiotis*: history and review. *Wildfowl* 47: 134–65.

Williams, M.D., Carey, G.J., Duff, D.G. and Xu, W. 1992. Autumn bird migration at Beidaihe, China, 1986–1990. *Forktail* 7: 3–55.

Williams, M.J. 1975. Black Swan. *Wildl. Rev. N.Z. Wildl. Serv.* 6: 19–22.

Williams, M.J. 1979c. The status and management of Black Swans *Cygnus atratus*, Latham at Lake Ellesmere since the 'Wahine storm', April 1968. *N.Z. J. Ecol.* 2: 34–41.

Williams, M.J. 1981a. The demography of New Zealand's *Cygnus atratus* population. In 2nd IWRB Swan Symp., Sapporo, 1980 (ed. G.V.T. Matthews and M. Smart), pp.147–61. IWRB, Slimbridge, UK.

Williams, M.J. 1981b. Hunting and management of *Cygnus atratus* in New Zealand. In 2nd IWRB Swan Symp., Sapporo, 1980 (ed. G.V.T. Matthews and M. Smart), pp.301–10. IWRB, Slimbridge, UK.

Williams, M.J., McKinney, F. and Norman, F.I. 1991. Ecological and behavioural responses of Austral teal to island life. *Int. Ornith. Congr.* 20: 876–84.

Williams, P.H. 1996. WORLDMAP iv WINDOWS: Software and user document 4.1. Privately distributed, London.

Williams, T.D. 1994. Adoption in a precocial species, the Lesser Snow Goose: inter-generational conflict, altruism or a mutually beneficial strategy? *Anim. Behav.* 47: 101–7.

Williams, T.D., Cooch, E.G., Jefferies, R.L. and Cooke, F. 1993. Environmental degradation, food limitation and reproductive output: juvenile survival in Lesser Snow Geese. *J. Anim. Ecol.* 62: 766–77.

Williams, T.D., Loonen, M.J.J.E. and Cooke, F. 1994. Fitness consequences of parental behavior in relation to offspring number in a precocial species: the Lesser Snow Goose. *Auk* 111: 563–72.

Wilmé, L. 1993. A recent record of the rare Madagascar Pochard (*Aythya innotata*) on Lake Alaotra, Madagascar. *Bull. BOC* 113: 188–89.

Wilmé, L. 1994. Status, distribution and conservation of two Madagascar bird species endemic to Lake Alaotra: Delacour's Grebe *Tachybaptus rufolavatus* and Madagascar Pochard *Aythya innotata*. *Biol. Cons.* 69: 15–21.

Wilmore, S.B. 1979. *Swans of the World*. Taplinger Publishing Company, New York.

Wilson, A.C., Cahn, R.D. and Kaplan, N.O. 1963. Functions of the two forms of lactic dehydrogenase in the breast muscle of birds. *Nature* 197: 331–34.

Wilson, H.J., Norriss, D.W., Walsh, A., Fox, A.D. and Stroud, D.A. 1991. Winter site fidelity in the Greenland White-fronted Goose *Anser albifrons flavirostris*: implications for conservation and management. *Ardea* 79: 287–94.

Wilson, L.K., Elliot, J.E., Langelier, K.M., Scheuhammer, A.M. and Bowes, V. 1998. Lead poisoning of Trumpeter Swans *Cygnus buccinator*, in British Columbia. *Canadian Field-Nat.* 112(2): 204–11.

Wilson, R. 1957. The Royal Spoonbill. *Notornis* 7: 107–9.

Wilson, R.E. 2002. A comparitive analysis of duckling distress calls. Unpubl. M.S. thesis, Univ. Minnesota, Minneapolis, US.

Wilson, R.T. 1992. Ornithological exploration in the Afrotropics. 2. James Bruce of Kinnaird, Esq., FRS. *Tauraco* 2: 63–72.

Wilson, R.T. 1993. Temporal and spatial distribution of the Anatidae in Ethiopia. *Annales Musée Royal de l'Afrique Centrale (Zoologie)* 268: 591–94.

Wilson, S.B. and Evans, A.H. 1890–1899. *Aves Hawaiiensis: the birds of the Sandwich Islands.* Porter, London.

Wilson, S.F. and Verbeek, N.A.M. 1995. Patterns of Wood Duck nest temperatures during egg-laying and incubation. *Condor* 97: 963–69.

Wilson, U.W. and Atkinson, J.B. 1995. Black Brant winter and spring-staging use at two Washington coastal areas in relation to eelgrass abundance. *Condor* 97: 91–98.

Winfield, I.J. and Winfield, D.K. 1994a. Feeding ecology of the diving ducks Pochard (*Aythya ferina*), Tufted Duck (*A. fuligula*), Scaup (*A. marila*) and Goldeneye (*Bucephala clangula*) overwintering on Lough Neagh, Northern Ireland. *Freshwater Biol.* 32: 467–77.

Winfield, I.J. and Winfield, D.K. 1994b. Possible competitive interactions between overwintering Tufted Ducks (*Aythya fuligula* (L.)) and fish populations of Lough Neagh, Northern Ireland. *Hydrobiologia* 280: 377–86.

Wink, M., Hofer, A., Bilfinger, U., Englert, E., Martin, M. and Schneider, D. 1993. Geese and dietary allelochemicals—food palatability and geophagy. *Chemoecology* 4: 93–107.

Winterbottom, J.M. 1968. A check list of the land and fresh water birds of the western Cape. *Ann. S. Afr. Mus.* 53: 1–276.

Winterbottom, J.M. 1971. *A preliminary check list of the birds of South West Africa.* S.W.A. Scientific Society, Windhoek.

Winterbottom, J.M. 1974. The Cape Teal. *Ostrich* 45: 110–32.

Wintle, C.C. 1981. Notes on the breeding behaviour of the White-backed Duck. *Honeyguide* 105: 13–20.

Wishart, R.A. 1983. Pairing chronology and mate selection in the American Wigeon (*Anas americana*). *Can. J. Zool.* 61: 1733–43.

Witherby, H.F., Jourdain, F.C.R., Ticehurst, N.F. and Tucker, B.W. 1939 (reprinted 1952). *The handbook of British birds*, Vol. 3. Witherby, London.

Wittenberger, J.F. and Tilson, R.L. 1980. The evolution of monogamy: hypotheses and evidence. *Ann. Rev. Ecol. Syst.* 11: 197–232.

Woebeser, G.A. 1981. *Diseases of wild waterfowl.* Plenum Press, New York.

Wood, C.C. 1985. Food-searching behaviour of the Common Merganser (*Mergus merganser*). II: Choice of foraging location. *Can. J. Zool.* 63: 1271–79.

Wood, C.C. 1986. Dispersion of Common Merganser (*Mergus merganser*) breeding pairs in relation to the availability of juvenile Pacific Salmon in Vancouver Island streams. *Can. J. Zool.* 64: 756–65.

Wood, C.C. 1987. Predation of juvenile Pacific Salmon by the Common Merganser *Mergus merganser* on eastern Vancouver Island. II: Predation of stream-resident juvenile salmon by merganser broods. *Can. J. Fish. Aquatic Sci.* 44: 950–59.

Woodall, P.F. 1975. A survey of duck shooting in Rhodesia. *S. Afr. J. Wildl. Man.* 5: 115–22.

Woodall, P.F. 1979. Food of the Redbilled Teal in Rhodesia. *S. Afr. J. Wildl. Res.* 9(1/2): 9–11.

Woodall, P.F. 1985. Waterbird populations in the Brisbane region, 1973–83, and correlates with rainfall and water heights. *Aust. Wildl. Res.* 12: 495–506.

Woodin, M.C. 1987. Wetland selection and foraging ecology of breeding diving ducks. Unpubl. Ph.D. thesis, Univ. Minnesota, Minneapolis, US.

Woodin, M.C. 1994. Use of saltwater and freshwater habitats by wintering Redheads in southern Texas. *Hydrobiologia* 279/280: 279–87.

Woodin, M.C. 1996. The wintering ecology of Red-heads (*Aythya americana*) in the western Gulf of Mexico region. *Gibier Faune Sauvage* 13: 653–65.

Woodin, M.C. and Michot, T.C. 1997. Feeding behavior of Redheads wintering in Texas and Louisiana: does resource limitation occur? Unpubl. ms.

Woodin, M.C. and Michot, T.C. 2002. Redhead (*Aythya americana*). The Birds of North America, No. 695 (ed. A. Poole and F. Gill). AOU, The Birds of North America Inc., Philadelphia.

Woodin, M.C. and Swanson, G.A. 1989. Foods and dietary strategies of prairie nesting Ruddy Ducks and Redheads. *Condor* 91: 280–87.

Woods, R.W. 1975. *The birds of the Falkland Islands.* Anthony Nelson, Oswestry, Shropshire, and Compton, Wiltshire.

Woods, R.W. 1988. *Guide to birds of the Falkland Islands.* Anthony Nelson, Oswestry.

Woods, R.W. and Woods, A. 1997. *Atlas of breeding birds of the Falkland Islands.* Anthony Nelson, Oswestry.

Woodworth, B.L., Port, J., McKinney, F., Harth, A., Sorenson, L.G. and Ruttan, L. 1993. Changes in local abundance and habitat use by the White-cheeked Pintail in New Providence Island, Bahamas, 1985–1992. *El Pitirre* 6: 12.

Woodyard, E.R. and Bolen, E. 1984. Ecological studies of Muscovy Ducks. *Southwest Nat.* 29(4): 453.

Woog, F. 2002. Distribution and timing of nesting in Hawaiian Geese in relation to food phenology in scrub-lands. *Wildfowl* 53: 79–107.

Wooldridge, A. and Wisniewski, P.J. 1993. The Western Cape Barren Goose at Martin Mere: a brief history. *Int. Zoo News.* 40: 24–27.

Wooley, J.B., Jr and Owen, R.B., Jr 1978. Energy costs of activity and daily energy expenditure in the Black Duck. *J. Wildl. Manage.* 42: 739–45.

Woolfenden, G. 1961. Post-cranial osteology of the waterfowl. *Bull. Florida State Mus. Biol. Sci.* 6: 1–129.

Woolington, D.W. 1993. Sex ratios of Canvasbacks wintering in Louisiana. *J. Wildl. Manage.* 57: 751–58.

Worthy, T.H. 1988. Loss of flight ability in the extinct New Zealand duck *Euryanas finschi. J. Zool., Lond.* 215: 619–28.

Worthy, T.H. 1995. Description of some post-cranial bones of *Malacorhynchus scarletti*, a large extinct Pink-eared Duck from New Zealand. *Emu* 95: 13–22.

Worthy, T.H. and Holdaway, R.N. 1994. Quaternary fossil faunas from caves in Takaka Valley and on Takaka Hill, northwest Nelson, South Island, New Zealand. *J. Roy. Soc. N.Z.* 24: 297–391.

Worthy, T.H., Holdaway, R.N., Sorenson, M.D. and Cooper, A.C. 1997. Description of the first complete skeleton of the extinct New Zealand goose *Cnemiornis calcitrans* (Aves: Anatidae), and a reassessment of the relations of *Cnemiornis. J. Zool., Lond.*: 243: 695–723.

Wrånes, E. 1988. Massedød av aerfugl på Sørlandet vinteren 1981/82. *Vår Fuglefauna* 11: 71–74.

Wright, B.S. 1954. *High tide and an east wind. The story of the Black Duck.* Stackpole, Harrisburg, Pennsylvania, and Wildl. Manage. Inst., Washington.

Wright, J.K. 1965. Observations of behaviour of the Andean Torrent Duck. *Condor* 67: 535.

WSGCOA 1994. *Waterbird Research in China.* East China Normal Univ. Press, Shanghai.

Würdinger, I. 1970. Erzeugung, Ontogenie und Funk-tion der Lautäußerungen bei vier Gänsearten (*Anser indicus, Anser caerulescens, Anser albifrons, Branta canadensis*). *Z. Tierpsychol.* 27: 257–302.

Würdinger, I. 1973. Breeding of Bar-headed Geese. *Int. Zoo Ybk* 13: 43–47.

Würdinger, I. 1975. Vergleichend morphologische Untersuchungen zur Jugendentwicklung von *Anser-* und *Branta-*Arten. *J. Orn.* 116: 65–86.

Würdinger, I. 1998. *Die Streifengans (Anser indicus vorm. Eulabeia indica)—Beschreibung und Analyse des Ver-haltens.* Franzbecker, Hildesheim.

Wynne-Jones, A. 1993. *The sport of shooting in southern Africa.* Oberon Press, Houghton.

Wypkema, R.C.P. and Ankey, C.D. 1979. Nutrient reserve dynamics of Lesser Snow Geese staging at James Bay, Ontario. *Can. J. Zool.* 57: 213–19.

Yahya, H.S.A. 1994. A survey of the White-winged Duck, *Cairina scutulata*, in India. *IWRB Threatened Waterfowl Research Group Newsl.* 5: 7–8.

Yamashina, Y. 1948. Notes on the Marianas Mallard. *Pac. Sci.* 2: 121–24.

Yamashina, Y. 1952. Classification of the Anatidae based on cytogenetics. *Pap. Coord. Comm. Res. Gen.* 3: 1–24.

Yamashina, Y. 1974. *Birds in Japan* (2nd edn). Kasumikaikan, Tokyo.

Yamashita, C. and de Paula Valle, M. 1990. Ocorrência de daus aves raras no Brasil Central: *Mergus octocetaceus* e *Tigrisoma fasciatum fasciatum. Ararjuba* 1: 107–9.

Ydenberg, R.C. 1986. Foraging by diving birds. *Int. Orn. Congr.* 19: 1832–42.

Ydenberg, R.C. and Prins, H.H.T. 1981. Spring grazing and the manipulation of food quality by Barnacle Geese. *J. Appl. Ecol.* 18: 443–53.

Ydenberg, R.C., Prins, H.H.T. and van Dijk, J. 1984. A lunar rhythm in the nocturnal foraging activities of wintering Barnacle Geese. *Wildfowl* 35: 93–96.

Yealland, J. 1951. Hartlaub's Duck (*Cairina hartlaubi*). *Avic. Mag.* 57: 156.

Yealland, J. 1957. The Hawaiian Duck. *Avic. Mag.* 57: 182.

Yelsukov, S.V. 1994. The Scaly-sided Merganser *Mergus squamatus* (Gould) in the central Sikhote-Alin Mountains, Far-East Russia. In *The Scaly-sided Merganser Mergus squamatus in Russia and China*, IWRB Threatened Waterfowl Research Group Spec. Publ., No. 1 (ed. B. Hughes and J. Hunter), pp.18–21. WWT, Slimbridge, UK.

Yerkes, T. 1998. The influence of female age, body mass, and ambient conditions on redhead incubation constancy. *Condor* 100: 62–68.

Yerkes, T. 2000. Nest-site characteristics and brood-habitat selection of redheads: an association between wetland characteristics and success. *Wetlands* 20: 575–80.

Yésou, P. and Trolliet, B. 1983. Anatidés et zones humides de France métropolitaine. *Bull. ONC* No. spéc. Déc.1983.

Young, A.D. 1993. Intraspecific variation in the use of nutrient reserves by breeding female Mallards. *Condor* 95: 45–56.

Young, A.D. and Titman, R.D. 1986. Costs and benefits to Red-breasted Mergansers nesting in tern and gull colonies. *Can. J. Zool.* 64: 2339–43.

Young, A.D. and Titman, R.D. 1988. Intraspecific nest parasitism in Red-breasted Mergansers. *Can. J. Zool.* 66: 2454–58.

Young, D.A. and Boag, D.A. 1981. A description of moult in male Mallards. *Can. J. Zool.* 59: 252–59.

Young, H.G. 1988. Data on the eggs of some bird species held at the Jersey Wildlife Preservation Trust. *Dodo* 25: 76–82.

Young, H.G. 1991. Sexual dimorphism in Meller's Duck *Anas melleri. Bull. BOC* 111: 225–28.

Young, H.G. 1994. The systematic position of Meller's Duck *Anas melleri*: a behavioural approach. Unpubl. M.Sc. thesis. Univ. Canterbury, Kent, UK.

Young, H.G. 1995a. Territoriality and reproductive behaviour of Meller's Duck *Anas melleri. Dodo* 31: 82–94.

Young, H.G. 1995b. The Madagascar Teal, a most enigmatic duck. *Bull. ABC* 2: 98–100.

Young, H.G. 1996a. Grey Teals in Asia. *Bull. OBC* 43: 54–57.

Young, H.G. 1996b. Threatened Anatinae and wetlands of Madagascar: a review and evaluation. *Gibier Faune Sauvage* 13: 801–13.

Young, H.G. 1999. Comparative study of the courtship displays of Meller's Duck *Anas melleri*, Yellow Billed Duck *A. undulata* and Northern Mallard *A. platyrhynchos. Ostrich* 70: 117–22.

Young, H.G. 2002. Predicting the ecology of Madagascar's endemic dabbling ducks using captive populations and related taxa: implications for conservation. Unpubl. Ph.D. thesis, Univ. Canterbury, Kent, UK.

Young, H.G. and Brayshaw, M. 2004. The downy young of grey teal (Anatidae) with first descriptions of the ducklings of Madagascar Teal *Anas bernieri* and Indonesian Teal *A. gibberifrons. Bull. BOC* 124: 62–68.

Young, H.G. and McCann, R. 2002. Sexual dimorphism in Hottentot Teal. *Wildfowl* 53: 225–27.

Young, H.G. and Rhymer, J.M. 1998. Meller's Duck: a threatened species receives recognition at last. *Biodiversity and Conservation* 7: 1313–23.

Young, H.G. and Robertson, I. 2001. The Yellow-billed Duck *Anas undulata* in West Africa. *Malimbus* 23: 56–58.

Young, H.G. and Smith, J.G. 1989. The search for the Madagascar Pochard *Aythya innotata*. Survey of Lac Alaotra, Madagascar October–November, 1989. *Dodo* 26: 17–34.

Young, H.G., Safford, R., Green, A., Ravonjiarisoa, P. and Rabarisoa, R.G.M. 1993. Survey and capture of the Madagascar Teal *Anas bernieri* at Lac Bemamba, Madagascar July–August 1992, July 1993. *Dodo* 29: 77–94.

Young, H.G., Tonge, S.J. and Hume, J.P. 1997. Review of Holocene wildfowl extinctions. *Wildfowl* 47: 166–80.

Young, H.G., Sorenson, M.D. and Johnson, K.P. 1998. A description of the Madagascar Teal *Anas bernieri* and an examination of its relationship with the Grey Teal *A. gracilis*. *Wildfowl* 48: 174–80.

Young, H.G., Lewis, R.E. and Razafindrajao, F. 2001. A description of the nest and eggs of the Madagascar Teal *Anas bernieri*. *Bull. BOC* 121: 64–67.

Young, J.G. 1965. Nests and eggs of Greylag Geese in Galloway. *Wildfowl* 16: 54–55.

Young, J.G. 1972. Breeding biology of feral Greylag Geese in south-west Scotland. *Wildfowl* 23: 83–87.

Zalakevicius, M. 1995. Birds of Lithuania 1994 with comments on status, number and distribution. *Acta Ornithologica Lituanica* 11: 1–110.

Zaloumis, E.A. 1982. Moult of carpal spur in the Spur-winged Goose. *Ostrich* 53: 235.

Zaloumis, E.A. 1987. The nesting requirements of southern African waterfowl. *S. Afr. J. Wildl. Res.* Suppl. 1: 76–81.

Zammuto, R.M. 1986. Life history of birds: clutch size, longevity, and body mass among North American game birds. *Can. J. Zool.* 64: 2739–49.

Zar, J.H. 1968. Standard metabolism comparisons between orders or birds. *Condor* 70: 278.

Zhao, Z.J. 1993. Is the Crested Shelduck extinct? *IWRB Threatened Waterfowl Research Group Newsl.* 3: 5.

Zhao, Z.J. and Pao, Z.J. 1998. The foraging behaviour of the Scaly-sided Merganser *Mergus squamatus* in the Changbai Mountains and Xiao Xingangling Mountains of China. *Forktail* 14: 76–77.

Zhao, Z.J., Han, X.D. and Wu, J.C. 1993. Current status of Scaly-sided Merganser in China and its distribution in winter. *Hong Kong Bird Rept.* 1993: 170–77.

Zhao, Z.J., Han, X.D. and Wu, J.C. 1994a. Current status and distribution of the Scaly-sided Merganser *Mergus squamatus* in China. In *The Scaly-sided Merganser Mergus squamatus in Russia and China*,

IWRB Threatened Waterfowl Research Group Spec. Publ., No. 1 (ed. B. Hughes and J. Hunter), pp.21–24. WWT, Slimbridge, UK.

Zhao, Z.J., Zhang, X.L., Zhang, S.H., Wu, J.C., Liu, P.Q., Han, X.D. *et al.* 1994b. The breeding biology and foraging ecology of the Scaly-sided Merganser *Mergus squamatus* in the Changbai Mountains, China. In *The Scaly-sided Merganser Mergus squamatus in Russia and China*, IWRB Threatened Waterfowl Research Group Spec. Publ., No. 1 (ed. B. Hughes and J. Hunter), pp. 24–28. WWT, Slimbridge, UK.

Zhao, Z.J., Han, X.D., Zhang, S.H., Wu, J.C. and Pao, Z.J. 1995. Breeding ecology of the Chinese Merganser in the Changbai Mountains. China. *J. Field Ornithol.* 66: 54–59.

Zharkova, Y. and Borzhonov, B. 1972. Nourishment of geese on the Taimyr Peninsula. In *Geese in the USSR*, Conf., Estonia, May 1970 (ed. E. Kumari), pp.117–26. Acad. Sci. Estonian SSR, Inst. Zoology and Botany, Tartu.

Zhuge, Y. 1990. *The avifauna of Zhejiang*. Science and Technology Publishing House, Zhejiang.

Zicus, M.C. 1990a. Nesting biology of Hooded Mergansers using nest boxes. *J. Wildl. Manage.* 54: 637–43.

Zicus, M.C. 1990b. Renesting by a Common Goldeneye. *J. Field Ornithol.* 61: 245–48.

Zicus, M.C. and Hennes, S.K. 1988. Cavity nesting waterfowl in Minnesota. *Wildfowl* 39: 115–23.

Zicus, M.C. and Hennes, S.K. 1989. Nest prospecting by Common Goldeneyes. *Condor* 91: 807–12.

Zicus, M.C. and Hennes, S.K. 1994. Diurnal time budgets of Goldeneye brood hens. *Wilson Bull.* 105: 680–85.

Zicus, M.C. and Riggs, M.R. 1996. Change in body mass of female Common Goldeneyes during nesting and brood rearing. *Wilson Bull.* 108: 61–71.

Zicus, M.C., Briggs, M.A. and Pace, R.M., III 1988. DDE, PCB, and mercury residues in Minnesota Common Goldeneye and Hooded Merganser eggs, 1981. *Can. J. Zool.* 66: 1871–79.

Zicus, M.C., Hennes, S.K. and Riggs, M.R. 1995. Common Goldeneye nest attendance patterns. *Condor* 97: 461–72.

Zijlstra, M., Loonen, M.J.J.E., van Eerden, M.R. and Dubbeldam, W. 1991. The Oostvaardersplassen as a key moulting site for Greylag Geese *Anser anser* in western Europe. *Wildfowl* 42: 45–52.

Zillich, U. and Black, J.M. 2002. Body mass and Abdominal Profile Index in captive Hawaiian Geese. *Wildfowl* 53: 67–77.

Zimmer, R., Erdtmann, B., Thomas, W.K. and Quinn, T.W. 1994. Phylogenetic analysis of the *Coscoroba coscoroba* using mitochondrial srRNA gene sequences. *Mol. Phyl. Evol.* 3: 85–91.

Zimmerman, D.A., Turner, D.A. and Pearson, D.J. 1996. *Birds of Kenya and Northern Tanzania.* Christopher Helm, London.

Zimmerman, D.R. 1970. *To save a bird in peril.* Coward, McCann and Geoghegan, New York.

Zink, R.M. 1996. Species concepts, speciation and sexual selection. *J. Avian Biology* 27: 1–6.

Zink, R.M. and McKitrick, M.C. 1995. The debate over species concepts and its implications for ornithology. *Auk* 112: 701–19.

Zubakin, V.A. 1981. Colonial birds of the Torei Lakes. In *Distribution and status of breeding sites of waterside birds in the USSR*, pp.132–34. Moscow.

Zubko, V.N. and Popovkina, A.B. 1999. The Ruddy Shelduck *Tadorna ferruginea* in Askania-Nova (Ukraine): population history, current status and prospects. *IWRB Duck Specialist Group Bull.* 2: 44–47.

Zusi, R.L. and Bentz, G.D. 1978. The appendicular myology of the Labrador Ducks (*Camptorhynchus labradorius*). *Condor* 80: 407–18.

Zusi, R.L. and Livezey, B.C. 2000. Homology and phylogenetic implications of some enigmatic cranial features in galliform and anseriform birds. *Annals of Carnegie Museum* 69: 157–93.

Zweers, G.A. 1974. Structure, movement and morphology of the feeding apparatus of the Mallard (*Anas platyrhychos* L.). A study of functional anatomy. *Netherl. J. Zool.* 24: 323–467.

List of Contributors

ALAN D. AFTON, Louisiana Cooperative Fish and Wildlife Research Unit, USA

DAVID G. ALLAN, Durban Natural Science Museum, South Africa

JANE E. AUSTIN, USA

PAUL C. BANKO, Pacific Island Ecosystems Research Center, USA

JEFFREY M. BLACK, Humboldt State University, USA

ERIC G. BOLEN, University of North Carolina at Wilmington, USA

JOHN BOWLER, RSPB, UK

HUGH BOYD, Canadian Wildlife Service, Canada

GWENDA L. BREWER, Maryland Dept. of Natural Resources, USA

DES CALLAGHAN, UK

ROGER CATTERMOLE, UK

ANWARUDDIN CHOUDHURY, The Rhino Foundation, India

EVAN G. COOCH, Department of Natural Resources, Cornell University, USA

F. GRAHAM COOCH, USA

CHRISTINE M. CUSTER, USA

CHRISTIAN P. DAU, US Fish and Wildlife Service, USA

CHRIS DAVEY, UK

GREG DAVIES, Natal Museum Pietermaritzburg, South Africa

SIMON DELANY, Wetlands International, The Netherlands

EDWARD C. DICKINSON, UK

KATHRYN DICKSON, Canadian Wildlife Service, Canada

ÁRNI EINARSSON, Mývatn Research Station, Iceland

A. J. ERSKINE, Canada

SUSAN EVARTS, USA

JON FJELDSÅ, Zoological Museum, University of Copenhagen, Denmark

TONY FOX, Ministry of Environment and Energy, Denmark

PETER FULLAGAR, Australia

OLIVIER GIRARD, Office National de la Chasse et de la Faune Sauvage, France

ANDY J. GREEN, Estación Biológica de Doñana, Spain

JOHN HARSHMAN, Field Museum of Natural History, Chicago, USA

†EDMUND HOFFMANN, USA

WILLIAM L. HOHMAN, Department of Animal Ecology, Iowa State University, USA

BAZ HUGHES, Wildfowl & Wetlands Trust, UK

JANET HUNTER, UK

NIGEL JARRETT, Wildfowl & Wetlands Trust, UK

†JANET KEAR, UK

TIM JONES, UK

†A.A. KISTCHINSKI, Russia

BRADLEY C. LIVEZEY, Carnegie Museum of Natural History, USA

ANN P. MARSHALL, US Fish & Wildlife Service, USA

ANTHONY R. MARTIN, British Antarctic Survey, UK

GEOFFREY V.T. MATTHEWS, UK

KEVIN G. McCRACKEN, University of Alaska Museum, USA

MARTIN McGILL, Wildfowl & Wetlands Trust, UK

†FRANK McKINNEY, USA

THOMAS C. MICHOT, US Geological Survey, National Wetlands Research Center, USA

CARL MITCHELL, RSPB, UK

NIAL MOORES, Wetlands and Birds Korea, South Korea

JENS NYELAND, Greenland

MALCOLM A. OGILVIE, UK

PETER OLNEY, UK

MYRFYN OWEN, UK

CLIVE PETERS, UK

STEPHAN PIHL, Denmark

JEFF PORT, Department of Biological Sciences, Bethel College, USA

JOHN L. QUINN, Edward Grey Institute of Field Ornithology, University of Oxford, UK

†PETER PRINCE, British Antarctic Survey, UK

AUSTIN REED, Canada

EILEEN C. REES, Wildfowl & Wetlands Trust, UK

JAMES A. ROBINSON, RSPB, UK

JOEL SCHMUTZ, Alaska Biological Science Center, USA

PHIL SHEPHERD, UK

LISA G. SORENSON, Biology Department, Boston University, USA

NANCY STAUS, Conservation Biology Institute, USA

RON SUMMERS, RSPB, UK

RODGER D. TITMAN, Department of Natural Resource Sciences & Avian Science & Conservation Center, McGill University, Canada

MURRAY WILLIAMS, Department of Conservation, New Zealand

TREVOR WILSON, UK

IRENE WÜRDINGER, Germany

PAT WISNIEWSKI, Wildfowl & Wetlands Trust, UK

MARC WOODIN, USA

GLYN YOUNG, Durrell Wildlife Conservation Trust, UK

MIKE ZICUS, Minnesota Dept. of Natural Resources, USA

†Deceased

Index

Species accounts may be found on the page numbers set in **bold** type. Plates appear between pages 172 and 173. Species other than wildfowl can be found by looking up their inverted English names, e.g. Falcon, Peregrine.